MATERIALS
of
CONSTRUCTION

MATERIALS
of
CONSTRUCTION

M. O. WITHEY

Emeritus Dean, College of Engineering
University of Wisconsin

G. W. WASHA

Professor of Mechanics
University of Wisconsin

JOHN WILEY & SONS, INC., NEW YORK
CHAPMAN & HALL, LIMITED, LONDON

Preface

Some fifty-five years ago the late Dean J. B. Johnson wrote the follow-ing pertinent statement in the preface of the first edition of *The Materials of Construction:*

The rational designing of any kind of construction involves a knowledge of:
The external forces to be resisted, transformed, or transmitted;
The internal stresses resulting therefrom;
The mechanical properties of the materials to be employed to accomplish the objects sought.

Of these three coordinate departments of knowledge the first two are founded on the sciences of mathematics and applied mechanics. The last one, however, does not rest on any deductive science, as this information can only be gained by patient, expensive, and competent research. For this reason the third essen-tial named above has not kept pace with the other two kinds of engineering science; but, on the other hand, it furnishes very much greater rewards to the skilled investigator.

During the past twenty-five years the number of such investigators has in-creased from a scattering few to hundreds and even thousands, and these are now found in all enlightened nations. The results of their original studies and experiments are pouring in upon us from all countries, in many languages; and no practising engineer can hope to even scan, much less to appropriate and as-similate, more than a very small part of this vast wealth of experimental knowl-edge.

The belief that it was essential that students and engineers should have a broad knowledge of this subject led Dean Johnson to compile his well-known treatise. His good judgment and foresight in so doing were con-firmed by extended use of the book both as a textbook and as a reference book for nearly a score of years with little revision. In 1918 under the editorial supervision of the late Dean F. E. Turneaure the present senior author with James Aston rewrote the book, producing the fifth edition. Since that time three editions embodying numerous changes have been published.

We believe that there is a distinct advantage in preserving the original aim of presenting a book that serves both as a textbook and as a reference book. Our aim has been to provide the essential information concerning the sources, manufacture, or fabrication of the principal materials; to give carefully selected data covering the more important mechanical and physical properties and the influences of various factors upon these prop-erties; to show the causes of defects and variations and how they may be discovered; to furnish an acquaintance with the technique of testing materials; and to present to the student some of the more general uses of the different materials. Care has been taken to illustrate adequately the revised work with material from the best sources.

Extensive changes have been made largely by G. W. Washa. A new page-numbering system has been used which will facilitate future revisions. Statistical data have been brought up to date. Chapter I has been revised to present new definitions, formulas, and information on energy losses in impact loading. Information on new testing machines and strain-measuring devices has been incorporated in Chapter II. A section on non-destructive tests has been added to Chapter III. In the chapters on timber, information on chemical seasoning, wood products, and timber connectors are presented. Changes in Chapters IX to XI include a résumé of the new types of cement and influence of alkalies on durability. The users of the book will derive satisfaction by noting that Chapter XII has been largely rewritten and presents descriptions of cement testing methods in place of the ASTM standards previously given. A separate chapter has been devoted to concrete aggregates and includes information on new testing methods and on lightweight aggregates. In Chapters XIV to XVI the information on mix design methods has been revised, methods of checking proportions of fresh and hardened concrete are given, and new information on concrete products is provided.

Additional material on the manufacture of iron and steel shapes is found in Chapter XX. The iron-iron carbide constitution diagram has been revised in accordance with the latest information. The chapters on wrought iron, alloy steels, non-ferrous metals, fatigue of materials, effect of mechanical work on the properties of steel, heat treatment of steel, and effects of temperature on the properties of metals have been largely or completely rewritten.

Acknowledgment of the many sources of information consulted in the compilation of this and previous editions of the book has been made in the text. We are much indebted to the engineering staff at the University of Wisconsin, especially to Dean K. F. Wendt, and Professors J. B. Kommers, R. J. Roark, P. G. Fluck, R. A. Ragatz, P. C. Rosenthal, and D. J. Mack. The cooperation of the staff of the Forest Products Laboratory, chiefly Messrs. L. J. Markwardt and A. D. Freas, and of Messrs. F. R. McMillan and H. F. Gonnerman of the Portland Cement Association Laboratory has been greatly appreciated. Gratitude to deceased friends Dean F. E. Turneaure, Professor E. R. Maurer, and Mr. J. A. Newlin is also acknowledged. We are grateful to all who have contributed illustrative material.

M. O. WITHEY
G. W. WASHA

Madison, Wisconsin
August, 1954

Contents

Synopsis of the Principles
of Mechanics of Materials

GENERAL NATURE OF DEFORMATION AND STRESS

1. Definitions. When a solid body is acted upon by external forces, two results are, in general, produced: (1) the body is deformed to a greater or less extent, and (2) there is developed in the body internal resisting forces which balance the external applied forces. The deformation produced is often called *strain,* but herein either deformation or strain will be used; that produced in a unit of length is termed unit deformation or unit strain. The internal forces acting between consecutive particles are called *stresses.* Unit stress is the amount of internal force per unit area. The stresses acting on any imaginary section taken through the body must be in equilibrium with the external forces acting on either side of such section.

If the external forces themselves are not in equilibrium, there is a third result produced, namely, that of acceleration of the body, but in most discussions of this treatise the motion of bodies is not considered; all external forces are assumed to be in equilibrium and the body at rest.

2. Kinds of Stresses. Depending upon the arrangement and direction of the external forces, the stress produced in a body may be

1. Tensile stress.
2. Compressive stress.
3. Shearing stress.
4. Bending stress.
5. Torsional stress.
6. Various combinations of the above stresses.

Tensile and compressive stresses are frequently called *direct* stresses. They act perpendicularly to the section in question. In the case of long prismatic bars or members of structures, if the external forces act along the axis of the member, direct stresses of tension or compression are produced, the section taken being assumed as a cross section transverse to the axis of the member.

Shearing stress is produced by forces tending to slide one particle upon another; it is a stress which acts parallel or tangential to the section in question. Where the resultant of all forces acts in a direction at right angles to a section, the stresses on the section are direct tensile or compressive stresses; where it acts at any other angle, there will exist shearing as well as direct stresses. Generally speaking, when a body is deformed under the action of external forces, both shearing and direct stresses will be produced throughout the body; it is only on particular sections that the stresses will be purely direct or purely shearing stresses. Thus, in the case of a tension bar, the stresses on a transverse section will be tensile only, but, on a section taken through the bar at any other angle, shearing stresses will also be present.

Tension, compression, and shear may be considered as the elementary stresses. The other kinds of stresses mentioned above are merely combinations of these elementary stresses resulting from special arrangements of the external forces. Thus, the so-called *bending stresses* are those which are produced by external forces that give rise to bending moments; the resulting stresses are compressive on one side of a neutral plane and tensile on the other side, whereas shearing stresses exist, in general, throughout the beam. The result of this combination of stresses is a bending of the member as a whole.

Torsional stresses are produced by forces which set up a torsional or twisting moment; this produces a rather complex combination of shearing, compressive, and tensile stresses. The member as a whole receives a twisting or torsional deformation.

Combined stresses are those resulting from a combination of direct and bending stresses which produce a bending of the member and at the same time an elongation or compression, those resulting from a combination of direct stresses, or those resulting from a combination of direct and shearing stresses.

Other common terms, frequently used in defining various conditions under which the external forces are applied, are: impact, repeated stress, and column action.

Impact is a term used to describe the application of external forces with such suddenness as to produce a shock or blow.

Repeated stresses indicate stresses which are applied and removed, in whole or in part, numerous times and at short intervals. In carrying out such tests, stresses are often repeated several millions of times.

Column action signifies a compression applied to a relatively long member so that lateral bending or buckling is likely to occur, thus giving rise to bending as well as compressive stresses.

3. Elastic and Plastic Bodies. When a body which has been deformed under the action of external forces is released from such action, a greater or less recovery of form takes place. To the extent to which the body recovers its original form, it is said to be *elastic*, and to the extent to which the body fails to recover its original form, it is said to be *plastic*. Most engineering materials are in part elastic and in part plastic, the relation between these properties varying widely in different materials. For relatively small unit stresses and deformations, most materials are nearly or quite perfectly elastic; that is to say, they fully recover their form when the load is removed, but, as the deformation increases, a point is reached beyond which the original form is not fully recovered.

Elastic Limit and Ultimate Strength. The maximum unit stress within which a body is elastic is called the *elastic limit*. Beyond this point, the material will recover only to a certain extent, and will show a certain amount of permanent change of form or set. When the load and deformation are increased still further, rupture generally ensues. The maximum unit stress carried by the material is termed the *ultimate strength*.

The amount of deformation which the material will undergo before rupture varies widely with different materials. Hard, brittle materials like glass will show very little deformation between their elastic limit and ultimate strength; materials like soft steel and wrought iron will undergo a very large deformation between these limits. Under compressive stresses materials like soft steel and wrought iron can hardly be said to have any definite ultimate strength, as their resistance to load increases continuously with their deformation.

4. Modulus of Elasticity. Within the limits of elasticity of solid bodies, the deformation is proportional to the stress, and the ratio of unit stress to unit deformation is a very important function in the study of materials. In general, this ratio is termed the *modulus of elasticity*, and we have moduli of elasticity in tension, compression, and shear. The moduli in tension and compression are usually equal. The modulus for either direct stress is known as *Young's modulus*, and is denoted by the letter E.

According to notation used in this work, we have the following for direct stresses:

P = end axial load.
l = length of bar.
A = area of cross section.
e = longitudinal deformation.
ϵ = unit longitudinal deformation.
S_t or S_c = unit stress of tension or compression.
E = modulus of elasticity.

Then
$$E = \frac{P/A}{e/l} = \frac{S_t}{\epsilon} \quad \text{or} \quad \frac{S_c}{\epsilon} \qquad (1)$$

5. Longitudinal and Lateral Deformation under Direct Stress. When a body is subjected to a direct stress, either tension or compression, it undergoes a certain amount of lateral as well as longitudinal deformation. The ratio of lateral to longitudinal deformation is called Poisson's ratio, denoted by λ. The values of this ratio for some of the more common materials are as follows: *

Glass	0.24	Brass	0.33
Steel	0.28	Aluminum	0.33
Copper	0.33	Lead	0.43
Magnesium	0.35	Tin	0.33
Platinum	0.39	Gold	0.42

6. Volumetric Deformation. If the length (l) of a body is increased by ϵl, its lateral dimensions are decreased in accordance with Art. 5 and the new volume of a rectangular bar having lateral dimensions of b and d would be

$$l(1 + \epsilon) \cdot b(1 - \epsilon\lambda) \cdot d(1 - \epsilon\lambda) = lbd(1 + \epsilon - 2\epsilon\lambda) \dagger$$

But the original volume was lbd; hence the change of volume is $lbd(1 - 2\lambda)\epsilon$, and the relative change is $lbd(1 - 2\lambda)\epsilon$ divided by the original volume, or $(1 - 2\lambda)\epsilon$.

If we now apply an equal direct tension in the direction of b, we would increase this dimension by ϵb, and the volume by $lbd(1 - 2\lambda)\epsilon$ as before. A similar result is produced by a tensile force in the direction of d; hence, for a direct tensile force in all three directions, the volume will be increased by $3(1 - 2\lambda)\epsilon$ times its original volume, and each dimension by $(1 - 2\lambda)\epsilon$ times its original value. For a compressive force in all directions the volume will be diminished in the same ratio.

The volumetric modulus of elasticity for equal stresses in all directions will be equal to the unit stress divided by the relative strain $3(1 - 2\lambda)\epsilon$ or, if $E_v =$ volumetric modulus, $E_v = S/3(1 - 2\lambda)\epsilon$.

But S/ϵ is the value of Young's modulus, or E; hence,

$$E_v = \frac{E}{3(1 - 2\lambda)} \tag{2}$$

If, for example, $\lambda = \frac{1}{4}$, then $E_v = \frac{2}{3}E$.

7. Shearing Deformation and Shearing Modulus of Elasticity. Let $ABCD$, Fig. 1, represent a very small element of a body subjected to the shearing stresses V. The dimensions perpendicular to the plane of the paper may be taken as unity. For equilibrium the shearing stresses V must be equal on all four faces, the couple formed by the two vertical

---

* For λ for concrete and stone see Art. VII-21 and XV-24.
† Omitting terms containing ϵ^2 and ϵ^3, as ϵ is a small quantity.

forces being balanced by that formed by the two horizontal forces. The unit shearing stress will be $V/l = S_s$.

Taking a diagonal section on the line AC, it will be found that the stress on this section will be purely tensile and equal in intensity to the shearing stress; that is, $S_t = S_s$. Likewise, on the diagonal DB, the stress is compressive and has an intensity of $S_c = S_s$. The element will be deformed into a rhombus, as shown in Fig. 2. Assuming that the diagonals retain their original directions, each side will be deflected through an angle θ, and the total change of angle of each apex of the original figure will be 2θ. This angular change is a measure of the unit shearing de-

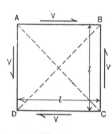
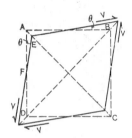

Fig. 1.   Fig. 2.

formation, and the unit shearing stress S_s divided by this relative deformation is called the *modulus of elasticity in shear;* or,

$$E_s = S_s/2\theta \qquad (3)$$

The value of θ can be calculated by a consideration of the effect of the direct tensile and compressive stresses S_t and S_c. The tensile stress S_t acts to increase the length along the diagonal DB by the amount $S_t l/\cos 45° E$, and to shorten the diagonal AC by the amount $S_t l\lambda/\cos 45° E$ where λ = Poisson's ratio. The compressive stress S_c causes a similar effect. The total lengthening of diagonal DB and total shortening of diagonal AC will then be equal to $S_s l(1 + \lambda)/\cos 45° E$.

From Fig. 2 the angle θ (in radians) is practically equal to $AE \cos 45/AF$; or, substituting from the preceding values, we have

$$\theta = S_s(1 + \lambda)/E \qquad (4)$$

The modulus of elasticity in shear is therefore equal to

$$E_s = \frac{S_s}{2\theta} = \frac{S_s E}{2S_s(1 + \lambda)} = \frac{E}{2(1 + \lambda)} \qquad (5)$$

This equation gives the theoretical relation between the shearing modulus and the modulus in direct stress.

In practice, it is difficult to determine experimentally the exact value of E_s corresponding to the theory herein given, on account of the presence of stresses other than those here considered and the fact that the shearing stresses vary from point to point in a test specimen. However, experimental values correspond approximately with the theoretical values determined by the above equation.

In steel, for example, $E = 30,000,000$ psi, $\lambda = 0.27$; hence, from eq. 5, $E_s = 30,000,000/2.54 = 11,800,000$. Bauschinger found from tests on round bars that $E_s = 13,600,000$, and from tests on square bars that $E_s = 11,500,000$ psi.

8. Characteristic Behavior of Materials under Stress. Materials differ very widely in their behavior under stress. Some of these differences, such as elasticity and plasticity, have already been mentioned. Other common characteristics are indicated by the following terms: ductile, brittle, stiff, flexible, tough, malleable, and hard.

Ductile materials are capable of being drawn out without necking down. Wrought iron, soft steel, and copper are ductile metals.

Brittle materials have little or no plasticity. Such materials show little deformation beyond the elastic limit, and will therefore fail suddenly and generally without warning. Cast iron, stone, brick, and concrete are materials that are comparatively brittle, but which have, however, a considerable amount of plasticity.

Stiff materials have a high modulus of elasticity, that is, a high ratio of stress to deformation. They deform little for a given load. Another sense in which this word is used is to indicate a material with relatively high elastic limit. Thus, a spring made of hard steel will have the same deformation per unit of load as one made of soft steel (the values of E being the same), but it will carry a greater load than the spring of soft steel, as the elastic limit is higher. It is therefore often called a *stiffer* spring. Technically speaking, the two have the same degree of stiffness.

Flexible materials will bend considerably without rupture. They have a low modulus of elasticity, or a low elastic limit and considerable ductility or plasticity beyond that limit. Willow and hickory are flexible woods.

Tough materials will withstand heavy shocks or will absorb a large amount of energy. Toughness is dependent upon strength and ductility or strength and flexibility. Mild steel, wrought iron, and hickory are tough materials.

Malleable materials can be hammered into thin sheets without rupture. Malleability is dependent upon the ductility and softness of the metal. Copper is very malleable, wrought iron and soft steel are somewhat malleable at ordinary temperatures but may be more easily worked at a red heat.

Hard materials offer high resistance to scratching or denting. They are not necessarily of great strength. White cast iron and chrome steel are such metals. Materials which offer high resistance to abrasion are also called hard, although they may not be highly resistant to indentation. Manganese steel is an example of such a material.

MATERIALS UNDER TENSILE STRESS

9. General Phenomena Accompanying Tensile Tests. When a body of uniform cross section is subjected to the action of a tensile force, it is elongated in the direction of this force by a proportionate amount equal to the average force per square inch divided by its modulus of elasticity; thus

$$e/l = \text{Proportionate elongation} = S/E$$

where e = total elongation, S = force or stress per unit area, and E = modulus of elasticity (Young's modulus). At the same time its lateral dimensions are reduced in accordance with Poisson's ratio, as described in Art. I-5. The rate of elongation in the direction of the force, and contraction in its transverse dimensions, continues in strict proportion to the amount of the external force, until the elastic limit is reached, when both the longitudinal elongation and the transverse contraction begin to increase at a more rapid rate, until finally, with the more ductile metals, the condition of perfect plasticity is reached, and the body elongates under a constant force, while the lateral dimensions reduce more and more, until rupture finally occurs.

If the external force or load, in pounds per square inch, is represented by vertical ordinates, and the corresponding elongations are represented by horizontal abscissas, then the action of the specimen under test may be indicated by what is known as a stress diagram, the vertical coordinates representing stress, and the horizontal coordinates the corresponding deformations. In Fig. 3 such stress diagrams are shown for zinc, cast iron, wrought iron, and steel. These lie on the upper side of the horizontal axis. If the same materials were to be subjected to compressive external forces, corresponding stress diagrams might be drawn in opposite directions, that is to say, downward and to the left, as indicated in Fig. 3, below the horizontal axis.

In Fig. 4 are shown portions of these same tensile diagrams with the deformation scale largely magnified, so as to bring out more clearly the characteristics of the various curves for small deformations. It will be noted that the diagram for zinc is curved almost from the beginning; the diagram for cast iron is straight for only a short distance; the diagrams for wrought iron and steel are straight until the stress has reached

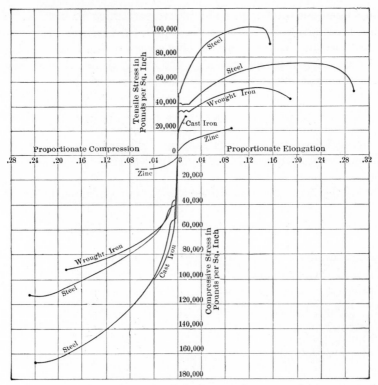

Fig. 3.   Typical stress diagrams of rolled zinc, cast iron, wrought iron, and steel in tension and compression.

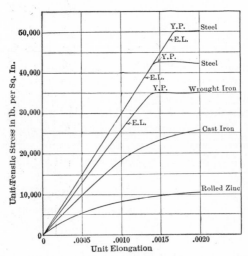

Fig. 4.   Typical tensile stress diagrams for rolled zinc, cast iron, wrought iron, and steel to enlarged scale.

50 to 60 per cent of the ultimate strength. The diagrams for zinc and cast iron are typical for materials of a non-homogeneous nature. Stone, brick, cement, concrete, and some of the brasses and bronzes behave in much the same way, as shown in Art. VII-22, XV-22, and Chapter XXX. Many of the more ductile metals behave in a manner similar to wrought iron and soft steel; when the point of plasticity is reached (Y.P.), a considerable deformation occurs with little or no increase of load, thus giving a horizontal notch in the curve.

10. The Significant Results of a Tensile Test. There are eight significant results of a tensile test, namely:

1. Proportional limit.
2. Modulus of elasticity.
3. Ultimate strength.
4. Percentage elongation.

5. Percentage reduction in area.
6. Modulus of resilience.*
7. Energy of rupture.*
8. Character of fracture.

11. The Elastic Strength and Its Indices. In Art. I-3, the elastic limit was defined as the maximum unit stress below which the material would fully recover its form on removal of the load. Since the determination of this critical stress involves a large number of applications and removals of loads, each somewhat larger than its predecessor, such determinations are tedious and rarely made. Approximations of the elastic limit are obtained from the proportional limit, yield point, and yield strength. The *proportional limit*, Fig. 4, a close approximation of the elastic limit, is the maximum unit stress within which the ratio of stress to deformation is constant. Since the stress diagram departs from a straight line at the proportional limit, the proportional limit may be determined from a large-scale diagram. This value has often been erroneously reported as the elastic limit.

In materials like timber, stone, and concrete, the elastic limit is low, since these materials show small permanent deformations or sets after low loads and exhibit stress diagrams which curve near the origin. For most metals, there is little or no set at low loads, the lower portion of the stress diagram is sensibly straight, and the elastic limit and proportional limit are relatively high. However, the exact point of departure of the curve from a straight line is difficult to determine, and its location depends on the precision of the observations and to some extent upon the scales of the stress diagram. The proportional limit is not, therefore, quickly determined. Hence in routine testing of wrought iron and structural steel the customary practice is to determine the *yield point*, the first unit stress at which deformation continues without an increase in load. The yield point is always higher than the elastic and proportional limits, commonly 5 to 15 per cent in structural steel.

* Defined on p. I-39.

To arrive speedily at a rough estimate of the elastic strength of metals like copper, aluminum, and their alloys, which have no yield point, determinations are now made of the *yield strength*. The yield strength is the unit stress corresponding to a small prescribed set. Thus, if a set of 0.001 in. per in. is specified, the yield strength may be found from the intersection of a line drawn 0.001 in. per in, from and parallel to the initial portion of the stress diagram (see Y.S., Fig. 5). The proximity of the yield strength to the proportional limit is dependent upon the magnitude of the set prescribed.

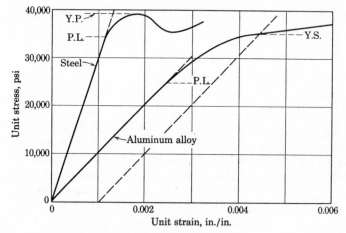

Fig. 5. Elastic portions of tensile stress diagrams for 1020 steel and 61S-T aluminum alloy.

Specifications for acceptance tests of metals sometimes require that the metal must develop a certain *proof stress* within a certain elongation. For example, structural steel might be required to sustain a proof stress of 30,000 psi, with a unit elongation not greater than 0.0012.

The original author of this work proposed that, in view of the difficulty of determining the elastic limit, *an apparent elastic limit* be taken *on the stress diagram at a point at which the rate of deformation is* 50 *per cent greater than at the origin*. This apparent elastic limit would approximate the yield point in materials having such a point and would give a reasonable elastic limit for such materials as cast iron or hard steel, for which this diagram shows a very gradual curvature. This meritorious criterion would accomplish the following results:

1. It always fixes one and the same well-defined point.

2. This point always corresponds to a permanent deformation so small as to be, for many practical purposes, the elastic limit.

3. It is equally applicable to all kinds of tests, whether on specimens or structures, where deformations can be correctly measured.

In Fig. 5 are shown the elastic portions of the tensile-stress diagrams for a steel and an aluminum alloy. Each has a proportional limit (P.L.) as shown, but the diagrams are quite different beyond the proportional limit. The diagram for the steel shows a definite yield point (Y.P.), whereas the diagram for the aluminum alloy shows the method of determining the yield strength (Y.S.) for a metal having no yield point.

12. The Modulus of Elasticity is determined from the initial slope of the stress diagram within the proportional limit. In finding this slope, the tangent of the angle between the curve and the deformation axis can be easily evaluated by using a multiple of unity as the deformation value. Thus, if we enter Fig. 4 with a unit deformation of 0.001, the corresponding unit stress for steel is 30,000 psi; hence $E = 30,000 \div 0.001 = 30,000,000$ psi. If an initial load is used, the slope may be easily read from a line drawn parallel to the original curve.

In materials having a curved diagram almost from the beginning, the modulus of elasticity is not so readily defined or determined. For very small unit stresses, it is taken as the slope of the tangent at the origin. Sometimes, however, as in concrete, the actual working stresses lie somewhat above the straight portion of the diagram; there will actually be a slight permanent set in such material under working loads. In such a case it is desirable to consider the modulus of elasticity to be the slope of the secant line (see Fig. XV-17) drawn from the origin to the point in the curve corresponding to the unit stress (S) in question. The slope of this line is then called the modulus of elasticity at the unit stress S. This use of the secant modulus is especially applicable to problems in reinforced concrete.

13. The Ultimate Strength of a specimen under tension is obtained by dividing the maximum load, which occurs at or just before rupture, by the original cross-sectional area. It is shown as the maximum ordinate on the stress diagram. For plastic metals the cross section at fracture is a third to a half the original area. Therefore, owing to such cold working of the metal, the actual breaking strength, found by dividing the breaking load by the final area, is two to three times the ultimate strength.

14. The Percentage of Elongation. This is found by dividing the increase in the gage length measured across the fracture by the original gage length. In the United States and England the standard gage length is usually 8 in. In Germany and France it is 20 cm, nearly the same length. The elongation of a specimen of plastic metal may be divided into two portions: (a) the elongation which is distributed uniformly along the length; (b) that part which is non-uniformly distributed in the vicinity of the fracture. Thus in Fig. 6 all specimens were originally of the length indicated by the untested specimen which stands on the right. The middle specimen has been stretched to the limit of the elongation indicated in (a) above, or until there is an indication of a local reduction of area. The left specimen shows the local elongation and reduction,

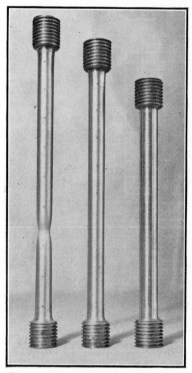

but the specimen was removed from the testing machine before rupture occurred. The middle specimen has been tested to the ultimate strength of the material, since, when the specimen begins to reduce locally, the ultimate strength has been passed, and the stress diagram begins to fall, or it is developed under a diminishing load.

By the amount, therefore, that the left specimen is longer than the middle specimen, by so much has the length been increased by the load drawing out on the section where failure will finally occur. The first elongation, therefore, is that portion which is uniformly distributed over the specimen, and the second is that which is concentrated in the vicinity of the final failure. Both of these elongations are, however, measured and included in the total elongation, from which the percentage of elongation is determined. The total elonga-

Fig. 6. The necking-down action of steel bars before rupture.

tion is obtained after rupture has occurred, by placing the two ends together and measuring the distance between the primitive gage marks. In specimens having shoulders at their ends the gage marks should be at least ½ in. inside the shoulder, since the metal adjacent to the shoulder does not elongate fully, because of the strengthening effect of the enlarged cross section at the ends.

The percentage of elongation is the result which indicates the ductility of the material, this being one of the most important qualities of the metals used in structural designing.

15. The Reduction of Area of Cross Section. This is found by determining the area of the broken cross section, subtracting this from the original area of cross section, and dividing the difference by the original area. This is not so important an indication or result as the others described above, but it is customary to determine it, and to add it to the record. For the ductile metals this reduction of area may be as much as 50 to 60 per cent of the original cross section.

16. Failure in Tension. Illustration of the types of failure common to brittle and ductile metals may be seen in Fig. III-6. In general, for ductile homogeneous materials the tensile elastic limit is reached when the shearing stress on any plane through the bar reaches the shearing elastic limit. This circumstance is followed and made evident by the appearance of fine lines called Luders lines on the surface, making angles of aproximately 45° with the axis of the test piece. The fracture of a ductile bar, like soft steel, shows a full cup and cone, the base angle of the cone also being about 45°. In the medium steels the cone is truncated, showing that the failure is partly shear and partly tensile. For very hard steels and other brittle materials the fracture is square across, showing that failure is due to tension.

Since the unit stress in shear on a 45° plane is $P/2A$ it follows that we may expect a cone or truncated-cone fracture whenever the ultimate shearing strength is less than half the *true* tensile strength * (i.e., tensile load divided by minimum area). When the true ultimate tensile strength is less than twice the shearing strength a square break will obtain.

Peculiarities in fracture are considered further under tests of various materials.

MATERIALS UNDER COMPRESSIVE STRESS

17. Two Classes of Engineering Materials. Engineering materials may be divided into two general classes, according to their manner of failure in compression.

Plastic or viscous materials are those which will flow without showing any other indication of failure, such as wrought iron, soft and medium steel, lead, copper, and zinc.

Brittle or comminutible materials are those which will crush to a powder, or crumble to pieces, or fail by shearing on definite angles under a compressive load, such as cast iron, hard or tempered steel, brick, stone,

---

* If we cut an oblique section through a bar under tension or compression and place upon the cut section equilibrating forces normal and tangential to it, the magnitude of the tangential component is $P \cos \theta$ and the intensity of shear stress is

$$S_s = P \cos \theta \div \frac{A}{\sin \theta} \quad \text{or} \quad S_s = \frac{P}{2A} \sin 2\theta$$

where P = end load, A = area of cross section, and θ = inclination of cut to axis of bar. $S_s = P/2A$, a maximum value when $\theta = 45°$.

and cement. The laws of failure of these two classes are very different, and they will, therefore, have to be discussed separately.

18. Crushing Strength of Plastic or Viscous Materials. There is no such thing as an "ultimate strength," in compression of a plastic body. There is, however, a definite yield point, the same as in tension. Beyond this limit the material simply spreads, and increases the area of its cross section indefinitely under an increasing load, as shown in Fig. III-11. This elastic limit in compression for wrought iron and steel is, fortunately, about the same in pounds per square inch as the elastic limit in tension. It is not customary, therefore, to test such materials in compression, but to assume that they have the same elastic limit in compression which they are found to have in tension.

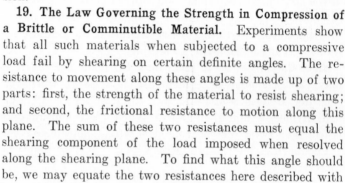

Fig. 7.

19. The Law Governing the Strength in Compression of a Brittle or Comminutible Material. Experiments show that all such materials when subjected to a compressive load fail by shearing on certain definite angles. The resistance to movement along these angles is made up of two parts: first, the strength of the material to resist shearing; and second, the frictional resistance to motion along this plane. The sum of these two resistances must equal the shearing component of the load imposed when resolved along the shearing plane. To find what this angle should be, we may equate the two resistances here described with the shearing force, and find the angle of rupture, the determining condition being that this angle shall be that which offers the least total resistance to failure under a crushing load. This angle, Fig. 7, may be found in the following manner:

Let S_s = shearing strength of the material per square inch.
A = area of prism = 1 sq in.
θ = angle of rupture.
S_c = crushing load per square inch.

The tendency to slide on the plane of rupture is $S_c \sin \theta$.
The resistance to sliding is $S_s \sec \theta + f S_c \cos \theta$, where f is the coefficient of friction = $\tan \phi$, where ϕ = angle of repose. Hence, at failure,

$$S_c \sin \theta = S_s \sec \theta + f S_c \cos \theta \qquad (6)$$

It is evident that the angle of rupture will be such as to cause failure under the least load; hence, if θ is taken as the independent variable, we shall have at rupture

$$dS_c/d\theta = -S_s(\cos^2 \theta - \sin^2 \theta + 2f \sin \theta \cos \theta) = 0$$

or
$$f = -\frac{\cos^2\theta - \sin^2\theta}{2\sin\theta\cos\theta} = -\frac{\cos 2\theta}{\sin 2\theta} = -\cot 2\theta \qquad (7)$$

Whence, since $f = \tan\phi$, we have

$$\tan\phi = -\cot 2\theta = -\tan(90° - 2\theta) = \tan(2\theta - 90°)$$

or $\qquad \phi = 2\theta - 90°$ and $\qquad \theta = \frac{90° + \phi}{2} = 45° + \frac{\phi}{2}$ $\qquad (8)$

That is to say, *the angle of rupture is 45° plus one-half the angle of repose.* If the friction had been omitted, we should have had

$$S_c \sin\theta = S_s \sec\theta \qquad \text{whence} \qquad dS_c/d\theta = -S_s(\cos^2\theta - \sin^2\theta) = 0$$

whence $\qquad\qquad \cos^2\theta = \sin^2\theta \qquad \text{or} \qquad \theta = 45° \qquad (9)$

It has been customary to neglect the friction, and to state that the planes of rupture make this angle of 45° with the horizontal; * but the actual plane of rupture, when the specimen has sufficient height, is about 55° with the horizontal, or 35° from the direction of the applied load. (See Fig. III-12, for photographic views of crushed specimens of cast-iron cylinders of various heights, showing angle of rupture.)

20. Relation of Crushing Strength to Shearing Strength. To show the relation of the crushing strength to the shearing strength, we have, from eq. 6 above,

$$S_s = S_c(\sin\theta\cos\theta - f\cos^2\theta)$$

also, from eq. 7,

$$f = -\cot 2\theta = -\frac{\cos 2\theta}{\sin 2\theta} = -\frac{\cos^2\theta - \sin^2\theta}{2\sin\theta\cos\theta}$$

Substituting this value of f, we find

$$S_s = \frac{S_c \cos\theta}{2\sin\theta} = \frac{1}{2}S_c \cot\theta \qquad (10)$$

or $\qquad\qquad\qquad S_c = 2S_s \tan\theta \qquad\qquad (11)$

21. Column Action. If the length of a compression member is more than ten times its least lateral dimension the member is likely to bend and the intensity of stress on the concave side of it will be augmented by the bending stress which arises from the eccentricity of the load. Strictly, the liability to lateral bending is dependent primarily upon the ratio of the length of the column to the least radius of gyration of the cross section—the slenderness ratio. In the short columns, where the

* *Coulomb* is responsible for this theory; *Navier* has given the true analysis. Most writers, including Rankine, have followed Coulomb, however.

slenderness ratio is less than 125, the effect of the lateral bending is of small moment; but in long columns it may be the controlling factor. Other factors which influence column action are the condition of the ends, the homogeneity of the member, stiffness, and the position of the load with respect to the center of resistance of the column.

There are four types of end conditions which are common: round end—the end is free to rotate; fixed end—the axis of the column has a fixed position near the column end; square end—end of column and abutting surface are perpendicular to the axis; pin end—rotation of the column end is permitted in one plane only. Figure 8 illustrates the be-

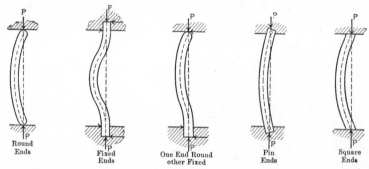

Round Ends   Fixed Ends   One End Round other Fixed   Pin Ends   Square Ends

Fig. 8.   Effects of various types of end conditions on the bending of columns.

havior of a column under these different end conditions. These theoretical conditions are not realized in practice. In the round- and pin-end columns friction at the bearings produces restraint; on the other hand, no support is sufficiently rigid to produce a fixed end.

Because of the uncertainty regarding conditions at the ends, regarding action between parts, and regarding the position of the load with respect to the axis of the column, theoretical analyses of column action are more or less rough and the main reliance of the designer is the information obtained from tests. The more important formulas for columns under axial loading will now be very briefly considered.

Euler's Formula. For straight and homogeneous long columns under axial loading a rational formula is that derived by Euler:

$$P/A = mE/(l/r)^2 \qquad (12)$$

where P = critical load which produces failure of the column by lateral bending; A = area of cross section; m = a constant depending on end conditions (theoretically $m = \pi^2$ for round ends, $4\pi^2$ for fixed ends, and $2.05\pi^2$ for one end fixed and the other round). With conditions of practice, $m = 3\pi^2$ for square ends and $1\frac{2}{3}\pi^2$ for pin ends, E = modulus of elasticity and l/r = slenderness ratio. Since the formula considers failure due to lateral flexure only and contains no term related to the compressive strength, it cannot be used to design or investigate short columns. Whenever the value of P/A computed by this formula exceeds one-third of the ultimate compressive strength of the material, Fig. 9, the result should be rejected and another column formula used. Safe loads are derived from this formula by dividing P by a suitable factor of safety.

The Secant Formula. This is the most precise column formula, but it is also unwieldy to use. For an ultimate load eccentric to both principal axes, this formula for steel columns with both ends round is

$$\frac{P}{A} = \frac{S_y}{1 + \frac{e_1 c_1}{r_1^2} \sec \sqrt{\frac{P}{AE}\frac{l}{2r_1}} + \frac{e_2 c_2}{r_2^2} \sec \sqrt{\frac{P}{AE}\frac{l}{2r_2}}} \tag{13}$$

where P = ultimate load, A = area of cross section, S_y = yield point of material, e_1 = eccentricity of load from principal axis 1–1, c_1 = distance to outer fiber from 1–1, r_1 = radius of gyration about 1–1, l = free length of column, and E = modulus of elasticity. The subscript 2 refers to the 2–2 principal axis. For round-end columns of structural steel with eccentricity in one plane,

$$\frac{P}{A} = \frac{36,000}{1 + \frac{ec}{r^2} \sec \sqrt{\frac{P/A}{29,400,000}\frac{l}{2r}}}$$

is an accurate formula.* For flat ends $0.56l$ should be substituted for l.

Rankine's Formula. A semi-rational formula which holds in a very rough way for a wide range of slenderness ratios is

$$\frac{P}{A} = \frac{S}{1 + \phi(l/r)^2} \tag{14}$$

where P = ultimate load, A = area of cross section, S = ultimate compressive strength of a short prism, ϕ = an empirical constant, depending upon end conditions and kind of material, and l/r = slenderness ratio. For roughly determining ultimate strength of structural steel columns, S may be taken at 40,000 psi, ϕ for pin ends = 1/18,000, and ϕ for flat ends = 1/36,000.

Straight-Line Formula. T. H. Johnson worked out a straight-line formula which, in conjunction with Euler's formula, gives results approximating the breaking values obtained by Tetmajer from experiments on medium-steel struts. The formula is

$$P/A = S - Cl/r \tag{15}$$

* See Report on Steel Column Research, *Trans. ASCE*, Vol. 98, p. 1388.

Materials of Construction

Here C = slope of tangent to Euler's curve at the point where l/r = $(3mE/S)^{1/2}$ and $P/A = S/3$, or $C = \frac{2}{3}S(S/3mE)^{1/2}$; P = ultimate load; A = area of cross section; S = ultimate strength of short prism; l/r = slenderness ratio; and $m = \pi^2$, $1\frac{2}{3}\pi^2$, and $2\frac{1}{2}\pi^2$ for round, hinged, and

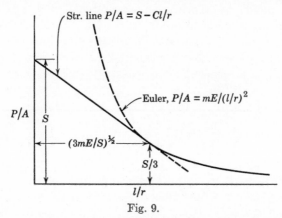

Fig. 9.

flat ends, respectively. Figure 9 shows the straight-line and the tangent Euler curves. Johnson's constants for steel and cast iron are given in Table 1. The data for the Duralumin is from the Aluminum Co. of Amer-

TABLE 1

Kind of Column.	S, lb./in.^{2}	C, lb./in.^{2}	Limit of $\dfrac{l}{r}$.
Cast iron:			
Flat ends....................	80,000	438	122
Duralumin (17 S-T)			
Fixed ends..................	43,800	175	166
Round ends.................	43,800	350	83
Structural steel:			
Flat ends...................	52,500	179	195
Hinged ends................	52,500	220	159
Round ends.................	52,500	284	123

ica *Structural Aluminum Handbook*, in which pin ends have been considered equivalent to round ends.

The straight-line type of column formula, on account of its simplicity, found considerable favor among architects and engineers; and such formulas have been used in specifications and in the building laws.

The Parabolic Formula. From a thorough study of the results of a large number of tests by M. Considère on small steel bars, from tests by Tetmajer on a variety of steel and iron sections, and from his own tests on timber, J. B. Johnson concluded that the strength of short columns was limited by the yield point of the material.* He proposed the following formula:

$$P/A = S_y - f(l/r)^2 \qquad (16)$$

This is the equation of a parabola which is tangent to Euler's curve if $f = S_y^2/4mE$. The ordinate of the point of tangency is $S_y/2$, and the corresponding abscissa is $(2mE/S_y)^{1/2}$. In the above expressions $P =$ ultimate load; $A =$ area of cross section; $S_y =$ compressive yield point; $l/r =$ slenderness ratio; $m = 1.6\pi^2$ and $3.0\pi^2$ for columns with hinged and flat ends, respectively; and $E =$ modulus of elasticity in compression. For structural steel $S_y = 36,000$ psi, $f = 0.72$ for pin ends and 0.36 for flat ends, and the limiting values of l/r for pin and flat ends are 158 and 224, respectively.

Numerous tests of rectangular columns with round ends, at the Forest Products Laboratory, indicate that a fourth-power parabola $P/A = S[1 - \frac{1}{3}(l/Kd)^4]$, and the tangent Euler curve, $P/A = (\pi^2 E)/12(l/d)^2$, best measure the strengths of timber columns with round ends. In these expressions S is the average ultimate compressive strength of short prisms, d is the least dimension, $K = (\pi/2)\sqrt{E/2S}$, and the other terms have the significance previously stated. The ordinate at the point of tangency of these two curves is $2S/3$, and the abscissa is a value of l/d equal to K. For values of l/d less than $K/2$ the strengths of timber columns are nearly constant and equal S.

For a working formula, the above laboratory has developed the fourth-power parabola and corresponding Euler tangent given in Art. VI-25. This fourth-power parabola has a factor of safety approximating 4, and its Euler tangent a factor of safety of 3 based on the formulas for ultimate strength of round-end columns. In applying the fourth-power parabola and its Euler tangent formula to building and bridge construction, no allowance for end restraint is recommended; hence for long columns with restrained ends the actual factor of safety is somewhat greater than 3.

Of the simple formulas for the strength of axially loaded columns, those of the parabolic type are the most accurate.

* A conclusion which the results of tests on large columns at the National Bureau of Standards Laboratory reaffirms. See *Eng. News*, Vol. 75, p. 190; also Vol. 76, pp. 49 and 81. See also Report on Column Research, *Trans. ASCE, op. cit.*

MATERIALS UNDER SHEARING STRESS

22. Two Manifestations of Shearing Stress. When all the opposing external forces which act on a body lie in one plane,* but not in the same line, the resisting stresses are those of simple shear and cross bending, without torsional stress.

When the opposing external forces do not lie in one plane the resisting stresses are those of torsional shear, with or without cross bending and simple shear.

In any case these three kinds of stress are determined separately, as follows:

(*a*) *For Parallel External Forces in One Plane.* The moment of resistance of the bending (direct) stresses at any transverse section is equal to the algebraic sum of the moments of the external forces on either side of that section taken about the neutral axis in that section.

The simple shearing stress on any section is equal to the algebraic sum of the transverse components of the external forces on either side of that section.

(*b*) *For Parallel External Forces Not in One Plane.* First replace all the forces by equal parallel forces acting in the plane of the axis of the body, and by couples equal in value in each case to the force multiplied by its displacement. Then the moments of resistance and the simple shearing stresses will be the same as in the last case, and in addition there will be the moment of torsion.

The torsional moment at any transverse section is equal to the algebraic sum of the moments of the couples of the displaced forces, acting on either side of the transverse section in question.

(*c*) *For Non-Parallel Forces Acting in Any Manner.* Resolve all forces into horizontal and vertical components at their points of application, and then solve for bending moments, and torsions at any section in these two planes.

The bending moment at this section will then be the square root of the sum of the squares of the bending moments at right angles to each other.

The total shear will also be the square root of the sum of the squares of the primary shears at right angles to each other.

The total moment of torsion will be the algebraic sum of the two moments of torsion found from the two sets of forces.

23. Shearing Stress Due to Torsion. In a solid or hollow member of circular cross section the twisting moment produces shearing defor-

---

* When a force is distributed over an area it is here supposed to act at the center of gravity of these force elements.

mations which, at any transverse section, vary from zero at the axis to a maximum on the surface. If the member is not deformed beyond its elastic limit the shearing deformations vary directly as the distance from the center of the cross section; consequently the intensity of stress varies in a like maner, Fig. 10a. If S_s is the intensity of stress on the outer fiber of a shaft having a radius r, the moment of stress on any element da at z distance from the axis is $(S_s z^2/r)\, da$ and the total moment of all stresses is $S_s J/r$, where J is the polar moment of inertia of the cross

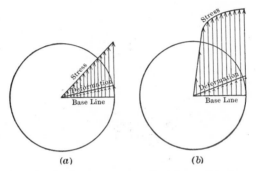

Fig. 10.   The relation of unit shear stress to unit deformation in a solid round shaft. (a) Stresses within elastic limit; (b) overstrained.

section about the axis. This is the resisting torsional moment and must equal the external twisting moment M_t, or

$$M_t = S_s J/r \qquad (17)$$

For a solid round shaft $J = \frac{1}{2}\pi r^4$, and, for a hollow shaft with inner radius r_1, $J = \frac{1}{2}\pi(r^4 - r_1^4)$.

Formula 17 does not hold exactly for sections other than circular. For other sections approximate values of the factor J/r may be computed from the radius of the inscribed circle. Thus for a square shaft, with sides $= d$, the exact analysis gives $M_t = 0.2083 S_s d^3$, which is about 5.9 per cent greater than the value for a solid round shaft of diameter d. For a solid elliptical shaft of major axis a and minor axis b the exact value for $M_t = (\pi/16)S_s ab^2$. If $a = 2b$ then the exact value of M_t is double that for a round shaft of diameter b. Similarly for a rectangular shaft $M_t = a^2 b^2 S_s/(3a + 1.8b)$, where a is the length of the long side and b the length of the short side. The greatest intensity of stress in an elliptical or rectangular shaft occurs at the ends of the minor axis.

If the shaft is deformed beyond its elastic limit the shearing deformation increases approximately as the distance of the fiber from the axis, but the intensity of stress does not vary directly with the unit shearing deformation, Fig. 10b. Values of the ultimate shearing stress in torsion cannot, therefore, be computed from $S_s = M_t r / J$. Upton has made a mathematical analysis by which the true intensity of shearing stress in a solid round shaft may be obtained as follows: In Fig. 11 the solid-line curve represents the relation of unit stress S_s on the outside fiber to the unit deformation of the same fiber. In plotting this curve, S_s is computed by formula 17 and ϵ_s must be determined by experiment. The true stresses are represented by ordinates to the EB' dashed line. To find the true stress DB' corresponding to a unit shearing deformation on the surface $= AB$, draw BD perpendicular to AD and prolong the tangent at B until it intersects the S_s axis at C; then $DB' = DB - (AC/4)$. For ductile materials the shearing stress-deformation curve is approximately parallel to the deformation axis at the maximum S_s; therefore the true ultimate shearing stress is

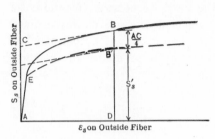

Fig. 11. Method of finding true unit shear stress in an overstrained solid round shaft (Upton).

$$S_s' = \frac{3}{4}\frac{M_t r}{J} = 0.477 \frac{M_t}{r^3} \tag{18}$$

For hollow shafts of ductile material in which the thickness is less than a fifth of the outer radius the intensity of shearing stress is approximately uniform throughout the cross section when the shaft is stressed to the ultimate; therefore the maximum unit shearing stress is approximately

$$S_s = \frac{2M_t}{\pi(r + r_1)^2(r - r_1)} \tag{19}$$

24. Shearing Deformations. As shown in Art. I-7, a shearing action of external forces results in angular deformation of the body. In simple shear, or where the forces lie in one plane, the angular deformation from shear is very small, the bending being mostly due to the longitudinal deformations resulting in the direct tensile and compressive resisting stresses on the two sides of the neutral plane respectively.* When the forces do not lie in one plane, or when there is a moment of torsion, the angular deformation gives rise to a twist of the body about the longitudinal axis. Thus in Fig. 12 assume the solid cylinder, anchored at O, to have a length l and a radius r. Let the torsional moment be $Pa = M_t$.

* Shear in beams is discussed in Art. I-28.

Then $S_s = M_t r/J = 2Pa/\pi r^3$. From Fig. 12 the unit shearing deformation of an outside fiber $\epsilon_s = r\theta/l$. From Art. 7, $\epsilon_s = S_s/E_s$; hence

$$\theta = M_t l/E_s J \qquad (20)$$

In the above and subsequent expressions θ is in radians. Formula 20 holds for hollow or solid round shafts for stresses within the elastic limit. The angle of twist for a square shaft of side d is $\theta = 7.11 M_t l/E_s d^4$, or 43 per cent more than θ for a solid round shaft. For an elliptical section $\theta = 4\pi^2 M_t J l/A^4 E_s$. A is the area of cross section, and J is the polar moment of inertia. This is also an approximate formula for the twist of rectangular shafts.

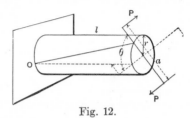

Fig. 12.

Both the torsional stiffness and torsional strength of shafts of any cross section can be accurately determined from soap-film experiments (see *Rept.* 334 of U. S. National Advisory Committee for Aeronautics).

The fracture of ductile materials under torsion is generally square across. Wrought iron and some of the brasses show a rope-like twisting of the fibers before a square break ensues. Brittle materials like cast iron, stone, brick, and concrete exhibit a helicoid fracture. These substances being weak in tension really fail through the secondary tensile stresses which are produced by two pairs of shearing stresses acting in planes tangent to the surface of the shaft. One of these pairs of forces acts perpendicular to the surface elements; the other pair acts parallel to the elements. Consequently, on a plane at $45°$ with the axis of the shaft, there is produced a unit tensile stress S_t, which is equal to the intensity of the shear stress S_s (Art. I-7).

MATERIALS UNDER CROSS-BENDING STRESS

25. Fundamental Principles. When a member is bent by forces applied transversely with respect to its axis, cross-bending stresses are produced. The simplest system of forces which will cause such stresses is a coplanar parallel system acting in a plane containing the longitudinal axis of the member. Such a member is called a beam. Frequently beams are horizontal, the loads are produced by gravity pulls on suspended masses and the supporting forces are upward. Under the action of these forces the beam is bent and observation shows that the fibers on its convex surface are elongated, those on its concave surface are shortened, and that there must be a plane of fibers between the convex and concave surfaces which suffers no deformation. This plane is called the neutral surface. Hence tension exists in the fibers between the neutral and the convex surfaces, and compression exists in the fibers between the neutral and the concave surfaces of the beam.

It will be assumed that the beam is symmetrical, initially straight, homogeneous, of material having equal stiffness in tension and compression, that it is not stressed beyond its elastic limit by the loads, that the bending is slight, and that the plane of the external forces coincides with a plane of symmetry. If the beam is severed transversely it will be necessary, in order that equilibrium may obtain, to place a system of forces on either cut surface similar to that shown in the lower part of Fig. 13. Then from the principles of statics we know that:

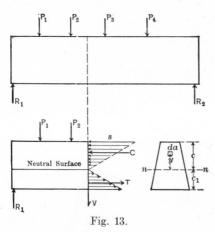

Fig. 13.

1. The vertical shear V equals the sum of the vertical forces on the left of the cut.

2. The total compression C equals the total tension T.

3. The sum of the moments of the tensile and compressive stresses on the portion shown equals the algebraic sum of the moment of the external forces to the left of the section.

From experimental evidence it is known that the unit deformations vary directly as the distance of the fiber from the neutral surface; consequently the intensity of stress varies in like manner.

From these considerations it is easily shown that the total horizontal stress on the cut is $0 = \dfrac{S}{c} \sum\limits_{c_1}^{c} y \, da$, where S is the unit stress on the extreme fiber at c distance from the neutral axis, y is the distance from the neutral axis to any elementary area (Fig. 13) and the summation is taken for the entire cross section. Since S/c is finite it follows that $\sum\limits_{c_1}^{c} y \, da = 0$, or the neutral axis must pass through the center of gravity of the cross section.

26. Resisting Moment Equals Bending Moment. Taking moments of the stresses about the trace of the neutral surface $(n\text{–}n)$ and using same notation, we have $M_R = \dfrac{S}{c} \sum\limits_{c_1}^{c} y^2 \, da = \dfrac{S}{c} I$. Since the resisting moment (M_R) equals the bending moment (M),

$$M = SI/c \tag{21}$$

For selecting a beam to carry a given loading, S is known and M can be computed by taking the algebraic sum of the moments of all forces on either side of the dangerous section; therefore I/c may be ascertained and the section designed. To determine the safe load for a given beam: S, I, and c are known or may be computed, and M is expressed in terms of the unknown load which can then be found. The third type of problem consists in finding the unit stress at a certain section of a given beam. In this problem M is computed for the given section; I and c are known, and S can be determined.

Values of the moment of inertia and resisting moment for several common beam sections appear in Table 2.

TABLE 2

Form of Cross-section.	Distance of Center of Gravity, or Neutral Axis, from the Most Distant Fiber. $=c$	Moments of Inertia about the Center of Gravity of the Section. $=I$	Moment of Resistance in Terms of the Stress in the Most Distant Fiber. $=M_r=\dfrac{SI}{c}$
	$\dfrac{d}{2}$	$\dfrac{bd^3}{12}$	$\dfrac{1}{6}Sbd^2$
	$\dfrac{d}{2}$	$\dfrac{\pi d^4}{64}$	$\dfrac{\pi}{32}Sd^3$
	$\dfrac{2}{3}h$	$\dfrac{bh^2}{36}$	$\dfrac{1}{24}Sbh^2$
	$\dfrac{d}{2}\sqrt{2}$	$\dfrac{d^4}{12}$	$\dfrac{1}{6\sqrt{2}}Sd^3$
	$\dfrac{h}{2}$	$\dfrac{bh^3-(b-t')(h-2t)^3}{12}$	$\dfrac{bh^3-(b-t')(h-2t)^3S}{6h}$
	$\dfrac{\frac{1}{2}t'h^2+t(b-t')(h-\frac{1}{2}t)}{t'h+t(b-t')}$	$\dfrac{bh^3-(b-t')(h-t)^3}{3}-Ac^2$	$\dfrac{SI}{c}$
	$\dfrac{b+2b'}{b+b'}\cdot\dfrac{h}{3}$	$h^3\left[\dfrac{3b+b'}{12}-\dfrac{(b+2b')^2}{18(b+b')}\right]$	$\dfrac{Sh^2}{6}\left[\dfrac{3(3b+b')(b+b')}{2(b+2b')}-(b+2b')\right]$

When the plane of the loads does not contain an axis of symmetry of the section, then the neutral axis is not in general perpendicular to the plane of the loads and the above formulas are inexact. In such cases the principal axes of the section (see moment of inertia in applied mechanics) may be determined; the bending moment is resolved into the planes of these axes; and the unit stress on a given fiber is found by adding algebraically the stress due to each moment considered separately. In finding the stress due to a component moment, the neutral plane for that moment is the plane of the principal axis perpendicular to that moment. Thus if x and y are the principal axes of the section and the z-axis coincides with the longitudinal axis of the beam,

$S_1 = \dfrac{M_y y_1}{I_x} + \dfrac{M_x x_1}{I_y}$. Where S_1 is the unit stress on fiber whose coordinates are x_1 and y_1 with respect to the principal axes, M_x is the component of the bending moment in the xz-plane, M_y is the component in the yz-plane, I_x is the moment of inertia about the x-axis, and I_y about the y-axis.

27. Stresses in Overstressed Beams. The flexure formula 21 does not hold for beams of materials where E_c does not equal E_t or for beams stressed beyond the elastic limit. In the latter case the intensity of

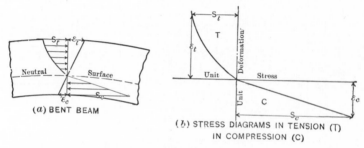

Fig. 14.

stress does not vary as the distance of the fiber from the neutral axis but follows the law of the variation of the stress ordinates to a stress diagram in which the extreme ordinate represents the stress on the extreme fiber of the beam. If the ultimate strengths in tension and compression are unequal, the neutral axis will shift toward the stronger side of the beam as the overstressing proceeds. Thus the stress variation in a beam of cast iron, which is much stronger in compression than in tension, is illustrated in Fig. 14. The unit deformation (ϵ_t) of the outside fiber in tension (Fig. 14a) corresponds to a unit stress S_t in the stress diagram of Fig. 14b. Similarly S_c for the bottom fiber and the unit stresses for other fibers may be found. If the load is increased until S_t equals the ultimate tensile strength of the cast iron, failure begins. Concrete, brick, and stone beams fail similarly; but a wooden beam, being weaker in compression, will fail first in compression.

If formula 21 be applied to find stresses beyond the elastic limit, it is evident from the foregoing that the results will be fictitious. In gen-

eral the value of S_m, found when M_m is the maximum moment, will lie
between the ultimate tensile and compressive strengths for the material.
It is called the modulus of rupture. If the shape and size of specimen
are maintained approximately constant, the modulus of rupture furnishes
a good index of the strength of different grades of material. For the
effect of variations in form on the modulus of rupture of cast-iron beams
see Art. III-22.

Upton has also worked out the true value of the unit stress on the
extreme fiber of an overstressed beam of rectangular cross section. A
curve is plotted as in Fig. 15 be-
tween the computed stresses on the
extreme fiber at the given section
and the unit deformations of the
same fiber. The true unit stress S'
corresponding to a given unit deformation OC is $CB' = CB - (OA/3)$,
AB being tangent to the curve OEB
at B. Ordinates to the dotted curve
EB' represents true unit stresses.
Use of the above method necessitates
measurement of the deflection and

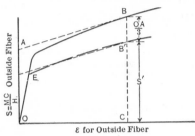

Fig. 15. Method of finding true unit
stress in an overstrained beam (Upton).

calculation of the values of ϵ, or direct measurement of the latter, which
is cumbersome. For ductile materials the stress-deformation curve is approximately horizontal when the maximum moment (M_m) is imposed;
therefore the true stress on the extreme fiber is two-thirds of the computed stress or

$$S_m' = \frac{2}{3}\frac{M_m c}{I} = \frac{4 M_m}{b d^2} \tag{22}$$

28. Variation in the Intensity of Shearing Stress within a Beam. If
a rectangular prism is cut from a beam and the forces necessary to equi-

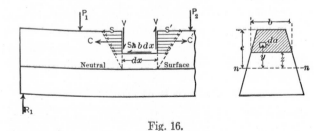

Fig. 16.

librium are placed on the cut surfaces as shown in Fig. 16, the occurrence
of a horizontal shearing stress acting along the surface which parallels

the neutral plane is noted. We shall now determine the average * intensity of this shearing stress S_h. Let M be the bending moment at the left end of the notch, M' the bending moment at the right end, S and S' the unit stresses on the extreme fibers at the left and right end of the notch, respectively, C the total stress on the right end, C' the total stress on the left end of notch, b the breadth of the bottom of the notch, and I the moment of inertia of the cross section about the neutral axis n–n. Then

$$C = \frac{S}{c} \sum_z^c y \, da \qquad \text{and} \qquad C' = \frac{S'}{c} \sum_z^c y \, da$$

therefore $C' - C = S_h b \, dx = \left[\dfrac{S'}{c} - \dfrac{S}{c} \right] \displaystyle\sum_z^c y \, da$

but $\dfrac{S'}{c} - \dfrac{S}{c} = \dfrac{M'}{I} - \dfrac{M}{I} = \dfrac{dM}{I}$

therefore $S_h b \, dx = \dfrac{dM}{I} \displaystyle\sum_z^c y \, da$

and $S_h = \dfrac{dM}{dx \, Ib} \displaystyle\sum_z^c y \, da$

Since $dM/dx = V$, we have

$$S_h = \frac{V}{Ib} \sum_z^c y \, da \tag{23}$$

In the above expression $\displaystyle\sum_z^c y \, da$ is the statical moment of the shaded area in Fig. 16 about the neutral axis n–n. Since it can easily be shown that the intensity of the vertical and horizontal shearing stresses at any point in a beam must be equal to produce equilibrium (see Fig. 1), it follows that values of the vertical unit shearing stress S_v may also be obtained by formula 23.

For a rectangular beam the intensity of the horizontal shear at any section varies, in accordance with the ordinates to a parabola, from zero at the outside fibers to a maximum at the neutral axis. For such beams the maximum value of the horizontal or vertical unit shearing stress is

$$S_h = S_v = 3V/2bd \tag{24}$$

where b = the breadth and d the depth of the cross section; that is, the maximum intensity is $\frac{3}{2}$ of the mean intensity of shearing stress. Figure

---

* The intensity of shearing stress on a horizontal plane is in general not uniform. For rectangular beams with $d > 2b$ it is nearly so.

17 shows how the total shear and the intensity of the horizontal and vertical unit shearing stresses vary in a rectangular beam under uniform load.

In a solid circular section the maximum intensity of shearing stress is $\frac{4}{3}$ of the mean intensity.

For an I-beam or plate girder the maximum intensity of shear stress is practically equal to the total shear at the section divided by the area of the web.

Shear in Wooden Beams. It becomes necessary to design wooden beams for horizontal shear when the safe load in shear is less than the safe load in bending. This condition occurs only in short deep beams. Thus for a uniformly loaded rectangular beam of simple span, the safe load in bending is $W_b = 4Sbd^2/3l$ and the safe load in shear is $W_s = \frac{4}{3}S_h bd$. If $W_s < W_b$, then must $S_h/d < S/l$.

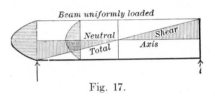

Fig. 17.

When the load is concentrated at the center, if $W_s < W_b$, then must $S_h/d < S/2l$. Here S and S_h are the allowable unit stresses in bending and horizontal shear, respectively, and b, d, and l are the breadth, depth, and length of the beam in the same linear units as those in which S is expressed.

29. Deflection of Beams due to Bending Moment. Let Fig. 18 represent a portion of a bent beam. We shall now derive an expression for

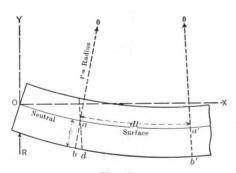

Fig. 18.

the radius of curvature and the differential equation by which the deflection of the neutral surface with respect to a set of axes may be determined. The elongation of the lower outer fiber of length dl, found by drawing ad parallel to $a'b'$, is bd. The unit elongation is $bd/dl = \epsilon$, and the unit stress in the fiber is $S = \epsilon E$. From the similarity of triangles oaa' and abd we have $r/dl = c/db$. Therefore $r = c/\epsilon = cE/S$. Since $S = Mc/I$ we have finally

$$r = EI/M \qquad (25)$$

From calculus, $r = \dfrac{[1 + (dy/dx)^2]^{\frac{3}{2}}}{d^2y/dx^2}$. Since in beams the curvature is slight, $(dy/dx)^2$ is negligible compared to 1, therefore approximately $d^2y/dx^2 = 1/r$. Substituting in eq. 25 we have

$$EI(d^2y/dx^2) = M \qquad (26)$$

In using this equation one must know the relation of E, I, and M to the variables y and x. Commonly E and I are constants and M can be expressed in terms of the variable x. The first integration gives the equation of the slope of the neutral axis with respect to the x-axis, the second

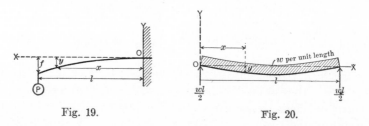

Fig. 19.   Fig. 20.

integration furnishes the equation of the neutral axis, or the elastic curve, with respect to the coordinate axes.

To illustrate the use of eq. 26 we shall determine the deflection of a cantilever beam with an end load, Fig. 19. The bending moment at any section, x distance from the support, is $-P(l - x)$; hence

$$(a) \quad EI\frac{d^2y}{dx^2} = -P(l - x)$$

$$(b) \quad EI\frac{dy}{dx} = -Plx + \frac{Px^2}{2} + c$$

$$[c = 0, \text{ since } dy/dx = 0 \text{ when } x = 0]$$

$$(c) \quad EIy = -\frac{Plx^2}{2} + \frac{Px^3}{6} + c_1$$

$$[c_1 = 0, \text{ since } x = 0 \text{ when } y = 0]$$

The deflection is a maximum when $x = l$;

$$\therefore y_{max} = f = -\frac{Pl^3}{3EI} \qquad (27)$$

The moment for this loading is a maximum at the support and equals $-Pl$.

As a second illustration consider a simple beam with a uniform load, Fig. 20. The moment equation for any section, x distance from the left support, is $\dfrac{wlx}{2} - \dfrac{wx^2}{2}$; hence

(d) $EI\dfrac{d^2y}{dx^2} = \dfrac{wlx}{2} - \dfrac{wx^2}{2}$

(e) $EI\dfrac{dy}{dx} = \dfrac{wlx^2}{4} - \dfrac{wx^3}{6} + c$

$$\left[\dfrac{dy}{dx} = 0 \text{ when } x = \dfrac{l}{2} \quad \therefore c = -\dfrac{wl^3}{24}\right]$$

(f) $EIy = \dfrac{wl^3}{12} - \dfrac{wx^4}{24} - \dfrac{wl^3x}{24} + c_1$

$$[x = 0 \text{ when } y = 0 \quad \therefore c_1 = 0]$$

The maximum deflection is found by substituting $x = l/2$ in equation f; therefore

$$y_{\max} = f = -5wl^4/384EI \tag{28}$$

The moment for this load is maximum at the center and equals $wl^2/8$.

The use of eq. 26 becomes more tedious when the bending-moment equation is a discontinuous function of x. In such cases it is generally necessary to determine the equation of the elastic curve for each portion of the beam. Elimination of the constants of integration is facilitated by remembering that the two slope equations for adjacent portions of the beam have a common value at the point of discontinuity; likewise the ordinate equations have equal values at this point. For the solution of the more complicated cases the student is referred to treatises on applied mechanics.

Values of the maximum moments and deflections for other beams under common types of loading appear in Table 3.

30. Deflection of Beams due to Shear. Besides the deflection due to bending moment there is a very slight deflection due to shear. This is of importance only in short deep beams where $l < 10d$. The shearing deflection may be closely approximated by equating the energy stored by the fibers in the beam to the work done by the load in moving through a distance equal to the shearing deflection.* For a rectangular cantilever with an end load P, the shearing deflection is $f_s = \%(Pl/E_sbd)$; for a rectangular simple beam with a load P at the middle it is $f_s = \frac{3}{10}(Pl/E_sbd)$.

* For other cases, see Timoshenko's *Strength of Materials*, Pt. I, Second Ed., 1940, D. Van Nostrand Co., Art. 39 and 66.

Materials of Construction

TABLE 3. MAXIMUM MOMENTS AND DEFLECTIONS FOR BEAMS

Method of Loading.	Max. Moment, M.	Max. Deflection, f.
	$M = -\dfrac{wl^2}{2}$	$f = \dfrac{wl^4}{8EI}$
	$M = \dfrac{Pl}{4}$	$f = \dfrac{Pl^3}{48EI}$
	$M = \dfrac{Pab}{l}$	$f = \dfrac{Pb}{27EIl}\sqrt{3[a(2b+a)]^3}$ for $x = \frac{1}{3}\sqrt{3[a(2b+a)]}$
	$M = Pa$	$f = \dfrac{Pa}{6EI}[\frac{3}{4}l^2 - a^2]$
	$R_1 = \dfrac{P}{2l^3}[3lb^2 - b^3]$ $M = R_1 a$, pos. $M = R_1 l - Pb$, neg.	$f = \dfrac{Pb^2}{6EI}(l-b)\sqrt{\dfrac{l-b}{3l-b}}$ for $x = l\left(1 - \sqrt{\dfrac{l-b}{3l-b}}\right)$ if $a > 0.414l$
	$R_1 = \frac{5}{8}wl$ $M = -\dfrac{wl^2}{8}$ for $x = 0$ $M = +\dfrac{9wl^2}{128}$ for $x = \dfrac{3l}{8}$	$f = 0.0054\dfrac{wl^4}{EI}$ for $x = 0.578l$
	$M = -\dfrac{Pl}{8}$ for $x = 0$ $M = +\dfrac{Pl}{8}$ for $x = \dfrac{l}{2}$	$f = \dfrac{Pl^3}{192EI}$
	$M = -\dfrac{wl^2}{12}$ for $x = 0$ $M = +\dfrac{wl^2}{24}$ for $x = \dfrac{l}{2}$	$f = \dfrac{wl^4}{384EI}$

For uniform loads equal to P in each of the above cases the deflection is only $\frac{1}{3}$ as much. From the above it appears that the deflection of a rectangular beam due to shear is to the deflection due to bending as Kd^2/l^2. Assuming $E_s/E = \frac{2}{5}$, then $K = \frac{3}{4}$ for a cantilever with an end load, 3 for a simple beam with a center load, $\frac{2}{3}$ for a cantilever with a uniform load, and 1.6 for a simple beam with a uniform load.

31. Curved Beams. When the axis of a homogeneous beam is curved, bending of the beam produces stresses which cannot be accurately calculated by the formulas of Art. I-26. If the axis of the beam lies in a

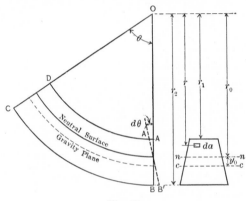

Fig. 21.

plane curve which cuts the principal axis of each cross section and the forces act in that plane, it is sufficiently exact, however, to assume that the total deformations vary as the distances of the fibers from the neutral surface; but since the fibers are of unequal length the unit deformations, hence unit stresses, will not so vary. As a result of this condition the neutral surface does not, in general, include the gravity axis of the beam.

Let Fig. 21 represent a small portion of a bent beam.* Consider the end CD fixed and suppose $A'B'$ to be the position assumed by AB after bending. Then the unit deformation of any fiber with cross section da is $\epsilon = (r \, d\theta - r_0 \, d\theta)/r\theta$ and the unit stress $\epsilon E = [(r - r_0)E \, d\theta]/r\theta$. The position of the neutral axis is obtained by equating the total stress on the cross section to zero; or $0 = \int_{r_1}^{r_2} [(r - r_0)E \, d\theta/r\theta] \, da$; since $E \, d\theta/\theta$ does not equal zero but is a constant for any given section we have

---

* For I-, T-, or U-shaped beams of sharp curvature, having web thickness less than $\frac{1}{2}$ the flange width, the radial stresses are important. See *Bull.* 195, Univ. Ill. Eng. Expt. Sta.

$$r_0 = \frac{A}{\displaystyle\int_{r_1}^{r_2} da/r} \tag{29}$$

The resisting moment

$$M_R = \frac{E\,d\theta}{\theta} \int_{r_1}^{r_2} \frac{(r - r_0)^2}{r}\,da \tag{30}$$

and the unit stress on the inner fiber due to a bending moment M is

$$S_1 = \frac{(r_1 - r_0)M}{r_1} \frac{1}{\displaystyle\int_{r_1}^{r_2} [(r - r_0)^2/r]\,da} \tag{31}$$

On the outer fiber,

$$S_2 = \frac{(r_2 - r_1)M}{r_2} \frac{1}{\displaystyle\int_{r_1}^{r_2} [(r - r_0)^2/r]\,da} \tag{32}$$

TABLE 4

Section.	r_0	$\displaystyle\int_{r_1}^{r_2}\frac{(r-r_0)^2}{r}da$
	$\dfrac{d}{\log_e \dfrac{r_1+d}{r_1}}$	$b\left[d\dfrac{(r_2+r_1-4r_0)}{2} + r_0^2 \log_e \dfrac{r_2}{r_1} \right]$
	$\dfrac{(\sqrt{r_1}+\sqrt{r_2})^2}{4}$	$\pi a^2 \left(\dfrac{r_1+r_2}{2} - r_0 \right)$
	$\dfrac{\left(\dfrac{r_2+r_1}{2}-U\right)d}{d-U \log_e \dfrac{r_2}{r_1}}$	$md\left[\dfrac{r_2+r_2 r_1+r_1{}^2}{3} - (r_0+U)\dfrac{r_2+r_1}{2} + Ur_0 \right]$ $m = \dfrac{b_2-b_1}{d}$

In solving eq. 29 to 32 the form of the section must be known in order that the relation of da to r may be properly inserted in evaluating the integrals. M is given a positive sign when it decreases the radius of curvature. A positive sign before the result in eq. 31 or 32 indicates tension. Table 4 contains values of r_0 and of the integral of eq. 30 to 32 for rectangular, circular, and trapezoidal sections.

Table 5 shows the ratios of unit stresses computed by eq. 31 and 32 to those obtained from $S = Mc/I$, when the curvature is sharp.

TABLE 5. RATIOS OF UNIT STRESS BY CURVED BEAM FORMULA TO UNIT STRESS BY STRAIGHT-BEAM FORMULA FOR EXTREME FIBERS [1]

$\dfrac{d}{r_1}$	RECTANGLE.		CIRCLE.	
	Concave.	Convex.	Concave.	Convex.
0.50	1.15	.87	1.17	.86
1.00	1.29	.81	1.33	.79
2.00	1.52	.73	1.62	.70

[1] Taken from Boyd's *Strength of Materials,* pp. 327 and 333.

In many practical problems a curved beam is bent by forces having components which are perpendicular to the cross section of the member. In such cases the values of r_0 do not indicate the position of the true neutral surface, but the position which it would occupy if bending only obtained. The bending moment in such cases is computed with respect to an axis through the center of gravity of the section considered and includes the moments of all forces on one side of the given section. The unit stress on any fiber is equal to the bending stress computed as indicated above plus or minus P/A.

EXAMPLE. A 4- by 2-in. rectangular bar is bent in an elliptical arc and loaded on either end with axial pulls of 3000 lb. The center of gravity of the remotest section is 5 in. from the line of action of the pulls. The inner radius (r_1) of that section is 8 in. and the outer radius (r_2) is 12 in. Find the unit stresses S_1' and S_2' on the inner and outer faces, respectively. Here $A = 8$ sq in.,

$$r_0 = \frac{d}{\log_e \dfrac{r_1 + d}{r_1}} = \frac{4}{0.1761 \times 2.3026} = \frac{4}{0.4057} = 9.865 \text{ in.}$$

$$b \left[d \frac{r_2 + r_1 - 4r_0}{2} + r_0^2 \log_e \frac{r_2}{r_1} \right] = -1.08 \text{ sq in.}$$

From eq. 31, $\quad S_1 = \dfrac{8 - 9.865}{8} \dfrac{(-5 \times 3000)}{1.08} = 3240 \text{ psi}$

$$S_1' = \frac{P}{A} + S_1 = \frac{3000}{8} + 3240 = 3615 \text{ psi tension}$$

From eq. 32, $\quad S_2 = \dfrac{12 - 9.865}{12} \dfrac{(-5 \times 3000)}{1.08} = -2470$ psi

$$S_2' = \frac{P}{A} + S_2 = +375 - 2470 = 2095 \text{ psi compression}$$

32. Strength and Deflection of Flat Plates under Normal Loads. Symbols in the following formulas * are:

W = total load.

w = load per unit area.

m = $1/\lambda$, reciprocal of Poisson's ratio.

r = radius of circular plate.

r_0 = radius of circle over which load is distributed.

$2a$ = long axis of rectangular or elliptical plate.

$2b$ = short axis of rectangular or elliptical plate.

k = b/a, a constant.

t = thickness of plate, less than $0.3r$ or $0.6b$.

S_r = maximum radial unit stress.

S_t = maximum tangential unit stress.

S_b = maximum unit stress parallel to $2b$-axis of plate.

D = maximum deflection, less than $0.2t$.

(a) *Flat Circular Plate Supported at the Circumference*

Uniformly loaded:

$$\text{At center, max } S_r = S_t = \frac{3}{8} \cdot \frac{3m+1}{m} \cdot \frac{wr}{t^2} \tag{33}$$

$$D = \frac{3}{16} \frac{(m-1)(5m+1)}{m^2} \frac{wr^4}{Et^3} \tag{33a}$$

Loaded over a small circle at center:

$$\text{At center, max } S_r = S_t = \frac{3(m+1)W}{2m\pi t^2} \left(\frac{m}{m+1} + \log_e \frac{r}{r_0} - \frac{m-1}{m+1} \cdot \frac{r_0^2}{4r^2} \right) \tag{34}$$

$$D = \frac{3(m-1)(3m+1)Wr^2}{4\pi m^2 Et^3} \tag{34a}$$

(b) *Flat Circular Plate Fixed at the Circumference*

Uniformly loaded:

$$\text{At edge, } S_r = \frac{3}{4} \frac{wr^2}{t^2} \qquad S_t = \frac{3}{4} \frac{wr^2}{mt^2} \tag{35}$$

$$\text{At center, } S_r = S_t = \frac{3}{8} \frac{(m+1)wr^2}{mt^2} \tag{35a}$$

$$D = \frac{3}{16} \frac{(m^2-1)wr^4}{m^2 Et^3} \tag{35b}$$

* Formulas 37 to 42 are from a digest of formulas for flat plates by R. J. Roark in *Formulas for Stress and Strain*. Formula 37 is from A. Morley's *Strength of Materials*, p. 441. Formulas 39 to 42 are based on Timoshenko's formulas and constants, in which $\lambda = 0.3$.

Loaded over a small circle at center:

$$\text{At edge, } S_r = \left(\frac{3}{2} - \frac{3}{4}\frac{r_0^2}{r^2}\right)\frac{W}{\pi t^2} \tag{36}$$

$$\text{At center, } S_r = S_t = \frac{3(m+1)W}{2m\pi t^2}\left(\log_e\frac{r}{r_0} + \frac{r_0^2}{4r^2}\right) \tag{36a}$$

$$D = \frac{3(m^2-1)Wr^2}{4\pi m^2 E t^3} \tag{36b}$$

(c) *Elliptical Plate Uniformly Loaded*

Edges supported:

$$\text{At center, max } S_b = \frac{1.25(2-k)wb^2}{t^2} \tag{37}$$

$$D = \frac{(2.34 - 1.6k)wb^4}{Et^3} \tag{37a}$$

Edges fixed:

$$\text{At edge, max } S_b = \frac{12wb^2}{2t^2(3 + 2k^2 + 3k^4)} \tag{38}$$

(d) *Rectangular Plate, Edges Supported*

Uniformly loaded:

$$\text{At center, max } S_b = \frac{3wb^2}{t^2(1 + 1.61k^3)} \tag{39}$$

$$D = \frac{2.27wb^4}{Et^3(1 + 2.21k^3)} \tag{39a}$$

Loaded over small concentric area, radius r_0:

$$\text{At center, } S_b = -\frac{3W}{2\pi m t^2}\left[\log_e\frac{b}{r_0}(m+1) + m\left(0.4 + \frac{0.914}{1 + 1.6k^5}\right)\right] \tag{40}$$

(e) *Rectangular Plate, Edges Fixed*

Uniformly loaded:

$$\text{At centers of long edges, max } S_b = \frac{2wb^2}{t^2(1 + 0.623k^6)} \tag{41}$$

$$D = \frac{0.454wb^4}{Et^3(1 + 1.056k^5)} \tag{41a}$$

Loaded over small concentric area, radius r_0:

$$\text{At center, max } S_b = \frac{3W}{2\pi m t^2}\left[\log_e\frac{b}{r_0}(m+1) + 5(1-k)\right] \tag{42}$$

RESILIENCE

33. Resilience Defined. Resilience is the work which a body can do in springing back after a deforming force has been removed. Within the elastic limit the work of the forces deforming the body equals the energy stored in the body, that is, it equals the resilience. If a body is stressed beyond its elastic limit some of the work of the forces is spent in permanently deforming the body through sliding of the particles over one another, thus causing a loss of heat. Under the latter condition the resilience equals that portion of the total work of deformation which the body can give back upon removal of the forces.

Since work is measured by the product of the force and the distance through which the application point moves in the direction of the force,

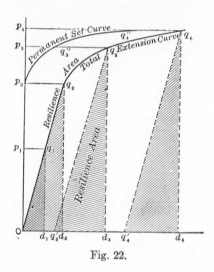

Fig. 22.

we find the work of deformation by multiplying the average stress by the total deformation. Thus the work of deformation (W) equals the resilience (K) for any unit stress (S) which is within the elastic limit and $W = K = \frac{1}{2}Pe$, where P is the maximum total stress and e the corresponding deformation.

If in the stress-deformation diagram for a body (Fig. 22) the total stresses (P) are plotted as ordinates and the displacements (e) as abscissas, then the work of deformation (W) equals the area (measured to scales of the diagram) between the curve and the e-axis. Within the elastic limit the resilience also is measured by this area. When the elastic limit has been exceeded experiment shows that the return curve is parallel to the elastic curve: q_3q_3' is parallel to oq_2, Fig. 22. Therefore the resilience equals one-half of the maximum stress multiplied by the corresponding elastic deformation. In Fig. 22 the shaded triangle marked resilience area represents, to scale, the resilience corresponding to a maximum stress q_3d_3 and an elastic deformation $q_3'd_3$, the corresponding total work of the deforming stresses is measured by the area $oq_2q_3d_3$, and the energy lost through friction by the area $oq_2q_3q_3'$. The total work of deformation to rupture is often called the *energy of rupture*.

If the permanent sets are laid off from the stress axis opposite to the corresponding stresses (p_3q_3'' equal to oq_3', p_4q_4'' equal to oq_4', etc.) then it may also be shown that the following sets of areas are equal: $op_1q_1o = oq_1d_1o$; $op_2q_2o = oq_2d_2o$; $op_2q_3''q_3q_2o = q_3'q_3d_3q_3'$; and $op_2q_3''q_4''q_4q_3q_2o = q_4'q_4d_4q_4'$. Therefore the resilience equals the work of the elastic deformations.

There are three varieties of resilience commonly met: resilience of direct stress, tension, or compression; resilience of cross bending; and resilience of torsion. Values for these different kinds of resilience will now be determined. In all cases it will be noted that the resilience is directly proportional to the square of the maximum unit stress divided by the modulus of elasticity (S^2/E), the volume (Al), and a coefficient which depends upon the kind of stress, the form of cross section and the method of loading.

34. Resilience of Bodies under Direct Stress. Consider a homogeneous prism of uniform cross section subjected to end axial pulls or pushes which are slowly increased until the value P is reached, P/A being less than the elastic limit. Then the total elongation due to P is $e = Pl/AE$ (see eq. 1) and the total work W_p, which is equal to the resilience K, is $W_p = \frac{1}{2}Pe$. Therefore

$$K = \frac{1}{2}SA\frac{SAl}{AE} = \frac{1}{2}\frac{S^2}{E}Al \qquad (43)$$

The factor $\dfrac{1}{2}\dfrac{S_e{}^2}{E}$, where S_e is the elastic limit, is the *modulus of resilience* for a material under the direct stress considered.

It should be noted in passing that, when P/A exceeds the elastic limit, the resilience may be computed by eq. 43, but it does not equal the work of P in this case. The latter can be found from the area of the stress-deformation diagram as previously indicated. It may also be approximated as follows:

For ductile materials having a stress diagram like mild steel (Fig. 3), the energy of rupture K_r per unit of volume is approximately

$$K_r = \left(\frac{S_y + S_u}{2}\right)\epsilon_m \qquad (44)$$

For materials like cast iron having a parabolic stress diagram, approximately,

$$K_r = \frac{2}{3}S_u\epsilon_m \qquad (45)$$

In the above S_y and S_u are the unit stresses at the yield point and maximum load, respectively, and ϵ_m is the ultimate unit elongation.

35. Resilience in Cross-Bending. Consider a homogeneous cantilever beam of uniform cross section with an end load which is gradually increased until it reaches the value P, the latter being of such value that the fibers of the beam are not stressed beyond the elastic limit. The deflection of the free end due to bending is $f = Pl^3/3EI$ (eq. 27), and the work (W_p) of the load is $W_p = \frac{1}{2}Pf$. Therefore the resilience $K = \frac{1}{2}Pf = P^2l^3/6EI$. Since the maximum unit stress on the extreme fiber at the support is $S = Plc/I$ we have

$$K = \frac{S^2 I l}{6Ec^2} = \frac{S^2 A r^2 l}{6Ec^2} = \frac{1}{6} \frac{r^2}{c^2} \frac{S^2}{E} Al \tag{46}$$

Here r = radius of gyration and the other symbols are in accordance with previous notation. The result in eq. 46 also holds for a simple beam loaded at the middle.

Equation 46 does not hold for stresses beyond the elastic limit because the flexure formula no longer gives the true value of S. The resilience for this case may be computed approximately from $K = P_1^2 l^3 / 6EI$, where P_1 is the maximum load.

For beams with a uniform load the resilience may be obtained by

$$K = \tfrac{1}{2} \int w \, dxy \; * \tag{47}$$

Here w is the load per unit of length, y is the deflection at any point and is expressed in terms of x, and the limits of integration include the entire beam. Thus for a simple beam with a uniform load

$$K = \frac{1}{2} \int_0^l w \, dx \left[\frac{w l^3 x}{24} - \frac{w l x^3}{12} + \frac{w x^4}{12} \right] = \frac{w^2 l^5}{240 EI}$$

For the value of y in the above, see eq. f, Art. I-29. Since $w l^2 = 8 S I / c$ the resilience in terms of the unit stress on the outside fiber at the center of the beam is

$$K = \frac{4}{15} \frac{r^2}{c^2} \frac{S^2}{E} Al \tag{48}$$

In all these discussions the resilience due to shear has been neglected because of its small effect.

36. Resilience in Torsion. Consider a homogeneous circular shaft held at one end and twisted by a couple, the magnitude of which increases to Pa without overstressing the shaft. Evidently the work of the couple is $W_c = Pa\theta/2$. Substituting in this equation $\theta = M_t l / E_s J$, $M_t = S_s J / c$, and $J = A r_0^2$ (where r_0 = polar radius of gyration) we have

$$K = \frac{Pa\theta}{2} = \frac{1}{2} \frac{r_0^2}{c^2} \frac{S_s^2}{E_s} Al \tag{49}$$

For a solid round shaft $K = \dfrac{1}{4} \dfrac{S_s^2}{E_s} Al$.

---

* An alternative method of computing the resilience for such cases is afforded by the equation $K = \int (M^2/EI) \, dx$ where the variables are expressed in terms of x and the limits of integration cover the entire beam.

37. Resilience a Measure of Shock Resistance. The magnitude or effect of a blow, or of a falling body, is measured by the energy stored in the moving body at the instant of impact. The energy of a body which has fallen freely in space under the action of gravity is Wh, where W is the weight of the body, and h is the distance through which the body has fallen freely. In any translation, the energy of the body is $Wv^2/2g$, where v is the velocity, and g is the acceleration of gravity. If a moving body, as a falling weight, is stopped by striking a fixed solid body, the energy of the moving body is spent in one or all of the following ways:

(a) In deforming the moving body itself, either within or beyond its elastic limit.

(b) In a local deformation of both bodies at the surface of contact, within or beyond the elastic limit.

(c) In moving the fixed body as a whole, with an accelerated velocity, the resistance consisting of the inertia of the body.

(d) In moving the fixed body against its external supports and resistances.

(e) Finally, in deforming the fixed body as a whole against the resisting stresses developed thereby.

If there is nearly absolute rigidity in all parts except in the body struck and if this yields only as a whole and not locally at the point of contact, then only can nearly all the energy of the moving body be absorbed through deformation in the body struck. When the energy of the striking body is due principally to its mass (measured by W/g) and only in small part to its velocity then 90 per cent or more of its energy may be absorbed by the body struck.

Assuming that all the energy of a blow is absorbed by the body struck, it becomes apparent that the work of deformation of that body must equal the energy of the blow. Studies of the relationships of resistance to deformation under impact, where the unit stresses have exceeded the elastic limit, have, in general, shown that a given deformation under impact is accompanied by a higher unit stress than in a static, or slowly applied, loading. For the tests on soft-iron wire illustrated in Fig. 23, the work of deformation in impact, as measured by the area under the impact stress-deformation curve, is about 30 per cent greater than the corresponding value for static stresses. Likewise Russell[*] found that the average energy of rupture of cast-iron bars tested in his pendulum impact machine was approximately 44 per cent greater than the average energy of rupture under gradually applied loads. When the stresses are

[*] See *Trans. ASCE,* Vol. 39, p. 246.

within the elastic limit it has been customary to assume that the moduli of elasticity for static loadings hold for impact. It has also been customary to argue from the above considerations that the modulus of resilience obtained from a static test is a measure of resistance to repeated shocks or blows and that the total area of the stress diagram (the energy of rupture) is a measure of resistance to a single blow.* In other words these quantities are considered indexes of toughness. That these conclusions do not apply, however, to all heat-treated materials is evinced by the behavior of burnt steel. This material often exhibits about as high energy of rupture in a static test as properly treated material but is far less tough.

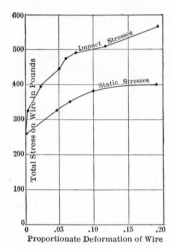

Fig. 23. Comparison of impact and static stresses when the deformations are the same. (*Rept. of French Com.*, Vol. 2, p. 344.)

A comprehensive study of the elastic portions of impact stress-deformation curves for our various building materials is badly needed in order that true value of the static modulus of resilience as an index of resistance to repeated shocks may be ascertained.

If we assume that all the energy of the blow is absorbed by the body struck and that the modulus of elasticity is independent of the speed of loading, we have for the case of direct stress under axial elastic impact

$$W(h + e) = \frac{1}{2}\frac{S^2}{E} Al \tag{50}$$

Here W = weight falling, h = distance dropped, e = maximum deformation of body struck (the deformation will oscillate from a maximum to a minimum value, as in a spring), S = maximum intensity of stress corresponding to deformation, E = modulus of elasticity, A = area of cross section, and l = length.

Similarly for a beam under impact of a center load we shall have

$$W(h + f) = \frac{1}{6}\frac{r^2}{c^2}\frac{S^2}{E} Al \tag{51}$$

Here f = the maximum deflection and the other quantities have usual significance. When h in either of eq. 50 or 51 is zero, namely, when

* H. C. Mann in *Proc. ASTM*, Vol. 35, Pt. 2, p. 323, gives a method of evaluating the impact energy of rupture from a static stress diagram which he checked closely by tests.

the load is suddenly applied, it is easy to show that the maximum intensity of stress is twice that for a static load, W.

It may also be shown that the deformation of a bar under axial elastic impact is given by $e = e' + e'[1 + (2h/e')]^{1/2}$, where e' is the elongation due to a static load W and e that due to the impact load W. Similarly for transverse impact we have $f = f' + f'[1 + (2h/f')]^{1/2}$, where f' is the deflection due to static W and f that due to impact of W.

Energy Lossses. Equations 50 and 51 are derived on the assumption that all the energy of the blow is used to produce elastic impact strain. Actually some energy is dissipated in producing local deformation of the resisting member. The energy so dissipated becomes important as the ratio of the weight w of the resisting member to the weight W of the moving body increases. The amount of the energy dissipated can be found by equating the momentum of the entire system before and after impact and is easily obtained by multiplying the energy of the moving body at the instant of contact by a factor n, whose value for several simple cases is given below:

(a) Axial impact on one end of a bar of uniform section with its other end fixed.

$$n = \frac{1 + \frac{1}{3}(w/W)}{[1 + \frac{1}{2}(w/W)]^2}$$

(b) Transverse impact at the center of a simply supported beam.

$$n = \frac{1 + \frac{17}{35}(w/W)}{[1 + \frac{5}{8}(w/W)]^2}$$

(c) Transverse impact at the center of a beam with both ends fixed.

$$n = \frac{1 + \frac{13}{35}(w/W)}{[1 + \frac{1}{2}(w/W)]^2}$$

The correction factors given above are not absolute because they are based on assumptions that are not always realized and because some factors such as the cumulative effect of reflected stress waves are not considered.

Consideration of Reflected Stress Waves. When a bar fixed at one end is subjected to axial impact at its free end, stress waves are produced that travel to the fixed end and are reflected back. Prof. L. H. Donnell * from the researches of St. Venant and Flamant developed the following formula for the approximate maximum unit stress S_I' to take into account the cumulative effect of the reflected stress waves.

* *Trans. ASME,* Vol. 52-I, 1930, APM-52-14, p. 153.

$$S_{I}' = V \left(\frac{wE}{lAg}\right)^{\frac{1}{2}} \left[1 + \left(\frac{W}{w} + \frac{2}{3}\right)^{\frac{1}{2}}\right] \tag{52}$$

In eq. 52, V is the velocity of the moving weight W, and l, A, and E are the length, area, and modulus of elasticity of the bar, respectively. As the ratio W/w varies from 1 to 20, S_{I}' varies from 2.3 to 1.2 times the maximum stress calculated from the equation obtained by equating the kinetic energy of the moving body to the strain energy of the bar.

Examination of the various formulas available for calculating stresses due to impact loading shows the need of clearly understanding the assumptions and limitations of each. It should also be apparent that the stresses and strains due to impact loads may exceed many times those due to static loads.

MATERIALS UNDER COMBINED STRESS

38. Direct and Bending Stresses. Consider the case of a simple beam under a transverse bending moment M and subjected to an eccentric end

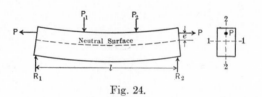

Fig. 24.

load P lying in a principal axis, Fig. 24, for example. Consider the force P resolved into a force along the axis of the beam and a couple Pe. Then the unit stress on the extreme fiber at the danger section is given by

$$S = \frac{P}{A} \pm \frac{Mc}{I} \tag{53}$$

Here M is the algebraic sum of the moments due to end loading (Pe) and transverse loadings taken on either side of the section, I is the moment of inertia of the cross section about the axis 1–1, c is the distance from 1–1 to the fiber considered, A is the area of the cross section. Unless the beam is long, deflection affects the moment arm of P but little and is, therefore, not considered in computing M.

Equation 53 may also be used in designing short columns $(l/r < 100)$ which are eccentrically loaded. It then reduces to

$$S = \frac{P}{A} \left(1 \pm \frac{ce}{r^2}\right) \tag{53a}$$

Here r is the radius of gyration of the section about the principal axis which is normal to the lever arm of P.

If P does not lie on a principal axis eq. 53a does not hold. The unit stress on any fiber is then given by

$$S = P\left(\frac{1}{A} + \frac{xx_1}{I_y} + \frac{yy_1}{I_x}\right) \tag{54}$$

Where x_1 and y_1 are the coordinates of the application point of the load P with respect to the principal axes (the x axis and the y axis), x and y are the coordinates of the fiber with unit stress S, I_x, and I_y are the principal moments of inertia with respect to the x and y axes, respectively. Due account of the signs of x, x_1, y, and y_1 must be taken in using eq. 54.

39. Shears and Direct Stress. One of the most common cases of combined stress is direct stress with pairs of equal shears perpendicular and

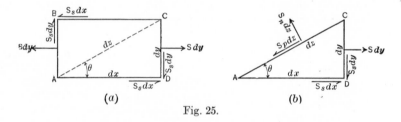

(a)   (b)

Fig. 25.

parallel to it. Let Fig. 25a represent the side elevation of an elementary rectangular parallelepiped, the thickness perpendicular to the paper being unity and the width and height dx and dy, respectively. Let the intensity of the direct stress be S and that of the shears S_s each. Then it is evident that on any oblique plane cutting the parallelepiped the total stress equals the resultant of $S\,dy$, $S_s\,dx$, and $S_s\,dy$. Consider the total stress on the plane AC to be resolved into normal and tangential components, $S_n\,dz$ and $S_p\,dz$, respectively; see Fig. 25b. We want to find the value of S_n and S_p in terms of S and S_s and then, by rotating the plane AC (allowing θ to vary), determine the maximum values for these stresses. Resolving the forces on CD and AD in Fig. 25b along AC and perpendicular to it, substituting $\sin\theta = dy/dz$, $\cos\theta = dx/dz$, and reducing, we have

$$S_p = (S/2)\sin 2\theta + S_s \cos 2\theta \tag{55}$$

$$S_n = (S/2)(1 - \cos 2\theta) + S_s \sin 2\theta \tag{56}$$

S_p is rendered a maximum or minimum when $\tan 2\theta = S/2S_s$; S_n is rendered a maximum or minimum when $\tan 2\theta = -2S_s/S$. Substituting the corresponding sine and cosine functions in eq. 55 and 56,

$$S_p = \sqrt{S_s^2 + (S/2)^2} \tag{57}$$

$$S_n = (S/2) \pm \sqrt{S_s^2 + (S/2)^2} \tag{58}$$

When the plus sign is used in eq. 58 the magnitude of the maximum unit stress of the same kind as S is found. If the minus sign is used, the minimum normal unit stress is found; but a negative sign obtains for the entire result indicating that the stress thus obtained is of opposite kind to S. These maximum and minimum values of S_n occur at the same point on mutually perpendicular planes. There is no shear stress on either of these planes.

The unit deformation in the direction of max S_n will be increased by the lateral deformation of min S_n acting at right angles to the maximum value (see Art. I-5 and I-6) or $\epsilon_n = \dfrac{\max S_n}{E} + \lambda\,\dfrac{\min S_n}{E}$, where ϵ_n is the unit deformation along max S_n and λ is Poisson's ratio. Substituting values of S_n from eq. 58 and changing sign of min S_n,

$$\epsilon_n = (S/2E)(1 - \lambda) + (1 + \lambda)\sqrt{S_s^2 + (S/2)^2} \tag{59}$$

If $\lambda = \frac{1}{4}$, a fair mean for metals, then

$$\epsilon_n = \frac{3S}{8E} + \frac{5}{4E}\sqrt{S_s^2 + (S/2)^2} \tag{60}$$

For analyzing the internal stresses in beams and shafting, eq. 57 and 58 are much used. In beams the horizontal and vertical shearing stresses provide the $S_s\,dx$ and $S_s\,dy$ forces of Fig. 25 and the flexure stresses make up the $S\,dy$ forces. In horizontal shafts the torsional shears in planes tangent to the shaft provide the pairs of shearing forces, and the stresses due to bending again introduce the normal forces. In vertical shafts the normal stress may be due to both direct stress (from the weight of the shaft) and lateral bending.

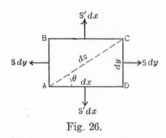

Fig. 26.

40. Biaxial Loading. Figure 26 shows an elementary parallelepiped of unit thickness under two pairs of mutually perpendicular tensile stresses. The following analysis with proper regard to sign holds, in general, whether both pairs of stresses are of like kind or not. We wish to find the value of the normal (S_n) and tangential (S_p) unit stresses on any plane such as AC. Resolving $S\,dy$ and $S'dx$ parallel to AC and perpendicular to it and substituting $\sin \theta = dy/dz$ and $\cos \theta = dx/dz$,

$$S_p = \frac{S - S'}{2} \sin 2\theta \qquad (61)$$

$$S_n = S \sin^2 \theta + S' \cos^2 \theta \qquad (62)$$

When $\theta = 45°$, $S_p = (S - S')/2$. Note, however, that for this case the greatest value of $S_p = S/2$, if $S > S'$. This stress occurs in a plane parallel to S' and making an angle of $45°$ with S. S_n is a maximum when $\theta = 90°$ if $S > S'$; when $\theta = 0°$ if $S < S'$.

Equations 61 and 62 are of value in determining stresses in boiler shells and pipes.

41. Conditions Determining Elastic Breakdown. There has always been much perplexity concerning what factors determine the breaking down of a metal at its elastic limit. Broadly speaking, the question is, does failure begin when a certain maximum unit stress is reached, regardless of the way in which that stress is produced, or does it commence when the unit deformation reaches a certain maximum. In studying these problems experimenters * have placed specimens of ductile metals under combined tension and torsion, compression and torsion, flexure and torsion, and under biaxial loadings. The three much-used theories which have been advanced are as follows:

1. Elastic breakdown begins when the maximum normal stress S_n reaches a certain value—*the maximum-stress theory.*
2. Elastic failure begins when the unit deformation (ϵ_n) in the direction of the maximum normal stress reaches a certain magnitude—*the maximum-strain theory.*
3. Elastic breakdown begins when the maximum shear (S_p) reaches a certain magnitude—*the maximum-shear theory.*

Most experimenters have held to the third theory, convinced that a ductile material under direct stresses, or direct and shear stresses, suffers elastic breakdown when some plane in the body experiences a shear stress equal to the shearing elastic limit, and that failure ensues when the ultimate shear stress is imposed on some plane (see S_p of formula 57 and discussion in Art. I-40). Becker,* however, from a very careful set of tests on thin steel tubes under biaxial loading has shown that elastic breakdown will ensue if the maximum unit strain exceeds a certain value, also if the maximum unit shear stress exceeds the shearing elastic limit. In other words, for biaxial loading he found that as the ratio of S'/S was increased the elastic limit was reached as soon as the maximum unit strain reached a certain value; when, however, as S'/S increased, the maximum

---

* See accounts of researches by J. J. Guest, *Phil. Mag.*, July, 1900; W. A. Scoble, *Phil. Mag.*, Vol. 12, 1906, p. 583; E. S. Hancock, *Proc. ASTM*, Vol. 5, p. 179; Vol. 6, p. 295; A. J. Becker, *Bull.* 85, Univ. Ill. Expt. Sta.

$S_p(=S/2$ if $S > S')$ reached the shearing elastic limit before the maximum unit strain ϵ_n reached its critical value, then failure was conditioned by the maximum-shear theory. The two limiting conditions for biaxial tensions are given by $\epsilon_n' = \dfrac{S}{E} - \lambda \dfrac{S'}{E}$ and $S_p' = \frac{1}{2}S$, where $\epsilon_n' =$ maximum unit elastic deformation which material can withstand and $S_p' =$ shearing elastic limit.

Two additional theories of elastic failure have received considerable attention: *the strain-energy theory* and *the shear strain-energy theory*. The strain-energy theory of Beltrami, more recently championed by B. P. Haigh, states that elastic breakdown begins when the quantity of strain energy stored per unit of volume exceeds the tensile modulus of resilience. If the three principal stresses are S_x, S_y, S_z, and S_e is the tensile elastic limit, the condition is

$$K_e = \frac{1}{2E}[(S_x^2 + S_y^2 + S_z^2) - 2\lambda(S_xS_y + S_xS_z + S_yS_z)] = \frac{S_e^2}{2E}$$

For biaxial loading this reduces to $S_x^2 + S_y^2 - 2\lambda S_xS_y = S_e^2$.

The shear strain-energy theory developed by Huber and von Mises, which assumes that the elastic failure is conditioned by the arrival of the unit shear strain energy at a certain limiting value, furnishes the following criterion for K_s, the modulus of resilience in shear:

$$K_s = \frac{1 + \lambda}{3E}[S_x^2 + S_y^2 + S_z^2 - (S_xS_y + S_xS_z + S_yS_z)] = \frac{1 + \lambda}{3E}S_e^2$$

For biaxial loading this reduces to $S_x^2 + S_y^2 - S_xS_y = S_e^2$.

Apparently none of the foregoing theories holds for all stress conditions. For ductile materials under biaxial loading where the principal stresses are of like kind, the principal stress or either of the strain-energy theories appears to be in accord with experimental evidence. For biaxial loading with stresses unlike in sign, the principal stress theory fails; but the maximum-shear, the strain-energy, or the shear strain-energy theories agree with observed data. In combined bending and torsion the maximum-shear-stress theory is the most conservative, the maximum-stress theory the least conservative; but for ratios of moment to torque (M/T) above 1.0 the discrepancies in the diameters obtained by designing by any of the theories is not large.

For triaxial loading neither strain-energy theory conforms to the observed facts when a ductile material is under compressive stresses of equal intensities, i.e., fluid pressure. Nevertheless, considering range of application, the shear strain-energy theory, which implies that the ratio of the elastic limit in shear to that in tension is 0.58, appears to be the most dependable of the above theories.

Evidence also indicates that the maximum-stress theory is in best accord with experimental evidence on brittle materials. A good resumé of these theories and numerical comparisons may be found in *Materials and Structures,* by E. H. Salmon, Vol. 1, Chapter XVI.

Machines and Appliances for Mechanical Tests

TESTING MACHINES

1. Definition. Since it would be obviously impossible to break, or even deform considerably, large specimens of strong material by the imposition of dead weights, a mechanical device called a testing machine is employed for this purpose. A testing machine may be said to consist of a base or frame which supports the crossheads used in loading the specimen, a means for applying the load, and a device for measuring it.

Universal Testing Machines

2. Classes of Universal Testing Machines. Universal testing machines—those in which tension, compression, or cross-bending tests can be made—are provided with at least one fixed crosshead against which the specimen rests and a movable crosshead by means of which the specimen is deformed. In accordance with the method employed to drive the movable crosshead, such machines may be divided into two classes: hydraulic machines and screw-gear machines. In American laboratories many of the testing machines are of the hydraulic type. Screw-gear machines, equipped with variable-speed electronic motor drives and pendulum-type weighing systems, are regaining some lost popularity.

With the exception of the Emery testing machine, which belongs in a class by itself, the chief advantages of hydraulic testing machines are freedom from vibration and noise, cheapness, and simplicity of construction and operation. On the other hand, most of the testing machines of this type have one or more of the following disadvantages: leakage of fluid, variable friction at the stuffing boxes and around the ram, or inaccurate means of measuring fluid pressures.*

In American screw-gear testing machines the load is generally reduced by a system of compound levers and weighed by balancing with a poise

---

* The University of Wisconsin has a 600,000-lb universal hydraulic testing machine designed and erected by the instructional staff. After installation in 1952 of a new pumping and load-indicating system the machine is well within the *ASTM* requirement for accuracy.

which is moved along a graduated scalebeam. In general these machines may be made very sensitive and accurate, but when built in large capacities are more expensive than those of the hydraulic type. Owing to the vibration and noise produced by the driving mechanism employed in screw-gear machines, hand power is necessitated when very sensitive apparatus is used to measure deformations.

Testing machines are often called horizontal or vertical in accordance with the position in which a tension or compression specimen is held. The advantage of the horizontal type lies in the accessibility of all parts of machine and specimen. In vertical testing machines, however, lateral bending due to the weight of the specimen is obviated.

3. General Conditions Which Should Obtain in Universal Machines. The following considerations apply to testing machines in general:

1. The weighing apparatus should be quite independent of the loading apparatus, the former usually being fixed and the latter movable.

2. In lever machines the length of the knife edges must be proportioned to the maximum loads in order not to be crushed down, and they should be so placed that all will receive their share of the load. They must also be so mounted as not to change the leverage by any reaction displacement which may occur. To insure this, the knife edges must be attached to the levers, and the bearings to the platform. Clearance between knife-edge bearings and levers must be sufficient to insure against frictional resistances, which greatly impair sensitiveness.

3. The knife edges and bearings of any beam must lie in the same straight line, and this line should lie in the gravity axis of the beam and its rigid attachments. This is especially necessary for the weighing beam itself, so that its vertical angular movement may not disturb the counter-balancing. If the poise is moved by a cord over a pair of pulleys, this cord should be attached to the poise hanger in this same axial line, so that the pulling of the poise may not supply a leverage on the beam to raise or lower it.

4. Manometer machines have many peculiar errors. For example, any air bubble in the indicating liquid vitiates the results by its own change in volume under pressure. Again, the exact area of surface subjected to pressure is always uncertain.

5. The weighing apparatus should be so constructed as to be readily verified by the imposition of known weights, and the parts should be open to inspection and easily repaired and kept in order.

6. A precision of 1 in 250 has been considered sufficient.* This is a proportional error of 0.4 of 1 per cent. Also, the imposition of a load

* For methods of verification and tolerances in testing machines, consult *Standards* of the ASTM.

equal to $\frac{1}{250}$ of that on the machine should produce an appreciable indication on the weighing device.

7. The loading should proceed gradually and uniformly, and the rate of loading should be under perfect control.

8. The machine should permit the free use of suitable appliances for measuring distortion of the specimen at all stages during tests.

9. A wide range of speeds should be available for the entire capacity of the machine, Art. III-10.

10. The axes of the jaws in the crossheads of the machine should be so placed that they will remain in line throughout any test provided that the specimen is properly centered in them.

11. There must be no twisting or rocking of the movable head when in motion.

4. Olsen Testing Machines. The Olsen screw-gear machine shown in Fig. 1 * affords a good illustration of the universal machines found in

Fig. 1.   Olsen's universal screw-gear testing machine.

American laboratories. Machines similar to this are built in capacities from 30,000 to 400,000 lb; others embodying similar principles are built

* Olsen testing machines made today have a hydraulic loading system or an electromechanical loading system which uses a variable-speed electronic motor drive, and have a pendulum-lever weighing system or a precision-type hydraulic gage indicating system.

in capacities up to 1,000,000 lb. Power is applied to the machine illustrated through a direct connected motor attached in the rear as shown. The main shaft (1) transmits power to the gear (2) which, through a

shaft and system of gearing, rotates four straining nuts. Each of these straining nuts bears against the underside of the bed plate of the machine (9) and revolves about one of the four vertical screws which are rigidly fastened to the pulling head (5). In this manner an upward or downward translation may be imparted to the screws and pulling head. A wide range in the rate of motion of the pulling head may be secured by means of the clutch levers (3) and (4). The pull on the specimen (6), which is held in the jaws of the crossheads by means of grooved wedges or liners, is transmitted downward through the four cast-iron columns (7) to the weighing table (8). The reaction of the straining nuts on the lower end of the screws produces an equal upward force beneath the bed plate (9). The weighing table is supported on knife edges fastened in the compound levers (10) and (11), which in turn are pivoted on pedestals formed on the bed plate (9); a closed circuit of forces is thus produced. The force on the weighing table is reduced by the levers (10), (11), and (12) and balanced by the poise (13) on the scalebeam. The poise (13) is driven by a screw running along the top of the scalebeam. The operator may drive the poise by

Fig. 2.   Low-cost 10,000-lb Olsen testing machine.   (Tinius Olsen Testing Machine Co.)

hand through the wheel (14), or the motion of the poise may be automatically controlled by the variable-speed cone drive (15) which is connected to the driving mechanism on the machine and drives the poise to the right as long as the scalebeam is up. When the beam drops an electric circuit is broken and the poise stops. The load in thousand-pound units or multiples thereof may be obtained from the graduations on the scalebeam. Intermediate values of the load are read on the dial (16) which is driven by the screw actuating the poise. The energy released by breaking of a specimen is dissipated through recoil buffers (17) and cushion-seated nuts.

Compression tests are made by attaching a spherical seat to the crosshead (5) and inserting the specimen on table (8).

The machine is arranged for bending tests by placing end bearings on the table (8) (or on an I-beam extension of the table) and attaching a knife edge on the movable head (5).

For testing low-strength specimens hand-operated or motor-driven (Fig. 2) machines of 10,000-lb capacity are very serviceable.

5. A Riehle Hydraulic Universal Machine. Figure 3 shows a 300,000-lb hydraulic testing machine made by American Machine and Metals, Inc.

Fig. 3. A 300,000-lb Riehle hydraulic testing machine.

The top head (1) and the table (2) of this machine are connected by four posts (3) and are always forced upward during a test by means of the ram in the base of the machine. The lower head (4) is held to the base of the machine by the two large screws and can be adjusted to the specimen by means of the small motor (5). The ram is supplied with oil from a 6-cylinder pump (6). The rate of speed of the ram is controlled by the hand wheel (7) which turns over a graduated dial. The load is weighed by a pendulum automatic indicating device which is equipped with two weights. These weights are usually arranged to provide load ranges of 0–30,000 and 0–300,000 lb. Both the cylinder on the ram and the pressure-measuring cylinder connected to the pendulum are very accurately ground and no packing is required. The measuring cylinder is rotated to reduce frictional effects to a minimum. The machine operates rapidly without disturbing noise or vibration and is very easy to handle.

6. Southwark-Tate-Emery Universal Testing Machines. The Southwark-Tate-Emery universal testing machines, such as the one shown in

Fig. 4. A 120,000-lb Southwark-Tate-Emery testing machine. (Baldwin-Lima-Hamilton Corp.)

Fig. 4, are made by the Baldwin-Lima-Hamilton Corp. These machines have three separate functional systems: loading, weighing, and indicating.

The loading system which is independent of the weighing and indicating systems consists of a motor-driven variable-discharge pump housed in the lower portion of the cabinet, micrometer loading valve (1), unloading valve (2), and the loading ram operating in a packed cylinder (3). Compression specimens are placed between the sensitive crosshead (4), which is moved into the proper position along the tension screws (5) by the adjusting motor (6), and the lower movable bed (7). Tension specimens are placed between the sensitive platen (4) and the upper movable head (10) which can be placed in several positions along the compression columns (8).

The weighing system consists of the weighing frame (sensitive crosshead, tension screws, and a bottom crosshead in the base) and an Emery capsule mounted between the bottom crosshead and the bottom of the hydraulic cylinder. As either a tensile or compressive load is applied the weighing frame moves up slightly and increases the pressure on the capsule. The dead weight of the weighing frame is supported by springs which maintain a datum pressure on the fluid in the capsule. Any additional load produces an instantaneous increase in the pressure on the fluid in the capsule and is transmitted to the indicating system. Flexure plates (9) between the cylinder and the tension screws help to resist horizontal load components while permitting vertical freedom of the weighing frame through the maximum displacement of 0.002 in. The Emery capsule is a rigid cylinder and piston unit with an enclosed oil film less than 0.03 in. thick. Lateral motion of the piston in the cylinder is prevented, and vertical motion caused by the pressure of the weighing frame increases the pressure on the oil film.

The air-operated indicating system uses the null method in which friction is overcome by using an outside source of power. Pressure changes in the Emery capsule are transmitted to and tend to deflect a Bourdon tube. Deflection is prevented by a restoring force which is measured by an isoelastic spring system which in turn activates the dial pointer.

Many Southwark-Tate-Emery high-capacity universal testing machines are used. The Aluminum Co. of America has a 3,000,000-lb machine; the machine at the University of California has a capacity of 4,000,000 lb and can test columns 33 ft long.

COMPRESSION TESTING MACHINES

7. A Field for the Hydraulic Press. To ascertain the compressive strengths of materials like concrete, stone, brick, and tile, a machine of great precision is not required. For work of this character a hydraulic press provided with an accurate gage for registering the fluid pressure in the ram has been found satisfactory.

The chief sources of inaccuracy in the hydraulic press are the variability of the friction between the piston and cylinder and at the stuffing box. In a well-designed press, however, these variations will be very small and may be neglected in rough work; or an average correction for friction may be made by calibrating the press with the packing tight and loose.

A great variety of testing machines of this type are in use in this country; two will be briefly described.

8. Precision Compression Testing Machines. Some testing machines have been designed solely for compression tests because of the large number of such tests made on non-metallic building materials. These machines are generally less expensive than universal testing machines and

Fig. 5. A 300,000-lb-capacity hydraulic compression testing machine with pendomatic indicating unit. (Riehle Testing Machines Division.)

give results quickly and accurately. Figure 5 shows a 300,000-lb hydraulic testing machine with a Pendomatic load-indicating unit. This Pendomatic indicating unit employs the pendulum dead-weight system for weighing loads. Compression testing machines of this type are usually available up to a maximum capacity of 400,000 lb.

9. The World's Largest Testing Machine. In Fig. 6 is shown the 10,000,000-lb compression machine built by Tinius Olsen Testing Machine Co. for the Laboratory of the National Bureau of Standards. This machine can be used to test specimens less than 25 ft long and 4 by 4 ft square within the capacity of the machine. The four screws are each 13½ in. in diameter. Connected to the screws by long power-driven nuts is the adjustable upper head, weighing 30 tons. The spherical-seated lower head of the same weight is mounted upon the end of the ram of a huge hydraulic press, not shown in the illustration.   To obviate uncertainty regarding frictional forces, the packing employed in this ram is so designed that these forces will vary directly with the pressure, a condition for which due allowance is made in the calibration.   The intensity of the fluid pressure in the ram is transferred to a smaller hydraulic chamber which is sealed with a diaphragm and supported on the pump well.   The pressure on the diaphragm is balanced through the lever system and screw-driven poise.   The scale-beam is graduated to read loads on the specimen up to 2,000,000 lb directly, and with end weights up to the capacity of the machine.   Fluid pressure is supplied to the ram by means of a triple-plunger variable-stroke pump driven by a 15-hp variable-speed motor.   This combination makes possible a considerable range in the speed of the lower head of the testing machine when desired.   An air reservoir inserted

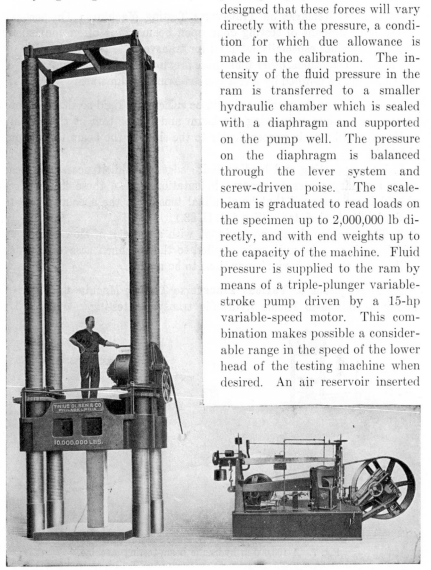

Fig. 6.   The largest testing machine in the world.   (National Bureau of Standards.)

in the supply line leading from the pump to the ram reduces the effects of the pulsations of the pump.*

* This machine is described in *Eng. Record,* Sept. 28, 1912, p. 353.

Transverse Testing Machines

10. General Remarks on Transverse Testing Machines. On account of the large amount of testing done upon beams, it is often convenient to have machines especially adapted for transverse testing.

The main conditions, other than those previously mentioned in Art. II-3, which should be fulfilled by a transverse testing machine are:

1. The parts of the machine should be sufficiently rigid so that the tops of the knife edges supporting the beam and the bottom of the loading knife edge will remain perpendicular to the sides of the beam throughout the test.

2. The supporting and loading knife edges should, if necessary, bear upon auxiliary plates to prevent indentation. Also, these knife edges should be so arranged that longitudinal tension in the specimen due to their rigidity is obviated. (See Art. II-33.)

3. The machine should be equipped with a variety of slow speeds by which loads may be uniformly applied to the specimen at a rate which will permit the necessary observations to be made.

11. Descriptions of Various Transverse Testing Machines. Figure 7 shows a 100,000-lb Riehle hydraulic transverse testing machine. By

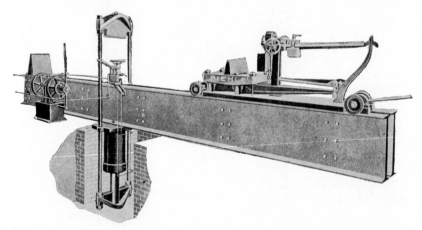

Fig. 7. A 100,000-lb hydraulic beam-testing machine.

means of the valve operated by the hand wheel at the center of the machine fluid from the pump can be forced into either end of the double-acting ram, which moves the loading knife edge. The support at the left end and the weighing apparatus at the right may be adjusted to spans varying from 4 to 20 ft. To save space this machine should be installed with the tops of the I-beam flush with the floor.

A portable concrete beam breaker, shown in Fig. 8, applies loads hydraulically at either the center-point or at the third-points. After the beam is positioned the load is applied at the proper rate by turning the

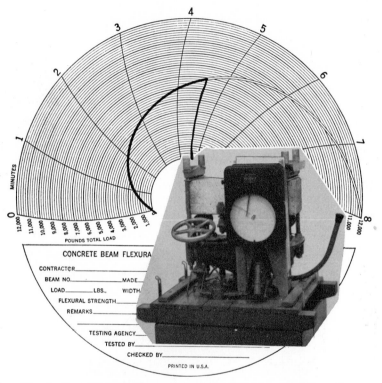

Fig. 8. Portable recording concrete beam breaker. (Rainhart Co.)

hand wheel of the hydraulic pump so that the recording pen keeps within the loading track as the chart rotates.

Cold-Bend Testing Machines

12. Methods of Making the Test. Up to this time, only machines in which the bending is accomplished by static pressure have been especially made for cold-bend tests. The power hammer is ordinarily employed when bending is accomplished by blows. The power-hammer method is subject to much wider variations than the pressure method, but properly made is a more severe test.

13. A Cold-Bend Attachment. The bending attachment shown in Fig. 9, designed by C. H. Scholer, can be inserted in a universal testing machine. The upper tool which is clamped in the movable head of the

Fig. 9. Scholer's bending attachment. (Baldwin-Southwark Corp.)

Fig. 10. Riehle cold bending machine. (Riehle Testing Machines Division.)

machine carries the pin around which the bar is bent. The bar rests on two cast-iron segmental rollers of 6-in. radius mounted on 2-in. hardened steel pins. The pins are supported in a frame consisting of two 4- by 6- by ¾-in. steel angles. The top of the angle frame is graduated to aid in setting the near bearing, in order to accommodate changes in thickness of specimen and pin. The device operates under low loads without imposing longitudinal forces due to roller friction, and can be used on specimens of short length.

14. Cold-Bending Machine. Figure 10 represents a motor-driven cold-bend testing machine used for bending rods, bars, and plates. The specimen is held between an adjustable platform and the lower pin as shown in the figure and is bent around the lower pin by the upper pin. By means of graduations on the dial behind the pins it is possible to determine the angle of bend. Various pins about which the specimen may be bent are shown in the lower right-hand corner.

SHEAR AND TORSION TESTING MACHINES

15. Transverse Shear-Test Appliances. Although it is impossible to produce in a body a transverse shearing stress unaccompanied by tension or compression, yet, on account of the frequent occurrence of shearing stresses in members subjected to cross bending—in rivets, bolts, pins, etc.—and on account of the weakness of timber in shearing along the grain, it is often desirable to obtain an approximate knowledge of the shearing strength of a material. Several devices have been employed for this purpose; two will be briefly described.

Fig. 11. Johnson's shear tool.

In Fig. 11 is shown a double-shear apparatus designed to determine the shearing strength of metals. With this appliance the end and central portions of the specimen are tightly gripped by hardened steel bearing plates which minimize bending distortion. However, on account of the small clearance between the central and end portions of the device, some frictional resistance is developed in testing. A comparison of the results of shearing tests on this apparatus with values obtained from torsion tests of very thin cylinders of like material indicates that the shearing device gives about 10 per cent higher unit stresses. The bars used in these tests were uniform in size. Grooving the bars in the planes of shearing would undoubtedly have lessened the error.

A simple and satisfactory apparatus for making shearing tests on small timber specimens is shown in Fig. 12. The specimens are nominally 2 by 2 by 2½ in. and are notched so that they fail on a 2- by 2-in. surface. The maximum applied load and the actual dimensions of the sheared surface are obtained, and the shearing strength is then calculated.

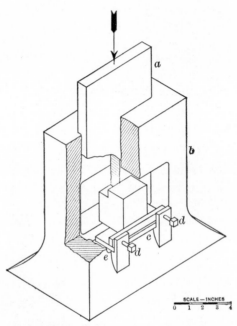

Fig. 12. Forest Products Laboratory shear tool. Specimen is cut with a projecting shoulder.

16. Torsion Testing Machines. Shafting, wire, and elements of machines which are to be subjected to twisting are often tested to determine their torsional strength and shearing modulus of elasticity. The machine shown in Fig. 13 is used for testing axles, crankshafts, airplane control rods, and other specimens. This machine is available in four models, with capacities ranging from 10,000 to 300,000 in-lb. Different lengths of specimens may be tested by sliding the torque-indicating unit along the rails to the desired position. Some models are equipped with an autographic device for plotting torque-twist diagrams.

The machine shown in Fig. 14 is adapted to test wires in torsion and combined tension and torsion. It consists of a motor-driven twisting head and a tailstock mounted on a base frame. The wire specimen is gripped in the chucks at each end, and the torque is applied at the left end. Tensile loads may be applied at the right end.

Fig. 13. Torsion testing machine. (Riehle Testing Machines Division.)

Fig. 14. Torsion machine for testing wire. (Baldwin-Lima-Hamilton Corp.)

IMPACT TESTING MACHINES

17. Essential Conditions for Impact Testing Machines. Since impact tests are made upon car wheels, car couplers, car axles, rails, and rail joints to determine the resistance of such structural forms to shock, it is very necessary that the machine in which the tests are made shall be so constructed that the energy absorbed by the specimen can be determined. Inasmuch as the effect of a blow on the specimen depends upon the resistance of the specimen as well as the energy and mass of the falling body, it follows that a standard impact test involves a standard anvil resting upon a standard foundation, a standard hammer or tup, and a standard fall. Furthermore, in drop machines the axes of the tup, guides, anvil, and specimen must be collinear; and the faces of the specimen, anvil, and tup must be parallel. On account of the impossibility of providing either an absolutely rigid anvil or tup, true quantitative results cannot be obtained. However, qualitative results of great value may be had from standardized tests. In practically all impact testing machines a transverse blow is delivered to the specimen by a pendulum revolving about a horizontal axis, by a falling weight, or by a rotating flywheel.

18. Pendulum Impact Testing Machines. The potential energy of a pendulum is a linear function of the versine of the angle through which it is raised from the lowest position. Hence if the initial angle to which the pendulum is raised and the final angle to which it rises after breaking the specimen are known, it is possible to calculate both the initial and residual energy of the pendulum. The difference between these energies closely approximates the energy used in breaking the specimen. Corrections for air resistance and bearing friction should be made.

The most widely used pendulum impact machines are adapted for Charpy, Izod, and impact tension tests. The machine shown in Fig. 15 can be made to operate over six different capacity ranges up to a maximum of 240 ft-lb by using different weight hammers and by releasing the pendulum from two possible positions. The impact velocities are 11 and 17 fps for the lowest and highest release positions, respectively.

The machine may be used for testing small simple end-supported beams (Charpy type) which are struck horizontally at midspan by the striking edge on the underside of the hammer. Beams of ductile materials must be notched across the side opposite the hammer if rupture is desired. Vertical cantilever beams (Izod type) are struck at a given distance above and on the same side as the notch by a different striking edge on the underside of the pendulum. Impact tension tests are made by removing the Izod vise holder, screwing one end of the specimen into an adaptor on the underside of the pendulum and the other end into a tension yoke, and then testing.

The dial on most machines is calibrated directly in foot pounds. Calibration is based on the principle that the difference between the versines of the angle of rise when the pendulum swings free from a given initial angle and the angle of rise when it starts from the same initial angle and breaks the specimen is a measure of the energy used in breaking the specimen.

With the ordinary type of pendulum impact machines the velocity of tup is low. A high-velocity tension impact testing machine was invented

Fig. 15. Sonntag universal impact testing machine. (Baldwin-Lima-Hamilton Corp.)

by Haskell and Mann of the Ordnance Department of the U. S. Army in 1935.* Figure 16 shows the principle of operation of this machine. The two rotating wheels carry a pair of horns and balancing counterweight, both of which can be released when the wheel speed has attained the desired value. The horns then engage the tup attached to the left end of the test specimen. The right end of the specimen is fastened to the pendulum, which hangs vertical until the tup is thus struck. The upward

* See *Proc. ASTM,* Vol. 36, Pt. 2, p. 85.

swing of the pendulum is indicated on the dial, which provides a means of calculating with reasonable accuracy the energy conserved in rupturing the specimen. Riehle Testing Machine Division of American Machine and Metals, Inc., now manufacture this machine, capable of producing a maximum velocity of 250 fps. In testing with this machine Mann used a specimen 3 in. long provided with threaded ends having an outside diameter of ¾ in. and a gage length of 1 in. with a diameter of 0.252 in.

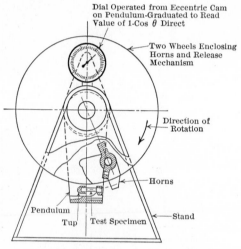

Fig. 16.   Principle of Mann-Haskell high-velocity tension impact testing machine. (*Proc. ASTM,* Vol. 36, Pt. 2, p. 85.)

The relation of diameters of end and gage portions is such that the work of deformation is restricted almost entirely to the reduced portion of this specimen.

19. Drop Impact Testing Machines. Figure 17 illustrates a Turner impact testing machine for either compression or transverse impact tests. In this machine the tup is hoisted by an electric motor placed at the top. Release of the tup is secured by reversing the current through the suspending magnet. A pencil moving over paper fastened to the revolving drum, shown just above the specimen, records the behavior of the specimen. The largest machine of this type has a capacity for beams 8 ft long and 12 in. wide; the maximum drop attainable is 6 ft, and the weights of tup range from 50 to 500 lb. With this type of machine tests can be made to ascertain the elastic properties in addition to the energy of rupture of a specimen.

Another example of this type is the standard drop testing machine adopted by the American Railway Engineering Association for making tests on rails. A noteworthy fact about this machine is the method of supporting the anvil. The latter weighs 20,000 lb and is supported on 20 MCBA Standard "C" springs arranged in groups of five at each corner of the anvil. No connection exists between the vertical guides and the anvil. For further information relating to this machine see *The Manual* of the AREA.

Apparatus for Determining Hardness

20. The Sclerometer. In 1886 Turner developed his sclerometer to measure hardness by ascertaining the weight required to cause a diamond to make a visible scratch. Martens modified this test by measuring the weight required to produce a scratch 0.01 mm wide with a conical diamond point. Such tests have attracted attention in this country. See *Rept. of Com.* E-4 of ASTM in 1926.

21. Ball Indentation Tests — Brinell and Rockwell. The penetration of a steel ball or diamond point into a finished surface is the most used method for testing the hardness of metals.

Both hand-operated and motor-driven Brinell machines are available. The specimen is placed on the anvil which caps the vertical screw shown in Fig. 18.

Fig. 17. A Turner impact testing machine.

By means of the screw the anvil is adjusted to permit admission of the specimen. The indentation of a 10-mm hardened steel ball, shown directly above the anvil, is imposed by hydraulic pressure. The pressure may be set and is registered on the dial. In hand-operated machines the load is regulated by accumulator weights which are lifted when the desired pressure has been imposed. The ratio of the load in kilograms to the surface area of the indentation in square millimeters forms the basis for the Brinell hardness scale. A specially constructed microscope is ordinarily used to measure the diameter of the indentation.

Devries of the National Bureau of Standards found that the indentation can be more accurately determined by measuring the difference in depth of indentation due to a light load applied before and after the test load. He also found that a linear relation exists between load and depth of indentation for pressures less than 3000 kg. Portable Brinell devices are also available.

Fig. 18. Machine-driven hardness tester. (Courtesy Detroit Testing Machine Co.)

For the Rockwell hardness tester, Fig. 19, two hardness scales are provided—the B scale in which the depth of indentation of a $\frac{1}{16}$-in. steel ball under an increase in load of 100 kg is the basis; and the C scale in which the penetration of a 120° conical diamond point (called a Brale) under a 150-kg increase in load is the basis. For very soft metals larger balls and lighter loads may be employed. Registration of penetration is made on a dial reading to 0.002 mm. The scale reading of the dial is arranged to increase with the hardness of the specimen.

In testing with the Rockwell machine the work is placed on the anvil (1) and forced upward against the penetrator by turning the hand wheel

(2) until a 10-kg initial load has been applied. The dial (3) is then set to read zero and the handle (4) pushed backward to release the major load 100, or 150 kg, which is superimposed at a given rate of speed by the dash pot. After the dial pointer (5) has come to rest the handle is pulled forward (6) releasing the major load but leaving the minor load imposed. The Rockwell hardness number (7) is then automatically registered by the dial pointer.

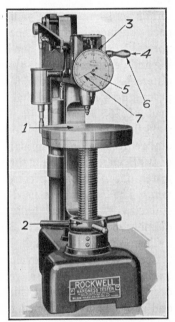

Fig. 19.   How to operate the   Fig. 20.   Shore sclero-
Rockwell hardness tester. (Wil-   scope.
son-Maeulen Co.)

22. The Shore Scleroscope.* In this apparatus the specimen is struck by a small diamond-pointed hammer falling freely. The rebound of the hammer is measured and gives an indication, according to its inventor, of the resistance to indentation or hardness. Figure 20 shows a recording type of scleroscope. In this device the tube is made vertical by adjusting the screws at the base of the instrument until the plumb rod, exposed at the front of the tube, is centered. The diamond-pointed hammer is elevated in the tube and released by turning the knurled knob near the bottom of the tube. The rebound of the hammer is recorded by the dial hand which remains fixed until the knurled knob is again turned for another test. In the older type of scleroscope the hammer is allowed to fall

* Manufactured by Shore Instrument and Manufacturing Co., Jamaica, N. Y.

in an accurately ground glass tube from a height of about 10 in. and the rebound is noted by the eye. Since slight differences in the sharpness of hammer points greatly affect the rebound, the hammer must be frequently tested on a standard surface. The surface ordinarily used is of hardened steel which gives a rebound of 100 on the scale.

23. Other Hardness Testers. The Rockwell superficial hardness tester was developed for testing thin materials and thin superficially hardened surfaces. It resembles the normal Rockwell tester, but its loading and depth-measuring systems are different. The superficial tester imposes a 3-kg minor load and a major load of 15, 30, or 45 kg. In the superficial tester one division on the dial represents an indentation depth of 0.001 mm, whereas for the normal tester one division represents 0.002 mm. The penetrators used are the standard $\frac{1}{16}$-in. steel ball and the diamond conical point (N Brale).

The Vickers pyramid hardness tester, Fig. 21, was developed for testing materials with a very high degree of hardness, very thin sheets, and superficially hardened material. Its principle is similar to that of the Brinell except that a diamond penetrator in the form of a square-base pyramid with an angle of 136° between faces is used. The load applied depends upon the material to be tested and varies from 1 to 120 kg. The application, duration, and removal of the load are automatic. After loading, the diagonals of the square impression are measured with a microscope to the nearest 0.001 mm and the average length is used to determine the hardness number. The Vickers pyramid hardness numbers are obtained by dividing the applied load in kilograms by the surface area of the impression in square millimeters. In testing, the specimen is placed on the stage which is then elevated by turning the handwheel until the specimen almost touches the diamond indenter. The loading and unloading cycles are performed automatically by tripping the starting handle. The stage is then lowered

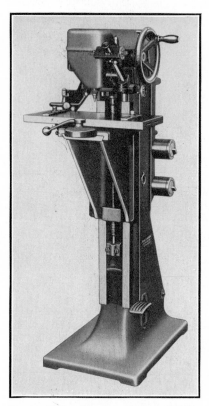

Fig. 21. Vickers hardness tester. (Riehle Testing Machines Division.)

and the microscope is positioned to read the dimensions of the impression. Finally, the foot pedal is depressed and the loading mechanism is brought into position for the next test.

The Monotron hardness tester also operates on the indentation principle. In testing, the $\frac{3}{4}$-mm spherical diamond penetrator is forced into the specimen under increasing pressure until an indentation of 0.0018 in. is noted on the depth dial. The load in kilograms required to produce this indentation, the Monotron hardness number, is then read directly from the load dial. For testing soft materials, cemented carbide balls 1 mm and $2\frac{1}{2}$ mm in diameter are used. The Monotron hardness tester is flexible and very rapid in its operation.

Microhardness testing has been developed for the testing of very thin materials, small precision parts, and also for the determination of the hardness gradients in surface-hardened materials. The surface to be tested, plane and free from scratches, is indented with a standard Knoop indenter by means of an instrument capable of accurately applying light loads such as the Tukon tester made by the Wilson Mechanical Instrument Co. The Knoop indenter is a diamond ground to a pyramidal form that produces a diamond-shaped indentation with the long diagonal about seven times as long as the short diagonal. The indenter has a longitudinal angle of 172° 30′ and a transverse angle of 130° 0′. Under the usual test loads, 25 to 3000 gm, the indenter penetrates to a depth of about $\frac{1}{30}$ of the length of the indentation. This length is carefully measured after testing by means of a metallurgical microscope with a filar micrometer eyepiece and is used to calculate the unrecovered projected area. It is assumed that the length of the indentation is not appreciably affected by the elastic recovery due to the removal of the load. The Knoop hardness number is calculated by dividing the load in kilograms by the unrecovered projected area in square millimeters. The load used should always be reported along with the hardness number.

ENDURANCE TESTING MACHINES

24. Reversed Bending Endurance Testing Machines. Figure 22 shows a type of rotating beam machine which has been extensively used both in the United States and in England. The machine shown is one which was used at the University of Illinois. The specimen A rests in ball bearings at B and E. The load is applied by means of two symmetrically placed ball bearings at C and D. This loading produces uniform bending moment between C and D. The revolutions counter is at N, and the machine has an automatic device (not shown) which stops the machine when the specimen breaks.

Figure 23 shows a widely used high-speed rotating cantilever-beam machine. The speed of operation, between 500 and 12,000 rpm, is controlled by a variable voltage transformer A. The specimen S is subjected to a constant bending moment by means of the application of a constant force at B to a spindle connected to the specimen. The applied force and

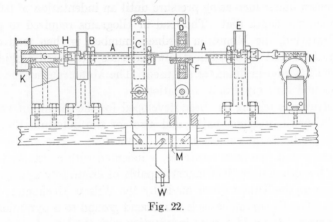

Fig. 22.

consequently the bending moment may be changed by moving the weight W along the weight beam. The machine is provided with a counter C to indicate the number of stress cycles and a microswitch which may be adjusted to stop the machine as soon as a certain deflection from the normal running position has occurred. Excessive deflection of the speci-

Fig. 23. A Krouse high-speed rotating beam fatigue machine.

men and spindle as the rotational speed is increased through the critical range is prevented by a loosely fitting collar at D.

Reversed bending tests are also run on sheet- and plate-type specimens in machines that maintain a constant peak force during the test or by machines that produce a fixed specimen deflection during test. An example of the first type is shown in Fig. 24. The machine consists of a synchronous motor M that rotates the drive shaft D and the eccentric mass E, a loading arm and yoke A that acts on the free end of the cantilever specimen, a specimen holder H, a cycle counter C, and a microswitch that cuts off the current when the amplitude of the motion of the loading

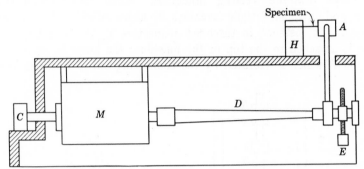

Fig. 24.   Constant-force-type fatigue machine for repeated bending tests of sheet materials.

yoke reaches a predetermined value.   The magnitude of the alternating force may be varied by moving the eccentric mass in or away from the axis of rotation.   Horizontal components of the force are absorbed, and the vertical components are transmitted to the loading yoke.

Fig. 25.   Fixed deflection-type fatigue machine for bending tests of sheet materials. (Krouse.)

In the fixed deflection-type machine, shown in Fig. 25, one end of the cantilever specimen S is held in a vise V, while the other end is loaded by a connecting rod C which is actuated by an adjustable throw crank driven by the motor.   The range and the ratio between the maximum and minimum stress may be varied by adjustment of the variable throw crank and by moving the specimen vise. An automatic switch stops the motor when the specimen fails, and the number of stress cycles may be obtained from a counter.

25. Other Fatigue Testing Machines.   Axial tension-compression, torsion, and universal fatigue machines are also available. In Fig. 26 the specimen S is fastened in threaded connectors T, T. The upper connector is attached to the top of the machine; the lower is connected to the lever B which is vibrated by the connecting rod R which in turn is

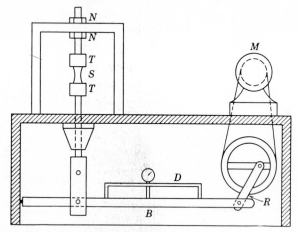

Fig. 26. Axial tension-compression fatigue machine.

driven by an adjustable-stroke crankpin. The ratio of maximum to minimum stress can be varied by proper adjustment of the nuts N, M, and the range of stress can be changed by adjustment of the variable-throw crank. The deflection of the lever B as measured by gage D provides information regarding the load on the specimen. The gage is removed while the machine is running.

Universal fatigue testing machines capable of direct axial stress, bending, and torsion fatigue tests are available. Generally such machines are limited in their axial tension-compression tests to small specimens because of the relatively large forces required for such tests in comparison with those necessary for bending and torsion fatigue tests.

Many special fatigue machines designed to test machine parts and complete structural units are in service. Adaptors of various types are available to make corrosion-fatigue, high-temperature and low-temperature tests. Some fatigue testing machines stress the specimen by causing it to vibrate at resonant frequency. Vibrations are produced by mechanical, electromagnetic, or pneumatic means.

AUXILIARY APPLIANCES EMPLOYED IN LOADING SPECIMENS

26. The Transmission of Load to a Specimen. In making tests of materials it is very desirable that the experimenter have control not only of the magnitude but also of the places of application and the directions of the forces applied to the specimen. Unless such conditions obtain, stresses of a different kind or of undesirable magnitude may be produced in the test piece. In most tension and compression tests an axial load is sought; in most transverse tests a loading which produces bending in a given plane is desired. On account of the devices employed to transmit pressure from the testing machine to the specimen, a brief description of some of these appliances will now be given.

GRIPPING DEVICES FOR TENSION TESTS

27. Wedges or Grips. By far the most frequently used device for holding tensile specimens in the jaws of the testing machine is a set of four

Fig. 27. Flat and grooved wedges for tensile tests.

serrated wedges. The flat wedges shown in Fig. 27 are for specimens of rectangular cross section; the grooved wedges are used with cylindrical test pieces.

Liners are placed in back of the grips in testing thin specimens. Figure 28*d* shows the proper method of gripping a test piece when wedges are employed. To prevent sticking in the jaws of the machine the backs of the grips should be coated with a heavy lubricant.

Wedges are often objected to on the ground that they crush the specimen and pull unevenly on opposite sides of a test piece, thus producing bending or oblique stresses. However, for rough commercial testing, experience has proved such grips to be satisfactory.

28. Spherical Seated Holders. In scientific testing to determine the elastic limit of a material, it is desirable to secure as close an approach to an axial loading as possible, and a method more refined than that indicated above should be employed. For such tests spherical seated holders of the type shown in Fig. 29 and 30 have been much used.

The efficiency of this device is dependent both upon the skill of the mechanic in making the appliance and in fashioning the specimen, and

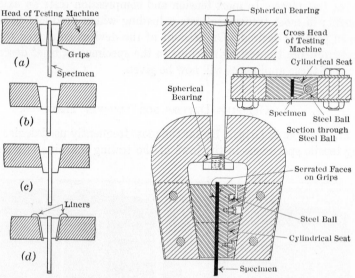

Fig. 28. Correct (*d*) and incorrect (*a, b, c*) methods of gripping tensile specimens with wedges.

Fig. 29. Gripping device for sheet materials. (See **ASTM** *Standards* for tension tests.)

upon the care exercised in using the device. To reduce the frictional resistance of the spherical seat to a minimum, the radius of the sphere should be made as small as a proper consideration of the crushing strength of the ball will permit, the ball and seat should be ground to fit, and the bearing should be lubricated with a thin film of oil. Even with a well-made holder and careful manipulation, extensometer measurements taken on opposite sides of a specimen will often differ considerably. This difficulty may be partly removed by applying a small load, reading the extensions, then removing the load and adjusting the specimen slightly to overcome the eccentricity.

A type of holder which is suitable for use with tempered steel specimens is shown in Fig. 30*b*. Portion *A* is a socket nut which is threaded to fit the lower end of the bolt *B*. The latter may be provided with a spherical head or threaded at the upper end to fit the holder of Fig. 30*a*. After the head of the test piece has been inserted through the hole in portion *A*, the halves of the spherical-seated washer *C* are slipped about the specimens and held in place by a rubber band or a split ring. Parts *A* and *B* are screwed together, and then the lower end of the specimen is socketed.

29. Crossed Knife-Edge Suspension. Figure 31 shows a form of crossed knife-edge suspension which has been successfully used at the Materials

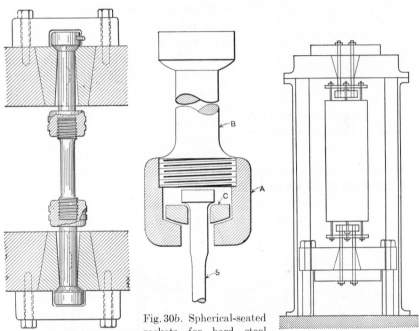

Fig. 30*a*. Holders with spherical seats for tensile tests.

Fig. 30*b*. Spherical-seated sockets for hard steel specimens. (After K. W. Zimmerscheid in *Trans. SAE*, Vol. 8, Pt. 2, p. 162.)

Fig. 31. A crossed knife-edge suspension for testing concrete cylinder in tension.

Testing Laboratory at the University of Wisconsin in making tension tests of concrete specimens.

LOADING APPLIANCES FOR COMPRESSION TESTS

30. Rigid Bearing Blocks. In rough testing, compressive loads are applied through heavy blocks, one of which is fastened to the lower side of the pushing head of the testing machine and the other of which is supported by the weighing table. With such bearing blocks it is very difficult to secure an axial load on the specimen.

31. Adjustable Bearing Blocks. For carefully conducted tests various appliances have been devised for imposing compressive loads. The spherical bearing block, shown in Fig. 32, has been extensively used. Some experimenters prefer to support this device on the weighing table beneath the specimen; others hang it from the moving head above the specimen. The latter position is the simpler for operation.

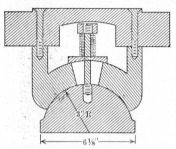

Fig. 32. A spherical bearing block used at the University of Wisconsin.

Ball-bearing blocks have also been widely used in compression tests. Figure 33 shows a form of block which is satisfactory for such tests.

In using any of the above devices great care must be exercised to make the axes of the bearing block, specimen, and testing machine collinear. If deformation measurements are being taken the load on the specimen may be made axial in the following manner: Readings of the shortening of elements on opposite sides of the specimen may be taken for moderate loads and the specimen adjusted on the bearing block until the deformations of all elements are equal.

In testing columns for the purpose of checking existing theories, most investigators have attempted to make the ends of the specimen free to

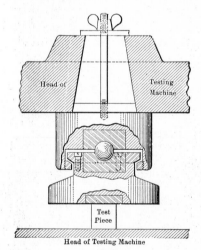

Fig. 33. Ball-bearing block for compression tests.

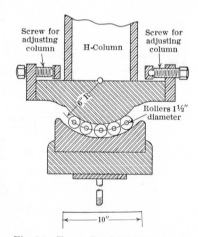

Fig. 34. Forest Products Laboratory roller-bearing block.

revolve. Professors Bauschinger, Considére, Tetmajer, and Lilly mounted their columns on cone or knife-edge bearings at the gravity axes. The roller bearings designed at the Forest Products Laboratory, Fig. 34, have also proved satisfactory. These bearings have been loaded to 800,000 lb. When the bearings are well greased, the coefficient of friction is about

0.025. The adjusting screws are convenient in centering the column as desired.

32. V-Blocks. Commonly the supporting tools for transverse tests are inverted V-blocks which are either fixed to the bed of the testing machine or which may be slid into the desired position. The edges of the blocks are rounded to produce line contact across the beam, and are surmounted by metal bearing plates when tests of non-metallic specimens are to be made. Through a similar V-block fixed in the jaws of the movable head of the testing machine and bearing upon a metal plate or saddle, the load is imposed upon the test piece. Obviously, with the above arrangement the beam is subjected to more or less longitudinal restraint. Furthermore, if the lines of contact on the beam are not parallel to the edges of the V-blocks, the test piece will be subjected to torsion.

33. Adjustable Bearing Blocks. To avoid the errors encountered in the use of fixed V-blocks it has been customary to mount the beam on

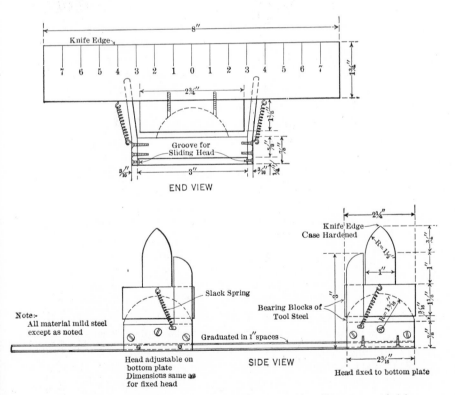

Fig. 35. Knife edges with spherical bearings for cross-bending tests on brick.

adjustable supports. A much-used form of support consists of a V-block mounted on a spherical seat. Figure 35 shows such a device which has been employed considerably at the University of Wisconsin in testing small specimens. Figure 36 illustrates the form of support which Tinius Olsen Testing Machine Co. advocates for testing large beams.

In careful work it is advisable to transmit the load from the pulling head to the specimen, or to the auxiliary beams used in loading, through

a spherical bearing block. If the specimen is loaded at more than one point, rollers resting on hard steel plates should be employed to apply the pressure of the auxiliary beams upon the test piece.

BEDMENTS

34. The Use of Bedments. Even though adjustable bearings are employed, it is necessary that the contact surfaces of the test piece be plane and approximately parallel. Metal specimens should always be machined or ground

Fig. 36. An adjustable supporting block used in testing large beams.

until the above conditions are fulfilled. For the best results, specimens of stone, brick, or concrete should also be ground. However, on account of the length of time and the equipment required to grind specimens, many experimenters bed such test pieces in some material which will lessen the effects of surface inequalities. If a bedment is used it should be made as thin as possible; also, it should be composed of a substance which will not spread or flow under pressure and which possesses the same strength and elastic properties as the specimen. The latter condition is difficult to satisfy and is, unfortunately, often disregarded.

35. Plaster of Paris. Bedments of plaster of Paris have long been used. In making such bedments it is good practice to place a sheet of sized paper between the plaster of Paris paste and the specimen to prevent the absorption of water by the latter, since this action invariably affects the strength of the test piece. The bedments should be made plane and perpendicular to the axis of the specimen after which a slight pressure should be brought to bear upon the soft bedment and allowed to remain until the plaster of Paris has set.

36. Cement Mortar. Laboratory practice for molding and capping concrete and mortar compression specimens is given in ASTM *Standard* C39. Where bedment is necessary, however, plaster of Paris and neat cement pastes are often used. Such bedments must be made long enough before the time of testing to permit the paste or mortar to harden. The addition of 2 per cent of calcium chloride, by weight, to a high early strength Portland cement paste gives a capping mortar with a compressive strength of 6000 psi at 1 day. (See also Art. XI-17.) In general, only the tops of the specimens need to be treated, the procedure being as follows: The specimen is placed upon a leveled surface and a thin coat of plastic mortar applied to the top. The bedment is then finished by pressing down upon it a piece of plate glass and truing with a spirit level.

37. Miscellaneous Bedments. Beaverboard, blotting paper, leather, millboard, and white pine board are occasionally used as bedments. Of the common sheet bedments, Beaverboard is most satisfactory; white pine board, millboard, and leather are of some benefit; blotting paper, sheet lead, and rubber are detrimental. (H. F. Gonnerman, *Proc. ASTM*, 1924.) Sulfur bedments are also used.

APPLIANCES FOR MEASURING DEFORMATIONS

EXTENSOMETERS

38. Essential Features of Extensometers. For measuring the elastic extension of materials subjected to tensile loads, a great variety of devices have been employed. Five principal types of extensometers are micrometer-screw with electric-contact, indicating dial, multiplying lever, optical lever, and electrical resistance apparatus. In any type of extensometer the following conditions should obtain:

1. The apparatus should be directly attached to the test piece.

2. It should be arranged to measure deformations on opposite sides of the specimen if the change in length of the axis is to be determined. If the maximum deformation of any element is desired, measurements along at least three elements, preferably 120° apart, are required.

3. The portions of the apparatus transmitting deformations should be parallel to and equidistant from the axis of the specimen. If only two measurements are made these should be along lines in the plane of the axis and equidistant from it.

4. The apparatus should be so arranged that the relative positions of all parts with respect to the axis of the specimen will remain the same throughout the test.

5. For precise measurements the instrument should read to at least 0.0001 in. and should be sensitive to half that amount. To determine the accuracy of the instrument, its readings should be checked by comparison with a standardized measuring device.

6. The apparatus should be so constructed that it may be quickly applied to or removed from a specimen without interfering with the application of the load.

39. A Micrometer-Screw Electric-Contact Extensometer. In Fig. 37 is shown a simple form of micrometer-screw extensometer reading to

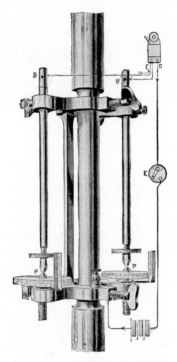

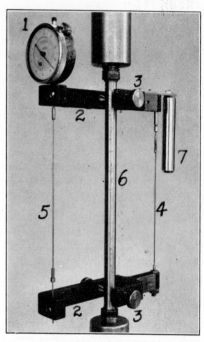

Fig. 37.　A micrometer-screw electric-contact extensometer.

Fig. 38.　An indicating dial extensometer.

0.0001 in. The upper and lower portions of the apparatus form parts of an open electric circuit. Contact between a micrometer screw and rod is announced by the bell which rings when the circuit is closed. Only a small constant current is used, since a large current will jump an appreciable gap between screw and rod. On account of the uncertainty of bell mechanisms telephone receivers are often substituted. To prevent a closed circuit through the specimen the vertical rods are insulated by gutta percha sleeves placed in the top collar of the instrument.

This common type of extensometer is quite satisfactory for student work, and with skillful handling will give accurate results. In operating the screws on this instrument, however, great care must always be exercised to make the plane of the turning couple exerted by the fingers perpendicular to the axis of the screw.

A similar type of instrument carries a rod at the left attached to the lower frame and pivoted on the upper. The micrometer on the right then reads double the average extension.

40. An Indicating Dial Extensometer. Indicating dials reading to 0.001 or 0.0001 in. have a very wide range of application in measuring deformations and deflections. Figure 38 shows an inexpensive extensometer in use at the University of Wisconsin. It is a modification of an earlier form devised by H. F. Moore. A 3-in. Federal dial (1) reading directly to 0.0001 in., equipped with adjustable scale and revolution counter, provides an easily read and accurate indicator. The upper and lower yokes (2) are of aluminum and pivot on the attachment screws (3). The vertical drill rods (4) and (5) connecting the yokes are provided with small ball-and-socket joints. Rod (4) acts as a pivot so that rod (5) transmits double the average elongation of the specimen (6) to the dial. The counterweight (7) serves to balance the weight of the dial.

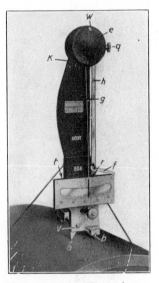

Fig. 39. A Huggenberger tensometer. (Baldwin-Southwark Corp.)

In assembling the device a gage bar, not shown, clamps the yokes at the desired distance apart until the instrument has been attached to the specimen. Care must be taken to center the device so that the plane of the rods contains the specimen axis and each rod is equidistant from that axis.

If it is desirable to read strains on opposite sides of the specimen, pivot rod (4) may be replaced by a rod similar to (5) and a second dial inserted on the top frame.

41. Multiplying Lever Extensometers. The Huggenberger tensometer is adaptable to a wide variety of strain measurements and especially to ½- or 1-in. gage lengths. The form shown in Fig. 39 has a strain range of 0.008 in. and a multiplication of 1200. The pointer (g) is balanced, and knife-edge fulcra are used. For ½-in. gage lengths the knife edge at (a) is reversed. In mounting the device the locking lever (f) is released and the pointers (g) and (k) are set at the proper ends of their ranges as the knife edges are adjusted to the scribed gage lines at (a) and (b). Care is taken to fasten securely the tensometer normal to the part measured. When the pointer reaches the limit of its range it can be reset by the screw (q).

An apparatus embodying both a multiplying lever and an indicating

dial is the Berry strain gage shown in Fig. 40. This device is particularly well adapted to the measurement of deformations in portions of
a structure. Any number of measurements on different portions of a
beam, column or floor may be made with one instrument provided a
pair of $\frac{1}{20}$-in. holes, spaced the gage length of the apparatus apart, are
drilled a short distance into each element at the proper place. In measuring, the left pivot which is rigidly attached to the Invar steel side bars

Fig. 40. Berry strain gage for measurements over 8-in. lengths, clamp for attaching
apparatus to specimen, and center punch.

is placed in one of the holes and the right pivot, which terminates the
short arm of a five-to-one bell-crank lever, is adjusted to the other hole.
The long arm of the bell crank rests against the pin of an Ames dial
reading to 0.001 in. The instrument is placed in the pair of holes several
times, and the average reading of the dial noted; the load is changed
and the reading repeated. By exercising great care readings accurate
to 0.0001 in. may be taken with this device. Side bars for 2-, 8-, and
20-in. gage lengths can be procured with this instrument.

The Porter-Lipp strain gage, Fig. 41, makes contact with the object
under test by means of one fixed and one movable knife edge usually 1 in.
apart. As the test specimen is strained the movable knife edge pivots,
and this motion is transferred through a lever system to a pointer which
moves across a scale. The gage has a range of about 0.008 in., and the
multiplication factor of the lever system is about 300. Its very small

size and light weight, less than half an ounce, along with low mounting pressures, are important advantages.

The General Motors photoelectric extensometer with gage lengths as short as ¼₆ in. has been developed for use in areas of high stress concentrations. A combination of mechanical and photoelectrical amplifications gives a multiplication factor of 30,000. The gage has two 120-line-per-inch optical gratings, one of which is fixed and the other of which is attached to the lever which is actuated by straining the surface

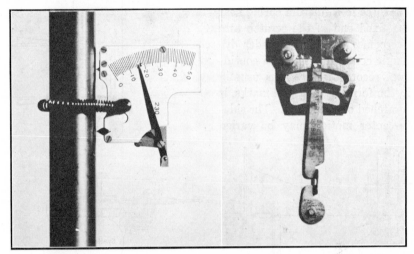

Fig. 41. Porter-Lipp strain gage (left) and deForest scratch recording strain gage (right).

to which it is attached. The amount of light that passes through the two gratings and onto a photoelectric cell depends on the relative motion of the movable grating with respect to the fixed grating. This motion in turn depends on the amount of strain in the surface to which the gage is attached. The magnitudes of the strains are determined from the readings of a microammeter which is actuated by the variable amounts of light falling on the photoelectric cell.

The deForest scratch-recording strain gage, Fig. 41, is used to determine deformations due to impact and dynamic loading. The gage is about as large as a latch key and weighs less than 2 gm. It can be easily attached to the object to be tested even in confined places, and it does not require any wire connections. A graphical record of the deformations which may be later studied at suitable magnification under a metallographic microscope is obtained on a polished target. The gage records deformations from 0.0001 in. to 0.050 in. over a 2-in. gage length with a fair degree of accuracy. The gage consists of two parts, a spring-loaded scratch arm with an emery grit coating at its tip, and a polished chrome-plated target. Both pieces are screwed or soldered to the surface of the test specimen. Friction between the scratch arm and a friction bar on the target under static conditions holds the scratch arm in any position it is placed. When strain is applied to the object under test the scratch arm moves at right angles to a previously established base line and also from the side to the center of the target. This latter motion is produced as the restoring force in a fulcrum spring near the fixed end of the scratch arm overcomes the friction under dynamic conditions. Thus a continuous record of the strain, usually in the form of V-shaped marks, is scratched on the target. The side-to-center motion may be varied

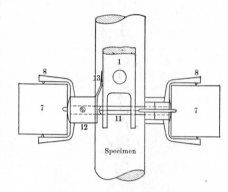

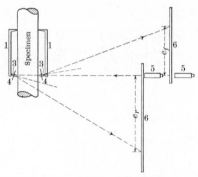

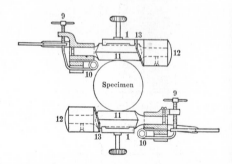

Fig. 42a. Diagrammatic sketch of Martens' mirror extensometer.　　　Fig. 42b. Fulcra and mirrors of Martens' extensometer.

by changing the stiffness of the restoring spring or by changing the friction between the scratch arm and the friction bar.

42. Optical Lever Extensometers. For greater refinement than 0.00005 in. in the measurement of deformations some form of optical lever is sometimes employed. One of the most accurate and adaptable instruments is the mirror apparatus devised by Martens. The sketch of this apparatus, Fig. 42a, indicates the principle of operation. In this instrument the multiplying levers shown in Fig. 39 are replaced by small mirrors, (4) (Fig. 42a), which are attached to the rhombic fulcra (3) so that the axis of each fulcrum passes through the reflecting plane of its mirror. The deformation of the specimen causes slight rotations of the mirrors. The rotations are determined by observing successive positions of the cross hairs in the telescopes (5) with respect to the images of the scales (6), thus finding e_r and e_f.

A better idea of the arrangement of the fulcra and mirrors can be had from Fig. 42b, which presents a view seen from the telescope. The mirrors (7) may be adjusted about a vertical line through the pivots of the frames (8) by means of screws (9). The springs (10) hold the mirrors against the screws. The mirrors may also be turned about the

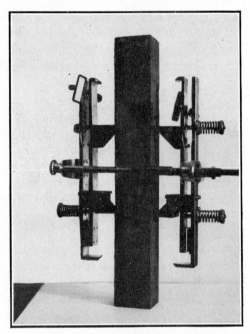

Fig. 43. Lamb's roller extensometer.

spindles connecting them with the fulcra (11). To balance the weight of the mirror each fulcra is provided with a counterweight (12). By making the vertical arms (13) parallel to the bars (1), the positions of the fulcra (11) may be accurately adjusted to the gage length for which bars were designed.

The entire apparatus is very light and may be quickly placed upon the test piece. If a flat scale is employed, proper correction to the readings must, of course, be made. With careful handling readings to 0.000002 in. can be taken with this instrument.

The Lamb's roller extensometer, Fig. 43, consists of two units clamped on opposite sides of the specimen. Each unit consists of two hardened steel plates separated at their lower ends by a ball bearing and at their upper ends by a carefully made hardened-steel roller. A knife edge on the inner plate contacts the specimen at the top gage point, while a knife edge on the outer plate makes contact at the lower gage point. As the specimen elongates, the two plates in each unit move relatively to each other. This motion causes the rollers and attached mirrors to rotate an amount that is proportional to the extension. The magnitude is obtained by noting the shift of the telescope cross hair on the image of the scale. The image is reflected from one mirror to the other and finally to the telescope. Since the multiplication factor depends on the distance of the scale from the mirror and on the distance between mirrors, it is variable and is limited only by the difficulty of reading the scale. Reliability and accuracy are the most important features of this extensometer. A companion instrument, Lamb's lateral extensometer, has been widely used for measuring lateral strains.

The Tuckerman optical strain gage is very accurate and sensitive and may be used for high-temperature measurements. The strain gage itself has a fixed knife edge at one end of the gage length and a stellite lozenge with one mirrored surface at the other end. As the specimen surface is strained, the lozenge pivots about its bearing point and the rotation of the lozenge mirror with respect to a mirror fixed in position in the frame is measured by the displacement of the reticule image in an autocollimator.

43. Electric Strain Gages. Three types of electric strain gages in use are the magnetic or reluctance type, the unbonded resistance wire (Statham type), and the bonded resistance wire (SR-4 type). The last is the most widely used, and discussion will be limited to it.

The SR-4 strain gage, Fig. 44, consists of resistance units of fine wire 0.001 in. in diameter cemented to the stressed surface and connected in a suitable bridge circuit. As the length of the fine resistance wires changes because of strains in the stressed surface the resistance of the wires also changes. The resulting unbalance in the bridge circuit is indicated by suitable equipment.

Each wire gage is made up of a number of loops of 1-mil wire cemented to a sheet of paper less than 0.001 in. thick with a cement that has a relatively low modulus of elasticity in comparison with that of the wire. In certain gage types a piece of felt is cemented over the wire for protection. Each wire is soldered at both ends to short copper lead wires. A large variety of SR-4 resistance wire gages made of different materials and requiring different cements for application are available. Single wire gages are used to measure strains in one direction only; the rosette types are used when strains in several directions are required as in the case where the directions of the principal strains are not known.

The most common nominal resistance of the gages is 120 ohms, but resistances between 40 and 2000 ohms are available. Nominal gage lengths vary from $\frac{1}{16}$ in. to 6 in.

Instrumentation required is dependent on whether static or dynamic tests are to be performed, necessary accuracy, number of readings to be

Fig. 44. Various types of SR-4 strain gages. (Baldwin-Lima-Hamilton Corp.)

taken, time available for readings, and whether or not a written record is needed. Recording oscillographs are used for dynamic measurements; potentiometers or galvanometers are used for static measurements. Where many gages are to be read in succession various types of balancing and switching units may be placed between the gages and the strain indicator.

Some of the many advantages of the SR-4 gages are their low cost, accuracy, small size, light weight, stable calibration, freedom from hysteresis, and wide field of usefulness. In addition they may be mounted in confined spaces and their resistance changes may be recorded or photographed at remote stations. Among their limitations are the necessity of amplifying the gage responses under certain conditions, and the high cost of instrumentation especially for dynamic studies and for automatic multiple recordings.

44. Autographic Stress-Strain Recorders. The requirements of speed and convenience in testing have led to the development of several types of automatic stress-strain recorders. Values of modulus of elasticity,

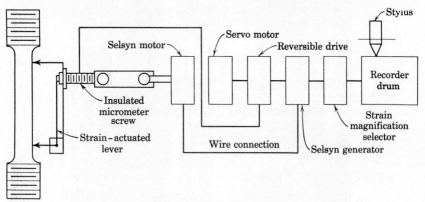

Fig. 45. Southwark-Templin strain recording system.

proportional limit, yield point, ultimate load, and shape of the curve may be determined.

Stress-strain recorders plot simultaneous values of load which may be converted to unit stresses and deformations which may be converted to unit strains. Loads and deformations may each be recorded in several different ways. Two widely used strain-recording systems are the Southwark-Templin type which uses a Selsyn motor and a Selsyn generator, and the Microformer type which uses miniature transformers with movable cores called Microformers.

A diagrammatic sketch of the basic parts of the Southwark-Templin strain recorder is shown in Fig. 45. As the specimen is strained the strain-actuated lever breaks an electric contact with the micrometer screw. When this happens the servo motor engages the Selsyn generator through the reversible drive, and also turns the recorder drum. Rotation of the Selsyn generator produces a similar rotation of the Selsyn motor, which advances the micrometer screw until contact with the strain-actuated lever is again made. This cycle is repeated every time

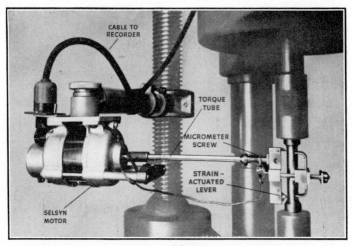

(a)

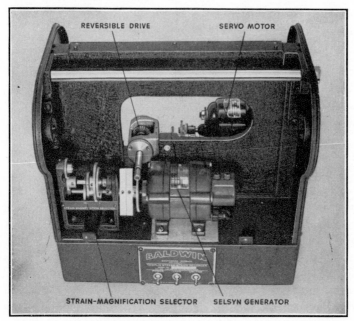

(b)

Fig. 46. a, Modified Templin-type extensometer on 0.505-in. round specimen. b, Recorder with covers removed. (Baldwin-Lima-Hamilton Corp.)

the electric contact is broken. Usual strain magnification ratios are 250:1, 500:1, and 1000:1. The extensometer and recorder units are shown in Fig. 46a and b.

A diagrammatic sketch of the Microformer type is shown in Fig. 47. As the specimen is strained the strain-actuated lever is moved and the core of the gage Microformer is displaced. This motion induces a change in the output of the gage Microformer and upsets the balance between it and a similar recorder Microformer. The unbalanced signal is amplified and used to drive the servo motor. The servo motor then rotates

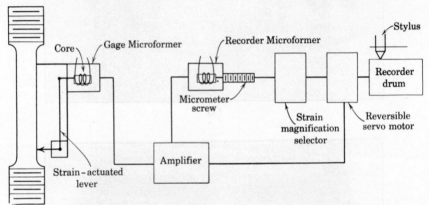

Fig. 47. Microformer-type strain recording system.

the recorder drum and also moves the core of the recorder Microformer to a new position such that the outputs of the two Microformers again balance. This cycle is repeated as the specimen continues to deform. Usual magnification ratios are the same as those given for the Southwark-Templin type.

Several load-recording systems are available. In one of them the load is recorded by a stylus that moves parallel to the axis of the recorder drum. The stylus is driven by a direct mechanical connection to the load-indicating portion of the testing machine. In another system the load is recorded by the rotation of the drum under the stylus. Bourdon tubes connected with the load-applying or the load-weighing portions of the testing machine control the amount of the drum rotation. In a third system the load is recorded by a stylus that moves parallel to the axis of the drum. The stylus is driven by a Selsyn motor which is actuated by a Selsyn generator whose rotation is in proportion to the movement of the counterpoise screw. In a fourth method the motion of a stylus parallel to the axis of the drum is caused by a Microformer unit attached to the load-indicating portion of the testing machine.

COMPRESSOMETERS

45. Essential Features of Compressometers. The conditions mentioned under essential features of extensometers apply with equal force to compressometers; and the use of an apparatus which measures the relative displacement of the bearing surfaces on either end of the specimen should never be permitted if the modulus of elasticity of the test piece is sought.

46. Brief Discussion of Various Types of Compressometers. Inasmuch as the principles of measurement are the same for both extensom-

Fig. 48.   An indicating-dial compressometer.

eters and compressometers, only types of the latter in which the method of attachment differs from that employed in the previously illustrated extensometers will be considered.

Figure 48 shows an indicating-dial compressometer used at the University of Wisconsin, primarily for tests on wood prisms. It is equipped with two Federal dials with adjustable scales reading directly to 0.0001 in. The collars are split and have three-point contact with the specimen. The gage length can be easily varied by changing the length of the rods. The gage bar is removed prior to test. Modification of the collars permits use for measuring strains in columns.

In Fig. 49 is shown a dial compressometer used at the University of Wisconsin in testing cylinders. The split rings at the top and bottom have three-point contact, and dials may be mounted on these to measure deformations along two or more lines parallel to the axis of the test piece. This apparatus also measures to 0.0001 in.

Fig. 49. A dial compressometer for cylinders and columns.

DEFLECTOMETERS

47. Essential Features of Deflectometers. To measure bending of beams, columns, floors, and other elements of structures an instrument called a deflectometer is employed. The essential conditions which should obtain in a deflectometer designed for accurate measurements are:

1. The apparatus should indicate the relative deflections of points in the neutral surface of the member. In many forms of deflectometers the apparatus itself is suspended from the neutral surface at four points directly above the supports and the deflections measured with respect to a plane through the points.

2. The parts of the deflectometer forming the datum to which the deflections are referred should be unstressed. This principle is often violated. A common practice is to measure deflections with reference to the bed of the testing machine, assuming this to be rigid.

3. Provision should be made for determining the deflections of both sides of the test piece.

4. For most work an apparatus which is sensitive and accurate to 0.001 in. will be found satisfactory.

48. A Dial Deflectometer. Figure 50 represents a dial deflectometer which has proved to be a very satisfactory instrument for measuring small deflections. The side bars (1) forming the datum plane of the device are freely supported on pins driven into the neutral surface above the end bearings. To prevent the bars from rubbing against the sides of the specimens, washers (2) are inserted as indicated. Clamp (3) holds

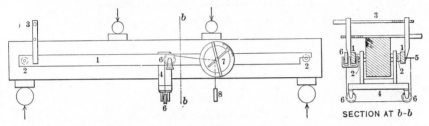

Fig. 50. Wire-wound dial deflectometer used at the University of Wisconsin.

the side bars in place and prevents them from vibrating during the test. Yoke (4) is clamped by means of thumb screws to the neutral surface at the point whose deflection is to be measured. In transmitting the motion of the yoke to the dial on the side bars, use is made of No. 38 covered copper wire. One end of the wire is attached to the pin (5) driven into the side bar shown at the right of the sectional view. The wire is then carried around the three idler pulleys (6) and wrapped around the drum of dial (7). Weight (8) serves to hold the wire taut. If the parts of the apparatus are properly arranged the increments in dial readings will be twice the deflection of the beam. If the deflection of each side is desired the device can be readily modified to meet such a requirement. With this instrument readings of deflections to 0.0001 in. may be made.

49. Multiplying-Lever Deflectometer. Figure 51 illustrates a common type of lever deflectometer reading to 0.001 in. The downward motion of the vertical spindle produces a rotation of the long arm with

Fig. 51. Multiplying lever deflectometer.

a consequent large magnification of the actual deflection. The deflec-tometer is shown at the left and in position for testing a cast-iron bar at the right. The indentation of the specimen at the supports enters into measurements made in this manner.

50. A Wire-Mirror-Scale Deflectometer. A very simple and conven-ient form of deflectometer for tests in which large deflections are to be measured is indicated in Fig. 52. In careful work the opposite side of the beam should be equipped with a duplicate of the appliance shown.

Fig. 52. A wire-mirror-scale deflectometer.

The fine wire (1) which passes over pulley (2) and is kept taut by weight (4), is attached to pins placed in the neutral surface above supports and forms the datum from which the deflections are measured. The highly polished scale (3), ordinarily graduated to 0.01 in., is also suspended from the neutral surface. In reading, the observer brings his eye into the plane of the wire and its image and notes the division intercepted on the scale.

MISCELLANEOUS APPARATUS FOR MEASURING DEFORMATIONS

51. Beam Deformeters. The device illustrated in Fig. 53 is employed to measure the deformations in the longitudinal fibers of a beam. Gen-erally such measurements are made upon the top and bottom fibers.

Fig. 53. Wire-wound dial deformeter device used to measure fiber stresses in beams.

Fig. 54.   Torsion indicator used at the University of Wisconsin.

Fig. 55.   Multiplying dividers for detecting the yield point.

If fibers nearer the neutral surface are to be measured, deeper U-shaped clamps must be provided.

Strain gages, both mechanical lever and electric types, are much used in measuring strains in beams.

52. A Dial Indicator of Detrusion. An apparatus for detrusion measurements which has been in use for many years at the University of Wisconsin is illustrated in Fig. 54. The twist of the section of the specimen between the arms (1) and (2) is transmitted through No. 38 covered copper wire to the drums (3) and (4), respectively. The spindle (5) carrying drum (3) actuates the pointer (6). Similarly dial (7) is connected to drum (4) by spindle (8). From this arrangement it is, therefore, evident that the twist between the two sections of the specimen can be obtained by noting the relative positions of pointer and dial corresponding to the increment in torque. In the apparatus shown the multiplying factor is 40, and the dial is graduated in one-half degrees. Any deflection produced by bending of the specimen during the test will, of course, affect the readings of this apparatus. However, a rough computation quickly demonstrates that such effects are negligible.

53. Multiplying Dividers. A very efficient device for accurately locating the yield point in a tension or compression test is the multiplying dividers shown in Fig. 55. In performing a test with this instrument the operator places the hard steel points located at the left end of the instrument in punch marks on the specimen spaced 2 in. apart. The instrument may be held in place manually or by means of a spring as shown. The motion of the pointer on the scale is hardly appreciable for elastic stresses, but when the yield point is reached the rapid increase in the rate of motion of the pointer instantly warns the operator of the fact.

(a)

(b)

Fig. 56. A wire-rope-extensometer. (a) View from telescope; (b) clamp for attaching scales to rope.

With such a device mistakes in the location of the yield point due to slipping of the grips are obviated. In tests of high-carbon steels, wire, and other materials having a high yield point the drop-of-beam method, Art. III-11, is very uncertain at best. By using the divider method, however, a distinct indication of the yield point can be readily obtained.

Simple multiplying dividers are also used at the University of Wisconsin to determine strains beyond the elastic region.

54. A Wire-Rope Extensometer. A simple and durable device for measuring the elongation of wire rope is illustrated in Fig. 56. Increments of elongation are determined by taking simultaneous readings on the upper and lower pairs of scales by transits or telescopes set up a short distance from the test piece. The scales are graduated to 0.01 in., and readings to half-hundredths may be established. Twisting of the rope does not materially affect the results if each telescope is placed on a level with the corresponding pair of scales. Furthermore, since the device is not delicate or expensive and the observer is well back from the test piece, readings may be taken until the specimen fails.

REFERENCES

1. *Indentation Hardness Testing,* by V. E. Lysaght; Reinhold Publishing Corp., New York.
2. *Textbook of the Materials of Engineering,* by H. F. Moore; McGraw-Hill Book Co., New York.
3. *Testing Materials of Construction,* by R. G. Batson and J. H. Hyde; E. P. Dutton & Co., New York.
4. *Materials and Structures,* by E. H. Salmon; Longmans, Green & Co., New York.
5. *The Testing of Materials of Construction,* by W. C. Unwin; Longmans, Green & Co., New York.
6. *Materials Testing Machines,* by C. H. Gibbons; Instruments Publishing Co., Pittsburgh.
7. *Commission des Méthodes d'Essai des Matériaux de Construction,* 4 vol., J. Rothschild, Editor, Rue des Saints-Pères, Paris. (This is often referred to as the *Report of the French Commission.*)
8. *Testing and Inspection of Engineering Materials,* by H. E. Davis, G. E. Troxell, and C. T. Wiskocil; McGraw-Hill Book Co., New York.
9. On the Reliability of Institutions, Machines and Experiments for Testing the Strengths of Materials, by A. Martens, *Proc. IATM,* 6th Congr., section **29,** 5.
10. The 600,000-lb screw-gear universal testing machine at the University of Illinois is described by W. C. DuComb in *Proc. ASTM,* Vol. 6, p. 476.
11. Large Testing Machine (4,000,000-lb) Built for California Laboratory; *Eng. News-Record,* Vol. 108, p. 217.
12. Phœnixville Testing Machine (a 2,400,000-lb horizontal hydraulic machine), *Eng. News,* Vol. 30, p. 512.
13. A 3300-ton Testing Machine (a horizontal hydraulic machine built in Germany), *Eng. News.* Vol. 67, p. 841.
14. A Large Hydraulic Testing Machine for Uniform Loads, by R. Cummings, *Proc. ASTM,* Vol. 5, p. 275.
15. A New Torsion Testing Machine (an autographic machine designed by W. E. Lilly), *Engineer,* Vol. 3, p. 175.
16. *Manufacturer's Literature.* Baldwin-Lima-Hamilton Corp., Philadelphia 42, Pa. Tinius Olsen Testing Machine Co., Philadelphia 23, Pa. Riehle Testing Machine Division, American Machine and Metals, Inc., East Moline, Ill.
17. Dynamic Tests by Means of Induced Vibrations, by R. K. Bernhard, *Proc. ASTM,* Vol. 37, p. 634.

18. *Fatigue of Metals,* by H. F. Moore and J. B. Kommers; McGraw-Hill Book Co., New York.

19. Repeated Stress (Fatigue) Testing Machines Used in the Materials Testing Laboratory of the University of Illinois, by H. F. Moore and G. N. Krouse, *Circular* 23, Eng. Expt. Sta., Urbana, Ill.

20. A Tool Steel Testing Machine and Results, by E. G. Herbert, *Am. Machinist,* Vol. 32, Pt. 1, p. 823.

21. Testing the Cutting Quality of Files, by E. G. Herbert, *Am. Machinist,* Vol. 30, Pt. 2, p. 946, also Vol. 34, p. 582.

22. Some Apparatus for Tension Tests of Rubber, by P. L. Wormley, *Proc. IATM,* 6th Congr., section 29, 3.

23. Symposium on Limitations of Laboratory and Service Tests in Evaluating Rubber Products, *Proc. ASTM,* Vol. 36, Pt. 2, p. 620.

24. Speed Control for Screw Power Testing Machines Driven by Direct Current Motors, by A. H. Stang and L. R. Sweetman, *Bull. ASTM,* Aug. 1937, p. 15.

25. Allowable Unit Loads on Knife Edges, by S. W. Bramwell, *Eng. News,* Vol. 55, p. 653.

26. Friction in Packings of Hydraulic Testing Machines, *Eng. News,* Vol. 58, p. 209; Vol. 59, p. 535; Vol. 60, pp. 19 and 154; Vol. 62, pp. 377, 386, 438.

27. On Measuring Small Strains in Testing Materials of Construction, by J. A. Ewing, *Proc. Roy. Soc. London,* Vol. 58, p. 123.

28. A New Mirror Apparatus for Measuring Elasticity, by B. Kirsch, *Eng. News,* Vol. 62, p. 619, and *Proc. IATM,* 5th Congr., section 8, 4.

29. *Photoelasticity,* Vol. 1 and 2, by M. M. Frocht; John Wiley & Sons, New York.

30. The Optical Determination of Stress, by E. G. Coker, *Phil. Mag.,* Oct. 1910, p. 740, and *Engineering,* Jan. 6, 1911, p. 1; also articles by the same author on similar subjects in *Engineer,* Vol. 94, pp. 134, 404, and 824.

31. New Developments in Electric Telemeters, by O. S. Peters and R. S. Johnston, *Proc. ASTM,* Vol. 23, Pt. 2, p. 592.

32. Optical Strain Gages and Extensometers, by L. B. Tuckerman, *Proc. ASTM,* Vol. 23, Pt. 2, p. 602.

33. A New Type of Mirror Extensometer, by M. F. Sayre, *Proc. ASTM,* Vol. 26, Pt. 2, p. 660.

34. The X-Ray Examinations of Materials in Industry, Edgar Marburg Lecture, by George L. Clark, *Proc. ASTM,* Vol. 27, Pt. 2, p. 5.

35. Symposium on Spectrographic Analysis. Relates uses in examinations of metals. *Proc. ASTM,* Vol. 35, Pt. 2, p. 47.

36. Symposium on Radiography and X-Ray Diffraction Methods, *Proc. ASTM,* Vol. 36, Pt. 2, 1936.

37. Concrete Beam Testing Machines, by A. T. Goldbeck, *Crushed Stone J.,* July-Aug., 1928, p. 4.

38. *Materials Testing,* by H. J. Gilkey, G. Murphy, and E. O. Bergman; McGraw-Hill Book Co., New York.

39. "Long-Time" or "Flow" Tests of Carbon Steels at Various Temperatures with Particular Reference to Stresses Below the Proportional Limit, by J. J. Kanter and L. W. Spring, *Proc. ASTM,* Vol. 28, Pt. 2, p. 80.

40. The Calibration of Extensometers, by R. L. Templin, *Proc. ASTM,* Vol. 28, Pt. 2, p. 714.

41. The Development of an Apparatus for Wear Tests on Flooring Materials, by D. W. Kessler, *Proc. ASTM,* Vol. 28, Pt. 2, p. 855.

42. Aircraft: Materials and Testing, Edgar Marburg Lecture, by L. B. Tuckerman, *Proc. ASTM,* Vol. 35, Pt. 2, p. 3.

43. Some Factors Affecting Strain Measurements in Tests of Metals, by R. L. Templin, *Proc. ASTM,* Vol. 34, Pt. 2, p. 182.

44. Predicting the Strength of Structures from Tests of Plaster Models, by R. J. Roark and R. S. Hartenberg, *Bull.* 81, Eng. Expt. Sta., Madison, Wis.

45. *The Whittemore Strain Gage,* Baldwin-Southwark Corp., Philadelphia.

46. The Electric Strain Meter and Its Use in Measuring Internal Strains, by R. E. Davis and R. W. Carlson, *Proc. ASTM,* Vol. 32, Pt. 2, p. 793.

47. Full-Load Calibration of a 600,000-Lb Testing Machine, by H. F. Moore, J. C. Othus, and G. N. Krouse, *Proc. ASTM,* Vol. 32, Pt. 2, p. 778.

48. *An Introduction to Experimental Stress Analysis,* by G. H. Lee; John Wiley & Sons, New York.

49. *Handbook of Experimental Stress Analysis,* by M. Hetényi; John Wiley & Sons, New York.

50. *Proceedings of the Society of Experimental Stress Analysis.*

Testing of Structural Materials

1. General Observations. Mechanical tests are those used to discover the qualities of the materials of construction under the action of external forces. Such tests, if they are to be of most value, should be made under conditions approximating as closely as possible those of practice. By standardizing these conditions the results become comparable wherever or by whomsoever they are made and are of very great importance in determining the properties and value of building materials. If such results can be made wholly independent of the means employed in making the tests, and hence to furnish a knowledge of the true characteristics of the material, they can be used safely in theoretical generalizations on the one hand, and in the practical designing of structures on the other. With many kinds of tests this ideal divorcement of the results from the conditions of the tests can certainly never be attained, as in the case of tests by impact, but it doubtless can be practically attained in some of the more simple tests, as in tension and compression. In the former case the most that can be accomplished is to prescribe uniform conditions in order that the results obtained by different experimenters may be comparable, although they may not serve for accurate scientific generalizations. They might also serve to give a relative value to the various materials or samples so tested, and to grade them with some degree of approximation to their true relative merits for a proposed purpose. Such tests, therefore, may serve fully their immediate object even though the results can be given no absolute significance whatever. If, however, the conditions of such tests are allowed to vary, they lose even this relative significance, and therefore become quite worthless. The standardizing of any particular kind of test evidently depends on the state of the science at the time; and, as our knowledge of any particular property of a material increases, it is probable that our standard methods of testing will also have to change. No such standards, therefore, can be fixed permanently, but certain methods can be agreed on and followed for a time, and when a change is made let all change together. To attain to this kind of unity of action it is necessary to have a world's representative body which will command the confidence and allegiance of both the theoretical and the practical users of materials in all civilized countries to decide such questions.

The efforts of the International Association for Testing Materials towards securing such unity of action in various countries have not thus far been productive of great reforms, although the outlook is hopeful. Within America, however, the American Society for Testing Materials and the American Standards Association have been successful in standardizing methods of testing and the specifications used in the United States.

Evidently no complete standardization can be effected for tests on entire structural forms, since these vary in shape, size, and disposition of parts, but specimen tests can be standardized since all significant conditions can be made uniform.

2. Mechanical Tests Classified. Mechanical tests may be classified under several headings. With reference to the rate and duration of the load application, the following classification may be made:

1. *Static Tests.* These are made with gradually increasing loads, such as the ordinary tests in tension, compression, cross bending, torsion, and shear.

2. *Dynamic Tests.* These are made with suddenly applied loads, as by a falling weight or pendulum. Charpy, Izod, and drop-impact tests would fall under this category.

3. *Wear Test.* These are made to determine resistance to abrasion and impact, as in the case of paving materials and coarse aggregate.

4. *Long-Time Tests.* These are made with loads applied to the object under test for a long period of time (months or years). This type of test is frequently used for materials such as wood and concrete to determine plastic flow characteristics, and also to determine the ratio of strength under a long loading period to the strength under a short loading period. Long-time tests that are run on materials at elevated temperatures are called *creep tests.*

5. *Fatigue Tests.* These are made with fluctuating stresses repeated a large number (thousands or millions) of times. The stresses may be completely reversed as in a rotating beam, partially reversed as from an axial tension to a smaller axial compression, or simply alternated between two values of a given kind of stress.

With reference to the type of test specimen, the following classification may be made:

1. *Raw or Processed Material Tests.* These are made upon specially selected samples of the material. Tests of cements, concrete aggregates, limes, asphalts, oils, etc., would be placed in this category.

2. *Specimen Tests.* These are made upon specimens of the material specially prepared and given standard forms and dimensions.

3. *Model Tests.* These are made upon models of structures or parts of structures. Plaster of Paris has been widely used for model tests because

of its straight-line stress-strain relationship. Models have also been made of Bakelite and similar materials and tested in a polariscope.

4. *Structural Tests.* These are made on full-sized structural forms, as floor systems, bridge members, brick piers, pipes, wire ropes, chains, riveted joints, etc., or on the structure as a whole, such as boilers, simple trusses, frames, and various machine parts.

With reference to the effect of the test on the specimen, the following classification may be made:

1. *Destructive Tests.* In these the specimens are made useless as a result of testing for their normal purposes. Tests to determine ultimate strengths of steel specimens in tension, concrete specimens in compression, and wood beams in cross bending are examples of this type of test.

2. *Non-Destructive Tests.* In these the specimens are not seriously harmed as a result of testing. Hardness, magnetic, and radiographic tests are common examples of this type. *Proof tests* are a special type of non-destructive test in which loads slightly in excess of the working load are applied to structural parts before they are used.

Complete standard rules for making routine tests on samples of raw and processed materials and on specially prepared specimens have been generally adopted. Such standardization is not usually possible for exploratory or research type tests or for tests of structural forms.

THE ACCURACY OF MACHINES AND APPARATUS

3. Methods of Determining the Accuracy and Sensitiveness of Testing Machines. General considerations of the accuracy, sensitiveness, and conditions which should obtain in testing machines are given in Chapter II. Since it is of vital importance that the user of a testing machine should know, approximately at least, the accuracy of his machine, a brief statement of methods commonly used for testing accuracy and sensitiveness will be made here.

In testing the accuracy of vertical static-load machines five to ten equal increments of dead load can be placed on the platform of the machine, or on extensions formed by I-beams, and the corresponding readings of the weighing device compared with the known loads. After each increment of load has been added the sensitiveness may be determined by finding the additional weight which is required to make a perceptible indication on the weighing device. This method, even when pig iron is used, is too cumbersome and laborious for loads above 10,000 to 20,000 lb. In calibrating machines of the lever type, loads of this magnitude are sufficient to determine the multiplying factor for the lever system and, assuming this factor constant, a correction coefficient applicable to the range of machine may be determined. It is not safe, however, to estimate the sensitiveness at high loads to be proportionately the same as at low loads. In calibrating hydraulic machines in which friction is a factor, it is desirable to test the machine to full capacity.

Standardized calibrating levers, with weights, in capacities up to 100,000 lb, are available. They furnish a more expedient means of calibrating over a greater range of loads than the dead-weight method. For procedure in calibrating testing machines, see ASTM *Standards*.

Fig. 1a. A Morehouse ring.

The comparatively large elastic deformation of a steel ring when subjected to a load in its diametral plane affords a reliable measure of the applied load. Morehouse rings (Fig. 1a) fitted with accurate permanently attached extensometers utilize this principle for calibrating testing machines. Calibrations by the U. S. Bureau of Standards indicate that these devices are accurate to 0.02 per cent between two-tenths capacity and full load. Rings with capacities up to 300,000 lb are obtainable.

Amsler boxes in capacities up to 1,000,000 lb provide compact means for calibrating testing machines. They are said to be accurate to 0.5 per cent in the upper nine-tenths of their load ranges. The volumetric elastic strain of a hollow cylindrical box indicated by a mercury gage measures the load applied by the testing machine. Hence temperature effects must be eliminated in calibrations.

Calibrated annealed steel bars or compression cylinders of high elastic limit so proportioned that they need not be stressed beyond two-thirds of their elastic limits are used for calibrating large testing machines to capacity. They should be axially loaded and fitted with self-indicating extensometers with gage length and accuracy such that the least reading will correspond to a load change not greater than 0.2 per cent of the capacity of the machine. If a compression cylinder is used, the slenderness ratio should not exceed 20; and, if hollow, the thickness should equal one-eighth of the diameter.

Calibrating test pieces should be standardized at the Bureau of Standards or on machines of known calibration. Care should always be taken to standardize such a test piece under the same conditions as will surround the specimen when it is used for calibration purposes. A half dozen or more increments of load may be applied to the calibrating specimen at a speed not to exceed 0.1 in. per min and corresponding readings of the deformations taken. After each increment of loading, the dead weight required to produce a movement of the weighing device furnishes a measure of sensitiveness.

Pressure gages on hydraulic machines should be frequently calibrated throughout the entire range of loading. If the pressure in the jack is measured to determine load on machine, calibrations under increasing and decreasing loadings should be made with the piston at different positions in the stroke. By so doing variations in the frictional resistances can be determined.

4. The Calibration of Apparatus for Measuring Deformations. For certain classes of testing, a knowledge of the accuracy and sensitiveness of apparatus used to measure deformations is of as great value as similar information concerning the testing machine. For most purposes an accuracy of 1 per cent is sufficient in such apparatus. Essential considerations for different types of deformation apparatus have been discussed in Chapter II. When conditions permit, the calibration of such devices may well be left to standard laboratories such as the Bureau of Standards or the Watertown Arsenal. If calibration is done in the home laboratory, the following method serves for a rough test of accuracy and sensitiveness. See also ASTM *Standards* Des. E83–52T.

The apparatus may be attached to a steel test piece for which the stress-deformation curve has been accurately determined, and the test piece gripped in a standard manner by the machine, so that slipping and improper distribution of stress are avoided. Increments of load are very slowly and uniformly applied to the test piece, and the corresponding readings of the apparatus are taken. After each increment of loading one may determine sensitiveness by observing the increase and decrease in load required to produce a readable change on the deformation apparatus.

If a standardized deformation apparatus is at hand, it may also be attached to a specimen under conditions similar to those surrounding the apparatus which is being calibrated. The unknown device can then be compared with the standard under loading conditions indicated above.

A more accurate method than the above for calibrating extensometers and compressometers consists in clamping one end of the apparatus to a dummy specimen held in a lathe chuck and the other end to the centering spindle of the tailstock. By using a microscope with a standardized micrometer eyepiece the movements of the pivot end of the spindle can be determined and compared with readings of the motions registered by the deformation apparatus. If a precision lathe can be had, one part of the extensometer may be attached to the spindle on the tailstock and the other to a specimen held on the lathe carriage. In this set-up the axes of specimen and spindle should be collinear. The lathe may then be set so that the carriage travels 0.02 or 0.01 in. per revolution of the chuck, and a comparison of the deformation apparatus with the lathe screw is determined.

Using a standardized linear dividing engine, reading directly to 0.002 mm or less, still greater refinement may be obtained. With such apparatus it is possible to calibrate scales, micrometers, and practically all the devices used in measuring deformations.

When calibrating apparatus in which accuracy in fabrication is based directly or indirectly upon the accuracy of a screw, readings of, say, one-tenth the range should be taken over the entire range of the apparatus to determine the cumulative error of the device. Periodic errors may be ascertained by a large number of readings of small increments of motion over a limited portion, say one-tenth, of the range. Furthermore, to eliminate periodic errors in the calibrating device it is essential that the apparatuses under comparison be shifted several times and the entire range and partial range calibrations repeated.

To avoid errors due to lost motion in screw-calibrating devices one must always approach the desired reading from the same direction. To accurately detect lost motion or lag and to determine the sensitiveness of the deformation apparatus, observations on minute forward and back motions of the moving part of the apparatus may be made under a microscope provided with a micrometer eyepiece.

SELECTION AND PREPARATION OF SPECIMENS

5. Selection of Specimens. It must be recognized at the outset that specimens are selected for testing with either of two objects in view—to compare the mechanical properties of certain materials or grades of the same material; or to ascertain the influence of certain conditions of fabrication, treatment, and usage on the mechanical properties. In comparing mechanical properties the size, shape, method of fabrication, and subsequent treatment of the specimens are generally standardized, but in ascertaining the effects of structural conditions one or more of these is made variable. When choosing specimens for any kind of test the inspector must constantly bear in mind that the test results are valueless unless the specimens are truly representative of conditions and properties under investigation.

The numerous specifications of the American Society for Testing Materials, American Society for Mechanical Engineers, the Society of Automotive Engineers, American Railway Engineering Association, and the Federal Government, in general, cover the method of selecting test specimens of metals which are to be used for various purposes. Test pieces may be cut from the finished casting or rolled product. If the quality of metal is to be ascertained, specimens of cast metals should be separately poured into vertical dry molds. If specimens are cut from castings, it must be remembered that shrinkage strains exert a pronounced effect upon strength at all corners and angles in the casting and that the outside, especially in cast-iron members, is often much stronger than the center. When specimens are cut from rolled structural shapes, one should consider that the metal in thin parts is harder, tougher, and stronger than that of thick portions which has received less work under the rolls. With wrought iron especially, specimens cut with the direction of the rolling are stronger and more ductile than those cut normal to the rolling. In steel plates there is little difference, and in rolled brass and copper plates there is no difference. In the case of the bronzes it is necessary to have test samples poured from different parts of the same melting, as the mixture changes its characteristics rapidly when in a melted state.

Piles of brick or building tile may be subdivided into small piles and one or two samples representing each small pile chosen. In selecting samples, color, depth of kiln mark, number and position of checks and spalls, and ring under the hammer should be considered. If the sampling is done at the kiln, the position of the specimens with respect to the source of heat must be considered.

Specimens of stone should be selected from the different strata which are being worked. If the surface has been exposed to the weather for a considerable time, specimens should be cut from the interior. The faces of specimens should be referenced with respect to the rift in the rock. Portions of rock adjacent to blast holes should be avoided.

In selecting timber specimens, the rate of growth of the tree as told by the annual rings, position in the tree, the proportion of heartwood and sapwood, the proportion of spring and summer wood, the moisture content, grain direction, the method of seasoning, and the character and position of defects must all be considered. (See ASTM *Standards*.)

The number of specimens to be selected to secure a representative average for a material will depend both upon the uniformity of the material and the uniformity of testing. Two or three specimens are sufficient for a tension test of a uniform metal, whereas 5 to 10 is a better number for compression tests of a variable masonry material requiring bedment. If n = the number of specimens such that the chances are 1 in 10 that the average of n will be in error less than x per cent and δ = the standard deviation of a large number of specimens (> 100) from their average, then from the laws of probability * $n = (1.64\delta/x)^2$. Hence if $\delta = 15$ and $x = 10$, $n = 6$.

* See paper by R. W. Crum in *Significance of Tests of Concrete and Concrete Aggregates*, ASTM publication, 1935. Also refer to Art. III-58.

6. The Preparation of the Specimen. In order that the specimen may fairly represent the material, plate, bar, or rolled form from which it is to be taken, it is necessary to observe a number of requirements.

The specimen must be obtained by cutting it out in a way that will leave it perfectly straight. If a metal test piece is bent in getting it out, it should be heated to straighten it; but this may often change the original molecular arrangement, and should be avoided if possible. When the specimen is cut from a larger portion of a plate or rolled form by shearing, it will invariably take a curved form. In this case *the plate, or form, should be sheared away from the specimen,* in narrow slices, so as to leave the test specimen unbent. If the specimen is bent and then straightened, the elastic limit is raised and the metal hardened, the same as any other kind of cold working. Instead of shearing, some milder process, such as planing or drilling or sawing, should be resorted to to obtain the test specimen. For, besides the bending action on the bar as a whole, the effect of the shearing or punching is to embrittle the metal for about $\frac{1}{8}$ in. beyond the sheared surface; hence under a tensile test these surfaces will be severed, causing a premature failure of the remainder of the cross section. To prevent this action on sheared or punched specimens, at least $\frac{1}{8}$ in. of thickness should be removed from all punched or sheared faces, by reaming, planing, or filing.

Final finishing of hard-metal specimens should be done with a file in order to avoid the torn and bruised surface conditions which result from the use of lathe and planer tools. Soft-metal test pieces should be finished with emery cloth. If the skin is removed from a casting by planer or milling device, it is well to remove the rectangular corners with a file in order that incipient cracks or irregularities caused by the tools may be eliminated. If soft-metal specimens must be straightened, wooden or copper mallets should be employed; a steel hammer should never be used. The ends of metal compression specimens should be accurately ground to parallel plane surfaces.

To avoid the inclusion of material which may have been weakened in quarrying, it is necessary to saw compression test pieces of stone from the interior of blocks somewhat larger than the test pieces; roughing out the specimen with hammer and chisel may cause a large reduction in strength. If the roughing-out method is permitted, care should be taken to make the sides of prismatic specimens plane. If accurate results are desired, it is well to grind to true planes the surfaces which are to be subjected to pressure. Specimens of brick, building tile, and concrete will show greater strength if similarly treated. Since the expense of this work is often prohibitive, bedments such as are described in Art. II-35, 36, and 37 are often used to overcome the effects of surface inequalities.

TENSION TESTS

7. Significance of Tension Tests.   Tension tests are more common, more readily made, and more useful in revealing the true character of a metal than any other kind of mechanical test.   In fact, when other kinds of tests are made it will commonly be well to accompany them with a few tensile tests for the purpose of being able better to coordinate the results with those obtained on other materials by similar tests, or on like materials by different tests.   In this connection, however, it is well to remember that all metals are wanting in strict homogeneity, and that they may be regarded as aggregations of more or less dissimilar elements embedded in a comon matrix, somewhat like granite.   (Art. XXI-7 and XXII-14.)   For instance, the planes of rupture will be different for different kinds of tests on the same specimen, and hence the strength developed will be that of a different combination of elements in each case. Also, the strength to resist various kinds of stress may lie in different elements of the aggregation, as, for instance, in gray cast iron the tensile strength is dependent both on the proportion of free graphite flakes and on the strength of the impure iron grains, whereas the compressive strength is primarily dependent upon the strength of the iron grains.

What we call the maximum strength of the material, therefore, or its strength at rupture, is not usually the sum of the maximum resistances of the several elementary portions of the cross section, since they do not all distort equally.   Often the actual rupture occurs successively over many elementary portions of the broken section before the final failure occurs. More especially is this true of the elastic limits of the material, whereas with iron and steel castings this failure in detail is so prominent as to cause the stress diagram to be a curve almost from the beginning of the loading.   Here, too, the irregular shrinkage often leaves very great internal stresses in the body, which causes some portions to come to their elastic limits and ultimate strength much earlier than others, again giving rise to a curved stress diagram.

The tension test is especially well calculated to show what local irregularities may be found in a finished product, and to indicate to what extent the work of forging (rolling or hammering) has produced that degree of homogeneity expected of it.

The tension test is more readily standardized than any other so as to be independent of "personal equation" and of variations in the testing machines employed.   It also demands the least amount of preparation of the test specimen, if tests are to be made only for commercial purposes. Except for the inherent want of uniformity or of homogeneity mentioned above, therefore, the tension test may be made to give typical and uniform results, and it should be considered as the best single test to make on any of the metals. The ASTM *Standard Methods of Tension Testing of Metallic Materials,* Des. E8–46, is of much value to students of this subject.

COMMERCIAL TENSION TESTS

8. Object. In routine tension testing of metals the ultimate strength, yield point, and per cent elongation are always determined, and usually the per cent reduction in area and the character of fracture are noted. From these properties the tensile strength, the limiting working unit stress, and the ductility are ascertained; the modulus of resilience and energy of rupture, both measures of toughness, can be computed; and the homogeneity and structure of the metals are judged. Therefore, such tests, performed speedily and cheaply, serve a very useful purpose.

9. Types of Tension Specimens. Experiments have shown that the form of a tension test piece has an influence upon both the strength and

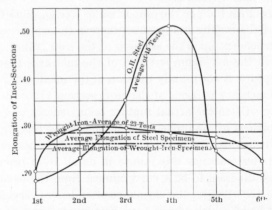

Fig. 1. The variation in the distribution of the elongation of the several inch spaces of 6-inch test bars of steel and wrought iron 0.56 in. in diameter.

elongation. Grooves or holes may cause the unit stresses at the roots of such contractions in cross section to be several times the average on a full cross section. Figure 1 shows the variation in unit elongation for successive spaces on steel and wrought-iron bars. Figure 2 illustrates the influence of the length of the gaged position on per cent elongation.

Tetmajer proposed that the elongation due to the neck be eliminated by subtracting the elongation in a 4-in. from the elongation in an 8-in. gage length and dividing by the difference in the gage lengths. The function, thus obtained, would be independent of the gage length of the specimen. This proposal has not, however, been widely adopted.

On account of the above considerations it has become quite necessary to prescribe certain types of specimens for commercial tests in which the grading and acceptance of material are involved. M. Barba has shown that the resistance and per cent elongation remain constant provided the *relative* dimensions are not changed and the method of gripping and loading are identical. As the result of his work and a large number of tests, the French Commission adopted the relation $l^2 = 66.67A$ or for cylin-

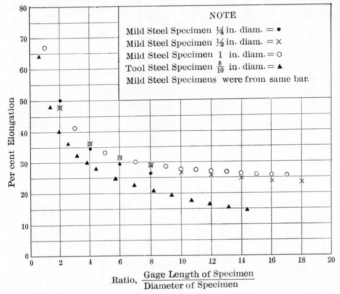

NOTE

Mild Steel Specimen ¼ in. diam. = •
Mild Steel Specimen ½ in. diam. = ×
Mild Steel Specimen 1 in. diam. = ○
Tool Steel Specimen $\frac{8}{10}$ in. diam. = ▲
Mild Steel Specimens were from same bar.

Per cent Elongation

Ratio, $\dfrac{\text{Gage Length of Specimen}}{\text{Diameter of Specimen}}$

Fig. 2. The influence of the ratio gage length/diameter on the per cent elongation of steel specimens.

drical specimens $l = 7.2D$, where l is the measured length on which the elongation is computed, D is the diameter, and A is the area of cross section. The German Commissions use $l = 11.3\sqrt{A}$, which is equal to $l = 10D$ if the specimen is cylindrical. Engineering societies in the United States have prescribed fixed standards for cylindrical and flat specimens (see Fig. 3c and e). For flat specimens of plate over ³⁄₁₆ in. thick, the gage length is 8 in. and the width 1½ in. The dimensions recommended for specimens used in testing sheets, strips, and flat wire under ½ in. in thickness may be found in the specifications of the ASTM on *Tension Testing for Metallic Materials*, Des. E8. The requirements for specimens of different products are listed under the specifications governing the testing of the products. When no specification is available for plate material, a width of five times the thickness and a gage length of twenty-four times the thickness with a minimum of 2 in. have been specified.

In Fig. 3 are shown seven types of specimens dimensioned in accordance with practice. For rough tests on ductile rounds or flats, form *a*

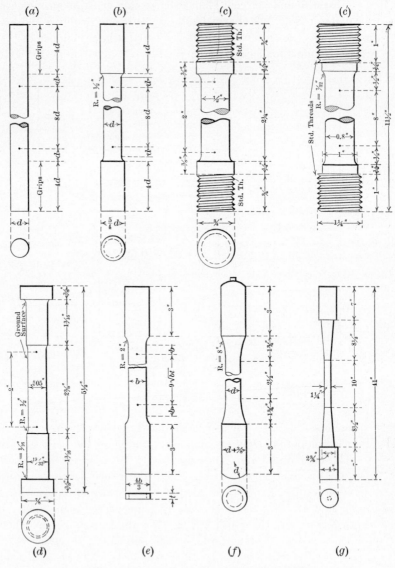

Fig. 3. Types of specimens for tensile tests.

is suitable. Form *b* is a more expensive specimen which is less liable to slip in the grips and which also receives a lower intensity of compression from the grips than does form *a*. For more careful tests in which it is highly desirable to avoid slipping at the grips, form c or c' is used in conjunction with the holder shown in Fig. 30a, Art. II-28. Automobile steels of very high elastic limit and great hardness cannot be readily fashioned into form c after hardening. If so fashioned before heat treatment, these steels are likely to become warped and weakened at the screw threads. For such steels form d * may be used in connection with the holder shown in Fig. 30b, Art. II-28. An inexpensive casting which makes a very satisfactory test piece for rough tests on cast iron, malleable iron, and similar brittle metals is form f. Form g has been used with success by Prof. W. H. Warren of Sydney University, Australia, in testing the tensile strengths of woods.†

10. Testing. The dimensions of cross section of the specimen are measured at several places along the gage length. If the test piece is cylindrical, mutually perpendicular diameters should be measured at each cross section. Measurements of metal should be accurate to ¼ of 1 per cent. The average cross section of deformed bars can be computed from the weight and length.

The specimen is then placed in a V-block and punch marked at intervals of 1 in. along the entire gage length. A laying-off gage or a multiple punch is a time saver in this operation. Fine wire and sections which would be weakened by punching may be marked with ink.

Although speeds of head up to 3 in. per min have little effect on the ultimate strength and elongation of hot rolled steels, the data of Fig. 4 for rods with a free length between grips of 10 in. show that the yield point is affected considerably by speeds of head above ¼ in. per min.

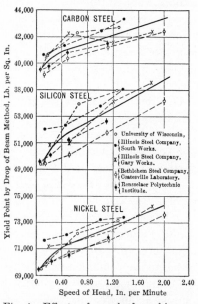

Fig. 4. Effects of speed of machine on yield-point of hot-rolled steel rods. (Rept. of Research Committee on Yield Point, *Proc. ASTM*, 1928.)

Data from the 1937 report of the same committee (see Fig. 4) indicate that for serrated grips the rate of straining or stressing increases very rapidly with the load. These considerations led the committee to recommend that the rate of straining or stressing be limited during such tests.

* See description of this type of specimen by K. W. Zimmerschied in *Trans. SAE*, Vol. 8, Pt. 2, p. 161.

† Forest Products Laboratory wood tension specimen is shown in Fig. VI-1.

Tentatively a rate of straining of 0.0015 in. per in. per min and a rate of stressing of 45,000 psi per min were suggested as maximum rates for determinations on the yield point of structural steel. In testing specimens of 8-in. gage length with serrated grips a speed of about 1 in. per min may be used to three-fourths of the estimated yield point, the proper rate of straining or stressing imposed until the yield point or yield strength is obtained, and finally a speed of 2 in. per min applied to rupture. For cast iron and similar brittle materials the speed throughout the test ought not to exceed 0.02 or 0.03 in. per min per in. of gage length.

Speed of testing may be measured by one of five methods, given in increasing order of precision: free-running crosshead speed in inches per inch of gage length per minute; rate of separation of the two heads of the machine during actual test in inches per inch of gage length per minute; elapsed time for completing a certain part of or all of a given test in minutes; rate of stressing the specimen in psi per minute; and rate of straining the specimen in inches per inch per minute. A simple check of any rate may be made with a stop watch and a satisfactory measuring device. Many new testing machines are equipped with pacing devices for measuring and controlling rate of stressing or rate of straining.

11. Observations for Record. The record should contain sufficient information so that the history of the specimen previous to the test may be traced. In inspection at the mill this includes heat number, specimen number, and other information needed to reference the specimen to the portion of the heat or to the member from which it was taken.

The first sign of weakening at yield point of the specimen should be carefully ascertained. In wrought iron and the low-carbon steels this is readily determined by the drop of beam, by the rapid increase in motion of the divider pointer and, in rolled material, by scaling. If rolled bars of uniform cross section are used, the scaling will appear first at the grips, owing to the combined stress existing there, and gradually extend toward the center of the specimen. It will be noted that the scaling advances on lines at about 45° with the axis of the specimen; i.e., on the surface traces of the planes upon which maximum shear stress exists. Of these, the divider method is the most reliable index of the yield point, with drop of beam a close second.

The maximum load is next determined. It will be found to occur simultaneously with the commencement of the "necking down" action in ductile materials, with rupture in brittle materials. After rupture the test piece is again laid in the V-block with the fractured ends in contact and a record of the length of gage across break is made. Methods of measuring the elongation when the fracture is near the end of the gage length are given in ASTM *Standards* on tension testing of metals.

If the specimen has a "cup and cone" fracture, it is best to join the fragments and measure the diameters of the minimum section with a screw-thread micrometer. The reduced areas of rectangular specimens can be most readily determined by measuring b, d_1, and d_2, as shown in Fig. 5. To measure fractures of irregular outline, a micrometer provided with a conical spindle and anvil will be found convenient.

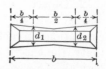

Fig. 5. Reduced area of a rectangular test piece $= b \dfrac{(d_1 + d_2)}{2}$

Two characterizations of fracture are generally made, one with reference to shape and the other with reference to texture. For example, mild-steel fractures are commonly "cup and cone" in shape and "silky" in texture; hard-steel fractures break squarely across—"square break"—and are more or less finely crystalline in texture. Figure 6 shows the

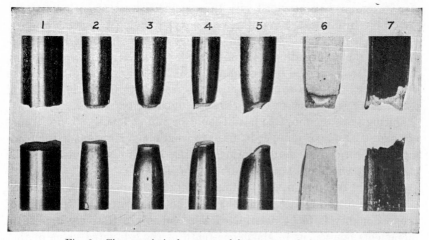

Fig. 6. Characteristic fractures of ferrous metals in tension.

1. Common in cast iron, designated as square break and fine or coarsely crystalline; also in very high-carbon steel, texture finely crystalline.

2. Common to high-carbon steel, called fin cup or flat cone with granular to crystalline texture.

3. Common to soft- and medium-carbon steels, called full cup and cone with texture silky.

4 and 5. Common in soft and medium steels (especially when eccentrically loaded), designated as three-quarter cup and cone (4), and half cup and cone (5).

6. Common in soft- and medium-steel bars of flat or square section, designated sheared cone with silky texture.

7. Common in wrought iron, designated jagged and fibrous. (Overheated soft or medium steel may also present a jagged break but not a fibrous break.)

fractures commonly observed in metals and suggested characterizations of the same. Unusual features in the fracture should always be recorded and their causes, if possible, ascertained. For the latter purpose the microscope is a valuable aid.

12. Object. In addition to the objects mentioned under commercial tension tests, the extensometer test affords a determination of the stress-elongation curve for the material. Consequently the modulus of elasticity, the elastic limit or the limit of proportionality, and the resilience may also be measured.

13. Testing. Specimens like form c or d, Fig. 3, are preferable for extensometer tests; but it is desirable that the gage length for the apparatus should be at least 8 in. For steels, a specimen fashioned as indicated with a diameter of 0.798 in. (area 0.5 sq in.), length between shoulders of 9 in., and a gage length of 8 in. is convenient and satisfactory.

To avoid errors arising from the bending of the specimen due to eccentricity in loading, non-homogeneity, or initial curvature in the specimen, extensometers provided with three-point contact at each collar are preferable to extensometers of the same type having two-point contact. The accuracy of the extensometer should be commensurate with the magnitude of the deformation to be measured. Ordinarily the least reading of the apparatus should be less than $\frac{1}{100}$ of the deformation at the elastic limit. For steel this requires apparatus reading to 0.0001 in. General requirements for extensometers may be found in Art. II-38.

During tests the movable head should be run at low speed, preferably not over 0.02 in. per min per in. of gage length, and stops made for readings. Vibrations or shocks during loading impair the accuracy of the extensometer readings and should be avoided.

There are two methods of loading which may be used, depending upon the nature of the material and the information desired. If the limit of proportionality is to be determined the load is progressively applied in increments equivalent to about one-tenth of the estimated value of that stress and the corresponding deformations observed. When a stress approximating the limit of proportionality is reached the increments are reduced to about one-tenth of their former value until the yield point has been passed. Instead of the foregoing method, some experimenters prefer to note the loads corresponding to equal increments of deformation until the yield point is determined. This may readily be done if a self-indicating extensometer is used. It is customary to remove the extensometer from the specimen after passing the yield point in order to avoid injury to the instrument. Subsequent measurements of elongation may be made with a pair of dividers.

The second method of loading is more often adopted with materials having a curvilinear stress-deformation diagram than with iron or steel. It consists of determining the maximum total deformation and set corresponding to repeated applications of each load. An initial load corresponding to one-twentieth the ultimate strength of the material, or thereabouts, may be applied and removed with determination of accompanying deformation and set. If set occurs the load is repeated and readings of deformation and set taken until the set becomes constant. Then the load is doubled and the same cycle of operations is repeated. This process is applied again and again until the load is reached at which the set continually increases. When this method is applied to a material having a true elastic limit it is well to decrease the increments of load in proximity of the elastic limit.

14. Stress-Deformation Diagrams. It is customary in the United States to plot curves using unit stress as ordinates and unit deformations as abscissas with the curve lying in the first quadrant. The scales for such diagrams should be so selected that the slope of the curve will lie between 30° and 70° with the horizontal; otherwise the curvature of the diagram is made too flat or too steep and there is also difficulty in determining the modulus of elasticity with accuracy. If the repetition method of loading has been employed in testing, curves showing the gross sets, gross deformations, and net deformations are generally plotted against unit stress. On such diagrams, in addition to a suitable title and proper labeling of the coordinates, it is good practice to indicate the value of the modulus of elasticity beside the line from which it was obtained, to indicate the limit of proportionality, the yield point, and the ultimate strength. The diagram is, in this way, made to furnish the most essential information secured in the test.

COMPRESSION TESTS

15. Objects of Compression Tests. Whereas tension tests are made for the purpose of determining many of the more significant mechanical properties of materials which are more or less ductile, compression tests are made chiefly to determine resistance to compression and the elastic properties under compression.* In testing materials possessing a high degree of elasticity, the elastic limit, yield point, and modulus of elasticity may be obtained. The determination of the ultimate strength is dependent upon the plasticity of the metal beyond the yield point. In the softer varieties of steel there is no well-defined point in the loading at which a complete disintegration of structure takes place. From tests of columns made of such materials it appears that the ultimate strength is limited by the elastic limit. Consequently it is quite common to regard

---

* Herein we shall refer to compression tests as practiced on short prisms. The testing of columns involves consideration of conditions of fabrication, end restraint, form, and position of load in addition to the characteristics of the material itself.

the elastic limit as a measure of ultimate strength in compression for these steels.

Materials possessing a high degree of plasticity, like the minor metals and their alloys, have poorly defined elastic limits, and the compressive strength is often based upon the load sustained at a given unit deformation. *These values furnish a basis of comparison but are far from criteria of structural strength unless determined from long-time applications of load.*

For brittle materials like concrete, building tile, stone, brick, and timber, the compression test is of most value in establishing criteria of mechanical properties of materials. In tests on these substances, the unit stress at first crack or first sign of failure, at elastic limit—if there is one— and at ultimate are found. The position of the first crack, the character of the explosion at rupture, and the shapes of the fragments are all noteworthy. The unit stress at first sign of failure coupled with a knowledge of the place of initial weakening may indicate faulty imposition of load or a local defect in material. The character of the explosion at rupture and the shape of the fragments are also of assistance in determining whether the load was axially or eccentrically applied. Flowing of the bedment often produces vertical splitting of the test piece.

16. The Form of Compression Specimens. The form of specimen which has been most frequently adopted is the cube. For materials which rupture on planes inclined more than 45° with the horizontal, the cube is not suitable, since the strength is increased by frictional restraint acting at

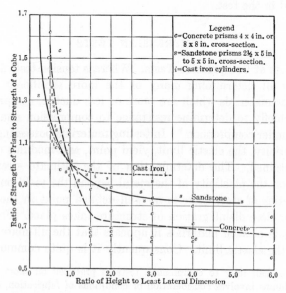

Fig. 7. Relations between the crushing strengths of prisms and cubes.

the surfaces under pressure. Prisms or cylinders with a height equal to twice the least lateral dimension are better types of test piece for such materials. Because of weaknesses at corners due to the methods of fashioning the specimen and to the impossibility of securing full resistance from the material in the corners, a cylindrical test piece is preferable.

In Fig. 7 appear three curves showing the relation of crushing strength to the ratio height/least lateral dimension. The results on cast-iron cylinders are digested from tests by Charles Bouton. For these tests over one hundred specimens were prepared from five bars of each of two kinds of cast iron. Comprehensive tests on Swiss sandstone prisms by Prof. J. Bauschinger furnished the data for the corresponding curve in Fig. 7.

From these tests on rectangular prisms, Bauschinger derived the following formula,

$$S_c = 5600 + 1400\sqrt{A}/h$$

in which S_c is in pounds per square inch, A is the area in square inches, and h is the height in inches. For a general formula he recommended

$$S_c = \sqrt{\frac{A}{u/4}}\,(a + b\sqrt{A}/h)$$

where u = perimeter of cross section; a and b are constants, and the other quantities are the same as above. A simpler relation for Bauschinger's tests on sandstone is given by

$$S_c = 5500 + 1565d/h$$

where d is the minimum lateral dimension.

The data for the third curve in Fig. 7 were obtained from 192 tests at several college laboratories in cooperation with the National Association of Cement Users.*

Numerous tests made by H. F. Gonnerman † indicate that the strength of concrete cylinders 28 days old varies with ratio of length to diameter; thus:

Ratio of Length to Diameter	0.5	1.0	1.25	1.5	2.0	3.0	4.0
Strength Ratio Percentage of 6 by 12-in. Cylinder	178	115	107	103	100	95	90

From the equation for the curve representing tests on sandstone prisms, Fig. 7, the following relation appears:

$$\text{Strength of prism}/\text{Strength of cube} = 0.788 + 0.222d/h$$

* *Concrete-Cement Age*, Vol. 4, p. 141.

† See *Bull.* 16, Lewis Institute, Chicago, entitled Effect of Size and Shape of Test Specimen on Compressive Strength of Concrete.

From the foregoing it appears that Gonnerman's data on concrete are in fair agreement with Bauschinger's data on sandstone. Hence we may expect a cube of such material to have a strength 15 per cent greater than a cylinder with length twice the diameter.

Best practice in testing ferrous and other hard metals for compressive strength calls for a cylindrical specimen with diameter of 0.798, 1, or 1.125 in. and height of 3 diameters; for modulus of elasticity determina-

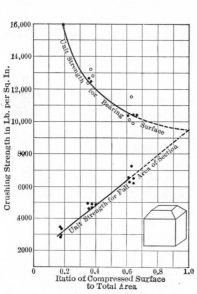

Fig. 8. Crushing strengths of cubes with chamfered edges. (Bauschinger.)

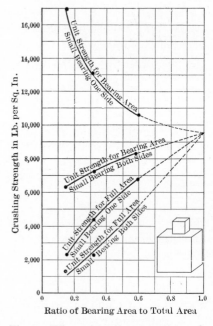

Fig. 9. Effect of loading a portion only of the surface of a cube.

tions the diameter should be 1.25 in. and the length 12.5 in. (see ASTM *Tentative Standards* Des. E9–52T); and for strength of bearing metals a length of 1 in. and a diameter of 1⅛ in. are satisfactory. For concrete specimens a 6- by 12-in. cylinder should be used when the aggregate is less than 2-in. maximum diameter (ASTM Des. C39). For larger aggregate, the cylinder diameter should be half its length and at least four times the maximum diameter of aggregate particle. For mortar either a 2-in. cube or a 2- by 4-in. cylinder is satisfactory. Cubes, because of the mass of existing data and because of relative ease of preparation, are preferred for tests on stone. For wood, 2- by 2- by 8-in. prisms are recommended (ASTM Des. D144 and D145).

The *modified cube* method makes possible good determinations of crushing strength on portions of concrete beams. Loads are applied to top and bottom surfaces through spherical bearings on opposite square capped areas of the same width as the beam (ASTM Des. C116–49).

17. Effects of Loading a Portion of the Cross Section.   Tests by Bauschinger on the effect of chamfered edges on the strength of sandstone cubes gave the results shown in Fig. 8.   The tests show that material symmetrically disposed outside the bearing surfaces increases the strength of the test piece.   This increase is less than 3.2 per cent, however, if the bearing area is more than 80 per cent of the gross cross section.

If the pressed surface is square and symmetrically located on a side of a cube the relations of resistances per square inch to the ratio of bearing area over total area are as shown in Fig. 9.

The effect of loading a rectangular zone having a width equal to 5 per cent of the side of the cube and a length equal to the side of the cube was also studied by Bauschinger.   In this case the resistance per square inch is a function of the

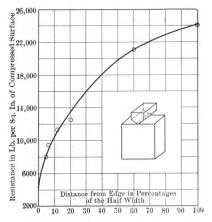

Fig. 10.   Effect of loading a zone on the surface of a cube. (Bauschinger.)

distance of the zone from the edge of the surface.   The results summarized in Fig. 10 show that the resistance per square inch of bearing area when the center of the bearing area is 4 per cent of width of the cube from the edge is 9500 lb, the normal strength of a cube.

18. Apparatus Required for Compression Tests.   Descriptions of testing machines, bearing blocks, compressometers, and bedments are found in Chapter II.   For tests on the modulus of elasticity the compressometer should be accurate and sensitive to $\frac{1}{100}$ of the deformation at the elastic limit.   It should record deformations on at least two sides of the specimen.   The yokes attaching the compressometer to the specimen should be placed not less than half the diameter of the specimen from the nearer bearing surface.   If the yield point of hard steel is to be determined, a pair of multiplying dividers will be found convenient.   A spherical seat to permit adjustment due to non-parallelism of the heads of the specimen is especially desirable in testing brittle materials.   The value of the seat is small, however, unless provision is made for properly centering the specimens with respect to it.

19. Testing.   The cross section of the specimen should be determined at several points along its length.   On cylindrical specimens measurements on mutually perpendicular diameters should be made.   Metals should be measured to $\frac{1}{400}$ part and non-metallic materials to 1 part in 200. Building tile, if scored, should be measured outside the scoring and no allowance made for the area of fillets. Although in specifications for all hollow building block and tile it is customary to demand a minimum strength in terms of the gross section only, it is worth while to obtain the net area in order that the strength of the material itself may be judged.

Great care should be exercised to adjust both the bearing block and specimen so that the line of pressure will pass through the axis of test piece, bearing block, and testing machine.

The speed of the movable head of the testing machine ought not to exceed 0.02 in. per min per in. of height in compressing iron or steel specimens. For plastic and brittle metals, stone, concrete, clay products, and wood, speeds should not exceed 0.005 in. per min per in. of height of test piece. Where strength only is desired the rate of loading may be made more rapid for loads less than half to three-fourths of the ultimate strength. For very plastic materials a much slower rate of loading should be used if a quantitative determination of the crushing strength is wanted. In any series of tests the method of applying the load should remain constant.

The manner of making compression tests with a compressometer is the same as that outlined in Art. III-13. Also, the method of plotting the curve sheet and the information desired may be obtained from Art. III-14.

In making a test for crushing strength only, it is well to surround brittle test pieces with wire meshing to prevent fragments from flying at rupture.

20. Observations during Test. Care should be taken to determine the position and character of the first crack together with the load at which

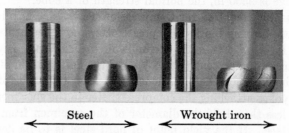

Steel   Wrought iron

Fig. 11.   Relative malleability of wrought iron and soft steel.

it occurs. With materials like low-carbon steel and wrought iron the yield point will be denoted by the drop of the beam, by the rapid increase in motion of the divider pointers, and—in rolled material—by scaling. In tests of brittle materials the shape of the fracture should be stated thus: "pyramidal," "plane inclined θ degrees to horizontal," or "cone"; and the texture of the broken surfaces examined and reported. Characteristic fractures of wrought-iron and cast-iron specimens may be found in Figs. 11 and 12, respectively. Typical fractures of concrete cylinders appear in Fig. 13.

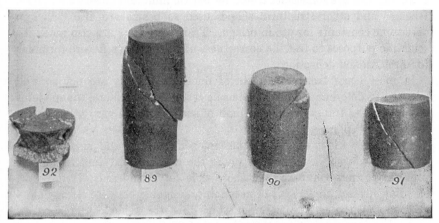

Fig. 12. Bouton's compression tests on cast iron.

Fig. 13. Typical failures of 6 × 12-in. concrete cylinders.

TRANSVERSE TESTS

21. Objects of Transverse Tests. For determining ultimate strength, elastic limit, yield point, resilience, and modulus of elasticity of brittle materials in cross bending, the transverse test is often used. This test is of especial value in determining the strength, stiffness, and toughness of brittle materials. Since the deflections of brittle specimens are many times larger than the elongation in tension tests, a much more accurate determination of resilience and energy of rupture can be made in the transverse test without expensive apparatus for measuring deformations. Furthermore, both the machine and the specimen required are inexpensive and the test may be rapidly made.

Cast iron, brick, stone, and concrete are tested principally for strength; sometimes the resilience and modulus of elasticity are obtained. Timber is tested for its strength, stiffness, and resilience. Springs and spring steel are tested for elastic limit, deflection under given loads, and resilience. Railroad rails are sometimes tested for elastic limit and ultimate strength. I-beams and other structural shapes used as beams are also tested to determine constants for use in design. Transverse tests are also made for scientific purposes to test the correctness of the ordinary flexure formulas for strength and deflection.

In most cases transverse tests of ductile materials are not so well adapted to determine quality as tensile tests. Furthermore, the modulus of rupture and transverse elastic limit of such materials vary greatly with the length of span.

Since three kinds of stress—tension, compression, and shearing—are developed when a beam is bent under the action of external forces, the problem is more complex than those thus far considered. Usually the shearing stresses are left out of account in designing both for strength and stiffness, but the conditions under which this stress should be recognized and taken into account are given in Art. I-28 for strength, and Art. I-30 for deflection.

22. Specimens for Transverse Tests. Although the data of Fig. 14 show considerable variability for transverse tests made on a 12-in. span,

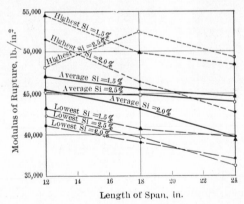

Fig. 14. Relation of span to modulus of rupture for cast-iron arbitration test, bars differing in silicon content. Each average represents 9 tests. (Mathews, in *Proc. ASTM,* Vol. 10, p. 303.)

present specifications permit diameters of specimens of 0.875, 1.20, and 2.00 in. and lengths of 15, 21, and 27 in., respectively. Corresponding test spans are 12, 18, and 21 in. Specimens are cast in conformity with the methods of molding the products represented. The use of a cylindrical specimen lessens shrinkage strains.

For transverse tests of malleable cast iron either a rectangular specimen 1 in. wide and ½ in. thick or a cylindrical test piece ¾ in. in diameter tested with center load over a 12-in. span is satisfactory. If the material has a good ductility, rupture will not occur in such tests.

When tests are made to determine constants for I-beams, T-bars, or similar sections, it is necessary that the specimen be geometrically similar (preferably of the same size to avoid differences due to rolling) to the section under investigation. Tests showing the variation in the transverse-strength properties of cast-iron specimens, due to changing the shape and thickness but not the area of cross section, appear in Table 1.

TABLE 1. THE EFFECT OF SHAPE ON THE TRANSVERSE STRENGTH OF CAST IRON

(C. H. Benjamin in *Machinery*, May, 1906)

Beams loaded at center over an 18-inch span

No. of Results Averaged.	SECTION. Shape.	SECTION. Area (in.²).	SECTION. $\frac{I}{c}$* (in.³).	Breaking Load, P (lb.).	Modulus of Rupture, $S_m = \frac{4.5Pc}{I}$, (lb./in.²).	Modulus of Elasticity, in 1,000,000 lb./in.²
2	●	4.42	1.31	7,375	25,270	8.28
2	■	4.44	1.55	8,125	23,450	9.25
2	▌	4.58	3.12	16,150	23,210	6.61
2	○	4.40	2.88	19,900	31,125	7.05
2	○	4.36	3.38	21,400	28,450	5.61
2	◊	4.41	3.22	25,250	35,300	6.49†
2	□	4.38	5.11	28,175	24,840	4.41
2	I	4.56	5.78	24,250	19,400	4.54
2	I	4.84	6.46	31,550	22,010	5.62
2	⊥	4.61	6.52	31,750	21,940	4.71
2	⊥	4.88	6.48	34,625	24,060	4.84
1	┌┐	4.51	0.81	5,400	30,000	10.74
1	└┘	5.10	1.99	8,350	18,900	8.57
1	┌┐	4.61	0.69	4,700	30,580	10.17
1	└┘	4.80	1.61	8,800	24,600	11.06
1	┰	4.41	0.83	4,400	23,700	
1	┸	4.60	2.30	12,250	24,000	9.34
1	┰	4.47	1.77	7,900	20,050	7.10
1	┸	5.02	4.36	22,600	23,250	7.88
1	┳	4.50	1.78	10,200	25,800	6.23
1	┻	5.18	5.95	25,000	18,900	7.28

* c is the distance to the extreme fiber in tension.   † Only one result.

For plate glass and flat springs, test pieces should be flat with a length ten or more times the depth. For timber, rectangular specimens are best. The Forest Products Laboratory uses 2- by 2- by 30-in. specimens with a 28-in. span for small-beam tests. In tests of larger timber beams the span should be fifteen or twenty times the depth. For cement and mortar, specimens 1- by 1- by 6-in. prisms with a 5-in. span, and, for concrete, 6- by 6-in., or 8- by 6-in. beams with an 18-in. span, are convenient.

23. Apparatus Required for Transverse Test. Descriptions and general considerations of apparatus are found in Chapter II. The testing machine should have a capacity two to four times the estimated strength of the specimen. If used, a deflectometer should be accurate and sensitive to $\frac{1}{100}$ of the deflection at the elastic limit, if E is to be measured, and to $\frac{1}{100}$ the maximum deflection for determinations of the maximum deflection. For measuring fiber strain, deformeters should be accurate and sensitive to $\frac{1}{100}$, or less, of the strain in the gaged length at the elastic limit. Wherever possible one should avoid fastening deformeters close to concentrated loads.*

Rocker supports or swinging links should be used at the ends of the specimen to prevent longitudinal compression in the lower fibers when the beam is loaded. Also, if a pair of loads is imposed through a loading beam, rollers should be used between specimen and loading beam to avoid compounding of the specimen and loading beam through friction at the load points. A high intensity of compression under the loads and over the reaction should be avoided by the use of metal bearing plates. For transmitting loads to 8 by 16-in. timber beams, the Forest Products Laboratory uses heavy laminated maple shoes which rest upon $\frac{5}{32}$-in. steel plates. The lower surface of each shoe is cut to a circular arc having a chord length of $13\frac{1}{2}$ in. and a mid-ordinate of $\frac{9}{16}$ in. See ASTM *Standards* Des. D198.

When structural shapes are tested, they should be braced and loaded as far as possible, in accordnace with the conditions of use. I-beams and girders should, in most cases, be laterally braced at the supports.

In general, the speed of loading should be based upon the rate of straining of the extreme fibers of the specimen. For tests of cast and brittle metals, the speed of moving head should not exceed 0.1 in. per min. The Forest Products Laboratory uses a speed of $\frac{1}{4}$ in. per minute on large timber beams and 0.1 in. per min on 2- by 2- by 30-in. specimens; see Art. VI-6. For tests on brick, concrete, stone, and similar brittle materials the rate of stressing the extreme fiber should be nearly constant as the maximum load is approached. In that vicinity suitable limiting

* For further data see *Bull.* 84, Eng. Expt. Sta., Univ. Wis., on Influence of Form and Scale on Strength, by R. J. Roark, R. S. Hartenberg, and R. Z. Williams.

rates are 500 to 1000 psi per min.* In the tests where deflections are being read, it is best to apply the load at a sufficiently low rate to permit the readings to be taken without stopping the machine. When defor-meters are being used the time intervals allowed for readings should be constant during such tests.

It is well to use increments of load of about one-tenth the estimated load at elastic limit and when in the proximity of the elastic limit reduce the increments to one-fifth of their former value.

24. Observations during Test. The transverse elastic limit of metals as determined from deflections is generally higher than the tensile elastic limit and not so plainly perceived. The yield point is denoted by the drop of beam and by scaling in the case of rolled sections. The position of the scaling and its advance over the test piece are well worth careful note. The ultimate strength of ductile metal specimens is often very hard to determine with exactness; but, if a slow speed is used, the maximum load may be approximately ascertained.

In testing brittle materials like cast iron, the observer must be alert if he is to note the load and deflection at failure. The character of the fracture should be recorded with care.

When testing timber, concrete, malleable cast iron, and like substances, the load at first crack should be noted and the position and character of the crack recorded.

25. Load Deflection Curves. Ordinarily, loads are plotted as ordinates and deflections as abscissas. The scales should be such that the initial portion of the curve has a slope of over 20° with respect to the load axis. On such diagrams it is good form to indicate the elastic limit, yield point, modulus of rupture (S_m), modulus of elasticity, and resilience.

IMPACT TESTS

26. Objects of Impact Tests. Inasmuch as the effect of speed of load-ing on the toughness of materials has not been well determined, it has been the practice to use data from impact tests for estimating resistance to shocks or blows. On the other hand, owing to the impossibility of accurately measuring the proportion of the energy of a blow which is absorbed by a specimen, and owing to the influence of form of specimen and other factors, the results of impact tests do not furnish absolute indi-cations of shock resistance. Nevertheless, by carefully standardizing machines, specimens, and the methods of testing, with respect to service conditions, it is possible from impact test data to make comparisons val-ued by the designer.

* Formulas for speed of the moving head of the testing machine appear in Art VI-6.

Transverse impact tests have long been used to determine the shock resistance of structural elements like rails, axles, car wheels, and car couplers, also for measuring shock resistance of brittle materials like wood or cast iron. In tests of such structural parts, acceptance is usually based on the capacity of selected pieces to withstand an arbitrary number of blows with a limited deformation. In tests of brittle materials the energy of rupture and type of fracture indicate the quality. (For methods of testing wood see ASTM *Standards,* Des. 143–52.)

When transverse impact tests are used to test ductile materials, it is necessary to groove the specimen to obtain rupture. Thus high concentrations of stress are caused at the groove, which makes the test results purely qualitative. Users of this test claim that it serves well in comparing the abilities of similar materials to serve in the form of intricate and severely stressed parts in correlating the effect of heat treatments of steel and of heat-treated forgings with service (see ASTM *Tentative Standards,* Des. E23–47T and its revision).

Tensile and compressive impact tests have been less frequently used than transverse impact tests. Difficulties in providing axial loading of specimens have militated against usage on brittle materials. For ductile materials, since small eccentricities of loading have little effect on the energy of rupture, tensile impact tests are far more accurate than notched-bar transverse tests. The applications of this test are deserving of much more attention than they have thus far received. (See Symposium on Impact Testing, *Proc. ASTM,* 1938.)

27. Specimens for Impact Tests. For brittle castings, bars similar to those recommended for transverse static tests are well adapted for transverse impact specimens. If service parts are to be used as cast, the skin should not be removed from specimens.

In transverse tests on ductile structural parts it is well to mark a number of equal intervals on both sides of the part where heavy stresses will occur to permit strain measurements after testing.

For transverse impact specimens of ductile materials, a great variety of specimens notched at midlength have been proposed. In order to make satisfactory comparisons, the size of the specimen and the type of notch should be standardized. Since defects have a more marked effect on small specimens they are usually preferable to large specimens.

The ASTM Committee E–1 in 1926 recommended the specimens shown in Fig. 14a. Concerning the notch, Fremont (*Proc. IATM,* 6th Congress, section 42) showed that slight variations in width of saw slot were not important. Thomas (*Proc. ASTM,* Vol. 15, p. 63) showed that the angle between the sides of the notch may be varied from 0° to 30° without material effect. Tetmajer, however, found that the curvature at the bottom of the notch should be maintained constant. Depth of notch must also be held constant.

For tensile impact tests of metals the specimen shown in Fig. 14a is recommended. Punch marks placed on the shoulders permit elongation measurements after failure. Additional types of metal impact specimens are shown in ASTM *Standards* Des. E23.

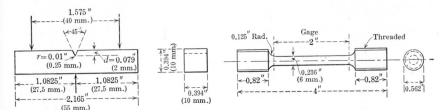

Specimen for transverse-impact tests of ductile metals.   Specimen for tensile impact tests of ductile metals.

Fig. 14a.

28. Considerations Involved in the Selection of an Impact Testing Machine. The fundamental conditions which one must consider in selecting an impact testing machine are briefly considered in Art. II-17. It must be pointed out, however, that machines are not standardized, although progress is being made. In the drop machines, with the exception of the machine for testing rails (see Art. II-19), there is a wide diversity of conditions. No standard relations of tup to anvil have been adopted, nor has there been any standardization of the height of drop. Fremont recommended a drop of at least 4 meters and an anvil weighing forty times as much as the tup. Experience seems to show that the hammer should be at least fifteen times as heavy as the specimen. When drop machines are used to apply blows smaller than required for rupture, some means should be provided to avoid secondary effects on the test piece, caused by rebounding of the hammer.

The Charpy pendulum machine has been adopted by the German Association for Testing Materials, and recommended by ASTM (see Des. E23–47T), but there are in use a large number of other types, in some of which the anvil is much too light. In such machines the loss of energy through vibration must be great. Universal impact machines which are equipped for Charpy (simple beam), Izod (cantilever beam), and impact tension tests are widely used.

Mann's tests (Art. II-18) indicate that many metals tested in impact tension exhibit constant energies of rupture for velocities below a certain critical value, termed the transition velocity, and for higher velocities they show a marked reduction in toughness. This fact should be given due consideration in all impact test programs and should receive proper attention in design. Friction effects in drop machines may be made small by freeing the guides of rust and wiping them with powdered graphite. Calibrations for friction losses can be made by measuring the elastic deflection of a spring attached to the anvil of the machine when subjected to different impacts and comparing the energy absorbed with that required to deflect the spring a like amount under static loading. The friction in drop machines equipped with a drum and tuning fork may be determined by comparing the slope of the velocity-time graph with the acceleration due to gravity.

The curvature of the knife-edges on the anvil and especially on the hammer is of importance. The hammer knife-edge on the Charpy machine has a radius of curvature of 2 mm.

29. Testing. In drop machines where successive blows are to be struck, provision should be made to keep the specimen from jumping off the supports during the test by means of slots or yokes near the ends; but fixing of the ends should be avoided. In tests on pendulum machines, the specimen must be placed tightly against the anvil. Where rupture is produced by a single blow it is best to adopt a uniform height of drop in order that the velocity of impact may be the same in all tests.

Pains should always be taken to see that every specimen is so placed that it receives the blow in the same position as its predecessors. Nicked specimens must be placed with the nick exactly opposite the hammer knife edge. If such specimens are round, the base of the nick should be parallel to the hammer knife edge when the latter is in contact with the test piece. Timber specimens should be struck normal to the annual rings.

The elastic limit is found by subjecting the specimen to progressively increased blows and plotting the energy of each blow against the square of the corresponding deflection. The elastic limit is the unit stress corresponding to the point at which the square of the deflection increases in faster ratio than the energy. In such tests it is impossible to measure the total energy absorbed by the specimen. The amount lies between the energy of the final blow and the sum of the energies in all the blows. In general, it is not possible to prescribe which of these qualities will form the better index for comparing ultimate resistance to impact, unless the forms of the load-deflection curves are known. Consequently, a single blow large enough to produce rupture is the preferable method of securing data on energy of rupture under impact.*

---

* For methods of testing axles and rails under impact consult the current *Standards* of the ASTM for axles and for rails; also see *Eng. News,* Vol. 75, p. 701.

30. Observation after Rupture. In tests on metals, the shape of the fractured surface, its inclination with respect to axis of the piece, and its texture should all be recorded. If the metal is ductile the relation of the plane of failure with respect to the notch or nick should also be carefully observed. When a rolled piece is tested the limits of the scaled area are noteworthy. On polished specimens, the area showing lines of strain and the character of these lines should be noted. Microscopic examinations of the portion next to the break are often very useful in determining structural defects which cause peculiar results.

HARDNESS TESTS

31. Kinds of Hardness. Hardness as applied to metals, minerals, and other solids is a term of variable meaning. Resistance to abrasion, to indentation, and to cutting have all been considered criteria of hardness; but no one of these serves in general, as a criterion for the others. Apparently abrasive resistance depends largely upon adhesion between the particles, resistance to indentation upon cohesion, and cutting resistance upon both cohesion and adhesion. Therefore, it seems likely, and the results of tests * show, that for pure metals which are nearly homogeneous these different resistances are closely related. However, for substances like cast iron, tempered steels, alloy steels, and alloys in which there is a decided difference in the mechanical properties of the constituent particles there appears to be no relation between these resistances. Since in practice distinct demands for the different sorts of hardness exist, it is quite desirable to standardize tests for the measurement of these properties. Thus far no single test has been devised which is in general well adapted to measure all of these different kinds of hardness; nor is it likely that one ever will be devised. Relative hardness of similar substances may be determined, but no absolute standard appears.

32. Types of Hardness Tests. The scratch test made with a diamond point is the oldest and simplest method of determining abrasive hardness. However, owing to difficulties in standardizing, this test has not come into general use. Probably the most satisfactory method of using it is that of Martens (see Art. II-20).

For measuring cutting hardness, especially of cast iron, use has been made of the Bauer drill test. In this test the quantity of metal removed by a standard drill operating under constant speed and pressure for a certain time interval is considered an index of cutting hardness.

Resistance to penetration has been the usual criterion for hardness of

* See T. Turner's tests, *J. Iron Steel Inst.*, 1909, No. 1, p. 426.

metals. The weighted pyramidal punch dropped from various heights was early standardized by Martel.* He concluded that the energy (D) required to displace unit volume of a given material is independent of the shape of the pyramid, the weight, or height of fall, and, hence, D is a suitable index of resistance to penetration for that material.

In most indentation testers the load is statically applied, and the penetrator is a sphere or is provided with a rounded tip to avoid the variations due to wear. The Vickers hardness tester, which utilizes a diamond-pointed pyramid, and the Knoop indenter (also a diamond-pointed pyramid) used in microhardness testing are exceptions. Penetrators should be used only under the specific conditions for which they were originally designed. Detailed consideration of the three widely used indentation tests, the Brinell, the Rockwell, and the Shore scleroscope (Art. II-21, 22), follows.

33. Objects of Indentation Tests on Metals. Indentation tests serve two very useful purposes: (1) to determine the quality or conditions of parts which—on account of size or shape—cannot be subjected to other mechanical tests or which must not be destroyed in testing; (2) to determine hardness. In either case comparisons must be made with materials of like nature, since none of these tests furnishes a satisfactory indication of the comparative hardness or other mechanical properties of all substances.

34. Relationships between Resistance to Indentation and Strength. In an excellent analysis of the Brinell test, R. H. Heyer (*Proc. ASTM*, Vol. 37, Pt. 1, p. 119) shows that the sink-in types of hardness impression arise from relatively large underlying shear strains and the ridging type comes from relatively large surface compressions. Hence, sink-in types usually connote a relative weakness in shear, whereas the ridging type indicate a high ratio of shear to compressive yield strength. From such evidence Heyer gave ratios for the shear yield strength in terms of the tensile or compressive yield strength for three classes of alloys which had been subjected to different amounts of work hardening.

Several investigators have found a rough linear relationship between the ultimate strength and hardness of steels. Unfortunately the equations for this relationship do not agree in all cases. Petrenko † in tests on a wide variety of steels calculated the tensile strength (S_t), in pounds per square inch, from $S_t = 515B$ for values of Brinell hardness (B) less

---

* The device was first used by Col. T. J. Rodman (U.S.A) before 1860; see his *Report of Experiments on Metals for Cannon and Cannon-Powder*, 1861. For standardization, see *Commission des méthodes d'essai des matériaux de construction*, Vol. 3, p. 261.

† *Tech. Paper* 334; National Bureau of Standards.

than 175. For Brinell hardness above 175 he used $S_t = 490B$. His equations for Rockwell hardness values follow.

For the B scale, using a $\frac{1}{16}$-in. ball and a 100-kg load (R_B),

$$S_t = \frac{3,750,000}{130 - R_B} \quad \text{for } R_B < 90$$

$$S_t = \frac{3,570,000}{130 - R_B} \quad \text{for } R_B > 90 < 100$$

For the C scale, using the diamond cone and a 150-kg load (R_C),

$$S_t = \frac{730,000,000}{(100 - R_C)^2} \quad \text{for } R_C < 10$$

$$S_t = \frac{695,000,000}{(100 - R_C)^2} \quad \text{for } R_C > 10 < 40$$

and $$S_t = \frac{12,250,000}{100 - R_C} \quad \text{for } R_C > 40$$

In all but a few cases Petrenko's calculated strengths were within 10 per cent of the experimental tensile strengths.

For non-ferrous metals Petrenko's tests failed to disclose any relationship between tensile strength and hardness.

35. Applications of Indentation Tests. Among the more important applications of indentation tests are the following: (1) to determine rapidly the carbon content of iron and steel parts; (2) to determine strength in parts which cannot be subjected to regular strength tests; (3) to test the uniformity and degree of tempering or hardening in steels; (4) to test the effect of cold working of steels; (5) to ascertain the condition of finished parts without injury.

36. A Comparison of the Brinell, Scleroscope, and Rockwell Methods. In general, the Brinell test is less rapid, requires a larger surface for test, produces a more pronounced disfiguration of the part tested, penetrates to a greater depth, and integrates the resistance of a larger number of particles than does the scleroscope or the Rockwell device. The chief error in the Brinell method arises in measuring the diameter of the impression. The error is due to the upward flow of metal around the sphere and the elastic deformation of the ball. This trouble is obviated by employing Devries' method of determining the depth of the impression; see Art. II-21.

On the other hand, it appears that the scleroscope indications are affected by properties of the specimen other than hardness, as the results in Table 2 show. Furthermore, the readings of the scleroscope are in-

TABLE 2

Material.	Plate Glass.	Ivory.	Cork.	Hemlock.	Hard Steel 0.70% C.	Soft Steel 0.14% C.	Lead.
Scleroscope Reading	116	45	37	31	23	12	12

fluenced by the method of holding the specimen, by the smoothness of the surface, by the rigidity of the support on which the specimen rests, by the shape of the hammer point, and also by the size of the indentation. The scleroscope tests conditions existing less than 0.01 in. from the surface.

Both the scleroscope and the Rockwell device may be used to test materials of any hardness. The Rockwell test is also rapidly made. Its readings are very consistent, and there is less chance of error due to maladjustment of apparatus or personal equation of operator than in tests with the scleroscope. The method of measuring the depth of indentation is superior to that commonly employed in Brinell tests. Although the indentations made by the Rockwell machine are usually deeper than those made by the scleroscope, they are not as marked as in Brinell tests. If desired, the disfigurations due to Rockwell tests may be made still less by the use of loads lighter than the standard. The fact that this machine has two standard scales, and a number of others more or less used, is a slight disadvantage in comparing materials which have marked differences in hardness. This objection is offset by the refinements in measurement thus obtained.

Petrenko found for a wide range of ferrous and non-ferrous metals that the Brinell number (B) may be estimated within 10 per cent from a Rockwell number by the following semi-empirical equations:

$$B = \frac{7300}{130 - R_B} \quad \text{for } R_B \text{ between 35 and 100}$$

$$B = \frac{1,420,000}{(100 - R_C)^2} \quad \text{for } R_C \text{ between } -20 \text{ and } 40$$

$$B = \frac{25,000}{100 - R_C} \quad \text{for } R_C \text{ above } 40$$

$$B = \frac{3710}{130 - R_B'} \quad \text{for } R_B' \text{ between 0 and 120}$$

Here R_B' signifies Rockwell reading for a $\frac{1}{8}$-in. ball under a 100-kg load and other symbols have their previous meanings.

37. Testing by the Brinell Method. The surface to be tested should be plane, free from scale, and smooth; it need not be polished. The balls should be made of hardened steel or other suitable material.* They should not suffer a permanent deformation greater than 0.0001 in. when loaded with 3000 kg against a steel piece having a hardness of 500 or greater. The balls should measure within 0.0025 mm (0.0001 in.) of 10 mm (0.3937 in.). Balls should be remeasured after every test in which the hardness exceeds 500.

The standard load for the ferrous metals is 3000 kg (6614 lb); for the minor metals and alloys, 500 kg is often used. Pressure should be applied slowly and kept on the specimen for 30 sec. The distance between the center of the indentation and the edge of the surface should equal at least 2.5 times the diameter of the impression. In no case should the side of a specimen exhibit a bulge after testing when compared with a straight edge. The thickness of the specimen should be at least ten times the depth of the indentation.

For tests on small or very thin specimens it is necessary to use a smaller ball than the standard. For such tests the applied load should be varied in proportion to the square of the diameter of the ball (D) in millimeters. Thus for iron and steel the load $P = 3000D^2/10^2$ or $30D^2$ kg. For brass, bronze, and other soft metals $P = 5D^2$.

If the depth of penetration is measured by Devries' method, a microscopic reading to 0.001 mm should be employed. If the diameter of the impression is desired, measurements should be made to at least 0.01 mm on two mutually perpendicular diameters.

The general equation for Brinell's numbers is

$$H = \frac{P}{(\pi D/2)(D - \sqrt{D^2 - d^2}\,)}$$

where H = hardness; P = pressure; D = diameter of ball; and d = diameter of impression.

In terms of the depth of impression, t, the equation is $H = P/\pi Dt$.

38. Testing with the Scleroscope. The surface of the specimen should be horizontal. If the specimen is soft, a fine file is sufficient to smooth the surface; but if a hard steel is to be tested the surface should be ground on the side of a fine emery wheel. In tests on very hard metal, it may be advisable to polish the surface. In any event care should be taken to avoid injury through overheating. Mill scale, blister, or decarbonized products of annealing must be removed before testing.

When parts are standardized by this test it is necessary that each should be held in the same manner. Since the rebound of the hammer is largely affected by the rigidity of the test piece, all small pieces should be

* See ASTM *Standards*, Des. E10–50T.

securely held. A vise can be employed in most cases, but for pieces of peculiar shape a jig or plaster cast may be more suitable.

The apparatus must be held in a vertical position. For ease in reading, the light should be directed downward toward the scale so that the top of the hammer glistens. An estimation of the rebound of the hammer should be made before the test, and the eye, about 20 in. from the apparatus, should be sighted slightly below the calculated scale reading. For accurate reading of small differences in rebound, the magnifier may be set after the range has been obtained.

Always avoid testing the piece twice in the same spot. Surfaces composed of widely varying constituents should be tested at several points to secure the range in rebound.

39. Testing with the Rockwell Machine. Prior to running a test, the machine should be equipped with the proper penetrator and tested several times on the standardized block provided by the makers. Tests should be made on one side of the block only, thus avoiding bearing troubles from indentations. After the surface has been covered with indentations the block should be discarded. The surface of the specimen should be smooth and normal to the axis of the penetrator. The specimen should rest solidly on the anvil. Care should be exercised to see that the specimen is properly forced against the penetrator and the dial turned to set mark. The time of applying the major load may be regulated to some extent by adjusting the dash pot, but it should not be made less than 4 sec. Whenever a reading above 100 is obtained on the B scale, a check should be made on the standard block. Erratic readings also should always be followed by check readings on the standard block. The diamond cones must be handled with care and should not be subjected to shock during loading of specimens. (See ASTM *Standards*, Des. E18–42.)

SHEAR TESTS

40. Essential Conditions in Transverse Shear Tests. In order to obtain the true shearing strength of any substance it is necessary to develop in it, along a given plane, shearing stress only, unaccompanied by the bending stresses of tension and compression. To accomplish this it is necessary to concentrate the external forces of action and reaction on planes an infinitely small distance (dx) apart. Any finite distance between these planes will develop a cross-bending action and its resultant direct stresses across the plane of shear. As it is impossible so to concentrate the external shearing forces, it is necessary to overcome the bending stresses due to non-concurrence of the external forces by preventing the bending of the specimen subjected to these forces. This is done by reinforcing the specimen between the shearing planes or by grooving the specimen in the planes of shear and supporting it by auxiliary clamps.[*]

41. Objects of Transverse Shear Tests. Although shear stress is present in nearly all cases where cross bending exists, it becomes of practical importance in only a limited number of instances. In the design of riveted joints, bridge pins, crankpins, short I-beams, and wooden beams especially, the shear stress must be considered. It is therefore of importance to be able to determine roughly at least, the shear strength of certain metals and of timber. It is, however, impracticable in the transverse shear test to determine the elastic limit or modulus of elasticity. These determinations on metals can be obtained best from torsion tests.

42. Specimens for Shear Tests. For shear tests of metals, specimens of rectangular cross section with a breadth equal to at least four times the depth are satisfactory for use with a Johnson shear tool. If round specimens are used, this shear tool should be modified so that the specimen is clamped in a circular die.

Wooden specimens cut in accordance with Fig. II-12, are satisfactory for use in the simple shear tool shown in the same figure. In preparing such specimens, one should remember that timber is weakest in longitudinal shear on planes tangent to the annual rings.

43. Testing. To avoid bending, it is necessary that the clamps on the shear tool grip the specimen tightly. Care must also be taken to place the specimen in the axis of the shear tool with the shear planes at right angles to the axis of the test piece. To avoid eccentric loading of the specimen, it is necessary to apply pressure to the shear tool through a crossed knife edge or through a spherical seat.

The speed of applying the load should not exceed 0.05 in. per min for metals and not over 0.1 in. per min for wood.

In addition to the ultimate load, observations of the shape of the fracture and its texture should be made.

TORSION TESTS

44. Objects. In general, torsional shear stress may be produced without bending; nevertheless one must not forget that on certain planes in a body under torsion these shear stresses combine to produce tensile or compressive stresses of equal intensity to the shear stresses. A torsion test differs from a transverse shear test in that the deformation acts over any predetermined length of the bar, and in that it varies from zero at the center of the bar to a maximum at some point on the outside. By using hollow cylindrical specimens having a large internal radius compared to thickness, it is possible to determine the ultimate shear strength of

---

[*] Both Dr. Kennedy and Mr. Barba grooved their specimens for double shear, and also held them in rigid forms. See *Rept. French Comm.*, Vol. 3, Plate 19.

many materials. If, however, the tensile strength of the material is less than its shear strength, failure in tension will result from combined shear stresses.

For elastic materials, the elastic limit, yield point, torsional modulus of rupture, modulus of elasticity, and torsional resilience may be obtained provided a cylindrical test piece is used. Torsion tests are made not only on shafting but also on variously shaped members of machines or structures which are subjected to twisting couples. In the latter tests the twisting moment at the yield point, the ultimate, and the angle of twist at the yield point and ultimate are the criteria of most use in design.

45. Specimens for Torsion Tests. For tests on torsional properties of materials, the round bar (either hollow or solid) is the only satisfactory form of specimen. Since it is possible to multiply the twist of the specimen by using radial arms of considerable length, it is not important in tests on the modulus of elasticity that a long gage length be used. Ten inches is generally ample. If the test is to be carried to rupture, it is well to have the portions at the grips about 20 per cent larger in diameter than the gage portion. The transition, however, from the enlarged ends to the gage portion should be made by fillets of large radius.

When it is desirable to determine the torsional strength and ductility of structural elements having non-circular cross sections, the test piece should be geometrically similar in form to the shape under consideration. It should also be remembered that in such sections the maximum shearing stress is produced at points on the periphery nearest the axis. Formulas for maximum intensity of stress in elliptical and rectangular sections are given in Art. I-23.

46. Testing. Descriptions of several machines and types of detrusion apparatus are given in Chapter II. The detrusion indicator should be accurate and sensitive to $\frac{1}{100}$ of the estimated angle of twist in the gage length at the elastic limit. The machine should be so constructed that end tension is not exerted on the specimen. In testing wire, means for making the end tension constant should be provided. Care must be exerted in gripping to insure against slipping. If the specimen is hard and has cylindrical ends, it is well to cut fine closely spaced grooves along elements of the surface to afford a grip for the teeth of the jaws.

The cross section of the specimen should be measured to 1 part in 1000 at several points along the gage length; and, to afford a rough determination of the angle of twist, a fine line may be scribed along a longitudinal element of the surface. If the modulus of elasticity is to be determined, it is well to secure about ten readings of twist within the elastic limit and to cut down the increments about 80 per cent when the twisting moment becomes 90 per cent of the estimated moment at the elastic limit. The speed of the twisting head within the elastic limit ought

Testing of Structural Materials   III-39

not exceed 0.005 rpm per in. of length of specimen. Beyond the elastic
limit this speed may be greatly increased.

At the yield point, scaling will be observed on rolled sections. The
location and the spreading of the scaling is of special note in tests on non-
cylindrical shapes. At failure, the texture of the fracture and the inclination and shape of the fractured surface should be observed. As a measure
of torsional ductility, the angle of twist per unit of length may also be
determined.

BEND TEST OF METALS

47. Significance of Bend Tests. A rough but very valuable test of
the ductility of malleable metals is afforded by the various types of bend

Fig. 15. Results of cold-bend tests. (1) ¾ × 1-in. wrought-iron bar, note crack; (2)
¾ × 1-in. mild-steel bar; (3) ¼ × 2-in. mild-steel flat; (4) ⅝ × ⅝-in. cold-rolled
bar; (5) ½-in. 0.90% carbon-steel rod; (6) ¾ × 1-in. wrought-iron bar nicked and
bent, note crystals at left; (7) mild-steel flat punched and bent with die side outside,
note cracks; (8) mild-steel flat punched and bent with die side inside; (9) mild-steel
flat drilled and bent; (10) mild-steel flat sheared along edges and bent with die side
inside; (11) mild-steel flat sheared along edges and bent with die side outside, note
cracks.

test commonly practiced in the shop. The test consists in sharply bending a bar or portion of a structural shape and noting the angle at which
rupture occurs on the convex surface of the bend. If the material can
be bent through an angle of 180° without rupture it is considered to have
exhibited a high degree of ductility. The test is also used to ascertain
the effects of cold work—punching, drilling, welding, and shearing—on
ductility. Figure 15 shows results of tests on wrought iron and steel speci-

mens. This easily made test is a more severe measure of ductility than the tension test but has not been so carefully standardized.

48. Various Kinds of Bend Tests.* Cold-bend, quench-bend, hot-bend, and nick-bend tests are all used more or less. Of these the cold-bend test is most commonly practiced. This test is ordinarily made at normal shop temperatures; sometimes, to test ductility at low temperatures, specimens are artificially cooled. Cold-bend tests are made on structural steel for bridges, buildings, ships, locomotives, reinforced concrete, rivets, splice bars, and on the various grades of wrought iron. The test, as commonly made, measures ductility of the metal at normal temperatures only.

For determining ductility of metal parts subjected to alternations of high and low temperatures, use is sometimes made of the quench-bend test. The specimen is first heated to a yellow heat and suddenly cooled by plunging in water at a temperature of about 80°F. It is then subjected to the bend test. Boiler-rivet steel is often subjected to this test.

To measure the ductility of wrought iron at welding heat, a hot-bend test is sometimes specified. The specimen is heated to a temperature of 1700 or 1800°F and immediately bent. This test is useful in detecting a high sulfur content.

Nick-bend tests are made on wrought iron to determine structure. The ASTM † requirement for the nick-bend test of engine-bolt iron follows: "The test specimen, when nicked 25 per cent around with a tool having a 60-degree cutting edge, to a depth of not less than 8 nor more than 16 per cent of the diameter of the specimen, and broken slowly shall show clean fibers, free from crystallization."

49. Specimens for Bend Tests. The cross section of specimens for bend tests may be round, square, or rectangular; finished shapes are sometimes tested. Rods and bolt stock are generally tested without machining. When specimens are sheared from plates the edges should be planed and the corners rounded with a file. If this is not done, cracks may start at the corners due to weakening of the metal by the shearing process. Martens advocated that the length of flats should be eighteen times the thickness, the breadth three times the thickness, and the radii of the sheared corners should be one-fourth of the thickness.‡

If the specimen is nicked it is preferable to use a planer or milling machine rather than the cold chisel, although the chisel method is the easiest. Martens recommended that the depth of the groove be between 10 and 20 per cent of the thickness of the test piece. It should extend across the surface which is under tension during the test.

---

* Ericksen and Olsen cupping tests are used to determine ductility and deep drawing qualities of thin metal sheets.

† See ASTM *Standards,* Des. A84–52T.

‡ *Handbook of Testing Materials,* p. 319; also ASTM *Standards,* Des. E16–39.

For bend tests on perforated specimens the hole should be located in the center of the test piece. It should be punched before the specimen is sheared from the plate. The diameter of the hole should bear a fixed relation to the thickness of the test piece. Martens recommended that the diameter of the hole should be twice the thickness and the width of the test piece should be five times its thickness.

50. Various Methods of Testing. Methods of starting and closing the bend vary considerably, and herein lies one of the main causes for discrepancies in this test. On small specimens it is possible to use a blacksmith's sledge and anvil. However, such practice is not recommended. When elongation measurements on the convex side of the bend are to be made, the specimen is lightly marked at intervals of 0.1 in. throughout the middle third of its length. The middle third of the specimen is then clamped in a vise and the end portions suitably bent with a hammer. The specimen is then subjected to axial compression in a vise, press, or testing machine and bending continued until failure of the outer fibers occurs, or until the maximum requirement has been fulfilled. In applying the load the speed may be as rapid as can be controlled but shock must be avoided. The elongation of the outer fibers in a length of 0.3 in. for specimens $\frac{1}{4}$ to $\frac{1}{2}$ in. thick and in 1 in. for thicker specimens can then be made with a flexible tape, making allowance for width of any included cracks (see ASTM *Standards*, Des. E16–39).

Bending attachments (see Art. II-13 and 14) yield concordant results and are recommended when numerous tests are to be made.

When nicked or perforated specimens are tested, the test piece should be so placed that the bend will occur at the minimum cross section. In testing punched specimens the die side should be subjected to tension in the bend test.

51. Influence of Thickness of Specimen. If we consider that the neutral plane remains in the center of the test piece during bending, the per cent elongation of the outer fiber is $100t/2R$, where t is the thickness and R the radius of curvature of the neutral surface. Tests show that although the above assumption is erroneous, the elongation of the outer fiber does vary directly with the thickness and inversely with the radius of curvature. Consequently, it is customary in specifications to increase the radius of curvature for thick test pieces. Thin steel plates are commonly bent flat through 180° (roughly $R = t$); those above $\frac{3}{4}$ in. are bent about a pin having a diameter equal to the thickness of the plate. It is common practice to bend rods about pins of equal diameter. (For examples of sizes of pins used in bend tests of various classes of steel and wrought iron bars and plates see current ASTM *Standards*.)

52. Observations during Tests. Owing to the congestion of metal on the concave side of the bend and restricted lateral expansion, the neutral axis of the specimen must approach nearer to the concave side as the angle of bend increases. Also, more of the specimen is severely stressed and deformed as the bend angle increases. Consequently the angle through which the specimen is bent without cracking forms a crude index of ductility. It is good practice in tests for comparative purposes to observe both the angle at first crack and at rupture. To make such measurements with accuracy the use of a cylindrical plug gage or a cone graduated on one element will be found convenient. Most American specifications omit elongation measurements and are so worded that no observations are required until the specimen has been bent a prescribed maximum amount.

THE VALUE OF MECHANICAL TESTS

53. A Resumé of the Utility of the Principal Mechanical Tests. In the following paragraphs appear a brief summary of the properties revealed by the various mechanical tests and the principal uses now made of these tests for ascertaining the quality of materials.

Tension Tests. With ductile materials the elastic and ultimate strengths, ductility, elastic resilience, toughness, modulus of elasticity, and an estimate of the composition and homogeneity can be had. Without an extensometer the test is not so informative for brittle materials; but it is effectively used to reveal strength and homogeneity.

Tensile tests are inexpensive and the most informative of the mechanical tests for ductile metals, rubber, fabrics, cloth, paper, and yarn. With brittle materials, they are much used to test cements and cast iron.

Compression Tests. With ductile materials the yield point or yield strength, elastic resilience, and a poor measure of toughness can be obtained. Usually, with brittle materials, only the strength and uniformity are ascertained. If a compressometer is used, the modulus of elasticity can be found.

Compression tests are used principally to test the strength of brittle materials like wood, concrete, brick, stone, and cast iron.

Transverse Tests. With ductile materials the yield point and modulus of elasticity can be found. With brittle materials, the strength, measured by modulus of rupture, the flexibility, toughness, modulus of elasticity, and an estimate of the composition and homogeneity can be obtained.

This test is the most informative and inexpensive of the mechanical tests for brittle materials like cast iron, wood, brick, cement, and concrete.

Bend Tests. Cold-, hot-, quench-, and nick-bend tests are sometimes used. The first three of these tests are measures of ductility for metals subjected to the respective conditions. Cold-bend tests detect very high carbon contents in steels normally cooled; they may detect brittleness due to a high phosphorus content or improper treatment in working or rolling. Failure in the hot-bend test may be due to a high sulfur content. Failure in the quench-bend test is likely to result if the carbon content is above 0.20 per cent. The nick-bend test is useful in determining the structure of the metal and to detect imperfect methods of manufacture.

These tests afford a simple, inexpensive, and valuable means for the shopman to determine the suitability of ductile metal like boiler plate, firebox steel, reinforcing bars, rivet metal, engine-bolt iron, and staybolt iron.

Hardness Tests. The resistance of metals and other materials to indentation is the form of hardness most often tested. The Brinell ball apparatus, the Rockwell machine, and the Shore scleroscope are the devices most used for the determination of this form of hardness. The Brinell test permanently deforms the specimen but is a better index of hardness (within the limits of the hardness of the ball) than the scleroscope test. The scleroscope indications are influenced by factors other than resistance to indentation, but the apparatus may be used on harder material than the Brinell device and does not seriously alter the surface of the specimen. The Rockwell test combines the advantages of both the Brinell and scleroscope tests, but it does somewhat more injury to the surface tested than the scleroscope.

The indentation tests afford an inexpensive and very valuable means for determining the quality of hardened and tempered metals, for standardizing the hardness of parts, and for detecting flaws in parts which on account of peculiarity in form cannot be subjected to other mechanical tests.

Impact Tests. Transverse impact tests afford a valuable measure of shock resistance for brittle materials. If the shock resistance of ductile metals is desired, the tensile impact test is more informative. If transverse impact tests are made on ductile metals a notched specimen is generally necessary.

Shear Tests. The transverse shear test affords an imperfect measure, due to the existence of bending stresses, of shearing strength.

These tests are used somewhat for metals, wood, and for riveted and nailed joints.

Torsion Tests. A measure of strength (the computed twisting strength), ductility, and toughness in torsion is afforded by this test. The shearing modulus of elasticity may be determined if a proper torsion indicator is used.

The test is occasionally used on ductile metals, shafts, and parts which are to be subjected to twisting.

Fatigue Tests. These tests are important when loads are repeated thousands or millions of times since stresses below the elastic limit may then cause failure. These tests provide information on the endurance limit and on safe design stresses. Mirror-polished metal specimens are commonly used, but the difficulty in applying these results to complicated structural assemblies has resulted in more testing of such assemblies.

Creep Tests. These tests are important when loads are maintained over long periods of time, especially if high temperatures are also maintained. Information on safe design stresses and flow or creep characteristics under such conditions are obtained.

NON-DESTRUCTIVE TESTS

54. Objects of Non-Destructive Tests. It is frequently necessary to know the probable properties of manufactured structural or machine parts before they are used. In other instances it is only necessary to know whether the parts are free from hidden defects. Non-destructive tests are required for these determinations because no damage to the parts is allowed. Most of the testing methods previously described are not satisfactory because they require partial or complete destruction. However, certain hardness testers, such as the Shore scleroscope, have been widely used to provide information on the properties of many manufactured parts. Some of the more important non-destructive tests are next described.

55. Descriptions of Non-Destructive Tests. Important information may frequently be obtained from a careful visual examination. Surface defects, size irregularities, and variations in structure may be quickly noted. Low-power magnifying glasses, scratch testers for checking hardness of metallic and clay products, binaural stethoscopes for checking soundness of welds, and hammers for checking soundness of materials such as clay tile and brick are all readily available and may be used to increase the usefulness of the visual inspection.

Magnetic analysis may be used to check ferromagnetic materials for uniformity and to detect flaws such as cracks, seams, and slivers in steel bars and tubes. In these tests a comparison of the magnetic properties of a standard object, free from defects and of known properties, and the test object is obtained. This comparison must then be carefully interpreted to identify the conditions that caused the difference in the magnetic characteristics.

Magnetic particle inspection (magnaflux method *) permits detection of cracks, tears, seams, segregation, inclusions, cold shuts, and other defects at or near the surface in ferromagnetic materials. The first step in the method consists of magnetizing the object to be inspected with either direct or alternating current. Longitudinal magnetic fields, pro-

---

* Complete information on this method may be obtained from the Magnaflux Corp., Chicago, Ill.

duced by means of a circular current, will best show transverse defects; circular magnetic fields, produced by means of longitudinal currents, will best show longitudinal defects. Surface defects cause sudden interruptions in the magnetic field and a local flux leakage. These flux leakage fields attract and hold finely divided magnetic particles and so indicate location, size, and shape of the defects. The magnetic particles may be used dry, in paste form when mixed with a light oil, or as an oil-base fluorescent paste.

Flaws in railway rails may be located by means of the Sperry Detector housed in a special car that is run over the track to be tested at a slow speed. The operation consists of sending a low-voltage, high-amperage direct current through the rail and noting the deviations in the magnetic field around the rail. These deviations are caused by changes in the direction of the current flowing through the rail, which in turn are caused by flaws in the rail.

Several other methods of detecting cracks have been developed by the Magnaflux Corp. One of these makes use of a fluorescent penetrant and is used to locate defects in non-magnetic metals and in other non-porous materials. The material is applied to the object by dipping, brushing, or spraying. Excess penetrant is removed, and the object is examined under black or near ultraviolet light (wave lengths between 3200 and 4000 angstrom units). A simple and rapid method of determining cracks in porous objects such as unfired clayware and sanitary ware consists of flooding the object with a special liquid suspension of colored particles and examining the object shortly after flooding. Cracks are clearly marked by the colored particles which penetrate into them. A method for locating surface defects in non-conducting materials such as ceramics, glass, and porcelain enamels consists of coating the object with a hot liquid penetrant conductor, drying the surface of the object, and blowing fine electrostatically charged particles on the surface. The particles, held electrostatically at the defects, quickly show them.

Radiographic examinations are used to locate defects such as gas and pipe cavities, slag inclusions, porosity, cracks, and segregation in the internal portions of metals and other materials. X-rays and gamma rays have very short wave lengths and consequently are able to penetrate opaque materials. If these rays are passed through materials that contain defects, selective absorption of the rays takes place—greater absorption by the sound dense material, and lesser absorption by the less dense regions with defects. A picture of the defects is obtained when the rays emerging from the material under test are caught on a photographic film and the film is developed. The X-ray method is rapid, excellent for detecting small defects in sections 2 in. or less in thickness, but is limited to a steel thickness of about $4\frac{1}{2}$ in. Gamma rays are produced by 100 to 300 mg of radium sulfate sealed in small capsules. The gamma-ray method is slow, but it has been successfully used for sections up to 12 in. thick.

Forced mechanical vibrations may be used to detect cracks and also to provide a quantitative measure of the modulus of elasticity. This type of test has been widely used in evaluating the effects of freezing and thawing on concrete beams. The magnitude of the damage due to freezing and thawing can be progressively determined from periodic tests. The test procedure consists of supporting the specimen on knife edges at its nodal points, and subjecting it to a vibratory center loading in a direction at right angles to the longitudinal axis of the specimen. The frequency of the loading is varied until a condition of resonance is obtained, and the natural frequency of the specimen is then noted. The dynamic or sonic modulus of elasticity may then be calculated. Vibratory loadings have also been used in field tests of structural members.

MISCELLANEOUS TESTS

56. Brittle Coatings. The flaking of mill scale off loaded steel members at the yield point has commonly been observed. Special coatings distributed by the Magnaflux Corp. under the trade name Stresscoat will also flake off the surface at certain strain values. However, before flaking, these coatings fracture at relatively low tensile strains and form strain patterns that may be used for stress determinations if the modulus of elasticity of the material under test is known.

The test procedure consists of first cleaning the surface of the part to be tested, spraying it and a companion calibration strip with an aluminum-colored undercoat to provide a uniformly brilliant background, and after a 15-minute drying period spraying the part and the calibration strip with a selected brittle coating until a thickness between 0.003 and 0.006 in. is obtained. Selection of the coating is dependent on the temperature, humidity, and desired sensitivity. The coating is usually allowed to dry for 15 to 24 hours. After proper drying the part is loaded and the start of the crack pattern formation is located. The cracks indicate the position and the direction of the principal tensile strain since they form at right angles to that direction. As the loads are increased the pattern spreads and starts at new sections. Since the cracks close on removal of the load or as dynamic loading is discontinued, it is desirable that the crack pattern that was formed during test be made visible for study. This is accomplished by applying a red dye etchant which reopens the cracks and leaves a permanent red stain in them.

In order to know the amount of strain required to start a crack pattern and to calculate corresponding stresses it is necessary that the previously coated calibration strip be loaded in a standard calibrator and then placed in the strain scale. The strain sensitivity, lowest strain for crack pattern formation, is usually between 0.0007 and 0.0008 in. per in., but it may be between 0.0005 and 0.0015 in. per in. Allowance for creep of the coating during the loading period may be made either by using a furnished "creep chart" or by loading the calibration bar in the same length of time as the test part.

Elastic compression strains may be determined in structural parts by utilizing the principle that brittle coatings acquire a neutral condition as long as the coated part is maintained under load for a required period, usually at least 3 hours. Release of the compressive strain then reacts on the brittle coating as if it were under tension, and characteristic crack patterns are obtained.

Brittle coatings are valuable for showing the strain distribution over an entire surface, for showing strain concentrations, and for determining weak spots in design. The results obtained with brittle coatings are affected by coating thickness, drying time, temperature, humidity, creep, and the method of applying the coating. Under very carefully controlled conditions accuracy within ±10 per cent may be obtained, but under usual conditions an accuracy within ±15 per cent may be expected.

57. Photoelasticity. Photoelasticity is an optical method of stress analysis based on the principle that polarized light passed through a temporary double-refracting

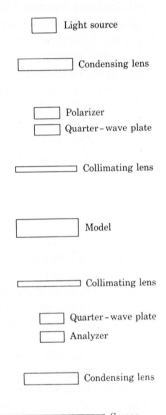

Fig. 16. Diagrammatic sketch of a standard circular polariscope.

material such as Bakelite or Celluloid will be retarded proportionally to the difference of the principal stresses.

Figure 16 shows a diagrammatic sketch of a standard circular polariscope used in photoelastic investigations. The light source may be an ordinary incandescent bulb, but frequently monochromatic light from a sodium-vapor or mercury-vapor lamp is used. The light waves pass through a condensing lens and then through a polarizer from which they emerge as plane-polarized light, and then pass through a quarter-wave plate set at 45° to the principal plane of the polarizer from which they emerge as circularly polarized light. After passing through a collimating lens, the beam of circularly polarized light impinges normally on the stressed Bakelite model which is temporarily doubly refracting while in the stressed condition. The beam of circularly polarized light is resolved into two equal components which travel through the model along the principal stress planes with different velocities and emerge 90° apart and out of phase. As the load on the model increases the phase difference, velocity difference between the two equal components, increases. The phase difference in wave lengths due to given load conditions at any point is called the fringe order at that point.

After passing through the model and another collimating lens the light waves pass through a second quarter-wave plate whose optical axis is inclined at 90° to that of the first quarter-wave plate. The second quarter-wave plate restores plane polarization, and the light then passes to another polaroid, called an analyzer, whose optical axis is at 90° with that of the first polaroid. In this polariscope, light rays retarded an integral number of wave lengths will not pass through the analyzer; those retarded an odd number of half wave lengths will pass through the analyzer and onto the screen with maximum intensity. The stress pattern on the screen is thus composed of areas that change from maximum darkness to areas of maximum brightness as retardations of integral and half wave lengths take place due to increasing load.

When the fringe order, the model thickness, and the model fringe value—determined from simple tension, compression, or bending tests under controlled load conditions—are known, it is a simple matter to calculate the principal stress at a boundary point. Stresses at other than boundary points may be calculated, but the procedure is more involved.

The photoelastic method is excellent for determining stress distribution at all points in two dimensional models. However, considerable knowledge of mathematics, physics, and mechanics is necessary if the method is to be generally used. In addition, while three-dimensional analysis is possible, it is involved and complex and has not been widely used.

STATISTICAL METHODS

58. Statistical Methods. In some testing operations it is necessary to test only a few specimens, but in other cases a large number of tests are required. When a large mass of original test data has been obtained it is necessary to use statistical methods to present the important features in a concise and interpretable form.

Statistical methods provide ways of calculating various average values. These averages measure central tendency or the value about which the data tend to center. Statistical methods also provide ways to measure the dispersion of the data with respect to the average or central value.

Central tendency is measured by the arithmetic mean, the geometric mean, the median, and the mode. The most widely used measure of central tendency is the arithmetic mean ($\overline{X}$) which is the familiar everyday average. It is defined as

$$\overline{X} = \frac{X_1 + X_2 + \cdots X_n}{n} = \frac{1}{n} \sum_{i=1}^{i=n} X_i$$

in which n is the number of the items X_1, X_2, etc. The geometric mean, not as widely used, is defined as

$$\text{Geometric mean} = \sqrt[n]{X_1 X_2 \cdots X_n}$$

The median is defined as the value of the middlemost item, and the mode as the value that occurs most frequently.

Dispersion or the variation of the results around the average is measured by range, standard deviation, average deviation, and coefficient of variation. Range is defined as the difference between the maximum and minimum values. The most commonly used measure of dispersion is the standard deviation (δ), which is defined as

$$\delta = \sqrt{\frac{(X_1 - \overline{X})^2 + (X_2 - \overline{X})^2 + \cdots (X_n - \overline{X})^2}{n}} = \sqrt{\frac{\sum_{i=1}^{i=n} (X_i - \overline{X})^2}{n}}$$

Average deviation, less frequently used, is defined as

$$\text{Average deviation} = \frac{\sum_{i=1}^{i=n} |X_i - \overline{X}|}{n}$$

where the symbol | | represents the absolute value of the deviation, disregarding signs. The coefficient of variation is the ratio of the standard deviation to the arithmetic average expressed as a percentage, or

$$v = \frac{\delta}{\overline{X}} 100$$

The information that should be presented after a large mass of data has been analyzed consists of a complete description of the test specimen and test procedure along with a discussion of the variables associated with them, the number of tests (n), the arithmetic mean ($\overline{X}$), and the standard deviation (δ). For information on required number of specimens see Art. III-5.

Characteristics, Physical Properties, and Uses of Wood

1. The Timber Situation. The original stands of timber in the United States are estimated to have contained 5200 billion board feet of timber. Much of this timber has been consumed, and much of it was destroyed to make way for agriculture. There remains, however, over 600 million acres of forest land on which, according to the best estimates, there is a stand of 470 billion cubic feet of timber of which 1600 billion board feet is saw timber in merchantable sizes.

The depletion of vigin forests without proper consideration of future reproduction has naturally resulted in a shifting of production centers and changes in species dominating the market. The principal centers of softwood production at the present time are the Southern and the Pacific Coast states, with southern yellow pine and Douglas fir, respectively, as the principal structural species. More specifically, about two-fifths of the present lumber cut is produced in each of these regions.

Extensive studies are under way to appraise the present forest situation with respect to future requirements. Whereas present consumption greatly exceeds annual growth, it is evident that second growth is becoming an important factor in augmenting the supply. With the practice of forestry on land unsuited to other crops, and with efficient timber utilization, the United States can reasonably be expected to meet its future needs, at least after an initial adjustment period.

Although the per capita consumption of lumber in the United States has decreased sharply since 1905, the decline in total lumber consumption has been less. One of the most significant causes of reduced per capita consumption is more economical use resulting from a better knowledge of the properties of wood, and the more extensive application of wood preservatives.

For structural uses, timber of excellent quality is still readily available. Better utilization of structural timber may be assured by the application of the improved grading rules, which have been adopted by the various organizations, including ASTM and AREA, and by the use of the working stresses and design formulas recommended by the Forest Products Laboratory. Significant trends having a far-reaching effect on utilization are the development of improved joints, through the medium of metal connectors, and the growth of the plywood industry.

Engineers are concerned principally with uses of timber for structural purposes. Each year they direct the use of large amounts of pine, hemlock, Douglas fir, cypress, oak, redwood, chestnut, ash, spruce, and cedar under many varied conditions. Consequently it is quite necessary that they should be well informed concerning the properties and uses of this very valuable building material, in order that they, too, may use it to best advantage and conserve it wherever possible.

GENERAL CHARACTERISTICS OF WOOD *

2. Structure and Appearance. Although color, weight, smell, and resonance are often helpful, the structure of wood is the only reliable means of identifying species. Structure is closely related to all the mechanical properties of wood and very often furnishes an explanation for observed differences in these properties. Furthermore, structure and color determine the beauty of wood, as seen in the hard pine ceiling, the quartered-oak desk, the "bird's-eye" maple dresser, the mahogany paneling, and many other examples of decorative woodwork. For the engineer a knowledge of structure is of most importance because of the relation of structure to species and mechanical properties. We shall, therefore, briefly consider the different classes of timber and certain of their more prominent structural characteristics before taking up their properties.

3. Classes of Trees. Two classes of trees furnish practically all the structural timber of the United States. They are the gymnosperms (naked seed-leaved trees), of which the conifers are the important family; and the dicotyledons (trees having two seed leaves), which are commonly termed broad-leaved trees. A third class, the monocotyledons, of which the yuccas and palms are the more prominent native members, are used to a small extent in some of the Southern states.

Sometimes trees are also classified by the way that they shed their foliage. The conifers which are of most importance in the lumber industry are evergreen, although the larch and bald cypress shed their needles annually. On the other hand nearly all the broad-leaved trees are deciduous in our northern latitudes.

Frequently, in the trade, the lumber of broad-leaved trees is called hardwood, and that of the conifers softwood. Here again the terms are inexact, since poplar, basswood, and horse chestnut (broad-leaved trees) are softwoods, and longleaf pine and yew (conifers) are hardwoods.

* In preparing this chapter reference was made to *Bull.* 10 of the U. S. Forestry Div., by F. Roth, to *Economic Woods of the United States,* and *Mechanical Properties of Wood,* by S. J. Record, and to *Wood Handbook,* U. S. Dept. Agr.

The classes of conifers which are of most importance structurally are pine, fir, hemlock, cypress, spruce, redwood, and cedar. Oak, maple, red gum, poplar, chestnut, birch, beech, basswood, elm, ash, and hickory are much-used broad-leaved trees.

Both conifers and broad-leaved trees grow in diameter as well as in height through the addition of yearly layers of wood, each of which forms immediately under the bark. On the other hand, the yuccas and palms increase principally in height. Although alike in manner of growth, conifers and broad-leaved trees differ markedly in structural detail and in character of wood elements. The wood of the conifers is characterized by a marked likeness in the wood elements and in their arrangement; the wood of the broad-leaved trees consists of a greater variety of fibers and cells which lack the regular arrangement seen in the conifers.

4. Structure of Wood in General. If one examines a sawn log of well-grown structural timber, he will perceive a small pith at the center of the cross section surrounded by numerous concentric rings of wood which are, in turn, encircled by the bark. The concentric rings represent the layers of wood added each year during the life of the tree. These *annual rings,* therefore, furnish valuable information regarding the age of the log, the rapidity and the uniformity of its growth. The thickness of the annual rings will be found to vary greatly in different trees of the same species and in different parts of the same cross section. Trees grown in the open or after a forest has been cleared (second growth) exhibit wider rings than those which grow more slowly in the forest. Generally the rings are widest at the center and become narrower nearer the bark. Also, the width of the same ring will vary from the bottom to the top of the tree. It is widest at the bottom in young thrifty trees, but in the old trees of the forest it is widest near the top. In thrifty forest trees the center rings are often $\frac{1}{2}$ in. or more in width, but in stunted specimens rings less than $\frac{1}{200}$ in. wide are found. With the conifers a medium rate of growth is conducive to high strength and toughness, whereas a rapid growth is desirable to produce maximum toughness and strength in hardwoods like hickory.

Closer observance of a single annual ring discloses that it is not uniform in composition. In many of the conifers the interior of the ring is decidedly lighter in color than the outer portion; the exact opposite is true in the oaks; in a cross section of hard maple no great variation in the color of a single ring is visible to the naked eye. These differences in color are due largely to variations in the size and structure of the wood cells and fibers. In the *non-porous* conifers the color of the earlier wood is due principally to cells which are less compact than those grown more slowly in the summer (Fig. 1). This difference in color and ring structure is not, however, very pronounced in white pine. The *ring-porous* woods like the oaks and the hickories owe the darker color of their early wood to the presence of numerous pores, each of which is large enough to admit a pin

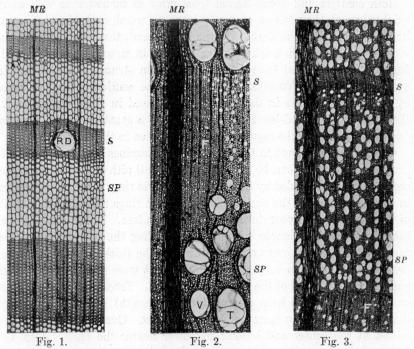

Fig. 1.　　　　　　　Fig. 2.　　　　　　　Fig. 3.

(All magnified about 27 diameters. Reduced from photomicrographs prepared by the Forest Products Laboratory, Forest Service, U. S. Dept. Agr.)

Fig. 1. Cross section of longleaf pine, a non-porous wood. (Note absence of pores; resin duct, *RD*; thick cell walls in summer wood, *S*; thin walls in spring wood, *SP*; narrow medullary ray, *MR*.)

Fig. 2. Cross section of white oak, a ring-porous wood. (Note large vessels, *V*, in spring wood, *SP*, some being clogged with tyloses, *T*; broad medullary ray, *MR*; also summer wood, *S*, and fibers, *F*.)

Fig. 3. Cross section of beech, a diffuse porous wood. (Note the uniform dispersion of vessels, *V*; fibers, *F*; medullary ray, *MR*, also spring wood, *SP*, and summer wood, *S*.)

point, and which are almost absent in the later wood (Fig. 2). *Diffuse-porous* woods, like beech and maple (Fig. 3), show little variation in the appearance of the early and late wood because of the more uniform dispersion of the pores across the ring. Owing to the time of growth in our climate, the early wood is called *spring wood,* and the later wood is termed *summer wood.*

Since the summer wood is denser, harder, and stronger than the spring wood, it follows that the percentage of summer wood in a stick of timber affords information concerning its mechanical properties (Art. VI-13). Furthermore, the contrast between the spring and summer woods is sometimes of assistance in distinguishing different timbers of the same class— the pines, for example.

The characteristic appearance of the annual rings after the log has been sawn into boards is seen in Figs. 4 and 5. Two important differences will at once be noted in these figures. The more open spring wood of the pine board is lighter colored than the denser summer wood, whereas in the oak the porous spring wood makes it appear darker than the more compact summer wood. Also, on the transverse section of the oak there are well-marked radial bands or *rays* which appear as light-colored parallel lines on the radial section. These rays, often termed *medullary rays*, are quite pronounced in many of the hardwoods but are less easily observed by the eye in the softwoods. They are, however, present in both classes of trees and serve as distributors of water and food supplies between the bark and adjacent layers of wood. In the oaks the rays lend the beauty to the grain of the quarter-sawn

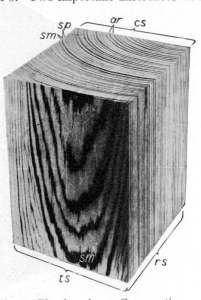

Fig. 4. Pine board. *cs*, Cross section; *rs*, radial section; *ts*, tangential section; *sm*, summer wood; *sp*, spring wood; *ar*, annual ring.

lumber. In all classes of timber they greatly influence shrinkage and thereby affect mechanical properties, as we shall see in Art. IV-11 and 12.

As a tree grows the cells near the pith gradually become inactive so far as the life of the tree is concerned. They do not decay, however, but remain a firm and strong support to the tree. This inner lifeless portion of the trunk is called the *heartwood*. The *sapwood* is the surrounding envelope, between the heartwood and the bark, which carries the water and alternately stores and supplies the food for the growing portions of the tree. Generally, through the infiltration of pigments, the heartwood is darker in color than the sapwood, although the contrast is not always marked. Red cedar, redwood, yew, tamarack, elm, and birch exhibit a strong contrast in the color of the sapwood and heartwood; but in fir, hemlock, and spruce the contrast is largely wanting.

The proportion of sapwood varies considerably in various parts of the same tree. Generally the envelope of sapwood becomes thinner near the top of the tree and in the limbs. Very thrifty rapid-growing trees generally have a larger proportion of sapwood than trees of like species having a stunted growth, but the latter often have more rings in the sapwood. The width of sapwood varies considerably for different kinds of wood;

Fig. 5. Oak board. *cs*, Cross section; *rs*, radial section; *ts*, tangential section; *r*, medullary rays.

it is small for longleaf pine, white pine and chestnut, and great for loblolly pine, Norway pine, ash, maple, hickory, and gum. Occupying the peripheral portion of the log, the sapwood always forms a large proportion of its mass.

In old tree trunks the sapwood is likely to be weaker, freer from knots, and more susceptible to decay than the heartwood. In comparatively young timber the difference in strength between heartwood and sapwood is small. Sapwood is more readily impregnated with preservatives than heartwood. Some workers claim that the sapwood of hickory is stronger and tougher than the heartwood, but tests by the Forest Service * have failed to substantiate this prejudice.

* *Bull.* 80, p. 50; also see Art. VI-14.

5. The Grain of Wood. The comparative width of annual rings, the direction and the arrangement of the cells and fibers are the causes of the *grain* of the wood. Thus trees of rapid growth having wide annual rings produce coarse-grained wood; those of slower growth produce wood with narrow rings or fine grain. When the wood elements are straight and run parallel to the pith the wood is said to be straight grained. When the wood elements do not run parallel to the axis of the piece, it is said to be *cross grained*. This includes *spiral, diagonal, interlocked* (succeeding layers winding in opposite direction), *wavy, dip* (one wave only), and *curly* grain.

The slope of the grain can be ascertained by noting the direction of the surface checks, resin ducts, and annual layers. Direction of grain can usually be told by observing the spreading of a drop of ink along the grain. Cross grain has a pronounced weakening effect on the strength of beams when the slope is 1:15 or greater.

6. Defects in Timber. Besides irregularities in the character of the grain, there are, from a structural standpoint, three important classes of defects in timber—knots, checks, and shakes.

Knots are the beginnings of branches which have been surrounded by the parent stem. Generally the piths of branch and stem join and the annual rings of the branch are continuous with the lower rings in the stem.

The size of a knot, unless otherwise specified, is measured by the average of the maximum and minimum diameters on the surface of a piece. *Pin knots* are under ½ in. in diameter, *small knots* are from ½ in. to ¾ in., *medium knots* from ¾ to 1½ in., and *large knots* are over 1½ in. in diameter. *Round knots* are oval or circular in form. When a knot is exposed by sawing lengthwise it is called a *spike knot*. *Sound knots* are as solid and hard as the surrounding wood. A *decayed* knot contains advanced decay and is softer than the surrounding wood. In an *encased knot* the annual rings fail to grow into the fibers of the surrounding wood. A *tight knot* is so securely fastened that it will hold its position in the finished piece. When the wood fibers deflect around one knot it is called a *single knot;* when they deflect about two or more knots as a unit, the group is called a *knot cluster*. Two or more knots radiating from a common center are termed *branch knots*.

Knots greatly affect the workability, cleavability, shrinkage, and the strength of wood (Art. VI-15). Knots in coniferous boards are likely to be filled with resin, a condition which renders them difficult to cover with paint.

A *check* is a longitudinal crack which is usually normal to the annual rings.

A *shake* is a longitudinal crack usually between the annual rings of growth.

Both shakes and checks adversely affect the durability of timber because they readily admit moisture and air. If present near the neutral plane of a beam they may materially weaken its resistance to horizontal shear.

7. Color and Odor. The colors exhibited by different woods or by the sapwood and heartwood of the same tree are due to chemical compounds impregnating the wood substance. Freshly formed wood is nearly colorless; the sapwood is lighter than the heartwood in all species having any pronounced demarcation between the two. Exposure to air deepens the color of wood, and immersion under water darkens it very materially. When wood is attacked by fungi it loses its luster and becomes dull in appearance.

Color, together with structure, is an important determinator of the beauty of mahogany, cherry, black walnut, red gum and sycamore. In many woods the color of the heartwood is a valuable aid to identification. Thus the white of the white spruce, the yellow of the osage orange, the yellow-brown of the tamarack, the light brown of the chestnut, white oak, and sycamore, the red-brown of the red oak, red cedar, and red gum, and the dark brown of the black walnut are all distinctive marks.

Odor is also due to chemical compounds in the wood substance. It is much reduced by exposure to the weather but can generally be determined by making a fresh incision in the wood. Heartwood gives a stronger odor than sapwood. Odor is undesirable in woods which are to be used as food containers. In cedar chests, however, it forms a protective against moths. As a means of identification the resinous odor of longleaf pine, the aromatic odor of cedar, the sour smell of oaks, the smell of kerosene emitted by catalpa are noteworthy. Decayed timber often has a smell which is pronouncedly different from the odor of the sound wood; decaying red oak, for example, smells like heliotrope.

PHYSICAL PROPERTIES OF WOOD

8. Density and Specific Weight. The true specific gravity of all wood substance is approximately 1.55, whereas the specific weight and *apparent* specific gravity (ratio of weight of given block to weight of an equal volume of water) vary with the density of the wood. Herein the term specific gravity will indicate the *apparent* value, which varies from 0.07 for balsa wood to 1.29 for black ironwood. This criterion conforms with our conceptions of heavy and light wood and the degree of its buoyancy in water.

The percentage of moisture in the wood has a very large effect upon the specific weight. Thus green wood is heavier than dry wood, the green sapwood of a given log is generally heavier than the accompanying heartwood, and the wood of the green sapling is heavier than that from the old tree. Since the moisture content greatly influences the specific weight, true comparisons of this important property can only be made on dry specimens.

Considering dry wood, we may say that the wood of a given tree is heaviest in the lower portion of the trunk, lighter in the limbs and branches, and lightest in the roots. The heaviest timber in old pine is found about half way between the center and the bark, where a medium rate of growth has obtained. In young pines and in ring-porous woods like oak the heaviest wood is at the center of the stump. In general the dry heartwood is much heavier than the dry sapwood. The dry wood of the oak sapling is heavier than that of the old tree, but in the pines and spruces the reverse is true. In the conifers high density is favored by a medium or slow rate of growth and a high percentage of summer wood. Thus the specific weight of shortleaf pine, redwood, western hemlock and Douglas fir has been found to vary linearly with the per cent of summer wood.* In the ring-porous woods like oak, chestnut, and elm a rapid rate of growth is attended by the production of a large proportion of thick-walled fibers, thus causing a high specific gravity; but in the diffuse porous woods like maple, birch, and beech, where the cell structure within the rings is more homogeneous, no relation between rate of growth and density is apparent. As in coniferous timber, however, the density of wood from broad-leaved trees increases with the proportion of summer wood.

Since the specific weight of dry wood is often a very important criterion of the strength and other mechanical properties of timber (Art. VI-11), it is well worth determining. In the laboratory small discs about 1 in. thick are cut from different portions of large sticks so that the variation in weight and moisture content may be represented. The pieces are then carefully weighed, dried in an oven to constant weight at 100°C, and again weighed. The specific weight is then computed from the volume and dry weight of the disc. Density is frequently based upon the volume at test and the oven-dry weight. In the field a rough but satisfactory method of determining density is afforded by boring holes of known diameter and depth in different portions of a timber and determining the specific weight from the dry weight of the shavings and the volume of the hole.

The range in average values for the specific gravity and specific weight of the more important native timbers are given in Table 1. All data

* See Fig. 17, *Bull.* 108, U. S. Forest Service.

were obtained from small clear specimens from the top 4 ft of 16-ft butt
logs of typical trees. Other results are given in Table 1, Chapter VI.

TABLE 1.   WEIGHTS OF DIFFERENT AIR-DRIED WOODS AT
12 PER CENT MOISTURE CONTENT [1]

Common Name of Wood.	Specific Gravity.	Specific Weight, lb./ft.^{3}
(a) VERY HEAVY WOODS:—Black ironwood..............	1.28	80
Live oak..	0.99	62
Canyon live oak; pignut hickory; blue gum; persimmon; mockernut, shagback hickory; buttonwood; blue beech; hop-hornbeam; black locust; mountain laurel; willow, white, post, swamp oak..........................	0.75–0.87	47–54
(b) HEAVY WOODS:—Sweet birch; bitternut hickory; chestnut, bur oak; beech; rock elm; honey locust; sugar maple; laurel, red, water oak; Pacific yew; yellow birch; water hickory; black oak; nutmeg hickory; white ash; southern red oak; longleaf pine; blue, green ash; black maple; California black oak.......................	0.64–0.74	40–46
(c) WOODS OF MEDIUM WEIGHT:—Paper birch; black walnut; Biltmore white, Oregon ash; red maple; loblolly, pond, shortleaf pine; slippery elm; hackberry; mountain pine; tamarack; pumpkin ash; western larch; gray birch; black cherry; American elm; black, tupelo gum; pitch pine; sycamore; black ash; Douglas fir (coast type); red gum; bigleaf maple; sand pine; eastern red cedar; silver maple; Norway pine; southern cypress; striped maple...	0.51–0.63	32–39
(d) LIGHT WOODS:—Mountain hemlock; western black willow; chestnut; Douglas fir (mountain type); jack pine; redwood; Alaska, Port Orford cedar; eastern cottonwood; lodgepole pine; pin cherry; eastern, western hemlock; Jeffrey, limber, western yellow pine; yellow poplar; black, red spruce; aspen; large tooth aspen; butternut; red fir; cabbage palmetto; Sitka, white spruce.....	0.43–0.50	27–31
(e) VERY LIGHT WOODS:—Basswood; incense cedar; balsam fir; black willow; white, sugar pine; black cottonwood; red, white cedar; alpine fir; Engelmann spruce; balsam poplar..	0.35–0.42	22–26

[1] Forest Products Laboratory, Technical Note No. 218.

Some very light woods, balsa and quipo, grown chiefly in Central America,
weigh only 4½ to 12½ lb per cu ft.

A practical rule for estimating the effect of small changes in moisture
content, less than 6 per cent, in air-dry wood (12 per cent moisture content) is to allow a change of 0.5 per cent in the specific weight for a
change of 1 per cent in the moisture content.

9. Moisture in Wood. Water is found in three portions of wood: (1) it constitutes over 90 per cent of the protoplasm in the living cells; (2) it saturates the cell walls; and (3) it fills, more or less completely, the pores of the lifeless cells. It occurs in all three portions of the sapwood but saturates only the cell walls in the heartwood. In the sapwood of white pine containing 100 per cent of water (in terms of the dry weight of the wood), about 5 per cent is found in the living cells, 35 per cent in the cell walls, and the remaining 60 per cent in the empty cells.* The water in the cells of the sapwood is drawn upward into the leaves of the tree and converted into sap. The sap is conducted down through the bark and provides nourishment for the wood forming immediately beneath the bark (the *cambium*). The water in the sapwood contains slight traces of mineral salts, and during the winter it may carry traces of sugar, organic acid, and gum. These substances apparently exercise little effect upon mechanical properties of wood, however, since only a trace of them can be found in it.

The wood immediately under the bark carries most of the water, and the proportion in any one cross section varies as the percentage of sapwood. It is, therefore, greatest in the roots and greater in the limbs and branches than in the trunk. The wood of saplings contains more moisture than that of old trees. Also, in the timber of thrifty trees, the per cent moisture is greater than in those of stunted growth.

It is impossible to remove moisture entirely from wood without setting it on fire, but all excepting a couple of per cent may be eliminated by drying at 100°C. Moisture determinations may be made on the same specimens used for determining density. The per cent moisture should, however, always be referred to the dry weight (100°C), in order to have a constant basis for comparison. The moisture content of green wood for a number of species is found in Table 1, Chapter VI.

10. The Drying of Timber. It is just as essential to dry properly, or "season," wood as it is to condition concrete by proper storage, or steel by proper heat treatment. Nevertheless the proper conditioning of timber has received far less consideration than it deserves. The chief reasons for drying timber are as follows: (1) to decrease shrinkage after placement in structure, (2) to increase its resistance to decay, (3) to reduce its weight, (4) to improve its strength and mechanical properties, (5) to prepare it for preservative treatments, and (6) to increase its workability. Since the water will not run out of the wood, some means of evaporating it must be used. It is impossible, however, to eliminate all moisture from timber without scorching it; and, furthermore, if the water were entirely removed the timber would reabsorb from the surrounding atmosphere and retain about 12 to 15 per cent of moisture.

* Roth, in *Bull.* 10, U. S. Forestry Div.

According to H. D. Tiemann * drying is much influenced by the following: (1) irregular shrinkage, (2) the different ways water is contained in the cells, (3) the manner in which it passes from center to surface, (4) the plasticity of the wood substance while in a hot and moist condition, and (5) the changes which are produced in the hygroscopic and chemical nature of the surface. The rate of drying is also affected by the ratio of the volume of the piece to its surface area. Logs with the bark left on dry very much more slowly and are more likely to decay than those without bark. End surfaces dry more rapidly than tangential or radial surfaces, but boards and long timbers lose most of their water through the sides. Within a given species, green timber of large moisture content dries in about the same length of time as that of lower moisture content. This is probably due to the fact that the sapwood, which contains most of the moisture, dries more rapidly than the heartwood. High temperatures soften the cell walls and promote the transfusion of moisture, thus favoring rapid drying.

Two methods of drying are practiced: air drying or "seasoning" and kiln drying. In air drying the temperature and humidity conditions of the atmosphere exercise an important influence upon the rate of drying. Thus, owing to warmer atmosphere, ties and structural timbers cut in the summer dry at a much more rapid rate than those felled in the late autumn. In fact, for many woods like oak and gum, timber felled in the summer often dries too fast and case hardens. For such timbers the cooler months with more humid atmosphere are a more favorable time for seasoning. A warm temperature and a free circulation of air are important requisites in air drying. The latter consideration, however, is often overlooked. In experiments conducted by the Forest Products Laboratory † it was demonstrated that ties piled 7 by 2, 7 by 1, or 8 by 1, in single piles, dried more rapidly than those piled 9 by 9. Coniferous wood may be dried to constant weight in a shorter time and at a more rapid rate than many of the hardwoods. Figure 6 shows drying charts for a number of tests on different kinds of ties. Large structural timbers of coniferous wood generally require seasoning for two summers; smaller ones require only one summer in our northern latitudes. On account of the long time required for successful air drying, a considerable proportion of certain woods like maple and gum rot before seasoning is completed.

There are a great many schemes in use for kiln drying lumber, but in most of them either warm moist air or superheated steam is the drying medium. Kiln temperatures varying from room temperature to 180°F, and drying periods of a few days to several months are used. In some

* See Principles of Kiln Drying Lumber in *Lumber World Review,* Jan. 25, 1915.
† *Bull.* 118, U. S. Forest Service.

yards working on hardwoods, a short period of air drying is followed by kiln drying.

For most successful kiln drying the timber should be brought to as high a temperature as it will stand without injury before drying is begun; otherwise the moisture in the hot outer fibers of the wood will tend to flow toward the cooler interior. The proper condition may be obtained by

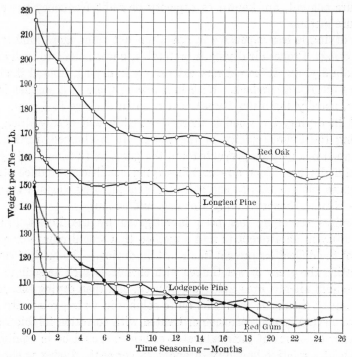

Fig. 6. Losses in weight of ties with long-continued seasoning. (W. H. Kempfer in *Bull.* 161, Am. Ry. Eng. Assoc., p. 215.)

circulating air with a high humidity until the wood is thoroughly heated, and then gradually diminishing the humidity to bring about drying. Tiemann * states that oak, western larch, and cypress require a high humidity (80–90 per cent) at the start and should be held at 50 per cent until toward the end of the run. Most of the conifers may, however, be run at lower humidities. With some green timbers initial temperatures of only 120°F or even less must be used; others can be started at temperatures above 212°F. Besides control over humidity and temperature, it is essential that the uniformity of both be secured by ample circulation.

The moisture content of wood may be determined by means of electric

* See footnote, p. IV-12.

moisture meters with an accuracy of ± 1 per cent if proper care is taken. The meters are easy to use, and only a few seconds are required to determine the moisture content of a given piece of wood. The resistance-type meter is based on the principle that the direct-current electrical resistance of wood changes at a very rapid rate as the moisture content changes between an oven-dry and a fiber-saturated condition. Other types, based on the change in the dielectric constant of wood with changes in the moisture content, are known as capacity or radio-frequency power-loss moisture meters.

Air drying is less expensive in operation but ruins more lumber than kiln drying. Proper air drying is preferable, nevertheless, to badly managed kiln drying. It is used very extensively in drying ties and the larger sizes of structural timbers. With kiln drying there is a smaller loss in timber, usually less than 10 per cent even in timbers like gum. Also, with kiln drying, the wood is more thoroughly and evenly dried, thus reducing the hygroscopicity of the wood. It is claimed, furthermore, that sap stains may be prevented and the gums and resins fixed by correct kiln drying. Poor air- or kiln-drying conditions produce stresses that cause such defects as end splitting, end checking, surface checking, case hardening, honeycombing, warping, and collapse.

Chemical seasoning has been investigated by the Forest Products Laboratory in an attempt to find a method that would relieve or correct some of the difficulties present in air or kiln drying. The method consists of treating the green or wet timber with chemicals such as sodium chloride, sodium nitrate, urea aldehyde, or urea, and then drying the timber. Satisfactory chemicals should be quite soluble in water, relatively inexpensive, naturally non-corrosive or treated with corrosion inhibitors, and the vapor pressures of their saturated solutions should be in equilibrium with air at a relative humidity of about 75 per cent. Lower vapor pressures are desirable for fast drying with minimum stress, but a relatively high vapor pressure is required to prevent condensation on treated wood in service.

The surface of a chemically treated timber will remain moist as long as the vapor pressure of the air equals or exceeds that of the chemical solution in the wood. Even though the moisture content of the surface remains high, the drying rate is not decreased because the water from the untreated interior portion of the timber moves toward and is evaporated from the surface at a rate that is dependent on the temperature and the relative humidity of the drying air. More severe drying conditions resulting in faster drying may be used with chemically treated timber, and such timber usually has fewer drying defects. Chemical seasoning has had only a limited commercial acceptance, but it may become an exceedingly important method if specifications require that the wood be dried to a specified moisture content and that it be virtually check free.

The figures in Table 2 furnish an approximation of the amount of water lost in drying green timber.

TABLE 2. POUNDS OF WATER LOST IN DRYING 100 POUNDS OF GREEN WOOD IN THE KILN [1]

Common Names of Species.	Sapwood or Outer Part.	Heartwood or Interior.
(1) Pines, cedars, spruces, and firs....................	45–65	16–25
(2) Cypress, extremely variable......................	50–65	18–60
(3) Poplar, cottonwood, basswood....................	60–65	40–60
(4) Oak, beech, ash, elm, maple, birch, hickory, chestnut, walnut, and sycamore.........................	40–50	30–40

The lighter kinds have the most water in the sapwood; thus sycamore has more than hickory.

[1] Roth in *Bull.* 10, U. S. Dept. Agr.

11. Shrinkage and Its Effects. For purposes of illustration consider a very small, thin transverse section of green wood, Fig. 7A. If this sec-

tion is very slowly and uniformly dried no change will be noted in the disc until the water in the pores is evaporated. Then the cell-walls will gradually become thinner and

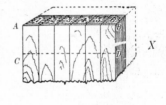

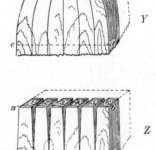

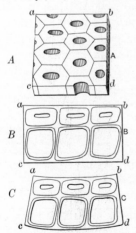

Fig 7. Warping of wood.   Fig. 8. Formation of checks.

the sides of the disc *ab*, *bd*, etc., will shorten. No contraction in length of the disc is, however, observable. Furthermore, since the thickness of the end walls of the cells or fibers is very small compared to their length, it is apparent that longitudinal shrinkage of a thicker disc composing several fiber lengths will be negligible. If we repeat the experiment with a disc like that of Fig. 7*B*, we will observe that the side *ab* shortens more than *cd* and that the surfaces *ab* and *cd* are curved, Fig. 7*C*. In other

words, thick-walled cells shrink more than those having thin walls. We shall, therefore, find that a curved disc of wood one annual ring in width will straighten in drying owing to the fact that the thick-walled cells of summer wood shrink more than the thinner walled cells of spring wood. This inequality in shrinkage between the various cells produces stresses of a serious nature during the drying of timber.

Again, if a stream of warm air is directed against the side *cd* of the moistened disc, Fig. 7*A*, it will be noted that it shortens much more rapidly than *ab*, owing to the more rapid evaporation of moisture. When all portions of the disc are equally dry, *ab* and *cd* are again of equal length. Thus a partially dried board exposed to the sun's rays becomes concave on the upper side, but may be straightened by turning the board over and allowing the moisture in the convex surface to be evaporated.

Fig. 9. Effects of shrinkage.

Since water is evaporated more rapidly from the ends of the wood elements than from the sides, a piece of wood like that in Fig. 8*X* will shrink more laterally at *AB* than at *CD*. This action produces bending in the piece, as shown in Fig. 8*Y*. If the rapidity of drying is sufficiently great, the resulting pull across the grain of the wood will exceed its tensile strength and checking ensues, Fig. 8*Z*. After the piece has completely dried many of these checks close, although the weakening effect remains. Rapid drying of the outsides of logs and timbers often causes similar cracks to appear on the longitudinal surfaces. Not all of these radial cracks close when seasoning is complete; some gradually open and remain a permanent source of weakness for a reason which we shall now explain.

Fig. 10. "Honeycombed" board. The checks or cracks form along the pith rays.

Looking at Fig. 14, we note that the cells in medullary rays are elongated in a direction perpendicular to the longitudinal elements. Since cells in the rays obey laws of shrinkage similar to those governing the behavior of the longitudinal elements, it is at once apparent that the rays will shrink in the longitudinal and tangential direction but not radially, whereas the longitudinal elements will shrink radially and tangentially but not longitudinally. Consequently, the lateral shrinkage of the ray in the longitudinal direction will be hindered by the adjoining longitudinal elements and the length of the ray will be shortened by the radial shrinkage of the longitudinal elements. The mutually perpendicular tensile and compressive forces thus produced are often sufficient to break the bond between the ray and the adjacent longitudinal fibers. Once the bond is broken, further circumferential shrinkage operates to widen rather than to close the breach.

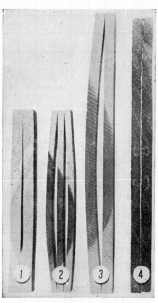

In woods like oak, where the number of pith rays is very large, it is probable that the slight longitudinal shrinkage is due principally to lateral shrinkage of the rays. Also, the resistance offered by the rays to oppose radial shrinkage of the wood and the great shrinkage of the summer wood are the reasons why the tangential shrinkage of wood is always more than the radial shrinkage. The difference in shrinkage in these two directions is the cause of much difficulty in drying. Besides producing the checks in logs and sawn timbers, this difference between the tangential and radial shrinkage also causes the flat surfaces of a sawn log to become convex, as shown in Fig. 9.

Fig. 11. The elimination of case-hardening in kiln-dry red gum by steaming at the end of the drying period. 1, Sawn after no final steaming; 2 and 3, after 18 minutes' final steaming; 4, after 36 minutes' final steaming. (J. E. Imrie, before Gum Lumber Mfrs. Assoc., Jan. 16, 1916.)

When hardwoods, like oak, are quickly dried the water is evaporated more rapidly from the outside than it can be brought to the surface. As a result the outer portion of the piece checks; or, if it has sufficient plasticity under the influence of heat and moisture, the surface may take a set and harden just as wood bent in steam retains its shape after drying. If drying continues, the interior of the stick shrinks and the circumferential tension in the outer shell is relieved. Further shrinkage of the piece, as a whole, is diminished by the rigidity of the outer shell. This brings about a gradual reversal of stress in the shell and causes radial tension in the interior. If the radial tension becomes excessive, rupture will occur, as shown in Fig. 10. This phenomenon is called *case hardening* or *honey-*

combing. It may exist in lumber without the cracks being noticed, but is revealed immediately upon sawing. A simple test for case hardening is that used by Tiemann (see Fig. 11).

Rapid drying of green cedar and redwood at high temperatures often produces a collapse of the cell walls. This is brought about by the radial

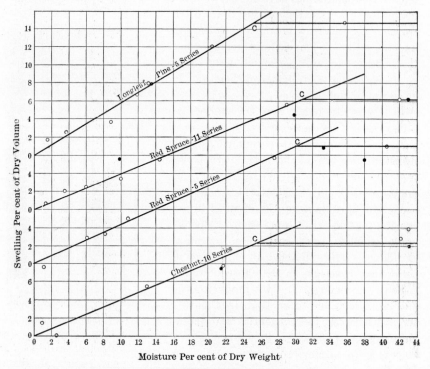

Fig. 12. Relation between swelling and moisture. Each point is the average of from 5 to 11 specimens. Black dots indicate specimens that were kiln dried and then allowed to reabsorb moisture. The fiber-saturation point is at C. (*Circ.* 108 of U. S. Forest Service.)

tensile stresses produced on the cell walls by the withdrawal of free water. Such defects lower the strength of the timber; they may be avoided by using lower initial temperatures in drying.

Dried pieces of wood greedily absorb water with an increase in volume until the cell walls are saturated and the *fiber-saturation point* is reached;[*] subsequent filling of the lumen in the cells is accompanied by no further swelling, Fig. 12.

[*] Tiemann reported in *Proc. Soc. Am. For.,* Vol. 8, p. 313, that blue gum is an exception to the above rule, since it "begins to shrink immediately from green condition, even at 70 to 90 per cent moisture."

TABLE 3

Species.	Per Cent.	Species.	Per Cent.
Southern yellow pine.....	25	Red spruce...........	31
Western hemlock........	31	Chestnut..............	25
Western larch..........	27	Tamarack.............	30
Norway pine...........	29	Red gum..............	25
Douglas fir.............	23	White ash............	20

The average values in Table 3 for per cent moisture at fiber-saturation point were obtained by Tiemann (*Circ.* 108, U. S. Forest Service). Each result represents 40 or more tests per species of wood. In some cases individual values varied as much as 10 per cent from the averages.

Repeated wetting and drying weakens timber, causes expansion and contraction, and, in addition, produces conditions which promote decay. Timber must, therefore, be protected from moisture, if constancy in volume and its life are to be conserved. The swelling of wooden pipes and tanks after water is admitted often produces large stresses in both bands and timber. The amount of swelling and the stresses caused by it should be given careful consideration in design.

12. Amount of Shrinkage. As a rule, if the sapwood is of the same density as the heartwood, the sapwood will shrink more than the heartwood; but heavy heartwood shrinks more than light sapwood. Coniferous woods like pine, spruce, cedar, cypress, and redwood shrink uniformly and do not check much in drying. Oak, beech, chestnut, elm, hickory, gum, and other hardwoods shrink considerably and check more or less, depending on the care exercised in drying.

In general, the radial shrinkage of wood is about 60 per cent of the tangential, and the longitudinal shrinkage is negligible. Therefore, the volumetric shrinkage is practically 1.6 times the tangential shrinkage.

TABLE 4. APPROXIMATE SHRINKAGE OF A BOARD, OR SET OF BOARDS, 100 INCHES WIDE, DRYING IN THE OPEN AIR

Common Name of Species.	Lateral Shrinkage, Inches.
(1) Hardy catalpa; redwood; white or red cedar.........................	$2 - 2\frac{1}{2}$
(2) Cedar (Alaska, Incense, Port Orford); chestnut, cypress; Alpine, balsam, white, red fir; locust; eastern hemlock; light pines..................	$3 - 3\frac{1}{2}$
(3) Ash; Douglas fir; tupelo or black gum; western hemlock, larch, heavy pines, poplar, spruce, sycamore, black walnut.....................	$3\frac{1}{2} - 4$
(4) Cottonwood, birch, maple...	$4 - 4\frac{1}{2}$
(5) Basswood, beech, elm, hickory, oak..............................	$4\frac{1}{2} - 5\frac{1}{2}$

Experiments by the Forest Products Laboratory show that the shrinkage for all species of wood varies roughly as the first power of the specific gravity (ρ). From Forest Products Laboratory *Bull.* 676 were obtained the following percentage relationships: volume shrinkage = 28ρ; radial shrinkage = 9.5ρ; tangential shrinkage = 17ρ.

Approximate values of the tangential shrinkage of air-dried material are given in Table 4. More accurate results appear in Table 1, Chapter VI.

PRINCIPAL NATIVE WOODS *

13. Sources, Characteristics, and Uses. In the list which follows, an attempt has been made to arrange the various classes of wood in order of economic importance. Within a given class, however, there may be individual species which are of less value than species in a class farther down in the list. For example: sugar pine, lodgepole pine, and tupelo gum are less valuable than hickory; but the pines and gums as groups are more valuable than hickory. The mechanical properties of many of these woods can be found in Chapter VI.

14. Southern Yellow Pine is the term applied to the species of yellow pine which are found in Southern states from Virginia to Texas; most of our supply now comes from Louisiana, Mississippi, Texas and North Carolina. Included in this group are longleaf, shortleaf, loblolly, Cuban and pond pine. Difficulty experienced in separating these species has brought about the use of this inclusive term and caused the adoption of grading rules for quality classification. From the standpoint of the lumber producer, longleaf and Cuban pine are the most desirable species. From the viewpoint of the consumer, if the standard grading rules are used in the selection of structural timbers of southern yellow pine the difference in strength and durability of members cut from trees of different species is unimportant. The heartwood of all species is durable in contact with the ground. The southern yellow pines are the most important source of dimension timber for all heavy construction. They also provide much lumber for joists, posts, piling, and building construction. When treated with preservatives the harder woods of this group make good ties and paving blocks.

15. White Pine is still found to a limited extent in the states north of the Ohio River and east of the Dakotas, most abundantly in Minnesota, Wisconsin, and Maine. A somewhat inferior grade of white pine is obtained along the Rocky Mountains. White pine is a soft, uniform white wood which shrinks very little in seasoning, works easily, nails without splitting, and takes paint well. It is not very strong but quite durable.

---

* Compiled largely from Hough's *Handbook of Trees,* Snow's *Principal Species of Wood,* and *Bull.* 232 of the U. S. Dept. Agr.; see also *Wood Handbook.*

For window sash, interior trim, and pattern making, the demand for this wood is very great.

16. Norway Pine is now found principally in the states bordering on the Great Lakes. It is a light wood of fair hardness and strength, but is not durable in contact with the ground. Some dimension timber, masts, spars, piling, and interior trim are made of it. It is often sold for white pine.

17. Western Yellow Pine grows on the eastern slopes of the Rockies and in country westward to the coast. It is lighter, softer, weaker, and less durable than longleaf pine, but heavier and stronger than white pine. It is considerably used for dimension timbers, ties, and mine timbers; although, unless treated, it is better fitted for trim and pattern making.

18. Sugar Pine, found in California and Oregon, is a very light soft wood resembling white pine; it has similar uses.

19. Lodgepole Pine, a timber found from the Rockies to the Pacific coast, is a light, brittle, straight-grained wood of low strength. It is also difficult to season. This pine is used principally for poles, posts, and ties.

20. White Oak of commerce includes true white, post, bur, overcup, swamp white, cow, and chestnut oaks. Oak of this class may be found in the states east of Colorado, but the principal supply comes from the Virginias, Tennessee, Arkansas, Kentucky, Ohio, and Missouri. These oaks are all hard, heavy strong, tough, dense woods which are durable in contact with the soil. They shrink considerably and are likely to check in seasoning. The wood is capable of receiving a high polish. White oak is much used for furniture, cross ties, agricultural implements, fence posts, wagon stock, cooperage, and baskets. These oaks are the most valuable of the hardwoods.

21. Red Oak of commerce includes red, pin, Spanish, and black oaks. The sources of supply are the same as for white oak. The wood of the red oaks, though hard and strong, is more porous, somewhat lighter and weaker, and far less durable in contact with the soil than white oak. It is used chiefly for interior finish and furniture. It is easily impregnated with preservative and when so treated makes excellent cross ties.

22. Live Oak is found along the coast of the southern Atlantic and Gulf states and in California and Oregon. The wood is very heavy, hard, tough, strong, durable, and difficult to work. It is used for implements, wagons, and in ship building.

23. Douglas Fir is grown along the Pacific coast, the most valuable forests being in Oregon, Washington, and British Columbia. The wood is strong and rather brittle. The heartwood is durable in contact with the ground. It is the best structural timber of the northwest. This clear, straight-grained wood is widely used for building construction, dimension timber, ties, piles, boats, paving blocks, tanks, conduits, and furniture.

24. Hemlock is found in the Great Lakes states, in southeastern Canada and from Maine to Georgia along the Appalachian range. Western hemlock grows on the Pacific coast from northern California to Alaska. The wood is light, soft, and brittle. Western hemlock is moderately strong and fairly durable, but eastern hemlock is weak and not durable in contact with the ground. Hemlock holds nails well and is much used in house framing. Western hemlock, known to trade as West Coast hemlock, is considerably used for dimension timber and cross ties.

25. Spruce. Red spruce is found principally in New York, New England, and West Virginia; white spruce in nearly all parts of central Canada and in the Great Lakes states; Sitka spruce in Washington, Oregon, and Idaho. The woods of these species are light and soft. They have low strength and fair durability. Spruce is used chiefly for paper pulp, railway ties, resonance wood, piles, airplanes, and lumber.

26. Cypress grows along the eastern and Gulf coasts from Maryland to Texas and along the Mississippi Valley as far north as Illinois. Louisiana, Florida, and Georgia are the chief producers. It is a wood of medium weight and strength which is rather difficult to season but very durable. Cypress is used for siding, shingles, sash, doors, tanks, silos, and railway ties. Excessive use has greatly depleted the supply.

27. Hard (Sugar) Maple grows in all the states east of Colorado but most abundantly in the Great Lakes region. The wood is heavy, tough, hard, and strong, but not durable. The grain is often curly or has "bird's eyes." It is used for interior finish, flooring, furniture, and ship and car construction. When treated, this wood may be used for cross ties.

28. Soft (Red) Maple is found in the region with hard maple. The wood is medium in weight, hard and strong, but inferior to hard maple. It is fairly easy to work and is used for furniture, cabinet making, turnery, and gun stocks.

29. Chestnut grows on both slopes of the Appalachian range, but is produced principally in the Virginias, Pennsylvania, Tennessee, and Connecticut. It is a light, soft, weak, and brittle wood which is very durable in contact with the ground. The wood shrinks considerably and checks in seasoning, but works easily. Chestnut is much used for fence posts, poles, and cross ties; also for exposed constructions, furniture, and cooperage. Supply is scanty owing to ravages of a blight.

30. Red (Sweet) Gum grows in the same regions as cypress and is supplied most abundantly from Arkansas and Mississippi. The wood is not durable in the ground, soft, rather brittle, and of moderate weight and strength. It is easily worked, but warps and twists in seasoning. When highly polished it makes attractive furniture and interior trim. Other uses are for flooring, slack cooperage, turnery, and wagon stock.

31. Tupelo (Sour) Gum is found with red gum, but is most abundant in the Gulf states. It has about the same weight and strength as red gum but is tougher. This wood also is difficult to season and finds more or less use in the manufacture of boxes, furniture, wagon boxes, flooring, and finishing.

32. Hickory is fast disappearing in the United States; the present supply is obtained from Arkansas, Tennessee, and the Ohio basin. The more abundant varieties of hickory furnish very heavy, hard wood which is stronger and tougher than other native woods. Hickory checks and shrinks largely in seasoning and is difficult to work. It is subject to insect attack and not durable. The chief uses are for wagon stock, agricultural implements, axe handles, hoops, and baskets.

33. Yellow Poplar (Whitewood) is found in nearly all states east of the Mississippi River and south of the Great Lakes; it is obtained from the Virginias, Tennessee, and Kentucky principally. The wood is light, soft, brittle, weak and easy to work. It shrinks considerably, but holds nails well and is fairly durable. Whitewood is a very valuable wood for interior finish, furniture, shelving, drawers, wagon-bodies and boxes; it is also used for siding and paneling.

34. Basswood is scattered over the eastern half of the United States with the exception of the southern Atlantic and Gulf coasts; Wisconsin, Michigan, West Virginia, and New York lead in production. The wood is soft, very light, weak, brittle, and not durable. It shrinks considerably, but is very uniform and works easily. Although slightly inferior to whitewood, it is used for similar purposes.

35. Redwood grows abundantly along the coast of California. The wood is light, soft, straight-grained, and very durable. In the West it is used for all kinds of lumber: ties, shingles, poles, paving blocks, tanks, and conduits.

36. Yellow and Sweet Birch are found in the region east of the Mississippi River and north of the Gulf states, also in southeastern Canada; Wisconsin, Michigan, and Maine lead in production. The wood is heavy, hard, stiff, strong, and tough; but it is not durable when exposed. Although hard, it works easily and takes a high polish. Birch is much used for interior finish, furniture, turnery, and carving.

37. Larch or Tamarack. The eastern variety of this wood, generally called tamarack, is abundant in the Great Lakes region, New England, and northern and eastern Canada. Western larch is found principally along the Columbia River valley. The western variety is of medium weight, rather tough, hard, and durable, but somewhat less strong than Douglas fir or western hemlock. It is used for lumber, lath, cross ties, poles, and slack cooperage. Tamarack is of approximately the same weight and strength as western larch. Its uses are similar.

38. Ash. Varieties of ash are found in nearly all states east of the Rockies. Black ash is confined to the Northern states of this region, but the white and green species are widely found. The wood of the white and green ashes is heavy, hard, strong, and fairly tough. It is straight grained, shrinks little in seasoning and can be polished. It is used for finishing lumber, in wagon construction, farm implements, furniture, and cabinet work. Black ash makes a lighter, inferior wood to that of the white or green ashes. It is used as a substitute for them and in basket making.

39. Red and White Cedar. White cedar is found along the eastern coast and around the Great Lakes; red cedar grows in the region east of Colorado and north of Florida. Western red cedar is grown largely in Washington, Oregon, Idaho, and Montana. Cedar wood is very light, soft, weak, and brittle. Its low shrinkage and great durability, when exposed, make cedar valuable for shingles, siding, posts, poles, and ties. Red cedar is much used for moth-proof chests.

40. Beech grows in the region east of the Mississippi and in southeastern Canada. The wood is heavy, hard, strong, tough, but not durable in contact with the soil. It shrinks and checks considerably in seasoning. It is used for furniture, plane stocks, handles, and shoe lasts.

41. Elm. White and slippery elms grow in the states east of Colorado; rock elm is found largely in Michigan and the states bordering on the Ohio River. The wood of the slippery and rock elms is heavy, hard, strong, tough, durable, and difficult to split. The wood of white elm is somewhat inferior to that of the rock and slippery elms. Elm wood is used for agricultural implements, wheel stock, boats, furniture, cross ties, posts, and poles.

42. Cottonwood is found scattered over the region east of the Rockies, except in Maine; abundantly in Arkansas, Mississippi, Louisiana, and Tennessee. It is a soft, weak wood similar to whitewood but inferior in quality. It is considerably used for slack cooperage, fencing, and paper pulp.

43. Black Walnut is found over the eastern half of the United States with the exception of southern Atlantic and Gulf coasts; Indiana, Ohio, and Missouri are principal producers. Some varieties are obtainable from New Mexico, Arizona, and California. The wood is of medium weight, hard, strong, and easily worked. It has a dark chocolate color and is susceptible of a high polish. Owing to scarcity, its usage is confined largely to making of cabinets, furniture, and gun stocks.

44. Sycamore is most abundantly grown in the Ohio and Mississippi basin, although common in most states east of Colorado. The wood is of medium weight, hardness, and strength. It is rather brittle, difficult to work, and likely to check and warp in seasoning. Sycamore makes a pleasing appearance when quarter-sawn. It is used for interior trim, cabinet making, tobacco boxes, and cooperage.

45. Eucalyptus is a rapidly growing Australian tree of which a large number of varieties have been transplanted in California. Blue gum (*Eucalyptus globulus*) is the most important of these. This durable wood is very heavy, hard, tough, and strong, comparing favorably in these respects with hickory. It is, however, extremely difficult to season, since it checks and warps very badly. From results obtained in Australia, it is predicted that the American blue gum will furnish a satisfactory wood for cross ties, fence posts, poles, piles, paving blocks and wagon stock.

46. Catalpa is grown in Mississippi, Alabama, Georgia, and Florida; and hardy catalpa in Missouri, Illinois, Indiana, Kentucky, and Tennessee. The wood of the two species is similar, being light, soft, and weak. It is very durable in contact with the ground and makes excellent fence posts and poles. If well protected with tie plates it also serves for cross ties. The very rapid growth which is characteristic of the tree has led to its planting for such purposes.

WOOD PRODUCTS

47. Description of Wood Products. Research in wood products has led to the development of additional methods of utilizing wastes from woodworking industries, and has resulted in modified forms of wood that are less subject to shrinkage and swelling with changes in the moisture content, and in new forms of wood that have more nearly equal strength properties in all directions.

Plywood panels are made by gluing three or some other odd number of plies in such a manner that the grain directions of the various plies are balanced with respect to the core layer. Plywood does not warp or split as easily as solid wood. A resin-impregnated paper-faced plywood is made by molding one or more resin-impregnated sheets of paper to the surface of the plywood so that the facing becomes an integral part of the panel. The facing material prevents surface checking, masks the grain of the wood, and provides a good paintable surface. Other developments in plywood include facing panels with metal, and molding plywood in compound curvature.

Wood-fibered materials are available for thermal insulation and for the manufacture of fiber boards used in curtain and exterior wall panels. Homogeneous rigid boards are made by placing wood fibers in a water suspension, reducing the suspension to a wet mat in a paper machine, compressing the mat, and drying. Laminated rigid boards are made by gluing and pressing together several thin homogeneous boards or many sheets of paper.

Sandwich construction of wood products is used to obtain a combination of strength and light weight, and consists of three or more plies with relatively thin, strong faces separated by a lightweight core. The face materials may be aluminum, steel, plywood, or fiber-reinforced plastic. The core materials, which must be strong enough in shear to develop the strength of the faces, may be balsa, firm sponge rubber, plastic, or a honeycomb made of resin-impregnated paper or cloth.

Wood-base plastics make up another important group of wood products. Cellulose nitrate and acetate made from wood pulp are widely used. Several modified woods and paper-base laminates are also considered as plastics. *Impreg* is made of thin sheets of wood that have been treated with synthetic resins that combine chemically with the cell-wall structure. After impregnation the sheets are dried, heated to set the resin, and glued together. Impreg is quite resistant to swelling and shrinking. *Compreg* is made by heating wood plies that have been treated with a stabilizing resin and compressing them while hot under pressures ranging between 500 and 3000 psi. The dimensional stability and all the mechanical properties of compreg, except toughness, are usually superior to those of ordinary wood. *Staypak* is made by compressing untreated wood under optimum conditions of temperature and moisture content so that it becomes relatively stable under future moisture variations. *Acetylated wood* is obtained from a vapor-phase treatment of wood veneer with acetic anhydride and pyridine. The method is effective in stabilizing dimensions, increasing decay resistance, and increasing toughness. *Papreg* is a paper-base laminate made by molding resin-treated strong paper sheets with a high degree of fiber orientation under heat and pressure.

THE IDENTIFICATION OF WOODS *

48. The Microscopic Structure of Wood. Thus far we have considered the structure of wood which is readily discerned by the naked eye. With a microscope it has been ascertained that a few definite types of cells and fibers form the structures of all woods. Inasmuch as the recognition of these types of cells, as well as their arrangement and condition, forms an important aid not only in identifying species but also in accounting for mechanical properties, a brief account of them is made. There are four main types of these microscopic elements which, with numerous transitional forms, make up the structure of timber. These are (1) *tracheids*, (2) *parenchyma*, (3) *vessels*, (4) *wood fibers*. The two first-mentioned

* For a more complete discussion of the microscopic structure and the identification of woods, the reader is referred to Record's *Economic Woods* and Hough's *American Woods*.

constitute the wood of the conifers, but all four types are found in varying amounts in broad-leaved trees.

Tracheids are slim polygonal cells provided with tapering ends. They are small and of little importance in the hardwoods; but in the conifers where they form the main constituents of the wood they range from 0.05

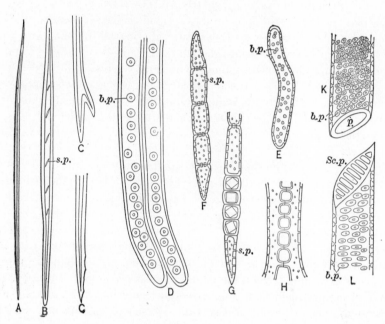

Fig. 13. Types of wood cells. *A*, Wood fiber with narrow lumen; *B*, wood fiber with wider lumen and simple pits (*s.p.*); *C*, wood fiber with saw-toothed end; *C′*, wood fiber with forked end; *D*, tracheids with bordered pits (*b.p.*) from pine; *E*, tracheid from oak; *F*, wood parenchyma fiber with individual cells and simple pits (*s.p.*); *G*, wood parenchyma with crystals of calcium oxalate from walnut; *H*, conjugate parenchyma cells; *K*, part of segment of a vessel with simple perforation (*p.*); *L*, part of segment of a vessel with scalariform perforation (*Sc.p.*). All much enlarged. (After Record.)

to 0.35 in. in length with a diameter of $\frac{1}{50}$ to $\frac{1}{100}$ of the length. The side walls of the tracheids are perforated with *bordered pits*, which are funnel-like depressions most thickly found near the ends of the cell (see Fig. 13). Through the thin walls at the bottoms of these pits the sap flows from one cell to another. In Douglas fir, spiral ridges are found on the inside of the tracheids; in longleaf and Norway pine the ray tracheids have irregular dentations on the inner surfaces.

Parenchyma are subordinate elements, which, like the tracheids, may be arranged end to end in a vertical line, thus forming the wood parenchyma fibers; or, grouped in bundles with their long axes extending radially, they compose the entire pith rays of the hardwoods and the main part of the rays in softwoods. Sometimes, as in white oak, chestnut, and hickory, the wood parenchyma fibers are arranged parallel to the vessels in the rings and appear as fine concentric lines on the cross section. In some woods they form the boundaries of the rings; in some they are scattered through the wood irregularly; in others they are arranged in radial planes; and in still others they surround the larger vessels. Parenchyma are minute, thin-walled elements tapering at the ends and subdivided by transverse walls into short, prismatic cells. The side walls of parenchyma are dotted with minute cylindrical depressions called *simple pits*, as in Fig. 13F. By pressure of large bordering vessels the parenchyma running vertically are sometimes flattened into the conjugate form shown in Fig. 13H. In oak, hickory, and walnut the individual cells of the vertical parenchyma are often separated by crystals of calcium oxalate, see Fig. 13G.

Vessels are small pipe-like elements of indefinite length, the walls of which are covered with bordered pits (Fig. 13K). The diameter of vessels is quite variable, sometimes reaching 0.02 in oak, but more often it is less than 0.01 in. While growing, constrictions are produced in the side walls, thus indicating the segments of growth. These segments may fit together (1) in a perfect transverse plane, (2) in an oblique plane, or (3) as in oak and gum, the faces of the segments may be oblique and have blind ends extending beyond the main line of constriction. In type 1 the opening from one segment to another is round, but in 2 and 3 the perforations may be scalariform as in Fig. 13L. Vessels in the sapwood serve as vertical water supply lines for the growing portion of the tree, but in the heartwood they are frequently clogged with sac-like protrusions from adjacent parenchyma cells. These protrusions are called *tyloses*.

Wood fibers are thin elongated cells tapering to a point at either end. They have thick walls which are ordinarily indented by inclined slit-like simple pits; see Fig. 13B. In mahogany the fibers are divided by cross partitions (septate fibers); in other woods the fibers are often forked at the ends (Fig. 13C′), a condition which decreases the cleavability of the wood. Wood fibers vary from $\frac{1}{50}$ to $\frac{1}{10}$ in. in length. They are found most commonly in the central portion of the annual rings of the hardwoods and are an important source of strength, toughness, and hardness.

As mentioned before, these various types of fibers grade into each other by transitional stages. Thus the wood fibers exhibit forms approaching the tracheids in some woods and approximating wood parenchyma in others, and the tracheids sometimes grade into the vessels.

49. The Structure of Coniferous Woods. In Fig. 14 are shown (1) a sector of spruce in natural size and (2) a part of one ring from the same magnified 100 times but oriented to correspond with piece 1. Looking at the upper face of piece 2 we are at once impressed by the regular arrangement of the tracheids in radial rows. From left to right they become flattened radially, showing the increase in density in passing from the spring wood to the summer wood. On the lower front portion of this piece we notice also the bordered pits, of which enlarged types are shown at $a, b,$ and $c.$

The dark lines in piece 1 represent the medullary rays of which five are exposed on the right face of piece 2. One of these rays is seen in section

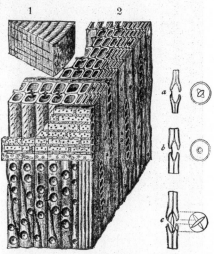

Fig. 14. Spruce wood. 1, Natural size; 2, small part of one ring magnified 100 times. The vertical tubes are wood fibers, in this case all "tracheids"; $a, b,$ and $c,$ bordered pits of the tracheids, enlarged more. Horizontal tubes are medullary or pith rays.

on the front face of piece 2. It will be noted that the cells in the rays are elongated radially and that each ray is 1 cell wide (uniseriate) and several cells deep. In this wood, the top and bottom cells of each ray are tracheids, but the intermediate cells are parenchyma.

The above example is typical of the regularity of arrangement of the cell structure in coniferous wood. In pine, spruce, Douglas fir, and tamarack vertical and radial resin ducts are found, which are interconnected here and there to permit the passage of resin. These ducts are often large enough to be distinguished by the naked eye. They are long canals bounded by groups of thin-walled cells, termed epithelial cells. Figure 15 shows a cross section of shortleaf pine which passes through a vertical resin duct. Radial resin ducts are commonly enclosed in multiseriate rays. Such ducts may often be formed by injury; chipping the outer sapwood of longleaf pine opens the resin ducts and affords a method of securing turpentine and allied products.

Tyloses are sometimes found in tracheids adjoining parenchymatous cells, but in conifers they are more often noticed in the resin ducts. Norway pine, western pine, white pine, and sugar pine are the main coniferous woods which have abundant tyloses (see Art. V-8).

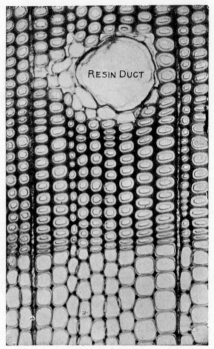

RESIN DUCT

Fig. 15.   Cross section of shortleaf pine, showing resin duct surrounded by epithelial cells.   (*Bull.* 101, U. S. Dept. Agr., Pl. 1.   Magnification = 125 diameters.)

50. The Structure of Wood from Broad-Leaved Trees. As we have previously mentioned, the arrangement of the cell elements in the wood of the broad-leaved trees is far more varied and complex than in the conifers. We shall consider two examples: red oak to illustrate ring-porous woods; and sugar maple to illustrate diffuse-porous woods.

The magnified cross-sectional view of red oak in Fig. 16 shows very clearly the irregular grouping of the large vessels in the spring wood, with a more or less gradual transition to smaller ones scattered here and there through the summer wood. In good oak these vessels occupy less than 10 per cent of the volume of the wood, but in poorer varieties they may amount to 25 per cent. In the middle of the annual ring the dark, solid-looking patches represent the cut ends of the wood fibers. The thicker the walls of these fibers and the greater the proportion of them in the wood, the stronger and tougher will it be. In good timber the fibers

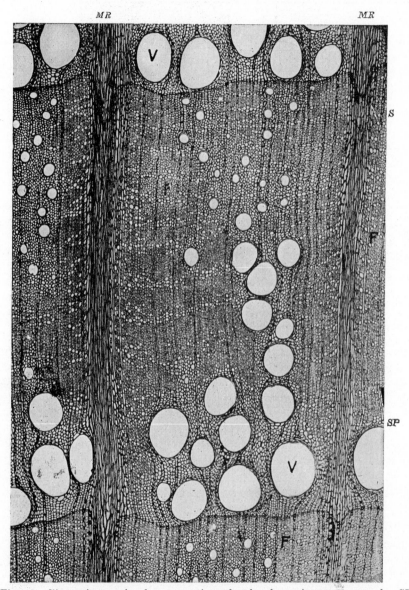

Fig. 16. Photomicrograph of cross section of red oak, a ring-porous wood. *SP*, Spring wood (note open pores); *S*, summer wood; *F*, fibers; *V*, vessels or pores; *MR*, medullary ray. (Prepared by the Forest Products Laboratory, Forest Service, U. S. Dept. Agr. ×40.)

constitute one-half the volume. Two medullary rays are also exposed in this view. The width of the band of cells composing these rays is a decided contrast to the uniseriate rays of the conifers. In the oaks, rays are often a hundred cells in width and an inch or more in height. It will be observed, however, that they always taper in width, at the top and bottom, to a single cell. Figure 17 brings out the comparative size of the medullary rays and the ring thickness in oak. All the cells in the rays of the dicotyledons are parenchyma. Some of the individual parenchyma can be distinguished in Fig. 16. Beside the medullary rays of large size other uniseriate pith rays of parenchymatous cells may also be seen in Fig. 16. The total proportion of rays in good white oak generally lies between 15 and 25 per cent.

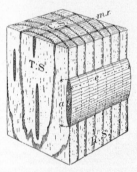

Fig. 17. Block of oak. *C.S.*, Cross section; *R.S.*, radial section; *T.S.*, tangential section; *m.r.*, medullary or pith ray; *a*, height, *b*, width, and *e*, length, of a pith ray.

The arrangement of pores in a ring-porous wood like the sugar maple is more uniform, the diameters are smaller, and the variation in size is less than in the oak (Fig. 18). Scarcely any difference is to be noted in the size of the vessels in the spring wood and summer wood, but there is a tendency toward radial grouping of 2 to 4 cells which is plainly marked. The medullary rays are much narrower than in the oak but broader than in the conifers. When the wood is quarter sawed these rays produce a silvery appearance. There are, however, numerous intermediate pith rays of 1-cell width in evidence. A further distinguishing feature of this wood is the distinct markings which limit the growth rings.

Tyloses are abundantly found in the vessels of the following hardwoods: in white, Garry, overcup, bur, swamp, cow, valley and post oaks, in most hickories, in chestnut, black locust, and osage orange. Tyloses apparently increase the resistance of the wood to the decay and also decreases the penetrance to preservatives.[*]

51. The Use of a Key in Distinguishing Woods.[†] Nobody need expect to be able to use successfully any key for the distinction of woods or of any other class of natural objects without some practice. This is especially true with regard to woods, which are apt to vary much, and when the key is based on such meager general data as the present. The best course to adopt is to supply oneself with a small sample collection of woods accurately named. Small, polished tablets are of little use for this purpose.

[*] From researches of Miss E. Gerry. See *J. Agr. Research*, Vol. 1, p. 464.

[†] For further study and additional references see *Wood Handbook* prepared by the Forest Products Laboratory; *Wood as an Engineering Material* by L. J. Mark-Wardt, *Proc. ASTM*, Vol. 43; *The Properties and Uses of Wood* by A. Koehler.

The pieces should be large enough, if possible, to include pith and bark, and of sufficient width to permit ready inspection of the cross section. By examining these with the aid of the key, beginning with the better-known

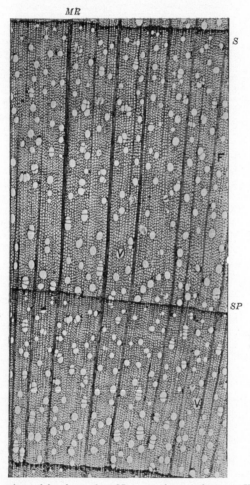

Fig. 18. Cross section of hard maple. Note tendency of pores, V, to form radial groups. Spring wood, SP, is much like the summer wood, S. Narrow medullary ray, MR. Fibers, F. Magnification = 34 diameters. (Photo prepared by Forest Products Laboratory, Forest Service, U. S. Dept. Agr.)

woods, one will soon learn to see the features described and to form an idea of the relative standards which the maker of the key had in mind.

An examination of a piece of wood for the purpose of identification should provide information on color of heartwood and sapwood, odor, hardness, specific weight, grain structure, pore structure, and character-istics of pith rays and resin ducts. The ASTM Timber Identification Kit is helpful for this purpose.

The Deterioration and Preservation of Timber *

DETERIORATION

1. The Durability of Wood. The durability of wood is a decidedly variable property. If well-seasoned and kept in a dry place, if immersed in water, or if buried in the ground, wood often lasts for centuries.

Fig. 1. Decay at joint and in strut supporting a bleachers. (Teesdale in *Am. Lumberman,* Oct. 3, 1914.)

Examples of sound wood piling which have been buried over a thousand years, wooden buildings which have stood for centuries, and many wooden relics can be cited as proof of this statement. When, however, unprotected wood is subjected to moisture, air, and moderate warmth, it decays.

* *Preservation of Structural Timber,* by H. F. Weiss, *Bull.* 78, 118, 107, and 126 of the U. S. Forest Service, were the principal sources for the compilation of this chapter.

The rapidity with which it decays depends on external conditions, the species of the wood, its preliminary conditioning, and its structure. Thus in mines the life of timber sets of untreated red oak and pine is not over 2 or 3 years, in ties or fence posts it may reach 4 to 6 years, and unprotected pine bleachers may last 10 years. In exposed structures decay nearly always starts at the sills and bottoms of posts and columns. Joints like those shown in Fig. 1 afford receptacles for the collection of water and snow with the result shown. On the other hand untreated fence posts of osage orange, black locust, and red cedar often last a quarter century or more; * the life of cedar poles may be estimated at 14 years, but those of loblolly pine are likely to decay in one-third of that time. In general, sapwood decays much more rapidly than heartwood; hence specifications call for a large proportion of heartwood in timbers to be exposed to the weather. Table 1 shows the relative resistance of the heartwood of common native timbers.

TABLE 1. DURABILITY OF HEARTWOOD OF TIMBERS UNDER
CONDITIONS FAVORING DECAY

High Durability	Medium Durability	Low Durability	Non-Durable
Cedar, red or white	Douglas fir	Beech	Aspen
Chestnut	Pine, southern yellow	Birch	Basswood
Cypress	Gum, red	Hemlock	Cottonwood
Locust, black	Larch, western	Maple	Fir, white
Oak, white	Pine, white	Oak, red	
Osage Orange	Tamarack	Pine, Norway	
Redwood		Spruce	

Besides being subject to decay, wood may be injured by the attack of insects, marine borers, and woodpeckers. It deteriorates under mechanical abrasion and may, of course, be entirely destroyed by fire.

2. Composition of Wood. Wood is essentially an organic substance, made up of a skeleton of cellulose impregnated with lignin. Cellulose is a whitish substance, like starch ($C_6H_{10}O_5$) in composition, but more highly resistant to alcoholic fermentation. Lignin is also composed of carbohydrate compounds, but it is more soluble in acid than cellulose. Chemically, dry wood contains 49 per cent carbon, 44 per cent oxygen, 6 per cent hydrogen, and 1 per cent ash.

3. Causes of Decay. The organic substances in wood are susceptible of attack both by bacteria and by fungi. The method by which bacteria decompose wood is probably similar in nature to a fungus attack. Fungi reproduce through thousands of minute particles, called "spores," which are blown about by the wind. The spores send out mycelia, which in turn

* See *Bull*. 219, Ohio Agr. Expt. Sta.

destroy the wood tissue by the action of solvent chemicals, enzymes, which the mycelia secrete.

Only a small proportion of fungi destroy wood. Of this number some attack the lignin, others the cellulose, and still others consume both these substances. The attack may proceed without any external evidence of the injury which the mycelia are inflicting within the wood, or it may be proclaimed by the appearance of mushroom growths, termed "fruiting bodies," on the surfaces of the timbers. In either case, after a considerable proportion of the cell walls has been destroyed by the mycelia, the wood becomes brittle and weak. Decaying timber is further characterized by a lack of resonance when struck with a hammer, by an abnormal capacity for absorbing water, and very often by an unnatural odor and color.

For life and propagation, fungi require air, moisture, warmth, and food supply. Not all fungi, however, thrive equally well under the same conditions. For example, the house fungus (*Merulius lachrymans*), Fig. 2, can live in air-seasoned timber surrounded by atmosphere with less than 70 per cent relative humidity, thrives at normal room temperatures, but is killed in an hour by a temperature of 115°F.* This fungus has

Fig. 2. Strands of the house fungus found on pine planks at the base of a lumber pile. (Photo by C. J. Humphrey.)

been known to lie dormant for several years in a seasoned stick of timber. All that is required to revive it is an increase in the humidity of its habitat. Frequently the house fungus furnishes no surface indication of its presence. In such cases boring into beams or planks which are thought to be contaminated may reveal the extent of the rotting. Rotted timber forms brownish chips. If the fungus is alive its presence may be detected by cutting small cubes from the edges of the brown wood region. These should be soaked in a 2 per cent citric acid solution for about 6 hours; they should then be removed and stored in a closed jar at 75°F for a couple of weeks. If filaments appear the fungus is alive. The insidious-

---

* This discussion of the house fungus and the dry rot is abstracted from a valuable article entitled "Dry Rot in Factory Timbers," by F. J. Hoxie, of the Inspection Dept. of the Associated Factory Mutual Fire Insurance Co., Boston.

ness of the attack of the house fungus makes it most dangerous, especially in buildings of mill-construction types. On account of the virility of the fungus under somewhat dry conditions, the name "dry rot" has been given to this form of decay.

Fig. 3. *Fomes roseus* on the end of a tie. (Photo by C. J. Humphrey.)

In contrast to the house fungus with its dry habitat and abnormal sensitiveness to heat, the following fungi which are characterized by many pores in their fruiting bodies may be mentioned: *Fomes roseus, Trametes serialis,* and *Lenzites sepiaria.* The *Fomes roseus,* Fig. 3, has a hard pink fruiting body covered with small round pores; it lives in a saturated

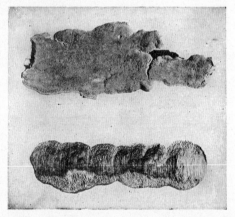

Fig. 4. *Trametes serialis.* Upper specimen from under side of a floor, lower specimen from side of a girder. (Photo by C. J. Humphrey. Reduced about one-half.)

atmosphere and works much mischief to wood exposed in damp basements. The fruiting body of the *Trametes serialis,* Fig. 4, is tough; the surface is white and covered with small pores. It also works in a very moist atmosphere. The *Lenzites sepiaria* has a semi-circular plate-like fruiting body which has side attachment to the wood. The underside of its fruiting body is covered with gill-like pores. It is very active in destroying warehouse platforms and railroad ties. This fungus lives even when the temperature approaches the boiling point of water.

Certain fungi attack with avidity the products stored in the cell walls of the sapwood. This attack is most common in woods which are air seasoned in a warm humid atmosphere. Despite the fact that no great damage to mechanical properties * appears to attend such action, at least in the early stages, yet the discoloration, which goes by the name of sap stain, is objectionable since it decreases the value of the timber.

4. Insects. Although decay is the principal cause of deterioration of timber, an immense amount of damage is done annually by the attacks of insects. Timber with the bark on is especially liable to injury from them, and the attack once started in the green log may continue after the wood has been seasoned. Insects are particularly active in mine timbers, posts, poles, hickory hoops and poles, wagon stock, and pulpwood. Two common insects described by Weiss † are the powder-post insect and the pole-borer. The larva of both these insects evolve from small beetles. The powder-post variety comes from a small brown or black bug which, when out of doors, deposits its eggs early in the spring on the surface of the wood. The eggs hatch into small white grubs. The grub bores into the wood and transforms it into a fine powder while selecting its food. After a period of growth the grub forms a cavity in the wood and lies dormant while its legs and wings are being developed. Since this beetle multiplies very rapidly, the deterioration of the infested timber proceeds quickly.

The pole-borer comes from a reddish-brown beetle about $\frac{2}{5}$ to $\frac{4}{5}$ in. long, which deposits its eggs near the ground line of posts and holes during the late summer and early fall. On hatching, the creamy white grub bores into the wood. It transforms the wood tissue into a reddish-brown or yellow dust which is packed into the burrow behind the worm. Like the powder-post insect, the pole-borer lies dormant in a cell in the wood until it metamorphoses into a beetle. During the late summer the beetle emerges from the pole through a large hole near the ground line. The pole-borer attacks both sound and decayed timber but is not active in the latter if it is water soaked. It has been found in poles within 2 years after setting in the ground.

Termites, insects resembling white ants, have done a large amount of damage to wooden structures in the Southern states and to a lesser extent in other portions of the country. The subterranean and dry-wood termites are the two classes operating in the United States. Both classes live very secretively in highly organized colonies and feed upon the cellulose in the wood without giving early external evidence of the damage being done.

* See tests in *Circ.* 192, U. S. Forest Service.
† See *The Preservation of Structural Timber,* Chapter II.

The subterranean variety inhabits dark, damp tunnels of properly regulated temperature well below the surface of the ground, and extends runways to the wood for food. The dry-wood termites do not require the humid earth habitat and, though less numerous, do much damage in the extreme south. Often the first warning of the presence of termites comes when a swarm of flying alates, young termites with wings, issues from an infested timber. These alates quickly lose their wings and die in large numbers, but the few survivors suffice to propagate new colonies.

Ravages of termites can be prevented by building tight concrete foundations, by keeping untreated timber out of contact with the ground, and by providing metal shields for all sills, foundation timbers, and conduits. Where termites have caused damage, badly infested members should be replaced by creosoted timbers. Timbers slightly damaged can be saved by treating with finely powdered Paris green or sodium fluosilicate.

5. Marine Borers. There are two classes of marine borers infesting the waters of both Atlantic and Pacific coasts: the mollusk and the crustacean types. Of the first class the *Teredo* and *Xylotrya*, which are very similar in appearance and mode of living, are the most important. Owing to their shape they are frequently called "shipworms." Either mollusk tunnels into the wood by means of a pair of shell valves and excretes the borings and a calcareous substance for lining the burrow through a posterior syphon. The food supply of the mollusk, which consists of low forms of animal life found in the water, is secured through a second posterior syphon. The *Teredo* rarely exceeds a length of 15 in. or a diameter of ⅜ in., but specimens of *Xylotrya* 6 ft long by 1 in. in diameter have been reported. Shipworms infest warm salt water or brackish waters and are said to prefer calcareous shores. They attack piling between mean tide and the low-water level; and at the Isthmus of Panama and along the coast of Florida have been known to ruin untreated timber in less than 1 year.

The *Limnoria* or wood louse is the crustacean which is most dangerous to timber. It grows to the size of a grain of rice and bores into the wood by means of sharp jaws. It lives on food from the wood substance which it penetrates radially to a depth of about ½ in. per year. It is active only in clear salt water and confines its attack to a narrow belt around the piling near the low-water mark. The *Limnoria* is particularly active in the Gulf of Mexico and along the north Pacific coast.

No native timber except the palmetto appears to be highly resistant to the attack of marine borers. The greenheart of South America and the jarrah of Australia are also said to be highly resistant to such attack. Pine and fir are the timbers largely used for piling in this country, but they must be protected to withstand the ravages of these pests. Creosoting by the boiling or Bethell processes, and encasing the piling in concrete jackets are the methods of protection ordinarily used. Impregnation with creosote even when well done is not always proof against shipworms, and concrete casings are expensive and likely to be cracked. Borers in an attacked pile may be killed by chlorine gas, which is generated as follows: The pile is enclosed with a canvas curtain and an electric current passed through the pile and the enclosed salt water. The treatment is expensive and requires frequent repetitions in waters which are heavily infested with borers.

6. Other Deteriorating Influences. Wood crossties, mine props, and wharf timbers suffer considerably from mechanical wear. It is estimated that a tenth of the annual tie loss could be saved by the use of suitable tie plates and improved spikes. It is not always possible or economical to protect timbers from mechanical wear, but in some cases iron plates may be effectively employed as shields.

Fire decomposes wood into carbon dioxide, water vapor, and ash. Wet wood is about twice as resistant to fire as dry wood. Structural timbers which are well seasoned will ignite with difficulty at temperatures in the vicinity of 400°F, and very quickly at temperatures around 600°F. Wood attacked by dry rot is more combustible than sound timber. Experiments by the National Fire Protection Association * show that the resistance of wood to fire can be much increased by saturating it with weak solutions (5 to 10 per cent) of ammonium sulfate or ammonium phosphate. Impregnation of the chemicals was accomplished by heating the solutions to 150°F and maintaining a pressure of 130 psi on the specimens for 2 hours while they were soaking. For wood exposed to moisture a treatment with zinc borate is effective. In this treatment the wood is first impregnated with a 10 per cent borax solution; it is then dried and again soaked in a 3 per cent zinc chloride solution. The two compounds react, forming the insoluble borate which remains in the wood. Pressure-impregnated fire-retardant lumber costs roughly twice as much as untreated lumber. Fire-retarding coatings such as sodium silicate solutions, water solutions of fire-retarding chemicals, linseed-oil-base paints with a material part of the pigment replaced with ground borax, and alginate paints which consist of aqueous gels of sodium or diammonium alginate and fire-retardant chemicals are also used.

Woodpeckers do considerable injury to poles by boring into them and building their nests. Where the holes are well above the ground line, they cause little direct loss in strength or stiffness, but they afford excellent breeding grounds for fungi and thus may foster decay.

* Report of Common Uses of Wood, *Proceedings,* 1915.

PRESERVATION

7. The Need of Preservation. Statistics compiled by the Forest Service * show that the average life in years of untreated structural timbers in the United States is approximately as follows: Mine props, 3; piles, 3½; ties, 7; posts, 8; lumber subject to decay, 8; poles, 13; and shingles, 18. Although statistics are not given, it is probable that between 17 and 20 billion board feet of structural timber are used annually for replacements. Weiss estimated that the amount of timber cut for such purposes could be decreased annually by nearly 7 billion board feet, if proper preservative methods were practiced. From a consideration of the low durability of wood and the great cost of the quantity required for replacements, the need of practicing comparatively inexpensive methods of preservation becomes evident. Furthermore, the proper use of efficient protectives would lead to the planting of more rapidly growing trees, the more effective utilization of inferior trees and top logs, the clearing of land occupied by fire-killed timber (since the latter can be effectively used if treated); in short, preservation would lead to better forest management in general.

In 1947 about 95 per cent of the crossties, a like proportion of the poles, and a fair proportion of the piling, building, and bridge timbers annually used in the United States were given a preservative treatment. The entire amount of timber treated in this country in a year is approximately 350,000,000 cu ft. To treat this amount of wood, about 200,000,000 gal of creosote, 60,000,000 gal of petroleum, about 4,000,000 lb of plain and chromated zinc chloride, and about 8,000,000 lb of other salts including pentachlorophenol and Walman salts are consumed.

8. The Relations of Structure to the Penetrance of Preservatives. Structure plays a very important role in determining the ease with which preservatives may be forced into wood and also in fixing the quantity injected. In most woods the sapwood is more easily impregnated and absorbs more preservative than the heartwood. However, in hemlock, alpine fir, and white spruce the sapwood is scarcely less resistant to penetration than the heartwood. Bark is nearly impenetrable and should always be completely removed from timber which is to be treated. The comparative resistance of the heartwood and sapwood should be considered in forming timbers which are to be treated. In the diffuse-porous woods and in those conifers which show little demarcation between spring and summer wood, the absorption of preservative is more uniform than in the ring-porous hardwoods or the hard pines. In the ring-porous woods most of the preservative will run into the spring wood, whereas in longleaf

* See *Bull.* 78.

pine the greater part will be found in the dense summer wood. Owing to the difference in the absorption of preservative by the spring and summer wood of the hard pines, a minimum limit on the number of rings per inch is often placed in specifications. The purpose of this restriction on rate of growth is to prevent wide variations in the distribution of the preservative.

Within a given species it is likely that the absorption of preservative varies inversely as the density of the wood, but no such relation exists between timbers of different species. Thus, red oak and hard pine, which are comparatively heavy woods, absorb much more preservative than the light white spruce.

Since nearly all the preservative is held in the cell cavities and only a small proportion permeates the cell walls, it follows that any condition which causes a plugging of these cells will interfere with the injection of preservatives. Such conditions are effected in many woods by tyloses (Art. IV-48, 49, and 50). If such woods are treated, the preservative is likely to be very non-uniformly distributed.

In coniferous wood the resin ducts, if unclogged by resin or growths, serve as canals for the rapid passage of preservatives. It is probable that the great absorption of the dense summer wood of the hard pines is due to the fact that it contains these ducts. Nearly all the pines also possess radial resin ducts which materially assist in the radial penetration of preservatives. Radial ducts are lacking in the larches, hemlocks, firs, and spruces; and it is much more difficult to secure a deep radial penetration in them than in the pines.

In some woods it is probable that the radial transmission of preservatives is affected through pit membranes in the cell walls. Tiemann and Weiss claim that slits which are opened in the cell walls during seasoning are another possible avenue of transmission.

Besides these physical characteristics of the wood structure, the chemical composition of the cell walls probably has an important influence on the absorption of preservatives.

Among the woods which are most readily injected with preservatives are longleaf pine, shortleaf pine, western yellow pine, lodgepole pine, loblolly pine, red birch, white elm, red elm, soft maple, beech and red oak. White oak, alpine fir, Douglas fir, tamarack, and white spruce are treated with difficulty. In this connection it should be recognized that the form of the timber often plays an important part in determining the penetration of preservative. For example, a Douglas fir pole can be easily impregnated with preservative because of its sapwood envelope. On the other hand, a large-dimension timber of this species having considerable exposed heartwood would be treated with much difficulty on account of the resistance of the heartwood to penetration.

9. The Treatment of Timber before Preservation.   Timber is best cut
in the fall or winter to avoid fungus or insect attack and to prevent checking produced by too rapid drying.   Bark should be promptly removed
from logs to prevent insect and fungus attack.   Such procedure also
renders the timber more permeable to preservatives.   Too-rapid seasoning
after bark removal should be avoided, since it causes case hardening and
thus increases resistance to penetration of preservatives.

Penetration of preservatives into woods lacking open radial ducts, like
fir, larch, maple, and birch, is materially improved by incising timbers by
toothed rolls to a depth of a half to three-fourths of an inch.   The use of
this treatment is growing rapidly.

It is desirable that all timber which is to be treated be thoroughly
seasoned in order that the penetration of preservatives may be facilitated.
With the exception of air seasoning, exposure to saturated steam is the
most-used conditioning process for timber which is to be preserved.   Under
this process the timber is placed in a large treating cylinder and subjected
to live steam at a pressure of 20 to 40 psi for 2 to 10 hours, the time
depending on the size and character of the timber.   A vacuum of about
25 in. is then applied for 30 minutes to 2 hours, after which the timber
is treated with preservative.   This process is a preliminary stage in
several of the common methods of treatment.   With a few creosoting
processes, seasoning is accomplished by running the timber into a cylinder
and soaking it in creosote.   The oil is gradually heated until the temperature is raised above the boiling point of water.   This causes the water to
vaporize.   The vapor is drawn off and condensed to free it of oil.   After
the moisture in wood has been sufficiently reduced, the cylinder is filled
full of preservative and pressure is applied until impregnation is completed.

SUPERFICIAL TREATMENTS

10. Conditions for Use of Superficial Treatments.   There are three inexpensive methods of treating the surface of timber to protect it against
decay and insects.   These methods are of value when the amount of timber
to be treated is too small to warrant the erection of a treating plant;
when it is impracticable to haul the timber to the work from a plant; or
when it is necessary to do the work at a minimum cost.   Since the value
of these treatments is based upon the maintenance of an unbroken film
which will resist the attack of fungi, it is very necessary that the timber
shall be thorouglhy air seasoned before treating.   If the timber is only
partially seasoned or green when treated, it is likely to check subsequently
and thus produce passageways for insects and mycelia.

11. Brush Treatments.   Probably the most-used superficial treatments
are those in which a liquid is applied to the surface of the timber by means

of a brush. Creosote, paint, oil, and whitewash are among the liquids used for the purpose. Creosote should be heated to about 200°F before being applied to the wood, since heating considerably decreases the viscosity of the oil and thereby aids in securing penetration of the preservative. Great pains should be taken to thoroughly coat all defects and fill checks, shakes, and joints. This method of treatment has been used considerably for the preservation of mine timbers, poles, and posts. It is well adapted to use on farms.

12. Dipping. By dipping the timber into the preservative and allowing it to soak for a few minutes, it is possible to secure a more complete coating of the defects than is had by brush treatments. The process requires the use of a large tank for holding the timber and necessitates a somewhat greater use of preservative, but the labor cost is less than in the brush process. It can be very effectively used for butt treatments on fence posts and poles. When used for this purpose the preservative should cover the pole for at least a foot above the ground line.

13. Charring. A very old and inexpensive method for protecting wood consists in charring the outer fibers of the timbers by fire. This process produces an envelope of charcoal which, being devoid of food elements, is not attacked by fungi. If the strength of the pieces treated is of great importance this process is detrimental, because it destroys the outer fibers and injures those immediately beneath. It has been used for treating the butts of posts and poles, but is not very efficacious.

NON-PRESSURE PROCESSES OF IMPREGNATION

14. The Value of Non-Pressure Processes. In the non-pressure processes the preservative is drawn into the wood by absorption or it is forced in by atmospheric pressure. By these processes it is not possible to secure as uniform and deep penetrations as with the pressure methods, but with woods like loblolly pine, shortleaf pine, red cedar, and beech, they can be successfully used. These processes require a longer time for treatment than the pressure processes. On the other hand, since they use no heavy treating cylinder with its expensive equipment, they afford cheap and effective means of preserving small quantities of poles, mine timbers, and ties, provided the wood is easily impregnated. The method is also of value when salts which would attack iron-treating cylinders are used.

15. Open-Tank Process. In this treatment the timber is placed in a tank and covered with the preservative. The charge is then heated to a temperature just above the boiling point of water. This serves to expel a considerable proportion of air and moisture from the cells in the wood. After soaking at this temperature for an hour or two the timber may be allowed to cool with the liquid, or it may be transferred to a cold tank where it is kept for another hour or more depending on how deep a penetration is wanted. As the wood cools a vacuum is formed in the outer cells and the preservative is injected by atmospheric pressure. Sometimes, when a deep penetration is desired with a minimum expenditure of preservative, the timber is drawn from the cooling tank before it has entirely cooled. As the interior of the stick gradually cools vacuums are formed which are filled by the excess fluid held in the outer cells.

The process may be used with creosote, zinc chloride, or crude oil. However, if the wood is boiled in the zinc chloride solution, its strength is likely to be impaired.

16. Kyanizing. In this process the timber, which must be thoroughly seasoned, is immersed in a 1 per cent solution of bichloride of mercury for a number of days. The time of treatment depends upon the thickness of the pieces and the depth of penetration desired. Ordinarily the time in days is equal to the thickness of the timber in inches plus 1, and the depth of penetration does not exceed ¼ in. Owing to the poisonous character of the salt great care must be exercised during the treatment of the timber; and the treated lumber should not be used where it is likely to be licked by animals.

As a means of preserving timber used in dry locations, this process ranks high; but, on account of the poisonous nature of the salt, the long time required for the process, and the solubility of the salt in water, it has not been widely used in the United States.

Pressure Processes of Impregnation

17. Field of Use. In general the pressure processes are the most satisfactory methods of treating large amounts of timber. Furthermore, these methods are the only ones which can be successfully used to impregnate many kinds of wood, such as hemlock, Douglas fir, and redwood.

18. Bethell or Full-Cell Process. The timber for treatment is placed on small cars and carried into horizontal steel cylinders which are ordinarily about 130 ft long by 7 ft in diameter. A vacuum is drawn to remove air from the cylinder and from the wood. Coal-tar creosote oil, heated to proper temperature, is then admitted to the cylinder and forced into the timber by a pressure of 100 to 180 psi. The pressure is maintained until the oil gages show the required impregnation. Then the oil is blown out of the cylinder into reservoirs, and the timber, after dripping for a few moments, is removed. In some plants dripping is accelerated by drawing a vacuum just before removing the timber. The process is much used both in the United States and abroad. It is especially valuable for wood block and piling where a heavy impregnation of oil is imperative. On account of the large expenditure of oil, 10 to 20 lb per cu ft, the process is very costly. The cost of treating crossties by it ordinarily runs between $1.25 and $2.00 each.

19. Burnettizing. This process is performed in the same manner as the Bethell process, but differs in the preservative. An aqueous solution containing from 2 to 5 per cent of zinc chloride is used and about ½ lb of salt per cu ft is the average impregnation in the process. Because of the solubility of zinc chloride in water, the process is not suited to treating timbers which are to be placed in damp locations. It is a very inexpensive process costing about one-third as much as the full-cell treatment. Burnettizing has been successfully used to treat ties and lumber both in the United States and in Europe.

20. The Boiling Process. In this process either green or seasoned timber is given a conditioning treatment in creosote oil (see Art. V-9) before impregnation with creosote. After the oil conditioning the remainder of the process is much like the Bethell method. The boiling method is used principally in preserving Douglas fir. Tests indicate that it may injure the strength of this wood (Art. VI-18).

21. The Rueping Process. One of the most important processes both here and abroad is the Rueping empty-cell process with creosote. Air-seasoned timber is preferred, although steam-treated material can be used. After the timber is placed in the treating cylinder, the cells of the wood are filled with compressed air which is admitted under a pressure of about 75 psi. Oil is then admitted at a slightly higher pressure until the wood has been immersed, when the pressure is raised to 150 psi or more. After the proper amount of oil has been injected, the creosote is forced out of the cylinder and the pressure released. As the pressure is withdrawn the compressed air within the wood expels the excess oil into the cylinder. It is thus possible to secure a deep penetration and to coat the cell walls with 5 to 7 lb of oil per cu ft of wood. Treatments by this process cost about two-thirds as much as the full-cell methods.

22. The Lowry Process. This process, like the Rueping, is planned to secure a deep penetration of oil with a small absorption. Air-dry timber is run into the cylinder and submerged in creosote oil at a temperature of about 200°F. Pressure is then applied, and the temperature and pressure are regulated until the timber has been filled with oil. After withdrawal of the oil a vacuum is drawn until the surplus oil in the wood cells has been removed. When the excess oil has been removed from the cylinder, the timber is taken out. The process is somewhat more expensive than the Rueping process but less costly than the full-cell. It is considerably used in the United States for treating crossties.

23. Preservatives. Inasmuch as fungi cannot thrive without moisture, waterproofing of seasoned wood will render it resistant to attack. Crude oil, paint, and stains are the common preservatives of this class. A far surer treatment is effected, however, by preservatives which poison the food supply of fungi and insects. The creosote oils, petroleum oils with chlorinated phenols, and the inorganic salts—chromated zinc chloride, mercuric chloride, copper sulfate, and Wolman salts—are members of the latter class.

The term crude oil includes three classes: (1) oil with a paraffin base, (2) oil with an asphaltic base, and (3) the product which is left after the lighter oils are distilled from crude oil, called residuum. All these oils are lighter than water but penetrate coniferous wood less readily than creosote. For successful treatment with them, the timber must be fully impregnated, thus rendering it heavy and likely to drip. The cost of sufficient oil to treat a cubic foot of timber runs from 5 to 10 cents. Crude oil is used but little in the United States.

Most of the paints used to protect wood consist of linseed oil, turpentine, and some inorganic coloring material. Although fungi will not attack a painted surface, most paint cannot be classed as an effective preservative when the wood is in contact with the soil, since it is somewhat porous and permits the passage of moisture. Stains having a creosote base with a vegetable- or mineral-oil body are poisonous to fungi. They also penetrate further into the wood than the paints, but are more volatile.

Creosote oils of three varieties are used in wood preservation: coaltar creosote, water-gas-tar creosote, and wood-tar creosote. They are all tar distillates and are very poisonous to fungi and insects. However, the volatile nature of the lighter fractions of these oils, their pungent odor, and the fact that they increase the flammability of wood render them unsatisfactory for some purposes. Creosote is also an expensive preservative; the cost ranges from 10 to 40 cents per cubic foot of treated wood, depending on the price of oil and the process used. Nevertheless, in spite of these objectionable features approximately 80 per cent of the timber annually treated in the United States is impregnated with coal-tar creosote.

Coal-tar creosote is a complex oil resulting from a double distillation of coal. In the first distillation the products are coke, gas, and tar. If the tar is again distilled three classes of compounds are formed—pitch, oils lighter than water, and oils heavier than water. The last are the creosotes. They consist principally of phenols, naphthalene, and anthracene. Tests made at the Forest Products Laboratory show that from 0.2 to 0.4

per cent of this oil in a culture medium is sufficient to kill fungi. For methods of sampling and analyzing creosote oil, see current ASTM *Standards*.

Water-gas tar is a by-product from the manufacture of water gas. By passing steam through red-hot coke or coal it is decomposed, and hydrogen, carbon monoxide, carbon dioxide, and methane are formed. These gases are then passed through a heated carburetor into which a spray of crude petroleum is simultaneously admitted. Gas and tar are thus evolved. By distillation the tar is separated into three components: oils lighter than water, pitch, and the creosote oils which are heavier than water. Very little water-gas-tar creosote is used as such for preservative purposes, but it is sometimes used as an adulterant of coal-tar creosote. It is probably no more volatile than the coal-tar product, but is less deadly to fungi.

Wood-tar creosote is derived from treble distillation of resinous woods. Owing to the expense of this oil its use has been largely confined to the manufacture of stains and patented coatings.

Petroleum oils fortified with pentachlorophenol and copper naphthenate are available where a clean, non-swelling, and paintable preservative treatment is required, as for window sash, flooring, mill work, and similar products. These preservatives consist of the toxic chemical, 5 per cent of pentachlorophenol or copper naphthenate equivalent to 0.75 per cent of copper metal, in volatile solvents or petroleum oils. These preservatives have also been used for treating structural timbers.

All the inorganic salts which are used for wood preservation are highly toxic to fungi. They are also non-volatile and odorless. Furthermore, timber into which these salts are injected can be covered with paint, whereas creosoted timber is coated with great difficulty. On the other hand, these salts are soluble in water and are likely to leach out of the timber if it is exposed to moisture.

Zinc chloride has been one of the most important of the inorganic salts, but it is now being largely displaced by chromated zinc chloride. These salts are equal in toxicity to coal-tar creosote but corrode the iron treating cylinders to a slight extent. The principal advantages of these salts are relative cheapness, cleanliness, lack of odor, and lack of fire hazard. The life of crossties treated with zinc chloride or chromated zinc chloride is about half that of crossties treated with coal-tar creosote.

Mercuric chloride is the most toxic preservative and on this account is often a menace to the users of the treated timber. It is less soluble in water than zinc chloride but much more corrosive to iron. From records, it appears to confer a somewhat longer life on treated timber. The cost of mercuric chloride per cubic foot of treated timber is about the same as that of zinc chloride.

Copper sulfate is a preservative of high toxicity, but readily leaches from the timber. It is fairly cheap and appears to be about as efficient a preservative as zinc chloride. The depth of penetration is readily determined by the blue stain which the liquid imparts to the wood. Since it attacks iron with great vigor, it cannot be used with the ordinary treating apparatus. The largest use of this preservative is made in France.

Wolman salts consisting approximately of 12½ per cent of dinitrophenol, 25 per cent of sodium fluoride, 25 per cent of disodium hydrogen arsenate, and 37½ per cent of sodium chromate have shown favorable performance characteristics when used on wood not in contact with the ground or with water. The material is relatively expensive.

Other water-borne preservatives in use are Celcure, zinc meta arsenite, and Chemonite.

24. Economy in Preservation. Economy is effected by the preservative treatment whenever the annual charge against the treated timber is less than the annual charge against any untreated timber (or other material) which would serve the purpose. The annual charge is defined as the amount of money which must be invested each year at a given rate of compound interest to provide a sum which, when the timber unit is no longer satisfactory, will equal the first cost of the installed unit plus interest charges. The annual charge for an untreated lodgepole pine tie with a life expectancy of 4 years is about $0.70, and for the same tie treated with 10 lb of creosote per cu ft or ½ lb of zinc chloride per cu ft it is about $0.35. The approximate life of the creosoted tie is about 15 years, and that of the zinc chloride-treated tie about 11 years.

The Mechanical Properties of Timber

1. Introduction. In order that the engineer may properly design columns and beams for various parts of wooden structures, he must be thoroughly conversant with the strength and stiffness of the available classes of timber. He must also know how various defects and conditions influence these properties. The architect must not only appreciate the beauty of the various species, the relative ease with which each may be worked, the tendency to shrink, warp, and check, but he must likewise be prepared to proportion joists and rafters to carry the imposed loads without excessive deflection. The wheelwright must understand how the toughness and strength of his axles, spokes, and shafts are influenced by species, rate of growth, density, and defects. The carpenter and the craftsman must also have knowledge of the mechanical properties of wood in order that they may work it to best advantage.

Furthermore, wood of a given species is extremely variable. Trees differ markedly in their rate of growth, due to climatic conditions, the density of the surrounding forest, the character of the soil, and the physiography of the region in which they grow. These conditions of growth, the position in the tree, the amount of moisture, and the defects all influence the mechanical properties of a piece of timber of a given species.

Recognizing the importance of a knowledge of the properties of wood and the factors influencing them, Dr. B. E. Fernow, then chief of the Forestry Division of the U. S. Department of Agriculture, inaugurated a series of timber tests in 1891. In the beginning, the microscopic and physical tests were conducted at Washington and the mechanical tests were made by J. B. Johnson, at Washington University, St. Louis. Later the mechanical tests were distributed among a number of technical laboratories in various parts of the country. In 1909 the major portion of the work done at the various laboratories was transferred to the Forest Products Laboratory * at Madison, Wis.

Mechanical tests of timber are only a portion of the work carried on at this laboratory. Studies of the physical and chemical properties, the microscopic structure, the methods of preservation of wood, and the utili-

* This laboratory is run by the U. S. Government in cooperation with the University of Wisconsin.

zation of wood products are among the other more important lines of investigation being conducted by this institution.

On account of the broad scope of these investigations, the great pains which are taken to identify species, to select properly both specimens and trees, and on account of the care taken to eliminate variables in testing, the results obtained are of very great value. Most of the data in this chapter are taken from publications of this laboratory. The *Wood Handbook* prepared by the laboratory contains much additional valuable information.

The mechanical tests which are most commonly made at the Forest Products Laboratory are: compression, shear, both static and impact, bending, tension, hardness, and cleavage. Observations are also made on the number of rings per inch, percentage of summer wood, percentage of moisture, density, and shrinkage. The more important conditions pertaining to the methods of testing wood considered in Chapter III are supplemented, when necessary, in the discussions on mechanical properties which follow.

THE STRENGTH OF WOOD

2. Compressive Strength. When wood is subjected to compressive forces acting parallel to the axis of growth (parallel to the grain), it is, in proportion to its weight, one of the strongest of structural materials. Columns and posts are, therefore, often fashioned of it. Inasmuch as the strength of such a member is a function of the compressive strength and the slenderness ratio, information concerning the former is of much importance. Furthermore, a knowledge of the compressive strength is of value in estimating strength in bending, since experiments have demonstrated that the yield point of a wooden beam is determined by the compressive strength of the wood. The compression test is not, however, as effective in demonstrating the weakening influences of defects as the cross-bending test.

When wood is subjected to compression parallel to the grain it may fail through collapsing of the cell walls or through lateral bending of the cells and fibers. In most of the conifers where the cells (tracheids) have thin walls, failure begins at pits in the walls of one of these cells and gradually causes a collapse of the entire cell. The plane of rupture is generally inclined about 60° to 75° with the axis of the cell. From the inclination of the plane of failure it appears probable that final collapse is due to the weakness of the cell wall in transverse shear. Adjacent cells are overstressed by the failure of the individual cell and a wrinkling of the surface, showing the progress of the breakdown throughout the specimen, becomes visible. In wet wood and in the hardwoods, which are composed of thick-walled fibers and vessels, incipient failure is due to bending of the individual fibers. Occasionally after the wrinkling begins, the specimen is separated into groups of fibers by longitudinal cracks. This condition is brought about by splitting of the fibers and not by failure of the bond between fibers. It will be generally noted that the line of failure on tangential surfaces of the specimen is inclined as previously stated; but on radial surfaces it is approximately normal to the axis of the test piece. The direction in the latter case is much influenced by the medullary rays. In cross-grained pieces the failure is likely to take place through shear parallel to the grain.

The strength of timber compressed across the grain is brought into play wherever a concentrated load is imposed on a beam. Since the compressive strength across the grain is only a small fraction of the compressive strength parallel to the grain, proper allowance for this discrepancy must be made in designing columns resting on wooden beams or the columns must be provided with a footing, to distribute the pressure.

Tests on compression across the grain are often made with the pressure distributed over only part of one of the loaded surfaces. Thus for tests on small specimens at the Forest Products Laboratory, a $2 \times 2 \times 6$-in. block is used and loads are applied over the lower 2×6-in. surface and the middle third of the upper surface. Although such procedure does not give the true cross-grained compressive strength, it more nearly approaches the loading condition ordinarily met in a structure. In such tests, as the load is increased, the upper bearing closes the cell cavities immediately beneath it and gradually indents the surface. Beam action in the upper fibers often produces splitting in planes perpendicular to the line of pressure, but there is no well-marked failure.

Strictly speaking, timber does not have a well-defined elastic limit, since it takes set after the imposition of low loads. Nevertheless, the initial portion of the stress-deformation curve is approximately straight and it has become customary to record the stress corresponding to the limit of proportionality as the elastic limit. This is the only value of importance in tests across the grain.

Values of the compressive strengths of 2×2-in. prisms of 85 woods in green condition appear in Table 1. In Table 2, similar values may be found for larger sizes of the common structural timbers when air seasoned. Table 3 shows the relation of air-seasoned to green material. Among the species having greatest compressive strength parallel to the grain we note locust, blue gum, hickory, white or green ash, walnut, yew, Cuban and longleaf pine, and lowland Spanish oak. The strongest structural timbers are oak, maple, bald cypress, Douglas fir, western larch, and the southern yellow pines.

For most of the conifers the compressive elastic limit across the grain varies between 12 and 18 per cent of the values determined for pressures

TABLE 1. RESULTS OF TESTS ON 85 SPECIES OF WOOD TESTED IN A GREEN CONDITION IN THE FORM OF SMALL CLEAR PIECES

From Bulletin No. 556 U. S. Dept. of Agriculture

[Test specimens are 2 by 2 inches in section. Bending specimens are cut 30 inches long; others are shorter, depending on kind of test.]

1	2	3	4	5	6	Specific Gravity, Oven Dry, Based on—		9	Shrinkage from Green to Oven-dry Condition			Static Bending			Work in Bending—		Impact Bending			Compression Parallel to Grain		23	24	25	Hardness, Load Required to Imbed a 0.444-Inch Ball to One-half Its Diameter	
Common Name	Locality Where Grown	Number of Trees Tested	Number of Rings per Inch	Summerwood (Per Cent)	Moisture Content (Per Cent)	Volume When Green	Volume When Oven-dry	Weight per Cubic Foot (Green) (Pounds)	In Volume (Per Cent of Dimensions When Green)	Radial (Per Cent of Dimensions When Green)	Tangential (Per Cent of Dimensions When Green)	Fiber Stress at Elastic Limit (Pounds per Square Inch)	Modulus of Rupture (Pounds per Square Inch)	Modulus of Elasticity (1000 Pounds per Square Inch)	To Elastic Limit (Inch-pounds per Cubic Inch)	To Maximum Load (Inch-pounds per Cubic Inch)	Fiber Stress at Elastic Limit (Pounds per Square Inch)	Work in Bending to Elastic Limit (Inch-pounds per Cubic Inch)	Height of Drop Causing Complete Failure, 50-pound Hammer (Inches)	Fiber Stress at Elastic Limit (Pounds per Square Inch)	Maximum Crushing Strength (Pounds per Square Inch)	Compression Perpendicular to Grain—Fiber Stress at Elastic Limit (Pounds per Square Inch)	Shearing Strength Parallel to Grain (Pounds per Square Inch)	Tension Perpendicular to Grain (Pounds per Square Inch)	End (Pounds)	Side (Pounds)
		3	4	5	6	7	8	9	10	11	12	13	14	15	16	17	18	19	20	21	22	23	24	25	26	27
HARDWOODS																										
Ash, black........	Mich., Wis.	15	24	53	83	0.46	0.53	53	15.2	5.0	7.8	2600	6,000	1020	0.42	12.4	7,200	2.5	32	1620	2,290	430	870	490	580	550
Ash, green.......	Mo., La.	10	18	58	48	.52	.61	48	12.5	4.6	7.1	5300	9,500	1400	1.14	11.8	11,400	5.0	34	3560	4,200	910	1260	590	960	870
Ash, white. (forest grown)	Ark., W.Va.	10	16	50	43	.52	.60	46	12.6	4.2	6.5	4900	9,100	1350	1.03	13.4	11,700	5.0	36	3230	3,800	800	1260	620	1000	900
Ash, white (second growth)..	N. Y.	5	9	63	40	.58	.71	51	14.0	5.3	8.7	6100	10,800	1640	1.30	16.3	13,800	5.9	47	3820	4,610	790	1600	790	1140	1080
Aspen...........	Wis.	5	8	...	107	.36	.42	47	11.1	3.3	6.9	2900	5,300	840	.65	6.9	6,900	2.5	28	1620	2,160	200	620	180	270	320
Basswood........	Penn., Wis.	8	19	29	103	.33	.40	41	15.8	6.6	9.3	2700	5,000	1030	.42	5.2	6,200	2.0	17	1710	2,210	210	610	280	280	250
Beech...........	Ind., Penn.	10	19	30	62	.54	.66	55	16.?	4.8	10.6	4500	8,200	1240	.99	12.5	10,400	4.2	40	2550	3,280	610	1210	760	950	820

Species	Locality	Values (as printed in row, columns unlabeled on this page)
Birch, paper	Wis.	5, 6, 30, 72, .47, .60, 51, 16.3, 6.6, 8.8, 2900, 5,800, 1010, .49, 15.0, 7,800, 2.7, 45, 1650, 2,210, 300, 790, 380, 380, 400, 490
Birch, yellow	Penn., Wis.	10, 19, 26, 68, .54, .66, 58, 16.8, 7.4, 9.0, 4600, 8,600, 1540, .80, 16.6, 11,700, 4.5, 40, 2760, 3,460, 450, 790, 430, 480, 820, 740
Butternut	Tenn., Wis.	10, 9, 104, .36, .40, 46, 10.2, 3.3, 6.1, 2900, 5,400, 970, .52, 8.2, 7,300, 2.5, 24, 1960, 2,420, 270, 760, 430, 430, 410, 390
Chestnut	Md., Tenn.	10, 10, 122, .40, .46, 55, 11.6, 3.4, 6.7, 3100, 5,600, 930, .59, 7.0, 7,900, 2.8, 24, 2040, 2,470, 380, 800, 430, 430, 530, 420
Cottonwood	Mo.	5, 6, 111, .37, .43, 49, 14.1, 3.9, 9.2, 2900, 5,300, 1010, .40, 7.3, 7,200, 2.3, 21, 1770, 2,280, 240, 680, 410, 380, 380, 340
Cottonwood, black	Wash.	5, 6, 132, .32, .37, 46, 12.4, 3.6, 8.6, 2900, 4,800, 1070, .44, 5.0, 6,800, 2.2, 20, 1770, 2,160, 200, 600, 270, 280, 280, 250
Elm, cork	Wis.	10, 28, 50, .58, .66, 54, 14.1, 4.8, 8.1, 4600, 9,500, 1190, .91, 19.8, 11,000, 4.1, 50, 2870, 3,780, 750, 1270, 660, 980, 990
Elm, slippery	Ind., Wis.	6, 16, 85, .43, .56, 56, 15.8, 4.9, 8.9, 4000, 9,000, 1230, .97, 15.4, 9,200, 3.4, 47, 2840, 3,320, 510, 1110, 650, 750, 660
Elm, white	Wis., Penn.	6, 18, 88, .44, .54, 54, 14.4, 4.4, 9.5, 3600, 6,900, 1030, .93, 11.0, 8,100, 2.9, 34, 2290, 2,880, 390, 920, 560, 610, 550
Gum, black	Tenn.	5, 27, 55, .40, .55, 45, 13.9, 4.4, 7.7, 4000, 7,000, 1030, .91, 13.0, 9,800, 4.7, 30, 2440, 3,040, 600, 1100, 570, 790, 640
Gum, blue	Cal.	5, 79, .62, .80, 70, 22.5, 7.6, 15.3, 7600, 11,200, 2010, 1.65, 13.3, 14,200, 4.7, 40, 4870, 5,250, 1020, 1550, 640, 1310, 1340
Gum, Tupelo	La.	6, 10, 97, .46, .52, 56, 12.5, 4.2, 7.6, 4200, 7,300, 1050, .96, 8.3, 9,000, 3.3, 30, 2900, 3,370, 590, 1190, 600, 800, 710
Gum, red	Mo.	10, 16, 91, .44, .53, 50, 15.0, 5.2, 9.9, 3700, 6,800, 1150, .51, 9.4, 10,000, 3.9, 33, 2360, 2,840, 460, 1070, 510, 630, 520
Hickory, big shell-bark	Miss., O.	19, 63, .62, 63, 10.2, 7.6, 12.6, 5600, 10,500, 1340, 1.36, 29.9, 14,200, 7.0, 104, 2740, 3,920, 1000, 1190
Hickory, bitternut	O., Va., Miss.	11, 63, .60, 63, 7.8, 5500, 10,300, 1400, 1.22, 20.0, 15,900, 8.5, 66, 4330, 4,570, 990, 1240
Hickory, mockernut	W. Va., Penn.	18, 64, .64, 64, 17.9, 7.8, 11.0, 6300, 11,100, 1570, 1.38, 26.1, 15,100, 6.7, 88, 3900, 4,480, 1000, 1280
Hickory, pignut	O., Miss., Penn., W. Va.	20, 65, .66, 64, 16.7, 7.2, 11.5, 6200, 11,700, 1650, 1.34, 31.7, 16,900, 8.8, 89, 3950, 4,810, 1140, 1370, 770, 1640, 1570
Hickory, shagbark	do.	19, 66, .60, 64, 9.8, 7.0, 10.5, 5900, 11,000, 1570, 1.28, 23.7, 14,400, 6.4, 74, 3430, 4,580, 1000, 1320, 930, 1440, 1390
Locust, black	Tenn.	11, 51, .66, 58, 11.6, 4.4, 6.9, 8800, 13,800, 1350, 2.36, 15.4, 18,300, 7.9, 44, 6280, 6,800, 1450, 1760, 600, 760, 620
Locust, honey	Mo., Ind.	9, 45, .60, 61, 12.5, 4.2, 6.6, 5600, 10,200, 1290, 1.40, 12.6, 11,800, 4.6, 47, 3320, 4,420, 1420, 1660, 580, 740, 600
Maple, Oregon	Wash.	12, 72, .44, 47, 11.6, 3.7, 7.1, 4400, 7,400, 1100, 1.02, 8.7, 8,500, 2.8, 23, 2380, 3,240, 550, 1110, 600, 760, 620
Maple, red	Penn., Wis.	5, 24, 70, .48, 51, 12.5, 3.8, 8.1, 4100, 7,800, 1420, .60, 10.0, 9,900, 3.7, 25, 2500, 3,350, 520, 1080, 580, 740, 600
Maple, silver	Wis.	7, 66, .51, 46, 12.0, 3.0, 7.2, 3100, 5,300, 940, .61, 11.0, 6,800, 2.6, 29, 1950, 2,490, 460, 1050, 560, 670, 590
Maple, sugar	Ind., Penn., Wis.	17, 21, 49, 60, .56, 56, 14.5, 4.8, 9.2, 5000, 9,100, 1480, 1.08, 11.0, 12,100, 5.0, 36, 3120, 3,860, 750, 1380, 770, 1000, 910
Oak, bur	Wis.	5, 12, 59, 70, .58, 67, 12.7, 4.4, 8.8, 3600, 7,200, 880, .89, 10.7, 10,000, 4.7, 44, 2310, 3,290, 840, 1350, 800, 1160, 1110
Oak, California black	Cal., Ore.	10, 16, 52, 106, .51, 58, 12.1, 3.6, 6.6, 3400, 6,200, 740, 1.03, 8.8, 8,200, 3.4, 30, 1880, 2,800, 890, 1140, 700, 910, 850
Oak, chestnut	Tenn.	5, 23, 50, 72, .57, 67, 16.7, 5.5, 9.7, 4600, 8,700, 790, .90, 9.4, 12,000, 4.6, 35, 2890, 3,520, 660, 1210, 690, 970, 890
Oak, Pacific post	Ore.	10, 16, 49, 64, .64, 75, 13.4, 5.0, 9.4, 4600, 7,700, 1510, 1.51, 13.7, 10,300, 4.8, 49, 2510, 3,570, 1380, 1630, 940, 1430, 1390
Oak, post	Ark., La.	10, 26, 54, 69, .60, 74, 16.2, 5.4, 9.8, 5000, 8,100, 1090, 1.31, 11.0, 10,900, 4.1, 44, 2840, 3,480, 1060, 1280, 790, 1160, 1130
Oak, red	Ind., Tenn.	21, 11, 62, 84, .56, 65, 14.2, 3.9, 8.3, 3700, 7,700, 1290, .65, 11.5, 10,400, 3.9, 41, 2330, 3,200, 730, 1120, 740, 1020, 950
Oak, Spanish (high-land)	La.	4, 20, 46, 90, .52, 62, 16.3, 4.5, 8.7, 4200, 6,900, 1140, .93, 8.0, 9,100, 3.1, 29, 2180, 3,030, 680, 930, 480, 910, 860
Oak, Spanish (low-land)	do.	3, 7, 63, 78, .61, 71, 16.4, 5.2, 10.8, 6500, 10,800, 1790, 1.32, 14.7, 12,300, 3.8, 54, 3760, 4,620, 940, 1320, 800, 1270, 1240
Oak, water	do.	5, 10, 61, 81, .56, 68, 16.4, 4.2, 9.3, 5600, 8,900, 1550, 1.14, 11.1, 11,600, 3.8, 39, 3200, 3,740, 770, 1240, 820, 1050, 1010

TABLE 1. RESULTS OF TESTS ON 85 SPECIES OF WOOD TESTED IN A GREEN CONDITION IN THE FORM OF SMALL CLEAR PIECES—*Continued*

1	2	3	4	5	6	Specific Gravity, Oven-Dry, Based on—		9	Shrinkage from Green to Oven-dry Condition			Static Bending			Work in Bending		Impact Bending			Compression Parallel to Grain		23	24	25	Hardness, Load Required to Imbed a 0.444-Inch Ball to One-half Its Diameter	
Common Name.	Locality Where Grown.	Number of Trees Tested.	Number of Rings per Inch.	Summerwood (Per Cent).	Moisture Content (Per Cent).	Volume When Green.	Volume When Oven-dry.	Weight per Cubic Foot (Green) (Pounds).	In Volume (Per Cent of Dimensions When Green).	Radial (Per Cent of Dimensions When Green).	Tangential (Per Cent of Dimensions When Green).	Fiber Stress at Elastic Limit (Pounds per Square Inch).	Modulus of Rupture (Pounds per Square Inch).	Modulus of Elasticity (1000 Pounds per Square Inch).	To Elastic Limit (Inch-pounds per Cubic Inch).	To Maximum Load (Inch-pounds per Cubic Inch).	Fiber Stress at Elastic Limit (Pounds per Square Inch).	Work in Bending to Elastic Limit (Inch-pounds per Cubic Inch).	Height of Drop Causing Complete Failure, 50-pound Hammer (Inches).	Fiber Stress at Elastic Limit (Pounds per Square Inch).	Maximum Crushing Strength (Pounds per Square Inch).	Compression Perpendicular to Grain—Fiber Stress at Elastic Limit (Pounds per Square Inch).	Shearing Strength Parallel to Grain (Pounds per Square Inch).	Tension Perpendicular to Grain (Pounds per Square Inch).	End (Pounds).	Side (Pounds).
		3	4	5	6	7	8	9	10	11	12	13	14	15	16	17	18	19	20	21	22	23	24	25	26	27
HARDWOODS—Con.																										
Oak, white......	Ark., La. [Ind.	20	17	60	68	.60	.71	62	15.8	5.3	9.0	4700	8,300	1250	1.08	11.5	10,700	4.2	42	2990	3,560	830	1250	770	1120	1060
Oak, yellow......	Ark., Wis.	8	15	71	78	.56	.67	63	14.2	4.5	9.7	4600	8,200	1180	1.20	12.3	10,800	4.4	40	2870	3,460	870	1180	830	1000	1060
Poplar, yellow....	Tenn.	5	14		64	.37	.42	38	11.4	4.1	6.9	3200	5,600	1210	.48	5.6	8,000	2.6	17	2000	2,550	310	790	460	420	340
Sycamore	Ind., Tenn.	10	16	77	83	.46	.54	52	14.2	5.?	7.6	3300	6,500	1060	.60	7.5	8,800	3.3	26	2390	2,920	450	1000	630	700	610
Walnut, black.....	Ky.	5	12		81	.51	.56	58	11.3	5.2	7.1	5400	9,500	1420	1.16	14.4	11,900	4.5	37	3600	4,300	600	1220	570	960	900
Willow, black.....	Wis., Mo.	10	5		138	.34	.41	50	13.8	2.6	7.8	1800	3,800	560	.36	10.8	5,100	2.0	36	970	1,510	210	620	430	350	360
CONIFERS																										
Cedar, incense....	Cal., Ore.	8	16	30	108	.35	.36	45	7.6	3.3	5.7	3900	6,200	840	.94	6.4	7,300	2.4	17	2870	3,150	460	830	280	570	390
Cedar, Port Orford.	Ore.	5	24	25	52	.41	.47	39	10.7	5.2	8.1	3900	6,800	1500	.59	7.8	9,300	2.7	25	2970	3,280	380	880	240	560	480
Cedar, western red.	Wash., Mont.	10	20	36	39	.31	.34	27	8.1	2.5	5.1	3300	5,200	950	.64	5.0	7,100	2.4	17	2500	2,840	310	720	210	430	260
Cedar, white......	Wis.	5	23	36	55	.29	.32	28	7.0	2.1	4.9	2600	4,200	640	.60	5.7	5,300	2.0	15	1420	1,990	290	620	240	320	230

Species	Locality	1	2	3	4	5	6	7	8	9	10	11	12	13	14	15	16	17	18	19	20	21	22	23	24	25	26
Cypress, bald	La., Mo.	10	16	31	87	.41	48	10.7	.47	3.8	6.0	4000	6.0	6,800	1190	.86	6.4	8,000	2.6	24	3100	3,490	470	820	280	470	380
Cypress, yellow	Ore.	5	31	..	40	.40	35	7.9	.44	1.9	5.0	3600	5.0	6,200	960	.77	9.5	8,600	3.2	27	2390	2,880	410	820	260	520	410
Douglas fir	Wash., Ore.	18	13	35	36	.45	38	12.6	.52	5.0	7.9	5000	7.9	7,800	1580	.86	6.7	9,400	2.9	25	3400	3,940	530	910	200	510	470
Douglas fir	Mont., Wy.	10	22	27	38	.40	34	10.6	.44	3.6	6.2	3600	6.2	6,400	1180	.65	6.8	9,100	3.0	20	2520	3,000	450	880	350	450	400
Fir, Alpine	Col.	5	15	14	47	.31	28	9.0	.32	2.5	7.1	2400	7.1	4,400	860	.39	4.4	5,300	1.6	21	1660	2,060	310	610	240	280	220
Fir, amabilis	Ore., Wash.	20	8	26	102	.37	47	14.1	.42	4.1	10.0	3900	6.0	6,300	1300	.60	4.7	7,800	2.3	23	2380	2,900	320	670	180	360	310
Fir, balsam	Wis.	10	12	26	117	.34	45	10.6	.41	2.8	6.6	3000	6.6	4,900	960	.52	4.7	6,900	2.2	16	2220	2,400	210	610	230	290	290
Fir, grand	Mont., Ore.	10	18	30	94	.37	44	13.6	.42	3.2	6.2	3000	6.2	6,100	1300	.58	5.6	8,100	2.6	22	2680	3,010	340	700	180	420	360
Fir, noble	Ore.	5	23	17	41	.35	31	10.2	.41	4.9	9.1	3400	9.1	5,700	1280	.53	6.2	7,900	2.2	20	2370	2,700	310	700	180	300	250
Fir, white	Cal.	5	10	30	156	.35	56	10.2	.39	3.4	7.0	3900	7.0	6,000	1130	.77	5.2	7,200	2.2	18	2610	2,800	440	730	260	380	330
Hemlock black	Mont.	10	23	45	70	.42	45	10.8	.48	4.4	7.1	3500	7.1	6,000	940	.78	9.4	8,800	3.6	36	2590	2,890	400	880	360	580	460
Hemlock (eastern)	Tenn., Wis.	10	20	34	105	.38	45	10.4	.44	4.0	6.4	4200	6.4	6,700	1120	.88	8.0	7,900	6.0	20	2710	3,270	500	880	360	510	410
Hemlock (western)	Wash.	5	10	27	71	.38	41	11.6	.43	4.5	7.9	3400	7.9	6,100	1190	.58	6.0	7,800	2.4	20	2290	2,890	350	810	260	540	430
Larch, western	Mont., Wash.	13	32	37	58	.48	48	13.2	.59	4.2	8.1	4600	8.1	7,500	1350	1.01	7.1	9,400	3.7	24	3250	3,800	560	920	230	470	450
Pine, Cuban	Fla.	5	17	44	47	.58	53	12.7	.68	5.9	7.5	5600	7.5	8,800	1630	1.10	7.9	11,300	3.9	37	3950	4,470	590	1030	290	570	630
Pine, jack	Wis.	5	7	30	105	.39	50	10.4	.46	3.4	6.5	3000	6.5	5,400	920	.55	5.9	7,800	3.3	30	2250	2,580	380	760	310	380	370
Pine, Jeffrey	Cal.	5	18	23	101	.37	47	9.9	.42	4.4	6.7	3200	6.7	5,000	980	.60	4.7	7,200	2.6	21	2030	2,370	350	690	260	320	340
Pine, loblolly	Fla., N.C., S.C.	15	8	42	70	.50	54	12.6	.59	5.5	7.5	4400	7.5	7,500	1380	.81	8.0	9,500	3.1	32	2870	3,580	550	900	280	400	450
Pine, lodgepole	Col., Mont.	28	24	22	65	.38	39	11.5	.44	4.5	6.7	3000	6.7	5,500	1080	.49	5.6	7,200	2.3	20	2100	2,610	310	690	220	320	330
Pine, longleaf	Fla., La., Miss.	34	18	39	47	.55	50	12.3	.64	5.3	7.5	5400	7.5	8,700	1630	1.00	8.0	10,800	3.5	34	3840	4,390	600	1070	290	550	590
Pine, Norway	Wis.	18	22	41	54	.44	42	11.5	.51	3.6	7.2	3700	7.2	6,400	1380	.59	5.8	7,500	3.2	28	2470	3,080	360	780	190	360	340
Pine, pitch	Tenn.	5	11	30	85	.47	54	11.7	.54	4.8	7.4	3700	7.4	6,700	1120	.75	8.5	9,100	3.4	29	2100	3,040	510	950	350	460	480
Pine, pond	Fla.	5	13	35	56	.50	49	11.2	.58	5.1	7.1	4500	7.1	7,400	1280	.93	8.7	9,400	4.0	33	2990	3,660	540	940	280	460	510
Pine, shortleaf	Ark., La.	12	12	40	64	.50	50	12.6	.58	5.1	8.2	4500	8.2	8,000	1450	.79	7.5	11,200	4.0	39	3650	3,810	480	880	330	490	560
Pine, sugar	Cal.	5	12	34	123	.36	50	8.4	.39	2.9	5.6	3300	5.6	5,300	990	.66	5.0	6,700	2.3	17	2340	2,600	350	710	330	330	560
Pine, table-mountain	Tenn.	5	15	29	75	.49	54	10.9	.55	4.4	6.8	4500	6.8	7,500	1270	.94	8.1	10,200	3.8	29	2980	3,540	560	960	320	480	490
Pine, western white	Mont.	5	28	33	58	.39	39	11.5	.45	4.1	7.4	3500	7.4	5,700	1330	.54	5.1	7,600	2.3	23	2770	3,070	300	710	250	330	330
Pine, westernyellow	Col., Mont., Ariz., Wash., Cal.	25	20	22	95	.38	46	10.8	.42	3.4	6.4	3100	6.4	5,200	1010	.54	5.1	6,700	2.3	19	2080	2,460	340	680	280	310	320
Pine, white	Wis.	5	16	31	74	.36	39	7.8	.39	2.2	5.9	3400	5.9	5,300	1070	.62	5.9	6,500	2.1	18	2370	2,720	310	640	260	300	300
Spruce, Engelmann	Col.	10	14	14	100	.31	38	10.4	.35	3.4	6.6	2500	6.6	4,200	830	.43	4.9	5,800	1.9	14	1740	1,980	290	590		250	240
Spruce, red	N.H., Tenn.	17	17	27	43	.38	34	11.8	.41	3.8	7.8	3400	7.8	5,700	1180	.56	6.1	7,200	2.3	18	2360	2,740	350	770	220	420	350
Spruce, red		9	9	24	53	.34	33	11.8	.37	4.5	7.3	3000	7.3	5,500	1180	.44	6.4	7,900	2.5	29	2280	2,600	330	780	230	430	350
Spruce, Sitka	Wash.	7	14	13	46	.36	33	14.18	.36	3.7	7.3	3300	7.3	5,400	980	.66	5.7	6,800	2.0	20	2280	2,380	270	675	200	300	280
Spruce, white	N.H., Wis.																										
Tamarack	Wis.	5	20	38	52	.49	47	13.6	.56	3.7	7.4	4200	7.4	7,200	1240	.84	7.2	7,800	2.7	28	3010	3,480	480	860	260	400	380
Yew, Pacific	Wash.	5	27	..	44	.60	54	9.7	.67	4.0	5.4	6500	5.4	10,100	990	2.46	20.2	13,100	6.2	38	3400	4,600	1040	1620	450	1340	1150

Materials of Construction

TABLE 2. AVERAGE STRENGTH VALUES FOR COMPRESSION PARALLEL TO GRAIN, COMPRESSION PERPENDICULAR TO GRAIN, AND SHEARING TESTS ON AIR-SEASONED MATERIAL OF DIFFERENT SIZES
(*Bull.* 108, Forest Service.)

Species.	Compression parallel to grain.						Compression perpendicular to grain.					Shear.		
	Size of specimen.	Number of tests.	Moisture.	Crushing strength at elastic limit per square inch.	Modulus of elasticity per square inch.	Crushing strength at maximum load per sq. in.	Stress area.	Height.	Number of tests.	Moisture.	Crushing strength at elastic limit per square inch.	Number of tests.	Moisture.	Shearing strength per square inch.
	In.		P. ct.	Lb.	1000 lb.	Lb.	In.	In.		P. ct.	Lb.		P. ct.	Lb.
Longleaf pine...	4×5	46	26.3	3480	.....	4800	4×5	4	22	25.1	572	52	20.2	984
Douglas fir.....	6×6	259	20.3	3271	1038	4258	4×8	16	44	20.8	732	465	22.1	822
	2×2	247	18.7	3842	1084	5002	4×8	10	32	18.1	584			
							4×4	8	51	20.2	638			
							4×4	6	49	24.0	613			
							4×4	4	29	24.8	603			
	6×6	29	15.7	4070	1951	6030	8×5	16	4	17.8	725	85	...	1135
Shortleaf pine...	2×2	57	14.2	...	.....	6380	8×5	14	3	16.3	757			
							8×5	12	5	15.1	730			
							5×5	8	6	15.0	918			
							2×2	2	57	13.9	926			
	6×6	112	16.0	...	.....	5445	8×6	16	17	18.8	491	193	15.0	905
Western larch...	4×4	81	14.7	...	.....	6161	8×6	12	18	17.6	526			
	2×2	270	14.8	...	.....	5934	5×4	8	22	13.3	735			
Loblolly pine ...	6×6	23	...	3357	1693	5005	8×5	16	12	19.8	602	156	11.3	1115
	5×5	10	22.4	2217	545	2950	8×5	8	7	22.9	679			
	4×8	8	19.4	3010	633	3920	4×5	8	8	19.5	715			
	2×2	69	...	...	.....	5547								
Tamarack......	6×7	3	15.7	2257	1042	3323	2×2	2	57	16.2	697	60	14.0	897
	4×7	3	13.6	3780	1301	4823								
	4×4	57	14.9	3386	1353	4346								
	2×2	66	14.6	...	.....	4790								
Western hemlock	6×6	102	18.6	4840	2140	5814	7×6	15	25	18.2	514	131	17.7	924
	2×2	463	17.0	4560	1923	5403	6×6	6	26	16.8	431			
							4×4	4	6	15.9	488			
Redwood.......	6×6	18	16.9	...	.....	4276	8×6	16	5	25.4	548	95	12.4	671
	2×2	115	14.6	...	.....	5119	6×6	12	6	14.7	610			
							7×6	9	5	14.8	500			
							3×6	14	2	12.6	470			
							2×6	12	2	16.2	498			
							2×6	10	4	14.3	511			
							2×6	8	2	13.2	429			
							2×2	2	145	13.8	564			
Norway pine. ..	6×7	4	15.2	2670	1182	4212	2×2	2	36	10.0	924	44	11.9	1145
	4×7	2	22.2	3275	1724	4575								
	4×4	55	16.6	3048	1367	4217								
	2×2	34	11.2	...	.....	7550								

TABLE 3. RATIOS OF AVERAGE STRENGTH VALUES FOR AIR-SEASONED MATERIAL TO THOSE FOR GREEN MATERIAL.* (*Bull.* 108, Forest Service)

Species.	Bending.				Compression parallel to grain.			Compression perpendicular to grain.	Shear.
	Fiber stress at elastic limit per square inch.	Modulus of rupture per square inch.	Modulus of elasticity per square inch.	Horizontal shear per square inch.	Crushing strength at elastic limit per square inch.	Crushing strength at maximum load per square inch.	Modulus of elasticity per square inch.	Crushing strength at elastic limit per square inch.	Shear strength per square inch.
	Lb.	Lb.	1000 Lb.	Lb.	Lb.	Lb.	1000 Lb.	Lb.	Lb.
Longleaf pine:									
Structural sizes.....	0.99	0.94	1.16	0.77	1.00	1.00	......	1.01	
Small specimens....	1.36	1.27	1.13	....	......	......	......	......	1.01
Douglas fir:									
Structural sizes.....	1.15	1.06	1.02	1.33	1.18	1.22	.73	1.12	
Small specimens....	1.28	1.25	1.06	....	1.10	1.24	.56	......	1.08
Shortleaf pine:									
Structural sizes.....	1.44	1.19	1.17	1.10	1.66	1.76	1.26	2.26	
Small specimens....	1.79	1.57	1.28	....	......	1.79	......	2.32	1.61
Western larch:									
Structural sizes.....	1.05	1.18	1.14	1.18	......	1.64	......	1.31	
Small specimens....	1.38	1.42	1.19	....	......	1.60	......	......	1.29
Loblolly pine:									
Structural sizes.....	1.16	1.19	1.07	1.30	1.47	1.46	2.20	1.31	
Small specimens....	1.26	1.19	1.02	....	......	1.71	......	......	1.77
Tamarack:									
Structural sizes.....	1.33	1.21	1.10	1.15	1.40	1.34	.98		
Small specimens....	2.33	2.26	1.09	....	......	1.60	......	......	1.32
Western hemlock:									
Structural sizes.....	1.25	1.21	1.20	1.07	1.67	1.73	1.32	1.09	
Small specimens....	1.44	1.42	1 17	....	1.55	1.59	1.11	......	1.47
Redwood:									
Structural sizes.....	.92	.87	.85	....	......	1.16	......	1.21	
Small specimens....	1.00	1.12	1.08	....	......	1.29	......	.99	.90
Norway pine:									
Structural sizes.....	1.63	1.57	1.25	1.20	1.48	1.66	1.36		
Small specimens....	1.88	1.64	1.21	....	......	3.01	......	......	1.94

* Ratios were based on the unit values indicated in column headings of Table 3.

parallel to the grain. Among the hardwoods the elastic limit in compression across the grain bears a higher ratio to the strength in compression parallel to the grain, the ratio being about 25 per cent for several of the varieties of hickory and oak and reaching 55 per cent for Pacific post oak.

With the exception of the longleaf pine specimens, which judging from their moisture content must have been pretty green, the air-seasoned structural timbers of every species were stronger in compression than the green timbers (see Art. VI-16).

3. Tensile Strength of Wood. When a properly shaped wooden stick is subjected to tensile forces acting parallel to the grain it is found to have greater strength than can be developed under any other kind of stress.

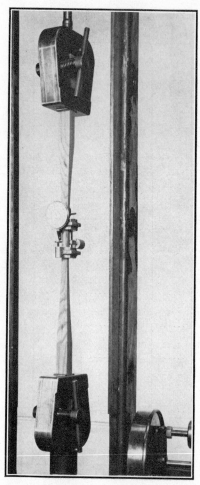

Fig. 1. Tension test assembly for determining strength parallel to grain.
(Forest Products Laboratory.)

Indeed, the tensile strength of wood parallel to the grain is so great that much difficulty is encountered in designing end connections so that the tensile strength of a piece can be developed. Therefore, wood tension members are rarely used. Moreover, since the tensile strength parallel to the grain is two to four times the compressive strength, the latter governs the strength of beams. The specimen used to determine the tensile strength of wood parallel to the grain is shown in Fig. 1.

The tensile strength parallel to the grain is influenced to some extent by the nature of the wood elements and their arrangement, but principally by the straightness of the grain and the thickness of the walls of the longitudinal elements. When failure occurs these elements are ruptured transversely. Knots greatly reduce the tensile strength parallel to the grain and are a great menace to strength when present in timbers subjected to such stresses (see Art. VI-15). The tensile strength appears to be less affected by moisture than are other mechanical properties.

Across the grain, the tensile strength of wood is small. It is a property closely related to cleavability, and it often determines the strength of a beam which has cross grain or spiral grain in the tension fibers. Failure in tension across the grain occurs through separation of the cells and fibers in longitudinal planes. Knots, shakes, and checks all reduce the tensile strength of wood across the grain. The form of specimen used by the Forest Products Laboratory in making the test is shown in Fig. 2.

Data in *Circ.* 213 of U. S. Forest Service show that the tensile strength of wood across a radial plane is less than the tensile strength across a plane tangent to the rings. This difference is especially pronounced in the oaks and other hardwoods having large medullary rays. It is probable, therefore, that these rays considerably weaken the tensile strength of wood across a radial plane.

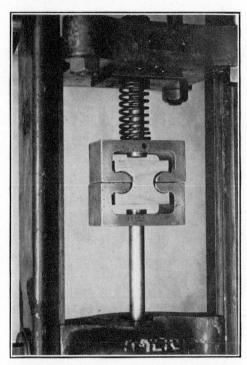

Fig. 2. Type of test used to find tensile strength of wood across grain. (Forest Products Laboratory.)

For the conifers, from which most structural timbers are secured, the cross-grained tensile strength of small perfect specimens of green wood runs between 180 and 450 psi, and for the oaks it varies between 500 and 1000 psi. The small size of these values must be remembered in computing the safe strengths of beams having cross grain in the tension fibers.

4. The Shearing Strength of Wood. Although shearing stresses are often of small moment in metal beams and other structural elements, they are frequently of very great importance in members made of wood. Thus the horizontal shear stress at the neutral axis of a short, deep wooden beam may be sufficiently great to produce a failure like that of Fig. 3.

If the shearing stresses act on planes tangent to the growth rings, the resistance of the various woods is quite small, ranging from about 600 to

1000 psi for small green specimens of the structural conifers and from 1000 to 1500 psi for similar pieces of oak, hickory, elm, maple, sycamore, beech, birch, and white ash (see Table 1). *Circ.* 213 of U. S. Forest Service shows that there is little difference between the strengths of small pieces of green coniferous wood subjected to shearing parallel to the rings (tangential shear), and the strengths of like pieces subjected to shearing stresses acting on vertical radial planes (radial shear). Among the hardwoods the resistance to radial shear appears to be slightly the greater.

DOUGLAS - FIR
LAMINATED BEAM NO. 4 E
MAXIMUM LOAD,53,870 LB.
TESTED APRIL 5 ,1946

Fig. 3. Failure of a large laminated wood beam by horizontal shear. (Forest Products Laboratory.)

Turning our attention to the results in Table 4 we find the calculated horizontal shear stresses developed in tests of beams of structural sizes. These shear stresses were computed from the formula $S_h = 3V/2a$, where S_h = horizontal shear stress, V = maximum vertical shear and a = area of rectangular cross section of beam. Comparing these results with the values for like woods found in Table 1, we observe that the computed stresses for the large beams are much lower than the shearing strengths of small specimens. This discrepancy is due principally to defects, shakes, and checks which cut down the area under shear. Since the formula assumes a full cross section, the results given by it will be smaller than the stresses in the net sections of wood. The lesson taught is to use values from the tests on large beams failing in shear as a basis for design. Both Tables 3 and 4 show that air-seasoned coniferous timber is, in most cases, stronger than green timber. Longleaf pine and redwood are, however, exceptions to this rule.

TABLE 4. CALCULATED SHEARING STRESSES DEVELOPED IN STRUCTURAL BEAMS

(From *Bull*. 108, Forest Service)

Species.	Total Number of Tests.		First Failure by Shear.				Shear following other Failure.				No Shear Failure.			
			Green.		Dry.		Green.		Dry.		Green.		Dry.	
	Green.	Dry.	Per cent of total.	Average calculated shear per square inch.	Per cent of total.	Average calculated shear per square inch.	Per cent of total.	Average calculated shear per square inch.	Per cent of total.	Average shear per square inch.	Per cent of total.	Average calculated shear per square inch.	Per cent of total.	Average calculated shear per square inch.
				Lb.		Lb.		Lb.		Lb.		Lb.		Lb.
Longleaf pine..	17	9	54	353	56	272	23	374	0	....	23	218	44	286
Douglas fir....	191	91	2	166	6	221	22	295	49	294	76	264	45	247
Shortleaf pine..	48	13	17	332	46	364	6	327	8	418	77	276	46	340
Western larch..	62	52	8	288	27	340	16	314	21	370	76	268	52	287
Loblolly pine..	111	25	7	335	28	434	2	356	16	546	91	237	56	255
Tamarack.....	30	9	10	261	33	299	3	263	0	....	87	228	67	283
Western hemlock........	39	44	5	288	23	307	28	281	68	438	67	250	9	417
Redwood......	28	12	7	302	0	......	11	218	17	250	82	283	83	227
Norway pine...	49	10	6	232	10	278	6	266	0	...	88	209	90	304

5. The Strength of Wood in Cross Bending. Because of the great use of wood for beams, stringers, joists, rafters, and other parts which are subject to bending, the cross-bending test is of much value in determining the quality of wood. By it one can measure the strength, toughness, and stiffness of the timber. Furthermore, the cross-bending test exposes weaknesses caused by defects better than any other test. Unless very large testing machines are at hand, it is the only test which can be used to find the strength of timbers of structural sizes.

It will be remembered from mechanics of materials that the modulus of rupture in cross bending is a fictitious measure of the ultimate unit stress on the extreme fiber at the danger section. The modulus of rupture is computed from the formula $S_m = M_m c / I$, where the modulus $S_m =$ unit stress on extreme fiber, $M_m =$ maximum bending moment, $c =$ distance from neutral axis to extreme fiber, and $I =$ moment of inertia of the cross section about the neutral axis. It will be recalled that the modulus of rupture as determined by this formula is intermediate between the tensile and compressive strengths and that it does not, therefore, truly represent the unit stress on the extreme fiber. The discrepancy between the calculated unit stress and the actual unit stress is due to the non-linear relation of stress to deformation when the elastic limit is exceeded, and also to the shifting of the neutral axis. The movement of the latter is brought about by the difference in the stress-deformation relations in tension and compression, although a fictitious stress, the modulus of rupture, is, nevertheless, a valuable index of quality of the wood. Also, if the elastic limit of the beam is determined, the ratio of the modulus of rupture to the unit stress on the extreme fiber at the elastic limit serves as a measure of the capacity of the beam to resist a momentary overload. Beams in which

Fig. 4. Tensile failure of a laminated wood beam. (Forest Products Laboratory.)

there is a well-marked difference between these stresses are preferable, since such members give ample warning of approaching failure.

The initial failure of long beams of uniform wood is indicated by a wrinkling of the overstressed compression fibers, much like the failure which occurs in compression prisms. Final failure of such beams is generally in tension. Figure 4 shows a typical tensile failure of a wood beam. Final failure is accompanied by more or less snapping as the individual fibers begin to break, and a loud report when the maximum load is reached. Very dry specimens sometimes fail very suddenly in tension before any wrinkling of the compression fibers is noticeable. On the other hand, green test pieces fail silently in compression without rupturing of the tensile fibers. Frequently, short deep beams fail by horizontal shear. This type of failure is sudden and is more common in well-seasoned timbers of structural sizes than in green timbers or in small beams. Very often shear failures result from defects.

Long, narrow beams must be restrained laterally and supported in such a manner that the wide sides are vertical. If the first condition is not fulfilled, the member will fail from column action in the compression fibers. Unless the second condition is met the strength of the beam may be very seriously reduced through the inclination of the neutral axis. In

TABLE 5. AVERAGE STRENGTH VALUES FOR AIR-SEASONED TIMBER BEAMS

(From Forest Service *Bull.* No. 108)

Species.	Sizes. Cross-section.	Span.	Number of tests.	Moisture.	Rings per inch.	Fiber stress at elastic Limit. Average per square inch.	Ratio to 2 by 2 inches.	Modulus of rupture. Average per square inch.	Ratio to 2 by 2 inches.	Modulus of elasticity. Average per square inch.	Ratio to 2 by 2 inches.	Calculated shear. Average per square inch.	Ratio to 2 by 2 inches.
	In.	In.		P.ct.		Lb.		Lb.		1000 Lb.		Lb.	
Longleaf pine...	8×16	180	5	22.2	16.0	3390	.50	4,274	0.37	1747	1.00	288	0.75
	6×16	132	1	23.4	17.1	3470	.51	6,610	.57	1501	.86	388	1.01
	6×10	177	2	19.0	8.8	4560	.68	7,880	.68	1722	.99	214	.56
	4×11	180	1	18.4	23.9	3078	.46	8,000	.69	1660	.95	251	.66
	6× 8	177	6	20.0	13.7	4227	.63	8,196	.71	1634	.94	177	.46
	2× 2	30	17	15.9	13.9	6750	1.00	11,520	1.00	1740	1.00	383	1.00
Douglas fir.....	8×16	180	91	20.8	13.1	4563	.68	6,372	.61	1549	.91	269	.64
	5× 8	180	30	14.9	12.2	5065	.76	6,777	.65	1853	1.09	218	.52
	2× 2	24	211	19.0	16.4	6686	1.00	10,378	1.00	1695	1.00	419	1.00
Shortleaf pine...	8×16	180	3	17.0	12.3	4220	.54	6,030	.50	1517	.85	398	.98
	8×14	180	3	16.0	12.3	4253	.55	5,347	.44	1757	.98	307	.76
	8×12	180	7	16.0	12.4	5051	.65	7,331	.60	1803	1.01	361	.89
	5× 8	180	6	12.2	22.5	7123	.92	9,373	.77	1985	1.11	301	.74
	2× 2	30	67	14.2	13.7	7780	1.00	12,170	1.00	1792	1.00	404	1.00
Western larch...	8×16	180	23	18.3	21.9	3343	.57	5,440	.53	1409	.90	349	.96
	8×12	180	29	17.8	23.4	3631	.62	6,186	.60	1549	.99	295	.81
	5× 8	180	8	13.6	27.6	4730	.80	7,258	.71	1620	1.04	221	.61
	2× 2	30	240	16.1	26.8	5880	1.00	10,254	1.00	1564	1.00	364	1.00
Loblolly pine....	8×16	180	14	20.5	7.4	4195	.81	6,734	.72	1619	1.10	462	1.45
	6×16	126	4	20.2	5.0	2432	.47	4,295	.46	1324	.90	266	.84
	6×10	174	3	21.3	4.7	3100	.60	6,167	.66	1449	.99	173	.54
	4×12	174	4	19.8	4.7	2713	.52	5,745	.61	1249	.85	185	.58
	8× 8	180	9	22.9	4.9	2903	.56	4,557	.48	1136	.77	93	.29
	6× 7	144	2	21.1	5.0	2990	.58	4,968	.53	1286	.88	116	.36
	4× 8	132	8	19.5	5.0	3384	.65	6,194	.66	1200	.82	196	.62
	2× 2	30	123	17.6	6.6	5170	1.00	9,400	1.00	1467	1.00	318	1.00
Tamarack......	6×12	162	5	23.0	15.1	3434	.45	5,640	.43	1330	.82	318	.75
	4×10	162	4	14.4	9.7	4100	.54	5,320	.41	1356	.84	252	.59
	2× 2	30	47	11.3	16.2	7630	1.00	13,080	1.00	1620	1.00	425	1.00
Western hemlock	8×16	180	44	17.7	17.8	4398	.69	6,420	.62	1737	1.04	406	1.06
	2× 2	28	311	17.9	19.4	6333	1.00	10,369	1.00	1666	1.00	382	1.00
Redwood.......	8×16	180	6	26.3	22.4	3797	.79	4,428	.57	1107	.96	294	1.05
	6×12	180	6	16.1	17.7	3175	.66	3,353	.43	728	.64	167	.60
	7× 9	180	6	15.9	15.2	3280	.69	4,002	.51	1104	.96	147	.53
	3×14	180	6	13.1	24.4	....	...	5,033	.64	....	...	291	1.04
	2×12	180	5	13.8	14.4	3928	.82	5,336	.68	1249	1.09	260	.93
	2×10	180	5	13.8	24.8	3757	.79	4,606	.59	1198	1.05	186	.67
	2× 8	180	6	13.7	20.7	4314	.90	5,050	.65	1313	1.15	166	.60
	2× 2	28	122	15.2	18.8	4777	1.00	7,798	1.00	1146	1.00	279	1.00
Norway pine....	6×12	162	5	16.7	8.1	2968	.56	5,204	.61	1123	.97	286	1.02
	4×10	162	5	13.7	12.0	5170	.98	6,904	.82	1712	1.48	317	1.13
	2× 2	30	60	14.9	11.2	5280	1.00	8,470	1.00	1158	1.00	281	1.00

laying joists for flooring these requirements are satisfied by diagonal bracing which the carpenter calls "bridging."

The relative strengths of the woods from various species of trees can be obtained from the values of the fiber stress at elastic limit and modulus of rupture which are tabulated in Table 1. It will be noted that the hardwoods as a class considerably exceed the conifers in static bending strength. Black and honey locust, the hickories, lowland Spanish oak, cork elm, blue gum, and white oak are the stronger varieties of the hardwoods. Among the softwoods, longleaf, Cuban, and shortleaf pines, yew, Douglas fir, and tamarack are the strongest.* Longleaf pine averages about the same in static bending strength as maple and red oak of the hardwoods. The ratios of the modulus of rupture to fiber stress at elastic limit range from 2.2 to 1.5 for the hardwoods and from 1.8 to 1.5 for the conifers. These ratios will be lower in beams of structural sizes because of defects.

In Table 5 strength values for cross-bending tests on air-seasoned timbers of structural size may be found. These results show very conclusively that the transverse strengths of small timbers are proportionately much higher than the strengths of large timbers. These discrepancies, which for the tests cited amount to 50 per cent in a number of instances, are largely due to the greater uniformity of the small test pieces and their freedom from defects. Selected structural timbers in green state are, in general, about three-fourths as strong as small, clear pieces taken from them.

Results in Table 3 show that air seasoning is somewhat beneficial to the strength of structural timbers. It is probable that a more complete drying would have made the strengths of the air-seasoned timbers still greater.

6. The Time Element in the Loading of Timber. Since timber yields more rapidly under heavy loads than most materials of construction, it is quite necessary to standardize the rate of loading in order that test data may not be influenced by this factor. Extensive tests by the U. S. Forest Service led it to adopt the following rates of unit deformation per minute for the testing program of the Forest Products Laboratory:

Bending tests on timber of structural size	0.0007
Bending tests on small beams	0.0015
Compression parallel to grain, large prisms	0.0015

* Bamboo is a very strong wood in cross bending, as the results of eight tests by J. B. Johnson show. He used pieces which varied in diameter (between joints) from 0.54 in. to 1.25 in., and in thickness from 0.08 in. to 0.17 in. The spans varied from about 28 in. for the larger pieces to 8 in. for the smaller. Values of the modulus of elasticity ranged from 1,960,000 to 3,020,000 and averaged 2,380,000 psi. The moduli of rupture varied from 19,600 to 41,100 and averaged 27,400 psi. The average elastic limit was 17,300 psi. All computations were based on the properties of the annular section. The average elastic resilience in inch-pounds per pound of weight of specimen was 216.

Compression parallel to grain, small prisms   0.0030
Shearing along the grain   0.0150

For the bending tests these rates apply to the extreme fiber at the dangerous section. The speed of the movable head (n) of the testing machine in bending tests is given by $n = \epsilon l^2/6h$ for a center load, and $n = \epsilon l^2/5.4h$ for a third-point loading. In these equations $\epsilon =$ unit deformation per minute, $l =$ span, and $h =$ depth of a rectangular beam. According to Tiemann * variations of 25 per cent in the above rates will not affect strength more than 2 per cent.

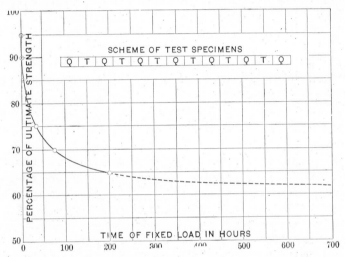

Fig. 5. Results of time tests on dry longleaf pine in compression endwise. The specimens marked Q were tested quickly, as in 1 or 2 minutes; those marked T were loaded with various percentages of the breaking load of the two adjacent specimens, and this load was left on until failure occurred, and the time noted.

In order that proper factors of safety may be established on a basis of testing-machine results, it is very desirable that the strength of timber under dead loads be determined. Experimentation by the Forest Products Laboratory indicates that the modulus of rupture in beams under load for several years is approximately 56 per cent of the value obtained in an ordinary test lasting 4 or 5 min and that the modulus obtained for a quick loading lasting about half a minute is about 10 per cent greater than the values obtained at normal speeds. In Fig. 5 appear the results of approximately 75 end compression tests by J. B. Johnson on $1\frac{5}{8} \times 1\frac{5}{8} \times 3$-in. prisms cut from a single plank. For dead-load tests the prisms were bedded on a nest of four vertical car springs which deformed about an inch under the imposed loads. By means of this elastic base the yielding

* For a more complete discussion see *Proc. ASTM,* Vol. 8, p. 541.

of the specimen was taken up and load of almost constant intensity maintained throughout the test. Each plotted point in Fig. 5 represents three to six tests. These data indicate that the long-time compressive strength of wood parallel to the grain cannot be taken greater than two-thirds of the usual testing-machine values. Compression tests on $1 \times 1 \times 4$-in. Douglas fir and Sitka spruce prisms have shown that the compressive strength obtained from tests of 1-sec duration is about 22 per cent greater than that obtained from tests of companion specimens tested in 5 min.

Moore and Kommers report that the fatigue strength in repeated bending tests of wood approximates one-fourth of the modulus of rupture determined at normal speeds. See also Art. XXXII-13.

STIFFNESS AND OTHER MECHANICAL PROPERTIES

7. The Stiffness of Wood. Stiffness in a structure is often of as much importance as strength, but it is much more frequently neglected in designing. Floors must be sufficiently stiff so that they will not deflect appreciably under working loads or else they give one the feeling of insecurity. If a floor sustains a plastered ceiling its deflection under working load should not exceed $\frac{1}{360}$ of the span. Likewise, the deflection of rafters should be limited, if it is desirable to avoid the disagreeable appearance of a sagged roof.

Stiffness in compression members is not often of moment in design. It is measured by the modulus of elasticity which is computed from the ratio of unit stress to unit strain. For beams the modulus of elasticity (E) may be computed from the equation $E = Pl^3/\beta fI$, where P = a certain load within the elastic limit of the beam, f = deflection corresponding to P, l = length of span, I = moment of inertia of cross section about the neutral axis, and β = a constant depending on the end conditions and the method of loading the beam. For a center load on a simple beam, $\beta = 48$; for the case of a simple beam loaded with two equal concentrated loads (P, P) at the third points of the span, $\beta = {}^{648}\!/_{23}$.

In general, the denser woods are the stiffer, as may be seen by reference to Table 1. There is not, however, much difference between stiffness of the softwoods as a class and the stiffness of the hardwoods, nor are there as wide variations in the stiffnesses of the various species of wood as in the strengths. Values in Table 3 show that green timber is less stiff than air-seasoned; and, from results in Table 5, it appears that the structural sizes of timber are about as stiff as the small clear sticks.

Figure 6 shows typical load-deflection and load-deformation curves for wood. These figures also indicate the method of finding the elastic limit and the correction of curve when it does not pass through the origin. Other load-deformation curves for wood may be seen in Fig. 13.

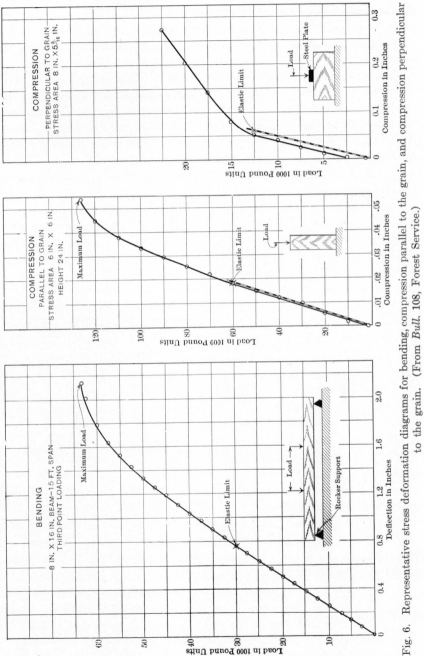

Fig. 6.   Representative stress deformation diagrams for bending, compression parallel to the grain, and compression perpendicular to the grain.   (From *Bull.* 108, Forest Service.)

8. Toughness. A wood which has a large capacity to resist shocks or blows is called tough. The spokes of an automobile or wagon, the tongue of a wagon and its axles, the handle of the axe or sledge all must be tough so that they may absorb without injury the shocks which they receive. In order to be tough a wood must have both strength and flexibility.

Toughness is best measured by the energy of the blow required to rupture a beam in transverse impact. A less reliable index of toughness is obtainable from the energy of rupture in cross bending. The latter test, however, is more easily made than the former and of more general value, since static strength and stiffness may also be determined from it. The torsion test has also been used to measure the toughness of wagon spokes.

In Table 1 the average work done in deforming a large number of small wooden specimens in both static and impact bending tests has been recorded. The methods of determining the various results in static bending have been considered in Chapters I and III. In the impact tests the height of drop was increased by 1- or 2-in. intervals until failure took place. The height of drop at the elastic limit was obtained by plotting height of drop h against the square of the deflection f and determining the value h' at which the curve deviated from a straight line. The fiber stress at elastic limit S_e was calculated from $S_e = 3Wh'l/fbd^2$; the modulus of elasticity E from $E = l^2 \times S_e/6hf$; and the elastic resilience K from $K = Wh'/lbd$. The undefined symbols are W = weight of hammer, l = length of span, b = breadth of beam, and d = depth of beam.

From the test results on green timber, it will be observed that the total work in static bending and the height of drop causing complete failure in impact bending vary with different species in approximately the same manner. With these calculated values as criteria, it is obvious that the hardwoods as a class excel the conifers in toughness. Among the hardwoods, osage orange, hickory, rock elm, slippery elm, honey locust, and hackberry are very tough; basswood and sycamore are more brittle than many of the softwoods. Longleaf pine is the only one of the conifers possessing much toughness.

Seasoning when unaccompanied by checking generally increases toughness, but in chestnut, gum, and willow it causes a marked decrease in toughness and, to a less extent, adversely affects hickory. In general, greenwood is tougher than seasoned material.

9. Cleavability is the measure of the ease with which wood may be split. This property is of considerable moment in the working of wood, especially in splitting fence rails and firewood. Woods which must be fastened by nails and screws should have a high resistance to splitting.

Since splitting is accomplished by wedging apart the longitudinal elements, it is closely related to tension, across the grain. At the Forest

Products Laboratory, the test piece of Fig. 7 is used to determine resistance to cleavage.

From data in U. S. Forest Service *Circ.* 213, it appears that most hardwoods split more easily along radial planes than along tangential surfaces. Among the conifers the difference in cleavage strength in the two directions is not great, but for longleaf pine and tamarack it is greatest across radial planes. Interlocking of the wood fibers causes high cleavage strength; defects like shakes and checks reduce it. Knots may affect it either way, depending upon the number, position, and character.

Honey locust, hickory, slippery elm, hard maple, and the oaks

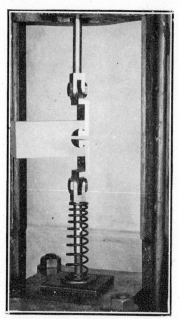

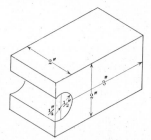

Fig. 7. Cleavage test specimen and test assembly. (Forest Products Laboratory.)

have the highest resistance to splitting. Basswood and the conifers split with comparative ease.

10. Hardness. Both resistance to indentation and resistance to scratching are important properties in woods which are to be used for finishing and for furniture. These properties, together with the ability to wear without splintering, determine the wearing resistance of wood for floors and pavements. Aside from the indentation tests no satisfactory type of test has been devised to measure these properties. However, experience shows that woods having marked difference in the character of the spring wood and summer wood (pine and oak), wear best when laid with the edge of the grain exposed to wear. With the fine-grained woods of uniform texture, like hard maple, the resistance to wear appears to be little affected by the method of sawing.

The resistance to indentation of a number of green woods is given in Table 1. Among the hardwoods, basswood, poplar, aspen, cottonwood, and willow are quite soft, whereas yew, a conifer, is remarkably hard.

In green wood the hardness appears to be independent of the surface indented. Seasoning greatly increases resistance of all surfaces to indentation but affects the resistance of the end surfaces most.

CONDITIONS AFFECTING MECHANICAL PROPERTIES OF TIMBER

11. Density. All the mechanical properties of clear wood are related to its density, which varies directly with the apparent specific gravity, ρ. Within a given species the relation is closer than between species. This is most pronounced in timbers of structural size where defects and moisture content considerably affect interspecies relationships.

From a large number of tests of small clear pieces made by the Forest Products Laboratory (see *Bull.* 676 and *Tech. Bull.* 158, U. S. Dept. Agr.) the data in Table 6 were obtained:

TABLE 6

Property.	Modulus of Rupture.	Modulus of Elasticity.	Work to Max. Load.	Compressive Strength		Shearing Strength (tangential).	Tension Across Grain.
				Parallel to Grain.	Normal to Grain.		
	lb./in.²	1000 lb./in.²	in lb./in.³	lb./in.²	lb./in.²	lb./in.²	lb./in.²
Green.....	$17{,}600\rho^{1.25}$	2360ρ	$35.6\rho^{1.75}$	$6{,}730\rho$	$3000\rho^{2.25}$	$2750\rho^{1.33}$	$1950\rho^2$
Air-dry....	$25{,}700\rho^{1.25}$	2800ρ	$32.4\rho^{1.75}$	$12{,}200\rho$	$4630\rho^{2.25}$	$4000\rho^{1.33}$	$2100\rho^2$

It will be observed that the general law is $Q = C\rho^n$, where n is an exponent between 1.0 and 2.25, and ρ is computed from the volume of the wood at test and the oven-dry weight.

Figure 8 shows the relation between modulus of rupture and the specific gravity for 113 varieties of wood in air-dry and in green condition. In standard specifications the value of specific gravity as a criterion of quality is evidenced by elimination of timbers of light weight from the select and dense select grades. Since specific gravity is affected by rate of growth, per cent summer wood, position of specimen in tree, and moisture content, the influence of these factors is next considered.

12. Effect of Rate of Growth. Figure 9 illustrates the previously made statement that coniferous wood having a medium rate of growth is the strongest and stiffest. There is, however, a wide range in the most effective rates of growth for different conifers. In the dense hardwoods rapid growth is more desirable. In tests on green hickory the best strength was obtained from material having a rate of growth of 10 to 20 rings per inch, and the best toughness from specimens with less than 10 rings per inch (*Bull.* 80, U. S. Forest Service).

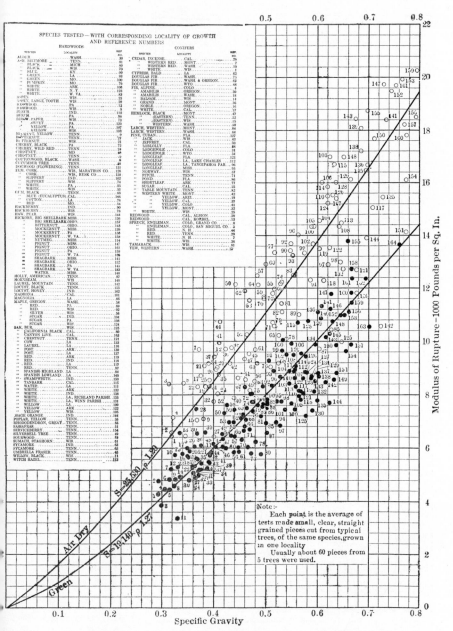

Fig. 8. Relation between bending strength (s) and specific gravity (ρ) for 113 woods. (Specific gravity is based on volume at test and dry weight. Diagram compiled at Forest Products Laboratory.)

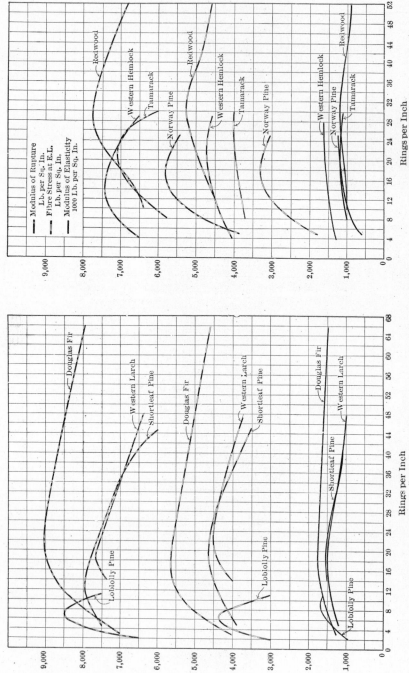

Fig. 9. Relation of modulus of rupture, fiber stress at elastic limit, and modulus of elasticity to rate of growth, as shown by number of rings per inch. (From *Bull.* 108, U. S. Forest Service.)

Whereas rate of growth is not so trustworthy a criterion of strength as the percentage of summer wood, the select grades of southern pine and Douglas fir are based on material containing not less than 6 nor more than 20 annual rings per linear inch.

13. Effect of Percentage of Summer Wood. With most coniferous wood the summer wood is readily identified and forms a valuable index of

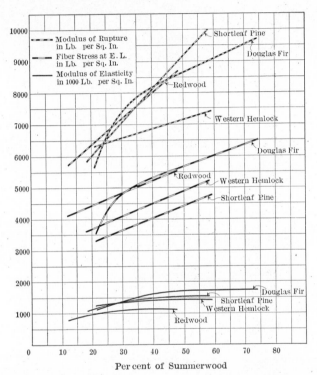

Fig. 10. Relation of modulus of rupture, fiber stress at elastic limit, and modulus of elasticity to percentage of summer wood. (From *Bull.* 108, U. S. Forest Service.)

the mechanical properties of the timber. The proportion of summer wood in a given coniferous timber is generally determined by estimating the ratio of the sum of the areas of the dark rings to the total cross section.

Figure 10 shows the relation of per cent summer wood to strength and stiffness for several coniferous woods. On account of the important relation which the per cent summer wood bears to mechanical properties a minimum percentage limit has been inserted in specifications for dense structural timber.

14. Relations of Mechanical Properties to Position in Tree. Since wood in the lower part of the trunk of a tree is more dense than that higher up, and since the densest wood at any given height is situated between the pith and the middle ring of the cross section, a small variation in the strength of wood due to position in the tree will be found. Figure 11 shows how the strength of wood in western larch trees varies with the height above ground.

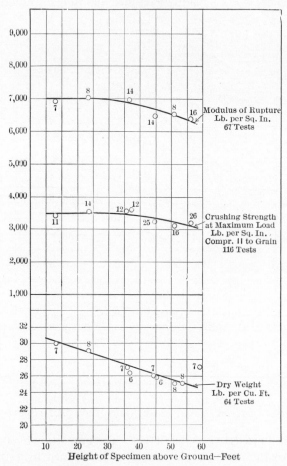

Fig. 11. Relation of strength values to height in trees. Specimens were small clear pieces of green western larch. (*Bull.* 122, U. S. Forest Service.)

15. The Influence of Defects on Mechanical Properties. Defects such as knots, checks, shakes, and inclined grain are limited in structural grades of timber, since they are a principal cause of variation in mechanical properties. The discrepancies in strengths of large and small specimens and the variation in properties of test pieces of the same wood are largely due to defects. *The magnitude of the influence of defects is determined* *by their character, size, and location,* and these factors are given consideration in the limitations for various structural grades.

Knots in heavy beams and posts which do not run directly through the member, or knots running normal to the top of a beam, reduce strength in direct proportion to their size. When knots run directly through joists and beams near the top and bottom surfaces in the midhalf of the length, their weakening effect is approximately in the ratio of twice the diameter to the depth of member. Knots near the ends of beams are less harmful than those near the middle, hence larger knots may be permitted in the end zones than near midlength. Since grain distortion and shrinkage strains are greater around large knots than around small knots, the maximum permitted size is varied with the width of the face of the timber containing the defect. The distribution and the sum of the knot diameters in the face of a post or beam also affect strength and are limited in grading rules.

From numerous compression parallel-to-grain tests on 6 by 6-in. wood prisms containing sound knots of various sizes, the comparisons shown in Table 7 were drawn from *Bull.* 108, U. S. Forest Service. These data show

TABLE 7. EFFECT OF KNOTS ON COMPRESSION PROPERTIES OF WOOD

Species.	Kind of Knot.	Diameter of Knot (Inches).	Percentages of Results Based on Compression Tests of Clear Specimens for		
			Elastic Limit.	Crushing Strength.	Modulus of Elasticity.
Douglas Fir.......	Pin	0– $\frac{1}{2}$	95	94	106
	Standard	$\frac{1}{2}$–1$\frac{1}{2}$	87	86	90
	Large	Over 1$\frac{1}{2}$	78	78	71
Western Larch....	Pin	0– $\frac{1}{2}$	112	104	119
	Standard	$\frac{1}{2}$–1$\frac{1}{2}$	98	89	100
	Large	Over 1$\frac{1}{2}$	98	85	94
Western Hemlock..	Pin	0– $\frac{1}{2}$	96	97	100
	Standard	$\frac{1}{2}$–1$\frac{1}{2}$	94	91	97
	Large	Over 1$\frac{1}{2}$	86	83	81

that the strength and stiffness of short compression members may be reduced 15 to 30 per cent by the presence of knots 1½ in. or over in diameter. In long columns, however, the effects of knots on stiffness is immaterial, hence the Euler loads are not reduced by the presence of knots.

Other tests by the Forest Products Laboratory have shown that knots have little effect on the elastic limits and stiffnesses of beams, but they decrease the modulus of rupture. Consequently knots in beams will adversely affect ultimate strength and toughness. Sound knots near the neutral plane have little influence on the shearing strengths of beams.

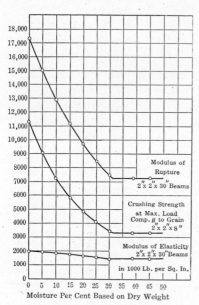

Fig. 12. Effect of varying degrees of moisture upon the strength of small, clear specimens of western (known to trade as West Coast) hemlock. (*Bull.* 115, U. S. Dept. Agr.)

Shakes and checks are most harmful to strength when they follow the neutral plane of a beam or run diagonally across the tension side of it. In the first case they weaken the resistance to horizontal shear, and in the second case they lessen the tensile strength.

In seasoned timber shakes and checks are more pronounced than in green timber; hence in grading rules for structural timbers the severity of the limitation on the proportion of the width of face occupied by check or shake varies with the grade and condition when inspected.

Inclination of grain to the axis of a beam less than 1:40 has little effect on strength. For greater slopes the strength is considerably reduced. Forest Products Laboratory tests indicate that grain slopes of 1:20 cause a decrease in beam strength of about one-eighth, 1:15 about one-fourth, 1:11 about three-eighths, and 1:8 about one-half. For posts, grain inclined 1:15 reduces strength about one-eighth, 1:11 about one-quarter, 1:8 about three-eighths, and 1:6 about one-half.

16. The Effect of Moisture on Mechanical Properties. Variations in the moisture content of the cell walls are accompanied by large changes in the strength and stiffness of wood. These effects are most noticeable in small, clear pieces which season with great rapidity. On account of the slowness with which large structural timbers dry it is, however, unsafe to count on any increase in strength due to air drying of such members. After years of seasoning, large timbers may lose enough water to effect an increase in tensile and compressive strength and in stiffness, but defects arising from shrinkage stresses often cause a decrease in the resistance to horizontal shear stresses. In kiln drying, the normal increase in strength due to loss of moisture is often nullified by case hardening, a condition

of the piece. If the exposure period is short and the temperature is not excessive, wood may recover practically all its original properties. Air-dry wood may withstand temperatures up to 150°F for over a year with-

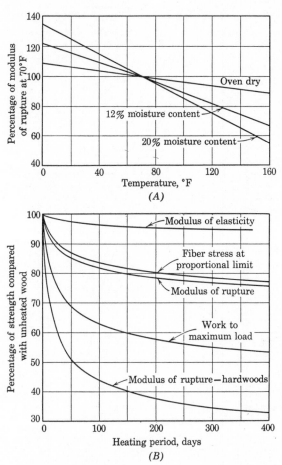

Fig. 14. *A*, Approximate immediate effect of temperature on modulus of rupture at several moisture-content conditions. *B*, Effect of heating on bending properties of wood exposed to water at 200°F for various periods and then tested at normal temperature and 12 per cent moisture content. All curves are for softwoods unless other-wise indicated. (Forest Products Laboratory.)

out an important permanent loss in strength, even though the strength while heated will be lower than that at normal temperature. Wet wood exposed to 150°F for 1 year will suffer an important strength loss.

Figure 14*A* shows the effect of temperature on the modulus of rupture of wood at three different moisture contents. This figure shows that dry wood is not affected by temperature as much as wet wood. The effect of heating on the bending properties of wood exposed to water at 200°F for various periods and then tested at normal temperature and 12 per cent moisture content is given in Fig. 14*B*. Under these conditions the modulus

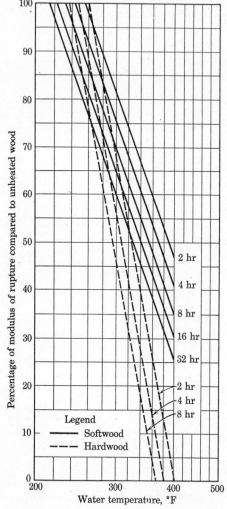

Fig. 15. Variation in modulus of rupture with temperature for softwoods and hardwoods soaked in hot water for various periods. Strength tests were made at normal temperature and 12 per cent moisture content. (Forest Products Laboratory.)

of elasticity is least affected; toughness is greatly affected. This figure also shows that hardwoods are affected to a considerably greater extent than softwoods.

The interrelation of temperature and period of exposure in hot water for softwood and hardwood is given in Fig. 15. As the temperature is increased above 220°F the modulus of rupture decreases rapidly. Exposure at 400°F for 2 hours reduces the modulus of rupture of softwood to about 45 per cent of the value for unheated wood and reduces the modulus of rupture of hardwood to 0.

The important strength properties of dry wood in bending and compression are much higher at a temperature of −300°F than at room temperature.

18. The Effect of Preservatives on Strength. Experiments made at the Forest Products Laboratory * show that creosote oil in itself is not injurious to the strength of timber, but excessive heat or pressure during the steaming and impregnation processes may injure strength considerably. From a boiling treatment (see Art. V-20) on Douglas fir timbers, both green and air-seasoned stringers lost about one-third of their normal strength. Tests by the U. S. Forest Service and others have shown that the boiling-under-vacuum method of treatment produces Douglas fir timber markedly superior to that treated by the ordinary boiling or steaming and boiling processes. In the U. S. Forest Service tests on 8 × 16-in. stringers, the temperature approximated 190°F, duration of boiling under vacuum was 21 to 22 hours, pressure period was 2 to 3 hours, and maximum pressure was about 125 psi. The ratios of strength of treated to strength of normal timbers varied from 87 to 94 per cent. The ratio was 93 per cent for the unseasoned and 90 per cent for the timbers seasoned before treatment. The tests indicated that the reduction in strength was less as the size of piece, temperature, length of boiling period, and pressure were reduced. However, the best combination of these variables still awaits a thorough investigation.

Zinc chloride solutions of the strengths commonly used in treating do not seriously weaken timber, but apparently do render it somewhat more brittle under impact.

19. Fire-Killed Douglas Fir. From the results of over 400 tests on beams of structural size and several hundred tests on smaller specimens,† it appears that fire-killed Douglas fir, if sound, is practically as strong and just as stiff as material obtained from growing trees. If such timber has stood for several years after the fire, it is likely to be badly eaten by beetles, borers, and fungi. Consequently careful inspection should be made to detect evidences of such deterioration before using fire-killed Douglas fir.

20. Effect of Bleeding on Strength of Longleaf Pine. The wood of pine trees which have been bled for turpentine is just as strong as that of unbled trees. This statement is based upon the results of over 1300 tests made by the U. S. Forest Service (*Circ.* 12) on air-dry material.

* See *Circ.* 39, U. S. Forest Service, and *Bull.* 286, U. S. Dept. Agr.
† J. B. Knapp in U. S. Forest Service *Bull.* 112.

Furthermore, these tests show that neither the shrinkage nor the specific weight are affected by bleeding; and that the resin loss, confined to the sapwood, is insufficient to affect the durability of the wood. Other tests indicate that the strength of longleaf pine is independent of the resin content.

STRENGTH OF NAILS AND WOOD JOINTS

21. Holding Force of Nails, Screws, and Spikes. *Nails.* A large number of tests at the Forest Products Laboratory indicate that the withdrawal force P for common nails or spikes per inch of embedment driven into side grain in seasoned wood approximates $P = 6900\rho^{2.5}d$, where ρ = specific gravity and d = nail diameter in inches. The safe quiescent load suggested for most species is $P/6$; for southern pine $P/8$ is preferable.

Resistance to withdrawal is increased from 90 to 200 per cent by chemically etching nails and increased about 40 to 50 per cent when cement-coated nails are used in softwoods. Barbed nails, nails with shanks longitudinally or spirally grooved, square or triangular in section, have resistance to withdrawal superior to that of common nails. When common nails are driven into green wood they usually lose part of their withdrawal resistance if the wood seasons; barbed and grooved nails usually retain most of their holding force. Nails with blunt tapered points and nails driven into lead holes exhibit greater holding forces than common nails and nails driven without lead holes. In softwoods the holding force parallel to the grain is only half to three-fourths the value normal to the grain. In hardwoods the direction of driving has little effect on the holding force.

Screws. Tests by the Bureau of Standards show that the withdrawal force P for common wood screws per inch of length when inserted normal to the grain in seasoned wood approximates $P = 10,200\rho^2 d$. In this expression it is assumed that the screws are of common lengths, embedded at least two-thirds of their lengths, and inserted in lead holes having a diameter about 70 per cent of the root diameter of the screw when placed in softwoods and 90 per cent when in hardwoods. A factor of safety of 6 is suggested for quiescent loads. Screws inserted parallel to the grain can carry about three-fourths of the foregoing values if splitting is avoided.

Railroad Spikes. In Table 9 are given results of tests made at the University of Illinois to determine the holding force of ordinary spikes and screw spikes in various woods. The common spikes were $5\frac{1}{2}$ and 6 in. long by $\frac{9}{16}$ to $\frac{5}{8}$ in. square; they were fairly smooth. The screw spikes varied from 5 to $5\frac{1}{2}$ in. in length and had a diameter at root of thread of $^{21}\!/_{32}$ to $^{22}\!/_{32}$ in. The thread projected $\frac{1}{8}$ to $\frac{3}{16}$ in. and the pitch was $\frac{1}{2}$ in. Spike holes were bored $^{11}\!/_{16}$ in. in diameter, thereby insuring a tight fit. The results in the table are corrected for a uniform

TABLE 9. RELATIVE HOLDING STRENGTH OF SCREW SPIKES AND ORDINARY SPIKES IN SEVERAL TIMBERS

(*Bull.* No. 6, Engr. Expt. Sta., University of Illinois)

Kind of Tie.	Kind of Spike.	RESISTANCE IN POUNDS FOR			RELATIVE RESISTANCES.		
		$\frac{1}{8}$-in. Pull.	$\frac{1}{4}$-in. Pull.	Max. Resist.	$\frac{1}{8}$-in. Pull.	$\frac{1}{4}$-in. Pull.	Max. Resist.
Water oak......	Ordinary..	2870	5,730	6,780	100	100	100
	Screw....	4888	9,180	12,190	170	160	179
Black oak......	Ordinary..	2910	5,890	7,230	100	100	100
	Screw....	4760	10,420	14,110	164	177	203
Red oak........	Ordinary..	2950	5,350	7,730	100	100	100
	Screw....	4900	10,400	13,560	166	194	176
White oak......	Ordinary..	3510	5,950	7,870	100	100	100
	Screw....	6250	11,900	12,630	178	200	188
Ash...........	Ordinary..	3570	5,200	7,730	100	100	100
	Screw....	5700	10,470	12,760	162	200	165
Beech.........	Ordinary..	2600	5,490	8,840	100	100	100
	Screw....	6450	13,140	16,230	248	221	238
Elm...........	Ordinary..	2380	5,580	7,500	100	100	100
	Screw....	5120	10,090	13,690	215	181	183
Poplar........	Ordinary..	2830	5,290	5,670	100	100	100
	Screw....	3880	6,210	7,490	137	117	132
Chestnut.......	Ordinary..	2850	4,070	5,200	100	100	100
	Screw....	3690	6,340	8,700	129	155	167
Sweet Gum.....	Ordinary..	3230	4,120	5,300	100	100	100
	Screw....	5430	7,710	8,280	167	162	156
Loblolly pine....	Ordinary..	2920	3,500	4,300	100	100	100
	Screw....	5750	9,050	10,620	197	258	247

depth of 5 in. Other tests made to determine the effect of depth of penetration on strength indicated that these factors were directly proportional. Blunt-pointed and bevel-pointed spikes were shown to be slightly superior to chisel-pointed spikes. Common spikes when redriven had about 60 to 80 per cent of the resistance of newly driven spikes.

Not only is the holding force of screw spikes much greater than that of plain spikes, but also their resistance to lateral thrust is consider-

ably higher.   Prof. W. K. Hatt * found that the lateral resistance of
screw spikes was 1.2 to 2.4 times the resistance of plain spikes similarly
tested. No support was provided for the head of the spike in these tests.
In timber treated with crude oil the holding force of plain spikes is considerably less than in untreated timber or in timbers treated by other commercial processes. For shortleaf pine treated with crude oil, Hatt found
the holding force of plain spikes to be only 45 per cent and of screw spikes
73 per cent of the values obtained for the respective spikes driven in untreated wood.

22. The Strength of Joints. *Nailed and Screwed Joints.* Extensive
tests by the Forest Products Laboratory resulted in the formula for the
safe lateral load for wire nail joints, $P = Kd^{3/2}$, in which P represents the
safe lateral load in pounds per nail, d the diameter of the nail, and K a
constant depending on species and condition of wood. With a factor of
safety of 6 and a moisture content of 15 per cent, the values of K given in
Table 10 apply. With reasonable spacing, the strength of the joint is in

TABLE 10.   VALUES OF CONSTANTS K AND K_s FOR WOOD JOINTS

Species of Wood	K	K_s
Cedar, white; Hemlock, eastern; Pine, lodgepole, sugar, white; Spruce, red, Sitka, white....................................	900	2100
Cedar, red; Cypress; Hemlock, western; Pine, Norway; Redwood; Tamarack...	1125	2700
Douglas fir (coast region); Larch, western; Pine, southern yellow..	1375	3300
Aspen; Basswood; Chestnut; Cottonwood; Poplar..............	900	2100
Ash, black; Elm, American; Gum; Maple, soft; Sycamore........	1250	2900
Ash, white; Beech; Birch, sweet, yellow; Elm, rock; Hickory; Locust; Maple, hard; Oak; Walnut.........................	1700	4000

proportion to the number of nails used. For safe lateral loads on wood
screws under conditions similar to the above, the Laboratory recommends
the equation $P = K_s d^2$, in which d is the diameter of shank of the screw,
with the values of K_s given in Table 10 and a penetration into the block
receiving the point of 7 or more diameters. The corresponding loads will
have a factor of safety of about 6, and the joints would be expected to slip
0.007 to 0.01 in.

Bolts and Connectors. In the *Wood Handbook* the Forest Products
Laboratory gives much valuable test data and information for the design
of wood joints fastened by bolts and by various types of modern ring or
plate connectors. Factors that influence the load-carrying capacity of a
bolted joint are the size of the main timber member, the safe bearing

* See *Bull.* 124, Am. Ry. Eng. Assoc.

stress, the ratio of the length of the bolt in the main timber to the diameter of the bolt, the direction of the load with respect to the grain direction, the character of the fit between the bolts and the bolt holes, the number and the properties of the bolts used, the center-to-center distance between the bolts, the distance between the bolts and the end of the timber member, and the splice plates used. For further information see *Tech. Bull.* 865 (1944), U. S. Dept. Agr.

Timber connectors have increased allowable joint loads and have expanded the use of structural timber. Joints made with timber connectors are relatively simple and efficient, perform well under adverse conditions, and may be prefabricated and assembled later in the field. Timber connectors are partially bedded in the pieces to be joined and act much like rigid dowels. Bolts placed in oversize holes are centered in these connectors to aid in assembling and maintaining tight joints. Four general types commonly used are the split-ring, toothed-ring, claw-plate, and shear-plate timber connectors. The split ring fits into precut grooves in the timber to be joined; the toothed ring is forced under pressure into the members to be joined; claw plates fit into prebored recesses and have short teeth that are forced into the timber; shear plates also fit into prebored recesses but have no teeth. Split rings and toothed rings are used in wood-to-wood joints; shear and claw plates are used in either wood-to-wood or metal-to-wood joints. The strength of timber-connector joints depends on the species of wood, dimensions of the wood members, type and size of the connector, edge and end margins, the direction of the load with respect to the grain direction, size of bolt hole, moisture content, and other conditions.

Glued Joints. The efficiency of glued joints depends on the kind and condition of the wood, the kind and condition of the glue, method of gluing, type of joint and method of conditioning it, and the protection given the joint. Among the woods that are easiest to glue are western red cedar, chestnut, white fir, redwood, and spruce; whereas beech, birch, gum, and hickory require special treatment in order to obtain good results.

Animal, casein, and resin glues all find use in gluing woodwork. Animal glues give best results when kept warm, set quickly without stain, and are much used for furniture, veneer, and millwork. Casein glues are mixed with cold water, set quickly, stain some woods badly, markedly dull woodworking tools, and are used in gluing lumber, veneer, plywood, aircraft, and automobile bodies. They are moderately durable under damp conditions. The most commonly used synthetic-resin glues are the phenol-formaldehyde and urea-formaldehyde types. Both are thermosetting. They are available in the form of dry film, dry powder, or in solution. When hot-pressed at 250°F, they are durable under severe exposure. Resin glues are used primarily in veneer and laminated wood construction.

High-frequency dielectric heating is used for rapid curing of glues in wood joints. When the electric field is perpendicular to a glue joint all the wood and glue between the electrodes is quickly heated. When the electric field is parallel to a glue joint containing some water the joint is heated selectively without appreciably heating the wood away from the joint.

The moisture content of wood to be glued should be less than 15 per cent; the optimum is slightly less than the content which will obtain under service. A uniform film of glue free from air bubbles or dirt and complete contact between the surfaces joined are essential to strong joints. Plain joints between side-grain surfaces can be made to develop the strength of the wood in longitudinal shear, in tension across grain, and in cleavage. By using a scarf joint having a slope with the grain not greater than 1 to 15 the tensile strength of the wood parallel to the grain can be equaled; with a butt joint only one-fourth of this strength can be secured.

Care should be taken to avoid finishing edge joints until the glue moisture has been dissipated. Artificial drying of glued wood should be carefully controlled. For moisture contents under 12 per cent, well-glued wood joints are permanent. The durability of joints may be materially increased by impregnation with preservatives.

23. Plywood signifies glued wood panels usually made of three or more thin layers of wood with the grain of one or more layers at an angle of 90° with the others. Usually 3, 5, or 7 plies are glued in such manner that the grain direction of the bands is balanced with respect to the core layer in order to avoid as far as possible warping due to shrinkage and swelling. Panels are commonly made 4 ft wide and 8 ft long and in thicknesses of $\frac{1}{4}$, $\frac{3}{8}$, $\frac{1}{2}$, $\frac{5}{8}$, and $\frac{3}{4}$ in.

Plywood does not check or split so easily when nailed or screwed and possesses better shear strength than solid wood if buckling is prevented.

It also has smaller dimensional changes due to moisture changes. The strength properties of plywood in all directions are more nearly equal than those of solid wood. The strength of plywood depends on the size of the member, the number of plies, the thicknesses of the various plies, the grain directions of adjacent plies, the properties of the various woods used in making the plies, and the direction of the applied load with respect to the grain of the face plies.

For computing the ultimate bending moment, M, of plywood, the Forest Products Laboratory uses $M = KSI/c$, where S is the modulus of rupture of the solid wood, I the moment of inertia of only the plies with grain parallel to the span, c the distance from the neutral axis to the outer fiber of the outermost ply with grain parallel to span, and K is a constant. For plywood with 3 or more plies having face-ply grain parallel to span, or with 5 or more plies having face-ply grain normal to span, $K = 0.85$; with 3 plies and face-ply grain normal to span, $K = 1.5$.

24. Glued Laminated Wood. Glued laminated wood may be defined as two or more layers of wood glued together so that the grain of all layers is parallel to the length of the member. The laminations may vary with regard to size, shape, species, number, quality of wood, and type of glue joint. Laminated wood members have strength properties that are about the same as those of solid wood members.

Five important advantages of glued laminated wood over solid wood follow: (*a*) Structural members of any size may be made from standard commercial sizes of timber. (*b*) The relatively small parts of a laminated member may be easily seasoned and dried to the right moisture content before fabrication and consequently seasoning defects may be avoided. (*c*) High-quality wood may be placed at points of high stress, and poorer material may be used at other points. (*d*) The size of the member may be varied from section to section in accordance with the strength requirements. (*e*) The members may be built up to provide distinctive architectural effects.

25. Working Stresses. From the results of extensive and carefully conducted tests the Forest Products Laboratory has compiled a *Guide to the Grading of Structural Timbers and the Determination of Working Stresses*. Both the ASTM * and the AREA have based their specifications for the different structural grades of timber on the limitations proposed by the Laboratory regarding stresses and defects. In the present specifications for structural timber issued by these bodies timbers are separated at the mill into grades in accordance with their inherent defects. From the laboratory data the safe strength of each grade under continuously dry conditions is known and used as the characteristic designation for that grade. Thus $1600f$, applied to a timber beam, indicates that the member can carry safely under dry conditions a maximum fiber stress of 1600 psi; likewise $1300c$ signifies that the member, as a short column, can safely carry a load of 1300 psi applied parallel to the grain.

Exposure is divided by the Laboratory into three degrees of severity: (*a*) continuously dry, as in protected locations of low humidity; (*b*) occasionally wet but quickly dried, as in bridges, trestles, grandstands, and exposed frames; (*c*) more or less continuously damp or wet, as exposed to waves or tides, in contact with ground or wet structures. Roughly, fiber stresses in bending and in compression parallel to the grain for condition *b* should not exceed seven-eighths of values permitted for condition *a*; and for condition *c* they should not exceed three-quarters the values for *a*. For compression perpendicular to the grain the stress ratios for conditions *b* and *c* should not exceed 0.7 and 0.6, respectively.

* See table of basic stresses for timber in ASTM *Standards* D245.

Impact stresses when less than 100 per cent of the live load need not be considered, if the working stresses are properly used.

Horizontal shear stress values are the maxima permitted at the neutral axis in beams. In calculating the shear near the end of a beam the loads concentrated between the ends and a point three times the depth of the beam from the end may be considered acting at that point. For moving loads on stringers of highway or railway bridges, however, it is permissible, in calculating the shear at one end, to ignore the wheel loads between the end and a point three times the depth of the beam from that end provided the remainder of the span is assumed loaded to produce maximum end shear.

Shear stresses in joint details may be increased 50 per cent above the values permitted for horizontal shear in beams.

Modulus of elasticity values given in the tables in ASTM *Standards* D245 are for loads of short duration. For calculating the deflections of beams under continuous loads, it is advisable to use one-half of the tabulated values to allow for sag due to continued loading.

The working unit stresses for compression parallel to the grain in the ASTM *Standards* are given for posts and struts with ratio of unsupported length to least dimension (l/d) not over 10. These values should also be used in calculating end bearing areas for compression members, since short struts are likely to fail at the ends because of differences in moisture content.

For columns of intermediate length a fourth-power parabola and for long columns a tangent Euler curve provide a combination of formulas which, the Forest Products Laboratory tests have demonstrated, represent the strength-slenderness-ratio relationship. The parabolic formula for columns of intermediate length is

$$P/A = S[1 - \tfrac{1}{3}(l/Kd)^4] \quad \text{between } P/A = S \text{ and } P/A = 2S/3$$

where P = safe load in pounds, A = cross-sectional area in square inches, S = working unit stress in compression parallel to grain for short column, l = unsupported length in inches, d = least dimension in inches. $K = (\pi/2)\sqrt{E/6S}$ is the abscissa of the point of tangency with the Euler curve; E = modulus of elasticity. Values of K for different species are given in ASTM *Standards* D245.

The tests have demonstrated that the detrimental influences of defects on the strengths of columns decrease as the ratio l/d increases until $l/d = K$. For longer columns the tests show that the Euler formula is accurate for pin-end columns. To obtain safe loads, a factor of safety of 3 is recommended. With the available data and usual conditions, the Laboratory does not find it advisable to increase the permitted loads for square end columns beyond those recommended in the following formula for columns with pin ends.

The Euler formula for long columns with a factor of safety of 3 is

$$P/A = \pi^2 E/36(l/d)^2 \quad \text{between } l/d = K \text{ and } l/d = 50$$

Tension. Where wood is used in direct tension the fiber stresses permitted in bending may be employed safely, provided joint details are properly designed. When the joists or beams of a given grade are used to carry tension, as in bottom chords of trusses, defects may be allowed to increase in size toward the ends of the members since the stress is gradually imposed in the members through splice plates.

Limitation on Defects. In the joist and plank grades restrictions are made so that allowable fiber stresses may be applied to either broad or narrow faces of these members. For material 5 in. and thicker loaded on the broad face, the knot requirement for the broad face is the same as that given in the rules for the narrow face. Timbers of square or nearly square section which are to be subjected to bending should be selected on the basis of beam and stringer grading rules, but care should be exercised to see that knot restrictions are applied to the proper faces.

In stringers of two-span length subject to moving loads the same restrictions should be imposed on defects occurring in middle two-thirds length as apply to the middle third of the length of a single-span stringer.

Basis of Working Stresses. In obtaining the tabulated working stresses for ASTM and other standards the Forest Products Laboratory considered both the elastic limit and ultimate strength, but adopted the latter as the more reliable basis for determining safe working stresses. The factors of safety vary with the duration of stress. Under the recommended stresses for timbers in dry locations, the average timber in a building has a factor of safety of 6 for impact loading, 4 for a load lasting 5 min, and $2\frac{1}{4}$ for a loading of long duration. Approximately 1 per cent of the pieces of very light weight carrying maximum defects permitted in a given grade would probably break if stressed 50 per cent above the recommended value for 10 years. New timbers in bridges have factors of safety about 15 per cent higher than the above.

The recommended working stresses are based upon the strength of the clear green wood of the given species and are varied in accordance with the following: Extreme fiber stresses in bending are varied with grade, type of exposure, and size of piece; horizontal shear stresses, with grade; stresses in compression parallel to grain, with grade and exposure; stresses in compression perpendicular to grain, with exposure. Modulus of elasticity values are considered constant for all grades, exposures, and sizes. In the highest stress grades, the allowable extreme fiber stresses range from 75 to 94 per cent of the basic stresses of green clear wood.

CHAPTER

VII

Building Stone*

1. Uses and Production. We shall include under the head of building
stone those stones which are used for ornamentation or for any form
of masonry construction, as in foundations, retaining walls, buildings,
bridges, pavements. In some of these constructions stone has been employed as a building material since the first Egyptian dynasty. The
tombs and pyramids of Egypt, the excavated ruins of ancient Troy, remains of Grecian and Roman structures, and the many old monuments
of stone scattered through England, France, Germany, and the Holy
Land all bear witness to the use which the ancients made of this material.
The conditions which govern in the selection of stone for structural purposes are cost, fashion, ornamental value, and durability; although the
latter property, it must be admitted, is frequently overlooked or disregarded. Cost is largely influenced by transportation charges, difficulties
in quarrying and cutting, ornamental features, and durability of the stone.
Color and arrangement, and shape of mineral constituents greatly influence fashion and ornamental value. Resistance to fire and power to
withstand weather conditions—factors which are largely influenced by
the mineral constitution of the rock—are the most important determinators of durability.

Suitable stone for structural purposes is widely distributed both in the
United States and abroad. Granite is found in large quantities in Canada,
England, Scotland, Sweden, and Norway; within the United States, California, North Carolina, Vermont, Massachusetts, Georgia, and Maine
lead in production. Limestone and marble are found in Canada, Italy,
England, Algeria, Germany, Belgium, France, and Austria. The following states lead in producing limestone: New York, Illinois, Ohio, Indiana,
Michigan. Vermont, Georgia, Tennessee, Alabama, and Missouri provide most of the domestic marble. Sandstone is obtainable in Canada
and Scotland; Ohio, Pennsylvania, West Virginia, New York, and California lead the states in production. Trap rock is produced principally
in New Jersey, Connecticut, Oregon, Washington, and Pennsylvania.

* References: Merrill's *Stones for Building and Decoration* (out of print), Ries'
Building Stones and Clay Products (out of print), Eckel's *Building Stones and Clays*
(out of print), Ries' and Watson's *Engineering Geology,* Bowles' *The Stone Industries.*

Slate is found in Canada, England, and France: within the United States the principal sources are Pennsylvania, Vermont, Virginia, New York, and Maine.

In 1950 the value of the building stone (except slate) produced in the United States was about $390 million. Production in short tons of the important building stones was: limestone, 180; granite, 23; basalt, 23; and sandstone, 9. More than half the stone was marketed as crushed stone, and other uses included rough or dressed building stone, monument stone, paving stone, rip-rap, and curbing. Over $30 million worth of limestone was sold as flux. The slate produced in the United States in 1950 was valued at about $15 million.

2. The Mineral Constituents of Rocks. Inasmuch as rocks are aggregations of minerals, their properties will be dependent upon the character of these constituents. Valuable aid in determining minerals is afforded by the blowpipe and by the reactions of the minerals with acids. For identifying minerals, for ascertaining their condition, and for observing the structural arrangement in a rock, the examination of thin sections under the microscope by an expert petrographer is often of great value. Chemical analyses of rocks are of little importance except in corroborating microscopic observations. The rapid determination of mineral constitution is ordinarily made, however, through recognition of certain physical properties. The more important of these properties are hardness, cleavage, streak, color, luster, specific gravity, and shape of crystals.

Hardness is probably of most importance for rapid determinations of minerals. It is measured by scratching the mineral with a series of substances of known variation in hardness, the following scale of Mohs being generally used:

1. Talc, scratches easily with the thumb-nail.
2. Gypsum, scratched by the thumb-nail.
3. Calcite, not scratched by thumb-nail, but easily cut by knife.
4. Fluorite can be cut by knife with greater difficulty than calcite.
5. Apatite can be cut only with difficulty by knife.
6. Orthoclase can be cut by knife with great difficulty on thin edges.
7. Quartz, not scratched by steel, scratches glass.
8. Topaz.
9. Sapphire.
10. Diamond.

If, for example, a given substance is scratched by calcite and not by gypsum its hardness is between 2 and 3.

Cleavage is the measure of the ease and distinctness with which a mineral may be separated on planes parallel to the crystal faces. All minerals do not exhibit cleavage, and only a few possess well-marked cleavage. Easy, distinct, indistinct, perfect, and imperfect are words often used to characterize cleavage.

Streak is the color of the mineral when in the form of a powder. It is generally determined by rubbing the mineral on a bit of unglazed porcelain, called a streak stone. Since the streak of a mineral is constant in color, it is of considerable importance in distinguishing the hematites and the sulfides of metallic minerals, which vary considerably in color of mass.

Color is a valuable characteristic of the metals but is a less reliable index of the non-metallic minerals, especially if they are contaminated by coloring agents.

Luster is the surface appearance of a mineral under reflected light. It is frequently described by the following terms: vitreous (glassy), greasy, pearly, resinous, dull, silky, and metallic.

Crystal form is of importance when a mineral has had opportunity to develop its natural shape. This is not the normal condition in rock structure. Nevertheless the form is often of much importance in microscopic examinations.

In the following list are found the most common mineral constituents of building stones together with their chemical constitution and more important physical properties.*

Quartz, silicon dioxide, is a most valuable constituent of many rocks. Hardness = 7; sp. gr. = 2.66. No cleavage. It is a colorless, white to gray sometimes brown to black mineral with a white streak and vitreous luster. It is soluble in hydrofluoric acid only and weathers well. *Flint* is a non-crystalline form of silica.

Feldspars are a group of silicates of alumina with potash (*orthoclase*) or with soda or lime (*plagioclase*). Hardness = 6; sp. gr. 2.62 to 2.75. Cleavage is good on two mutually perpendicular planes. The streak is white and the luster vitreous to pearly. Orthoclase varies in color from deep pink to whitish pink, plagioclase from gray to white. Feldspars are less durable than quartz.

Micas are silicates of alumina with hydrogen and potash (*muscovite*) or with iron, magnesia, and hydrogen (*biotite*). Hardness = 2 to 3; sp. gr. = 2.7 to 3.2. Micas may be split along one plane into very thin tough plates. Their luster is vitreous to pearly and their streak is colorless or gray. In color, muscovite is colorless or gray to brown; and biotite is brown to black. Micas, especially biotite, do not weather well.

Amphibole commonly occurs as *hornblende,* a complex silicate of iron, lime, magnesia, and alumina, or sometimes as *tremolite,* a silicate of lime and magnesia. Hardness = 5 to 6; sp. gr. = 2.9 to 3.5. Cleavage is perfect on two planes 124° apart, but the mineral does not separate into flakes like mica. Luster is vitreous and streak uncolored, grayish or brownish. Hornblende is dark green to black, tremolite is white to gray. Hornblende weathers fairly well, tremolite poorly.

Pyroxene is chiefly found as *augite,* a silicate of lime, alumina, magnesia, and iron. Hardness = 5 to 6; sp. gr. = 3.2 to 3.6. Cleavage is good on two planes 93° apart. Color is green to black. Resembles hornblende and weathers fairly well.

* For further information see *Engineering Geology* by Ries and Watson or *Optical Mineralogy* by N. H. and A. N. Winchell.

Olivine, a silicate of iron and magnesia, is a round-grained, greenish mineral having a hardness of 6 to 7. Its cleavage is indistinct, luster vitreous, and streak uncolored. It weathers poorly.

Chlorites are a group of aluminum silicates containing iron and magnesia. They are of greenish color and have cleavage properties like mica, but less elastic leaves. Hardness = 2 to 2.5. Streak is white to green.

Garnets are commonly silicates of iron and alumina; less often the silicates may contain lime or magnesia. Hardness = 6.5 to 7.5. Cleavage is poor, streak white, color red, and luster vitreous. They render stone difficult to dress and polish.

Serpentine is a hydrous silicate of magnesia having a greenish color and soapy feel. Hardness is usually about 4. The streak is white and luster greasy. It is soluble in hydrochloric acid and has poor resistance to weather.

Talc, another hydrous silicate of magnesia, has a hardness of 1. Splits into thin, brittle plates. Color is white to green, luster pearly. *Soapstone* is a massive form of talc.

Calcite, calcium carbonate, effervesces in dilute cold hydrochloric acid. Its color is quite variable, white when pure. Hardness = 3. Sp. gr. = 2.72. Cleavage is perfect in three directions. Slowly dissolved by waters containing traces of acids; not very durable.

Dolomite, calcium-magnesium carbonate, resembles calcite. Hardness = 3.5 to 4. Sp. gr. = 2.85. Its color is often pink and white. Effervesces in hot dilute acid but not in cold. Less soluble than calcite but not very durable.

Gypsum, hydrous calcium sulfate, is a colorless or white mineral. Its hardness is 2; sp. gr. 2.32, cleavage perfect in one plane, streak white. It is soluble in hydrochloric acid and slightly so in water.

Limonite, a hydrous sesquioxide of iron, has no cleavage. Its streak is yellowish brown. Hardness = 5 to 5.5. Sp. gr. = 3.6 to 4. Color varies from yellow to dark brown. Soluble in hydrochloric acid.

Magnetite, a combination of ferrous and ferric oxides of iron, is a black, strongly magnetic mineral. Hardness = 5.5 to 6.5; sp. gr. = 5.16 to 5.18. Cleavage is indistinct, luster metallic, and streak black. Slowly soluble in hydrochloric acid. Rusts on weathering.

Pyrite, iron disulfide, is a very common impurity in rocks. Color is brassy yellow, streak green to black, luster metallic. It has no cleavage. Hardness = 6 to 6.5; sp. gr. = 4.95 to 5.1. Oxidizes readily when exposed to the weather.

IMPORTANT STONES FOR STRUCTURAL PURPOSES

3. Classes of Rocks. In accordance with geological origin, rocks may be classified as *igneous*, formed by the more or less rapid cooling of molten material from inside of the earth; *sedimentary*, consolidated from particles of decayed rocks which have been deposited from streams of water; and *metamorphic*, either igneous or sedimentary rocks which have undergone structural change due to pressure or heat. For structural purposes, granite, gneiss, trap rock, limestone, marble, sandstone, quartzite, and slate are the most important rocks. Of these, granite and trap rock are igneous, limestone and sandstone are sedimentary, and gneiss, marble, quartzite, and slate are metamorphic rocks.

4. Granites are hard crystalline rocks of igneous origin which have cooled before coming to the earth's surface. True granites consist chiefly of orthoclase feldspar and quartz plus small amounts of mica or hornblende. In commerce, and among quarrymen and engineers, the term granite has a broader meaning; it includes practically all the crystalline igneous rocks such as the syenites, which consist of feldspar plus mica or hornblende; the diorites, which are mainly hornblende plus plagioclase feldspar; the coarse-grained gabbros, which are chiefly pyroxene plus feldspar; pyroxenites, which are composed essentially of pyroxene; and peridotites, which commonly consist of olivine plus pyroxene or hornblende. Although the large majority of American stone sold for granite is correctly named from the geological standpoint, we shall use the term as applied commercially herein. For most granites the chemical constitution percentages will fall within the following limits: silica, 65 to 75; alumina, 12 to 18; potash, 3 to 6; soda, 2 to 5; with lime, magnesia, and the oxides of iron less than 2 each.

The uses to which granite may be put depend largely upon the size of the crystal grains, the uniformity of the structure, the color, and the durability. Only those fine-grained granites, in which the crystals are $\frac{1}{5}$ in. or less in diameter, are suitable for work which is to be polished or carved. The medium-grained stone may be used in building construction, but the very coarse-grained rocks are, in most cases, only fit for crushed stone. Photomicrographs of thin sections of granites are shown in Figs. 1a and 1b.

The uniformity of the structure of granite is often broken in several ways. *Rift* is an obscure plane, often nearly horizontal, along which the rock can be most easily split; *grain* is the plane perpendicular to the rift along which the rock splits, but with more difficulty than along the rift; and *head* or *cut-off* is the plane upon which the stone does not split. It is likely that both rift and grain were caused by strains set up in cooling from the molten state. *Joints* are fractures, produced by internal cooling strains or temperature changes, which separate the rock into sheets or beds running parallel to the surface. The above-mentioned structural imperfections generally render the stone easier to quarry; although, in some cases, where the layers are very thin or the joints are badly disintegrated, they are detrimental to its use. Segregations of minerals, which cause spots or knots, and inclusions of rock fragments, are, however, defects which may render the rock worthless for ornamental purposes.

Most of the valuable granites are gray or red, although green, black, and yellow stones are in use. The color of the lighter stones is largely determined by feldspar, whereas biotite, hornblende, augite, olivine, and chlorite color the darker rocks. Since biotite, olivine, and chlorite weather

(a) Finely crystalline granite

(b) Coarsely crystalline granite

(c) Hornblende schist

(d) Diabase, a variety of trap rock

(e) Limestone

(f) Marble

(g) Very fine-grained sandstone

(h) Coarse-grained sandstone

Fig. 1. Photomicrographs of various stones, ×14. Crossed nicols used on a, b, d, e, f, and h. (Taken by L. W. Brown. Descriptions, courtesy of Prof. A. N. Winchell.)

(a) Principally feldspar (several large crystals) and mica (feathery structure). (b) Largely quartz (white) and feldspar (dark gray); strongly interlocked crystals. (c) Principally hornblende (gray), feldspar and quartz (white); some magnetite (black); interlocking crystals. (d) Largely augite (gray), and plagioclase (long, black and white crystals); interlocking crystals. (e) Nearly all calcite; some of the grayish portions are limonite. (f) Nearly all calcite crystals; not well interlocked. (g) Chiefly quartz grains (white) with abundant magnetite (black). (h) Mostly quartz (white), feldspar (white with fine parallel lines), biotite and magnetite (both black), lime carbonate cement.

poorly, rocks containing them are less durable than the light-colored rocks, which are likely to be free from them.

5. Gneiss. A granite which has become laminated through metamorphism is called a gneiss. Evidently there are as many varieties of gneiss as there are granites. Many of the gneisses of the Eastern states are very hard and durable; they are much used in construction but rarely for ornamentation. Gneiss in which the foliation is very fine is called a schist, Fig. 1c.

6. Trap Rock. Originally trap rock was the term applied to certain igneous rocks which occurred in massive layers, or in columns that presented a stepped appearance. At the present time trap rock includes the heavy dense igneous rocks which are of dark color and which, due to rapid cooling, are very fine grained. Basalt, diabase, the fine-grained gabbros, and occasionally fine-grained diorites are the main types of rocks so classified.

Basalt is a black, imperfectly crystallized rock which consists mainly of augite and plagioclase feldspar. It is found quite commonly in California and the Northwestern states. Diabase (Fig. 1d), is quite similar to basalt in mineral composition, but is more perfectly crystallized. In color it varies from green to a grayish black, the green diabases being colored by olivine or chlorite. Sheets and dikes of diabase associated with red or brown sandstone are widely found in the states along the Atlantic coast. The chief difference between gabbro and diabase lies in the kind of pyroxene, gabbro containing a foliated form. Gabbro is found in Maryland and in Minnesota. Diorite is a dark gray or greenish rock consisting of plagioclase feldspar and hornblende sometimes with a small amount of biotite. It is found in New York, Pennsylvania, and Texas.

Owing to their somber colors, toughness, and the difficulty experienced in quarrying and cutting trap rocks, little use has been made of them for building construction. When crushed they make good road metal and aggregate for concrete. In California trap rock is also considerably used for paving blocks.

7. Limestone. It is quite probable that most of the limestone deposits of the United States were formed from the remains of corals, mollusks and other calcareous organisms when the ocean covered these portions of the earth's surface. Limestone is the trade name for all stratified rocks, which consist principally of calcite or a combination of calcium and magnesium carbonates. Limestones which contain a considerable proportion, say 15 to 40 per cent, of magnesium carbonate are called magnesium limestones; those which contain approximately equal amounts of the two carbonates are dolomites; and those which consist principally of magnesium carbonate are termed magnesites.

In the majority of limestones the content of lime plus magnesium carbonates will run over 75 per cent. When the silica content is high the stone grades into a sandstone; if the clay content runs high, it approaches shale. Many limestones are contaminated with some or all of the following compounds: clay, flint, sand, iron carbonate, iron oxide, iron sulfide, gypsum, and alkali carbonates. Of these impurities, quartz veins, flint seams, and pyrite inclusions are objectionable if the rock is subjected to the weather.

Generally the grain of limestone is so fine that individual crystals are not readily distinguished by the eye (see Fig. 1e). In color, limestones vary from white to black, although the gray and blue rocks are the most abundant. Iron compounds are responsible for the pink, red, and yellow varieties; the presence of carbonaceous material is commonly the cause of the blue, gray, or black color.

In addition to the varieties already mentioned several other classes of limestone are sometimes used for building construction. Among these are the famous oölitic limestone of Indiana (Bedford stone), which is composed of minute round grains cemented together; the fossiliferous limestones of Ohio; the coquina of Florida, a soft limestone which consists of a cemented aggregation of more or less broken shells; and the travertine of Italy, the calcareous constituents of which were deposited by running streams or springs of hot water. Italian travertine was used for the interior of the Pennsylvania Railroad Terminal in New York City and the old Coliseum at Rome.

8. Marble. When a limestone or dolomite has become crystallized through the combined influence of great heat and pressure it is called a marble. Commercially, however, the term marble is often applied to any limestone which is capable of taking a polish, for example, the non-crystalline fossiliferous marbles of Tennessee. Besides calcite and dolomite, marbles often contain impurities, such as mica, pyrite, iron oxide, quartz, tremolite, and carbon. With the possible exception of carbon, any of these impurities in segregated form is likely to cause the stone to weather non-uniformly; mica and pyrite are especially bad in this regard.

Most of the more desirable marbles are finely crystalline rocks (Fig. 1f), of white or gray color. Many of the marbles of the New England states, New York, Georgia, and Alabama are of this type. However, both in texture and color, marble is subject to considerable variation. In some stones crystals ¼ in. in diameter are in evidence; in the ornamental but non-weathering brecciated marbles the stone body is made up of small particles of crushed rock cemented by mineral matter. The colors of marbles range from beautiful shades of pink, yellow, and red to blue, brown, and black. Iron compounds are generally responsible for the yellow and red shades; carbonaceous material produces the gray, blue, and black hues.

Onyx marble is another type of ornamental stone which is of some importance commercially. These translucent rocks consist of colored bands of nearly pure calcium carbonate which have been formed by the deposition of layers of colored calcareous sediments from springs and streams of cold water. California, New Mexico, Arizona, and Utah produce small quantities of onyx marbles.*

9. Sandstone. For the most part, sandstones consist of quartz grains cemented together by silica, clay, iron oxide, or lime carbonate. Feldspar, mica, and pyrites are common accessory minerals. Sandstones are of sedimentary origin and have resulted from the consolidation of sand and gravel beds which either contained the cementing substance or were impregnated with it during the process of solidification.

Inasmuch as the color, hardness, strength, and durability of sandstone are due largely to the binding agency, a knowledge of the character and condition of the cement is of great importance in judging of the value of this stone. Silica forms the most enduring binder, but it is likely to render the stone hard and difficult to work. Clay in combination with silica often makes a good binder; when segregated in seams it forms planes of weakness. Also, since a clay cement greedily absorbs water, it probably weakens the resistance of the stone to freezing. Iron oxide is the main coloring agent and provides good bond. Probably the poorest cement is lime carbonate, which, although strong, is somewhat soluble in rain water, and consequently weathers poorly.

Sandstones with a lime carbonate cement are termed calcareous; those containing an iron oxide binder are called ferruginous; and those having a clay cement are sometimes called argillaceous sandstones. *Quartzite* is a hard, metamorphic sandstone containing a siliceous cement.

The textures of sandstones vary greatly. In most of the ornamental varieties the grains are less than $\frac{1}{50}$ in. in size, whereas some of the stones used for rough work contain stone particles several inches in diameter. Figures 1*g* and 1*h* show fine- and medium-grained sandstones. Sandstones containing rounded pebbles are called *conglomerates;* those having inclusions of angular stone are *breccias.*

The yellow, red, and brown sandstones are generally colored by the oxides of iron; bluish and greenish shades are often caused by pyrite or iron carbonate; clay is likely to make the stone gray.

The following varieties of sandstone are of chief importance in building construction in the United States: Brownstone, a sandstone of granitic origin containing more or less feldspar and mica which is found in the

* True onyx is a translucent siliceous rock of wavy banded structure,

Connecticut River valley and in the middle Atlantic states; Medina red sandstone of New York; Potsdam sandstone, a hard, red to brown rock quarried extensively in New York and to some extent in northern Wisconsin; and Berea sandstone, a finely crystalline stone of uniform texture and light yellow-gray color found in Ohio. Bluestone, a thinly bedded argillaceous sandstone found in New York and Pennsylvania, makes hard, tough flagstone. Gray Medina sandstone from New York, the Kettle River sandstone from Minnesota, and the Ablemans sandstone from Wisconsin are used for paving blocks.

10. Slate. When a clayey shale has been consolidated by great pressure to form a rock which may be cleaved into thin sheets, the name slate is applied. A few slates, also, have originated from the metamorphism of igneous rocks. From the compilation of a large number of analyses by Eckel * it appears that most slates contain from 55 to 70 per cent of silica, 9 to 25 per cent of alumina, with small percentages of iron oxide, lime, magnesia, and the alkalies. The presence of iron sulfide is undesirable, since in weathering it is likely to produce rust discolorations on the surface of the slate. Slates exhibit a wide range in color from green to black. The green varieties commonly owe their color to the presence of chlorite. Most of the non-fading slates are gray or black.

About three-fourths of the slate produced in the United States is made into roofing, and the majority of the remainder is used for structural and electrical purposes, blackboards, and grave vaults.

THE DURABILITY OF STONE

11. The Weathering of Structural Stone. This term includes the resistance of stones, when exposed to the weather, to all the disintegrating actions of heat and cold, water, frost, and chemical action, which combine in this climate to effect the rapid decomposition and destruction of most of the rocks, and of many of those which have been selected for building purposes. Stone buildings or monuments should remain in good preservation for hundreds of years, but more commonly they begin to scale and crumble before they are 25 years old. The life of a rock may be many thousands of years in Egypt, or Italy, or Greece, when it would not last as many scores of years in the United States.

In quarrying and cutting the stone certain conditions arise which affect its weathering properties. Stone from the top ledges of limestone, granite, and slate and from the exposed faces of the rock bed is likely to be less hard and durable than material unexposed to ground water and the weather. The method of blasting and cutting also influences the strength

* *Building Stones and Clays*, p. 97.

of the stone and its resistance to freezing and temperature changes. Small charges of powder uniformly distributed have a lesser weakening effect than large concentrations of explosives. Repeated hammering in cutting is also likely to injure the stone. Some authorities claim saw-cut stone is more durable than that finished by the hammer. Doubtless polished stone is more enduring than rough-surfaced work, since the rain slides off the former more easily. Quarrying of highly absorbent stone, like the more porous sandstones, in freezing weather is bad practice, since the rock is full of quarry water and is likely to be split by freezing action. Although most stones work more readily when freshly cut and full of quarry water, yet it is unwise to lay stone in a wall immediately after quarrying. Such procedure hinders evaporation of the water and thereby lessens the strength of the stone.* In laying stratified rock, like argillaceous sandstones, brownstones, or gneisses, the natural beds should be placed horizontal in order to secure maximum weathering resistance.

Probably the most important disintegrating agent of relatively impervious rocks is the variation of temperature. If one considers that most of the rocks are composed of minerals, each of which may have a different coefficient of expansion, and that the crystals of a given mineral have different coefficients along their different axes, it will be appreciated that the unequal temperatures in various parts of a stone due to the way it is exposed must produce large stresses and deformations within it. Furthermore, experiments have shown that there is always some set after the temperature has been reduced (see Art. VII-17). Consequently, the alternate expansion and contraction due to unequal heating by the sun slowly but surely breaks down the structure of the stone.

The porosity of the stone and the character of its pores affect its resistance to freezing. A porous stone is less resistant to freezing than a dense stone of like pore structure and composition. It is probable that a porous stone having large pores and small tubes connecting the pores is weakened more by freezing than a stone having large pores and large connecting tubes. Also, rocks with tortuous pores and tubes are more apt to be injured by freezing than those of equal porosity having straight pores and tubes.

Pyrite, magnetite, and iron carbonate oxidize in weathering and cause discoloration of the stone in which they are present. Since this oxidation is accompanied by a change in volume, the surrounding structure is weakened. When, however, pyrite is very finely and uniformly distributed through the stone, as in Berea sandstone, the structural injury due to oxidation seems to be negligible. Pyrite inclusions in limestone, or in a

---

* It is claimed that the evaporation of the quarry water leaves the mineral matter which it contains in the pores of the rock, thus producing a denser and stronger surface on the stone.

calcareous sandstone, are very objectionable since they may form sulfuric acid during the weathering process and the acid attacks the lime and magnesia compounds.

Inasmuch as the atmospheric water and rain of most large cities contain appreciable quantities of acid, mainly carbonic and sulfuric, the solubility of the carbonates, and to a lesser extent biotite, plagioclase feldspars, and hornblende should be remembered when selecting building stones for such localities. Limestones, marbles, the laminated micaceous brownstones, and calcareous sandstones are the greatest sufferers from the solvent action of acidulated water.

Table A, prepared by Dr. A. A. Julien, shows the estimated life of various building stones when exposed to weather in New York City.

TABLE A [1]

Kind of Stone	Life
Coarse brownstone	5–15 years
Fine laminated brownstone	20–50 years
Compact brownstone	100–200 years
Bluestone (sandstone)	Untried, probably centuries
Nova Scotia sandstone	Untried, perhaps 50–200 years
Ohio sandstone (best siliceous variety)	Perhaps 1 to many centuries
Coarse fossiliferous limestone	20–40 years
Fine oölitic (French) limestone	30–40 years
Marble, coarse dolomitic	40 years
Marble, fine dolomitic	60–80 years
Marble, fine	50–100 years
Granite	75–200 years
Gneiss	50 years to many centuries

[1] *Rept. Tenth Census*, 1880, Vol. 10, p. 391.

Efflorescence on limestone can often be removed by a blast of steam at 125 psi pressure, followed by an immediate washing with a 5 per cent solution of formic acid.*

12. Preservative Coatings for Stone Work. Among the more valuable preservative treatments applied to deteriorating stone work are boiled linseed oil, paraffin, and paraffin or wax in volatile solvents. Before application of the preservative the stone work must be clean and dry. Under severe exposures treatment renewals will occasionally be required.

Boiled linseed oil is brushed on in two or three coats and followed by a coat of dilute ammonia in warm water. The latter application unifies the discoloration produced by the oil.

Melted paraffin is sometimes applied by a brush and then forced into the pores of the stone by heating the surface to a temperature of about

* See *Bull.* 33, Purdue University; also *Proc. ASTM*, Vol. 28, Pt. 2, p. 695.

60°C. The paraffin used in treating the surface of the Egyptian obelisk in New York City contained a solution of creosote and naphtha. The purpose of the creosote was to prevent organic growth on the stone.

For stone of medium or coarse texture, D. W. Kessler (see National Bureau of Standards *RP*771) states that paraffin with a melting temperature above 60°C, dissolved in proportion of 6 to 12 oz to 1 gal of naphtha, makes an effective and durable treatment when sprayed or brushed on the work. For fine-pored stone the addition of 3 to 6 oz of China wood oil increases ease of penetration, but may cause an oily discoloration.

13. The Value of Durability Tests. By far the best, and perhaps the only infallible, test of the weathering qualities of any given stone is the examination of a ledge of it which has been long exposed, or of an old building, slab, or monument made from the same ledge in the quarry. Inasmuch as this test cannot be applied to a new quarry without an exposed face, and because durability is by far the most important property of any building stone, the following artificial tests are sometimes used to determine durability: freezing and thawing tests, acid tests, and fire tests.

14. Freezing and Thawing Tests. A satisfactory procedure consists of preparing 10 representative 2-in. cubes and subjecting 5 to freezing and thawing. Before freezing and thawing the cubes are weighed and immersed for 24 hours in clean water; then they are placed in a freezer at 10 to 20°C. The test is more drastic if the specimens are frozen while immersed in water. After they are thawed for 1 hr. in circulating water at 20 to 25°C, the cycle is repeated. After intervals of 25 cycles, losses in weight are determined, and, whenever an appreciable effect has been produced, all cubes are crushed in wet condition. The number of cycles withstood prior to marked disintegration and the ratio of frozen to normal strength afford indices of durability. Kessler in *Tech. Paper* 349, National Bureau of Standards, reported that 25 out of 65 types of native limestones withstood more than 1000 cycles of freezing (in air) and thawing before exhibiting marked disintegration. Reduction in strength, due to freezing and thawing, may also be determined by the sonic method described in Art. XV-45.

The resistance of crushed stone can be estimated by finding the reduction in particle size after 100 or more cycles of freezing and thawing.

From a large number of tests on 2-in. cubes of Wisconsin stones in which 35 repetitions of freezing were used, Buckley found that granites and rhyolites * lost less than 0.03 per cent, limestones less than 0.30 per cent, and sandstones less than 0.62 per cent by weight. In crushing tests, frozen samples showed less strength than normal specimens, some of the

---

* A dense, fine-grained igneous rock with occasional large crystals of quartz or feldspar which has cooled near the surface of the earth and which has much the same mineral constitution as true granite; often termed quartz porphyry.

frozen specimens exhibiting less than 50 per cent of the strength of equally perfect normal test pieces. Other results by Bauschinger on the effect of freezing on crushing strength appear in Table 6.

Tests by Hirschwald * show that the resistance to freezing depends on the percentage of pore space occupied by water. In experiments on a number of different rocks he showed that a comparatively small number of freezings would rupture rocks which were saturated with water under pressure, whereas 25 to 30 freezings affected but little those which were immersed at atmospheric temperature and pressure. Consequently, in making the freezing test, conditions surrounding the soaking of the specimens should be uniform and the aim should be to fill the pores as much as they ever would be filled in service.

Owing to the length of time and cost of freezing tests, accelerated soundness tests, based on the expansive action of crystallizing salt, such as sodium or magnesium sulfate, are often used. Essentially, the sodium sulfate test † consists of 5 or 10 cycles of the following procedure: Submerge a 5000-gm sample of crushed rock sized in a standard manner in a saturated solution of sodium sulfate maintained at 21°C for 18 hours, dry at 105 to 110°C for 4 hours, then cool in air for 2 hours. The losses in weight retained on the standard sieves serve as an index of damage, but failure in the test should not be considered conclusive evidence of unfitness of a stone.

15. Acid Tests. To ascertain the resistance of stone to acidulated waters and the acid atmosphere common to the large cities, tests have been made to determine the disintegrating effect of sulfurous and carbonic acid gases upon samples of stone. In making such tests carefully prepared cubes of equal size are dried to constant weight at 110°C. They are then placed in a large jar provided with a humidifier of some sort, and so made that it may be hermetically sealed. A stream of washed gas is then pumped through the jar until all air is expelled. The jar is then sealed for 2 or 3 days, when another application of gas is administered. At the conclusion of a couple of months the test is discontinued, and the specimens are examined and weighed.

In tests on ¾-in. cubes of a number of stones, chiefly from New York, Wilber ‡ found the maximum percentage losses in weight shown in Table 1.

In 44-day tests on 11 limestones of Wisconsin, Buckley found a maximum loss in weight of 1.13 per cent in sulfurous acid gas and 0.11 per cent in carbonic acid gas. His 1-in. and 1½-in. cubes were badly discolored

---

* Reported in *Handbuch der Bautenischen Gesteinsprüfung,* Hirschwald; also *Engineering Geology,* Ries and Watson.

† See Test for Soundness of Coarse Aggregates, *ASTM Tentative Standard.*

‡ *Bull.* 10, New York State Museum, p. 357; also see *Building Stones and Clays,* by E. C. Eckel, p. 209 (out of print).

TABLE 1. THE EFFECT OF ACID ATMOSPHERES UPON DIFFERENT STONES. (WILBER)

Kind of Stone	No. of Tests	Maximum Per Cent Loss in Weight when Immersed in	
		CO_2*	HS_2†
Granite........................	4	.029	024
Marble........................	4	.017	.250
Limestone.....................	13	.087	.250
Sandstone.....................	30	.104	.250
Slate..........................	1	.004	.070

* Tested 52 days.   † Tested 31 days.

and some showed magnesium incrustations on the surface. Besides the weight lost the effect of the carbonic acid gas was not perceptible.

Slate is sometimes tested for resistance to acidulated waters by immersing small fragments in a very dilute mixture of hydrochloric and sulfuric acids and noting the losses in weight. Merriman * in his tests used 1 part hydrochloric, 1 part sulfuric acid, and 98 parts of water. He immersed 3 × 4-in. specimens in this solution and determined the dry weight before and after a 63-day immersion period. The average loss in weight of the varieties which he tested ranged from 0.286 to 0.768 grain; all but one variety had less than 0.4 grain loss.

It should be always borne in mind when making tests or comparing weight losses in corrosion tests that a knowledge of the segregated intensity of the action of the acid is often of more importance than the total loss in weight.

16. Fire Tests. During conflagrations stone buildings often suffer severely. Under such conditions stone must be classed as inferior to structural clay or Portland cement products. The comparatively low resistance of building stone to high temperatures is undoubtedly due to a combination of stresses set up by the great differences in the coefficients of expansion of the constituent minerals, and also to the low heat conductivity of the rock. Quenching with a fire hose accentuates the stressed condition and often badly cracks the stone or causes thin slabs to spall off.

The relative resistances of different stones to high temperatures may be compared and the effect of structural and mineralogical differences observed by placing cubes in a muffle furnace and subjecting them to temperatures ranging from 500° to 900°C. The temperatures should be read by pyrometers so placed that the temperature of the specimens and not the flame is determined. In this connection it is well to have one or two specimens bored to take a thermocouple, so that the inside temperature

* *Bull.* 275, U. S. Geol. Survey.

of the specimens may be estimated. When testing cubes 4 in. or less in diameter, the temperature should be held constant for at least ½ hour. The effect of variations in temperature on the strength of stone is a subject deserving of study.

For determining the resistance of stone work to fire, the only satisfactory method of testing is to build a small hut or a wall panel of stone and mortar and subject one side of the structure to high temperature; 1700°F after 1 hour to 2300°F after 8 hours are the furnace temperatures specified in ASTM *Standards*.

From a considerable number of tests on small cubes, reported by W. E. McCourt (*Bull.* 100, New York State Museum), and others by E. R. Buckley (*Bull.* 4, Wisconsin Geol. and Nat. Hist. Survey), the following conclusions seem justifiable:

None of the common building stones, granite, gneiss, limestone, marble, or sandstone, will withstand temperatures above 850°C. Coarsely grained granite, gneiss, porous sandstones, and the coarsely crystallized marbles begin to show signs of disintegration at temperatures as low as 550°C. Limestone and marble withstand heating as well as any of the igneous rocks until the temperature is reached at which calcination begins (600 to 800°C); then they rapidly disintegrate. Fine-grained, dense sandstone with siliceous cement is very resistant to fire, but the good aspect of badly disintegrated cubes which had been heated to 850°C indicates that the appearance of this material after a fire is misleading. Fine-grained granite at 850°C exhibits more or less cracks but is not badly disintegrated.

Fire tests of panels of stone which were laid with broken joints in cement mortar and backed with brick or tile are reported in *Bull.* 370 of the U. S. Geol. Survey. The tests were made as indicated in Art. XV-47. Granite, sandstone, limestone, and marble panels were tested, the stone for these panels being bought in the Chicago market. The stones composing the panels were $4 \times 7\frac{3}{4}$ in. in cross section. Part were laid with the narrow edge and part with the wide edge exposed. After being subjected to a temperature of 900° to 1000°C for 1 hour and then soaked with a fire hose, none of the panels were in good condition. The majority of the stones in each panel were badly cracked, and in some cases the faces were spalled to the depth of 2 or 3 in. No satisfactory comparison of the resistance of different classes of stone can be made on the basis of these tests.

THE PHYSICAL PROPERTIES OF STONES

17. The Thermal Expansion of Stone. Aside from its effect in weathering of stone, Art. VII-11, thermal expansion has a marked effect on stresses set up in stone when restrained and subjected to temperature changes. Usually stones show variations in their coefficients in different ranges of temperature; coefficients for limestones are less at room temperatures, or slightly below, than at 100°C. Most stones exhibit permanent expansion after heating to the boiling point of water: thus in *Tests of Metals*, 1895, bars of granite, sandstone, limestone, and marble heated in water exhibited permanent average unit expansions of 0.00019, 0.00026, and 0.00037, respectively. Apparently, from a few tests conducted with copper-jacketed bars, a third of this expansion was due to entrance of water into the stones.

The maximum, average, and minimum values from the accurate tests made by J. H. Griffith, and reported in *Bull.* 128 and 131 of the Iowa Eng. Expt. Sta., are summarized in Table 2. In Griffith's tests the bars were

TABLE 2. PHYSICAL PROPERTIES OF AMERICAN ROCKS (Griffith)

Maximum, mean (in bold face type), and minimum observed values are recorded

Kinds of Stone	No. of Kinds	Shore Hardness Number	Coef. of Thermal Expansion $\times 10^{-7}$ per °F.	True Specific Gravity	Weight in lb./ft.[3]	PERCENTAGE		Crushing Strength, lb./in.[2]
						Absorption by Weight	Porosity by Weight	
Rhyolite-Granite.........	22	104 **89** 51	66 **44** 19	3.04 **2.66** 2.59	187 **163** 155	1.7 **0.6** 0.2	4.1 **1.5** 0.4	42,500 **23,100** 8,830
Andesite-Diorite.........	5	93 **78** 66	57 **36** 23	3.02 **2.75** 2.49	185 **177** 139	4.9 **1.2** 0.0	10.8 **2.8** 0.1	32,700 **24,490** 13,610
Basalt-Gabbro...........	11	96 **79** 54	50 **31** 20	3.00 **2.83** 2.70	184 **172** 138	10.0 **1.1** 0.0	22.0 **2.6** 0.0	38,000 **23,260** 6,540
Sandstone..............	8	86 **57** 22	65 **54** 37	2.66 **2.61** 2.52	161 **146** 133	13.8 **4.8** 0.7	26.4 **10.4** 1.6	33,350 **15,940** 4,920
Limestone-Dolomite......	18	96 **54** 28	68 **42** 17	2.80 **2.71** 2.65	170 **166** 143	6.0 **0.9** 0.1	13.7 **2.1** 0.2	26,900 **16,270** 8,470
Gneiss.................	5	99 **87** 71	44 **35** 13	3.15 **2.77** 2.62	195 **171** 163	0.8 **0.4** 0.1	2.2 **1.0** 0.3	29,400 **20,030** 12,950
Quartzite..............	3	97 **90** 78	61 **60** 60	2.68 **2.65** 2.63	167 **165** 163	0.3 **0.2** 0.1	0.6 **0.5** 0.3	43,800 **33,680** 23,440
Slate..................	4	75 **56** 30	49 **44** 35	2.88 **2.80** 2.76	174 **172** 169	1.3 **0.5** 0.0	3.6 **1.4** 0.0	19,100 **18,370** 17,770
Marble................	8	66 **48** 38	51 **45** 38	2.88 **2.68** 2.50	179 **166** 156	0.8 **0.3** 0.1	2.0 **0.7** 0.3	32,450 **20,070** 13,180

heated in an electric furnace, without immersion in water. His data show that for rocks containing silica the thermal expansion increased with the proportion of free silica. Rocks having the most free silica expanded most, whereas those having the most combined silica expanded least.

18. Specific Gravity and Specific Weight. The specific gravity is an important property for two reasons: The higher the specific gravity the greater the stability of a hydraulic structure built of the stone; also for a given kind of stone the strength increases with the specific gravity or density. The superiority of heavy stone for dam or retaining wall construction is apparent if one computes the ratio of the weights of a light and a heavy stone when submerged in water.

There are three ways of determining the specific gravity of substances like stone, all of which are in use to some extent. In the first method, used by Griffith, the dried stone is pulverized and the specific gravity is found by the method used in testing cement (Art. XII-5); this method if properly applied gives the true specific gravity of the stone substance. The second method consists in drying the stone to constant weight, coating it with a thin film of paraffin, and then determining the weight of the stone immersed in water. The loss in weight divided into the dry weight gives the bulk specific gravity (i.e., the specific gravity of the stone, including its pores). The third method differs from the second in that the dried stone is saturated (?) with water and then weighed under water. Since it is impossible to fill completely the pores of the stone, the third method gives results intermediate between those of the first and third methods. If the specific weight is computed by multiplying the specific gravity by 62.4, the results from the second method are of most importance to engineers. Values of specific gravity and specific weight appear in Tables 2 to 4.

19. Porosity and Density. The porosity of a stone is the ratio of the volume of its pores to the entire volume of stone plus pores. Density = 1 − porosity. Porosity may be accurately computed as follows: The stone, dried to constant weight, is coated with paraffin and weighed suspended in water. The loss in weight in water divided by the weight of 1 cubic unit of water gives the volume of stone plus pores. The volume of the stone substance may be obtained by dividing the dry weight of the stone by the product of the specific gravity of its powder and the weight of 1 cubic unit of water. The porosity or the density is then readily computed. Griffith's values for porosity are given in Table 2.

In tests on a large number of Wisconsin and Missouri stones, E. R. Buckley found the following ranges in porosity for the different classes of rock: granites, 0.019 to 1.45; limestones, 0.32 to 13.38, and sandstones, 4.81 to 28.28 per cent.[*] In calculating the pore space Buckley determined the volume of water absorbed by the stone under vacuum at a temperature of 100°C.

[*] See *Bull.* 4, Wisconsin Geol. and Nat. Hist. Survey, p. 400; and *Bull.* 2, Mo. Bureau Geol. and Mines, 2d series, p. 317.

TABLE 3. · PHYSICAL PROPERTIES OF BUILDING STONES

Condensed from Merrill's *Stones for Building and Decoration*

Kind of Stone.	Locality.	Position.	Strength per Square Inch.	Specific Gravity.	Weight per Cubic Foot.	Percentage of Absorption by Weight.	Number of Specimens averaged.
			Lb.		Lb.		
1. Granite	Grape Creek, Brownsville, Lawson, Platte Cañon, Cotopaxi, Monarch, Gunnison—*Colo.*	Bed Edge	15,531 18,536	2.68	167.0	1.1	8
2. Granite	New London, Millstone Point, Mystic River, Stony Creek—*Conn.* Vinalhaven, Fox Island, Dyer's Island, City Point, Dix Island, Jonesboro, Sprucehead, Hewitt's Island, Hurricane Island—*Maine.* Huron Island—*Mich.*	Bed	16,200	2.65	166.0	0.4	20
3. Granite	East Saint Cloud, Saint Cloud, Watab, Sauk Rapids, Beaver Bay—*Minn.*	Bed Edge	24,464 24,464	2.65	165.8	0.5	7
4. Granite	Cape Ann, Rockport, Quincy—*Mass.*	Bed	16,079	2.67	167.0	0.7	4
5. Granite	Fall River, Monson — *Mass.* Keene — *N. H.* Tarrytown, Morrisania, Staten Island, North River, Madison Avenue, Chaumont Bay—*N. Y.* Westerly — *R. I.* Richmond —*Va.*	Bed	15,570	2.69	168.0	0.4	14
6. Granite	New Haven — *Conn.* Duluth, Taylor's Falls, Beaver Bay—*Minn.* Jersey City Heights, Pompton—*N. J.* Goose Creek (Loudoun County)—*Va.*	Bed Edge	21,272 20,740	2.82	176.2	0.3	6
7. Limestone (oölitic)	Putnamville, Greensburgh, Saint Paul, Harrison County, Mount Vernon, Bloomington—*Ind.*	Bed	14,054	....	156.2	1.4	6
8. Limestone	Spencer, Ellettsville, Bedford, Salem—*Ind.*	Bed	9,297	....	145.9	3.6	8
9. Limestone	Bardstown—*Ky.*	Bed Edge	16,250 15,000	2.67	166.9	1.2	1
10. Limestone	Lee—*Mass.*	Bed Edge	22,323 21,728	....	....	....	3
11. Limestone	Frontenac, Stillwater, Winona, Red Wing, Kasota, Mantorville—*Minn.*	Bed Edge	16,320 16,643	2.52	157.3	3.1	7
12. Limestone	Glens Falls, Lake Champlain, Canajoharie, Kingston, Garrison's Station, Williamsville—*N. Y.*	Bed Edge	16,971 15,533	2.58	168.1	....	6

PHYSICAL PROPERTIES OF BUILDING STONES—*Continued*

Kind of Stone.	Locality.	Position.	Strength per Square Inch.	Specific Gravity.	Weight per Cubic Foot.	Percentage of Absorption by Weight.	Number of Specimens averaged.
			Lb.		Lb.		
13. Limestone (marble)	Montgomery County—*Pa.*	Bed Edge	13,112 11,055	....	....	....	4
14. Limestone (marble)	Dorset—*Vermont.*	Bed Edge	10,506 8,670	2.64 2.68	164.7 167.8	....	2 1
15. Limestone (marble)	Italy.	Bed	12,156	2.69	168.2	....	1
16. Sandstone	Buckhorn (Larimer Co.), Trinidad (Las Animas Co.), Manitou (El Paso Co.), Ralston, Left Hand, Saint Vairus, Fort Collins (Larimer Co.), Stout (Larimer Co.)—*Colo.* Thistle —*Utah.*	Bed Edge	11,141 12,434	2.13	132.9	6.6	9
17. Sandstone	Coal Creek, Oak Creek (Fremont Co.), Gunnison (Gunnison Co.), Manitou (El Paso Co.), La Porte (Larimer Co.), Brandford (Fremont Co.)—*Colo.*	Bed Edge	5,481 4,941	2.12	133.0	13.8	9
18. Sandstone	Middletown, Portland — *Conn.* East Long Meadow—*Mass.* Marquette—*Mich.*	Bed	6,639	2.27	142.2	3.5	3
19. Sandstone	Hinckley, Fort Snelling—*Minn.*	Bed Edge	16,625 18,750	2.23	139.0	6.0	2
20. Sandstone	Dresbach, Jordan, Fond du Lac, Dakota—*Minn.*	Bed Edge	5,789 4,102	1.99	124.4	9.9	6
21. Sandstone	Taylor's Falls, Kasota, Frontenac—*Minn.*	Bed Edge	7,483 9,725	2.28	142.3	5.9	3
22. Sandstone	Haverstraw, Hudson River, Albion—*N. Y.*	Bed Edge	8,925 7,687	2.28	142.2	2.6	2
23. Sandstone	Medina—*N. Y.*	Bed Edge	17,500 14,812	2.42 2.39	150.8 149.3	1.6 2.0	2 1
24. Sandstone	Vermilion—*Ohio*	Bed Edge	7,840 6,875	2.16	135.0	5.2	5 1
25. Sandstone	Seneca—*Ohio.*	Bed Edge	9,687 10,500	2.39	149.3	3.1	1
26. Sandstone	Cleveland—*Ohio.*	Bed Edge	6,800 7,910	2.24	140 0	2.8	1
27. Sandstone	Marblehead—*Ohio.*	Bed Edge	7,937 6,850	2.31	144.4	5.2	1
28. Sandstone	North Amherst—*Ohio.*	Bed Edge	6,212 5,450	2.16	133.7 135.8	5.2	2 1
29. Sandstone	Berea—*Ohio*	Bed	9,236	2.13	133.0	5.5	2

The per cent porosity in conjunction with the per cent absorption is of value in judging of the resistance of porous materials to freezing.

20. Absorption. Methods for testing the absorption of stone differ. After drying 5 or more samples for 24 hours at 110 to 120°C and cooling before weighing, the absorption can be found after submersion in distilled water for 14 days, or after boiling 5 hours (see Art. VIII-18).

The proportion of the pore space filled with water and the rate at which the rock will expel absorbed water are important criteria of resistance to freezing. Rocks which absorb enough water to fill the pores and which expel slowly are very likely to be weakened by freezing.

Values of the percentage of absorption for different stones may be found in Tables 3 and 4. Griffith soaked his specimens overnight, boiled them 3 hours, and cooled them in water several hours before determining absorption.

TABLE 4.   TESTS OF AMERICAN BUILDING STONE MADE AT THE
WATERTOWN ARSENAL

Name of Stone.	Weight per Cubic Foot.	Compression Tests.		Ratio of Lateral Expansion to Longitudinal Compression.*	Shearing Strength.	Coefficient of Expansion in Water per °F.
		Strength in Pounds per Square Inch.	Modulus of Elasticity for Working Loads.			
	Lb.		Lb./In.²		Lb.	
Brandford granite (Conn.)...	162.0	15,707	8,333,300	0.250	1833	.00000398
Milford granite (Mass.).....	162.5	23,775	6,663,000	0.172	2554	.00000418
Milford granite (Mass.).....	.....	....	....	....	....	.00000415
Troy granite (N. H.)........	164.7	26,174	4,545,400	0.196	2214	.00000337
Milford pink granite (Mass.)	161.9	18,988	5,128,000	....	1825	
Pigeon Hill granite (Mass.)..	161.5	19,670	6,666,700	....	1550	
Creole marble (Georgia).....	170.0	13,466	6,896,500	0.345	1369	
Cherokee marble (Georgia)..	167.8	12,618	9,090,900	0.270	1237	.00000441
Etowah marble (Georgia)....	169.8	14,052	7,843,100	0.278	1411	
Kennesaw marble (Georgia)..	168.1	9,562	7,547,100	0.256	1242	
Lee marble (Mass.).........	.....	....	....	....	....	.00000454
Marble Hill marble (Ga.)...	168.6	11,505	9,090,900	0.294	1332	.00000194
Tuckahoe marble (N. Y.)....	178.0	16,203	13,563,200	0.222	1490	.00000441
Mt. Vernon limestone (Ky.).	139.1	7,647	3,200,200	0.250	1705	.00000464
Bedford blue limestone (O.)	.....	10,823	7,250,000	0.270	1017	.00000389
North River bluestone (N. Y.)	.....	22,947	5,268,800	.		
Monson slate (Maine).......		....	....	....	....	.00000519
Cooper sandstone (Oregon)..	159.8	15,163	2,816,900	0.091	1831	.00000177
Sandstone, Cromwell (Conn.)	.....	10,780				
Maynard sandstone (Mass.).	133.5	9,880	1,941,700	0.333	1204	.00000567
Kibbe sandstone (Mass.).....	133.4	10,363	1,834,900	0.300	1150	.00000577
Worcester sandstone (Mass.).	136.6	9,762	2,439,000	0.227	1242	.00000517
Potomac sandstone (Md.)....	.....	....	....	....	....	.00000500
Olympia sandstone (Oregon).	.....	12,665	....	....	....	.00000320
Chuckanut sandstone(Wash.)	.....	11,389	....	....	1352	
Dyckerhoff Portland cement, neat......................	.....	....	....	....	....	.00000578

* Poisson's ratio.

THE MECHANICAL PROPERTIES OF STONE

21. The Strength of Stone. The compressive strength of building stone is the most commonly tested mechanical property, although shearing and transverse tests are sometimes made.

For rock which is to be used in road construction toughness and resistance to abrasion are common determinations (see Art. VII-23 and *Standard Specifications* of AASHO). The preparation of specimens and methods of making compression tests are considered in Chapter III. Considerable uncertainty exists concerning methods of preparing and bedding used in obtaining the older data reported herein, but in Griffith's tests the bed planes were ground and no capping was used. He found the difference between tests run parallel and normal to the rift was only 5 to 10 per cent.

From a study of the relation of the percentage of absorption A by weight to the ultimate crushing strength S_c in pounds per square inch, Griffith concluded that practically all the reliable test averages fell within the zone $S_c(A + 4) = 80,000 \ (1 \pm \frac{1}{4})$.

Although a high crushing strength is important where a heavy load is to be borne by a single stone, other properties may be more desirable in masonry constructions where the maximum stresses are commonly less than 800 psi. Crushing strengths of the more important stones of the United States are given in Tables 2, 3, and 4.

Owing to faulty methods of quarrying, discrepancies between the rift and planes of bedment in the wall, and owing to irregularities in foundations and mortar bedments, stone is much more likely to crack because of the imposition of bending stresses than by crushing. Cracks in lintels due to transverse stresses and in walls due to excessive shear stresses are quite common. Consequently, the resistance of stone to these stresses is of importance.

In Table 4 are given the shearing strengths for a number of American stones. Inasmuch as the majority of these tests were made by a method similar to that outlined in Fig. 15, Art. XV-17, the values are probably lower than the true shearing strength due to bending. While testing the transverse strength of Wisconsin stones, Buckley found the following ranges in modulus of rupture: granite, 2713 to 3910; limestone, 1164 to 4659, and sandstone, 363 to 1324 psi. A series of tests on Bavarian building stones was made with great care and precision by Prof. Bauschinger and reported in his *Communications*, Vol. 10. The results show that there is no fixed relation between the various kinds of strength of stone.

A considerable number of transverse tests were made by Prof. Merriman [*] on slate specimens which were secured from a number of the eastern

* *Bull.* 275, U. S. Geol. Survey.

states. The specimens were 24×12 in. in plan and $\frac{3}{16}$ to $\frac{1}{4}$ in. thick. They were tested flatwise on a 22-in. span. The values of the average modulus of rupture for nine varieties ranged from 6410 to 9880 psi, and the average maximum deflection varied from 0.19 to 0.23 in. It seems reasonable, therefore, to expect good slate to have a modulus of rupture of 7000 psi and to deflect 0.20 in. at rupture.

Experiments made at the Watertown Arsenal * have shown that a very great loss in transverse strength results from immersing stone in hot and cold water. The granites were the least affected and the marbles most. The loss in strength of the granites, for the most part, was less than 25 per cent, whereas several of the marbles lost 50 per cent of their strength due to this treatment. Consequently, one must be careful that specimens of stone for transverse tests are not subjected to large temperature variations. Furthermore, this fact would be borne in mind in designing lintels and stone beams which will be subjected to wide variations of temperature.

22. The Elastic Properties of Stone. Like cast iron, brick, and concrete, stone is a material which does not obey Hooke's law. The granites, limestones, and marbles, however, exhibit less curvature and less set in their stress-deformation curves than the more porous sandstones. These facts will be evident after an examination of Figs. 2, 3, 4, and 5. Bauschinger has shown, however, that for a given specimen the moduli of elasticity on the first loading in tension, compression, and cross bending are practically the same.

In Table 4 appear values of Poisson's ratio for stone. With one or two exceptions the values are about the same as those given for the ferrous metals; one-fourth is a fair average.

23. Resistance to Abrasion and Shock. The abrasion on pavements, sidewalks, and doorsteps is a matter of considerable importance in determining the life of stone used for such purposes. A number of tests have been devised for measuring abrasive resistance, but none have been universally adopted. Two types of test have been considerably used. In one, a carefully prepared stone specimen with a plane face is held against a horizontal table which revolves about a vertical axis, and abrasion is produced by sand or emery. In the other test a graded sample of crushed stone or gravel is subjected to abrasion in a rattler.

Bauschinger experimented considerably with the first method, using a cast-iron table 5 ft in diameter. He placed two specimens each 4 in. square at a distance of 19.5 in. from the axis and weighted each with 30 kg. The table was run at a speed of 20 rpm, and 20 gm of fine emery (No. 3) was fed to the plate every 10 revolutions, the old emery being

---

* *Tests of Metals,* 1905.

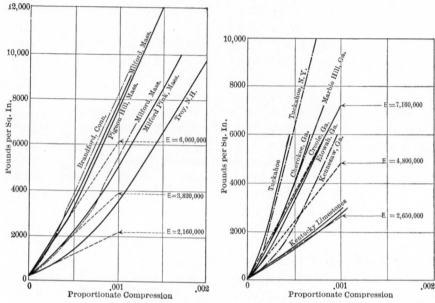

Fig. 2. The elastic properties of various granites under compressive stress. (*Watertown Arsenal Rept.*, 1894.)

Fig. 3. The elastic properties of various limestones and marbles under compressive stress. (*Watertown Arsenal Rept.*, 1894.)

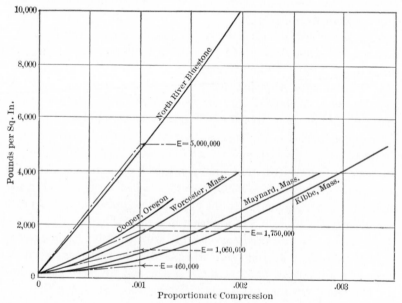

Fig. 4. The elastic properties of various sandstones under compressive stress. (*Tests of Metals*, 1894.)

brushed off. Two attendants constantly kept the emery in the path of the specimen.*

The results of some of Bauschinger's preliminary tests to determine proper pressure and rate of feeding the emery are shown in Fig. 6. The average results which he obtained in testing various materials indicate:

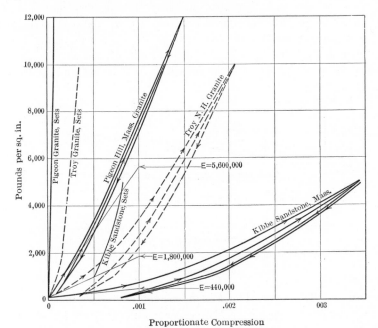

Fig. 5.   Elastic properties of various stones under compressive stress. (*Tests of Metals,* 1894.)

1. The wet grinding was about twice as effective as the dry grinding.

2. There was no fixed relation between crushing strength and abrasive resistance.

3. The limestones wore about five times and the sandstones about four times as fast as the granites, porphyries, and basalts.

4. The clay-slate showed the best results in abrasion, but only a few specimens were tested.

5. The brick and tile wore about twice as fast and the cement compositions about three times as fast as the primitive rocks.

6. The resistance of asphalt paving to abrasion fell between the cement mixtures and sandstone.

* Bauschinger's test does not differ greatly in principle from the Dorry hardness test used in France and the United States for road metal. In the Dorry test the abrasive agent is standard quartz sand passing a 30-mesh and retained on a 40-mesh sieve; the diameter of each specimen is 1 in.; and the speed is 30 rpm for 1000 revolutions.

Materials of Construction

The introduction of the Los Angeles abrasion machine * marked an advance in methods of testing the wear resistance of crushed slag, or gravel. The machine consists of a cylindrical drum 20 in. long and 28 in. in diameter, inside, fitted with a removable dust-tight cover, mounted on horizontal trunnions which are coaxial with the drum. In this test a 5-kg representative dry sample, graded in one of four specified manners which most nearly represents the actual grading, is used. An abrasive charge, dependent on the grading, of cast iron or steel spheres similar to those used in testing paving brick is also introduced into the drum. After 500 revolutions at 30 to 33 rpm the charge is withdrawn and sieved on a

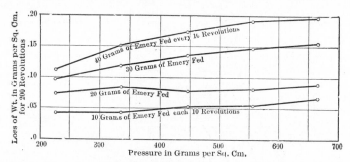

Fig. 6. The relation between the abrasion, pressure, and energy used in abrasion test. (Bauschinger.)

standard No. 12 sieve. The loss in weight expressed in terms of the original sample is reported as the percentage of wear. On account of the size of the rattler drum and the impact of the abrasive charge the test also measures, to some extent, toughness. Typical ranges in per cent wear for different stones follow: basalt 10–15; dolomite 20–40; gneiss 30–65; granite 20–40; gravel 25–60; limestone 20–45; marble 40–70; quartzite 25–30; sandstone 20–60; schist 35–50.

Extensive tests with this machine demonstrate that its indications agree with service records of materials tested. Test samples are easily prepared, the test is rapidly made, and the results are not influenced by the dust in the rattler or personal equation in the preparation of the sample. The influence of friable, soft, or elongated particles is also detected by this machine. Good aggregate for road work will usually show less than 40 per cent wear in this test.

The toughness of rock for road-construction † purposes is often measured by the Page impact machine. This device consists of a 50-kg anvil at the base, upon which the cylindrical test sample 1 in. in diameter

* See D. O. Woolf, *Proc. Highway Research Board,* Vol. 16, p. 174; *Proc. ASTM,* Vol. 35, Pt. 2, p. 511; also ASTM *Standards.*

† See 6000 test results in U. S. Dept. Agr. *Misc. Pub.* **76.**

and 1 in. high is clamped, a 1-kg plunger, which rests on top of the specimen, and a 2-kg hammer mounted above the specimen and sliding in
guides. The guides are so arranged that the hammer can be dropped at
heights progressively increased by 1-cm intervals. The toughness index
for a stone is the height of the last drop causing rupture. Kessler * gives
the following toughness ranges for stones: limestone 4–21; slate 10–56;
sandstone 3–47; quartzite 14–30; serpentine 6–17; rhyolite 6–42; diorite
12–36; schist 6–34; granite 7–31. Rocks of low toughness give indexes
below 13, those of high toughness above 19.

Toughness tests of gravel can be made by subjecting a representative
sample of 50 or more particles between $\frac{3}{4}$ in. and 2 in. in diameter to impact between two $2\frac{1}{2}$-in. steel spheres. The lower sphere rests on a cast-
iron base, and the upper sphere falls inside of three vertical guide rods.
Particles of sedimentary origin having average minor diameters (d)
should withstand without cracking blows from heights (h) greater than
$4(d - \frac{1}{4})$. For particles of igneous or metamorphic origin the heights
should be greater than $4d$.

* *Tech. Paper* 349, National Bureau of Standards.

Structural Clay Products *

1. Introduction. Clay products form one of the most important classes of structural materials. In building construction, brick and terra cotta are desirable on account of their pleasing appearance, strength, and durability. Partition and floor tile form walls and floors of light weight which possess high strength and resistance to fire. Paving brick make economical and durable, although somewhat noisy, pavements. Clay pipe on account of their durability, strength, light weight, and cheapness are successfully used in sewers, drains, and conduits.

Structural clay products may be classified as follows:

Brick
- Building brick
- Paving brick
- Firebrick

Building tile
- Load-bearing tile
- Bakup tile
- Partition tile
- Fireproofing
- Roofing tile
- Floor tile
- Wall tile

Terra cotta

Pipe
- Sewer pipe
- Drain pipe
- Conduit pipe

The total value of the clay products produced in the United States in 1950 was about $327 million. Of this amount the value of unglazed brick was about 50 per cent; vitrified sewer pipe, 17 per cent; drain tile, 3 per cent; unglazed structural tile, 5 per cent; hollow facing tile, glazed and unglazed, 7 per cent; and floor and wall tile, glazed and unglazed, 19 per cent.

MATERIALS, MANUFACTURE, AND TESTING OF CLAY PRODUCTS

THE RAW MATERIALS

2. Classes of Raw Materials. In addition to the various types of clay there are also many forms of shale which are used in the production of

* The following books have been freely consulted in preparing this chapter: *Clays: Occurrence, Properties and Uses,* also *Building Stones and Clay Products,* by H. Ries,

clay products. Clays are those substances resulting from the decay of rocks, which possess plasticity on being tempered with water and which are capable of retaining their shape when molded into various forms and dried. When such bodies are heated to redness or above they resemble rocks in hardness and strength. Shale is a hardened form of clay which has been consolidated by the weight of overlying earth, but which after being reduced to a powder exhibits the above-mentioned characteristics of clay.

Residual clays are formed from the decay of the underlying rocks. They constitute important sources of high-grade clays for pottery. Those clays which have been removed from the parent rock by glacial action, by water, or by wind are called transported clays. Such clays are often termed sedimentary since they have been carried as sediment by the current and deposited in places where the velocity of flow decreased. On account of the changes in conditions which surrounded the deposition of sedimentary clays, they generally consist of strata of material which often vary considerably in composition and properties. Frequently such clays have sandy laminations or are mixed with sand.

Since the largest and most homogeneous deposits of sedimentary clay are those precipitated in large bodies of still water, the marine clays, deposited on former ocean bottoms, or lacustrine clays, found on the bottoms of extinct lakes or in swamps, form the most valuable sources of raw materials for the manufacture of structural clay products. The soft clays, either glacial or residual, which are found at or near the surface, are often termed surface clays. Fire clay is a term, loosely applied, to include those sedimentary or residual clays which vitrify at a very high temperature and which, when so burned, possess great resistance to heat. Impure fire clays are contaminated with certain fluxes such as lime, iron oxide, or the alkalies which reduce the vitrification temperature. In many of the coal-producing states fire clays underlie the coal beds.

3. Composition of Clays. In determining the suitability of clays for the manufacture of clay products a knowledge of both the mineral and chemical constitution is of assistance. From the mineral constitution the proportion of true clay substance may be determined, whereas the chemical constitution affords indications of the purity, refractoriness, color, and shrinkage or swelling in burning.

The minerals most commonly found in clays and shales are kaolinite $(2SiO_2 \cdot Al_2O_3 \cdot 2H_2O)$ and other hydrated silicates of alumina; quartz (SiO_2); feldspar (principally silicate of alumina combined with potash; or lime, or soda and lime); limonite $(2Fe_2O_3 \cdot 3H_2O)$; hematite (Fe_2O_3); siderite $(FeCO_3)$; pyrite (FeS_2); calcite $(CaCO_3)$; magnesite $(MgCO_3)$;

John Wiley & Sons; *The Clay Workers' Handbook,* by A. B. Searle, Griffin & Co.; *Modern Brick Making,* by A. B. Searle, Scott, Greenwood & Son.

gypsum ($CaSO_4 \cdot 2H_2O$), and sometimes rutile (TiO_2). Of these minerals, kaolinite and other hydrated silicates of alumina are the most desirable constituents. They generally form the major part of those high-grade clays, termed kaolins, which are used in the production of crockery and white burning pottery. These silicates constitute the finer portion of the clay which is called the clay substance. Clay substance is defined by Seger as the material less than 0.004 in. in diameter.

Chemical analyses of good clays will show that they consist mainly of the following elements:

Silica	(SiO_2)
Alumina	(Al_2O_3)

Ferric oxide	(Fe_2O_3)	
Lime	(CaO)	Fluxing ingredients (generally
Magnesia	(MgO)	less than 20 per cent)
Alkalies	($K_2O + Na_2O$)	

Water	(H_2O)
Carbon dioxide	(CO_2)
Sulfur trioxide	(SO_3)

Silica generally forms from 40 to 80 per cent of the raw materials used in making structural clay products other than firebrick. In firebrick the silica content may rise to 98 per cent. Although a large percentage of sand or uncombined silica in clay is undesirable, it is sometimes added to decrease shrinkage in burning and to increase the refractoriness of low alumina clays.

The alumina content ordinarily ranges from 10 to 40 per cent except in silica brick. Wares having an exceedingly high alumina content are likely to be very refractory.

Iron oxide, which in most cases constitutes less than 7 per cent of a clay, is a most important factor in determining the color of the clay and the burned product. It also tends to lower the fusion point of the clay, especially if present as ferrous oxide.

Lime normally constitutes less than 10 per cent of clay, but in some glacial deposits, which are successfully used in making common brick and tiling, a higher lime content obtains. In carbonated form lime lowers the fusion point. Since the carbonate breaks up into carbon dioxide (CO_2) and lime (CaO) at a temperature of 900°C, it is desirable, in clays burned at this temperature, to finely crush the lime pebbles. If this is done, danger from "popping" in the burnt ware, due to slaking of the lime, may be avoided. If the burning temperature is considerably higher than the above, complex combinations of lime, silica, and alumina are formed with the result that the lime effects a change in the color of the product. Red-burning wares are often made buff-burning by increasing the lime content.

Magnesia rarely exceeds 1 per cent in clay. In burning it causes the clay to soften at a slower rate than does lime and lessens warping.

The alkalies, forming less than 10 per cent of the raw clay, are of great value as fluxes, especially when combined with silicates of alumina. Feldspar is much used as a flux with kaolin in making white ware.

A large proportion of free water generally causes clay to shrink considerably in drying; combined water causes shrinkage in burning.

Carbonaceous material in the form of bituminous matter or carbon greatly affects the color of the raw clay. Unless proper precaution is taken to effect complete removal of such matter by oxidation, the burned product is likely to have a black core.

Sulfur is most commonly found in clay as the sulfate of calcium, magnesium, potassium, sodium, or iron, or as iron sulfide. Generally the proportion is small. If, however, there is carbon in the clay and insufficient time is given during burning for proper oxidation of carbon and sulfur, the sulfur will cause a spongy swollen structure in the burned product. Most of the sulfates are soluble and give evidence of their presence by the formation of a scum on the dried ware. As a result, unless considerable care is exercised in burning, the product will be discolored by white blotches. The use of water containing small quantities of magnesium or calcium carbonates, together with a sulfurous fuel, often causes similar effects. Wall white, which appears after brick have been laid, may be due to soluble salts in the brick or in the mortar, which are brought to the surface by absorption of water and subsequent drying.

4. Physical Properties of Clays. Plasticity, tensile strength, texture, shrinkage, porosity, fusibility, and color after burning are the physical properties which are of most importance in determining the value of a clay. A knowledge of these properties is of more benefit in judging the quality of the raw material than a chemical analysis.

By plasticity is meant the property which wetted clay has of being permanently deformed without cracking. The amount of water required by different clays to produce the most plastic condition varies from 15 to 35 per cent. Although plasticity is probably the most important physical property of clay, yet there are no methods of measuring it which are entirely satisfactory.* The simplest and most used test is afforded by feeling of the wetted clay with the fingers. Personal equation necessarily plays a large part in such determination.

Since clay ware is subjected to considerable stress in molding, handling, and drying a high tensile strength is desirable. The test is made by determining the strength of specimens which have been molded into briquet

---

* For a more complete discussion of the physical properties and their measurement, see *Clays, Their Occurrence, Properties, and Uses,* Third Edition, by H. Ries, Chapters IV and V.

form * and very carefully dried. The tensile strength of clays will vary from almost nothing in highly siliceous fire clays to over 400 psi in some common brick clays. Kaolin generally shows low tensile strength.

The texture of a clay is measured by the fineness of its grains. In rough work the per cent passing a No. 100 sieve is determined, but for measuring the size of the clay grains a more refined device such as the Schöne washing apparatus or a centrifugal separator is used. No numerical limit to the grain size or desired relation between sizes has been established. Tests by Beyers and Williams † indicate that the sizes of grain from 0.004 in. down should be uniformly graded to obtain maximum tensile strength. Ries' tests showed that an excess of either very fine material or of sand grains decreased the tensile strength of the clay. Very fine-grained clays free from sand are more plastic and shrink more than those containing coarser material.

A knowledge of the shrinkage both in drying and in burning is required in order to produce a product of required size. Also, the amount of shrinkage forms an index of the degree of burning. The shrinkage in drying is dependent upon pore space within the clay and upon the amount of mixing water. The addition of sand or ground burnt clay lowers shrinkage, increases porosity, and facilitates drying. Fire shrinkage depends upon the proportion of volatile elements, upon texture, and upon the way that clay burns. Tests of shrinkage are made by determining the volume of benzine displaced by a small prism of clay when green, after drying at a temperature slightly above the boiling point of water, and also after burning. Beyer and Williams, in tests on a number of Iowa clays, reported air shrinkages varying from 4.86 per cent to 27.00 per cent and fire shrinkage from −2.88 per cent (swelling) to 5.92 per cent.

By porosity of clay is meant the ratio of the volume of pore space to the dry volume. Since porosity affects the proportion of water required to make clay plastic, it will indirectly influence air shrinkage. Large pores allow the water to evaporate more easily and consequently permit a higher rate of drying than small pores. Inasmuch as the rate at which the clay may be safely dried is of great importance in manufacturing clay products, the effect of porosity on the rate of drying should be considered.

The temperature at which a clay fuses is determined by the proportion of fluxes, texture, homogeneity of the material, character of the flame, and its mineral constitution. Owing to non-uniformity in composition, parts of the clay body melt at different rates so that the softening period extends over a considerable range both of time and temperature. Wheeler divides the period into (1) incipient vitrification, at which the clay has softened sufficiently to cause adherence but not enough to close the pores or cause

* See briquet molds and testing machines in Art. XII-16 and XII-21.
† *Iowa Geol. Survey*, Vol. 15, p. 102, 1904.

loss of shape—on cooling the material cannot be scratched by the knife; (2) complete vitrification, more or less well marked by maximum shrinkage, coalescence of particles, smooth fracture, and no loss in shape; (3) viscous vitrification, produced by a further increase in temperature which results in a soft molten mass, a gradual loss in shape, and a glassy fracture after cooling.

Experiments roughly indicate that the higher the proportion of fluxes the lower the melting point. Fine-textured clays fuse more easily than those of coarser texture and the same mineral composition. The uniformity of the clay mass determines very largely the influence of various elements; the carbonate of lime in large lumps may cause popping when present in small percentages, but when finely ground 15 per cent of it may be allowed in making brick or tile. Lime combined with silicate of alumina (feldspar) forms a desirable flux. Iron in the ferrous form, found in carbonates and in magnetite, fuses more easily than when present as ferric iron. If the kiln atmosphere is insufficiently oxidizing in character during the early stages of burning, the removal of carbon and sulfur will be prevented until the mass has shrunk to such an extent as to prevent their expulsion and the oxidation of iron. When this happens a product with a discolored core or swollen body is likely to result.

Since a determination of the fusibility of a clay is of much importance both in judging of the cost of burning it and in estimating its refractoriness, experiments are often made on small prisms to determine the rapidity with which the clay may be burned, the temperatures at which incipient, complete, and viscous vitrification occur, how the clay behaves in annealing, and the color of the burned product. Temperatures are commonly measured by means of Seger cones,* in refined work by a pyrometer.

METHOD OF MANUFACTURE

5. Preparation of the Clay. Many of the large deposits of clay or soft shale are worked in open cut with a steam shovel. The hard shales adjacent to coal veins are frequently mined. Generally the raw material is drawn from the pit in cars on a narrow-gage track by horses or by dinky engines. For pressed brick and terra cotta it is sometimes advantageous to weather the clay, before using it. This is accomplished by loosely spreading the clay in a layer a couple of feet thick over a flat surface where it will be exposed to the action of the elements. Such action causes a rusting of iron particles and a breaking down of pyrite inclusions.

* Seger cones are made from mixtures of clay and fluxes so proportioned that their melting-points form a temperature scale. Two or more cones differing in fusibility are inserted in the furnace or kiln and the temperature is estimated from their appearances.

Most clays, however, are hauled directly to a crushing or disintegrating device. For the hard shales jaw-crushers are sometimes used. Dry pans like the one shown in Fig. 1 are often employed to break up the softer shales and tough clays. For certain dry shales, toothed or corrugated

Fig. 1. A 9-ft dry pan.

rolls are effective where coarse grinding only is required. After the clay has been crushed it is conveyed to a pug mill (Fig. 2), in which it is tempered with the proper amount of water and thoroughly mixed. Wet clays

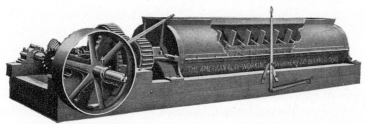

Fig. 2. A double-shaft pug mill.

are generally ground and tempered simultaneously in large ring pits, in pug mills, or in wet pans. In the ring pits a heavy iron wheel, which rolls over the bottom surface of the pit in a spiral path, serves to stir and grind the clay. This method is used only at small plants. The wet pan is much like the dry pan, with the exception that the bottom of the wet pan is not perforated.

6. Molding. Building brick are molded by the soft-mud, the stiff-mud, or the dry-press process. The stiff-mud process is employed in making nearly all other structural clay products. Firebrick is sometimes made by the soft-mud process, and roofing, floor, and wall tile by the dry-press process.

In the soft-mud process the clay, or mixture of clayey materials, is tempered with enough water to form a mass of soft consistency. The mixture is then introduced into wooden molds which are lined with sand

Fig. 3.   A small auger equipped with device for making side-cut brick.

to avoid sticking. Either hand or machine molding is employed in this process. Soft-mud brick exhibit five sides to which more or less sand adheres. The soft-mud process can be used with a greater variety of clays than any other method of molding, and very uniform brick may be made with it.

Less water is used in the stiff-mud process so that the mixture is much more rigid than in the soft-mud process. It is well applied to mixtures which are of medium plasticity. The clay from the pug mill is forced through a tapered die by means of an auger, and the issuing bar is cut into the required lengths. Owing to the motion imparted by the auger and friction on the sides of the die, various portions of the clay bar are given different velocities; consequently more or less laminations are present in the product of auger machines. Brick are made either end or side cut by this machine. Figure 3 shows a side-cut machine. Auger brick machines have considerably greater capacities than the machines of the vertical press type used in the soft-mud or dry-press processes. For molding common brick, machines equipped with double or triple dies are sometimes used. Partition tile, conduits, fireproofing and the smaller sizes of drain tile are molded in a manner similar to stiff-mud brick. For sewer pipe and the larger sizes of drain tile, vertical presses are employed. The uniformity in shape and size of stiff-mud or soft-mud brick can be improved, the surfaces made smoother and harder, and the density and strength increased by repressing. This auxiliary process is often employed in making high-grade face brick and in molding paving brick.

In the dry-press process the tempered clay is pulverized, screened through a No. 16 sieve, and then fed into molds on a vertical press. The molds of hard steel are steam heated to prevent adherence of the clay. Vents are provided to allow the escape of entrapped air. Owing to the heavy pressures used, it is possible to obtain pieces with sharp corners and of more uniform shape than can be had from auger machines. This process also does away with air drying although considerable free water must be driven off in the kiln. Face brick are commonly dry pressed.

Improvement in the uniformity, density, strength, and toughness of certain stiff-mud and dry-pressed clay products has been effected in the laboratory by de-airing. This is accomplished by often using high pressures in repressing or by evacuating air just before the clay is molded or passes into the die of the auger machine. De-airing has been successfully applied in the manufacture of paving brick.

Terra cotta is generally hand molded or cast in plaster molds.

7. Drying. Great care is required to dry soft-mud and stiff-mud products at maximum rate without causing checking. In some yards the open-air driers are provided with roofs, which can be opened during fine weather, and are means for heating in bad weather.

Artificial driers are of two types, the hot-floor drier and the tunnel drier. The former is the older and is used for firebrick, clay pipe, and terra cotta. The hot-floor drier is heated either by a furnace placed at one end of the drier or by exhaust steam from the engine used to furnish power. Tunnel driers are periodic—filled, dried, and emptied in rotation—or continuous—the green ware being loaded into one end of the tunnel and the dried product removed at the other. Tunnel driers are heated by flues underneath, by steam pipes, or by hot air from cooling kilns. They are more economical than hot-floor driers. In artificial driers the temperature rarely exceeds 120°C. The time required in drying varies from 1 to 3 days, depending upon the temperature of the drier, the character of the clay, and the shape of the body.

In some brick plants the green ware is set in a kiln and dried by waste heat from cooling kilns. This method requires more kilns, but effects a saving in handling of brick.

8. Kilns. In the brick industry four types of kilns are in use: the scove kiln, the up-draft kiln, the down-draft kiln, and the continuous kiln. Of these types the down-draft and continuous kilns are used in burning other clay products. Terra cotta is generally burned in round down-draft kilns provided with muffles to prevent contact of flame and ware.

The scove kiln shown in Fig. 4a is much used in burning common brick. Brick are laid about 40 courses high and the entire kiln enclosed with a

Fig. 4a. Setting a scove kiln. Temporary end and side walls not in place. (*Bull.* 15, Wisconsin Geol. and Nat. Hist. Survey, Pl. 6.)

Fig. 4b. Circular down-draft kiln used for burning brick. (*Bull.* 15, Wisconsin Geol. and Nat. Hist. Survey, Pl. 6.)

Fig. 4c. Haigh continuous kiln (American Clay Machinery Co.)

Fig. 4. COMMON TYPES OF KILNS.

course or two of special brick containing a small proportion of coal. The outside is then plastered with mortar and fires started in the arches. Wood or oil is used as fuel. The temperature of the outer and inner portions of the kiln is equalized to some extent by the combustion of the coal brick. Although the cost of the scove kiln is low, the loss in brick and in heat is high.

Up-draft kilns provided with permanent walls and roof are an improvement over the scove kiln, but they are more wasteful of heat and are heated less uniformly than the down-draft kiln.

The down-draft kiln (Fig. 4b) is either rectangular or circular in plan, the former being used largely in burning the better grades of building brick and in burning paving brick. As the name implies, heat from the fire after passing through up-takes to the top of the furnace is drawn downward through the kiln and passes through flues in the floor. Thence the waste gases are led through tunnels either to a stack passing up through the center of the kiln, or to a detached stack serving several kilns. With the down-draft kiln a more uniform distribution and better regulation of heat can be obtained than with either of the kilns previously described. Since the hardest burned ware, which becomes the softest in burning, is found at the top of the kiln, it cannot be misshapen by the weight of overlying courses.

Continuous kilns (Fig. 4c) are often built oval in plan and divided by vertical walls into a large number of compartments. These are loaded from the interior of the ring and unloaded from the outside. Each compartment is provided with an adjoined firebox, a flue leading to a cental stack and by-passes in the side walls through which the compartment can be connected with the adjacent compartments. Pockets are also provided in the top of each chamber for additional fires. Chambers are charged, fired, and unloaded in rotation. A chamber is first isolated and heated by the side firebox until the ware is freed of combined water. Then the waste heat from the adjoining chamber is admitted until a red heat is attained when the top pockets are fired until burning has been completed. This type of kiln effectively utilizes fuel and is used to burn brick, fireproofing, and tile.

The tunnel or fixed fire zone form of continuous kiln is the most modern. It is becoming increasingly important because of its flexibility, excellent temperature control, and uniformly burned product. The dried ware is entered at one end, and as it is slowly moved through the tunnel the temperature is raised to the maximum desired at midlength, and then gradually reduced as the ware reaches the exit.

9. Burning. The burning of clays, requiring from 60 to 100 hours, may be divided into three main stages: (1) dehydration or "water smoking," (2) oxidation, (3) vitrification, or period of settlement in the kiln.

During the dehydration period the water which has been retained in the pores of the clay after drying is driven off, some of the carbonaceous matter is burned, a portion of the sulfur is distilled from pyrites, hydrous minerals like kaolinite and ferric hydroxide are dehydrated, and the carbonate minerals are more or less decarbonated.* The speed with which these eliminations occur depends upon the water and mineral content of the clay, its porosity, and its texture, and upon the method of handling the kiln. Too-rapid heating causes cracking or bursting of the ware. On the other hand, if alkali is contained in the clay or much sulfur is present in the coal, too-slow heating produces a scum on the surface of the product. During the "water-smoking" stage, frequent measurements of the draft and temperature are made in order to standardize the procedure for a given clay. This period is generally completed before a temperature of 700°C is reached.

During the oxidation period, which is nearly always completed at 900°C, the remainder of the carbon must be eliminated and, to promote stability, the ferrous iron must be oxidized to the ferric form. Although some of these changes begin before the completion of the water-smoking stage, it has been pretty well demonstrated that the removal of sulfur cannot be completed before the carbon has been eliminated. Sulfur, on account of its affinity for oxygen, also holds back the oxidation of iron. Consequently, in order to avoid black or spongy cores, oxidation must proceed at such a rate as will allow these changes to occur before the heat becomes sufficient to soften the clay and close its pores. Grog or sand is often added to the raw clay to produce a more open structure and thus provide for the escape of gases generated in burning.

The different stages in vitrification have already been mentioned. It should be borne in mind that but few clay products are vitrified to the point of viscosity; indeed, many common brick and tile cannot be called vitrified in any sense of the term. On the other hand, paving brick must be burned to the stage which Wheeler called complete vitrification if the maximum combination of hardness and toughness is to result. There is, consequently, a wide range in the maximum burning temperature to which the clay must be submitted, depending upon the character of the raw material and the purpose of the ware. In the manufacture of tile and building brick this range varies between 900° and 1200°C.

The degree of burning is frequently determined by the settlement of the goods in the kiln, in some cases by pyrometers. For ware which is to be completely vitrified, it is advantageous to have the points of incipient and viscous vitrification separated as widely as possible. This is desirable in order that goods from different parts of the kiln may not vary widely owing to non-uniform distribution of heat

* Prof. E. Orton, Jr., *Trans. Am. Ceramic Soc.*, Vol. 5, p. 393.

10. Glazing. By glazing clay products, it is possible to give a pleasing appearance to the ware, to increase its imperviousness to water, or to accomplish both of these ends without incurring the cost of complete vitrification. Slip clays, which have a high fluxing content and which may be so adjusted in composition that different coloring effects can be produced, lead compounds, barium compounds, and common salt are among the substances uses for glazes. Decorative terra-cotta goods are sprayed with a thin mixture of slip clay before burning. Sewer pipe is salt glazed by the addition of common salt to the fires during the vitrification stage. Enamel brick are given a coating of slip containing oxide of tin or similar compound to render the glaze opaque.

11. Flashing. Colors ranging from gold to dark reddish-brown may be produced on many kinds of ware by flashing. The process consists in exposing the ware to a reducing atmosphere during a part or whole of the burning period. Front brick are often so treated with pleasing results. Flashing, however, is likely to deceive even experts concerning the degree of burning.

12. Annealing. Great care is necessary in cooling the goods below a cherry-red heat in order to avoid checking and cracking. Hastening the annealing process may destroy the product of an otherwise successful burn. To make paving brick of maximum toughness requires an annealing period of 7 to 10 days.

13. Sorting. In up-draft kilns the overburned ware is found at the bottom near the top of the arches and the under-burned material is at the top. The converse is true for down-draft kilns. In either kiln, the best of the product is found in the intermediate courses. In the manufacture of paving brick, high-grade building brick, and drain tile, these different classes of goods are separated in unloading the kiln and the poorer grades of material sold for different purposes. Overburned paving brick and building brick are used in sewer construction. Soft-burned paving brick are used for exterior walls in building construction; the soft-burned building brick serve as filling.

METHODS OF TESTING STRUCTURAL CLAY PRODUCTS

14. Tests. Two classes of tests are used in judging the quality of clay products: (A) tests which may be readily made on the job; (B) those which require laboratory equipment. The field tests are: (1) appearance, (2) hammer test, (3) hardness, (4) absorption, (5) specific gravity. In the laboratory, the following additional tests are sometimes made: (6) crushing, (7) transverse bending, (8) rattler test * (paving brick), (9)

* See Art. VIII-21.

abrasion (paving brick), (10) resistance to freezing and thawing (Art. VII-14 and VIII-23).

15. Appearance. Shape, color, kiln marks, checks, laminations, and blisters all form more or less valuable indications of quality. The color of the outside of the goods is often misleading in regard to the degree of burning. This also applies to the color of the interior, unless one is familiar with the changes which the given clay undergoes in burning. The presence of lime pebbles over ⅛ in. in diameter is undesirable. Black or spongy cores show improper burning as previously mentioned. In brick, well-defined kiln-marks indicate that the brick have been hard burned, but do not serve to distinguish between hard-burned and overburned brick. Checks and cracks may be due to improper drying or annealing. They decrease the strength and resistance to frost; if well-marked they are sufficient cause for rejection. Checks produced in annealing generally indicate brittleness. Pronounced laminations in the cross section of the ware are objectionable since they weaken the structure and lessen resistance to freezing. Broken blisters on the surfaces of sewer pipe or drain tile are due to air imprisoned in molding. They should not be tolerated on the inner surface. When present on the outer surface they should not exceed one-fifth of the thickness of the tile in depth, and in diameter they should not exceed one-eighth of the diameter of the pipe.

16. The Hammer Test. When properly burned and free from cracks, dry clay products emit a highly metallic ring if struck with a hammer. A rough notion of the toughness of brick is also afforded by breaking specimens with the hammer.

17. Hardness. To secure evidence of the degree of burning, the interior of the clay body may be scratched with a knife. Sewer pipe and paving brick which have been burned to incipient vitrification or above cannot be scratched. Well-burned tile will be scratched with difficulty.

18. Absorption. The percentage of absorption is a very valuable indication of the degree of burning provided one knows the limit of the given clay corresponding to a properly burned product. According to Orton * vitrification, in the true sense, corresponds to such a degree of compactness that the absorption of the product is not over 3 per cent after 48 hours' immersion. He also stated that if the absorption was less than 5 per cent danger from frost was negligible. Since the expansive force of water freezing in the pores of a clay material depends upon the proportion of pore space occupied, the ratio of the absorption after 24 hours' submersion to absorption after boiling 5 hours (C_{24}/B_5 ratio) appears to be a better criterion of resistance to freezing than the percentage of absorption (Art. VIII-27). McBurney's recommendations on methods for

* *Proc. ASTM*, Vol. 15, p. 263.

procedure in absorption tests in *Proc. ASTM*, Vol. 36, Pt. 1, p. 260, should be studied.

Tests by Palmer and Parsons * show that bricks in condition to absorb 10 to 35 gm of water in 1 min when immersed ⅛ in. on one face develop the strongest mortar bond. Too-rapid withdrawal of water from the mortar by brick produces a weak bond. These tests and others indicate that the suction rate is an important property of brick and tile. It should be controlled by the manufacturer and builder and determined on the job.

No standard method of making the absorption test has been adopted for all structural clay products. Five half brick from different units or 15 uncracked square fragments of structural clay tile, drain tile, or sewer pipe selected from 5 units constitute suitable samples for the respective materials. The fragments should be 12 to 20 sq in. in area. In all procedures specimens should be oven dried to constant weight at temperatures just above the boiling point of water. Usually a temperature of 110° to 120°C for 72 hours is sufficient. Weighing should be done on scales sensitive to 0.1 per cent of the weight of the specimen. Where the C/B ratio is to be determined, as for brick, specimens are submerged for 24 hours in distilled, or rain, water at room temperature (15 to 30°C) and carefully surface dried with a towel before weighing. They are then boiled for 5 hours in distilled or rain water, cooled in the water, and again surface dried and weighed. The difference between weights after soaking or boiling and the dry weight divided by the dry weight and multiplied by 100 gives the weight percentage of absorption. Absorption after boiling is prescribed by the ASTM (see *Standards*) for the following intervals: for structural clay tile, 1 hour; for drain tile and sewer pipe, 5 hours.

If the absorption by volume is desired, it can be obtained by multiplying the weight percentage by the apparent specific gravity.

19. Specific Gravity. Other factors being constant, the higher the bulk specific gravity the stronger the clay product. This rule does not hold for vitrified products since Purdy and Moore's tests † show that the specific gravity of a clay decreases as vitrification advances. *Specific gravity* may be determined on the pulverized product (Art. VII-18). It is often less accurately found by dividing the dry weight in air by the difference between the dry weight and the weight when submerged cold after boiling 5 hours. The *bulk specific gravity* may be found by dividing the dry weight in air by the difference between the weight saturated in air and the weight saturated when submerged.

20. Strength Tests. The methods of making the crushing and transverse tests of brick and building tile are the same as outlined in Art.

* *Research Paper RP683*, National Bur. Standards.
† *Trans. Am. Ceramics Soc.*, Vol. 9, p. 203.

III-15 to III-24. The crushing test is generally made on half brick bedded flatwise, but this method is not satisfactory both on account of the uncertainty in determining the final load and on account of the lack of opportunity for shear failure. These considerations have led some experimenters to bed the brick on the edges. The strength of side-cut brick on edge is sometimes 30 to 60 per cent less than the strength of specimens bedded flatwise.

The crushing test affords a means of comparing the quality of brick or tile but is of little value in determining the strength of a wall, since the

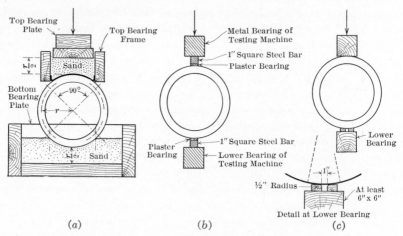

Fig. 5. Methods of supporting drain tile for strength tests. (*ASTM*, Des. C4-24.)
(*a*) Sand bearings. (*b*) Two-edge bearings. (*c*) Three-edge bearings.

latter depends primarily on the strength of the mortar. As a criterion of structural strength for brick, the transverse test is of more value than the crushing test, since transverse failure in a wall or pavement is likely to occur on account of improper bedment. Brick which are improperly annealed or checked in air drying exhibit a lower transverse strength than properly treated specimens. Moreover, the transverse test can be made in a small machine without the expense of a bedment.

Drain tile and sewer pipe are often tested under gradually applied loads placed as indicated in Fig. 5. The tile should be thoroughly wet when tested, and not less than 5 specimens should be tested. The supporting strength (W) is defined as the load per lineal foot which the tile can carry when loaded through sand bearings. Under this condition the moment, $M = 0.20RW/12$, where R is the radius of the center line of the tile in inches. To determine supporting strength from a three-point bearing test, multiply the breaking load per foot by 1.50; if hydraulic bearings are used multiply by 1.25. The three-point bearing method is simpler in application, but it is more severe on warped pipe than either hydraulic or sand bearings. Sand bearings also approximate quite closely the loading conditions to which the pipe is subjected in a ditch.*

21. The Rattler Tests on Paving Brick. Although the rattler test has never been shown to be a true index of the life of brick in a pavement, yet as a means of standardizing resistance of paving brick to combined impact and abrasion it is considered valuable. For details in performing this test, see ASTM current *Standards*. The test consists in placing one representative sample of 10 whole brick which pass visual inspection requirements in a metal barrel 20 in. long and 28 in. in diameter, together with a 300-lb charge of cast-iron spheres, and subjecting the bricks to the action of the charge during 1800 revolutions at 30 rpm. The barrel is mounted on horizontal axial trunnions which are parallel to the sides. Openings between the 14 staves of the barrel permit escape of dust. Good pavers 3 by 4 by 8½ in. will usually show less than 21 per cent loss in this test, although 24 per cent is permitted by the specifications.

22. Pavement Determinators. Numerous laboratory tests of sample pavements have been made. Usually the samples of the types of pavement form segments of a circular track which rests on a permanent foundation. The abrading apparatus consists of one or more loaded wheels, which may be shod with rubber tires or more abrasive devices. These wheels are rolled over the track in paths of variable radii through connection with a vertical axle in the center of the track. After a suitable number of rolling cycles the condition of the pavement is examined visually, and where the wear is sufficient measurements are made.

One of the earliest of these determinators was used by the city of Detroit. The Road Research Laboratory at Harmondsworth, England, has 3 tracks, the largest of which operates a 10-ton truck chassis on a track with a mean diameter of 110 ft. The U. S. Bureau of Public Roads and the Crushed Stone Association also have tracks for such tests.†

23. Alternate Freezing and Thawing Test. Committee C–6 of the ASTM has prescribed an alternate freezing and thawing test* for drain tile which may be applied to other clay products. The test is made on 3 or more specimens from each of 5 separate tiles. The specimens are so chosen that they represent the ends and center of each tile. They must be sound, approximately square, and between 12 and 20 sq in. in area. After being dried to constant weight at 110°C, or above, the specimens are cooled to 20° or 25°C, reweighed, and immersed in pure water. For freezing the specimens are placed with their concave faces upward in trays of ice

* For more complete information see Standard Specifications for Drain Tile, Serial Des. C4–24, ASTM *Standards*.

† See *Eng. Record*, Vol. 68, p. 457; *Highways and Bridges*, Apr. 29, 1936; *Public Roads*, Jan. 1934; *The Crushed Stone Journal*, Dec. 1935.

water. After the specimens have acquired the temperature of the water, the water should be drawn off until ½ in. remains in each tray. The trays are placed in a suitable rack and immersed in a freezer. The freezer temperature must be reduced to $-10°C$ or below within 30 minutes after the specimens are introduced, but should not fall below $-20°C$ during the test. After the water in the trays has been frozen solid the trays are taken out of the freezer and immersed in water at a temperature of 18° to 24°C. The specifications demand 24 alternate freezings and thawings for farm drain tile, 36 for standard drain tile, and 48 for extra quality drain tile. Failure in this test is conditioned by (1) superficial disintegration or spalling with a loss of more than 5 per cent of the dry weight, or by (2) cracking badly in other than planes of laminations, or by (3) serious loss in structural strength.

PROPERTIES OF STRUCTURAL CLAY PRODUCTS

Building Brick

24. Manufacture. A variety of clays is used in making building brick ranging from the common surface clays used for common brick to the better grades of shale or impure fire clays used in producing face brick. The essential properties of the clay are sufficient plasticity for proper molding, low shrinkage in drying and burning, and low fusibility. The clay should not crack or warp during the drying or burning processes, and for face brick or ornamental brick it should burn to a uniform color.

Common brick are frequently burned in scove kilns, but the better grades of building brick are fired in permanent kilns of the up-draft, down-draft, or tunnel, type. The temperature of burning varies from 900 to 1200°C, depending upon the composition of the clay.

25. Classes of Building Brick. Brick are often classified by method of molding as soft-mud, stiff-mud, dry-pressed, or re-pressed brick.

By the degree of burning, brick are sometimes sorted into three classes (1) pale or salmon brick which are underburned, (2) body brick which occupy the central portion of the kiln and are well burned, (3) arch or clinker brick which are overburned.

Two irregular forms of brick commonly used in construction are compass brick and feather-edge brick. Compass brick have tapering broad faces; feather-edge brick have tapering narrow faces.

Cored brick extruded with 14 or 16 holes normal to the broad faces are easily and uniformly burned and light in weight.

From the standpoint of usage, the following classification may be made: common brick, front brick, and ornamental brick. Common brick comprise the poorer grades of building brick which are used for filling, backing and in walls where appearance is of small moment. They often vary greatly in color, degree of burning, and shape. Front or face brick are made more carefully than common brick. They are generally pressed or re-pressed and are used in fronts of buildings and in walls for which a pleasing appearance is desired. Red, white, cream, buff-burning brick, and buff-burning brick speckled by the addition of manganese, all of which burn to an even tone, are much used as front brick. Tapestry brick, rug brick, and stipple-faced brick are stiff-mud products which have had their edges roughened in different ways in order to create pleasing effects in wall constructions. Ornamental brick include enameled and glazed brick. Enameled brick constitute the major portion of the ornamental brick produced in the United States.

26. Requirements of Good Brick. The essential requirements for building brick are sufficient strength in crushing and bending, durability, a proper suction rate, and a pleasing appearance when exposed to view. Common brick of good quality should be free from checks or cracks, should emit a metallic ring when struck with the hammer, and should exhibit a fine-grained, uniform, dense structure free from laminations or large lime pebbles. Well-burned face brick should not be easily scratched by the knife. They should possess the previously mentioned characteristics, and also be uniform both in color and size. Regularity in size of brick and joints is important where high wall strength is required. Good brick should be free from soluble salts which cause efflorescence, such as the sulfates of lime, magnesia, and the alkalies. The liability to effloresce may be determined by allowing 3 or more brick to stand on end immersed in $\frac{1}{2}$ in. of distilled water for a week and then noting the appearance of the upper portions.

In a structure the durability of brick may be tested by frost action, by alternate wetting and drying, and by fire. Tests of fire resistance are generally made on wall panels. Resistance to frost action is best ascertained from alternate freezing and thawing tests, which are, however, quite expensive. The absorption test has long been considered a measure of durability, although the basis for this assumption is questionable.

As indicated in Art. VIII-18, the suction rate of a brick at the time it is laid exercises a marked influence on mortar bond. Although the suction rate can be regulated by wetting prior to laying, such procedure is always a nuisance and impracticable in cold weather. Hence brick which in normal condition have suction rates between 10 and 35 gm per brick per min are preferred for their superior bonding qualities.

The standard size for common and rough-face building brick of shale or clay is $8 \pm \frac{1}{4}$ by $3\frac{3}{4} \pm \frac{1}{8}$ by $2\frac{1}{4} \pm \frac{1}{16}$ in.; for smooth-face brick the width is $3\frac{7}{8} \pm \frac{1}{8}$, with other dimensions the same.

TABLE 1.　WEIGHTED AVERAGES OF STRENGTH AND ABSORPTION FOR BUILDING BRICK FROM VARIOUS PLACES IN THE UNITED STATES (McBurney and Lovewell).

District or City	Type of Brick	Average Compressive Strength, lb. per sq. in.	Average Modulus of Rupture, lb. per sq. in.	Average Water Absorption, per cent			Average Ratio, $\frac{C_{48}}{B_5}$
				5 hr. Cold	48 hr. Cold	5 hr. Boiling	
Maine, New Hampshire and Vermont	Hard	10,330	1505	5.7	6.3	8.7	0.70
	Salmon	5,520	995	13.9	14.5	17.2	0.84
Boston, Mass.	Hard	8,240	1360	7.7	8.2	10.6	0.74
	Salmon	3,710	645	16.4	17.1	19.6	0.88
Massachusetts, except Boston	Hard	5,940	1100	9.8	10.3	13.2	0.77
	Salmon	3,410	700	15.7	16.4	19.8	0.84
Connecticut	Hard	7,210	1155	12.9	13.5	16.2	0.82
	Salmon	4,670	770	18.6	19.1	21.8	0.87
Hudson Valley	Hard	4,740	745	14.0	14.6	17.7	0.80
	Salmon	2,580	425	19.5	20.0	24.3	0.83
New York, except Hudson Valley	Hard	4,770	1005	14.4	15.4	18.3	0.83
New Jersey	Hard	5,410	900	9.1	10.0	13.6	0.73
	Salmon	2,080	530	17.7	18.9	22.1	0.86
Delaware	Hard	8,040	1210	6.9	7.7	12.0	0.63
	Salmon	2,800	450	12.9	13.8	16.0	0.86
Baltimore, Md.	Hard	5,990	1330	8.0	9.1	12.3	0.75
	Salmon	3,130	645	17.3	18.2	20.9	0.88
Maryland, except Baltimore	Hard	4,440	960	8.4	9.2	13.4	0.68
	Salmon	2,680	570	14.1	15.4	18.5	0.83
Philadelphia, Pa.	Hard	6,580	855	8.9	9.8	14.5	0.67
	Salmon	2,520	355	16.7	17.9	22.9	0.79
Eastern Pennsylvania, except Philadelphia	Hard	8,080	1415	7.8	8.7	11.8	0.73
	Salmon	3,250	580	17.0	18.0	21.3	0.82
Pittsburgh, Pa.	Hard	11,060	2055	4.8	5.5	7.7	0.69
	Salmon	4,880	955	11.4	12.1	14.1	0.85
West Virginia and Western Pennsylvania, except Pittsburgh	Hard	11,450	1845	4.9	5.6	8.0	0.69
	Salmon	4,810	940	11.7	12.5	14.6	0.85
Cleveland, Ohio	Hard	9,820	1185	8.2	8.7	11.1	0.78
	Salmon	7,780	1285	9.7	10.3	12.0	0.85
Northern Ohio, except Cleveland	Hard	12,110	1720	7.1	7.9	10.4	0.68
	Salmon	3,910	620	12.6	13.5	14.6	0.79
Detroit, Mich.	Hard	4,330	900	15.6	16.5	19.5	0.81
	Salmon	2,540	555	18.9	19.4	20.8	0.93
Wisconsin	Hard	5,330	1110	15.6	16.6	20.3	0.81
	Salmon	2,320	470	24.4	25.2	28.0	0.90
Chicago, Ill.	Hard	3,450	1265	13.2	15.2	19.0	0.79
	Salmon	2,400	420	20.0	22.4	26.5	0.85
Illinois, except Chicago	Hard	13,050	1580	5.2	6.2	8.0	0.75
	Salmon	6,330	780	14.3	15.2	17.2	0.88
Kentucky	Hard	7,780	1255	10.3	11.2	15.5	0.73
	Salmon	4,010	720	14.7	15.8	19.0	0.84
Southern Indiana	Hard	16,280	2360	1.8	2.3	5.4	0.37
St. Louis, Mo.	Hard	11,040	1465	6.0	6.7	9.1	0.70
	Salmon	5,940	585	13.8	14.7	16.3	0.90
Missouri, except St. Louis	Hard	14,660	2020	2.9	3.8	5.7	0.61
	Salmon	6,430	1170	12.9	13.8	15.8	0.88
Nebraska	Hard	8,300	1025	8.7	9.7	13.3	0.73
	Salmon	2,480	460	14.0	15.3	20.6	0.76
Kansas	Hard	15,850	1915	3.2	3.8	5.1	0.59
	Salmon	4,500	600	15.2	16.0	17.6	0.91
Denver, Colorado	Hard	5,050	620	10.4	11.3	13.5	0.82
	Salmon	4,210	415	13.6	14.4	16.4	0.88
Colorado, except Denver	Hard	7,340	1145	10.3	11.1	13.3	0.83
	Salmon	4,900	740	15.5	16.0	17.8	0.90
Utah	Hard	7,490	1305	13.0	14.2	16.6	0.78
Wyoming	Hard	6,310	1410	7.2	8.1	12.1	0.68
	Salmon	5,680	300	13.4	13.9	16.3	0.85
Washington and Oregon	Hard	7,600	1245	9.5	10.3	14.1	0.70
	Salmon	3,240	580	15.9	17.0	20.1	0.85
Los Angeles, Calif.	Hard	3,690	600	11.2	11.8	14.2	0.83
California, except Los Angeles	Hard	4,640	735	11.9	12.7	15.2	0.84
Texas	Hard	7,285	1020	11.1	12.0	14.3	0.82
Mississippi, Louisiana and Arkansas	Hard	6,320	911	11.4	12.3	16.5	0.79
	Salmon	2,580	485	10.1	11.1	16.8	0.67
Alabama, Tennessee and North Carolina	Hard	9,700	1525	7.0	7.9	10.6	0.72
	Salmon	4,510	750	17.6	18.9	21.0	0.89
Richmond, Va.	Hard	9,350	1315	7.4	8.3	11.1	0.74
	Salmon	4,120	650	15.0	15.9	18.0	0.88
Virginia, except Richmond	Hard	9,470	1815	6.7	7.5	10.0	0.75
	Salmon	6,560	1440	11.2	11.9	13.8	0.87
Washington, D. C.	Hard	5,700	875	8.3	9.4	12.9	0.72
	Salmon	3,500	385	14.3	15.4	16.7	0.91
Weighted average of all samples, both hard and salmon		7,246	1154	10.12	10.92	13.99	0.764
Weighted average of all Hard Samples		7,434	1183	9.77	10.56	13.66	0.758
Weighted average of all Salmon Samples		4,094	678	15.94	16.77	19.41	0.851

27. Tests on Building Brick. A summary of tests on building-brick samples from 255 plants located throughout the United States and representing 37 per cent of the 1929 production is reported in Table 1. These tests were made at the Bureau of Standards by representatives of the Common Brick Manufacturers Association,* using ASTM procedure (see Serial Des. C67–31). Table 2 shows distribution of properties of hard

TABLE 2. DISTRIBUTION OF PROPERTIES OF "HARD BRICK" FROM ALL PARTS OF THE UNITED STATES (McBurney and Lovewell)

Compressive Strength, Flatwise		Modulus of Rupture		Water Absorption				Ratio, 48 hr. Cold to 5 hr. Boiling Water Absorption	
Range, lb. per sq. in.	Percentage of Production Within Range	Range, lb. per sq. in.	Percentage of Production Within Range	Range, per cent	Percentage of Production Within Range			Range	Percentage of Production Within Range
					5 hr. Cold	48 hr. Cold	5 hr. Boiling		
21,001 to 22,500	0.46	2101 to 3450	6.95	0 to 2.00	3.87	2.65	0.53	0.16 to 0.30	0.37
19,501 to 21,000	0.69	1951 to 2100	3.00	2.01 to 4.00	8.05	4.96	2.77	0.31 to 0.35	0.45
18,001 to 19,501	0.46	1801 to 1950	2.74	4.01 to 6.00	14.99	13.00	3.27	0.36 to 0.40	0.21
16,501 to 18,000	2.04	1651 to 1800	7.57	6.01 to 8.00	13.73	14.22	9.94	0.41 to 0.45	0.64
15,001 to 16,500	1.49	1501 to 1650	8.34	8.01 to 10.00	16.52	15.82	13.77	0.46 to 0.50	1.28
13,501 to 15,000	3.71	1351 to 1500	5.34	10.01 to 12.00	11.80	11.77	11.19	0.51 to 0.55	1.17
12,001 to 13,500	4.76	1201 to 1350	7.12	12.01 to 14.00	11.14	14.29	13.88	0.56 to 0.60	3.30
10,501 to 12,000	7.78	1051 to 1200	10.55	14.01 to 16.00	8.84	8.24	13.09	0.61 to 0.65	8.64
9,001 to 10,500	8.61	901 to 1050	10.44	16.01 to 18.00	5.01	5.52	11.02	0.66 to 0.70	12.37
7,501 to 9,000	11.92	751 to 900	13.60	18.01 to 20.00	2.42	4.77	9.14	0.71 to 0.75	16.80
6,001 to 7,500	15.47	601 to 750	11.74	20.01 to 22.00	2.22	2.31	5.72	0.76 to 0.80	19.41
4,501 to 6,000	16.81	451 to 600	7.52	22.01 to 24.00	1.31	0.64	2.14	0.81 to 0.85	15.65
3,001 to 4,500	17.97	301 to 450	4.35	24.01 to 26.00	0.00	0.68	1.95	0.86 to 0.90	13.89
1,501 to 3,000	7.46	151 to 300	0.37	26.01 to 28.00	0.11	0.00	0.75	0.91 to 0.95	5.32
0 to 1,500	0.36	0 to 150	0.37	28.01 to 34.00	0.00	0.11	0.75	0.96 to 1.00	0.51
Total per cent	99.99		100.00		100.01	99.98	99.91		100.01

brick covered in this survey. The terms hard and salmon were applied by the manufacturer and indicated brick which he estimated to be satisfactory and unsatisfactory in weathering resistance. Table 3 shows the effect of freezing and thawing on brick of doubtful weathering resistance.

These tests indicate that shale brick can be separated into resistant material by requiring either a compressive strength not less than 7500 psi or a modulus of rupture not less than 1200 psi or an absorption after 5 hours' boil not more than 12 per cent. Bricks with compressive strengths of 4500 psi or more, C/B ratios less than 0.8, or compressive strengths over 6000 psi and C/B less than 0.85 appear satisfactory in resistance to freezing and thawing.

From a consideration of the existing data, the grades and requirements suggested for building brick of *clay or shale* are shown in Table 4.

Grade A brick is suggested for use where strength and resistance to freezing and thawing in presence of moisture are required; grade B is

* Reported in *Proc. ASTM*, Vol. 33, Pt. 2, p. 636.

TABLE 3. EFFECT OF 51 CYCLES OF FREEZING AND THAWING ON INDIVIDUAL BRICK CLASSIFIED ACCORDING TO FLAT COMPRESSIVE STRENGTH AND RATIO OF 48 HOURS' COLD TO 5 HOURS' BOILING WATER ABSORPTION (McBurney and Lovewell)

S = satisfactory.   U = unsatisfactory (loss 3 per cent or more in weight).   Figures show number of brick.

Range, Compressive Strength, Flatwise, lb. per sq. in.	Range, ratio 48 hr. cold to 5 hr. boiling water absorption.																			
	0 to 0.40		0.40 to 0.60		0.60 to 0.70		0.70 to 0.75		0.75 to 0.80		0.80 to 0.85		0.85 to 0.90		0.90 to 0.95		0.95 to 1.00		Total No. Bricks	
	S	U	S	U	S	U	S	U	S	U	S	U	S	U	S	U	S	U	S	U
0 to 1,500			0	1*	4	3*	1	0	1	6	3	12	0	5	0	1	0	2	9	30
1,501 to 2,500			1	0	6	2*	1	0	9	7	10	13	6	15	2	7	0	2	35	46
2,501 to 3,500			1	0	2	0	1	0	3	0	11	9	18	39	4	14	1	3	41	65
3,501 to 4,500			1	0			3	1*	12	0	7	7	13	20	9	24	1	0	46	52
4,501 to 6,000					1	0	3	0	8	0	21	8	17	15	3	11			53	34
6,001 to 8,000					1	0	1	0			13	0	14	4	3	1			32	5
8,001 to 12,000			2	0	2	0	2	0	1	0	2	0	5	1	1	1			15	2
12,001 to 15,000			2	0	3	0	2	0											7	0
15,000+	2	0	5	0	2	0													9	0
Total	2	0	12	1	21	5	14	1	34	13	67	49	73	99	22	59	2	7	247	234

* From Hudson Valley.

TABLE 4

Grade	Compressive Strength (tested flatwise), lb. per sq. in.		Modulus of Rupture (flatwise on 7-in. span), lb. per sq. in.		Ratio of Absorptions* $\frac{C_{24}}{B_5}$	
	Mean of 5 Tests	Individual Minimum	Mean of 5 Tests	Individual Minimum	Mean of 5 Tests	Individual Maximum
A	4500 or over	3500	750 or over	550	0.75	0.80
B	2500–4500	2000	500 or over	350	0.80	0.85
C	1500–2500	1250	300 or over	200	No Limit	

* Requirement may be waived if brick are not exposed to freezing and thawing or where the compressive strength exceeds 8000 lb./in.^{2} and the absorption after 5 hr. boil is less than 8 per cent.

suggested for use where lower strength is acceptable and where brick are not saturated when exposed to freezing and thawing; grade C is intended for back up or interior masonry, or for exteriors not exposed to freezing.

First-quality sewer brick should show an average compressive strength of 8000 psi or more, a modulus of rupture of 1000 psi or more, a C_{24}/B_5 ratio of 0.75 or less, and an average absorption not over 6 per cent.

From the properties of the clay brick shown in Table 5 it will be observed that the ratios of the average tensile strength to the average

TABLE 5. AVERAGE PHYSICAL PROPERTIES OF BRICK USED IN
WALLS OF TABLE 6

Locality Represented or Kind	Absorption		Strength in Pounds per Square Inch			
	5 hr. Boil	48 hr. Immersion	Modulus of Rupture Flatwise	Compression Flatwise	Tension	Punching Shear
Chicago............	16.5	11.7	1225	3280	417	1100[a]
Detroit.............	22.3	20.7	670	3540	222	1165[a]
Mississippi.........	21.7	16.7	820	3410	317	1590[a]
New England.......	9.2	6.9	1550	8600	601	3550[b]
Sand Lime..........	13.2	....	560	4150	210	1230[c]

Each average represents 50 tests except as noted: [a] represents 10 tests; [b] represents 4 tests; [c] represents 70 tests.

modulus of rupture range between 30 and 40 per cent and that the ratio of the average punching shear strength to the average compressive strength flatwise varies from a third to a half. Data from other sources indicate that the compressive strength of brick tested on edge or on end is usually lower than that obtained when tested flatwise.

Griffith also found that the approximate relationship between the crushing strength and absorption of stone (Art. VII-21) holds for brick and other structural silicates.

The modulus of elasticity of brick generally lies between 1,500,000 and 4,000,000 psi.

28. Specific Gravity of Brick. The bulk specific gravity of brick ranges from 1.6 to 2.5, depending upon the character of the raw materials and the degree of burning. Brick made from impure fire clays generally have a lower specific gravity than those made from shales. For well-burned brick the bulk specific gravity will usually lie between 2.0 and 2.4. Specific gravity of pulverized building brick runs from 2.5 to 2.9.

29. Crushing Tests on Brick Masonry. The main conditions governing the strength of brick masonry under concentric loading are: (1) the strength of brick, (2) the strength and elasticity of mortar, (3) quality of workmanship in laying, (4) method of laying, (5) regularity in form of brick. The stiffness of masonry is dependent largely upon the modulus of elasticity of the mortar, the quality of workmanship in laying, and the modulus of elasticity of the brick.

Transverse failure of individual brick usually begins at loads between 50 and 80 per cent of the maximum (Tables 6 and 7). The pier or wall then gradually separates into a number of slender columns, and failure ensues. The failures of plain and reinforced brick columns are shown in Fig. 6 and 7. Both columns were made with a brick having a crushing

TABLE 6. COMPRESSIVE STRENGTH OF BRICK WALLS *

Walls 8 and 12 in. thick, 6 ft. long, and 9 ft. high. Solid construction, common bond, headers every sixth course, joints $\frac{1}{4}$ to $\frac{1}{2}$ in. thick. Workmanship A, beds furrowed vertical joints not filled; B, beds well spread and vertical joints filled.

Work-man-ship	No. Walls Tested	Mortar Mix by Vol. C : L : S	Compressive Strengths, lb./in.²				Secant Modulus of Elasticity in 1,000 lb./in.²	Average Ratios		
			Brick Flatwise (B)	Mortar 2×4-in. Cylinders (M)	Walls Av. (W)	Walls Min.		$\frac{W}{B}$	$\frac{W}{M}$	Load at First Crack to Max. Load
B	5	1 : 0.1 : 3	3280	3260	905	755	1300	0.28	0.28	0.94
	6	....	3540	....	1145	895	830	0.32	0.35	0.69
	6	....	3410	....	1510	1335	1420	0.44	0.46	0.88
	6	....	8600	....	2710	2040	2500	0.31	0.83	0.75
B	6	1 : 1 : 6	3540	1100	945	760	680	0.27	0.86	0.59
	6	....	3410	....	1230	965	1160	0.36	1.10	0.92
	6	....	8600	....	1840	1710	2260	0.21	1.65	0.62
A	5	1 : 0 : 3	3280	3580	660	580	620	0.20	0.18	0.94
	6	....	4150†	....	905	800	1300	0.22	0.25	0.77
A	6	1 : 1¼ : 6	3280	1070	585	575	510	0.18	0.55	0.88
	6	....	4150†	....	625	550	740	0.15	0.58	0.80
A	6	0 : 1¼ : 3	3280	90	285	250	62	0.09	3.15	0.71
	6	....	4150†	....	300	280	93	0.07	3.35	0.69

* Data from U. S. Bureau of Standards, *RP108*, and *Tech. Paper* No. 276.
† Sand lime brick.

strength of 14,420 psi, tested flatwise. They were 12 by 12 in. in cross section and 6 ft high. The column shown in Fig. 7 had 3.1 per cent vertical steel and two $\frac{3}{8}$-in. hoops per joint. The reinforced column was considerably tougher and stronger. It failed at a load of 605,000 lb; the plain column failed at 361,500 lb.

Because of differences in ratio of height to least width, a homogeneous pier or wall having a height to width ratio between 6:1 and 10:1 should have only 70 per cent of the crushing strength of a brick tested flatwise. Owing to mortar joints, strength and elastic properties of masonry never reach this ratio. The data by Stang, Parsons, and McBurney given in Table 6 and those of Talbot in Table 7 show that the strengths of walls and piers made from ordinary bricks and mortars usually run between 0.1 and 0.4 of the compressive strength of the component brick tested flatwise.

Supporting evidence on the influence of the strength of the component brick is afforded by the tests reported by Bragg in *Tech. Paper* III. These tests were made at the U. S. Bureau of Standards on large piers 30 by 30 in. by 10 ft, built of four grades of brick ranging in crushing strength from 1600 to 12,000 psi with three mortars. They indicate that the strengths of piers can be raised by increasing the depths of the units or by breaking joints every few courses rather than every course. These tests and others at Watertown Arsenal also show that a decided advantage in masonry strength obtains when brick are laid on edge. Insertion

TABLE 7. AVERAGE RESULTS OF COMPRESSIVE TESTS ON BRICK COLUMNS

[See *Bull.* 27, Eng. Expt. Sta., Univ. Ill.]

Columns were $12\frac{1}{2}\times12\frac{1}{2}$ in.$\times10$ ft. and consisted of 40 to 43 courses of brick laid with $\frac{3}{8}$-in. joints.

No. of Tests.	Characteristics of Columns.			Average Ultimate Strength Lb./In.²†	Proportion of Load at which Popping Occurred.‡	Ratio of Strength of Columns to Strength of			Modulus of Elasticity in 1000 Lb./In.²
	How Laid.	Mix of Mortar.*	Age Days.			Brick	First Set.	6-in. Mortar Cubes.	
					SHALE BUILDING BRICK				
3	Well	1 P : 3S	67	3365	.56	.31	1.00	1.17	4783
2	Well	1 P : 3S	181	3950	......	.37	1.18	.....	5025
2	Well	1 P : 3S	68	2800 ¹	.66	.26	.83	.....	4400
2	Poorly	1 P : 3S	67	2920	.62	.27	.87	1.05	3525
2	Well	1 P : 5S	65	2225	.52	.21	.66	1.30	3250
1	Well	1 N : 3S	67	1750	.40	.16	.52	5.75	800
2	Well	1 L : 2S	66	1450	.43	.14	.43	.....	104
					UNDERBURNED CLAY BRICK				
2	Well	1 P : 3S	63	1060	.76	.27	.31	.37	433

* P = Portland cement; S = sand; N = natural cement; L = lime.
† The maximum range in strength for any set of columns was less than 13 per cent.
‡ Popping was probably due to transverse rupture of brick.
¹ These columns were loaded with 1-inch eccentricity.

of wire mesh in every horizontal joint also caused a small increase in strength. As a result of these tests, Bragg proposed the expression $P = Kp$, where P = unit crushing strength of pier, p = unit compressive strength of brick, and K is a constant depending on the mortar. For brick laid flatwise in 1:3 Portland cement mortar, he suggested $K = 0.27$, and for 1:6 lime mortar, $K = 0.11$.

Tests made at the Watertown Arsenal clearly show the advantage of using mortar stronger than a 1:3 mix with very hard-burned brick. In tests of piers of wire-cut brick having a crushing strength of approximately 13,000 psi, those laid in neat Portland cement had a strength of 31 per cent of the brick, whereas those laid in 1:3 Portland cement mortar possessed only 19 per cent of the strength of the brick.

The advantage of stiffness arising from the use of strong mortar in the joints is also well illustrated in the data of Tables 6 and 7.

The data in Table 6 and other evidence from the Stang, Parsons, and McBurney tests show that increases of 30 to 100 per cent in the crushing strength and material gains in stiffness of brick masonry can be realized if the *mortar* is spread on *horizontal joints* and *filled into vertical joints* rather than grooved on the beds and omitted from the vertical joints.

The existing data indicate that the crushing strength of well-laid brick masonry varies directly with the crushing strength of the brick and roughly with the cube root of the compressive strength of the mortar.

Fig. 6. Failure of unreinforced   Fig. 7. Failure of brick column
         brick column.   reinforced with horizontal steel
                                                 hoops and vertical steel bars.

30. Resistance of Brick Walls to Fire. In a series of fire tests on 6 × 9-ft wall panels at the Underwriters' Laboratories, in Chicago, brick panels showed marked resistance to fire and low conductivity. Tests were made on (1) a 12-in. wall of well-burned Chicago brick, (2) an 8-in. panel of hydraulic-pressed brick from Indiana, (3) an 8-in. panel of common brick from St. Louis, and (4) an 8-in. panel of sand-lime brick from Indiana. The strengths and absorptive properties of these bricks are given in Table 8. With the exception of the panel made of hydraulic brick which was laid in lime putty, cement mortar was used. The tests were

TABLE 8.　EFFECTS OF HIGH TEMPERATURE ON BRICK AND BRICK WALLS

[*Bull.* 370, U. S. Geological Survey]

Wall panels fired for two hours, for one hour at maximum temperature.

Kind of Brick	Hard-burned Clay (1)	Hyd-pressed Brick (2)	Com-mon Clay (3)	Sand-Lime (4)
Thickness of panel, in.	12	8	8	8
Maximum average temperature on exposed face in °C	770	850	850	790
Maximum average temperature on unexposed face after 2 hr. in °C	18	35	58	55
Mean temperature of air on unexposed face	3	3	23	19
No. unexposed brick tested transversely	2	2	5	5
Average modulus of rupture of unexposed brick, lb/in.^{2}	482	718	1178	319
No. exposed brick tested transversely	0	0	0	5
Average modulus of rupture of exposed brick, lb/in.^{2}	. . .	. . .	. . .	56
No. unexposed brick crushed	13	13	5	5
Average crushing strength of unexposed brick, lb/in.^{2}	2729	4440	3866	2035
No. exposed brick crushed	13	13	0	5
Average crushing strength of exposed brick, lb/in.^{2}	2793	3701	. . .	1750
No. unexposed * brick immersed	2	2	5	5
Average per cent absorption, unexposed brick, after forty-eight hours' immersion	20.2	10.7	6.2	15.9

* Absorptions of exposed brick were about the same as for unexposed brick.

made by subjecting the face of the panel to a temperature which rose to about 800°C in ½ hour and then varied between 800° and 900°C for 1½ hours, at which time the panel was removed and the face quenched by water from a fire hose. Each high temperature recorded in Table 8 represents an average of a number of pyrometer readings, the thermocouples being arranged to secure the variation in temperature at different parts of the furnace and at various points on the face of the wall.

The panels of clay brick withstood the tests better than the panel of sand-lime brick. The panel of hydraulic-pressed brick was in the most perfect condition after quenching. About 18 per cent of the brick on the face of this panel were cracked through, and a very few were spalled. The

Chicago brick contained lime knots which caused a large percentage of the exposed brick to crack when quenched. In 60 to 70 per cent of these the cracks were sufficiently large to permit picking off portions of the brick. About half the faces of the St. Louis brick were so cracked at the conclusion of the test that they could be readily removed, and the face of the wall was discolored to a depth of about 1 in. After firing, the face of the panel of sand-lime brick looked soft and chalky. It was washed away to a depth of ⅜ to ¾ in. when the hose was applied. Only about 20 per cent of the exposed brick could be removed from the wall intact.

Sand-Lime Brick *

Although not a clay product, the fact that a million dollars' worth of sand-lime brick are used annually as a substitute for clay brick warrants a brief discussion of their manufacture and properties in this chapter.

31. Definition. Sand-lime brick are made from a lean mixture of slaked lime and fine siliceous sand, molded under mechanical pressure and hardened under steam pressure.

32. Manufacture. The sand should be free from clay or mica. It should all pass a 20-mesh and three-fourths of it should be retained on 100-mesh. If the grains run larger than a 20-mesh, the coarse particles must be screened out or reduced in a tube mill. A high-calcium lime is preferred to a brown or dolomitic lime owing to the rapidity with which the high-calcium lime hardens. The requisite percentage of lime varies between 4 and 10 per cent. Generally the lime is slaked before mixing with the sand by placing it beneath the brick cars in the hardening cylinder and allowing the steam to act upon it. Often the sand and lime are mixed dry in a tube mill and the mixture is then tempered in a special type of pug mill. In some plants the quicklime is slaked, the sand ground, and an intimate mixture secured by running the wet sand and lime through a wet and dry grinding mill, an apparatus similar to a dry pan. Molding is done in powerful presses, some of which can exert a compression of 20,000 psi on the surface of the brick. After removal from the press the brick are stacked on cars which are run into the hardening cylinders. In the latter a steam pressure of 100 to 150 psi is used. After hardening for 6 to 10 hours the brick are ready for use.

33. Comparison of Clay and Sand-Lime Brick. On account of their smooth surfaces, even shape, freedom from efflorescence, uniform color, and satisfactory strength, sand-lime brick are sometimes preferred to clay brick. Some of the American sand-lime brick, however, have not been

* For further information on sand-lime brick see *Cements, Limes and Plasters,* by E. C. Eckel. An interesting article on *The Chemistry of Sand-lime Brick,* by T. R. Ernest, appears in *Trans. Am. Ceramic Soc.,* Vol. 13, p. 649.

as durable when exposed to the weather as good grades of clay brick. Unless made with great care sand-lime brick do not resist frost action or fire as well as clay brick.

34. Physical Properties of Sand-Lime Brick. Good sand-lime brick bedded flatwise have a compressive strength between 2500 and 5000 psi. In cross bending the modulus of rupture should exceed 450 psi. After boiling 5 hours good brick should not show more than 18 per cent absorption. The bulk specific gravity commonly lies between 1.8 and 2.0.

PAVING BRICK *

35. Manufacture. Paving brick are made from three classes of clay: surface clays, impure fire clays, and shale. Owing to the narrowness of the vitrification range for most surface clays, they are apt to produce either underburned or overburned brick. Impure fire clays make a good brick when sufficiently vitrified, but require a high temperature. The shales are by far the best source of raw material for paving brick. Wheeler suggested that shales suitable for paving brick should approximate the following percentage analysis: silica (SiO_2) = 56, alumina (Al_2O_3) = 22, ignition loss = 7, lime (CaO) = 1, magnesia (MgO) = 1, alkalies (K_2O and Na_2O) = 4. Fluxing impurities in the above analysis total 13 per cent.

Approximately three-fourths of the paving brick produced in the United States are vertical fiber lug brick made in three standard depths: $2\frac{1}{2} \pm \frac{1}{8}$, $3 \pm \frac{1}{8}$, and $3\frac{1}{2} \pm \frac{1}{8}$ in., with a width of $4 \pm \frac{1}{8}$ in. and length of $8\frac{1}{2} \pm \frac{1}{4}$ in. Of these sizes the 3-in. depth is the most used. These brick have plain wire-cut faces with two or more lugs on one side and a vertical bar lug or lugs on each end. Lugs extend from $\frac{1}{8}$ to $\frac{1}{4}$ in. beyond the body dimensions mentioned above. A small proportion of the older re-pressed lug variety with four lugs on one side, still standard in the $3\frac{1}{2} \pm \frac{1}{8}$ by $4 \pm \frac{1}{8}$ by $8\frac{1}{2} \pm \frac{1}{4}$ in. size, is also marketed.

De-airing has been introduced in molding paving brick with accompanying improvements in density, strength, and resistance to abrasion.

Paving brick are generally burned in down-draft or continuous kilns. From 7 to 10 days are required in burning and a like period for proper annealing. The temperature required to bring shales to complete vitrification (Wheeler) is 850 to 1100°C. Impure fire clays require a temperature from 100 to 200°C higher.

By employing impure fire clay, with which danger of overburning is small, as high as 90 per cent of first-class paving brick may be produced.

* Additional information on methods of manufacture may be obtained from *Vitrified Paving Brick*, by H. A. Wheeler, Randall & Co.; and from *Burning Brick in Down-Draft Kilns*, by W. D. Richardson, Randall & Co.

Using shale, it is not possible to average more than 75 per cent of first-class pavers.

36. Requirements of Good Paving Brick. Every brick should be free from marked distortion, should have one plane face, and should be free from cracks, checks, blisters, and kiln marks over $3/16$ in. deep. It should give a high metallic ring when struck with a hammer and should, when broken, exhibit a uniform close-grained structure free from laminations. The interior of a properly burned brick cannot be scratched with a knife. *Uniformity in quality is of vital importance in order that the pavement may wear evenly.*

37. Physical Properties of Paving Brick. Good brick should have a crushing strength in excess of 8000 psi. The transverse strength (modulus of rupture) should not be less than 1500 psi. Low transverse strength may be due to either overburning or improper annealing. After immersion 24 hours in water at room temperature, shale brick when properly vitrified generally absorb between 0.5 and 2 per cent; brick made of impure fire clay may absorb as high as 5 per cent. An absorption less than 0.5 per cent generally denotes overburning. In bulk specific gravity, shale pavers commonly range between 2.2 and 2.5, impure fire clay between 2.1 and 2.3. The better grades of paving brick lose less than 20 per cent by weight, in the rattler test. Wide variation in the losses of individual brick indicate non-uniformity in methods of manufacture and are sufficient cause for rejection of brick even though the average loss is small.

REFRACTORY BRICK *

38. Introduction. Certain classes of brick are much employed to line flues, hearths, and the various classes of furnaces used in metallurgical processes. Such brick must be able to withstand high temperatures without undue softening or change in volume, must resist the action of gases and slags generated during the process, must resist abrasion when hot, and must possess low thermal conductivity. In accordance with the character of the chemical reaction which different refractory brick resist, they are divided into three classes: acid, basic, and neutral.

39. Acid Brick. The brick which are commonly used to resist the action of siliceous and other acid slags are firebrick and silica brick.

Firebrick are made from fire clays which are sometimes grogged with small percentages of sand to reduce shrinkage. The clay generally consists of 50 to 75 per cent silica, 20 to 40 per cent alumina, and less than 10 per cent of fluxes. The more refractory brick are made from clays

---

* For additional information on refractory materials reference should be made to Havard's *Refractories and Furnaces,* from which considerable of this material has been drawn.

having low flux contents and high alumina contents. A very high alumina content, however, gives the brick a basic reaction. The brick are molded by either the soft- or stiff-mud processes and re-pressed after partial drying.

First class firebrick should have a modulus of rupture of at least 500 psi and should withstand a load of 25 psi at a temperature of 1350°C without deforming over 6 per cent. They should not soften at a temperature less than 1700°C.*

40. Silica Brick. Quartzite, sandstone, or silica sand, which consists of 95 per cent or more pure silica, are the main constituents used in making silica brick. If the siliceous rock contains small percentages of clay it is sometimes possible to mold the brick without artificial additions. The English ganister brick is made from such material. Ordinarily, however, the ground siliceous rock or the sand are not sufficiently plastic when tempered with water and are adulterated either with very small percentages of fire clay or about 1½ per cent of high-calcium lime. Silica brick are burned at temperatures slightly higher than firebrick.

On account of their brittleness and expansibility when heated, silica brick must be laid with wide joints. The compressive strength of silica brick tested flatwise often exceeds 2000 psi. The softening temperature ranges from 1700° to 1800°C.

41. Basic Brick. For lining basic Bessemer converters, basic open-hearth furnaces, blast furnaces, copper furnaces, and other vessels subjected to the action of basic slags, magnesia brick are quite generally used. Magnesia brick are made from magnesite, nearly pure magnesium carbonate, of which the most satisfactory supplies are found in Greece and in Styria, an Austrian province. The magnesite is first calcined at 800°C, a temperature which is sufficient to free the carbon dioxide. This preliminary calcination of Grecian magnesite is generally done at the mines. At the brick plant a large proportion of the calcined product is sintered at a temperature of 1800°C. It is then mixed with 1 to 50 per cent of calcined magnesia, and the mass is tempered with a small proportion of water. For brick which must resist high temperatures the proportion of calcined magnesia must be low. Since such mixtures are of low plasticity a very little tar or magnesium chloride is sometimes added for a binder. The brick are then hand molded, partially dried, and re-pressed. After further drying, the brick, which have very little tenacity, are carefully stacked in a double layer in a down-draft kiln and burned.

Styrian magnesite is sorted, dead-burned, and again freed from impurities. The sintered magnesia is then ground, tempered with a small proportion of water, and molded into brick which are burned at a temperature

* See *Tech. Paper* **7**, National Bureau of Standards.

above 1700°C. Brick made from Styrian magnesite are considered more refractory than others. Their softening temperature is approximately 2000°C.

Although not so satisfactory as magnesia, calcined dolomite, the double carbonate of magnesia and lime, is often used to make refractory brick. The natural rock or a mixture of the rock and clay is ground, tempered with water, and molded into shape. After drying, these are burned like magnesia brick. Dolomite brick suffer greater contraction at high temperatures than magnesia brick.

In making bauxite brick, the bauxite, which consists of 50 per cent or more of alumina, with water, iron oxide, and silica for principal impurities, is calcined and crushed to a fine powder. It is then mixed with 15 to 30 per cent of fire clay, tempered with water, and molded into bricks. Although properly burned bauxite brick are highly refractory, they have such a large shrinkage when heated to high temperatures that they have not come into general use. In experiments by Kanolt * on 8 samples of brick, the melting points varied from 1565 to 1785°C.

42. Neutral Brick. At the slag line in a basic furnace and in certain ports, and flues where the reaction of the surrounding medium may be either acid or basic, refractory brick which are neutral in reaction are used.

Chromite, the oxide of iron and chromium, is the principal raw material used for making neutral refractory brick. The ore is crushed and mixed either with fire clay or with magnesia and tempered with water in a wet-pan. The brick are molded, dried, and burned in much the same way as magnesia brick. Ordinarily the brick contain from 30 to 40 per cent chrome (Cr_2O_3), with alumina, iron oxide, magnesia, and silica in varying amounts. Chrome brick, although very resistant chemically to the action of slags and gases, are less refractory and weaker than magnesia brick. One sample tested by Kanolt had a melting point of 2050°C.

BUILDING TILE

43. Wall Tile, Partition Tile, and Fireproofing. For manufacturing wall tile, structural floor tile, partition tile, and fireproofing, plastic clays or shales mixed with clay are used. They burn to a hard, dense structure at a fairly low temperature, generally between 1100° and 1300°C. These forms are molded in machines of the auger or plunger type and are commonly burned in down-draft or continuous kilns. Figure 8 shows typical shapes of these four classes of building tile. Most of such forms contain 45 to 55 per cent of air space or voids. Sections so made are sometimes inaccurately called terra cotta blocks. Hollow blocks, frequently termed

* *Tech. Paper* 10, National Bureau of Standards.

load-bearing tile, are used in load-bearing walls and partitions. For un-
plastered outside walls they are often salt glazed. For walls which are
to be plastered, blocks, tile, and fireproofing are often scored in order to
furnish a better bond for the plaster. Load-bearing tile and structural
floor tile are harder to burn and stronger than partition tile. Partition
tile are used principally for partitions which carry no superimposed load.
Fireproofing differs from partition tile chiefly in shape and size.

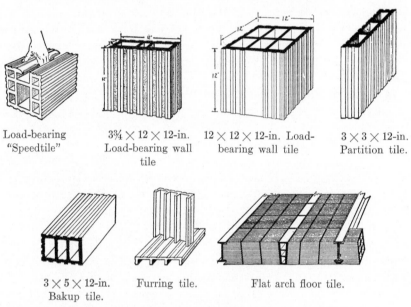

Load-bearing   3¾ × 12 × 12-in.   12 × 12 × 12-in. Load-   3 × 3 × 12-in.
"Speedtile"   Load-bearing wall   bearing wall tile   Partition tile.
              tile

3 × 5 × 12-in.   Furring tile.   Flat arch floor tile.
Bakup tile.

Fig. 8. Types of clay building tile. (National Fireproofing Corporation.)

The advantages of hollow block and fireproofing are lightness, low permeability to water, low heat conductivity, and a rough surface to which
plaster may be directly applied, thus avoiding the necessity of furring and
lathing. Fire tests have shown, however, that partition tile and hollow
blocks are likely to split at the junctions of webs and faces, especially
when the hose is turned upon hot partitions.* It is, therefore, safe practice to insist on fire tests of hollow block panels when they are to be used
for fire protection.

Load-bearing wall tile of good quality should be true in shape and
dimensions. They should have a compressive strength when loaded on
the sides in excess of 700 psi of gross area and double that value when
loaded on the ends. The better grades of wall tile exhibit strengths of
two to three times these amounts. After boiling for 1 hour, good wall

* *Bull.* 370, U. S. Geol. Survey.

tile for service exposed to the weather should show less than 16 per cent absorption.

Structural clay load-bearing floor tile for arch construction, when loaded on sides, should exhibit compressive strengths in excess of 1600 psi of net area, and double that amount when loaded on the ends.

The variability of wall tile and the necessity for testing them are shown by a large series of tests reported in *Proc. ASTM*, Vol. 17, Pt. 1, p. 334. Tile were selected by manufacturers to represent their product fairly. The compressive strengths in these tests ranged from 95 psi of gross area, for a soft-burned tile loaded flatwise, to 6000 psi for a medium-burned tile tested on end. Absorption, by weight, after boiling 5 hours, ranged from 1.8 per cent for a hard-burned specimen to 20.3 per cent for a very soft tile.

44. Tests of Pilasters and Hollow Block Columns. Crushing tests on 16 pilasters between 12 by 12 and 20 by 24 in. in cross section, laid in 1L:1C:4S mortar and loaded to duplicate structural conditions, were made by Shank at Ohio State University in 1936 (see Expt. Sta. *Bull.* 57). On pilasters made of common forms of load-bearing tile faced and capped with Detroit common brick the range in strength based on gross area was 489 to 805 psi, average 550 psi. For pilasters of Detroit common brick the values ranged from 802 to 928 and averaged 864 psi.

In *Bull.* 27, Eng. Expt. Sta., Univ. Ill., Talbot reports two series of tests on columns made of hollow blocks 8 in. high, 4 in. wide, and 8 in. long, containing about 15 per cent of cell space. The blocks were laid in Portland cement mortar. Their compressive strengths varied between 3350 and 9070, averaging 5451 psi of net cross section.

The seven columns tested in 1907 were approximately 12 ft high; the twelve columns of the 1908 series were 10 ft high. Columns of the earlier series ranged in cross section from $8\frac{1}{2} \times 8\frac{1}{2}$ in. to $17\frac{1}{2} \times 17\frac{1}{2}$ in.; all the columns of the later series were $12\frac{1}{2} \times 12\frac{1}{2}$ in. in cross section. The columns of the earlier series were laid in 1:2 mortar. Most of the columns of the series of 1908 were laid in 1:3 mortar. The strengths of the columns tested in 1907 varied from 2710 to 3440 psi; those tested in 1908 had strengths ranging from 3040 to 4300 psi, the latter value being estimated. By reference to Art. VIII-29 it will be noted that the strengths of these hollow block columns compare very favorably with the strengths of first-class brick columns. The initial modulus of elasticity of the columns varied between 1,910,000 and 2,860,000 psi.

45. Roofing Tile. For making roofing tile, the clay must not only be plastic, but it must also dry and burn without suffering distortion. Considerable care is also required in preparing the raw material. After being ground in a dry-pan and finely screened the clay is pugged in a wet-pan and made into balls which are stored in bins until wanted. The balls are then taken to an auger machine and molded into tile or, if interlocking tile are to be made, they are formed into clots. The clots are then formed into tile on a press. Common types of tile are shown in Fig. 9. After drying, roofing tile are burnt in saggers in down-draft kilns. Tile which are to serve as insulation against heat are soft burned and porous. Where tile are to be subjected to freezing they are burned harder or glazed.

Roofing tile should be strong, durable, free from soluble salts, and impervious to water. Roofing tile, when properly made, form a strong, durable, fireproof roof which is a poor conductor of heat. The chief objections to tile roofing are the expense and the heaviness of the construction.

46. Floor Tile. White-burning and red-burning clays, fire clays, and shales are used in making tile for floor surfaces. The chief considerations are color when burned, freedom from soluble salts, and absence of distortion and checking in burning. The dry-press process is used in molding, and down-draft kilns in burning.

Floor tile may be divided into two classes in accordance with the method of molding the design into the tile. They are face tile, commonly called encaustic tile because they have a burnt-in design, and plain tile.

Plain tile are composed of the same clay or mixture of clay throughout. Frequently these are made in the form of mosaics. They may be either vitreous or semi-vitreous.

Plain face tile are made by covering the die forming the base of the mold with a thin layer of specially prepared clay, filling the mold with a clay backing, and compacting in a hand press. In making inlaid face tile, a cellular frame is placed on the bottom of the mold and clays which have been properly colored are screened into the different cells in accordance with the pattern scheme. The frame is then removed, the backing inserted, and pressure applied to compact the tile.

Floor tile should show little absorption, have a high transverse strength, and a high resistance to abrasion.

47. Wall Tile. Tile for surfaces of walls differ from floor tile principally in design and degree of burning. Wall tile are burned at a comparatively low temperature, glazed, and fired again in a muffle kiln at a still lower temperature. Wide difference in color, in shades of a single color, and in relief design can be obtained. Wall tile are much used in wainscotings and to some extent in arches and ceilings. Floor- and wall-tile designs appear in Fig. 10.

TERRA COTTA

48. Terra Cotta. For the ornamentation of buildings and structures decorative terra cotta is often used. It is less costly than stone when a

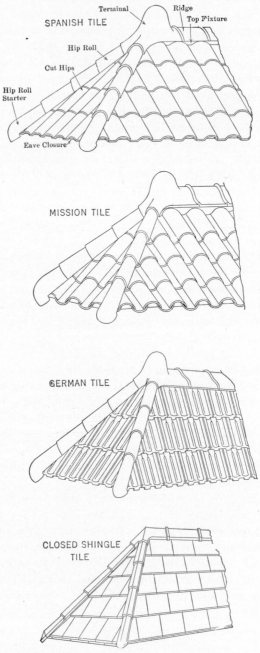

Fig. 9.   Examples of various roofing tiles.

number of pieces of a given pattern are frequently repeated in a structure. This economic advantage is especially worthy of consideration when the repeated patterns are of intricate design. When properly made the material weathers well and because of its glazed surface can be cleaned more easily than a porous stone.

Terra cotta is made from a finely ground mixture of fire clay and shale, or fire clay and impure clay, which is adulterated with ground brick or other burnt-clay product to reduce shrinkage. Plain forms of uniform section are extruded through dies; other simple shapes are hand molded in

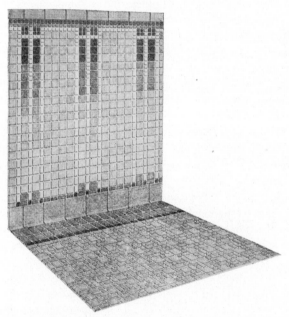

Fig. 10. Typical design in ceramic tile of the wall and floor above the pool in a natatorium. (American-Olean Tile Co.)

plaster molds. Intricate patterns are modeled in green clay by sculptors and used for making plaster molds. Thirty to fifty pieces can be reproduced from a given mold. After being molded, terra cotta parts are slowly dried to avoid checking and warping. They are then sprayed with a slip to impart the desired color to the goods on burning. To some parts glazes of bright or dull finish are also applied. Burning is done in muffle kilns or in continuous tunnel kilns. In the latter, a period of about 5 days is required to burn the product. The maximum temperatures attained are about 1100° to 1200°C. To avoid kiln marks each piece is independently supported on fire-clay tile. After burning, rough edges are removed and parts are assembled and ground to fit.

CLAY PIPE

49. Sewer Pipe. In the construction of sewers clay pipe has long been successfully used. Sewer pipe must have high strength in order that it may carry the ditch filling. To successfully withstand the action of acids and gases in the sewage, the pipe must be hard burned and impervious. They should be reasonably straight, smooth on the interior, and substantially free from cracks, blisters, pimples, and laminations.

Sewer pipe is made from red-burning clays, fire clays, shales, and mixtures of shale and fire clay. It is generally molded in vertical double-cylinder presses from a stiff-mud mix, although some pipe is made by the dry-press process. Sewer pipe is commonly burned in down-draft kilns at temperatures between 1050° and 1300°C. The term vitrified pipe is often a misnomer, since the burning temperature frequently is insufficient for vitrification. However, the firing should be carried to the stage of incipient vitrification. Salt glazing is generally practiced to insure a smooth and impervious surface. The pipe is made in lengths of about 3 ft and in diameters up to 42 in. Sewer pipe are commonly provided with a bell on one end, into which the small end of an adjacent pipe is fitted. Joints are filled with 1:1 Portland cement mortar.*

In general, small fragments from good pipe will have an absorption less than 7 per cent after boiling 5 hours in distilled water. Results of crushing tests in which the lower portion of the pipe was bedded in sand and the load applied on the top through a hardwood strip 1 in. wide appear in Table 9.

50. Drain Tile. Clay drain tile are made principally from shales and impure clays. The smaller sizes are molded in auger machines, but the larger ones are made in sewer-pipe presses. The tile are burned in a variety of kilns sometimes with brick or fireproofing. Kiln temperatures are lower than those used in burning sewer pipe, although the better grades of tile are burned until steel-hard. Salt glazing is sometimes employed. Drain tile are generally cylindrical in form and laid with uncemented butt joints through which the drainage water seeps.

Drain tile and sewer pipe should conform to the strength requirements in Table 10. These values are the same as the crushing loads per foot of length under sand bearings (see Art. VIII-20). For relation of load to strength requirements for other bearings, see ASTM *Specifications*.

* The remarks in Art. VIII-36 concerning appearance, hardness, texture, and ring under the hammer of paving brick apply with equal force to sewer pipe and the better grades of drain tile.

TABLE 9. CRUSHING TESTS ON SEWER PIPE MADE BY THE MUNICI-
PAL SEWER-PIPE TESTING LABORATORY OF BROOKLYN, N. Y., IN 1909

[See *Municipal Journal*, Vol. 38, p. 160.]

Size of Pipe, In.	Total Number Tested.	Number Tested to Destruction.	Crushing Strengths in Pounds per Linear Foot of Pipe.			Required Strength, Lb. per Ft.†	Percentage of Failures.
			Maximum.	Minimum.	Average.		
6	170	169	2333	1033	1537	1000	0
12	245	245	2900	933	1542	1150	2.04
15	72	72	2800	1300	1935	1300	0
18	25	25	3100	1734	2389	1450	0
24	17	14	3800	2200	2825	2000	0
30	2	2	3280	3240	3260	....	0
30*	2	2	3240	3080	3160	....	0

* Double strength pipe. † Local standard.

TABLE 10. AVERAGE STRENGTH REQUIREMENTS FOR CLAY AND
CEMENT DRAIN TILE AND SEWER PIPE

(From ASTM *Standards*)

	Drain Tile			Sewer Pipe		
	Minimum Average Ordinary Supporting Strength, pounds per linear foot, for			Minimum Strength, pounds per linear foot, Sand Bearings		
Internal Diameter of Tile, inches	Standard Drain Tile *a*	Extra-Quality Drain Tile *b*	Internal Diameter of Pipe, inches	Clay, Standard Strength	Pipe, Extra Strength	Concrete Pipe
4	1200	1600	4	1430		1500
5	1200	1600	6	1430	2850	1650
6	1200	1600	8	1430	2850	1950
8	1200	1600	10	1570	2850	2100
10	1200	1600	12	1710	3200	2250
12	1200	1600	15	2000	3925	2620
15	1300	1600	18	2430	4700	3000
18	1400	1800	21	2860	5500	3300
21	1500	2100	24	3430	6300	3600
24	1700	2400	27	3930		
27	1850	2700	30	4570	7100	
30	2000	3000	33	5000		
33	2150	3300	36	5570	8575	
36	2300	3600				
42	2600	4200				

a Standard drain tile is for ordinary land drainage at moderate depths and widths.

b Extra-quality drain tile is for land drainage where the depth or width is large and
an extra-quality pipe is needed.

Three methods of testing tile are outlined in Art. VIII-20.

The maximum absorptions permitted by ASTM specifications for the three classes of drain tile are shown in Table 11. For sewer pipe the maximum absorption should not exceed 8 per cent.

TABLE 11

Kind of Tile	Maximum Percentage of Absorption	
	Standard	Extra Quality
Clay	13	11
Concrete	10	8

51. Conduit. In large cities considerable use is now made of clay conduits for carrying underground cables and wires. Hollow rectangular prisms rounded at the corners and traversed by several longitudinal ducts are much employed in lengths of about 3 ft. Conduits are made of the same material and molded in the same manner as fireproofing. They are, however, hard burned and salt glazed to render them impervious to water.

52. Reinforced Brick Masonry. Impetus has been given to the use of reinforced brick masonry since 1922 by the results of numerous strength tests * of slabs, beams, and columns, and applications in small structures.

Tests were made in 1932 at the University of Wisconsin on twenty-five 8 by 12-in. beams loaded at the third-points of an 8-ft span. These beams contained 0.5 to 2.3 per cent of longitudinal steel and variable amounts of Z-shaped steel stirrup reinforcement. The data indicate that formulas used in designing reinforced concrete beams can be applied to reinforced brick beams provided due attention is given to mortar bond, filling of joints, coursing, and proportion and arrangement of reinforcement. Two beams of Chicago common brick laid in 1L:3C:12S mortar (by weight), carrying $1\frac{1}{4}$ per cent of longitudinal steel and a stirrup ratio of 0.0045, gave M/bd^2 values of 397 and 543 psi. With a stronger brick, a beam having 2.3 per cent of longitudinal steel and a stirrup ratio of 0.0048 failed in compression and developed $M/bd^2 = 840$ psi and $v = 294$ psi.

Tests on thirty-two $12\frac{1}{2}$ by $12\frac{1}{2}$-in. brick columns 6 ft and 12 ft high, reinforced with longitudinal rods and hoop steel placed in the joints, were also made at the University of Wisconsin. These tests and others made at Lehigh University show that the strength of such a column varies directly with the strength of the plain masonry, and with the percentages of longitudinal and hoop steel. Hoops serve to prevent sudden fail-

---

* See *Bull.* 37, Eng. Expt. Sta., Univ. Mo.; *Bull.* 9 and 15, Eng. Expt. Sta., Virginia Polytechnic Inst.; *Proc. ASTM*, Vol. 33, Pt. 2, p. 651, and Vol. 34, Pt. 2, p. 387; *J. Am. Ceramic Soc.*, Nov. 1933, p. 584.

ures. In the Wisconsin tests a column made with a high-strength brick, 1L:3C:7½S mortar, and loaded with 1½ per cent of hoops and 4 per cent of vertical steel carried a maximum load of 5050 psi on gross area.

Since the integrity of reinforced brick masonry depends upon the development of a strong permanent bond, all joints must be carefully filled. In the lower courses of beams the use of brick of special shapes or tile keyed to the mortar and reinforcement promotes durability of such courses.

Reinforced brick masonry requires little form work and has many architectural possibilities. It appears well suited for buildings, retaining walls, culverts, bridges, reservoirs, sewers, bins, and chimneys.

Brick beams and columns subjected to sustained loading undergo plastic flow. The rate of plastic flow is high at the start of loading and decreases rapidly with time. About three-quarters of the total ultimate flow may be expected during the first half year. The magnitude of the plastic flow deflection of a brick beam depends on many variables, such as the type of brick, properties of mortar or grout, number and position of mortar joints, magnitude of load, workmanship, dimensions of beam, span length, amount and position of reinforcing steel, and temperature and humidity conditions.

Portland Cement

1. The Cements of Construction. The cementing materials which are most used in engineering constructions may be classified as follows:

1. Hydraulic cements
$\begin{cases} \text{Portland cement} \\ \text{Natural cement} \\ \text{Puzzolan cement} \\ \text{Blended cement} \\ \text{High alumina cement} \end{cases}$ Will set under water

2. Limes
$\begin{cases} \text{Quick lime} \\ \text{Hydrated lime} \\ \text{Hydraulic lime (sets under water)} \end{cases}$

3. Gypsum plasters
$\begin{cases} \text{Plaster of Paris} \\ \text{Wall plaster} \\ \text{Hard finish plaster} \end{cases}$

4. Bitumens

Only the first three classes will be discussed herein; for the properties and uses of bitumens, reference may be made to *Asphalts and Allied Substances*, by H. Abrahams, and to *Highway Design and Construction*, by A. G. Bruce, or to other standard works on pavements.

NATURE OF PORTLAND CEMENT

2. Definition and Characteristics of Portland Cement. Portland cement may be defined as the product obtained by finely pulverizing a clinker consisting essentially of hydraulic calcium silicates, with no additions subsequent to calcination other than water and/or untreated calcium sulfate, except that additions up to 1.0 per cent of other approved materials may be interground with the clinker.

Five different types of Portland cement are covered in ASTM *Standard* C150. Type I is used for general construction and is frequently referred to as normal Portland cement. Type II has a moderate heat of hydration and is used in concrete that is exposed to moderate sulfate action. Type III, frequently referred to as high early Portland cement, is used when a high early strength is required. Type IV is used when a cement with a low heat of hydration is required, and Type V when high sulfate resistance is required.

In addition to the five types named above, ASTM *Standard* C175 covers Types IA, IIA, and IIIA air-entraining Portland cements which correspond respectively with Types I, II, and III. In the process of manufacture of Types IA, IIA, and IIIA certain additions are interground with the normal clinker to produce air-entraining properties. The additions accepted by ASTM for this purpose are Vinsol resin, which is essentially the petroleum-hydrocarbon-insoluble fraction of a coal-tar hydrocarbon extract of pine wood; Darex, which is essentially a triethanolamine salt of a sulfonated hydrocarbon; and N-Tair, which is essentially a sodium resinate produced from the hydrocarbon extract of pine wood stumps from which the bulk of the soluble resin acids have been removed. Relatively small amounts of the air-entraining agents, usually between 0.01 and 0.05 per cent by weight of the cement, are added.

Portland cement is a flour-like powder which varies in color from a greenish gray to a brownish gray. White Portland cement is also successfully produced. In general, the specific gravity of Portland cement is higher than that of other hydraulic cements, lying between 3.10 and 3.20. The specific weight is variable, ranging from 75 to 95 lb per cu ft, depending upon the compactness; it is considerably higher than the specific weight of natural cement.

3. Composition and Constitution of Portland Cement. *Composition.* The three fundamental constituents of hydraulic cements are lime, silica, and alumina. In addition to these, most cements contain small proportions of iron oxide, magnesia, sulfur trioxide, alkalies, and carbon dioxide. In the manufacture of the high early strength cements, additions subsequent to calcination, not exceeding 1 per cent of harmless materials other than gypsum or water, are permitted. The usual limits in oxide composition for Type I and for high early strength Portland cements (Type III) produced in the United States are tabulated here from the published analyses of a large number of cements.

	Usual Percentage Limits	
Oxide	Type I Portland	Type III Portland
Lime (CaO)	62–65	63–66
Silica (SiO$_2$)	19–22	19–21
Alumina (Al$_2$O$_3$)	4–7	4–7
Iron oxide (Fe$_2$O$_3$)	2–4	2–4
Magnesia (MgO)	1–4	1–4
Sulfur trioxide (SO$_3$)	1.5–2	2–2.5
Alkalies (K$_2$O + Na$_2$O)	0.3–1	0.3–1
Water (H$_2$O) and carbon dioxide (CO$_2$)	1–3	1–3

Although the oxide composition has been the basis of proportioning the raw materials in manufacturing Portland cement, and although good cements are made by following rule-of-thumb methods and giving especial care to details, nevertheless the properties of the mineral compounds formed in the burning process determine the quality of the cement. Studies of the properties of these mineral compounds by petrographers and physical chemists have led to a better understanding of their function in Portland cement and to better methods of proportioning raw materials in manufacture.

Constitution. From the investigations of Le Châtelier,[*] the French chemist, Törnebohm, the Swedish petrographer, Day, Shephard, Rankin, and Wright [†] at the Geophysical Laboratory at Washington, and the studies of Brownmiller and Bogue [‡] of the Portland Cement Association, it has been shown that the four principal mineral compounds in a well-burned Portland cement are:

		Symbolized by
1.	Tricalcium silicate, $3CaO \cdot SiO_2$	C_3S
2.	Dicalcium silicate, $2CaO \cdot SiO_2$	C_2S
3.	Tricalcium aluminate, $3CaO \cdot Al_2O_3$	C_3A
4.	Tetracalcium aluminum ferrite, $4CaO \cdot Al_2O_3 \cdot Fe_2O_3$	C_4AF

Under certain circumstances the alumina may be partially combined as $5CaO \cdot 3Al_2O_3 = C_5A_3$, and some uncombined or "free" lime may be present. American cements also usually carry small amounts of free magnesia.

4. The Setting and Hardening of Portland Cement. If Portland cement clinker is pulverized with 2 or 3 per cent of gypsum and tempered with water, the resulting soft paste slowly loses its plasticity, stiffens, and hardens into a rock-like mass. When the paste has lost its plasticity and become sufficiently coherent to withstand a certain arbitrary pressure, it is said to have acquired *initial set*. On acquiring a rigidity which enables it to withstand a higher intensity of pressure, it is said to have attained *final set*. After final set the paste exhibits a marked increase in rigidity, strength, and hardness with time. This transformation is termed *hardening*.

There has been much dispute concerning the nature of the intricate setting and hardening processes, but there seems to be good evidence to support the following statements concerning the actions of the mineral components in the setting and hardening § of Portland cement mortars and concretes.

[*] *Constitution of Hydraulic Mortars,* by H. Le Châtelier (trans. by Mack).

[†] *Eng. News,* Vol. 65, p. 350; also *J. Ind. Chem.,* April 1911.

[‡] *Am. J. Sci.,* Vol. 23 (1932), p. 501; also National Bureau of Standards, *Research Paper* 684.

[§] See Portland Cement Assoc. *Fellowship Papers,* 17 and 27, by R. H. Bogue and by R. H. Bogue and W. Lerch; also *The Chemistry of Cement and Concrete,* by F. M. Lea and C. H. Desch.

1. The flash set of the unadulterated, finely ground clinker is due to the rapid hydration of the aluminates C_3A and C_4AF. The rapidity of the action increases with the proportion of the aluminates present and is regulated by the addition of 2 or 3 per cent of gypsum. The gypsum reacts with the hydrated aluminates to form fine crystalline needles of calcium sulfoaluminate, which action retards crystallization of the calcium aluminates and thus delays set. The strengthening effects of the aluminates is most potent during the first 24 hours and does not extend beyond 28 days.

2. The action of water on tricalcium silicate, C_3S, proceeds less rapidly, forming supersaturated solutions from which emerge crystals of calcium hydroxide and amorphous masses of colloidal * calcium hydrosilicate. The colloid swells slightly as it takes on water and shrinks as it solidifies into a gel. This gel envelops groups of unattacked cement grains, which are gradually hydrated and further increase the density, impermeability, and strength of the hardened paste. This hydrolysis of the C_3S grains is well under way in 24 hours and has made a marked advance in 7 days. The rate of hydrolysis of C_3S and the character of the gel developed are the main causes for the early hardness and strength of cement pastes.

3. The beta dicalcium silicate, C_2S, is hydrolized into a gel at a very slow rate. Its influence on strength and hardness is small at ages less than a month, but at 1 year it contributes proportionately nearly as much strength as C_3S.

The colloidal theory of setting and hardening of Portland cement was first advanced by W. Michaelis, Sr., in 1893.† Those who believe in this theory maintain that, when a finely ground cement is gaged with water, a supersaturated solution containing calcium oxide, calcium aluminate, calcium sulfate, and calcium ferrite is formed. Owing to the insolubility of the calcium sulfoaluminate in lime water, it crystallizes as previously mentioned. Then the oversaturated solution coagulates in a gel formation about the cement grains, many of which are unattacked. This plastic hydrogel containing calcium hydrosilicate, calcium hydroaluminate, calcium hydroferrite, and a small proportion of lime gradually hardens, partly by withdrawal of water by the unattacked cement grains and

---

* There are a number of solids which, when very finely pulverized and mixed with certain liquids in highly supersaturated solutions, will form more or less rigid bodies by coagulation and subsequent desiccation. No crystalline structure is evinced during or after desiccation. On account of the glue-like properties which such substances exhibit in hardening, they have been named colloids. Some substances may form either colloids or crystalloids, depending upon the degree of supersaturation of the liquid solution. Colloidal solutions will not pass through a parchment membrane, whereas crystalloid solutions will. A colloidal aqueous solution is often called a hydrosol. When it becomes gelatinous it is termed an hydrogel. The boiling-point of a hydrosol is the same as the boiling point of water.

† *Cement and Eng. News* (trans.), Vol. 21, p. 299.

partly by crystallization of these components. The hardening of cement in air is hastened by the evaporation of a portion of the water. Owing to the evaporation of water during air hardening, however, more cement grains are imperfectly hydrated than in water hardening, and shrinkage of the colloid is very marked.

Since crystals are formed from solutions of low supersaturation, Michaelis claimed that the addition of gypsum, which brings on crystallization, will therefore retard the setting process. This follows since, owing to the low supersaturation of the initial mixture, some crystallization must take place before coagulation of the hydrogel.

Michaelis' theory has been partially verified by the microscope. Sections of hardened Portland cement paste have revealed the colloidal structure surrounding grains of unattacked clinker. In fact, Stern * estimated that only half the cement grains are attacked by water in ordinary pastes of cement. That the attack of water is incomplete may be proved by holding the broken ends of cement briquets in contact under water for several days, after which cohesion will have taken place. It has been demonstrated that the powder formed by crushing and grinding neat cement briquets has cementitious properties, and briquets made after a second regrinding possessed a low strength.

5. The Calculation of Compound Composition of Portland Cements.

Bogue † developed a method for calculating the compound composition from the oxide analysis of a cement. This method is based upon cooling of the clinker at such rate that equilibrium is maintained. Although equilibrium does not usually obtain in commercial operations, valuable information can be derived from such calculations. The method is summarized in the following steps and Table A. An accurate chemical analysis is entered in the first column of the table as shown.

Since the ratio of the atomic weight of $CaO:SO_3 = 56.07:80.065 = 0.70:1$, each percentage of SO_3 combines with 0.70 per cent of CaO to form 1.70 per cent of $CaSO_4$. Hence the percentage of lime required to satisfy $SO_3 (= 0.7 \times$ per cent $SO_3)$ is recorded as c_1 in column 4 of the table, opposite CaO; the percentage of SO_3 is also entered in column 4; and the $CaSO_4$ content is summed and entered at the bottom of column 4.

Similarly, since the atomic ratios $Al_2O_3:Fe_2O_3 = 101.92:159.68 = 0.64:1$ and $4CaO:Fe_2O_3 = 224.28:159.68 = 1.40:1$, it is evident that each percentage of Fe_2O_3 enters into combination with 0.64 per cent of Al_2O_3 and 1.40 per cent of CaO to form 3.04 per cent of $4CaO \cdot Al_2O_3 \cdot Fe_2O_3$. Therefore $0.64 \times$ percentage of Fe_2O_3 is entered as a_1, opposite Al_2O_3 in

* Chem.-Ztg., 1908, No. 47 and 85; Stahl u. Eisen, Vol. 28, p. 1542; Mitt. kgl. Materialprüfungsant, Vol. 27, p. 7, and Vol. 28, p. 173.

† Portland Cement Assoc. Fellowship Paper 21, Calculation of Compounds in Portland Cement.

TABLE A. RECORD OF SIGNIFICANT DATA FOR COMPUTING COMPOUND COMPOSITION

Oxides	Analysis	Compounds					
		Free CaO	SO_3+	Fe_2O_3+	Al_2O_3+	c and s	C_2S and C_4
CaO	63.0	0.2	$c_1=1.0$	$c_2=4.9$	$c_3=5.4$	$c=51.5$	$c_4=10.3$
MgO	3.0						
Al_2O_3	5.5	....	....	$a_1=2.2$	$a_2=3.3$		
Fe_2O_3	3.5			3.5			
SiO_2	22.0	....	....	....	....	$s=22.0$	63.2 approx.
SO_3	1.5	....	1.5				
Ig. Loss	1.2						
Ins. Res.	0.1						
Free CaO	0.2						

Ignition Loss	Free MgO	Free CaO	$CaSO_4$	C_4AF	C_3A	C_3S	C_2S
1.2	3.0	0.2	2.5	10.6	8.7	42	32

column 5, and 1.4 × percentage of Fe_2O_3 is entered as c_2, opposite CaO in column 5; the percentage of Fe_2O_3 is reentered in the same column; and the percentage of C_4AF is summed at the bottom.

Since practically none of the magnesia is combined, it is entered as free at the bottom of column 2.

The total alumina minus a_1, entered as a_2 in column 6, is available to combine with lime to form C_3A in the ratio $3CaO:Al_2O_3 = 168.21:101.92 = 1.65:1$. Hence each percentage of this available alumina × 1.65 is the percentage of CaO required for C_3A, and it is entered opposite CaO as c_3 in column 6. Summing quantities in column 6 gives percentage of C_3A.

The CaO available to combine with SiO_2 is total CaO minus (free CaO + c_1 + c_2 + c_3); call this difference c. Then the total silica (s) is calculated first to combine with CaO to form C_2S. Since the ratio $2CaO \cdot SiO_2 : SiO_2 = 172.20:60.06 = 2.87:1$, each percentage of s × 2.87 is the percentage of C_2S. This first approximation of C_2S is entered in column 8, opposite SiO_2. By subtracting this value of C_2S from the sum $s + c$, the amount of CaO (called c_4) available for combination with $2CaO \cdot SiO_2$ to form $3CaO \cdot SiO_2$ is determined. Since the ratio $3CaO \cdot SiO_2 : CaO = 228.27:56.07 = 4.07:1$, multiplying c_4 by 4.07 gives the amount of C_3S which is entered at the foot of column 7. By subtracting this value of C_3S from $c + s$, the true percentage of C_2S is found and entered in column 8.

Should the computed percentage of C_3S be greater than $c + s$, no C_2S is present. In that case the content of C_3S is found from the ratio $3CaO \cdot SiO_2 : SiO_2 = 228.27:60.06 = 3.8:1$. Hence the percentage of C_3S is obtained by multiplying the percentage of SiO_2 by 3.8. This latter value of C_3S, subtracted from $c + s$, gives the percentage of uncombined lime. This last condition can only obtain when lime is in excess of the amount required for equilibrium and the free lime has not been deducted.

Since errors in chemical analysis of 0.2 per cent in determinations of lime, alumina, silica, or iron oxide will make errors up to 1.5 per cent in certain compounds, percentages for the compounds should be rounded off to whole numbers. If the ignition loss is high, the analysis should be reduced to a clinker basis prior to compound calculations.

As previously mentioned, Bogue's method of calculation is based on the assumption that the clinker is slowly cooled at such rate that equilibrium is maintained and the crystallization is complete. Lea and Parker * have shown that values calculated by the Bogue method may be considerably in error if the clinker liquid crystallizes independently of the solids formed, or if cooling is so sudden that no crystallization takes place and glass is formed. For the case of independent crystallization and a clinkering temperature of 1400°C, they show that Bogue's method is correct for cements with Al_2O_3/Fe_2O_3 ratios between 0.9 and 1.7, but for ratios between 1.7 and 6.1 their corrections to be added are:

$$C_3S, +(1.8Al_2O_3 - 2.8Fe_2O_3)$$

$$C_2S, +(2.1Fe_2O_3 - 1.4Al_2O_3)$$

$$C_3A, +(2.5Fe_2O_3 - 1.6Al_2O_3)$$

$$C_4AF, \text{ Nil}$$

Thus for a cement with $Al_2O_3 = 7$ and $Fe_2O_3 = 3$ per cent, their correction to $C_3S = 4.2$, to $C_2S = -3.5$, and to $C_3A = -3.7$ per cent.

For very rapid cooling of the clinker, the liquid is formed into glass and they show that *no* C_3A or C_4AF appear but the amount of glass is $+ (2.95Al_2O_3 + 2.2Fe_2O_3)$. For this case their corrections to Bogue's values for C_3S and C_2S are: $C_3S, +(1.8Al_2O_3 - 2.8Fe_2O_3)$; $C_2S, + (1.9Fe_2O_3 - 2.1Al_2O_3)$.

Out of 21 commercial plant clinkers examined at the Bureau of Standards (see *RP*1066, January 1938), 11 had 5 per cent or less of glass and 18 had 10 per cent or less.

A short method of approximating the proportions of the main constituents of Portland cements follows the section on chemical requirements in ASTM Standard C150.

6. The Proportioning of the Main Constituents. From the foregoing it will be evident that care must be exercised by the cement chemist in proportioning the raw materials to obtain clinker of proper constitution. Since about 1925 there has been a marked tendency to increase the lime content and C_3S in order to increase the early strength of mortars and concretes. An excess of lime beyond that combined with silica and alumina, *free lime*, promotes unsoundness in the hardening paste. Un-

---

* See *Building Research Tech. Paper* 16 (1935); also *The Chemistry of Cement and Concrete,* by Lea and Desch, p. 119.

soundness is characterized by checking and cracking of the hardened paste. Lea and Parker (*loc. cit.*) state that the maximum lime which can be carried is given by $CaO = 2.8SiO_2 + 1.18Al_2O_3 + 0.65Fe_2O_3$.

European specifications limit only the weight ratio of $CaO/(SiO_2 + Al_2O_3 + Fe_2O_3) \gtreqless 1.7$. In the United States this ratio may run to 2.3 or 2.4 for the high early strength Portlands.

Control is exercised over the rate of setting by regulating the ratio $SiO_2/(Al_2O_3 + Fe_2O_3)$. Where the development of much heat during hydration is undesirable the silica content is increased to 21 per cent or above, the alumina and iron oxide contents are limited to 6 per cent each, the C_3A is limited to 8 per cent, and the ratio Al_2O_3/Fe_2O_3 is limited between 0.7 and 2.0.* Resistance to the action of sulfate waters is increased by raising the silica to a minimum of 24 per cent, reducing the alumina and iron oxide contents to 4 per cent each, reducing C_3A to 5 per cent, and holding the ratio Al_2O_3/Fe_2O_3 between 0.7 and 2.0.*

In a general way it can be said that raising the C_3S content of a cement is desirable in so far as it renders the clinker easier to grind, promotes strength at early ages, and increases resistance to freezing and thawing; but it has the undesirable effect of increasing the heat of hydration and increasing the solubility of the cement in water. Raising the C_2S content renders clinker harder to grind, reduces early strength, decreases resistance to freezing and thawing at early ages, decreases the heat of hydration, but promotes high strength after a year or more. Raising the C_3A content reduces the time of set, increases strength up to 28 days, but lowers the ultimate strength, increases the heat of hydration, increases the contraction during air hardening, and weakens resistance to sulfate attack. Raising the C_4AF content appears to reduce strength slightly.

7. Iron Oxide. Ferric oxide (Fe_2O_3) exercises a very important influence on the color of the cement. Pure white cements are made from materials containing very little of this compound. Most cements contain 2 to 3 per cent of this oxide. If it enters into combination with lime and alumina to form C_4AF, it serves to neutralize some of the undesirable properties contributed by alumina when combined with lime alone. When iron oxide is combined with lime as $2CaO \cdot Fe_2O_3$ it promotes instability. Small percentages of iron oxide render highly siliceous raw materials easier to burn, but a high iron content produces a hard clinker which is difficult to grind.

8. Magnesia in ordinary proportions does not combine with the other elements in burning. It hydrates very slowly when tempered with water but expands markedly after a long attack.

The precentage of magnesia which can be safely carried in Portland cement has been the subject of much experimentation with variable re-

---

* See Federal Specifications for Portland cement.

sults. Tests by P. H. Bates at the Bureau of Standards on cements made from clinker burned in a small gas-fired rotary kiln showed normal results in setting, in soundness, and in strength up to 1 year, when the magnesia content was less than 7.5 per cent (*Cement Age,* Cement Mill Ed., March 1914). In 1934, H. F. Gonnerman of the Portland Cement Association Laboratory reported an extended series of tests to the ASTM, showing the effects of magnesia on strength, durability, and volume change. His tests indicated undesirable properties in cements containing over 5 per cent magnesia. Tests by Prof. E. D. Campbell at the University of Michigan on neat prisms made of cements containing 3 per cent of free magnesia exhibited over 1 per cent expansion after 13 years immersion in cold water, although the 1-year expansion was normal.

Since magnesia can be locked up in the glass formed by sudden cooling of the clinker, it seems likely that some of the discrepancies in the tests described are due to differences in the proportions of *free* magnesia. Because of the detrimental effects of free magnesia on strength and expansion after prolonged hydration, the magnesia content of Portland cement is limited. In American specifications the maximum allowed is 5 per cent.

9. Sulfur Compounds. Sulfides in cements tend to cause unsoundness. Ordinarily they are not present in harmful amounts in Portland cement clinker. The sulfate of calcium, gypsum ($CaSO_4 + 2H_2O$), is added after burning in amounts less than 3 or 4 per cent to retard setting. The hydration of gypsum also appears to counteract to some extent the weakening attending the hydration of the alum'nates. In specifications for normal Portland cements the limit on SO_3 is 2.0 per cent. For the high early strength Portlands the limit is raised to 2.5 per cent.

10. The Alkalies (K_2O and Na_2O) are found in very small amounts in most Portland cements. They appear to accelerate the setting time, and to enter into combinations with lime and alumina.

Deterioration of concrete in many instances has been attributed to the use of high-alkali cements in conjunction with certain aggregates such as opaline chert, siliceous magnesium limestone, andesite, rhyolite, phyllite, and others. The intensity of the alkali-aggregate reaction depends on the amount of the reactive mineral in the aggregate and on the alkali content of the cement. Although the ASTM has set no specification on the maximum allowable alkali content in Portland cement, other groups have done so. In California, where this problem has been particularly troublesome, state specifications have placed a maximum limit of 0.6 per cent on the alkali content.

11. Water and Carbonic Oxide. Aeration of cement clinker, which is commonly practiced to slake free lime, also causes an absorption of some moisture and carbon dioxide. The per cent CO_2 absorbed depends on the completeness of the exposure to air. The amount of moisture absorbed by cement depends principally on the completeness of exposure and the moisture in the surrounding atmosphere. Absorption of moisture tends to increase the time of setting, but absorption of CO_2 accelerates setting.

American specifications limit the loss on ignition, which is due mainly to the presence of water and carbonic oxide, to 4 per cent.

MODERN METHODS OF MANUFACTURE

12. Growth and Importance of the Portland Cement Industry. On account of the many excellent properties possessed by Portland cement, its great field of usefulness, the widely distributed sources of the raw materials from which it is made, its cheapness, and the decline in the supply of timber, the Portland cement industry has had a marvelously rapid growth. Although the process of manufacture of this material was patented in 1824, by Joseph Aspdin, of Leeds, England, it was not until 1859 that any considerable quantity was used in England, and not until 1875 that any progress was made in the manufacture of this cement in the United States. An estimate of the growth and economic importance of the industry may be formed by comparing the 42,000 barrels produced in the United States in 1880 with the 230,000,000 barrels produced in 1950. The value per barrel at mill in 1880 was $3, in 1950 it was $2.35. The 1950 production in the United States was about 30 per cent of the world production.

The following percentages show the trend in modern usage of Portland cement: for roads and pavements, 23; buildings and similar structures, 34; conservation projects, 14; rural uses including products for farms, 9; sewerage and drainage, 7; bridges, 4; miscellaneous, 9.

13. Raw Materials. In general the calcareous ingredients are present in raw materials in the form of lime carbonate $(CaCO_3)$ and the silica and alumina are combined in the form of clay or other argillaceous ingredients. These essential ingredients are proportioned in accordance with the principles mentioned in Art. IX-6.

Arranged in order of importance, the raw materials most commonly used in the manufacture of Portland cement and the parts of the United States in which they are employed are:

Materials		Where Used in Making Portland Cement
Calcareous	*Argillaceous*	
1. Limestone	+ shale or clay	Widely used, N. Y., Mich., Ill., Ind., Cal., Iowa, Kan., Tex.
2. Limestone	+ cement rock	Eastern Pa., N. J., Cal., Kan.
3. Limestone	+ blast furnace slag	Ill., Ohio, Pa.
4. Marl	+ shale or clay	Central N. Y., Ohio, Mich., Ind.

Limestone for the manufacture of Portland cement should be soft and consist largely of calcite or calcite and clay. If 20 per cent or more of clay is present with the calcite it is called cement rock. The limestone should not contain over 5 or 6 per cent of magnesium carbonate and should be comparatively free from sulfur and quartz. According to Eckel * phosphorus pentoxide (P_2O_5) is also an undesirable element.

Marl, another calcareous substance much used in the wet process of manufacture, is a soft deposit found in the bottoms of shallow lakes, swamps, and extinct fresh-water basins. It should conform to the restrictions placed upon limestone and be free from sand and gravel.

For origin and composition of clays, reference should be made to Art. VIII-2.

With reference to the proportions of the constituents of clay suitable for Portland cement manufacture, Meade states that the ratio of the silica to the alumina content should be between 2.5 and 4 to 1, and that there should not be more iron oxide than alumina, and that the alkalies and magnesia should each be less than 3 per cent.† A considerable proportion of sand larger than a 100-mesh sieve renders the clay unfit for cement manufacture.

Blast-furnace slag suitable for the manufacture of Portland cement should be basic in character. The analysis should conform roughly to the following: two-fifths to one-half lime; one-third silica; one-eighth to one-sixth alumina plus iron oxide; magnesia less than 3 per cent. Calcium sulfide is considered undesirable.

The first step in the process of manufacture of Portland cement is the winning of the raw materials from nature. Hard raw materials are blasted, loaded onto small cars, and drawn to the cement mill. Soft materials like marl or clay are dug or excavated by steam shovel or dredge, depending upon the nature of the deposit. Such materials are often pumped directly to the mill. Slag is granulated into a sand-like substance by running the molten material from the blast furnace into a vat of water. It is then loaded on cars by clamshell buckets and transported to the cement plant.

The Dry Process of Manufacture

14. Preparation of Raw Materials. In general, only the comparatively dry raw materials, such as limestone and cement rock, limestone and shale or clay, and limestone and blast-furnace slag, are used in the dry process of manufacture of Portland cement. The steps in the process of manufacture are: 1, crushing of raw materials; 2, drying; 3, grinding; 4, propor-

* Eckel's *Cements, Limes and Plasters*, p. 389.
† Meade's *Portland Cement*, p. 54.

tioning; 5, pulverizing of raw materials; 6, burning; 7, cooling and storing the clinker; 8, adulteration to retard set; 9, reduction of clinker to an impalpable powder; 10, seasoning of cement; 11, bagging. The order of the first four of these operations varies at different plants, and it depends to some extent upon the character of the raw materials.

The hard materials are usually crushed in gyratory crushers, although jaw and roll crushers of large capacities are also used. Generally, the

Fig. 1. An Allis-Chalmers dry-grinding preliminator.

material must be passed through a large and a small crusher in order that the requisite fineness for successful operation of the grinding mills may result.

Since it is necessary to have the raw materials in an approximately dry state before grinding, most of these materials must be passed through some sort of a drying apparatus. In most plants a dryer consists of a hollow steel cylinder about 50 ft long and 5 ft in diameter, revolving about its geometrical axis which is inclined at a small angle with the horizontal. The raw materials enter at the upper end and pass out at the lower end of the cylinder. The source of heat, which is commonly an attached furnace or waste gas from the rotary kilns, enters at the lower end and passes out at the upper. To increase the circulation of the materials through the hot gases, lugs which serve to elevate and scatter the charge are riveted on the inside of the dryer.

15. Preliminary Grinding. In order to secure proper combinations in the kiln between the lime, silica, and alumina, it is necessary to have the raw materials ground so finely that 90 per cent will pass a No. 200 mesh. This is usually done in two stages, preliminary and final.

Preliminary grinding is quite extensively done in some type of ball mill. One form of such machine is the preliminator shown in Fig. 1. The preliminator consists of a cylindrical steel drum lined with chilled iron or hard steel and equipped with trunnions. The right end of the drum is encircled by a large gear by means of which the mill is rotated. Through a hole in the left trunnion raw material is fed into the mill. Pulverizing is accomplished by the rolling and hammering received from 6 to 8 tons of forged steel balls which range in diameter from 2½ to 5 in. The ground material passes through narrow longitudinal slots shown near the right end of the mill onto a circumferential screen. Residues are returned to the grinding compartment. The fines pass through the screen and are chuted to a conveyor. Working on 3-in. limestone and shale, a preliminator 8 ft in diameter and 5½ ft long can produce about 50 barrels per hour of material which will pass a No. 20 mesh.

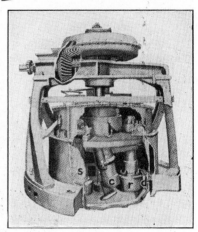

Fig. 2. A Hercules mill. (Bradley Pulverizer Co.)

The Hercules mill shown in Fig. 2 has come into extensive use for preliminary grinding of either raw materials or clinker. The material enters the grinding chamber through 3 chutes (*c*). Pulverizing is accomplished by 3 rolls (*r*) which revolve at approximately 375 rpm about a vertical central axis and crush the material against a circumferential die (*d*). The fines pass through the circumferential screen (*s*) surrounding the grinding chamber and are collected in a downspout below the mill. The makers claim that this mill, equipped with a 350-hp motor, will reduce in 1 hour 40 to 60 tons of dry raw mix, or 135 to 200 barrels of clinker up to 2½-in. diameter, to the following fineness: 90 to 95 per cent through a 20-mesh, 45 to 55 per cent through a 100-mesh, and 35 to 45 per cent through a 200-mesh sieve. A Hercules mill and a tube mill provide a flexible combination of grinding units with low power consumption.

16. Proportioning. Since correct proportioning of the raw materials is of prime importance in securing a clinker of proper constitution, accurate automatic scales are installed for weighing the raw materials. This operation can usually be done best after the preliminary grinding of the raw materials; although at some plants, where the raw mix runs very uniform in character, the proportioning is done earlier in the process.

17. Final Grinding. At many plants the final stage in grinding is done in a tube mill. This mill is also a steel-jacketed cylinder revolving about its geometrical axis. Commonly, such a mill is about 26 ft long and 7 ft in diameter. The inside is lined with alloy steel or chilled cast

Fig. 3. A wet-grinding Compeb mill. (Allis-Chalmers.)

iron. The mix from the preliminary mills or proportioning scales is fed by a worm through one trunnion into the tube mill. Pulverizing is accomplished by the impact and abrasive action of a heavy charge of cast-iron slugs between 1 and $1\frac{1}{4}$ in. in diameter. A 7- by 26-ft tube mill will reduce about 30 tons of raw material per hour, 80 per cent to pass a 200-sieve or reduce 70 barrels of clinker to cement, 90 per cent passing a 200-sieve.

The Allis-Chalmers Manufacturing Co. claims that a much greater efficiency can be obtained in grinding operations by dividing the drum of the tube mill into compartments by means of one or more transverse diaphragms. Figure 3 shows one of their Compeb mills suitable for wet grinding, but which can be modified for dry grinding. By the use of such mills the company claims the preliminary grinding can be done in the short compartment and the final grinding in the long compartment. The efficiency is said to be increased by inserting a vibrating screen between the preliminator and the second compartment and by using an air separator to remove the fines in the latter. Added efficiency is claimed for two stages in the final grinding with air separators applied on each compartment to remove the fines as they accumulate. With their No. 726 mill equipped with a 500-hp motor, the company claims raw material may be dry ground from 1-in. mesh to 80 per cent through a 200-mesh at 22 tons per hour, or ground wet at 25 tons per hour. On clinker, with air separation, 64 barrels per hour with 90 per cent through a 200-mesh sieve is claimed for that mill.

18. Burning. The purpose of burning the raw mixture is to secure a union of the different constituents in the form of mineral compounds, primarily the formation of silicates of lime and alumina as we have seen in Art. IX-3.

After the raw materials have been proportioned, intimately mixed, and very finely ground, the powdered product is conveyed to kilns to be burned. Formerly the vertical intermittent type of kiln, somewhat like that used in the production of natural cement, was employed to burn Portland cement. In Europe, use is still made of this type, and in Germany the Hoffman ring kiln is quite extensively employed. However, in the United States the continuously operated rotary kiln is favored to the exclusion of all others.

From Fig. 4 one can obtain a notion of the appearance of a rotary kiln. It consists of a cylindrical jacket made of riveted steel plates lined with refractory firebrick. The lower end of this cylinder is covered by a detachable hood provided with two openings. Through one of these openings is passed a nozzle for the admission of fuel. The fuel most commonly employed is powdered coal. In order to introduce the coal into the kiln and to secure both rapid and complete combustion, it must be so finely pulverized that 95 per cent will pass a No. 100 sieve. The coal is blown through the nozzle by an air blast. The second opening in the hood is provided to enable the operator to observe the interior of the kiln during calcination. The steel jacket is surrounded by two or more heavy steel tires, by means of which it is rotated on friction roller bearings. These bearings are so adjusted that the axis of the kiln has an inclination with the horizontal of about $\frac{1}{2}$ in. per ft. By thus inclining the axis, the material is slowly moved downward from the upper end as the kiln is rotated. Rotation is produced by a motor placed near the center and geared to a girth gear attached to the jacket. The upper end of the kiln enters a brick flue from which the products of combustion escape to the stack. Passing through this flue is an inclined spout which discharges the finely powdered raw material into the kiln.

Soon after the entrance of the material, it begins to ball up into small marble-like shapes. During the first half of the passage toward the hood any entrained water is evaporated and the material is heated to a temperature sufficient to expel carbon dioxide (CO_2) from the limestone. By the time the clinker has reached within a few feet of the lower end of the kiln its temperature has risen to 1400° or 1450°C, all carbon dioxide, sulfur, and organic matter have been expelled, and the little soft yellowish-brown balls have now partially fused into hard, greenish-black clinker.* At many plants the degree of calcination is left to the skill of

Fig. 4. An 8½ by 10 by 260-ft rotary kiln for dry process. (Allis-Chalmers.)

the burner, who regulates the speed of rotation of the kiln so that the clinkering zone is kept back a few feet from the discharge end. He is able to judge of the position of this zone by the abrupt change in the color of the flame where the material begins to burn and form clinker. Under ordinary conditions a speed of 45 or 60 revolutions per hour secures the requisite degree of calcination. At the end of about 1 hour the burning process is completed and the clinker falls out of the kiln through a trap in the lower side of the hood, whence it is conveyed to the cooler. The clinker is quite irregular in shape and varies from the size of a hen's egg

* For further information concerning the chemical changes in a rotary kiln, see R. K. Meade's *Portland Cement,* pp. 176 to 199.

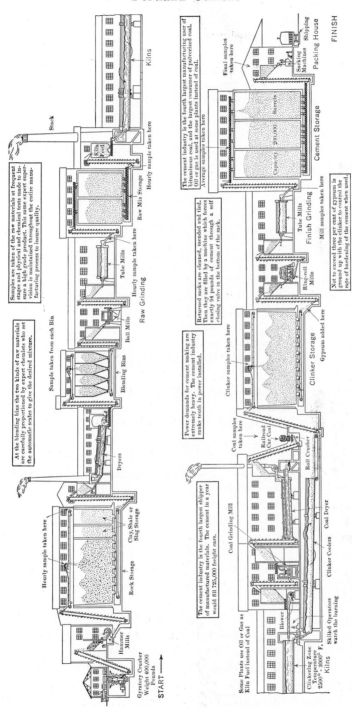

Fig. 5. Sequence of operations in the manufacture of Portland cement by the dry process. (Portland Cement Association.)

down to a buckshot. It is very hard, has more or less vitreous luster, and is generally black or greenish-black.

In the dry process, kilns usually vary from 150 to 250 ft in length and 8 to 10 ft in diameter. The larger modern kilns will produce 1000 to 1400 barrels of clinker per day. In producing a 376-lb barrel of Portland cement, by this process, 500 to 600 lb of raw materials and 70 to 90 lb of coal, or the equivalent, are consumed.

19. Grinding of the Clinker. To facilitate grinding, the clinker is passed through a cooler. Frequently the cooler consists of a vertical or horizontal steel cylinder equipped with devices for agitating the material in a forced air draft, which rapidly lowers its temperature. Rapid quenching of the clinker promotes the formation of glass, which action appears to counteract the detrimental influences of tricalcium aluminate and magnesia. After seasoning, about 2 per cent of gypsum is added to retard the time of set of the resulting cement. The adulteration is often done after the clinker has been through the ball mill. In grinding the clinker the same kind of machinery is generally used as is employed in pulverizing the raw materials. Whatever grinding machinery is used, the resultant fineness is such that 90 to 95 per cent will pass a sieve with 200 meshes per linear inch. For the high early strength Portlands the percentage passing this sieve is usually over 96.

20. Storage and Bagging of Cement. From the grinding mills a conveyor carries the cement to the storage bins, in which it is generally kept for a few weeks before being bagged for shipment. This seasoning period reduces the heat which the cement will generate during setting and hardening. Storage also allows time for free lime to hydrate and carbonate and thus become inert.

In accordance with the demand of the trade the cement is conveyed from the storage bins to the packing house. Here it is automatically weighed and packed by machines sometimes in wooden barrels containing 376 lb, net, but usually in cloth or paper sacks which hold 94 lb net. Cement is often shipped in bulk to central proportioning plants.

21. Typical Dry-Process Plant Operation. The schematic drawing, Fig. 5, shows the sequence of operations and more important steps in the manufacture of Portland cement by the dry process.

THE WET PROCESS OF MANUFACTURE

22. General. Although the dry process has been much used in the United States, the advent of longer kilns and waste heat boilers has effected such economies in wet-process operations that most of the new installations are of this type, and more cement is now produced by the wet than by the dry process in this country. Where marl is used it is excavated by an orange-peel bucket or pumped in thin mud form from the deposit to tanks near the kilns. The clay is excavated by a steam

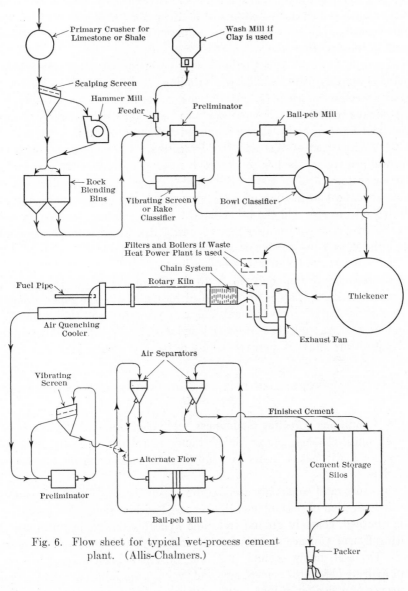

Fig. 6. Flow sheet for typical wet-process cement plant. (Allis-Chalmers.)

shovel and ground in a wet pan or in a dry pan, Fig. VIII-1. Limestone, when used, is quarried in the usual manner and ground in a ball mill or preliminator. Next the marl and clay, or the limestone and clay, are mixed in predetermined proportions and then ground. This mixture, called slurry, containing from 30 to 50 per cent of water, is placed in storage tanks and held there until analyzed and corrected to the desired composition. The slurry is then pumped into especially constructed long rotary kilns, which in the newer installations are 200 to 400 ft in length, and burned. The succeeding steps in manufacture are similar to those used in the dry process.

Figure 6 shows an Allis-Chalmers flow sheet for a typical wet-process plant equipped with classified wet grinding on the raw side. The company's recommendations for installations of vibrating screens, air-quenching clinker cooler, and air separators are also indicated. A slurry thickener and filters are also shown immediately before the kiln.

23. Comparison of Wet and Dry Processes. The chief advantages of the wet process are the low cost of excavating and grinding raw materials, the accurate control of composition and homogeneity of the slurry, and the economical utilization of fuel through the elimination of separated drying operations. On the other hand the longer kilns, essential in the wet process, cost more and are less responsive to a variable clinker demand than the short kilns which can be used in the dry process.

In Germany the Lepol kiln was developed to utilize the heat from the kiln so effectively that only 43 to 45 lb of coal are required to burn a barrel of clinker. This is accomplished by nodulizing the finely ground raw mix by the addition of small amounts of water, and subjecting the nodules to decarbonization prior to admission to the kiln. Perhaps the advent of this kiln will increase the use of the dry process in America.

EFFECTS ON PROPERTIES DUE TO CONDITIONS OF MANUFACTURE OR TESTING

24. Conditions Affecting Soundness. Although some of the effects of the chemical elements present in Portland cement have already been referred to, it will not be amiss to recall them in considering the properties affected.

The cause most commonly ascribed for unsoundness in Portland cement is the hydration of uncombined lime encased within the cement particles. High-burned, coarsely ground free lime hydrates slowly, but ultimately with sufficient violence to endanger the integrity of the surrounding mortar. Exposed, finely ground free lime, in small percentages at least, will hydrate before the cement sets and produces no injurious effect. The presence of uncombined lime may be the result of either underburning the clinker or overliming the mixture before burning. Infrequently freshly ground cement will be unsound due to the presence of uncombined lime which may be partially exposed in the grinding process. By allowing the cement to aerate for 2 or 3 weeks, thus allowing the lime to hydrate, it is often possible to overcome unsoundness.*

Other chemical elements which may produce unsoundness are magnesia and the alkalies. In most cements the proportions of these elements are well within the danger limit.

It is probable that the action of the retardant assists in overcoming unsoundness, since it tends to hold the mixture in a plastic state and permit the lime to slake. Meade cites several examples of unsound cements which were rendered sound by adding from 0.5 to 3.0 per cent of plaster of Paris.†

Fine grinding of both raw materials and the clinker are very essential if a sound cement is to be secured. Fine grinding of the raw materials makes possible the production of a more homogeneous mixture before burning so that a uniform distribution of the lime content may obtain. It has also been shown that coarsely ground cements which are unsound in the accelerated test may often be rendered sound by fine grinding.‡ Remembering that the addition of free lime in small percentages does not affect the soundness of a normal Portland cement, it seems evident that the coarser grains of cement may imprison minute particles of uncombined lime which do not become hydrated until after the cement has set. The expansion, which then occurs due to the crystallization of calcium hydrate, produces disintegration. This view seems to be quite generally held by authorities on this subject. The reasonableness of the above explanation of the action of the coarser particles in promoting unsoundness is made more evident by the experiments of Brinckley.§ The results of his tests show that the particles of a cement passing a No. 100 and caught on a No. 200 sieve may have some hydraulic properties, but that pats made of them break down when subjected to the soundness test (Art. XII-11).

25. Conditions Affecting Strength. Recapitulating, we will recall that either a high lime or high alumina content tends to make the cement strong at an early age. Gypsum and Plaster of Paris in small percentages also tend to increase the strength of Portland cement, but when present in quantities larger than 3 per cent these substances produce variable effects.¶ However, it is certain, as has been mentioned before, that the

---

* For example, see *Proc. ASTM*, Vol. 3, p. 376.

† *Portland Cement*, p. 474. See "Free Lime in Portland Cement," by Kiefer, *Chem. Eng.*, Vol. 15, p. 219; also "Soundness Tests of Portland Cement," by Taylor, *Proc. ASTM*, Vol. 3, p. 374.

‡ *Portland Cement*, p. 472.

§ *Eng. Record*, Vol. 61, p. 212.

¶ See results of experiments given in Eckel's *Cements, Limes and Plasters*, pp. 536–544 (out of print); also a paper by P. H. Bates in *Proc. ASTM*, Vol. 15, p. 126.

Materials of Construction

compounds formed determine the properties. As evidence of the effects of variations in tricalcium silicate, C_3S, and tricalcium aluminate, C_3A, on the strengths of cement mortars and concretes, Figs. 7, 8, and 9 have been inserted from the 1934 tests of Gonnerman at the Portland Cement Association Laboratories. The cements were prepared from commercial raw materials and carefully burned in an experimental kiln. The effects

Cement	C_3S	C_2S	C_3A	C_4AF	C_2F	MgO	Free CaO	Cement	C_3S	C_2S	C_3A	C_4AF	C_2F	MgO	Free CaO	Cement	C_3S	C_2S	C_3A	C_4AF	C_2F	MgO	Free CaO
No. 46.....	56	24	0	16	1	3.2	0.1	No. 42.....	61	17	7	12	0	3.1	0.2	No. 58*....	62	13	14	7	0	3.3	0.7
No. 6.....	41	39	0	14	3	3.0	0	No. 24.....	41	37	7	12	0	2.8	0	No. 2B Dupl.	43	32	15	7	0	2.9	0.2
No. 45.....	28	52	0	15	2	3.1	0	No. 41.....	29	49	7	12	0	3.0	0	No. 37.....	16	58	16	6	0	3.0	0.2

*Cement Double Burned

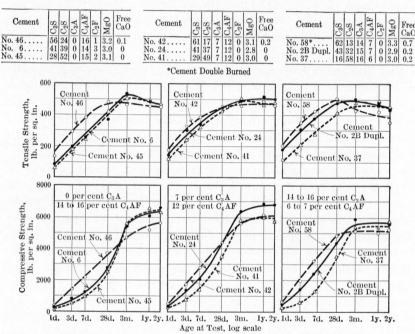

Fig. 7. Age-strength relations for cements differing in tricalcium silicate content. (H. F. Gonnerman, *Proc. ASTM,* Vol. 34, Pt. 2, p. 244.)

of C_3S and C_3A in producing high early strengths are patent in all three diagrams. It is also apparent that the strengths at a year or more of the mortars of cements having high C_2S contents are as high or higher than those containing cements of high C_3S contents. Figure 9 indicates that, at ages of a year, high C_3A contents are detrimental to the strengths of mortars and to some of the concretes.

In addition to effects of composition, the strength of cement is greatly influenced by the degree of burning, the fineness of grinding, and the aeration it receives. If underburned the cement is likely to be deficient in strength. Assuming the clinker properly burned, increasing the proportion of fine particles between 5 and 20 microns (1 micron = 0.001 mm) in diameter causes an increase in mortar or concrete strength. It appears questionable if there is material advantage to be gained from particles below 5 microns in diameter, and those above 100 microns exhibit no cementitious properties.

Cement	C₃S	C₂S	C₃A	C₄AF	C₂F	MgO	Free CaO
No. 45	28	52	0	15	2	3.1	0
No. 6	41	39	0	14	3	3.0	0
No. 11	51	29	0	15	2	3.0	0.1
No. 46	56	24	0	16	1	3.2	0.1
No. 61	56	24	0	16	1	3.1	0.1
No. 62*	74	5	0	15	2	3.1	0.4

*Cement Double Burned

Cement	C₃S	C₂S	C₃A	C₄AF	C₂F	MgO	Free CaO
No. 41	29	49	7	12	0	3.0	0
No. 24	41	37	7	12	0	2.8	0
No. 4	43	34	7	13	0	3.1	0
No. 59	52	26	6	13	0	2.9	0.6
No. 9*	53	25	7	13	0	3.0	0
No. 60	55	20	7	12	0	3.0	2.3
No. 60A	57	20	6	13	0	2.8	0.2
No. 42	61	17	7	12	0	3.1	0.2

Cement	C₃S	C₂S	C₃A	C₄AF	C₂F	MgO	Free CaO
No. 37	16	58	16	6	0	3.0	0.2
No. 8 Dupl.	42	33	15	7	0	3.1	0.1
No. 2B Dupl.	43	32	15	7	0	2.9	0.2
No. 57	45	28	15	7	0	2.9	2.1
No. 2B	47	26	16	7	0	3.0	0.3
No. 38A*	61	14	14	7	0	3.3	0.3
No. 53	62	13	14	7	0	3.3	0.7

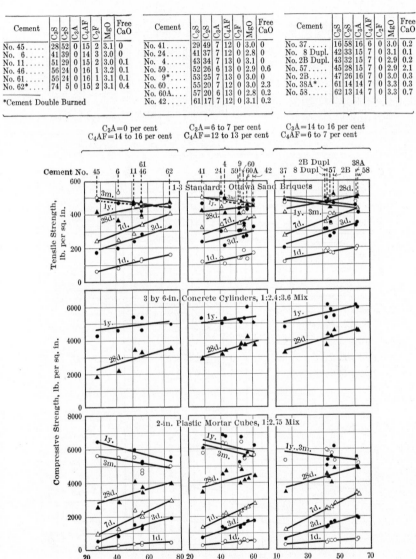

Fig. 8. Relations of strength to tricalcium silicate content of cement. (H. F. Gonnerman, *loc. cit.*)

In Bates' experiments (*Proc. ASTM*, Vol. 15, p. 126) the effect of fineness of grinding on the compressive strength of 1:1½:4½ concrete was determined. Ten brands of cement, varying in fineness from 75.4 to 82.2

per cent passing a 200-mesh sieve, were used as received and also after being reground so that the fineness of the individual brands varied from

Cement	C₃S	C₂S	C₃A	C₄AF	C₂F	MgO	Free CaO
No. 50*....	47	37	4	8	0	3.0	0.5
No. 16.....	42	38	9	6	0	2.9	0.9
No. 53*....	47	35	10	4	0	3.0	0.3
No. 28.....	44	34	11	6	0	2.8	0.3
No. 2B Dupl.	43	32	15	7	0	2.9	0.2
No. 57.....	45	28	15	7	0	2.9	2.1
No. 8 Dupl.	42	33	15	7	0	3.1	0.1
No. 2B.....	47	26	16	7	0	3.0	0.3
No. 1.....	43	27	18	4	0	2.8	1.4
No. 1 Dupl.	45	28	20	4	0	2.9	0.2

Cement	C₃S	C₂S	C₃A	C₄AF	C₂F	MgO	Free CaO
No. 6.....	41	39	0	14	3	3.0	0
No. 51.....	38	45	2	13	0	3.3	0
No. 26.....	42	38	3	15	0	2.7	0
No. 4.....	43	34	7	13	0	3.1	0
No. 24.....	41	37	7	12	0	2.8	0
No. 29.....	40	33	11	13	0	2.8	0
No. 12.....	41	32	12	12	0	2.8	0.1
No. 20.....	42	30	12	13	0	2.8	0
No. 30.....	39	32	13	13	0	2.8	0.1

Cement	C₃S	C₂S	C₃A	C₄AF	C₂F	MgO	Free CaO
No. 19.....	44	33	0	19	1	2.5	0
No. 27.....	41	35	1	20	0	2.9	0
No. 17.....	39	37	3	18	0	2.9	0
No. 25.....	44	32	4	18	0	2.5	0
No. 23.....	38	33	5	20	0	2.8	0
No. 13.....	38	31	7	21	0	2.7	0
No. 21.....	40	30	10	17	0	2.8	0

*Cement Double Burned

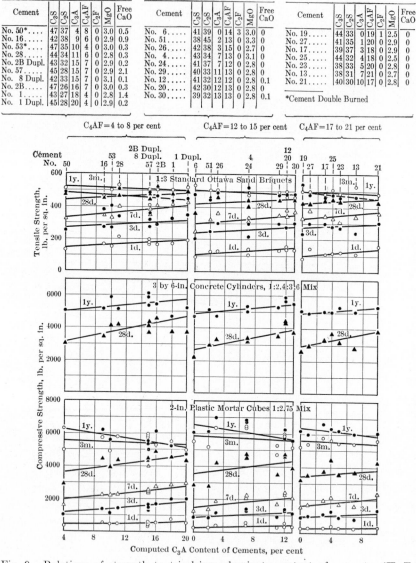

Fig. 9. Relations of strength to tricalcium aluminate content of cement. (H. F. Gonnerman, *loc. cit.*)

86.8 to 92.7 per cent passing the same sieve. At an age of 28 days the concrete made from the finer cements exhibited an average strength of 28 per cent greater than the concrete made from the normal cement. At 90 days the concrete made from the finer cements averaged 17 per cent more strength.

The relation of the compressive strength of 1:3 standard sand mortars to the surface area of the particles of commercial cements of like composition is well shown in Fig. 10.* Since all nine of the cements represented in Fig. 10 had residues less than 10 per cent on the No. 200-mesh sieve, it is evident that the surface area as determined by the turbidimeter affords

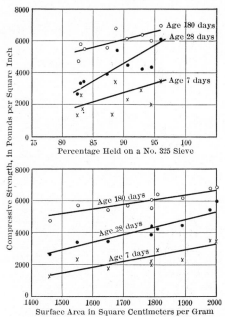

Fig. 10. The effect of fineness of cement on the compressive strength of mortar.

a better criterion of the effects of fineness than the residue on the No. 200 sieve. Also, the data shown in the lower part of the figure exhibit a more consistent relation to strength than those plotted against the percentages passing the No. 325-mesh sieve in the upper part of the figure.

From the above it appears evident that a well-burned, finely ground cement can carry a greater proportion of sand than a more coarsely ground cement and will be more economical, provided the cost of the additional grinding does not offset the advantage derived.

The amount of "seasoning" or aeration which the cement has received subsequent to final grinding influences its strength markedly.

The results of tests reported by the Director of Research of the Portland Cement Association, 1928, are shown in Fig. 11. These and other tests indicate that cement can be kept indefinitely in good condition in tight bins

* From data by H. J. Casey, *J. Am. Concrete Inst.*, Jan.–Feb. 1937, p. 279.

or cans, but it deteriorates considerably when stored in sacks exposed to the air. During the exposures represented in Fig. 11, the moisture and carbon dioxide contents and the loss on ignition all increased with age and severity of the exposure. Thus cement stored in sacks in a shed for 3 years carried 2.5 per cent CO_2, 1.1 per cent H_2O, and 5.3 per cent loss on ignition, whereas the corresponding quantities for cement stored in mill bins were 0.4, 0.3, and 1.2 per cent, respectively. Hence a high loss on ignition is one index of long storage.

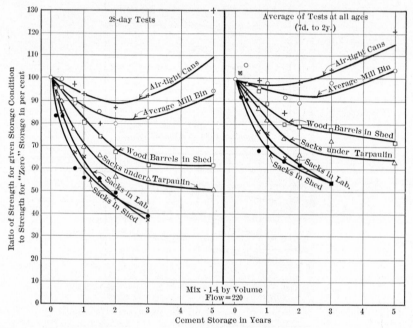

Fig. 11. Effects of storage of cement on concrete strength. (Tests made at Portland Cement Association Laboratory.)

Many tests have been made to determine the effect of the percentage of mixing water upon the strength of cement mixes. Data for concrete tests showing the relation of the strength to the water-cement ratio appear in Art. XV-13. For purposes of testing the strength of cement, use is made of mortars containing standard Ottawa sand passing a 20-mesh and held on a 30-mesh sieve, or a more finely graded variety of this sand. A plastic consistency determined as indicated in Art. XII-8 is used in making standard sand mortars of 1:3 proportions, by weight. Such mortars will show a flow between 35 and 60 per cent when given twenty-five ½-in. drops in 15 sec on a 10-in. flow table (Art. XII-34). With the methods of hand mixing and molding standard in the United States, the use of such consistencies promotes optimum strengths and minimum deviations from strength averages. A wetter consistency having a flow of 100 to 130 per cent has been used as a means of standardizing cement strength in compression, with the mortars being made of finely graded Ottawa sand in 1:2.75 proportions, by weight, with water equal to 53 per cent of the weight of the cement. Since changes of 1 per cent in the amount of mixing water are likely to reflect somewhat greater inverse changes in strength, the water must be accurately weighed.

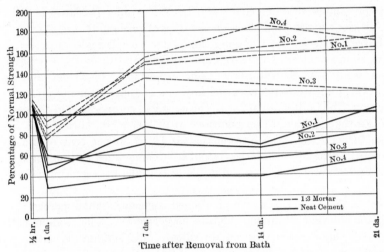

Fig. 12. Effects of drying on the tensile strengths of neat and 1:3 standard sand mortars. Age at removal from bath was 28 days; 4 tests per point.

If briquets are removed from water before testing, a considerable effect, depending upon the time they dry, may be produced upon their strength. Figure 12 has been compiled from the results of experiments by A. J. Barclay,* on four different brands of cement. Similar tests have been reported by Prof. J. L. Van Ornum in *Eng. News*, Vol. 51, p. 24, and by Prof. R. P. Davis in *Eng. News*, Vol. 61, p. 581.

26. Conditions Affecting the Time of Set. The factors which influence the setting properties of the cement are its composition, the percentage of retardant, the degree of calcination, the fineness of grinding, the aeration subsequent to grinding of clinker, the percentage of water used in gaging the paste, the temperature of the mixing water and cement, the humidity and temperature of the moist closet or of the atmosphere in which the cement paste is placed, and the amount of manipulation the paste receives

The effect of lime, silica, and alumina in controlling the set have already been referred to in Art. IX-4. Although the proportion of these oxides

* Thesis, University of Wisconsin, 1912.

exercises a marked influence on set, nevertheless finely ground clinker sets too quickly when mixed with water; hence some provision must be made by the manufacturer to increase the time of setting of freshly ground cement so that it will be sufficiently slow setting for use in construction. This is commonly done by mixing gypsum ($CaSO_4 + 2H_2O$) or plaster of Paris ($CaSO_4 + \frac{1}{2}H_2O$) with the clinker before final grinding, or by adding one of these compounds just after the clinker has received preliminary grinding. (The addition of gypsum before calcination causes it to decompose into lime and sulfur trioxide. Since the latter is liberated in the kiln the resulting effect on the time of set is nil.)

Experiments by Le Châtelier, and later ones by Meade and Gano,[*] have shown that anhydrous calcium sulfate, plaster of Paris, or gypsum may be used as the retardant. The experiments of Meade and Gano, however, indicate that increasing any one of these elements up to 2 or 3 per cent (the limit will vary with the chemical composition of the cement) retards the set, but further additions of plaster of Paris cause the setting time to decrease. The introduction of 10 to 20 per cent of plaster of Paris will generally cause the cement to become quick setting again. The latter effects were not observed in the tests made with gypsum ($CaSO_4 + 2H_2O$) or dead burned gypsum ($CaSO_4$).

In addition to the above-mentioned elements, small percentages of calcium chloride, aluminum chloride, magnesium chloride, sodium hydroxide, potassium hydroxide, sodium silicate, and sodium carbonate [†] also exercise a marked acceleration upon the setting properties of cement. Nihoul and Dufossez showed that strontium sulfate, barium sulfate, calcium sulfate, and calcium aluminate in small percentages also effected a rapid increase in set.

Often an underlimed cement will become quick setting after seasoning. This fault can be overcome by increasing the lime content in the raw materials, or the remedy mentioned below may be applied to the cement. Examples of cements which become slower setting with age are common, and some cases have been cited where cements that are slow setting when fresh have become quick setting and then slow setting after aging for some time. Quick setting may often be avoided by adding to the cement 1 or 2 per cent of hydrated lime or the fraction of a per cent of plaster of Paris.

The fineness to which a cement is ground produces an effect upon its time of set, as the results in Table 1 [‡] indicate. In general, it may be said that the more finely the cement is ground the more rapidly it will set.

[*] *Chem. Eng.*, Vol. 1, p. 92; see also the tests of Nihoul and Dufossez, abstracted in *J. Soc. Chem. Ind.*, Vol. 21, p. 859.

[†] *Concrete-Cement Age*, November, 1912, p. 68.

[‡] From a paper by Meade, *Proc. ASTM*, Vol. 8, p. 410.

TABLE 1. INFLUENCE OF FINE GRINDING UPON THE INITIAL SET
OF CEMENT (MEADE)

Per Cent Passing a No. 200 Sieve.	SETTING TIME IN MINUTES OF CEMENT NO.							
	1	2	3	4	5	6	7	8
75	255	105	120	240	240	200	100	115
80	246	106	115	200	210	190	100	105
85	192	100	100	180	110	175	90	100
90	75	100	95	115	55	100	80	75
95	12	22	60	60	15	25	25	30
100	2	6	35	30	5	2	5	10

However, the relation between time of set and fineness as measured by
the 200-mesh sieve is not rectilinear, as inspection of the table will show.
The results also indicate that grinding to a fineness of 90 per cent through
the No. 200 sieve does not decrease the time of set below the customary
limits.

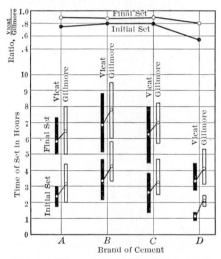

Fig. 13. A comparison of Gillmore and Vicat determinations on time of set.

An increase of 1 per cent in the amount of mixing water used in testing
cement pastes above that required for normal consistency may cause an
increase of a half hour or more in either initial or final set. A comparison
of Gillmore and Vicat methods is shown in Fig. 13, compiled from the
Report of Committee C1 of the ASTM for 1930. These data represent
the range in results from four laboratories operating on each of the four
cements. The results show that the Vicat method indicates lower times
of set than does the Gillmore. The ratios at the top of Fig. 13 indicate

that the discrepancy is likely to be greater for a quick-setting cement like D than for a slower-setting cement like B.

The influence of temperature upon the time of set is shown in Table 2. Cements stored in warm rooms will, in general, be quicker setting than

TABLE 2.   INFLUENCE OF TEMPERATURE ON THE SETTING OF PORTLAND CEMENT †

Sample No.	Initial Set in Minutes. Temperature ° F.				Final Set in Hours. Temperature ° F.			
	100	80	60	40	100	80	60	40
1	$1\frac{1}{2}$	4	6	13	$1\frac{1}{4}$	$1\frac{1}{2}$	2	$2\frac{1}{2}$
2	3	5	6	8	1	$1\frac{1}{4}$	$1\frac{3}{4}$	$2\frac{1}{2}$
3	4	10	15	20	$\frac{1}{2}$	$\frac{3}{4}$	$1\frac{1}{2}$	$6\frac{1}{4}$
4*	5	9	15	30	$\frac{1}{2}$	$\frac{3}{4}$	1	6
5	6	10	14	25	1	$1\frac{1}{2}$	2	$2\frac{1}{2}$
6*	7	12	15	20	$1\frac{3}{4}$	2	$2\frac{1}{4}$	$2\frac{1}{2}$
7*	9	10	15	17	$3\frac{1}{2}$	6	7	12
8	10	15	35	40	$\frac{3}{4}$	1	$1\frac{1}{4}$	$1\frac{3}{4}$
9	11	15	20	57	3	5	6	10
10	11	13	15	30	$2\frac{1}{2}$	3	$3\frac{1}{2}$	6
11	19	32	60	120	3	6	7	15
12	15	35	70*	360	$3\frac{1}{2}$	6	7	22

* Contain a considerable admixture of Kentish Rag.
† From Butler's *Portland Cement*, p. 267.

those stored in a cold atmosphere. Cold mixing water retards set; warm water accelerates it. For the range of temperature ordinarily met in the laboratory, say 65° to 75°F, the effect is not very marked. However, due consideration of the influence of temperature should be given in reporting on cements which are quick setting in a hot laboratory but which will be used in a colder atmosphere.

Cements exposed to a thoroughly saturated atmosphere will set much more slowly than those exposed to a dry atmosphere. If, however, a considerable proportion of moist CO_2 is present in the air, the experiments of Gadd * seem to indicate that the setting time will be greatly reduced.

By lengthening the time of mixing and by prolonged troweling of the surface mortars it is also possible to considerably delay the time of set.

27. Conditions Affecting Fineness. The percentage of flour contained in a cement depends principally upon a number of variables in the method of manufacture. The chemical composition and the degree of calcination influence the hardness of the clinker and consequently affect the fineness to which the clinker is ground. Clinker high in iron or silica is apt to be

* See *Concrete-Cement Age*, Cement Mill Section, Feb., 1914; also paper by G. M. Williams, *Proc. ASTM*, Vol. 14, p. 174.

hard and difficult to grind. The same is true of a hard-burned clinker. It does not always follow, therefore, that a difference in fineness indicates the relative quality of two cements since the one more finely ground may have been underburned. Furthermore, the fineness will be influenced by the time of grinding and the character of the pulverizing machinery employed in grinding.

To some extent seasoning also affects fineness. It has been found that cement becomes slightly finer with age provided that it does not absorb too much moisture. This is probably due to the decrepitation of the coarser grains resulting from hydration of the embedded lime particles.

Methods for testing the fineness of cement, and the errors in sieves are discussed in Art XII-6.

28. Conditions Affecting Specific Gravity. In the majority of cases, the specific gravity affords little if any information concerning the relative value of two cements made from different materials, unless the average specific gravity of each brand is known. The test is chiefly used to detect abnormal conditions in a brand of known specific gravity.

The detection of adulteration by this test depends upon the specific gravity of the adulterant and upon the proportion used. A simple computation reveals that a clinker having a specific gravity of 3.15 may be adulterated with 14.3 per cent of limestone having a specific gravity of 2.8 before the specific gravity of the mixture will be reduced below the normal minimum usually taken as 3.10. If, instead of limestone, a blast-furnace slag or natural cement with a specific gravity of 3.0 is employed, 6.7 per cent of the adulterant may be used before the specific gravity of the adulterated cement is reduced 0.01. Furthermore, it is permissible under the above methods of testing to ignite the sample if its specific gravity falls below 3.10. Experiments have shown that this procedure will raise the specific gravity of many adulterated mixtures considerably above the specified limit. So it is evident that, although adulteration lowers specific gravity, a low result is not necessarily a sign of adulteration, nor is a high value an indication of the absence of it.

Long seasoning is the chief cause of a low specific gravity in an unadulterated cement. This is due to the fact that freshly ground cement when exposed to the air rapidly absorbs moisture and carbon dioxide. A month's seasoning will often reduce the specific gravity from 3.15 to 3.08, or thereabouts, and a long period of seasoning may reduce it to 3.00.* Drying seasoned samples at 212°F will slightly raise the specific gravity; igniting will, in general, raise the specific gravity to the original value. Seasoning the clinker lowers specific gravity.

* For example see *Chem. Eng.*, Vol. 6, p. 19; or Taylor's *Practical Cement Testing*, p. 48.

The chemical composition of a cement also affects its specific gravity. Cements with high contents of iron oxide will have specific gravities 0.05 to 0.10 higher than those with low iron contents, provided both have been subjected to similar storage conditions.

Formerly the degree of calcination was supposed to affect the specific gravity, but numerous experiments have completely disproved this theory.* The effects of fineness of grinding upon specific gravity are slight. Very finely ground cements on account of the readiness with which they absorb moisture and carbon dioxide are likely to have lower specific gravities than cements made from the same materials but more coarsely ground.

RESULTS OF VARIOUS TESTS ON PORTLAND CEMENT

29. General. We shall now consider some results of tests on Portland cement pastes and standard sand mortars. Only those results which are especially affected by the cement itself will receive attention herein. The effects produced upon mortars by variables in the aggregate are considered in Chapter XV.

30. Strength Tests. Strength-age curves for 1:3 standard Ottawa sand mortars of standard consistency and similar curves for 1:2.75 mortars made of graded Ottawa sand with a water-cement ratio of 0.53, by weight, are shown in Fig. 14 for 7 normal Portland cements and in Fig. 15 for 5 high early strength Portland cements. These data were taken from the tests of Committee C1 reported in *Proc. ASTM*, Vol. 1, 1934, p. 322. Each point for a given curve represents the average of 120 tests made in 10 laboratories. The compositions of these cements are given in Table 3 and physical properties in Table 4. From the average curves shown in the lower part of Fig. 15, one obtains a good comparison of the early compressive strengths of normal and high early strength Portlands. Figure 16 shows average strength-age curves for compressive and bending strength tests of 4 types of cement differing in C_3S and C_2S contents. The Cowe Bay sand used in most of these tests was a well-graded quartz sand. It passed a No. 4 sieve, had 49 and 96 per cent retained on the No. 28 and 100 sieves, respectively. Its fineness modulus was 2.7. The water-cement ratio for the 1:2 mortars averaged 0.43 and for the 1:4½ mortars, 0.40, by weight.

These data show, as do those of Fig. 7, that, although cements high in C_3S exhibit the highest early strengths, those of lower C_3S and higher C_2S contents show the highest strengths after a year or more of moist curing.

* See *Chem. Eng.*, Vol. 6, p. 17; and *Proc. Inst. Civil Eng.*, Vol. 166, p. 342.

The data in Fig. 17 show 10-year tests of mortars of standard consistency made with 4 cements commonly used in the Middle West in 1923. These cements were not so finely ground as the normal Portlands

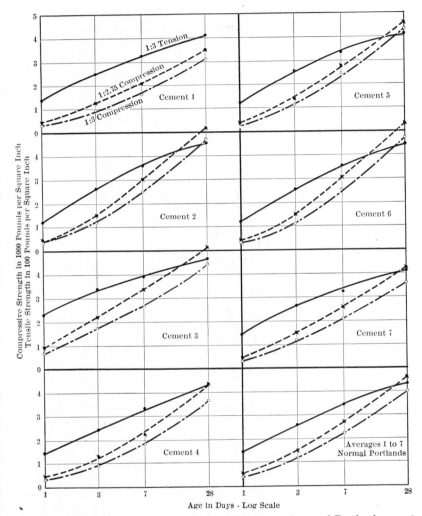

Fig. 14. Strength-age curves for standard sand mortars of normal Portland cements.

of today and in composition would now be classed as low in C_3S. They all exhibit satisfactory gains in mortar compressive strengths. Cured outdoors under an average humidity of 70 per cent, after an initial 28-day period in water, the 1:3 mortars at 10 years were 44 to 96 per cent stronger in compression than similar mortars cured continuously in water.

Cured in water, the tensile strengths of the mortars, Fig. 17, show retrogressions which are less pronounced in the specimens of graded Janesville

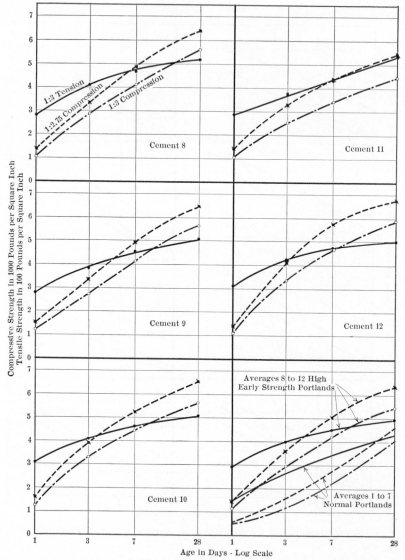

Fig. 15.   Strength-age relations for standard sand mortars of high early strength Portland cements.

sand and in specimens cured outdoors.   Neat cement briquets of these cements cured outside were in many instances cracked and exhibited tensile strengths of only $\frac{1}{10}$ to $\frac{1}{3}$ of the 28-day strength, whereas water-

TABLE 3. CHEMICAL COMPOSITION AND COMPUTED COMPOUND COMPOSITION FOR CEMENTS 1 TO 12
(See Figs. 14 and 15.)

Cement	Oxide Analysis, percentage by wt.						Loss on Ignition	Insoluble Residue	Computed Compound Composition Calculated to Clinker Basis, percent			
	SiO_2	Fe_2O_3	Al_2O_3	CaO	MgO	SO_3			C_3S	C_2S	C_3A	C_4AF
Normal Portland Cements												
1	20.91	3.00	5.20	63.69	3.02	1.61	1.58	0.19	60	18	9	10
2	21.21	2.57	5.26	63.52	4.20	1.52	1.36	0.12	56	21	10	8
3	21.13	3.02	3.96	65.05	3.20	1.48	1.36	0.19	72	9	6	10
4	20.98	2.98	5.65	63.91	2.14	1.34	1.83	0.08	58	20	11	10
5	21.00	2.31	6.12	64.44	2.08	1.52	1.42	0.16	57	21	13	8
6	20.32	3.31	5.64	64.78	2.50	1.14	1.49	0.10	66	11	10	11
7	20.45	4.16	6.23	64.42	1.32	1.48	1.15	0.20	57	18	10	13
High Early Strength Cements												
8	19.91	4.30	5.99	64.03	1.47	2.46	1.18	0.20	59	16	9	14
9	19.87	2.76	6.05	65.35	1.40	2.34	1.73	0.27	68	9	12	9
10	19.63	3.55	6.33	63.13	2.44	2.37	1.42	0.19	57	17	12	12
11	20.34	2.75	5.11	64.93	1.28	2.09	1.96	0.18	68	12	10	9
12	19.74	2.25	5.52	65.81	2.03	2.17	1.22	0.12	76	3	12	7

TABLE 4. AVERAGES OF PHYSICAL PROPERTIES OF CEMENTS 1 TO 12
(All cements were sound in pat tests.)

Cement No.	1	2	3	4	5	6	7	8	9	10	11	12
Water (per cent)	23.9	25.4	26.3	23.7	23.5	24.7	22.4	26.8	25.6	27.0	25.7	24.9
Initial Set,* h.m.	4:12	4:36	3:42	3:22	3:38	4:24	4:06	3:07	2:37	1:34	3:23	4:24
Final Set,* h.m.	6:31	7:02	5:51	5:58	5:29	6:32	6:25	5:18	4:34	5:14	5:14	7:22
Per cent Passing No. 200 Sieve	93	95	98	98	89	96	92	100	99	100	99	98
%<11 microns	28	27	43	36	27	31	31	46	43	48	39	39
%<21 "	45	45	66	54	42	48	44	69	61	73	61	60
%<31 "	62	66	84	73	60	68	62	89	79	91	83	79
%<44 "	71	76	90	82	68	78	71	94	88	97	91	86
Surface Area cm²/gm.	1520	1530	2130	1830	1470	1660	1600	2230	2070	2320	2000	1970

* Gillmore Method. ←——— Normal Portlands ———→ ←——— High Early Strength ———→

cured neat cement briquets at 10 years exhibited strengths averaging from 505 psi for cement 5M to 775 psi for cement 3M. In compression the 2- by 4-in. neat cement cylinders cured outside averaged between 10,210 psi for cement 5M and 16,455 psi for cement 4M.

In conclusion, we may say for cements low in C_3A that C_3S exercises a marked influence on rate of increase in strength of moist-cured mortars up to 1 year; thereafter the effect of C_2S is more potent. The compressive strengths of mortars generally show an upward trend for ages beyond 1 year, but the tensile strengths often show retrogression. Retrogression in tensile strength is most pronounced in mixes rich in cement which are subjected to periods of wetting and drying, and in lean porous mixes which are stored continuously under water. Curing at low humidities is detri-

mental to strength of all mixes. Curing 1:3 mortars of standard sand in
moist air usually produces lower strengths than curing in running water

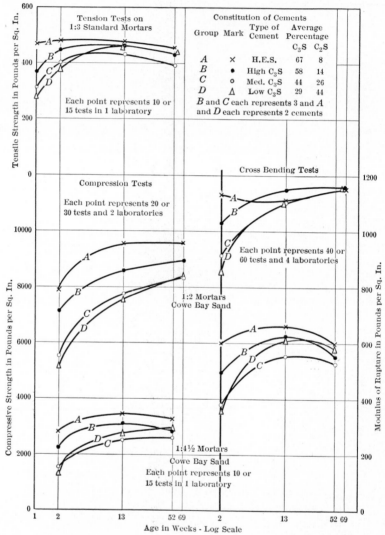

Fig. 16.   The influence of compound composition on mortar strength.   (Compiled
from *Proc. Highway Research Board,* Vol. 16, 1936, p. 135.)

at ages up to 6 months, but subsequently the specimens cured in moist
air become stronger.

31. Expansion and Contraction Due to Variations in Moisture Content.
Owing to its colloidal nature, Portland cement pastes and mortars undergo

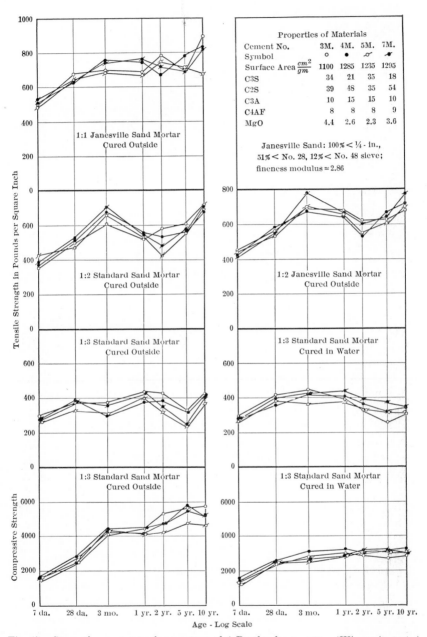

Fig. 17. Strength-age curves for mortars of 4 Portland cements. (Wisconsin tests.)

Materials of Construction

a volumetric contraction when they are allowed to dry in air and to a less extent an expansion when hardened in water.

The contraction in air varies with the decrease in the proportion of free water in the pores plus water held in the colloids.* It may be increased by the water released by carbonation of calcium hydroxide. The expansion in wet curing depends upon the increase in the proportion of water combined with the cement.

The existing evidence shows that both hygral expansion and contraction vary with the paste content of the mix and with the ratio of water

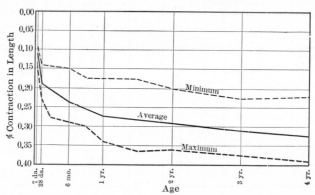

Fig. 18. The linear contraction of prisms of neat cement stored in air. (White.)

to the cement. The contraction in air varies with (1) the humidity of the surrounding atmosphere, (2) the ratio of the exposed surface to the volume, (3) the thickness of the mortar or concrete, (4) the proportion of cement grains hydrated, which is largely dependent on the length of the moist curing period, (5) the length of the drying period, and (6) the proportion of tricalcium aluminate in the cement.

A summary of important experiments by Prof. A. H. White is given in *Proc. ASTM,* Vol. 11, p. 531, and Vol. 14, p. 204. All cements used by White passed the standard soundness tests. After being cured 24 hours in moist air, the initial readings were taken on the 1- by 1- by 4-in. prisms, a micrometer with probable error of 0.003 per cent being used.

Figure 18 shows the average contraction of air-cured neat cement prisms at various ages up to 4 years. Five or six different brands are represented up to 2 years, and 3 brands for the remainder of the time period. The effect of prolonged seasoning on contraction was negligible.

Figure 19 gives the expansion time curves for water-cured neat prisms made of 4 brands of cement and also shows the effects of removal from water and subsequent immersion. It will be noted that the bars shrank

* Y. Yoshida, *J. Am. Concrete Inst.,* Vol. 9, No. 1, 1937.

very slowly after removal from water but expanded very rapidly within a day when subsequently immersed. The behavior of the duplicate bars 146A3 and 146A4 well illustrate this phenomenon. The former, after being subjected to short immersion periods and long drying periods, exhibited no pronounced change in mean length during 3 years' treatment, whereas bar 146A4, which received long periods of soaking and short periods of drying, increased in mean length about 0.15 per cent during the same time. No diminution in the proportionate expansion or con-

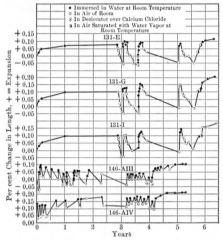

Fig. 19. Changes in length of neat cement bars when alternately wetted and dried at room temperature. (White.)

traction of the bars appeared after repeated applications of the wetting and drying process. In several instances the changes in length increased with repetitions of this treatment. A saturated atmosphere caused expansion comparable to that obtained by immersion in water.

Alternate wetting and drying caused more rapid changes in 1:3 mortar specimens than in those made of neat cement. Prisms cut from sound and strong sidewalk tops, which had seen 20 years' service, exhibited changes in length similar in kind and intermediate in magnitude to the changes observed in the neat and mortar bars. Experiments on compound bars made of equal layers of neat cement and 1:3 mortar led White to the conclusion that such specimens expanded and contracted together but not at the same rate nor to the same degree, the difference in expansion varying from 0 to 0.15 per cent.

Table 5 gives average values of expansion obtained by the Bureau of Standards Laboratory for neat and 1:3 mortar prisms made from 10 different American brands of Portland cement.

TABLE 5.   AVERAGE LINEAR EXPANSION OF NEAT AND 1:3 STANDARD
SAND MORTAR PRISMS OF 10 DIFFERENT BRANDS OF PORTLAND CE-
MENT CURED IN WATER

(*Proc. ASTM*, Vol. 15, p. 141)

Mix	Percentage Linear Expansion at 13 Weeks [1]					
	Normal Cement			Reground 87–93% < No. 200 Mesh		
	Maximum	Minimum	Average	Maximum	Minimum	Average
Neat	0.120	0.057	0.066	0.132	0.056	0.085
1:3	0.024	0.005	0.012	0.027	0.005	0.013

[1] Average results represent 20 specimens.   Each specimen was measured several times
with a Berry strain gage.

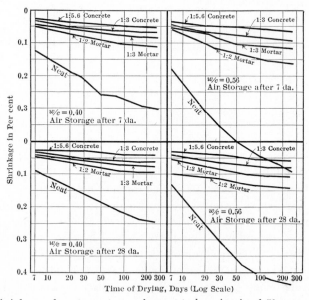

Fig. 20.   Shrinkage of neat, mortar, and concrete bars in air of 50 per cent relative
humidity (*Proc. Am. Concrete Inst.*, Vol. 34, p. 38).   Mortar contained sand passing No. 8 sieve, $m = 2.57$.   Concrete contained gravel 0 to ¾ in., $m = 4.85$.   Bars 1½
by 1½ by 12 in. were given an initial moist storage.

A comparison of the contractions of 1½- by 1½- by 12-in. bars due to variations in paste content is well shown in Fig. 20 from the tests by Y. Yoshida.

The effect of tricalcium aluminate on expansion of cement mortars was reported by Gonnerman (refer to Art. IX-25). Length measurements were made on 3- by 3- by 15-in. mortar bars of 1:3.6 proportions, by weight. He found that the contraction, after 2 years in air at 50 per cent relative humidity and room temperature, following 3 months of moist curing, varied from 0.07 per cent for mortars with cements having no tricalcium aluminate, C_3A, to 0.11 per cent for others having a C_3A content of 20 per cent. The contractions after moist curing 7 days and drying 14 months were approximately the same. His data indicate that the contraction caused by tricalcium aluminate was proportionately three times as much as that due to C_2S or C_3S.

For data on hygral changes of concrete see Art. XV-25.

32. Effect of Remixing and Retempering on Strength of Cement. From the results of tests made at the Watertown Arsenal, Fig. 21 has been

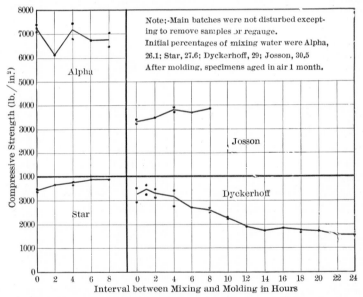

Fig. 21.   Effect of remixing after setting upon the compressive strength of neat cement cubes.

plotted. This diagram shows the strengths of 6-in. neat cement cubes made from pastes which were remixed by hand after setting for different intervals of time. The initial percentage of water is indicated in the figure. Sufficient additional water was added whenever the paste became dry to secure the original consistency.

Materials of Construction

The influence of retempering and remixing of concrete mixes of 1:4½ proportions, by volume, with and without admixtures, is shown in Fig. 22, from the Report of the Director of Research of the Portland Cement

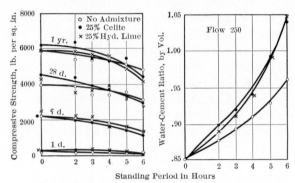

Fig. 22. Effect of retempering and remixing on strength of 1:4½ concrete. (Portland Cement Assoc. tests.)

Association. These data indicate that the strength was reduced in proportion to the increase in the water-cement ratio caused by retempering. After standing 6 hours the compressive strength of the retempered mixes without admixtures was reduced 15 to 20 per cent. When no retempering was done, the strengths were not materially affected by standing 6 hours, but the workability as expressed by the flow was reduced from 250 to 160 per cent.

Table 6 shows the strengths at 1 month of grouts made from various cements which were allowed to remain for 15 or 16 hours in the mixing board and were then remixed with an addition or removal of water, if necessary, to obtain the consistency ordinarily used by masons.

TABLE 6. EFFECT OF RETEMPERING ON THE COMPRESSIVE
STRENGTH OF NEAT CEMENT GROUTS *

Specimens were 6-in. cubes. Age at test = 1 mo.

Brand.	Kind of Cement.	Per Cent Water (by Wt.) at		Interval between Mixing and Molding (Hr.).	No. of Spec.	Compressive Strength (Lb. per Sq. in.)		
		Mixing.	Molding.			Max.	Min.	Average.
Alpha......	Portland	44.9	43.9	15	8	3706	3302	3480
Dyckerhoff.	Portland	43.3	43.3	15	8	2250	1908	2113
Josson.....	Portland	48.6	43.7	15	8	2304	1976	2087
Steel.......	Slag	50.9	50.9	15	8	585	519	554
Mankato...	Natural	68.8	68.8	16	7	316	255	294
Norton.....	Natural	59.0	64.5	15	8	377	305	343

* *Tests of Metals*, 1901, p. 520.

33. Effects of Low Temperatures on the Strength of Cement. In general it may be stated that the setting of cement proceeds at a very slow rate when the temperature falls below 40°F. When the temperature falls below freezing the particles of cement in unset specimens are separated by the expansion of water in freezing. A minimum amount of water should, therefore, be used in cement work subjected to freezing temperature in order that this expansive action may be as small as possible. Alternations in freezing and thawing before the cement has attained hard set generally cause a loss in cementing power owing to the repeated breaking of the bond between adjacent particles. If the work freezes before setting but thaws without refreezing, it will in time secure 50 per cent of normal strength if moisture is provided for proper curing.

From the result of a very large number of compression tests on neat cement made at the Watertown Arsenal, the data in Table 7 have been selected. These tests show that there is considerable chemical activity in neat cement when setting at 0°F. It appears that neat cement specimens subjected to such low temperatures immediately after mixing gain strength at a very much slower rate than specimens cured at room temperatures; but that after several years the test pieces stored at low temperatures develop a considerable proportion of their normal strength. It also appears that specimens hardening at 70°F for a given period will attain a greater strength than specimens which are allowed to harden for a like period after an exposure to freezing temperatures. If neat specimens are allowed to set for 1 day at room temperature before being subjected to freezing temperatures, the rate of growth in strength is more rapid than if immediately frozen.

Tests on mortars and concretes indicate that high early strength Portland cements and cements high in tricalcium silicate have resistance to freezing and thawing superior to the modified cements or those low in tricalcium silicate. This is especially true if freezing takes place at an early age. A high tricalcium aluminate content also appears detrimental to resistance to freezing and thawing. For additional data on effects of low temperatures on concrete, see Art. XV-42.

34. Effect of High Temperatures on the Strength of Neat Portland Cement. In *Tests of Metals*, 1902, a report is made of a number of tests on 4-in. cubes of neat cement which were cured for 1 year in air or water and then gradually heated to temperatures of 600° to 1000°F. The cubes were cooled in asbestos or sawdust and aged for 4 days to 4 months before they were tested. After being heated most of the cubes showed faint cracks, which gradually enlarged when the cubes were allowed to stand in air for several days. In several of the specimens subjected to temperatures of 900°F, these cracks became so large that the specimens were rendered unfit for testing. Specimens subjected to temperatures of 800°F

Materials of Construction

TABLE 7. THE EFFECTS OF LOW TEMPERATURES ON THE COMPRES-
SIVE STRENGTH OF 2-IN. CUBES OF NEAT PORTLAND CEMENT

(*Tests of Metals,* 1901, 1902, and 1907)

Brand of Cement.	Per Cent Water.	TIME OF SETTING IN AIR AT TEMPERATURES OF			Total Age. Days.	COMPRESSIVE STRENGTH * IN LB.-IN.² AFTER STORAGE.	
		70° F. Days.	0° F. Days.	70° F. Days.		Treatment Indicated.	In Air at 70° F for Total Age.
Star.........	23.4	0	31	1	32	1350	4570
		0	31	7	38	2340	4820
		0	89	1	90	1720	
		0	89	30	119	3620	4410
		0	1 yr.	1	.....	2724	
Star.........	24.0	0	5 yr.	1	.....	3250	
Alsen........	28.2	0	30	1	31	986	3900
		0	30	7	37	2440	3450
		0	90	1	91	1210	4040
		0	90	29	119	2520	3510
		0	1 yr.	1	.....	1580	
Alpha........	25.0	.....	.....	1	1	....	582
		1	7	1	9	2400	4990
		1	179	1	181	3670	5910
	25.0	1	5 yr.	1	.....	6320	
		1	5 yr.	36	.....	8100	
Alpha........	23.0	.....	.....	7	7	....	5550
		7	9	1	17	5160	5730
		7	188	1	196	5350	5940
		7	5 yr.	1	.....	7310	
		7	5 yr.	41	.....	7650	
Atlas........	24.0	.....	.....	1	1	....	689
		1	7	1	9	2140	4130
		1	181	1	183	2950	5410
		1	5 yr.	1	.....	4160	
		1	5 yr.	40	.....	6780	
Atlas........	24.0	.....	.....	7	7	....	3730
		7	7	1	15	4210	4890
		7	18	1	192	4500	5790
		7	5 yr.	1	.....	6640	
		7	5 yr.	40	.....	7410	

* Each result is averaged from five or more tests.

or above showed a marked decrease in strength, especially those hardened
in water. Of the cubes made from Dyckerhoff cement and gaged with
29 per cent of water, those hardened in air showed a loss of weight varying from 7.7 per cent after being subjected to 700°F to 10.5 per cent after
1000°F; those hardened in water lost 17.7 per cent after being heated to
1000°F.

35. Experiments on the Rise in Temperature during Setting. In large
masses of concrete the heat evolved in setting is dissipated so slowly that
a marked rise in temperature occurs. Eventually the interior cools and
contracts, thus inducing tensile stresses in the interior of the mass. If
these are sufficiently high, they may cause cracks, which in turn may unite
with surface shrinkage cracks and thus promote leakage and subsequent
disintegration. Hence special attention is given to the selection of the
cement, the proportioning of the mix, and the rate of placement for such
structures. The average heats of hydration for various types of cement
reported by the Bureau of Reclamation in *Special Cements for Mass Concrete* (1936) are shown in Table 8.

TABLE 8

Type of Cement	No. of Cements Averaged	Specific Surface Cm²/gm.	C₃S PerCent	Heat of Hydration in Calories per gram of Cement after		
				3 days	7 days	28 days
High Early Strength.......	12	2030	56	102	108	114
Standard................	11	1770	43	79	86	91
Modified................	12	1930	42	63	74	82
Low Heat...............	14	1930	20	44	52	65

The computed relative effect of various types of cement on adiabatic
temperature rise (no heat loss permitted) in concrete containing 1 barrel
of cement per cu yd is shown in Fig. 23.* For an initial temperature of
40°F, the rise above that initial temperature is less during the first few
days, but at 28 days somewhat greater than for an initial temperature
of 70°F.

Professor R. W. Carlson † has computed temperature rise in dams due
to various rates of placement. Figure 24 shows the computed temperature
rise at various distances above the foundation at the end of the fourteenth
day after the initial lift was placed, when 5-ft lifts were cast every 4 days.
For 10-ft lifts cast every 8 days, Carlson's computations indicate somewhat greater temperature rises. For 4 lifts of 2.5 ft cast at 2-day intervals,

* From paper by J. W. Kelly, *Proc. Am. Concrete Inst.*, Vol. 34, p. 577.
† *Proc. Am. Concrete Inst.*, Vol. 34, p. 497.

the calculations show a maximum temperature rise of 24°F, as compared to 42°F 4 days after placing a single 10-ft lift. He indicated that less

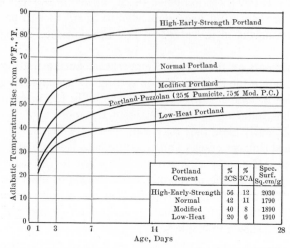

Portland Cement	% 3CS	% 3CA	Spec. Surf. Sq.cm/g
High-Early-Strength	56	12	2030
Normal	42	11	1790
Modified	40	8	1890
Low-Heat	20	6	1910

Fig. 23. Relative effect of type of cement on adiabatic temperature rise of concrete. (J. W. Kelly.)

temperature rise will occur if a given height is placed in several small lifts and then time is allowed for the heat to dissipate prior to further placement.

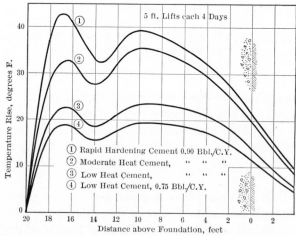

① Rapid Hardening Cement 0.90 Bbl./C.Y.
② Moderate Heat Cement,   "   "   "
③ Low Heat Cement,   "   "   "
④ Low Heat Cement, 0.75 Bbl./C.Y.

Fig. 24. Calculated temperature distribution in a mass of concrete. (R. W. Carlson, *Proc. Am. Concrete Inst.*, Vol. 34, p. 501.)

36. The Resistance of Cement to the Action of Alkali Waters and Sea Water. Under laboratory conditions neat cement may be disintegrated by the combined chemical and mechanical action of waters containing various salts, such as the sulfates of magnesia and sodium, the chlorides of magnesia, sodium and calcium, and the carbonate of soda. The sulfates and chlorides are chemically active in removing lime from the cement, whereas the carbonate of soda alone or in solution with sodium sulfate or sodium chloride withdraws silica.* If the test pieces are subjected to alternate wetting and drying a mechanical action greatly accelerates the breakdown of the cement. Under such conditions, crystals of large size are rapidly formed and expansive forces are produced. Under the action of these forces neat cement pastes are disintegrated more rapidly than lean mortars.†

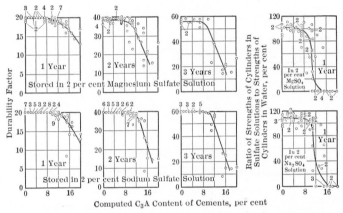

Fig. 25. Influence of tricalcium aluminate content of cement on the durability and strength of concrete exposed to sulfate solutions. Numerals indicate number of identical values. (Gonnerman, *Proc. ASTM,* Vol. 34, Pt. 2, p. 244.)

In the investigation mentioned in Art. IX-25, Gonnerman reported tests of mortar briquets and cubes and 3- by 6-in. cylinders, the latter with a water-cement ratio of 0.56, by weight, all of which were subjected to the action of 2 per cent magnesium or sodium sulfate solutions after moist curing for 28 days. The strength of the solutions was periodically adjusted to maintain constancy. From time to time, visual ratings of the appearance of the specimens were made, also strength tests. The data from Gonnerman's tests in Fig. 25 show that the resistance of the concrete specimens was lessened as the tricalcium aluminate content of the cement was raised above 7 per cent. Similarly he noted that the expansions of concrete cylinders subjected to sulfate attack became more pronounced when the C_3A content of the cement exceeded 7 per cent.

* *Action of the Salts in Alkali Water and Sea Water on Cements, Tech. Paper,* 12, National Bureau of Standards, by Bates, Phillips, and Wig.

† "The Effect of Alkali Water on Cement Mortars," A. J. Fisk, *Eng. News,* Aug. 18, 1910.

Materials of Construction

Stanton and Meder * reported an extensive investigation by the California Division of Highways on the resistance of cements to the attack of sea water and alkali soils. After analyzing soils and waters which had caused disintegration in concrete roads and structures, they subjected 6- by 6-in. cylinders of concrete containing 5 and 6 sacks of cement per cu yd to the action of the aggressive alkali soil. Specimens were moist cured for 28 days and then buried to two-thirds their depth in pans of soil placed on the laboratory roof. In dry season tap water was added once or twice a week to maintain free moisture in the soil. The soils contained

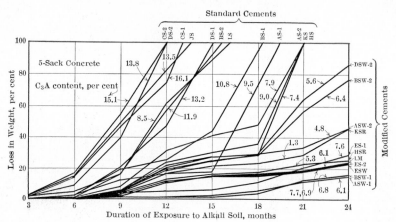

Fig. 26. Comparison of performance of standard Portland cements with that of modified sulfate-resistant cements. (*Proc. Am. Concrete Inst.*, Vol. 34, p. 449.)

approximately 19 per cent of water-soluble salts, of which about ¾ was sodium sulfate and ⅙ magnesium sulfate, the remainder of the salts being largely calcium sulfate, calcium chloride, and bicarbonate of soda. The specimens were examined every 3 months and losses in weight determined.

Figure 26 shows the relation of the loss in weight to duration of exposure for cylinders of 5-sack concrete made with various standard and modified cements marketed in California. Of the modified cements, ASW, BSW, and DSW were made by additions of iron or iron oxide to the raw mix prior to burning, thus reducing computed C_3A and increasing C_4AF. They were intended to be satisfactory for use in sea water and have moderate resistance to sulfate attack. Cements HSR and KSR with high iron contents were designed to have high resistance to sulfate attack. Cement LM was a puzzolan cement made by blending siliceous material with the clinker. The advantage of this procedure arises from combination which this siliceous material makes with any free lime in the clinker, thus fore-

* *Proc. Am. Concrete Inst.*, Vol. 34, p. 433.

stalling the attack of the alkali sulfate on the free lime. These data show that the resistance to alkali attack is related to the computed content of tricalcium aluminate. With the exception of standard cements ES and ESW, the modified or blended cements, all of which were low in C_3A, were much more resistant than the standard Portland cements used in these tests. Cements ES and ESW were more resistant than their computed C_3A contents would indicate. This may have been due to conditions in manufacture which reduced the content of this component below the computed value.

37. Effects of Oils and Acids on Cement and Mortar. Most mineral oils show no tendency to disintegrate well-cured cement mortars.[*] Lean mortars (1:4) may develop less strength when partially immersed in such oil after 7 days than when moist cured for a month or more prior to immersion. Soaking the surface of a floor in a mineral oil of low viscosity will cause a marked reduction in its abrasive resistance. When mineral oils are incorporated into the mixing water they materially retard the set of the cement and reduce the strength.

Animal and vegetable oils, which contain organic acids or which become rancid on exposure, will attack the lime compounds in the cement, form lime soap, and cause surface disintegration. Toch[*] suggests that this attack is due to the expansion during crystallization of the oleate and stearate of calcium. Therefore in lubricating molds only mineral oil should be used and the amount should be as small as possible.

Seeds [†] in shells like andaassu, ayry, tucum, and urucury, when subject to moisture, generate uluric acid, which attacks the lime in the cement. Crushed seeds which in moist surroundings generate considerable carbonic acid will also react adversely on lime compounds. Usually the acetic or lactic acids in silage are too weak to attack a dense, well-made mortar, but the spillage of milk and cream on creamery floors produces pronounced attack on cement surfaces and mortar joints. Light, refined molasses [‡] may attack concrete containers in time. Tannic acid, commonly found in the top soil overlaying sand and gravel deposits, may cause a marked reduction in the strength of a cement mortar if 0.1 per cent is present in the sand or gravel.

Weak solutions of sulfuric or hydrochloric acid (less than 0.3 per cent) will cause a marked attack on cement mortars and concrete. Natural water with pH above 7.0 has a negligible attack on cement, but with a lower pH value the lime is removed from the cement in proportion to the decrease in the pH number; and the strength of the mortar is thereby

[*] J. C. Hain, *Eng. News,* Vol. 53, p. 279, 419.

[†] F. W. Friese, *Concrete and Const. Eng.,* Vol. 27, p. 347.

[‡] M. N. Clair and M. A. Morrissey, *Eng. News Record,* Vol. 111, p. 775.

reduced.*   Mine waters are likely to run high in acidity and consequently aggressively attack mortars and concretes.†

38. Effects of Sugar on Cement.   The addition of sugar to cement, even in amounts as small as 0.10 per cent, appears to produce a marked delay in the time of set, to practically destroy early strength, and to greatly decrease strength at 28 days.   Concrete failures have been attributed to the sugar introduced into concrete by the use of old sugar sacks to transport fine aggregate or by the use of such sacks in curing concrete. Hardened concrete is not affected by dry sugar, but should be protected against repeated wetting and drying with sugar solutions.

* Bailey Tremper, *Contract Record,* Vol. 45, p. 1441.

† A tabulation summarizing the effect of oils and miscellaneous liquids on concrete and method of protective treatment where required is given in Art. XV-55.

Natural and Other Hydraulic Cements

NATURAL CEMENT

1. Definition. Natural cement is made by burning a natural argillaceous limestone at a low red heat which is sufficient to drive off carbonic oxide (CO_2). Additions up to 5 per cent of non-deleterious materials are permitted after burning. The clinker must be finely ground to provide hydraulic properties.

2. Process of Manufacture. The limestone, containing from 15 to 35 per cent clay, is burnt in vertical kilns 30 to 40 ft high and 10 to 15 ft in diameter. The common type of kiln consists of a cylindrical steel shell open at the top and lined with firebrick. In operating a kiln, thick layers of limestone and thin layers of soft coal are alternately dumped into the top of the furnace and the burnt clinker is drawn off at frequent intervals from the bottom. As the limestone descends in the kiln, water is first driven off from the rock. At a temperature of about 700°C, magnesium carbonate begins to decompose. Lime carbonate dissociates at 900°C and clay at a somewhat higher temperature. The alumina and iron oxide set free by the decomposition of the clay combine with the lime and magnesia and, if the final temperature is high enough, lime and magnesium silicates will be formed. The process is run continuously, and about one-third of the charge, in the form of clinker, is daily withdrawn from the kiln.

On account of the variations in the quality of the raw material and on account of non-uniformity in burning different parts of the charge, a considerable portion of the resultant clinker is either underburned or over-burned. According to Eckel, from 10 to 33 per cent of the resultant product cannot be used. After the clinker has been removed from the kiln it is allowed to season in the air in order that any underburned clinker may be slacked before grinding. Sometimes slacking is accelerated by steaming the clinker.

The burnt clinker is first passed throught a stone crusher and then fed to some form of apparatus for grinding it to the requisite fineness. Formerly, all mills used the millstone grinders commonly employed in flour mills. Currently, however, a decided improvement in the fineness of grinding has been effected by the introduction of ball mills, tube mills, and other modern equipment used in grinding Portland cement.

Natural cement is sold by the barrel (4 one-cubic-foot sacks). The weight per barrel is 282 lb net.

3. Characteristics of Natural Cement. Natural cement is an impalpable powder varying in color from yellow to brown and in specific gravity from 2.80 to 3.00. It resembles hydraulic lime inasmuch as it is made from a natural argillaceous limestone and will set when mixed with water either in air or under water. On the other hand, natural cement clinker slakes but little, if any, when water is poured upon it. Most natural cements are not so finely ground as Portland cements.

Natural cement requires more water for normal consistency and sets much more rapidly but with a less evolution of heat than Portland cement. For pastes of normal consistency the time of initial set will usually vary from 15 minutes to 1 hour, and final set will generally occur within 3 hours. An excess of water greatly retards the setting of natural cement pastes. Aeration also retards the set of natural cement.

On account of the variability of the raw materials employed in manufacture, natural cements differ considerably in chemical composition. Even in the same brand considerable differences in the composition are common owing to variations in the rock and degree of calcination. The approximate ranges in amounts of the chief chemical compounds found in natural cements, as obtained from over 100 analyses given in Eckel's *Cements, Limes and Plasters*, Chapter XIX, are as follows: 30 to 60 per cent of lime (CaO); 15 to 35 per cent of silica (SiO_2); 1 to 25 per cent of magnesia (MgO); 2 to 20 per cent of alumina (Al_2O_3); 1 to 19 per cent of iron oxide (Fe_2O_3); and, in general, less than 10 per cent of water (H_2O), carbon dioxide (CO_2), the alkalies (K_2O, Na_2O), and sulfur trioxide (SO_3).

4. Properties of Natural Cement. Because of variations in composition and manufacture, the properties of natural cements, even those of the same brand, often differ considerably. In Fig. 1 are shown the average tensile strength results of numerous tests made by W. P. Taylor on different brands of natural cement. Attention is called to the regular increase in tensile strength which accompanies an increase in the age of briquets. Although natural cement gains its full strength much less rapidly than Portland cement, it does not, in general, exhibit marked retrogression in strength, even when tested neat. This fact is well illustrated by Fig. 2 which shows the results of long-time tensile tests on 3 brands of natural and 1 brand of Portland cement used on the Croton Dam. In these tests the mortars were made with crushed quartz passing a No. 20 sieve and retained on a No. 30 sieve. The number of specimens per point on the diagram ranged from 15 to 14,740. Nearly all the tests were made by one operator.

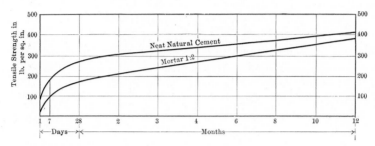

Fig. 1. Tensile strength-age curves for neat and 1:2 natural cement mortars. (From Taylor's *Practical Cement Testing.*)

Wheeler found the ratios of tensile strengths of 1:2, 1:3, and 1:4 natural cement mortars to those of neat natural cement when moist cured 6 months to be 0.65, 0.45, 0.35.

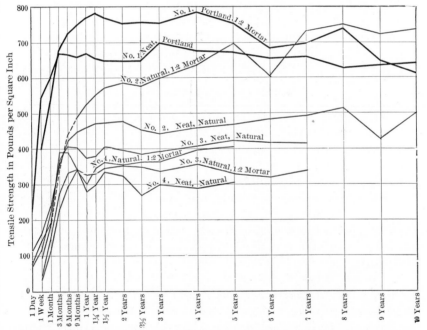

Fig. 2. The effects of age on the tensile strengths of natural and Portland cements used in the Croton Dam. (G. G. Honness, *Trans. ASCE,* Vol. 76, p. 1038.)

Natural cement in good condition should exhibit minimum tensile strengths in 1:3 mortars of standard sand and standard consistency (Art. XII-8) not less than 75 psi after 7 days and 150 psi after 28 days of moist curing. In compression, the strength of similar mortars at 7, 28, and 360 days should average 450, 1000, and 2500 psi, respectively.

Exposure of natural cement to air is likely to cause a reduction in the tensile strength of mortars made from the aerated cement. Regaging neat natural cement mortars with water adversely affects their strengths. Some of Wheeler's tests indicate that the reduction in tensile strength for a single regaging at the end of 1 hour was 30 per cent and regaging three times in 3 hours caused a reduction of 40 per cent. Natural cement mortars are adversely affected by freezing and thawing in about the same proportion as Portland cement mortars, but their final strengths after such action are much lower.

5. Uses and Production. Until the beginning of the twentieth century natural cement had been extensively used in monolithic constructions in concrete in which great strength was not required. The quicker-hardening and superior strength properties of Portland cement and the lowering of the price of the latter have practically eliminated natural cement from that field. Natural cement now finds use chiefly in masonry mortars for sewers, buildings, and various types of unit masonry constructions. The quantity of natural cement produced annually in the United States approximates 2 per cent of the production of Portland cement. Its cost is about 20 to 30 per cent less than that of Portland cement.

MISCELLANEOUS CEMENTS

6. White Portland Cement. Stainless white Portland cements of high strength are used in ornamental work both interior and exterior, in making building blocks, cast stone, stucco, stainless mortar, and in marking highway lanes. In order to obtain the white color it is necessary to use raw materials with a low content of iron oxide, to use fuel free of pyrite, and to burn at a temperature above the normal. Generally less than 1 per cent of this oxide is present in the finished cement. In physical properties, white Portland cements conform to the standard specification for Portland cements, although the strength at 1 and 7 days is sometimes low.* About 1,100,000 barrels of white Portland cement were produced in 1950 in the United States. The value at the mill was $4.75 per barrel.

7. High Early Strength Portland Cements are made from high-limed mixtures, burned twice, and very finely ground. They contain a higher proportion of tricalcium silicate than ordinary Portland cements. Consequently, although setting at about the same rate as ordinary Portlands, they harden much more quickly and with greater evolution of heat. Briquets of 1:3 standard sand mortar should obtain a strength of 275 psi at 1 day and 375 psi at 3 days.

---

* For data on properties, see P. H. Bates, *Trans. Am. Ceramic Soc.*, Vol. 16, p. 551.

Comparing strength of concretes of high early strength (Type III) cements to strength of concrete made of other types of Portland cements, both having water cement ratios of 0.80, by volume, it will be found that in compression the ratio of the former to the latter is approximately 3:1 at one day, 2.5:1 at 3 days, and 2:1 at 7 days. In flexure, the concrete made of high early strength Portland cement and $w/c = 0.8$ is approximately twice as strong at ages of 1 to 3 days as that made of Type I Portland cement. For further data on properties see Art. IX-30.

Since high early strength Portland cements (Type III) usually cost somewhat more than other types of Portland, they are economically used when a high strength is wanted at 1 or 2 days. When 3 days or more curing can be permitted, rich mixes of Type I Portland cement will usually give the required strength at less cost.

About 6,700,000 barrels of high early strength cements were produced in the United States in 1950. The value at the mill was $2.74 per barrel.

8. Blended Cements. A blended cement is the impalpable powder obtained by mixing Portland cement with more than 1 per cent of an admixture, other than a retardant, for the purpose of altering the normal properties of the Portland cement. Mixing is preferably done prior to grinding of the clinker. There are four varieties of admixtures used in making blended cements: (a) puzzolanic material; (b) inert siliceous sands or rocks; (c) natural cement or lime; (d) accelerators, retarders, plasticizers, and waterproofing materials. Of these the first and second have been used to a considerable extent in marine structures abroad and to some extent for dams and other hydraulic constructions in the United States. These two types are high silica cements with low heats of hydration and relatively high resistance to the action of alkali or sea water.

9. Portland-Puzzolan cement is made usually by intergrinding about 30 per cent of puzzolanic material with 70 per cent of Portland cement clinker. Puzzolan is a corruption of the Italian pozzuolana, signifying a volcanic ash. Although not cementitious by itself, a puzzolan carries a type of siliceous material which when finely ground will combine with lime in the presence of water and form stable compounds. The more important puzzolanic materials found in nature are volcanic ash and its derivatives, pumicite, tuff, and trass; diatomaceous earths and shales; certain siliceous rocks. Among the artificial puzzolans are burned clay, slag, and the very finely divided fly ash from the burning of powdered coal.

The Los Angeles Aqueduct was built of concrete made with cement containing equal parts of Portland cement and tuff. The tuff was consolidated pumiceous rock approximating 70 per cent silica, 12 to 14 per cent alumina, and smaller amounts of iron oxide, lime, magnesia, and alkalies. Since this cement was prepared by grinding the pulverized tuff with the Portland cement to a fineness of 90 per cent passing a No. 200

sieve, the finished product was much finer than normal Portland cements of that period. This cement produced 1:2:4 concrete somewhat slower in hardening than those made of the Portland cement, but eventually acquired 80 per cent of the strength of similar mixes of Portland. Concrete of this cement was very impervious and showed little shrinkage.

On the Arrowrock, Elephant Butte, and Lahontan Dams, Portland cements interground with equal parts of sand or siliceous rock of low puzzolanic activity were used with satisfactory results.

In the constructions of the Bonneville Dam and the Golden Gate Bridge piers, Portland-puzzolan cements were used after exhaustive investigations [*] by R. E. Davis of the University of California and the U. S. Bureau of Reclamation under J. L. Savage. Of the four common types of Portland cement, Davis tests indicated that a high-lime clinker is the best for making these blended cements. Considering grindability of clinker, strength of concrete, and resistance to sodium sulfate attack, the diatomaceous silicas were the most desirable puzzolans, especially if calcined at 1450°F prior to blending; but mortars of these cements contract more than those of normal Portlands on drying. The mortars made with cements containing volcanic silicas exhibited less contraction on drying, but were somewhat less strong and resistant to sulfate attack. The mortars made of cements containing siliceous rock such as puzzolan had low contractions on drying but were considerably lower in strength and sulfate resistance. Also the clinker of these latter cements was harder to grind. In general, the Portland-puzzolan cement concretes exhibited less separation of water after standing in molds and higher impermeability than concretes of the Portland cement. The reduction in heat of hydration of Portland-puzzolan cements is roughly proportional to the percentage of puzzolan. With 30 per cent of puzzolan the heat of hydration is about the same as for low-heat Portlands. Portland-puzzolans made with diatomaceous silicas, volcanic silicas, or limestone are more resistant to sodium sulfate action than the corresponding Portland cements. The plastic deformation of Portland-puzzolan cement mortars under sustained loads is somewhat greater than that of corresponding Portland cement mortars.

Davis' tests on Portland cement blended with fly ash indicate that the latter when containing less than 10 per cent of carbon has excellent puzzolanic properties.

A comparison [†] of the properties of concretes made with a high-grade commercial Portland-puzzolan, No. 4, and others made with different types of Portland cement, is shown in Fig. 3. Test ages were 28 days.

---

[*] See *J. Am. Concrete Inst.*, March–April 1934, p. 369; Sept.–Oct. 1935, p. 80; May–June 1937, p. 577; *Special Cements for Mass Concrete*, U. S. Bureau of Reclamation.
[†] From 1938 thesis by G. W. Washa, Ph.D., at University of Wisconsin.

About 1,400,000 barrels of Portland-puzzolan cement were produced in 1950 in the United States. The value at the mill was $2.45 per barrel.

In England and in Germany blast-furnace slag has been used considerably, interground with Portland cement to form Portland blast-furnace

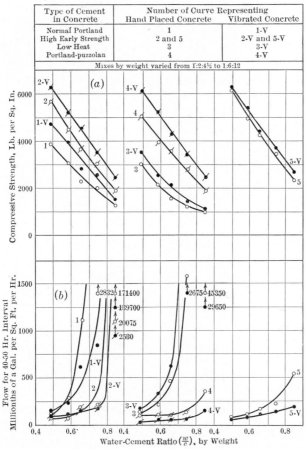

Fig. 3. The effects of different types of cement on the strength and watertightness of gravel concrete placed by hand; also by an internal vibrator (Washa).

cement and Eisen Portland cement. The British Portland blast-furnace cement meets the physical test requirements of their standard Portlands but has a lower heat of hydration and high resistance to sulfate attack.

10. Portland Cement Blended with Natural Cement. The use of this blend has been revived to some extent. Tests were made at Purdue University on all the more important properties of concrete containing a given brand of normal Portland cement and the same cement blended with 25 per cent of natural cement. In strength and elasticity the concretes of normal cement were slightly superior; but in plastic flow, resistance to fatigue, and in low heat of hydration the blended cement concretes were somewhat better.

In New York State Portland cements blended with 14 to 28 per cent of natural cement have been used in concrete pavements, on account of the superior resistance of concrete so made to the attack of salt used in sanding ice-covered pavements in the winter.*

11. Puzzolan Cements. Since the beginning of the Christian era the Italians have successfully employed puzzolan cement for various kinds of construction. This cement is made by grinding two to four parts of puzzolana with one part of hydrated lime.† Besides puzzolana, granulated slag, trass, or tuff may be used. When granulated slag is employed, the product is often called slag cement. In 1937 two Alabama plants made from slag and lime all the puzzolan cement produced in the United States.

12. Properties of Slag Cement. Slag cement may be recognized by its freedom from grit, the extreme fineness to which it is ground, and its lilac color. When a fractured surface of hardened neat paste is exposed to the air, its color gradually turns from a bluish green to white, owing to the oxidation of the sulfides present in the slag. When freshly made, slag cement sets in about the same time as Portland cement but hardens much more slowly. If the slag cement is old, the effect of the caustic soda, which is added to accelerate the set, disappears and the cement becomes very slow setting. Slag cements require 2 to 4 per cent less water than Portland cement to form pastes of normal consistency. In specific gravity, slag cements vary from 2.7 to 2.9. The proportions of the chemical elements in the puzzolans range about as follows: CaO, 45–55 per cent; SiO_2, 27–30 per cent; Al_2O_3, 10–14 per cent; $Fe_2O_3 < 2$ per cent; $MgO < 4$ per cent; $CaS < 3$ per cent. Most of the American slag cements have a lime ratio between 1.0 and 1.3.

The compressive strengths of rich mixes made from slag cement are less than those of similar Portland cement mixes. In lean proportions, however, the differences in strength are not so great. Mortars of puzzolan cements are tough but have little resistance to attrition. According to the report of the United States Army Engineers ‡ puzzolan cement mortars and concretes should not be used where they will be continually exposed to the air since such exposure produces disintegration by oxidation of the sulfides in the slag. Inasmuch as these cements possess hydraulic prop-

---

* See W. F. Kellerman and D. G. Runner, *Proc. ASTM*, Vol. 38, Pt. 2, p. 329.

† In the setting and hardening of these cements, it is probable that the main reactions are similar to those discussed in Art. IX-4 and X-9.

‡ *Eng. News*, Vol. 46, p. 180.

erties and are highly siliceous, they are commonly believed to be less affected by sea water than Portland cements.*

13. Masonry Cements are used in laying brick, tile, concrete block, stone, or other masonry units. In 1934 Rogers and Blaine, of the U. S. Bureau of Standards, reported (*Research Paper* 746) on the properties of 41 commercial masonry cements then marketed in the United States. These cements were of the following types: 7 largely Portland; 8 Portland and hydrated lime mixtures; 10 Portland mixed with unidentified plasticizing material—probably limestone dust or siliceous material; 2 mixtures of Portland and natural cements; 4 natural cements; 6 containing large amounts of slag; 2 hydrated or hydraulic limes; and 2 not identified. About half these cements contained water-repellent additions of petroleum products or fatty acid derivatives. These water repellents increased watertightness and resistance to freezing but caused more air to be entrapped in the mortars, and thus increased yield. Some conception of the variability and desirability of standardizing these cements is given below:

Specific weight, 40–90 lb/cu ft (rodded).
Water retentivity of 1:3 mortar after 1 min suction, 53 to 98 per cent.
Shrinkage during first 24 hours, 0.087 to 0.585 per cent.
Compressive strength of 1:3 mortar at 28 days, 50 to 3650 psi (13 cements were
    below 300 psi and 22 below 600 psi).
Only 16 of the 41 masonry cements showed high resistance to freezing and thawing
    by withstanding over 250 cycles, whereas 16 withstood 10, or fewer, cycles.

Such cements should pass the autoclave test for soundness; should not take initial set within 1 hour; and should acquire final set in 24 hours. The compressive strength of three 2-in. cubes of 1:3 mortar of standard sand made with a flow of 100–115 per cent after twenty-five ½-in. drops in 15 sec should exceed 250 (Type I) or 500 psi (Type II) at 7 days, and 500 (Type I) or 1000 psi (Type II) at 28 days. The same type of mortar made with an initial flow of 100 to 115 should have a flow greater than 70 per cent of the initial value after being subject for 1 min to a suction of 2 in. of mercury. Mortars of such cements should not shrink or expand unduly in hardening, should spread easily under the trowel, should bond well to the masonry, should be durable, and should not effloresce or stain masonry (ASTM C91). About 11,200,000 barrels of masonry cement were produced in 1950 in the United States. The value at the mill was $2.84 per barrel.

14. High Alumina Cement consists essentially of alumina (Al_2O_3) 40.0, lime (CaO) 40.0, iron oxides 15.0, and silica, magnesia, insoluble material, etc., 5.0 per cent. It is manufactured from limestone and bauxite, either

* For further results see tests by W. K. Hatt, *Eng. News,* Vol. 45, p. 164.

by the dry process used in making Portland cement or by fusion in an electric furnace. The American product Lumnite cement is much darker colored than Portland cement.

High alumina cement is more finely ground than Portland, 5 to 8 per cent being held on a 200-mesh sieve. It acquires initial set a bit more slowly and hardens much more rapidly and with a greater evolution of heat than Portland cement. In order to obtain best results it is necessary that concrete made with Lumnite cement be sprinkled or sprayed frequently after final set has occurred until it is at least 24 hours old. If the curing water is applied too soon, or the surrounding atmosphere becomes too dry, a weak scaly surface forms on the work. Strength of Lumnite cement mixes wet-cured for 24 hours at room temperature are somewhat higher than the strengths of similar mixes of Portland cement at 28 days. Owing to the high temperatures generated in hardening, Lumnite cement mixes are less sensitive to cold temperatures than Portland cement mixes. Mortars of Lumnite cured in a dry atmosphere contract about as much as similar Portland mixes, but in moist atmosphere they expand more than Portland mortars.

Owing to the high cost of bauxite, Lumnite is three to four times as costly as Portland cement. However, on account of its remarkable early strength, a saving in forms and earlier availability of construction attends its use. Other advantages claimed for this cement are superior resistance to sea water, sulfate-bearing waters, industrial wastes, and organic acids.

Lumnite cement, along with crushed firebrick, or Haydite, or other heat-resistant materials, is also used to make refractory concrete for furnace linings.

15. Oil Well cement used to protect the casing of an oil well from subsurface fluids under pressure is made by adding a fraction of 1 per cent of a non-harmful retarding agent to normal Portland cement. A retarded cement has no tendency to stiffen when water is added and maintains excellent pumpability during the period of retardation, after which it hardens normally with rising temperature and rapidly at high temperatures. It is claimed that slurries made with these cements remain pumpable for more than 4 hours at temperatures of 180° to 200°F, and that fluidity remains satisfactory under combinations of high pressure and temperature. Slurries commonly used contain 4.5 gal of water per sack of cement. About 1,800,000 barrels of oil well cement were produced in 1950 in the United States. The value at the mill was $2.59 per barrel.

Limes and Plasters

LIMES

1. Quicklime. Pure lime, generally called quicklime, is a white oxide of calcium. Much of the commercial quicklime, however, contains more or less magnesium oxide, which gives the product a brownish or grayish tinge. Quicklime slakes when mixed with water. The specific gravity of pure lime is about 3.40.

Essentially, the process of making lime consists in heating calcite ($CaCO_3$), or magnesium limestone ($xCaCO_3$) $\pm$ $yMgCO_3$, to a temperature sufficiently high to drive off the carbon dioxide (CO_2). For pure lime carbonate the temperature at which such dissociation takes place is approximately 900°C. Since a considerable length of time is required to calcine limestone at such temperatures, it has been found good practice in operating kilns to use higher temperatures, depending upon the character of the impurities of the stone. However, to avoid burning, which seriously injures the setting properties, high magnesium limes should not be subjected to temperatures above 1000°C and high-calcium limes should be burnt at temperatures lower than 1300°C.*

Under Serial Des. C51–47 and C5–26, the ASTM † recommends that quicklime be classified as shown in the accompanying table.

Properties Considered.	Calcium Lime.	Magnesium Lime.
Calcium Oxide, min., per cent......	75	
Magnesium Oxide, min., per cent...	......	20
Calcium and Magnesium Oxides, min., per cent.................	95	95
Silica, alumina, and oxide of iron, max., per cent.................	5	5
Carbon Dioxide, max., per cent:		
(a) If sample is taken at kiln....	3	3
(b) If sample is taken any other place.....................	10	10

Lump Lime: Quicklime as it comes from the kilns.

Lump Lime Screened: Lump lime after forking or screening to remove the finer portion.

NOTE.—The portion removed is usually that which will pass a ½-in. sieve.

Pulverized Lime: Quicklime which will pass a fine sieve of specified size.

NOTE.—The size of the sieve is usually ¼ in.

2. Burning of Lime. Limestone is usually burnt in some form of vertical kiln. The raw material is fed in at the top and the finished product

* *Trans. Am. Ceramic Soc.*, Vol. 13, p. 618, article on burning of limestones by A. V. Bleininger and W. E. Emley.

† See ASTM *Standards* for the specifications.

drawn off through an opening in the side near the bottom. In general
the stacks of these kilns consist of cylindrical steel shells lined with re-

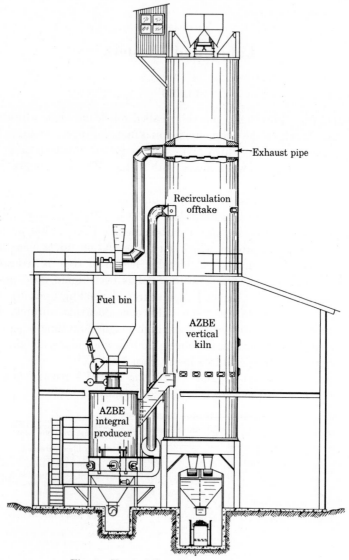

Fig. 1. Vertical lime kiln. (AZBE Corp.)

fractory brick. Kilns may be operated continuously or intermittently.
To secure the greatest efficiency continuous operation is imperative. The
common types of kiln are the mixed-feed and separate-feed kilns. In the
mixed-feed type, bituminous coal and limestone are fed into the top of

the kiln in alternate layers; in the separate-feed type, limestone is not brought into contact with the fuel during the burning process. To accomplish this the fuel is burned in a grate which is attached to the sides of the kiln (see Fig. 1), and which is so arranged that the heat produced will ascend into the stack. The majority of the separate-feed kilns burn coal, some wood, and a few producer gas. The mixed-feed kiln is more economical of fuel but does not produce as high-grade product as the separate-feed kiln. Most American concerns now use the separate-feed kiln to burn lime.

Rotary kilns about 150 ft long, similar to those used in burning Portland cement, account for about one-half the lime produced in the United States. These kilns have a greater production per man-hour and provide better control over the properties of the product. They have, however, a much higher initial cost, and require steady operation for maximum productive capacity. They have a 24-hr capacity of about 150 tons.

3. Production Statistics. Lime is made in nearly all of the United States. Leaders in production are Ohio, Pennsylvania, Missouri, and West Virginia. The total output for the country is about 7,500,000 short tons, with an average value of approximately $11 per ton. About one-fourth of the lime produced is sold in hydrated form. About one-half is used in chemical and metallurgical operations, one-sixth in building construction, and the remainder for refractories and agricultural purposes.

4. The Slaking and Hardening of Lime. The mixing of 56 parts of pure quicklime with 18 parts of water, by weight, causes considerable evolution of heat and an increase of nearly 100 per cent in absolute volume in forming calcium hydroxide, $Ca(OH)_2$. To avoid burning and to promote workable pastes, masons usually slake limes with $1\frac{1}{2}$ to 2 times as much water as lime. Slaking proceeds best at temperatures near the boiling point of water, but care should be taken to avoid overheating as evidenced by the issuance of jets of steam. Limes from coarse-grained stone, lump limes, and pulverized limes usually slake rapidly; limes from fine-grained stones, and dense lumpy limes usually slake slowly. Over-burning or underburning of the limestone causes the lime to slake more slowly and injures the mortar strength. With rapid-slaking limes (showing decrepitation and marked evolution of heat within 5 min) it is best in slaking to add the lime to the water and keep the lime covered with water, thus avoiding overheating. With slower-slaking limes the water should be added to the lime in amounts sufficient to promote a vigorous reaction without the formation of steam jets. In order to avoid popping of plaster and undue expansion in masonry mortars subjected to moisture, both the lime and magnesia should be hydrated. Since the latter hydrates at ordinary temperatures much more slowly than the former, dolomitic and high magnesium limes will require a longer time to hydrate than the high-calcium limes. By maintaining the temperature of the batch at 180°F, either can be hydrated in a couple of days. If the batch is allowed to cool down to room temperature in 6 or 8 hours, it may then require a week or two to hydrate 80 per cent of the magnesia in a dolomitic lime.

In construction, both the shrinkage and the cost of lime mortars are much reduced by adding 4 or 5 volumes of sand to 1 volume of lime putty.

In the hydrating of lime, part of the calcium hydroxide crystallizes and part forms colloids. These components secure a certain amount of rigidity through evaporation and absorption of the surplus water by the surrounding masonry. Final hardening is attained, however, through desiccation of the water and replacement by carbon dioxide from the air. Thus the paste is slowly converted into a carbonate of approximately the same composition as the original limestone. Owing to the inaccessibility of the interior of a masonry joint, this hardening action progresses very slowly and, if the wall is thick, may take years for its completion.

When stored in air, quicklime soon decrepitates because of the absorption of moisture and carbon dioxide and is in time reduced to lime carbonate. Therefore, in order to preserve its hardening power, quicklime must be stored in tight containers. Since ground lime keeps better than lump lime, ground lime can be shipped in open cars, although ground lime for construction is commonly shipped in paper sacks of 67-lb capacity.

There are two methods of marketing lime designed to overcome the imperfections of job slaking. In a number of metropolitan areas, plants with specially equipped slakers, tanks, and trucks can supply properly hydrated putty in desired quantities. Hydrated lime in powder form is also available.

5. Hydrated Lime. When quicklime is finely crushed, slaked with a minimum amount of water, and screened or ground to form a fine homogeneous powder, the product is called hydrated lime. If the lime from which it is made is pure, hydrated lime is a white powder having a specific gravity of 2.08; the specific gravity of some dolomitic hydrates may reach 2.40. The magnesia of dolomitic hydrates may not be hydrated owing to insufficient time and temperature used in hydrating. Unless presoaked, mortars made of the hydrates are less plastic than those made of the putties. Hydrated lime is sold in paper bags of 50-lb capacity or in 100-lb burlap or cloth sacks. In such containers it may be stored for a much longer time than lump lime without serious deterioration.

6. Testing of Limes. The ASTM specifications for structural lime specify certain tests in addition to chemical analysis. A fineness test on lime is recommended to determine the percentage of inert material. For this test a representative 5-lb sample of lime broken to pass a 1-in.

ring and be retained on a ¼-in. sieve, is carefully slaked with sufficient water to form the maximum amount of lime putty, care being taken to avoid drowning or burning. After standing for 1 hour the paste is washed through a 20-mesh sieve. The stream of water should flow under moderate pressure and rubbing of the material through the screen should be avoided. Not more than 15 per cent of a ground lime or slaked lime should remain on the sieve after washing 30 min.

Less than 15 per cent of a commercial hydrate of lime should be retained on a No. 200 sieve after 30 min washing of a 100-gm sample with water. Methods are also specified in the ASTM *Standards* for soundness tests and for estimating the consistency of mortars. Lime mortars are tested for water retention after suction for 60 sec. The autoclave test provides a simple method for determining the completeness of hydration.

Tensile strength tests of lime mortar briquets are also sometimes made. When compression or transverse tests are made it is necessary to specify a certain size of test piece, since the rate of carbonation is affected by the specimen thickness. Large cubes have lesser strengths than small ones.

The yield or volume of lime paste which can be made from a given weight of lime is an important factor in estimating the quantity of lime required to make a given amount of mortar. The test can be made in the same manner as indicated in Art. XII-38.

7. Properties of Lime. From a long series of experiments on the strength of lime mortars made at Iowa State College the results shown in Table 1 have been derived. For some unknown reason the strength of these mortars was somewhat greater at 9 months than at 1 year, although the carbonation process was still incomplete at the end of a year. In general the greater strengths were obtained with the lower percentages of water and sand. The hardening of the calcium limes was more uniform and rapid than that of the magnesium limes, but the latter exhibited higher strengths.*

Compressive tests by W. E. Emley and S. E. Young, of the Bureau of Standards laboratory, show that the size of the sand grains has a pronounced effect upon the strength of lime mortar.† The tests were made upon 2-in. cubes of 1 part quicklime to 3½ parts sand, by weight. The age at breaking was 90 days. The results of these tests appear in Table 2*b*. It should be noted that the mortars of fine sand gave the highest strength, a condition not true in mortars made of hydraulic cements. Probably the loss in strength due to the lack of density in the fine-sand pastes is offset by the complete carbonation which is obtained on account

---

* For further data see *Bull.* 1, Vol. 4, Eng. Expt. Sta., Iowa State College, Ames, Iowa; *Bull.* 4, Ohio Geol. Survey; *Proc. ASTM*, Vol. 10, pp. 328–340; also Vol. 14, p. 339.

† Reported in *Proc. ASTM*, Vol. 14, p. 346.

Materials of Construction

TABLE 1. RESULTS OF TENSILE TESTS OF LIME-MORTAR BRIQUETS
MADE AT IOWA STATE COLLEGE

Proportions, Lime : Sand.*	% Water.†	Average Strength of 10 Briquettes in Lb./in.²									
		Age 3 Months.					Age 6 Months.				
		Calcium Limes.		Magnesian Limes.			Calcium Limes.		Magnesian Limes.		
		Mason City.	Spring-field.	Eagle Point.	Mason City.	Maquo-keta.	Mason City.‡	Spring-field.	Eagle Point.	Mason City.	Maquo-keta.
1 : 1		65	96	111	78	128	63	109	154	159	184
1 : 2	100	76	94	100	92	130	68	97	113	137	167
1 : 3		55	68	90	86	130	53	73	94	119	154
1 : 1		45	61	98	54	105	47	62	113	75	153
1 : 2	200	51	55	90	81	105	53	57	88	98	125
1 : 3		50	55	101	81	100	54	48	104	91	108
1 : 1		43	41	120	75	101	42	45	140	96	123
1 : 2	300	41	45	112	77	86	41	45	114	91	113
1 : 3		46	53	87	70	82	48	51	99	88	96

* A river sand passing a No. 20 and held on a No. 30 sieve was used in all tests.
† Calculated in terms of the weight of the dry hydrate.
‡ Age = 16 weeks.

ANALYSES OF LIMES

Locality.	CaO	MgO	$Al_2O_3+Fe_2O_3$	Loss on Ignition.	Insol. Res.	CO_2
Mason City, Ia........	95.40	0.43	2.98	0.00	1.02	
Springfield, Mo.......	94.70	0.40	1.80	2.08	1.00	trace
Eagle Point, Ia........	58.19	33.48	6.60	slight	2.01	
Mason City, Ia........	72.40	15.23	6.03	3.36	2.32	0.10
Maquoketa, Ia........	60.60	35.70	2.10	2.30	0.63	

of their porous structure. The effect of the proportion of sand on the compressive strength of lime pastes is also shown in Table 2.

High-calcium limes expand more in slaking and shrink more in setting than the magnesium limes. They are also more liable to injury through "burning" in slaking. When completely hydrated the dolomitic limes produce stronger mortars and work as smoothly under the trowel.

8. The Uses of Lime. In construction, slaked lime is chiefly used to make mortar for laying brick and stone masonry and for plastering walls of buildings. When so used, quicklime should be completely hydrated by slaking from 3 to 14 days, depending upon the kind of lime, temperature, and slaking conditions. Hydrated lime, although immediately usable, is usually improved by soaking overnight or longer. Hydrated limes are often added to Portland cement mortars in proportions varying from

TABLE 2.   THE VARIATION IN THE COMPRESSIVE STRENGTH OF LIME
WITH (a) AMOUNT OF SAND AND (b) SIZE OF SAND GRAINS
(Tests by Emley and Young)
Each result is averaged from 3 tests.

	(a) AMOUNT OF SAND.		(b) SIZE OF GRAINS.		
	Compressive Strength Lb. per Sq.in.		Size of Sand Grains between Meshes No.	Compressive Strength Lb. per Sq. in.	
Sand Parts,.	High Calcium	Dolomitic.		High Calcium.	Dolomitic
½	273	372	10–20	98	166
1	151	267	20–30	118	214
2	116	217	30–40	138	312
3	112	202	40–60	186	335
4	116	203	60–80	260	444

5 to 85 per cent of the weight of the cement.   This is done to increase
plasticity and workability.   In order to avoid excessive expansion, it is
not advisable to incorporate more than 10 per cent of dolomitic hydrate
in such mortars if they are to be subjected to moist conditions, unless the
magnesia in the lime is known to be pressure hydrated, or has been hydrated by presoaking for 2 or 3 weeks.   Hydrated lime is used also in
making the popular stucco finish for exterior walls * and to increase the
imperviousness of Portland cement concrete (see Art. XV-36).

9. Hydraulic Lime.   In the middle of the eighteenth century John
Smeaton, the celebrated English engineer, was confronted with the problem of finding a cement which could be used in the construction of the
famous Eddystone Lighthouse.   The only cementing material then in
use was quicklime, which does not harden under water.   After a series of
experiments he discovered that an impure limestone containing a small
amount of clay, if calcined in the ordinary way, would produce a lime
which would slake upon the addition of water and would harden under
water.   On account of the latter property the name hydraulic lime was
given to this material.   In France and southern Europe it is still used
to a considerable extent.   On account of the prevalence of raw materials
suitable for the manufacture of Portland and natural cements no hydraulic lime is manufactured in the United States.   However, Lafarge
cement, a by-product in the manufacture of hydraulic lime, is used to
some extent in this country.

Hydraulic lime is manufactured in the same way as quicklime, although
a somewhat higher temperature is required in burning.   In slaking, con-

* See specifications for Portland cement stucco, *Proc. NACU*, Vol. 7, p. 586.

siderable care is required to provide just sufficient water and no excess, since an excess would cause the lime to harden. After slaking, the coarse material is screened out and the fine product bagged for market. The coarse particles are finely ground and sold for Grappier cement. The specific gravity of hydraulic lime is about the same as that of the natural cement. Mortars made from the famous limes of Tiel, France, also have about the same strength as those made from natural cement.

10. Lafarge Cement. This cement is used in America for stucco work and in laying marble and other masonry which is stained by natural or Portland cement mortars. It is a Grappier cement made as indicated above. Published analyses show it consists principally of lime (58–59 per cent) and silica (27–31 per cent) with 2.6 to 4.5 per cent of alumina and smaller percentages of iron oxide, magnesia, and the alkalies. According to the manufacturers' circular this cement has a specific gravity of 2.6, an initial set in 4 hours, final set in 10 hours, and a residue on 100-mesh sieve of 0.6 per cent. Its strength neat and in a 1:2 mortar is about 60 per cent of that demanded of a standard Portland cement at 7 and 28 days. At 2 years the record gives a neat strength of 665 psi.

GYPSUM PLASTERS

11. Introduction. On account of the wide use of gypsum plasters in the arts and in building construction a brief resumé of some important facts concerning them will be given. In the United States plaster of Paris, stucco, wall plaster, and hard-finish plaster are extensively used in wall construction. In Germany, flooring plaster, made by calcining gypsum at a high temperature, has been considerably used. In all these powders, gypsum in a more or less dehydrated state is the essential element. When water is added to these substances they become rehydrated, forming compounds similar to those existing before calcination.

12. Gypsum. There are two commercial varieties of crude gypsum, rock gypsum and gypsum earth or gypsite. These substances consist principally of a hydrous sulfate of lime ($CaSO_4 + 2H_2O$), with varying percentages of silica, carbonate of lime, carbonate of magnesia, and iron oxide. Pure gypsum is a white translucent crystalline mineral, so soft that it can be scratched with the fingernail. When heated to 400°F, pure gypsum loses its luster and its specific gravity is increased from 2.3 to approximately 2.95 due to the loss of water of crystallization.

Deposits of gypsum are numerous and widely scattered. The rock deposits occur in beds commonly traversed by thin strata of limestone and often adjacent to rock-salt deposits. Gypsite formations consist of masses of gypsum crystals interspersed with clay and sand. The states leading in the production of gypsum are New York, Iowa, Michigan,

Texas, California, Nevada, and Oklahoma. Among the countries of the world the United States ranks first and produces about one-third of the total supply. About 8,200,000 short tons of crude gypsum were mined in the United States in 1950 and 3,200,000 tons were imported. Approximately 60 per cent of the gypsum is calcined. Over 1,700,000 short tons at an average price of $3.23 were used in the manufacture of Portland cement.

13. Manufacture of Plasters. For making the refined grades of plaster of Paris in which a uniform degree of calcination is required the oven process is much used in Europe. In the United States, however, on account of the expense and time required, this method has been discarded in favor of the kettle and rotary process, the former being used in nearly all plants making plaster of Paris or cement plaster. Hard-finish plasters are made in kilns similar to the mixed-feed kilns used in calcining lime.

After the raw material has been excavated or mined it is put through one or more crushers, and, if the kettle process is used, is then ground by buhr-stones or like mills until about 60 per cent will pass a No. 100 sieve. In the rotary process the final pulverization is done after calcination.

The kettles employed for calcination are 8 or 10 ft in diameter and about 6 or 7 ft high. The sides are made of sheet steel and the bottoms of cast iron. Each kettle is placed with its top just above the working floor. The lower portion of the kettle is enclosed in a masonry chamber which serves to support the kettle and distribute the heat from the grate fire about it. Two or four horizontal flues running through the kettle increase the circulation of heat. A power-driven stirrer is used to agitate the contents of the kettle and thus prevent the bottoms from burning out. The hot gases and steam are led away through a stack.

After the pulverized material has been chuted into a kettle, heat is very slowly applied until the mechanically held water is driven off. At a temperature just above the boiling point of water the whole mass bubbles up violently and then sinks. At 290°F, the combined water begins to boil out; and between 340° and 396°F the process is stopped. The impure gypsites generally require a higher temperature than the purer rock gypsums. In many plants the final temperature is judged by the appearance of the boil, although thermometers are often used in making plaster of Paris.

By the kettle process, it requires about 2 or 3 hours to calcine a charge yielding 5 or 6 tons. The calcined product is then run from the bottom of the kettle into a cooling vat, whence, after partially cooling, it is sent to the screens. Residues from the screens are reground; the fines are stored in large bins.

In the rotary process the raw material is crushed to pass a 1-in. mesh and is then fed into the upper end of a cylinder which rotates about an axis slightly inclined to the horizontal. Calcination is accomplished by the introduction of hot furnace gas, the temperature of which can be regulated by an admixture of a forced draught of air. When properly roasted the material is conveyed to brick-lined calcining vats in which further changes are brought about by the heat within the material. The product from the vats is then finely ground and screened. Continuous operation is the main advantage which this process possesses over the kettle process.

In order that the workman may properly handle plaster of Paris or stucco, it is necessary to delay the time of setting. This is accomplished by adding a fraction of 1 per cent of a retardant like glue, sawdust, or blood after the plaster has cooled.

To increase the cohesiveness of wall plaster, cattle hair or wood fiber is introduced. For this purpose about 2 or 3 lb of finely picked hair or 60 to 100 lb of finely pulverized wood fiber is added to each ton of plaster.

Wall plasters made from pure raw materials are generally adulterated with 15 to 20 per cent of hydrated lime to increase the plasticity of the product. The term "stucco" is sometimes applied to a plaster so treated. Wall plasters made from raw materials containing considerable clay do not require such addition.

14. Plaster of Paris. Plaster of Paris is produced by incompletely dehydrating pure, finely ground gypsum at a temperature somewhat less than 370°F. Most plasters closely approach the theoretical composition $CaSO_4 + \frac{1}{2}H_2O$, which contains about 6.2 per cent of water. Plaster of Paris is a white powder having a specific gravity of 2.57. When tempered with sufficient water to form a plastic paste it sets in 5 to 10 min.

The setting of plaster of Paris is attributed to the formation of gypsum crystals from a supersaturated aqueous solution. Why the rapidity of setting is so very much greater when the powder consists of plaster of Paris than when it consists of anhydrous gypsum plus water is a point not yet settled. When substances of a colloidal nature (glue, for example) are mixed with the plaster the formation of crystals is hindered and the time of set retarded.

In hardening, plaster of Paris first shrinks and then expands. The latter property makes the material valuable in making casts, since a sharp impression of the mold can be secured. Owing to the rapidity of set and difficulty in working, its use in structures is limited to ornamental work.

15. Gypsum Wall Plasters are divided into four classes * as follows: *Gypsum neat plaster* consists of 60.5 per cent or more calcined gypsum, the remainder being material added at the mill for controlling workability, time of set, and cohesiveness. Calcined gypsum signifies commercial plaster of Paris, $CaSO_4 + \frac{1}{2}H_2O$. *Gypsum wood-fibered plaster* carries

* This classification is based on ASTM *Standards,* Des. C28–50.

60.5 per cent or more by weight of calcined gypsum, 1 per cent or more of wood fiber to increase the cohesiveness, and other materials to control workability and time of set. *Calcined gypsum* for finishing coat, which may or may not carry a retardant, is divided into two grades, "white" and "gray." *Gypsum ready-sanded plaster* consists of a cementing material, predominantly calcined gypsum, which has been mixed at the mill with the proper proportions of sand and other desirable constituents. It is prepared for use simply by adding water. The two grades of gypsum ready-sanded plaster are scratch, or first coat, and the browning, or second coat. Scratch coat ready-sanded plaster contains not over two parts sand by weight to one part of cementing material. The cementing material carries at least 60.5 per cent by weight of calcined gypsum plus other ingredients for controlling workability, time of set, and cohesiveness. Second coat ready-sanded plaster contains not over three parts sand with the same type of cementing material as in first coat ready-sanded plaster.

Specifications of the ASTM require that gypsum neat plaster mixed with three parts of standard sand shall set in 2 to 32 hours and, when mixed with two parts of standard sand, shall have a compressive strength when dry of not less than 750 psi when dried in air between 70° and 100°F at a relative humidity of 50 per cent. Gypsum wood-fibered plaster shall set in not less than 1½ hours nor more than 16 hours, and shall develop a compressive strength of 1200 psi. Gypsum gaging plaster for finishing coat shall, when not retarded, set in from 20 to 40 min (when retarded, not less than 40 min), and shall have a compressive strength of 1200 psi. Gypsum ready-mixed plaster shall set in from 1½ to 8 hours, and shall have a compressive strength of 400 psi when dry.

A large number of tests (*Rept. Iowa Geol. Survey*, Vol. 12, p. 232) indicate that gypsum plasters gain one-half of their 1-month strength in a day, and gain but little strength after 1 month. Plaster and sand mortars of 1:1 proportions may be expected to develop 80 per cent of the neat strength at corresponding ages; those of 1:2 proportions generally possess one-half to two-thirds of the neat strength. Compressive strength of plasters 1 week old and air cured vary from 887 to 2236 psi. These tests also show that the adhesion of plaster mortars to a fractured surface of plaster is approximately two-thirds of the strength of the mortar.

Gypsum wall plasters have become quite popular because they are ready for use when brought to the job and also because they harden more rapidly than the older lime plasters. However, lime plasters are more plastic and may, therefore, be loaded with three or four parts of sand, whereas the gypsum plasters can carry only two or three parts; also, when properly slaked, lime plasters form eventually just as satisfactory walls as those made from cement plasters.

16. Hard-Finish Plasters. By burning gypsum to a considerably higher temperature than the calcining temperature of cement plaster, treating with certain solutions like alum and Glauber's salts, there may be produced plasters which set slowly but ultimately become very hard. Such plasters may be polished to form a smooth surface and make a very satisfactory finish for interior walls. Often walls of these plasters are marked to imitate tiling with pleasing results.

Keene's cement is made by burning a very pure rock gypsum at a red heat (1300°F), cooling, and then adding less than 1 per cent of potassium and aluminum sulfates to accelerate the set. Subsequently the material is ground so that 80 per cent or more will pass a No. 100 sieve. Keene's cement is thus nearly pure calcium sulfate ($CaSO_4$) of pure white color. It is not injured by storage, and mortars of it may be retempered. Set should occur between 20 min and 6 hours. The neat tensile strength should exceed 400 psi, and the compressive strength 2500 psi.

Mack's cement is made by burning gypsum at a very high temperature and adding about 0.4 per cent of burnt Glauber's salts (Na_2SO_4) or potassium sulfate (K_2SO_4). It is said to form an unusually hard, dense, and durable surface which will take paint well.

17. Other Gypsum Building Materials. Blocks and tile made from wall plaster and suitable for floor and interior wall construction are now on the market. These forms are light, can be easily sawn to desired shape, possess sufficient strength for many types of construction and have a high resistance to fire. Mixed with fine cinders or wood chips and sufficient water to form a thin consistency, wall plaster has been used in making floors for buildings. Such floors can be much more rapidly constructed than concrete floors, owing to the rapidity with which the plaster hardens. However, they are neither so resistant to fire nor so strong as concrete floors.

Another product of recent origin is plaster board. It is made of thin layers of cardboard or wood cemented together by wall plaster. Thin sheets of this material are used in place of lath; sheets ⅜ in. thick, 3 to 4 ft wide, and 6 to 10 ft long are used in place of lath and plaster. Some types have a close-grained light-colored surface, some have a printed replica of a wood surface on one side, some have a wood veneer applied on one side, and some are made to resemble a ceramic tile surface.

Pyrocell is a finely ground gypsum powder containing an admixture which, on being mixed with water, forms a gas and expands the mixture to 3 or 4 times its volume. This inflated paste hardens into a light, cellular, fire-resistant mass possessing good acoustical and insulating properties.

To cap concrete, brick, and other masonry materials for compression tests, gaging plaster, Hydrocal, and Hydrostone may be used. In a consistency of thick cream they attain the following strengths in 2-in. cubes after 2 hours in air: gaging plaster, 1400 psi; Hydrocal, a casting plaster, 3500 psi; and Hydrostone, a special type of Hydrocal, 4500 psi. Hydrocal is also mixed with sand, emulsified asphalt, and crushed stone or gravel, when wear resistance is required, to make a mastic floor finish, $\frac{3}{4}$ to $1\frac{1}{2}$ in. thick, that is quick setting and durable. It is claimed that these floor finishes are resistant to dusting, cracking, and wear, but they are not recommended for use under extreme acid, oil, or moisture conditions.

CHAPTER

XII

Methods of Testing Hydraulic Cements

1. Necessity for Testing Cement. Experience has shown that it is practically impossible to make large quantities of cement without any variation in quality. To be sure, some mills working with raw materials which run very uniformly and using the best of equipment and methods of operation will have very few unsuccessful "burns" in a year, whereas others will be less fortunate. Nevertheless the consumer has little chance of ascertaining how his particular carload of cement was made; therefore, if he has under way a construction of any importance, he ought to satisfy himself regarding the quality of his purchase. He should test his cement not only to see that he gets what he has paid for but also to forestall the possibility of a failure through the use of defective material.

In engineering construction the main qualifications demanded of a cement are permanency of structure, strength, and a rate of setting suitable to the demands of the work. To determine these qualifications, both physical and chemical tests are made, the former, on account of importance, more often than the latter.

As a result of long experience the physical tests which have come into general use in determining the acceptability of cement are: (1) soundness or constancy of volume, (2) strength, (3) time of set or activity, and (4) fineness. In order that the results of such tests made by different parties may accord as nearly as possible, it is necessary that a standard method be rigidly adhered to and that only experienced operators, who fully appreciate the necessity of eliminating personal equation from all manipulations, be employed.

Standard specifications for the performance of physical and chemical tests of Portland cement may be found in the ASTM *Standards* and also in the *Federal Standard Stock Catalog*. These specifications are the results of cooperative work and discussion between the various groups interested in the manufacture and use of Portland cement. They are frequently revised to keep abreast with the many technical advances being made. If a comparison of results between various laboratories is to be obtained, or if the results are to have more than a strictly local significance, it is necessary that standard methods be followed. Any divergence by the operator should be stated with full explanation in reporting the results of tests.

2. Sampling. Test samples may be individual or composite, as required, and ordinarily should represent not more than 500 barrels. Each test sample should weigh at least 8 lb. Bearing in mind the importance of obtaining a fair and representative sample of the cement, it is well to exercise much care in the selection, storage, and mixing of it. If the cement is stored in bags in a car or warehouse the selection of the bags to be sampled should be made in such manner that the entire lot will be represented. It is not sufficient to select bags from the outside of a pile, but those within should also be sampled.

In all cases a sufficient quantity should be collected so that the contemplated series of tests may be duplicated without resampling. Although it is not always possible to obtain a second sample, it is still worth while in sampling bags or barrels to number the bag and sample alike. The sample may be taken conveniently by the auger shown in Fig. 1 or by a long-handled spoon.

Storage of the Sample. Because it is important that the properties of the cement shall not be influenced by changes in the humidity and temperature of the air, standard storage conditions should be maintained. If paper or cloth sacks are used in collecting samples, they should be enclosed in a tight waterproof container for shipment to the laboratory. In the laboratory, clean cans fitted with tightly fitting covers will be found

Fig. 1. Cement sampler.

convenient receptacles for samples which must be stored for several weeks. The storage room should be dry and its temperature maintained at approximately 70°F.

Mixing Samples. If information concerning the uniformity of a quantity of cement is desired, the individual samples should be tested separately. If a fair number of samples are taken from a carload, say 10 to 20, such procedure would be very costly if all the tests were made on each sample. In order to cut down the expense of testing and at the same time secure information regarding the uniformity of the material, the accelerated soundness may be run on every sample and the remaining tests made on a composite sample consisting of equal portions taken from each individual sample. Before making any tests, each individual or composite sample should be placed on a smooth dense surface and turned over 30 or 40 times with a trowel.

Quartering. The portions of a sample required for the various tests may be fairly obtained by spreading the cement into a flat cylindrical pile and removing sector slices sufficient in quantity for each test. Such proceeding is sometimes called "the method of quartering." Sample splitters are also manufactured for such purposes.

CHEMICAL DETERMINATIONS

3. Purposes. Chemical analyses are regularly made by the manufacturer to whom they afford very valuable indications concerning the proportioning and burning of the cement. Sometimes analyses are made by consumers who wish to determine whether the cement has been adulterated or has excessive amounts of injurious substances such as magnesia and sulfur trioxide. As a rule the results of an analysis are of much less value to the consumer than the physical test indications. Chemical determinations of the four major oxides—silicon dioxide, ferric oxide, aluminum oxide, and calcium oxide—are regularly made, and the results are used to calculate the compound composition. The amounts of magnesium oxide, free calcium oxide, and sulfur trioxide are important because of their adverse effects on soundness. Determinations of the sodium and potassium oxides as well as of the water-soluble alkalies are important under circumstances as described in Art. IX-10. The loss on ignition determination provides information mainly on the presence of water and carbonic acid, whereas the insoluble residue test gives information on the amount of acid insoluble substances in the cement. Determinations of phosphorus pentoxide and manganic oxide as well as tests for air-entraining agents and various fatty acid compounds are also made. Complete detail for all tests is given in ASTM *Standard* C114.

4. Purity Test. The so-called purity test affords a speedy determination of the presence of adulterants. The test may be made as follows: Place about ½ teaspoonful of cement in a test tube. Stir the cement with a glass rod and cover with a 50 per cent solution of hydrochloric acid. If the cement is pure, it will effervesce slightly and form a yellow or orange-yellow jelly; the presence of an adulterant consisting mainly of calcium carbonate will cause violent effervescing. Slag will cause the emission of sulfurated hydrogen; other insoluble adulterants form a dark sediment at the bottom of the jelly.

PHYSICAL TESTS

5. Determination of Specific Gravity. In order to determine the density of mortar or concrete, the specific gravity of the cement must be known. The specific gravity test is also useful in detecting adulteration.

Apparatus. The determination of specific gravity shall be made with a standardized Le Châtelier apparatus which conforms to the requirements illustrated in Fig. 2. This apparatus is standardized by the National Bureau of Standards. Kerosene free from water, or benzine not lighter than 62° Baumé, shall be used in making this determination.

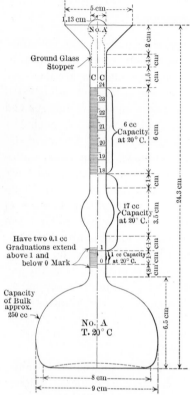

Fig. 2. Le Châtelier apparatus.

Method. The flask shall be filled with either of these liquids to a point on the stem between 0 and 1 cc, and 64 gm of cement, of the same temperature as the liquid, shall be slowly introduced, care being taken that the cement does not adhere to the inside of the flask above the liquid and to free the cement from air by rolling the flask in an inclined position. After all the cement is introduced, the level of the liquid will rise to some division of the graduated neck; the difference between readings is the volume displaced by 64 gm of the cement.

The specific gravity shall then be obtained from the formula

Specific gravity

$$= \frac{\text{Weight of cement (gm)}}{\text{Displaced volume (cc)}}$$

The flask, during the operation, shall be kept immersed in water, in order to avoid variations in the temperature of the liquid in the flask, which shall not exceed 0.5°C. The results of repeated tests should agree within 0.01.

FINENESS

6. Methods of Determining Fineness. *Sieve Tests.* Tests to determine the fineness of Portland cement have in the past been performed by either hand or machine, sieving on a No. 200 sieve with a nominal opening of 0.0029 in. Some laboratories still make sieve tests, but in most cases fineness is now determined by other methods described later. The details of the sieve test are given in ASTM *Standard* C184, but no requirement on the maximum residue is now specified by ASTM.

The sieves used must have correction factors certified by the National Bureau of Standards. The bureau also furnishes standard samples of cements with certified fineness so that laboratories may calibrate and periodically check their sieves. Hand sieving is given preference in the specifications, but mechanical shakers are frequently used. A 20-min shaking period has frequently been used with satisfactory results for shakers such as the Hunt shaker manufactured by the Humboldt Manufacturing Co., Chicago, and the Ro-tap shaker made by the W. S. Tyler Co., Cleveland.

Since many Portland cements have less than 10 per cent retained on the No. 200 sieve, the test does not give a good indication of fineness. Sieves finer than the No. 200 are so expensive and difficult to standardize that other means of determining the particle-size distribution of Portland cements are now being used.

Turbidimeter Method. The method specified by ASTM for determining fineness by means of the Wagner turbidimeter * is given in *Standard* C115. This method covers the determination of the surface area of a known fraction of a gram of cement expressed as total surface area in square centimeters per gram of cement.

In this test the cement sample, usually 0.3 to 0.5 gm, is dispersed in clear white kerosene in a plate-glass sedimentation tank. Parallel light rays passing throught the suspension onto the sensitive plate of a photoelectric cell generate current, which is measured with a microammeter. Readings taken at regular intervals indicate the changing turbidity of the suspension as the cement particles settle out. The specific surface is then calculated by substituting the experimental data in the equation derived for the turbidimeter.

Figure 3 shows a diagrammatic sketch of a turbidimeter. The source of light is a 3- to 6-candlepower lamp which is usually operated by a 6-volt storage battery. The light intensity is regulated by two rheostats, and the light rays are approximately parallel as they leave the parabolic reflector. They next pass through a water cell which absorbs the radiant heat, and then through a light-retarding filter which reduces the intensity of the light. The light rays then pass through the sedimentation tank which contains the suspension of kerosene and cement, and then on to the sensitive plate of the photoelectric cell. The current generated is measured by an attached microammeter with a range of 0 to 50 μa. The lamp and reflector, water cell, filter, and photoelectric cell are mounted on a movable shelf which may be moved up or down so that the turbidity of the suspension may be determined at any desired depth. The sedimentation tank remains fixed in position. During a test, the first readings are taken with the shelf in the lowest position, and as additional readings

* See papers by L. A. Wagner, *Proc. ASTM,* Vol. 33, Pt. 2, p. 553; also by H. S. Ponzer and D. R. MacPherson, Vol. 38, Pt. 2, p. 441.

are taken the shelf is raised to predetermined levels. Readings are taken at definite time intervals determined by means of a timing burette.

Air-Permeability Method. The fineness of Portland cement may also be determined by an air-permeability method which is described in detail in ASTM *Standard* C204. The result obtained with the Blaine air-permeability apparatus is the specific surface expressed as total surface area in square centimeters per gram of cement. In this test, a bed of cement about 1.27 cm in diameter and 1.5 cm high is placed in a permeability cell. The weight of the cement used is such that the bed of cement

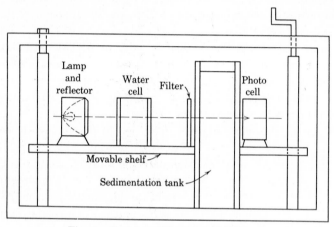

Fig. 3. Sketch of Wagner turbidimeter.

will have a porosity of 0.530 ± 0.005 when compacted in the specified manner. A definite quantity of air is then drawn through this cement bed of definite porosity. The size of the particles is related to the number and size of the pores in the prepared cement bed which in turn determines the rate of air flow through the bed. When this rate for a given cement along with constants for the apparatus are known, the specific surface can be calculated.

Mixing Cement Pastes and Mortars

7. Description of Methods. Detailed methods of mixing cement pastes and mortars are given in ASTM *Standard* C109, C187, and C190. Tolerances on the scales, weights, and glass graduates used are all carefully specified. The temperature of the dry materials and the room in which the mixing is performed should be maintained between 68°F and 81.5°F. The temperature of the mixing water, moist closet, and water in the storage tanks should be maintained at $70 \pm 3°F$. The relative humidity of the moist closet should be greater than 90 per cent.

Neat cement mixtures are usually made with 500 gm of cement and enough clean water to produce the proper consistency. The dry cement is placed on a clean non-absorbent surface and a crater is formed in the center. After the water has been poured into the crater the dry cement on the outer edge is turned into the crater within 30 sec with a trowel. The batch is left to stand for an additional 30 sec and is then vigorously mixed and kneaded for a period of $1\frac{1}{2}$ minutes by an operator whose hands are protected by rubber gloves. In kneading the mixture, the operator covers the pile of material with his hands, placed palms downward, with his fingers pointing away from him. He then quickly forces his wrists forward while keeping the ends of his fingers fixed and exerting a downward pressure of about 20 lb with his palms. After three or four similar movements, the pile is turned through an angle of 90°, any loose material is gathered in, and the above manipulation is repeated. The pile should be given 20 to 25 turns in 1 min.

Cement-mortar mixtures for tension briquets are made with 1:3 proportions by weight of cement to standard sand. The common quantities of dry materials used are 1000 to 1200 gm for 6 briquets and 1500 to 1800 gm for 9 briquets. The amount of water used may be obtained from Table 1 after the normal consistency of the neat cement has been determined.

TABLE 1. PERCENTAGE OF WATER FOR STANDARD MORTARS.

Percentage of Water for Neat Cement Paste of Normal Consistency	Percentage of Water for Mortar of One Cement, Three Standard Ottawa Sand[a]	Percentage of Water for Neat Cement Paste of Normal Consistency	Percentage of Water for Mortar of One Cement, Three Standard Ottawa Sand[a]
15	9.0	23	10.3
16	9.2	24	10.5
17	9.3	25	10.7
18	9.5	26	10.8
19	9.7	27	11.0
20	9.8	28	11.2
21	10.0	29	11.3
22	10.2	30	11.5

[a] When the proportions of cement to sand are other than one to three by weight, the amount of mixing water shall be calculated from the following formula, upon which Table 1 is based:

$$y = \frac{2}{3}\frac{P}{n+1} + K$$

where y = the percentage of water required for the sand mortar,
P = the percentage of water required for neat cement paste of normal consistency,
n = the number of parts of sand to one of cement by weight, and
K = a constant which for standard Ottawa sand has the value 6.5.

After the dry materials are placed on a clean non-absorbent surface, they are mixed with a trowel until a batch of uniform color is obtained. The remaining mixing procedure is the same as that described for mixing neat cement pastes.

Cement mortar mixtures for compression cubes are made with 1:2.75 proportions by weight of cement to graded standard sand. The usual quantities of dry materials are 500 gm of cement and 1375 gm of sand to make 6 cubes or 700 gm of cement and 1925 gm of sand to make 9 cubes. Enough water is added so that the final mortar has a flow of 100 to 115 when subjected to twenty-five ½ in. drops in 15 sec on a standard flow table. The mixing operation consists of first placing the water in a 6- to 8-qt mixing bowl made of non-absorptive non-corroding material and then adding the cement. The cement and water are vigorously mixed for 30 sec with one hand which is protected by a rubber glove. Then about half the sand is added and the batch is again mixed for 30 sec, and finally the rest of the sand is added and mixing continued for an additional 1½ min.

Normal Consistency

8. Method for Determining Normal Consistency. The test for the determination of the correct amount of water expressed in percentage by

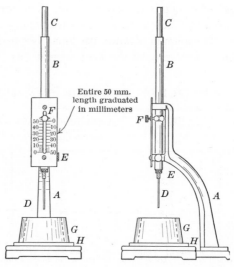

Fig. 4. Vicat apparatus.

weight of the dry cement to make neat cement pastes of satisfactory workability is described in detail in ASTM *Standard* C187. In this test, 500 gm of cement is mixed with an estimated quantity of water in the manner described in Art. 7. The neat cement is formed into a 2-in. ball which is then tossed six times through a distance of 6 in. from one hand to the other. An approximation of the proper water content may be obtained at this point by dropping the ball from a height of 2 ft upon the mixing table. For normal consistency, the ball should flatten not more than one-half its diameter without cracking. For the actual determination of the normal consistency, the ball is pressed into the larger end of the conical ring G, shown in Fig. 4. The ring has an inside diameter of 7 cm at the base, 6 cm at the top, and a height of 4 cm. The excess material at the larger end is removed by a single movement of the palm of the hand, and the ring is then placed on a glass plate H. The excess material at the smaller end is sliced off with a single stroke of a trowel, and the ring with the contained paste is then centered under the rod B, which is set so that the plunger end C is down and in contact with the surface of the paste. The rod B weighs 300 gm, and the diameter at the end C is 1 cm. After the initial reading of the indicator F is obtained, the rod is released and allowed to penetrate the cement paste for a period of 30 sec. The paste is considered to be of normal consistency when the rod B settles a distance of 10 mm below the original surface. Additional trials with fresh paste must be made with varying percentages of water until the normal consistency is obtained.

After the normal consistency of the cement has been obtained, the consistency of standard mortars made with the cement may be taken from Table 1. The values given in the table are expressed as percentages of the combined dry weights of the cement and standard sand.

9. Le Châtelier's Test for Soundness. A good many accelerated tests for soundness have been devised. One of these, which was recommended

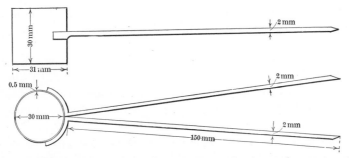

Fig. 5.   Le Châtelier's tongs for testing constancy of volume of cement pastes.

by the Committee on Accelerated Tests of the IATM and specified in both the British and French standard specifications, is the rough measurement of the expansion of a cylindrical test piece by Le Châtelier's tongs, shown in Fig. 5. The method of making the test, which was originally proposed by Le Châtelier and adopted by the committee, follows: "The cement is gaged and filled into a mold on a plate of glass, the edges of the mold being held together. When the mold has been filled it is covered with a plate of glass held down by a small weight and the whole is immersed in water at 15°C for twenty-four hours. Any tie or band which has been used to keep the edges of the mold together during setting is then removed. The distance between the indicator needles is measured and the mold is placed in cold water, which is raised to a temperature of 100°C in the course of half an hour and is kept boiling for six hours. The mold is removed from the water and after it has cooled the distance between the indicator needles is again measured. The difference between the two measurements represents the expansion of the cement. This must not exceed 10 mm when the cement has been aerated for twenty-four hours and 5 mm when the cement has been aerated for seven days."

10. The Boiling Test. The boiling test recommended in 1870 by Dr. Michaelis has been considerably used for detecting unsoundness. In making this test a 2-in. ball of neat cement paste of standard consistency is allowed to harden in the moist closet for 24 hours, or longer if hard set has not been obtained. It is then placed in a pan of pure water at normal room temperature. The temperature of the water is gradually raised to the boiling point in not less than 30 min. After boiling for 3 hours the ball is removed, allowed to cool without sudden chilling, then examined for signs of disintegration.

11. The Pat Test. This test procedure to check the soundness of cement has been used for a considerable period, and the method is still given in detail in ASTM *Standard* C189. The pat is made from a cement paste of normal consistency on a clean glass plate. It is about 3 in. in diameter, ½ in. thick at the center, and is tapered to a thin edge. The pat is stored in a moist closet for 24 hours, after which it is placed in steam at a temperature between 98° and 100°C, upon a support 1 in. above boiling water, for 5 hours. The apparatus used for making this test is shown in Fig. 6. Within 1 hour after steaming, the pat should be examined for unsoundness, which is usually indicated by a change in volume which causes distortion, cracking, checking, or disintegration, as shown in Fig. 7b. Shrinkage cracks such as those shown in Fig. 7a are not considered as evidence of unsoundness.

12. The Autoclave Test. This more stringent test provides quantitative information and is now standard. It is described in detail in ASTM *Standard* C151. In this test, prisms 1 by 1 by 11¼ in. are made from paste of normal consistency and are provided with ¼- by ⅝-in. stainless-steel reference plugs centered in each end. The effective gage length of 10 in. is considered as the distance between the innermost points of the reference plugs. After 24 hours in the moist closet, specimens are removed from the molds and measured for length at 70°F in a dial comparator reading to 0.0001 in. They are then placed in an autoclave so that the four sides of each specimen are exposed to saturated steam. In the course of 1 to 1¼ hours the steam pressure is raised to 295 psi (420°F) and held constant for 3 hours. Then the autoclave is gradually cooled until the pressure is 10 psi or less, in an hour. The specimens are then removed and placed in water which is at a temperature above 194°F. The temperature of the water is then cooled at a uniform rate down to 70°F in 15 min and is kept at that temperature for an additional 15 min. The specimens are then removed, surface dried, and again measured.

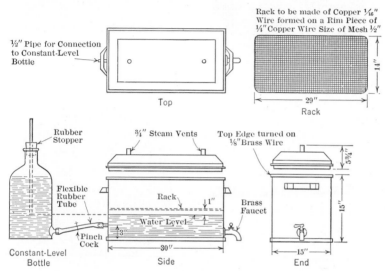

Apparatus to be made of sheet copper weighing 22 oz per sq ft tinned inside. All seams to be lapped where possible. Hard solder only to be used. Dimensions are optional except distance between water level and top of rack which must be 1 inch as specified.

Fig. 6. Apparatus for making soundness test of cement.

The action of the autoclave causes a rapid hydration of the free lime and the free magnesia and consequently provides a good indication of unsoundness. Specifications limit the autoclave expansion for Portland cement to a maximum value of 0.50 per cent.

13. The Value of the Soundness Test. The steam pat soundness test is useful in detecting unsoundness caused by the hydration of finely ground free lime. Lerch, after confirming the foregoing statement, in *Portland Cement Assoc. Fellowship Paper* 20, states that the amount of free lime necessary to cause unsoundness may vary with different cements; that a cement with less than 1 per cent of free lime will usually be sound, whereas a cement having 3 per cent or more is likely to be unsound.

If a cement contains free lime which is coarsely ground and highly burned, it is doubtful whether the steam pat test will always reveal the

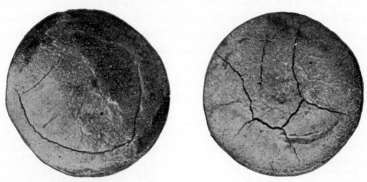

(*a*) Shrinkage cracks due to exposure of pats to dry air during setting.

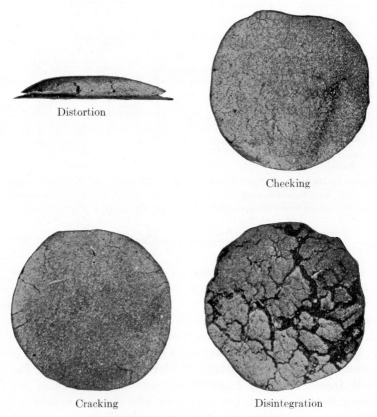

Distortion

Checking

Cracking   Disintegration

(*b*) Typical failures in soundness test.

Fig. 7. SOUNDNESS TEST PATS.

unsoundness. (See *Tech. Paper* 43, p. 58.) It is contended, however, that the autoclave test will. Extensive tests made by the U. S. Bureau of Standards (*Tech. Paper* 47) on the cements which passed and failed in the autoclave test and on concretes made from them did not show that the strength of the concrete made from cements which failed in the autoclave was materially affected after a 2-year curing out of doors.

From the results of Prof. E. D. Campbell,* it appears that the steam pat test does not always detect free magnesia. His tests show that only 4 per cent of free magnesia is needed to cause water-cured cement prisms to expand linearly over 2 per cent.

That the autoclave test is a valuable criterion of the expansive influences of magnesia in moist-cured mortars is evidenced in the tests by Withey and Wendt.† Its value in indicating the influence of free lime is shown in Young's tests.‡ The test is also a valuable index for cements which are to be used in making steam-cured concrete products.

Time of Setting

14. Methods of Determining Time of Set. Two methods of determining the time of set are given in ASTM *Standard* C191 and C266. One of the methods involves the use of the Vicat apparatus shown in Fig. 4. In this method, the cement paste of normal consistency is molded in the ring G and placed on the glass plate H. This specimen is kept in a moist room during the test. In determining the time of set, the specimen is placed under the needle D of rod B and the needle D is brought in contact with the surface of the specimen. Initial set has occurred when the needle, after being released, ceases to pass a point 5 mm above the glass plate within 30 sec; and final set occurs when the needle does not sink visibly into the paste.

The second method involves the use of the Gillmore needles shown in Fig. 8. In this test, a pat of paste of normal consistency, about 3 in. in diameter and $\frac{1}{2}$ in. thick at the center, Fig. 8a, is made on a flat, clean glass plate. The pat is stored in a moist room. Initial set has occurred when the pat will carry without appreciable indentation the lighter needle with an end diameter of $\frac{1}{12}$ in. and weighing $\frac{1}{4}$ lb; and final set has occurred when it will carry without appreciable indentation the heavier needle with an end diameter of $\frac{1}{24}$ in. and weighing 1 lb.

The determination of the time of set is only approximate because it is affected by the percentage and temperature of the water used, the amount

* *J. Ind. Eng. Chem.*, Vol. 8, p. 1101.
† *Proc. ASTM*, Vol. 35, Pt. 2, p. 426.
‡ *Proc. Am. Concrete Inst.*, Vol. 34, 1937, p. 13.

of kneading in making the cement paste, the temperature and humidity of the air, and the skill of the observer.

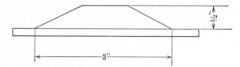

(*a*) Pat with top surface flattened for determining time of setting by Gillmore method.

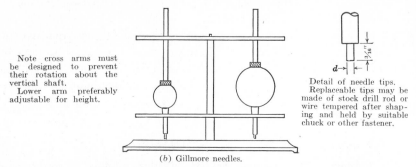

Note cross arms must be designed to prevent their rotation about the vertical shaft.
    Lower arm preferably adjustable for height.

Detail of needle tips. Replaceable tips may be made of stock drill rod or wire tempered after shaping and held by suitable chuck or other fastener.

(*b*) Gillmore needles.

Fig. 8.   Apparatus for time of setting test.

15. Comparison of Vicat and Gillmore Methods.   It will be appreciated that the determinations afforded by either of the above methods are purely empirical and that there is no reason why the results obtained by one method should agree with those by the other.   The only conclusion which can be stated is that either time of set determined by the Vicat apparatus is less than that from the Gillmore needles.   The discrepancy may range from a few minutes to over an hour.   In a series of tests involving 594 specimens, 6 cements, and 34 laboratories [see *Rept. of Joint Conference on Uniform Methods and Standard Specifications for Cement* (April 28, 1915)], the discrepancies averaged about 20 per cent for either initial or final set.*   A comparison of these methods made in 1930 is shown in Art. IX-26.

TENSILE STRENGTH

16. Method of Test.   Complete details for making tensile strength tests of cement mortars are given in ASTM *Standard* C190.   The briquets used in tensile tests have the form and dimensions shown in Fig. 9 and are usually made in 3-gang molds shown in Fig. 10.   The mortar for the briquets is proportioned and mixed as described in Art. XII-7.   Imme-

---

* For devices invented to record automatically the setting of cement, see *Eng. News*, Vol. 46, p. 95, and Vol. 97, p. 66; *Cement Age*, Vol. 13, p. 138, and Vol. 14, p. 88.

diately after mixing, the mortar is placed loosely in the molds. The simultaneous application of both thumbs, 12 times to each briquet, is used to provide the required compacting pressure of 15 to 20 lb. The molds are then heaped full, smoothed off with a trowel, turned over upon a plane plate, and the filling, compressing, and smoothing operations are repeated. After molding, the briquets in the molds are placed in a moist closet maintained at standard temperature and humidity conditions for 24 hours. The briquets are then removed from the molds and placed in clean water in storage tanks until test. At the proper test age, the briquets are taken out of the water and carefully centered in the clips, Fig. 11, of the testing machine. The briquets are tested in machines such as those shown in Figs. 13 and 14 which apply the load continuously at a rate of 600 ± 25 lb per min. Strength results differing more than 15 per cent from the average value should not be used.

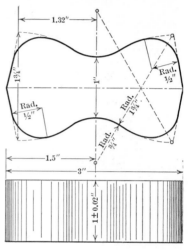

Fig. 9. Details for briquet.

17. Reasons for the Tension Test. Although little reliance is placed upon the low tensile strength of concrete in making structural designs, a great many strength tests on cements are tensile. This anomalous condition is due chiefly to three causes: first, the tensile strength is supposed to be a measure of the compressive strength; second, the tensile strength affords quicker indications of defects in the cement than other strength tests; third, this test is more conveniently

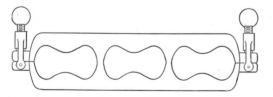

Fig. 10. Briquet gang mold.

made than the compression test since the small specimens used may be tested on an inexpensive machine of small capacity. The first of the above arguments is decidedly fallacious, since the ratio of the strength in tension to the strength in compression varies considerably with the strength of the mortar or concrete and to some extent with the type of cement. It may also be argued with considerable force that the form of

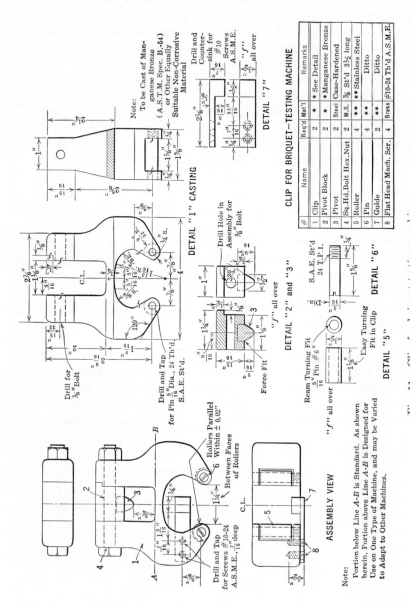

Fig. 11. Clip for briquet-testing machine.

test piece, methods of mixing and molding, and the method of gripping are of such nature that compression tests of cubes can be made with as little variation as tensile tests on briquets. Figure 12 shows average ratios of compressive strengths of concrete made with a water-cement ratio of 1, by volume, to the tensile and to the compressive strengths of 1:3 mortars of standard Ottawa sand (from the 1934 report of Committee C1 of the ASTM). It will be noted that the ratios of the compressive strengths are much more nearly constant. Further data on the comparative reliability of mortar tension and compression tests was reported by Committee C1 in 1938.

The data presented by the Project Committee on Cements of the Highway Research Board (see *Proc.*, 1936), show that 2- by 2- by 10-in. prisms can be made to yield reliable indices of both the flexural and compressive strengths of cements. Since the flexural strength is directly related to the tensile strength, this test appears ideally fitted to give information both with regard to tensile and compressive strengths when the supply of material for testing is small.

Specifications for Portland cement now include requirements for both tension tests of briquets and compression tests of 2-in. cubes made of standard mortars.

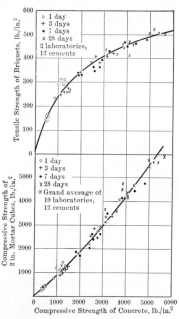

Fig. 12.   Relation of strengths of standard Ottawa sand mortars to compressive strength of concrete. (*Rept.*, Com. C1, ASTM, 1934.)

18. Indications Afforded by Neat and Mortar Tension Tests. Neat cement paste, though unstable under atmospheric conditions, is occasionally tested in tension after 12 to 24 hours to ascertain the rate of hardening.

Tension tests of mortars must be considered as rather sensitive indices of quality *provided standard conditions are maintained*. As measures of the compressive strength of concrete they are only rough criteria.

When the time allowed for testing is short, tests on 1:3 mortar briquets of standard sand give valuable indications of quality. Such briquets should exhibit a strength of 210 psi at 3 days. Care must be taken, however, to maintain moist closet and water bath at 70°F, since tests at the University of Wisconsin have shown that the strength of 3-day mortar briquets may be decreased 20 lb and that of 7-day briquets 10 lb by immersion in water at 60°F.

19. The Theory of the Distribution of Stress over the Minimum Section of a Cement Briquet has been developed by M. Durand-Claye in *Annales des ponts et chaussées*, June, 1895. He found for the form of briquet shown in Fig. 9 that the ratio of the maximum to the minimum unit stress was 2.12:1 and the ratio of the maximum to the average unit stress was 1.54:1. Prof. Coker in *Proc. IATM*, 6th Cong., 1912, gave proof based on experiment that the latter ratio was 1.7:1. These investigations show that the intensity of stress is greatest along the sides of the minimum section and least at the center.

20. Precautions to Observe in Molding Briquets. The operator should note well that ASTM *Standard* C190 prohibits the use of rammers in filling the molds. When such devices are used, or when the molds are filled in thin layers, the early strength of the specimens will be greater than if made in the standard manner. Care should also be taken to see that the minimum cross section of the briquet is exactly 1 in. thick. Briquets varying in thickness from the above dimension will be eccentrically loaded when tested in standard grips, and, as a result, their load-carrying capacity will be decreased. To assist in estimating the correct pressure in molding, inexperienced operators should practice molding on platform scales or on delimeters.

21. Types of Testing Machines. A very efficient and simple device for testing the strength of briquets is shown in Fig. 13. In starting the test, sufficient fine shot is placed in the bucket *b* to counterbalance the weight *w*. After the briquet is adjusted in the grips or clamps *g*, the

Fig. 13.   An Olsen automatic shot briquet tester.

Fig. 14.   A Riehlé motor-driven automatic briquet tester.

trigger *t* at the bottom of the bucket is released; this opens a valve which allows shot to flow down into the cup *c*. As the shot flows from the bucket the weight *w* moves downward; and, through the lever system, a stress is produced upon the briquet which is proportional to the shot lost. To keep the beam in the central position, the crank *k* is turned in the clockwise direction. When the briquet breaks, the lever l is tripped, releasing the spring in trip-lever r; thus the valve is immediately closed and the flow of shot stopped. The spring balance is graduated to read the load on the briquet to the nearest 5 lb.

Figure 14 shows a precision automatic briquet tester in which the load is applied to the specimen by a poise traveling along the single loading lever. The rate of loading is positive and constant. Poise stops instantaneously with the fracture of the test piece, and the load is read directly from the loading lever.

22. The Effect of Eccentric Loading on the Strength of Briquets. In making briquet tests it is of great importance that the load shall be centrally applied. To avoid errors from such eccentric loading, the roller and pivot alignment of new sets of grips should be carefully checked to see that the load line coincides with the axis of the specimen. Similar checks should be periodically made on grips subject to severe usage. Furthermore, the operator should see that any projecting edges are removed from the specimens, that the rollers work freely and have a bearing over the entire width of the briquet, and that the specimen rests against the bars on the back of the clips. Tests made at the Massachusetts Institute of Technology * show that a displacement of $\frac{1}{16}$ in. will decrease the strength from 15 to 20 per cent.

Since briquets become more brittle with age, the effect of a slight eccentricity or any torsional strain will be more marked in long-time tests than in those made at an early age.

23. The Effect of the Rate of Loading on the Strength of Briquets. A number of series of experiments have been made to determine the effect of rate of loading on the tensile strength of briquets. These show that the strength increases with the rapidity of loading. Since variations of 100 lb per min in the rate of loading may cause changes of 2 per cent in the observed strength,† the operator should frequently check his machine to see that the speed of loading conforms to requirements.

24. Number of Specimens. It is good practice to break from 3 to 5 briquets at each period. If the work is carefully done an individual result should not vary more than 10 per cent from the mean.

25. Calibration and Standardization of Equipment. The National Bureau of Standards maintains a Cement Reference Laboratory which, upon request, will furnish instruction with regard to standard methods of making tests and proper procedure in care and calibration of equipment. The bureau's *Circ.* 9 gives requirements for graduates and burettes; *Handbook M*85 covers calibration of balances and weights. Periodically the weights, diameters, and conditions of the ends of Vicat and Gillmore

---

* *Trans. ASME,* Vol. 9, p. 181.

† See experiments by W. P. Taylor in his *Practical Cement Testing,* p. 148; also Wheeler's tests, *Report of Chief Engrs.,* U. S. A., 1895, p. 2951.

needles should be checked. Briquet molds should be checked to see that they are properly mated, and the thickness and width at the minimum section should be measured. Briquet-testing machines should be tested for accuracy and sensitivity and, if necessary, the knife edges should be sharpened. Roller bearings on grips and rate of flow of shot should be checked daily for freedom of revolution and at least once a month for alignment.

COMPRESSIVE STRENGTH

26. Methods of Test. Complete details for making compressive strength tests of hydraulic-cement mortars are given in ASTM *Standard* C109. The proportioning and mixing of the mortar for making the 2-in. compression cubes is described in Art. XII-7. Standard procedures should be followed in filling the molds in order to secure uniform specimens. The specimens in the molds are stored for 24 hours in a moist closet, and are then removed from the molds and stored in clean water until test. In testing, the load should be applied, through a spherically seated bearing, to the cube faces that were in contact with the plane surfaces of the mold. If the cube faces to be loaded are not plane, they should be ground on a sheet of fine emery cloth glued to a plane surface. Any convenient rate of testing may be used up to 50 per cent of the expected maximum load, except that only 25 per cent should be applied at such a rate for expected maximum loads of less than 4000 lb at ages of 7 days or less. After the initial load has been applied, the rate of loading should be between 1000 and 6000 psi per min to failure. Three or more specimens are required for each test age.

Compression tests have also been made on 2- by 4-in. cylinders. These cylinders may be easily molded in cold-drawn brass tubing split along one element. The average unit strengths of 2-in. mortar cubes and 2- by 4-in. cylinders are practically the same. The 2-in. cube has become the standard compression mortar specimen, probably because it requires less material than the cylinder and because it need not be capped.

Compression tests are also made on the halves of beam specimens after transverse tests have been performed. In making this test, the beam is placed on its side on a hardened bearing block whose width is about equal to the original depth of the beam, and a similar block is placed on top of the beam directly over the bottom block. The modified cube so enclosed is then loaded to failure.

THE INTERPRETATION OF THE RESULTS OF STANDARD TESTS

27. General Recommendations. The operator should always bear in mind that the tests are only of qualitative value for the purpose of comparing the sample with a standard, adopted after long experience, or to compare it with previous samples of the same brand of cement. Therefore, before accepting or rejecting a cement, he should carefully consider the relative value of the results of each test and the conditions under which the cement is to be used. Furthermore, one should not condemn a sample unless certain that the conditions surrounding each test were standard. Any uncertainty in regard to a result should be removed by performing a second test under standard conditions. Below will be found a brief discussion of the criteria determining the acceptability of Portland cement arranged in order of the importance of the various tests.

28. Soundness. If one or more steamed pats show signs of distortion, checking, disintegration, or radial cracks (Fig. 7) the cement should be rejected; or if conditions permit the cement may be stored and further soundness tests made.

Although the accelerated soundness test is made under abnormal conditions, yet the results of 1000 boiling tests made by W. P. Taylor on different brands of cement bear witness to its value. He found that about one-third of the cements failing in the boiling test gave evidence of unsoundness in air-cured pats or a retrogression in strength inside of 28 days; within 1 year approximately seven-eighths of these cements had given like evidence of unfitness. Furthermore, only $\frac{1}{2}$ of 1 per cent of the cements which passed the boiling test showed signs of unsoundness in the air pat tests and only 13 per cent retrograded in strength within the year.

The autoclave test is now usually accepted as the standard test for soundness. This test is more drastic than the pat test and provides quantitative information. Specifications permit a maximum expansion of 0.5 per cent for Portland cement.

29. Strength. Reject the cement if the strength at 28 days is less than required by the specifications. If the strength of the mortar cubes or briquets at 28 days is less than that at 7 days, reject. If the mortar strength is a trifle below the standard at 7 days but is above at 28 days, accept the cement. If judgment must be passed upon a sample at the end of 7 days, reject on a decidedly low mortar test. Hold for 28 days if the mortar strength is slightly below the standard.

30. Time of Set. If the cement does not pass the specification in the laboratory test, determine its behavior under conditions in which it will be used before condemning it. Slow final set may be due to coarseness, which will also affect the tensile strength of the mortar briquets.

31. Fineness. Inasmuch as no sieves made at the present time are sufficiently fine to determine the percentage of flour, the important cementing element, this test has only corroborative value. Generally, a coarse cement will exhibit a low mortar strength and will often fail in the sound-

ness test. Surface area measurements are more informative than the
results of sieve tests and are commonly used.

For further information on interpretation of results of cement tests,
consult W. P. Taylor's *Practical Cement Testing* or R. K. Meade's *Portland Cement.*

MISCELLANEOUS TESTS OF CEMENTS AND MORTARS

32. Tests on Cement for Research Purposes. Cement for research
purposes should be tested in strict accordance with the standard specifications. In order to obtain representative results and to eliminate personal
equation and variable laboratory conditions, it is desirable to make at
least 5 specimens for each variable of the test. Such specimens should
be made on different days so that each final average of 5 or more specimens will represent as many different batches.

For ascertaining the concrete-making properties of cements, tests made
on concrete according to the Standard Methods of Making Compression
Tests of Concrete (ASTM *Standard* C39) are more effective than briquet
tests.

33. Preparation of Materials for Mortar Tests. Mortar tests are
usually made to determine the quality of the mortar or the suitability of
fine aggregate for making mortar or concrete. The Portland cement used
in such tests should conform to standard specifications, unless it is one of
the variables of the test.

In determining the quality of a mortar, the aggregate should be screened
to a size suitable for the specific purpose for which it is intended. In determining the concrete-making qualities of a fine aggregate, the aggregate
should be passed through a No. 4 sieve or a $\frac{1}{4}$-in. screen.

Aggregate should preferably be air dry. When sands are to be used
on the job without drying, they should also be tested with their natural
moisture content. The quantity of water they contain may be determined
on separate samples and the weights of sand and water used in the tests
determined accordingly.

34. Determination of Normal Consistency in Mortar Tests. A small
flow table having a top diameter of 10 in. is a satisfactory device for measuring the relative consistency of mortars. A conical frustum having a top
diameter 2.75 in., bottom diameter 4 in., and altitude 2 in. is placed in the
middle of the table. After the mortar has been mixed in the standard
manner (Art. XII-7), it is placed in the frustum in two layers. Each
layer is rodded 15 times with a $\frac{3}{8}$-in. rod, and the mold is removed. By
means of a cam, the table is then raised $\frac{1}{2}$ in. and dropped 25 times in
15 sec. The index of consistency, the flow, is determined by calcu-

lating the ratio of the diameter of the mass after vibrating to the original base diameter of the frustum and expressing the ratio as a percentage.

In mortar tests on the structural strength of fine aggregate, standard consistency obtains when the mortar exhibits a flow of 100 ± 5 after being subjected to 30 ⅛-in. drops in 30 sec.

35. Transverse Tests. Although transverse bending tests of cement mortars have been used to some extent, they have not been a specification requirement. Such tests can be made with less expensive molding and testing equipment than required for either the tension or compression test. When properly made they furnish as concordant results as either of the latter.

M. Durand-Claye has shown by very extended series of tests in tension and in cross bending, on identical samples of neat Portland cement, that the average ratio of the modulus of rupture in cross bending to the tensile strength, as determined upon standard forms of briquets, is 1.92 at 7 days and 1.86 for 28 days, or an average of 1.89. This relation was found to subsist between averages made up from the means of the 3 tests in each set of 6, in both tension and cross bending. The mean error of a single test at 28 days was found to be 2.10 per cent for the tension tests and 2.13 per cent for the tests in cross bending, thus showing that the two methods of testing were equally accordant.

For mortars of aggregates under ¼-in. in size, a prism 1 by 1 by 6 in. tested under center load over a 5-in. span makes a satisfactory specimen. Gang molds of non-corrodible metal holding 5 such prisms can be made very cheaply; 1200 gm of dry material is ample for making 5 such specimens.

At least 3, and preferably 5, specimens should be broken at each test period. The automatic shot briquet-testing machine (Fig. 13) can be provided with an auxiliary breaking attachment for these prisms in the space between the frame and shot bucket (b).

By inserting non-corrodible plugs in the ends of the cross-bending prisms, they can also be used for expansion measurements, although a longer prism is preferable.

36. Methods of Testing the Adhesion of Cement and Cement Mortars to Various Substances. While the tensile strength of briquets shows the cohesion of the mortar, it has been found by experiment that its adhesion either to other mortars or to the same mixture which has already hardened, or to brick or stone or metal, is very much less than its cohesion. It is important, therefore, to have a standard test of adhesion, as well as of strength. Because tests of this kind are comparatively rare, no general custom has been established in America on the subject; but the following recommendations have been made by the French Commission:

1. For tests of adhesion of cements and cement mortars use will be made of a special form of briquet, molded in two parts, these two parts consisting of the two materials whose adhesion is to be tested, provided both can be molded, or containing between them a prism of the solid body to which the adhesion of the mortar is to be determined. The form of this briquet, as modified for English units, with 1 sq in. of area on the surface of adhesion, is shown in Fig. 15. This mold is formed in two parts, and is used to form in succession the two halves of the complete briquet.

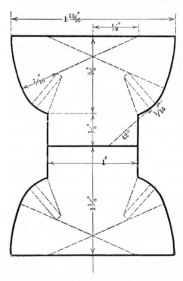

Fig. 15. Form of briquet for adhesion test of cement as adopted by the French Commission and adapted to English units.

2. *To compare the force of adhesion of different cements to a given material, normal adhesion blocks* will be prepared as follows: Use for these always one kind of standard Portland cement which has passed a sieve of 80 meshes to the linear inch, mixed with the standard sand No. 3 (sand passing a No. 15 and held on a No. 11 sieve) in the proportion of 1 of cement to 2 of sand. These normal adhesion blocks will be molded in the form of one half of the briquet shown in Fig. 15.* It will be gaged with 9 per cent of water and rammed into the mold. At the end of 24 hours in air it will be placed in fresh water for a period of at least 28 days. When it is to be used, it will first be dried and its adhesion surface polished with emery paper.

3. The cement to be tested for adhesion with these standard blocks prepared as above will be mixed as a normal plastic mortar, 1 of cement to 3 of sand (the consistency advocated is about the same as the ASTM recommends), which will be introduced into the mold with a trowel, this mold now being placed with a normal adhesion block at the bottom in place of the movable metallic disc. The mold will remain upon this completed block until it is ready for testing, and the block will be allowed to harden either in air or water, and for such period as the test requires. It is recommended that the number of tests, the periods of time, the methods of hardening, and the recording of the results should comply with the conditions given for tension tests of cement.

* The detail drawings of these molds are given in *Com. des methodes d'essai mat. const.*, Vol. 4, p. 284.

4. *To compare the force of adhesion of a given cement to different materials:* For this purpose the test specimens will be prepared as described above, except that in place of the normal adhesion blocks similar blocks of the various materials to be tested will be prepared and allowed to harden, provided these are such as can be molded in this manner. If such materials are solid, small discs, about ⅜ in. thick, will be prepared, and these will be used in the bottom of the mold in place of the metallic disc, the adhesion block to be completed by using neat Portland cement mortar. After this has hardened the briquet will be completed by making the other half of a standard plastic mortar, 1 part cement to 3 sand, using the particular kind of cement whose adhesion to these various substances is to be tested.

If the normal plastic mortar is not used in adhesion tests, a full description of its composition should be indicated on the records.

These adhesion briquets should be broken on a standard tension-testing machine, using the regular tension clips.*

In connection with the methods of testing adhesion, one should also examine the report of Feret, The Adhesive Strength of Hydraulic Cements, *Proc. IATM*, Brussels Congress, 1906, Problem 10. As the result of a number of experiments Feret advocates the use of a prismatic specimen 4 by 4 by 16 cm (1.6 by 1.6 by 6.4 in.) in dimensions, one end of which is bonded to the body with which adhesion is to be tested. He outlines very careful methods for mixing, molding, and curing the specimens and recommends that the prisms be torn apart by subjecting them to a uniform bending moment.

Tests for the adhesion of mineral wool or vermiculite thermal insulating cements to steel are described in ASTM *Standard* C195 and C196, respectively.

37. Methods of Determining Mortar Bond Strength. Tests to determine the bond of mortar to brick or other masonry units are frequently performed, but methods have not been completely standardized. Test arrangements frequently used are shown in Fig. 16 and 17. Figure 16 shows the method of testing a crossed brick couplet for determining the tension bond

Fig. 16. Method of testing tension bond of a mortar joint.

of a mortar joint. The area bonded on one brick is 12 to 15 sq in. Figure 17 shows the method of testing for determining shear bond properties.

* In order that the specimens may fit ASTM grips, a slight modification of the above form will be found necessary.

A cantilever test on a parallel brick couplet has also been used to determine bond characteristics with fair success.

Bond tests are usually rather variable, and consequently at least 5 specimens per point should be made. In addition, uniformity must be maintained in conditioning the brick, making the joints, curing, and in centering the apparatus on the specimens in testing.

Fig. 17. Method of testing shear bond of a mortar joint.

38. Methods of Determining Yield. This test is used primarily to determine the volume of paste, mortar, or concrete which can be obtained from given proportions of the ingredients. It is also possible to determine the density of the mixture from the test, if the weights and specific gravities of each ingredient are known.

The French Commission recommended that the yield be determined in either of the following ways: The volume of 1 kg of neat cement paste or mortar of proper consistency should be measured by compacting in a glass burette about 2⅜ in. in diameter, due care being taken to expel any entrained air; or, the set paste may be weighed in air and in water and the yield computed from the loss in weight.

39. Method of Determining the Air Content of Portland Cement Mortar. A check on the air-entraining properties of cements may be obtained from tests of the air content of mortars made with the cements, as described in ASTM *Standard* C185. The apparatus required for the test consists of the usual weighing and mixing items and in addition a 400-ml measure, a mixer, bowl, paddle, and a 10-in. flow table conforming to ASTM Des. C230.

The test procedure consists in determining the correct amount of water to be used with 300 gm of cement and 1200 gm of standard sand to obtain a mortar with a flow between 80 and 95 per cent on the flow table, and then to determine the weight of 400 ml of the mortar. When these values are known, the air content, per cent by volume, may be calculated from the equation

$$\text{Air content} = 100 - 2.5W\,\frac{(182.7 + P)}{(5000 + 10P)}$$

where W = weight in grams of 400 ml of mortar.
  P = percentage mixing water based on weight of cement used.

In making the flow test the flow mold is filled and removed in standard manner and the table dropped ½ in. ten times in 6 sec. The flow is the resulting increase in average diameter of the mortar mass expressed as a percentage of the original diameter.

40. Method of Determining Water Retention. One of the most important properties of a masonry mortar is its ability to retain its water when

Fig. 18. Apparatus for determining water retention.

it is subjected to the suction of brick or block during construction.   A test for water retentivity is described in ASTM *Standard* C91.   For this test, 500 gm of cement, 1500 gm of sand, and enough water to produce a flow between 100 and 115 per cent are mixed together.   The flow test is performed immediately after mixing on a 10-in. flow table which is dropped through a height of ½ in., twenty-five times in 15 sec.   After the mortar within the required initial flow range has been made, it is placed on a sheet of dampened filter paper which covers the bottom of a perforated disc.   This disc has an inside diameter of about 155 mm, is about 19.5 mm deep, and has 217 holes approximately 1.5 mm in diameter in its base.   The disc filled with mortar is then placed on the moistened rubber gasket sealed to the wide edge of a glass funnel, Fig. 18, and is then subjected to a vacuum of 2 in. for 60 sec, which is produced by a water aspirator and controlled by a mercury column relief.   After suction, another flow test is performed.   Flow after suction is usually required to be greater than 70 per cent of the initial flow.

Concrete Aggregates

1. Introduction. Aggregates are the relatively inert particles that act as filler and usually constitute from 66 to 78 per cent of the volume of the concrete. Although no hard-and-fast division can be made, sands, screenings, mine tailings, pulverized slag, etc., in which the maximum particle diameter is less than $\frac{1}{4}$ in., may be classed as fine aggregates; crushed stone, gravel, cinders, slag, and the like, containing larger particles, are called coarse aggregates.

Results of numerous experiments and records of failures caused by the use of poor aggregates have convinced engineers that a knowledge of the aggregate properties is as important as knowledge of the cement properties. Acceptance tests of aggregates are now widely used and serve to eliminate most of the poor ones. However, the acceptance tests sometimes advocated for aggregates are not always true criteria of the relative values of the concretes made from them, and sometimes cause the rejection of satisfactory aggregates. Consequently, the quality of a questionable aggregate should be tested by making it into concrete and determining its performance characteristics before the aggregate is accepted or rejected.

The various desirable qualities of aggregates, discussed later in greater detail, include: toughness to resist impact; durability to resist freezing and thawing, wetting and drying, and temperature variations; hardness to resist abrasion; strength to withstand heavy loads; cleanliness to allow the cement paste to bond with the aggregate, and to permit the setting and hardening of the cement; proper grading to make economical, workable concrete; uniformity to avoid frequent changes in mix proportions.

2. Sampling Aggregate. Due attention must be given to securing representative samples of aggregate. If the character of the deposit, or supply of material, is variable, then individual samples of the different grades may well be taken and tested separately, or mixed together, depending upon the degree of variation. For preliminary examinations, the samples of fine aggregate should not weigh less than 25 lb, and samples of coarse aggregate should not be less than 100 lb. For more complete tests or for mix designs, much larger quantities may be required.

In sampling the open face of a sand or gravel pit, the character of the overlying material, the stripping, should be noted and the face of the opening sampled from the bottom to the top. This may be conveniently done by scooping vertical troughs out of the face of the bank with a pail, which should be so manipulated that an equal amount of material is secured from every portion of each trough. If sharply defined strata of fine and coarse particles are present, it is well to secure separate samples of the material composing these layers.

When one is sampling a pile of aggregate, it should be remembered that the coarse particles tend to separate and flow towards the bottom of the pile; consequently it is desirable either to flatten the pile and employ the "method of quartering" (Art. XII-2) or, if the pile is very large, to proceed in the same manner as suggested in sampling a pit. Standard procedure for sampling aggregates may be found in ASTM *Des.* D75.

TESTS OF AGGREGATES

3. Silt is the impalpable dust which is present, at least in small proportion, in nearly all aggregates. The amount of silt can be determined with the apparatus shown in Fig. 1. One or two hundred grams of dry fine aggregate is carefully weighed, placed in the percolator and washed by a stream of pure water from the bottle (*b*). The silt is continuously stirred with a glass rod until the effluent from the percolator becomes clear. The residue in the percolator is then dried, and the loss in weight determined. If an analysis of the silt is desired the effluent from the percolator is filtered, and the residue on the filter is dried and analyzed. In order to obtain consistent results the dimensions of the percolator, velocity of flow of water, size of orifice, and method of stirring should be standardized.

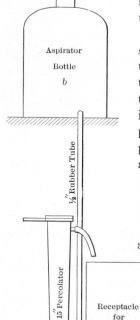

Fig. 1.   Apparatus for determining amount of silt in aggregate.

A standard method for determining the amount of material finer than the No. 200 sieve for both fine and coarse aggregates is described in ASTM *Standard* C117.

4. Specific Weight. The weight of an aggregate contained in a measure of unit volume is called its specific weight. Generally the units of volume used in this country are the cubic foot and the cubic yard.

Inasmuch as this determination is affected by the moisture content of the aggregate due consideration of the latter should be given. In specific weight determinations on fine aggregate the results for dry material cannot be accurately computed from tests in which the moisture content is sufficient to wet the surfaces of the particles. (See Art. XIII-16.) Obviously the degree of compactness of the material also greatly influences the specific weight; hence the adjectives rammed, compacted, shaken-down and loose are used. Loose measurement is often used in the field.

The method recommended in ASTM *Standard* C29 for aggregates having a maximum size of 2 in. or less consists of filling a cylindrical measure of $\frac{1}{10}$-, $\frac{1}{2}$-, or 1-cu ft capacity and determining the net weight of the aggregate in the measure. The sample of the aggregate shall be room dry if possible, and thoroughly mixed. The measure shall be filled one-third full, leveled off, and tamped twenty-five times with a $\frac{5}{8}$-in. pointed rod. The measure is filled two-thirds full and tamped twenty-five times as before. The measure shall then be filled to overflowing, tamped twenty-five times, and the surplus aggregate struck off, using the rod as a straight-edge. No effort should be made to fill holes left by the rod when the aggregate is damp. The size of measure to be used is determined by the size of aggregate, the $\frac{1}{10}$-cu ft to be used for aggregate whose particles are under $\frac{1}{2}$ in. The $\frac{1}{2}$- and 1-cu ft measures are for aggregates whose particles are under $1\frac{1}{2}$ in. and over $1\frac{1}{2}$ in., respectively.

The jigging procedure is recommended for aggregates having a maximum size greater than 2 in. and not over 4 in., and also for lightweight aggregates. The measure is filled in three approximately equal layers and each layer is compacted by raising alternate sides of the measure about 2 in. above the floor and allowing it to drop fifty times. The surface is leveled after the last layer has been compacted, and the net weight of the aggregate is obtained.

5. Specific Gravity and Absorption. Standard methods for determining the specific gravity and absorption of fine and coarse aggregates are completely described in ASTM *Standards* C127 and C128.

In the fine aggregate tests, about 1000 gm of oven-dry aggregate is placed in a pan, covered with water, and allowed to stand for 24 hours. The aggregate is then spread on a flat surface and is uniformly dried by a moving current of warm air until it approaches a free-flowing condition. The aggregate is then loosely placed in a conical mold ($1\frac{1}{2}$ in. top diameter, $3\frac{1}{2}$ in. bottom diameter, and $3\frac{1}{2}$ in. high) and the surface is lightly tamped twenty-five times with a metal rod. The cone of fine aggregate will retain its shape when the mold is removed if any free moisture is present; and the test is repeated after further drying until a surface-dry condition is indicated by the slumping of the aggregate on removal of the mold. A 500-gm sample of the surface-dry aggregate is then placed in a flask, and the necessary quantity of water required to fill the flask to the 500-ml mark is determined. Finally, the aggregate is removed, dried to constant weight, and weighed. The following information obtained from the test is used to calculate the bulk specific gravity, the bulk specific gravity (saturated surface-dry basis), the apparent specific gravity, and the absorption: weight in grams of oven-dry sample in air (A), volume in milliliters of flask (V), and weight in grams or volume in milliliters of water added to flask (W).

The bulk specific gravity (defined as the ratio of the weight in air of a given volume of a permeable material, including both permeable and impermeable voids, at a given temperature, to the weight in air of an equal volume of distilled water at the same temperature) may be calculated from

$$\text{Bulk specific gravity} = A/(V - W)$$

The bulk specific gravity on a saturated surface-dry basis may be calculated from

$$\text{Bulk specific gravity} = 500/(V - W)$$
(saturated surface-
dry basis)

The apparent specific gravity (defined as the ratio of the weight in air of a given volume of the impermeable portion of a permeable material, solid matter plus impermeable pores, at a given temperature, to the weight in air of an equal volume of distilled water at the same temperature) may be calculated from

$$\text{Apparent specific gravity} = \frac{A}{(V - W) - (500 - A)}$$

The absorption may be calculated from

$$\text{Absorption, per cent} = \frac{500 - A}{A} \times 100$$

The absorption of an air-dry fine aggregate may be approximated in the following manner:

Weigh to nearest half gram a representative 3000-gm sample of sand. In all succeeding operations avoid loss of sand. Spread approximately two-thirds of the sample in a shallow pan 16 by 16 in., or larger, sprinkle with a small amount of water, and mix thoroughly. Allow some of the moistened sand to flow from a smooth tin scoop into pan. Observe whether it flows freely, or forms balls. If it flows freely, spray on more water; if it balls up, add some sand from the remainder of the original sample. When the moisture content has been raised until the sand is just on point of balling up as it flows from scoop, determine weight of moistened sand; also weight of residue of original 3000-gm sample. Calculate the percentage of moisture to the nearest 0.1 per cent. Repeat the determination at least once.

The tests of a coarse aggregate require approximately a 5-kg sample of the material held on a $\frac{3}{8}$-in. sieve. The aggregate is first thoroughly washed and then dried to constant weight. After that it is immersed in water for 24 hours, taken out of the water, and all surface moisture removed by rolling in a large absorbent cloth. The weight of the surface-dry aggregate is then determined in air and in water. Finally, the oven-dry constant weight is determined. The test data, weight in grams of the oven-dry sample in air (A), weight in grams of the saturated surface-dry sample in air (B), and weight in grams of the saturated sample in water (C), may then be used to calculate the desired results as follows:

$$\text{Bulk specific gravity} = A/(B - C)$$

$$\text{Bulk specific gravity} = B/(B - C)$$
(saturated surface-
dry basis)

$$\text{Apparent specific gravity} = A/(A - C)$$

$$\text{Absorption, per cent} = 100(B - A)/A$$

The bulk specific gravity for both fine and coarse aggregates is usually used for calculations pertaining to Portland cement concrete.

6. Voids. If an aggregate is poured into a container of any sort it will be observed that not all of the space within the container is filled. To the vacant spaces between the particles of aggregate the name voids is applied. Necessarily, the percentage of voids like the specific weight is affected by the compactness of the aggregate and the amount of moisture which it contains. Generally void determinations are made on material measured loose.

There are two classes of methods commonly employed for measuring voids, the direct and the indirect. The most-used direct method consists in determining the volume of liquid, generally water, which is required to fill the voids in a given quantity of material. Since in pouring water into fine aggregate it is impossible to expel all the air between the particles, the measured voids are smaller than the actual. It therefore becomes evident that the above direct method should not be used with fine aggregates unless the test is conducted in a vacuum. By the indirect method, the solid volume of a known quantity of aggregate is obtained by pouring the material into a calibrated tank partially filled with water; the difference between the apparent volume of material and the volume of water displaced equals the voids. If very accurate results are desired void measurements should be corrected for the porosity * of the aggregate and the moisture it contains. Figure 2 shows a convenient device for measuring voids by this indirect method.†

When the bulk specific gravity of the aggregate is known the voids may be calculated thus:

$$\text{Per cent voids} = \frac{62.4 \times \text{Sp. gr. of aggregate} - \text{Wt. per cu ft of aggregate}}{0.624 \times \text{Sp. gr. of aggregate}}$$

Fig. 2. Voidmeter.

The method for determining the voids in concrete aggregates is given in ASTM *Standard* C30.

The variation in the size of particles in the aggregate greatly affects the voids. If a mass of spheres of equal diameters is piled as compactly as possible it may be shown that the per cent voids is approximately 26.‡ If spheres of smaller diameter, which will just fit into interstices in the original pile, are added, it is evident that the voids may be reduced. By the insertion of a third lot of still smaller spheres within the voids left in the pile a further reduction in voids may be made. Although particles of aggregate cannot be assigned to such definite positions, especially if they are loosely piled, yet experiments have shown that the voids in loose material may be greatly decreased by properly grading the sizes of the constituent particles.

7. **Mechanical Analysis** consists in determining the proportionate amounts of particles held on or passing through a series of sieves differing in size of mesh. Such analyses indicate whether the material is properly graded to produce the minimum voids, when it is made into mortar or concrete. They also provide a means of studying how the gradation of particles may be improved by making proper addi-

* See Art. VII-19.

† For other devices for determining voids see *Bull.* 329, U. S. Geol. Survey.

‡ See *Concrete Plain and Reinforced,* by Taylor and Thompson, 3rd Ed., p. 130, for demonstration.

tions and how different grades of aggregates may be combined with cement to form the most efficient mix.

For analyzing fine aggregate it is common practice in this country to employ sieves made of woven-brass wire. In some laboratories sheet brass perforated with circular holes is used instead of the wire cloth. The number of meshes per linear inch, the diameter of wire and size of opening of the more commonly used sieves of the United States Standard Sieve Series are given in Table 1. The sieves marked * are sufficient for most

TABLE 1. REQUIREMENTS FOR SIEVES FOR TESTING CONCRETE AGGREGATE

Standard Sieve Series Number	Sieve Opening mm	in.	Tolerance in Average Opening, per cent	Tolerance in Maximum Opening, per cent	Wire Diameter mm	in.
3-in.*	76.2	3.00	±2	+3	4.8 to 8.1	0.190 to 0.320
2-in.	50.8	2.00	±2	+3	4.1 to 6.2	0.160 to 0.245
1½-in.*	38.1	1.50	±2	+3	3.7 to 5.3	0.145 to 0.210
1-in.	25.4	1.00	±3	+5	3.43 to 4.50	0.135 to 0.177
¾-in.*	19.1	0.750	±3	+5	3.10 to 3.91	0.122 to 0.154
⅜-in.*	9.52	0.375	±3	+5	2.11 to 2.59	0.083 to 0.102
¼-in.	6.35	0.250	±3	+5	1.60 to 2.11	0.063 to 0.083
4 *	4.76	0.187	±3	+10	1.14 to 1.68	0.045 to 0.066
8 *	2.38	0.0937	±3	+10	0.74 to 1.10	0.0291 to 0.0433
10	2.00	0.0787	±3	+10	0.68 to 1.00	0.0268 to 0.0394
12	1.68	0.0661	±3	+10	0.62 to 0.90	0.0244 to 0.0354
16 *	1.19	0.0469	±3	+10	0.50 to 0.70	0.0197 to 0.0276
20	0.84	0.0331	±5	+15 †	0.38 to 0.55	0.0150 to 0.0217
30 *	0.59	0.0232	±5	+15 †	0.29 to 0.42	0.0114 to 0.0165
40	0.42	0.0165	±5	+25 †	0.23 to 0.33	0.0091 to 0.0130
50 *	0.297	0.0117	±5	+25 †	0.170 to 0.253	0.0067 to 0.0100
60	0.250	0.0098	±5	+25 †	0.149 to 0.220	0.0059 to 0.0087
80	0.177	0.0070	±6	+40 †	0.114 to 0.154	0.0045 to 0.0061
100 *	0.149	0.0059	±6	+40 †	0.096 to 0.125	0.0038 to 0.0049
120	0.125	0.0049	±6	+40 †	0.079 to 0.103	0.0031 to 0.0041
140	0.105	0.0041	±6	+40 †	0.063 to 0.087	0.0025 to 0.0034
200	0.074	0.0029	±7	+60 †	0.045 to 0.061	0.0018 to 0.0024
325	0.044	0.0017	±7	+90 †	0.031 to 0.040	0.0012 to 0.0016
400	0.037	0.0015	±7	+90 †	0.023 to 0.035	0.0009 to 0.0014

* Most used sieves. For additional sieves see ASTM *Standard* E11.
† Not more than 5 per cent of the openings may exceed the nominal sieve opening by more than one-half the tolerance in the maximum opening.

gradation tests on aggregates. Sieves for fine aggregate are generally made 8 in. in diameter and 2¼ in. deep. They are so fashioned that they may be nested one above the other with the sizes arranged in order of fineness of mesh from the bottom upwards. These sieves are frequently designated by their micron number, which is equal to 1000 times the sieve opening in millimeters.

For coarse aggregate, sieves are made from woven-wire meshing or sheet metal perforated with round holes. The size of opening, generally in the clear, is stated in fractions of an inch. Wooden-rimmed sieves 16 to 20 in. in diameter and 4 in. deep, equipped with meshing or perforated metal varying in diameter of opening as indicated in the upper part of Table 1, are satisfactory.

Before using, all sieves should be carefully calibrated to ascertain the variation in shape and size of openings and the average diameter of the mesh. For fine sieves a linen-tester's microscope may be used to count

Fig. 3. A Ro-tap mechanical shaker equipped with a Stop-Rite time switch.

the meshes, but a microscope fitted with a graduated eyepiece is necessary to measure accurately the size of the wire. Coarser sieves may be measured by means of micrometer calipers. The most accurate calibrations can be made by shaking materials of known analysis upon the given sieve and determining the per cent passing. The diameter of wire and size of opening in a given sieve should conform to the tolerances specified in Table 1.

The standard method of test for determining the sieve analysis of fine and coarse aggregates is given in ASTM *Standard* C136. In making sieve tests, a representative sample of the aggregate should be dried and weighed on scales accurate and sensitive to 0.1 per cent of the weight of the total sample. The size of the sample to be used depends on the maximum particle size, and should be increased as the maximum particle size is increased. For the usual fine aggregate, a 500-gm sample is satisfactory, and for coarse aggregates up to 1½ in. in size, a 15,000-gm sample is satisfactory. In making sieve tests of fine aggregates, the sieves are frequently nested in a mechanical shaker such as the one shown in Fig. 3, which was developed by the W. S. Tyler Co. This shaker is so designed that six 8-in. standard sieves or 13 half-height sieves may be shaken at one time. The driving mechanism is arranged to rotate

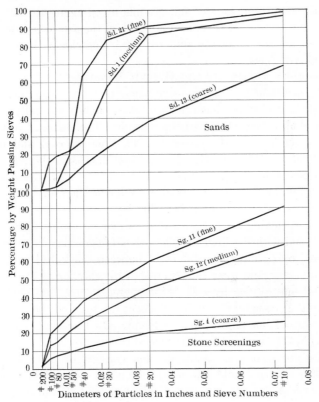

Fig. 4.   Mechanical analyses curves for typical sands and screenings. (*Bull.* 331, U. S. Geol. Survey.)

the sieves and tap them 150 times a minute. The time switch automatically stops the shaker at the end of the predetermined period. Sieving should be continued until not more than 1 per cent by weight of the residue passes any sieve in 1 min. Coarse aggregates are frequently sieved by hand, starting with the coarsest sieve. The Gilson Testing Screen is another type of mechanical shaker which is very helpful in making these tests.

When weighing, it is best to place the residue on the coarsest sieve in the scale pan first, then add the residue on the next finer sieve, and so on. Thus successive weight readings may be easily converted into percentages retained, and the discrepancy between the final and initial weight of the sample gives a check on losses.

Interpretation of the results of mechanical analyses are readily made by diagrams (see Fig. 4). In these diagrams, percentages by weight passing a given mesh are plotted as ordinates and the diameters of openings in the mesh as abscissas. The *fineness modulus, m,* is a less informative but useful measure of the size and grading of an aggregate. It is found by adding the percentages coarser than each of the asterisked sieves listed in Table 1, and dividing the sum by 100. For calculations of m, see Table 2 in Art. XIII-15.

8. Deleterious Substances and Organic Impurities. Clay lumps, soft fragments, coal and lignite, excessive amounts of material finer than the No. 200 sieve, and other deleterious substances such as shale, mica, iron pyrites, and absorbent cherts are undesirable. The standard test for clay lumps is given in ASTM *Standard* C142, that for coal and lignite in ASTM *Standard* C123, and that for material finer than the No. 200 sieve in ASTM *Standard* C117.

The test for clay lumps consists of oven drying the sample of aggregate to constant weight, spreading it in a thin layer on the bottom of the container, and removing all particles that cannot be broken into finely divided material with the fingers. The percentage of clay lumps may then be obtained by dividing the difference between the initial weight of the sample and the weight after the removal of the clay lumps by the original weight and multiplying by 100. Fine aggregate tests are performed on the material coarser than the No. 16 sieve; the tests on the coarse aggregate are carried out on the four following size fractions: No. 4–$\frac{3}{8}$ in., $\frac{3}{8}$–$\frac{3}{4}$ in., $\frac{3}{4}$–$1\frac{1}{2}$ in., and over $1\frac{1}{2}$ in.

The test for coal and lignite in sand consists of pouring a 200-gm sample of oven-dried sand into about 250 ml of a liquid that has a specific gravity of 2.0. A process of agitation and decantation repeated many times will separate the coal, lignite, and other low-specific-gravity particles from the heavier sand particles. An approximate percentage of coal and lignite may then be obtained by dividing the weight of the decanted particles by the weight of the original sample and multiplying by 100. Coal and lignite in coarse aggregate may be determined from simple visual inspection.

The test for material finer than the No. 200 sieve consists of washing an air-dry sample over a No. 200 sieve until the wash water is clean, drying the washed sample, and then calculating the percentage of material finer than the No. 200 sieve by dividing the difference between the original dry weight and the dry weight after washing by the original dry weight and multiplying by 100.

Aggregates may be tested for soft-piece content by scratching them with a hard yellow brass scribe. According to D. O. Woolf the brass scribe will not scratch good-quality limestone but will scratch badly weathered materials (see *Proc. ASTM*, Vol. 47, p. 967).

Organic impurities in sands for concrete may be determined by the method given in ASTM *Standard* C40. The test consists of filling a 12-oz glass bottle to the $4\frac{1}{2}$-oz level with sand to be tested. Then a 3 per cent solution of sodium hydroxide in water is added until the liquid is at the 7-oz level. The liquid and sand are shaken and allowed to stand for 24 hours. If the clear supernatant liquid is then colorless, or has only a light yellow color, the sand has a low organic content and may be considered satisfactory. If the color is dark brown, a high organic content is indicated, and the sand should not be used unless it has been proved satisfactory by the mortar strength test.

9. Soundness. The method for testing the soundness of aggregates by use of sodium sulfate or magnesium sulfate is described in ASTM *Standard* C88. The resistance of aggregates to the disintegrating action of cycles of immersion in saturated solutions of sodium sulfate or magnesium sulfate followed by oven drying is considered to provide information on the durability of aggregates subject to weathering action. Such information is particularly desirable when actual service records of the aggregate are not available.

The sodium sulfate solution should have a specific gravity of not less than 1.151 and not greater than 1.174, and may be made by using at least 350 gm of Na_2SO_4 or 750 gm of $Na_4SO_2 \cdot 10H_2O$ per liter of water. The magnesium sulfate should have a specific gravity between 1.295 and 1.308, and may be made by using at least 1400 gm of $MgSO_4 \cdot 7H_2O$ (Epsom salt) per liter of water.

The aggregate to be tested should be washed, oven dried, and separated into the various specified sizes. It is then immersed in the required sulfate solution, kept at $21 \pm 1°C$ for a period of 16 to 18 hours, and then oven dried at 105–110°C to constant weight. The aggregate is cooled to room temperature, and the cycle is then repeated the required number of times. After the final cycle, the aggregate is washed, oven dried, and sieved on the same sieve on which it was held before the test. The percentage loss for each size fraction is then calculated. Careful consideration should be given to setting up specification requirements for these tests because the two salts do not give the same results. Aggregates that fail to pass the sodium or magnesium sulfate accelerated soundness test are considered satisfactory if they pass a freezing and thawing test.

10. Abrasion. Methods for testing the abrasion of coarse aggregate by the use of the Los Angeles machine are given in ASTM *Standard* C131, for testing the abrasion of rock by the use of the Deval machine in

ASTM *Standard* D2, and for testing the abrasion of graded coarse aggregate by the use of the Deval machine in ASTM *Standard* D289.

The Los Angeles test described in Art. VII-23 consists of subjecting a sample of definite weight and grading to the abrasive action of a definite weight of steel and cast-iron spheres in a rotating drum. After the completion of 500 revolutions of the drum, the amount of the sample retained on a No. 12 sieve is determined. The percentage of wear is then calculated by dividing the loss in weight by the original weight and multiplying by 100.

The Deval machine consists of one or more hollow cast-iron cylinders 20 cm in inside diameter and 34 cm long. They are closed at one end, have a tightly fitted cover at the other, and are attached to a shaft at 30° with the axis of rotation of the shaft. The abrasion test of graded coarse aggregate consists of introducing a specially graded sample, weight dependent on the specific gravity of the material, along with an abrasive charge of 6 spheres weighing about 2500 gm, in the Deval machine, and rotating the machine at a rate of 30 to 33 rpm for 10,000 revolutions. The material is then removed, sieved on a No. 12 sieve, washed, dried, and weighed, and the percentage wear calculated. The abrasion test of rock consists of placing about 50 pieces of broken dry rock weighing 5000 gm in a cylinder and rotating for 10,000 revolutions at a rate between 30 and 33 rpm. The amount of wear may be given either on a percentage basis, or the French coefficient of wear may be calculated by dividing 400 by the weight in grams per kilogram of rock of the material passing the No. 12 sieve.

11. Alkali-Aggregate Reactivity. The expansive reactions that take place between certain aggregates such as opal, opaline chert, siliceous dolomitic limestone, aggregates containing volcanic glasses, and cements containing more than 0.5 to 0.6 per cent of the alkalies sodium hydroxide and potassium hydroxide are of great concern to engineers. Standard tests to determine alkali-aggregate reactivity have not been adopted, but certain tests have been suggested and some experimental work on each type has been carried out.

An alkali etching test has been proposed * in which polished specimens of the aggregate are immersed in a 10 per cent sodium hydroxide solution for 18 to 24 hours. During the test, the temperature of the solution should be kept at 50°C. After immersion, the aggregates are examined for signs of etching. If etching has occurred and if no calcite or dolomite are present, the aggregate should be regarded as potentially reactive with alkalies.

* Alkali Etching Tests on Concrete Aggregate, by W. H. Parsons and H. Insley, *J. Am. Concrete Inst.*, Vol. 40, p. 229.

Mortar bar expansions have been proposed for determining alkali-aggregate reactions.* These mortar bars, 1 by 1 by 10 in. with brass end plugs, should be made of mortar consisting of 1 part of cement to 2 parts of aggregate by weight, the mortar having a flow of 100 ± 10 per cent. After 24 hours in the molds, the bars should be kept at approximately 100 per cent relative humidity and at the desired temperature, usually between 70° and 100°F. ' Expansions are measured with a standard comparator. Coarse aggregate may be tested by crushing it into sand sizes.

12. Moisture Content. The *total moisture* content of an aggregate can be accurately found by determining the loss in weight of a representative 1000-gm sample of sand, or a 2000-gm sample of coarse aggregate after it has been dried to constant weight. Drying can be done in an oven, over a hot plate, or by saturating fine aggregate with alcohol and igniting. The *moisture absorbed* by the aggregate may be obtained by the methods given in Art. 5. The *free or surface moisture* used in water-cement ratio calculations may be found by subtracting the absorbed moisture from the total moisture.

The free moisture can also be found from the differences in specific gravities of moist and surface dry sand as outlined in ASTM Des. C70–30. A more serviceable device for field use developed by the Portland Cement Association is shown in *Proc. Am. Concrete Inst.*, Vol. 25, p. 266. In this connection also refer to ASTM Des. 128 and 127.

When the moisture in sand varies 1 or 2 per cent from batch to batch, the above methods requiring 20 to 30 min per determination are slow and cumbersome. C. E. Wuerpel in construction of the Alton lock on the Mississippi River measured the electrical conductance of a portion of the sand in the measuring hopper (see *Eng. News-Record*, Vol. 115, p. 52). The method is based upon the principle that the conductance of a given volume of sand under a given degree of compaction increases with the moisture content. By making calibrations for the type of water used and for different temperatures in the sand he was able to determine rapidly average moisture contents to 0.3 per cent of the sand weight.

CHARACTERISTICS AND PROPERTIES OF FINE AGGREGATE

13. Requirements for Fine Aggregate. The fine aggregate should consist of a mixture of hard, tough grains of different sizes. Particles of approximately equal dimensions are preferable to elongated grains, since the former, with similar gradation of sizes, produce more compact mixtures containing less voids than the latter. The sharpness of the grains is of little importance. The fine aggregate should be free from any

* A Study of Alkali-Aggregate Reactivity by Means of Mortar Bar Expansions, by T. M. Kelly, L. Schuman, F. B. Hornibrook, *J. Am. Concrete Inst.*, Vol. 45, p. 57.

minerals of a weak, friable nature and from other impurities such as organic or vegetable matter, the presence of which in very small percentages may be very injurious. The presence of 10 per cent or more of clay or loam is, in general, objectionable. Smaller percentages of these impurities may impair the efficiency of fine sands.

The effects of natural impurities like clay and loam are dependent upon: 1, the gradation of the sand particles; 2, the richness of the mortar; 3, the chemical constitution and the fineness of the particles in the clay or loam. Lumps of clay or loam are decidedly harmful. Their weight should not exceed 1 per cent of the fine aggregate. The addition of finely ground clay to a coarse sand may improve its grading and reduce voids. Hence lean mortars deficient in fines may be improved both in density and in plasticity by additions of small percentages of such clays.* A rough qualitative test for detecting small percentages of loam or clay may be made by rubbing the sand between the palms and noting the amount and character of the stain thus produced. If present in large percentages clay imparts a greasy, slippery feeling to the sand when it is wetted; and loam is generally readily detected by its dark color.

Coal and lignite should not be permitted in excess of $\frac{1}{4}$ per cent. For concrete subjected to abrasion, the amount of material in the aggregate passing a No. 200 sieve should be under 2 per cent. Alkali, mica, coated grains, and soft particles should not exceed 1 per cent, and the weight of all impurities should not exceed 3 per cent of the fine aggregate.

Organic and vegetable impurities, which often injure the hardening properties of the cement, are usually found in the silt. Hence sands containing more than 6 per cent by volume, or 3 per cent by weight, are likely to be unsatisfactory and should always be subjected to a mortar strength test before using.

Preferably, the percentages of fine aggregate retained on the respective sieves should be limited for general concrete construction as follows: none on a $\frac{3}{8}$-in. sieve, 0 to 5 per cent on a No. 4, 20 to 55 per cent on a No. 16, 70 to 90 per cent on a No. 50, and 90 to 98 per cent on a No. 100 sieve. The fineness modulus m should usually be between 2.5 and 3.2.

Whenever time permits, strength tests should be made of mortars containing the fine aggregate. In fact, it is unsafe to use sands of unproven quality unless such strength tests are made. Sands for construction purposes should possess at least 90 per cent of the strength of standard sand mortars of like proportions and consistency. Compression tests are the most valuable, although tension or transverse tests are permissible. If the sand is to be used in making concrete, it should be mixed with the proper proportions of the cement and stone with which it is to be used and

* See paper by Withey and Wendt, *Proc. ASTM*, Vol. 35, Pt. 2, p. 426.

the strength of the hardened mixture should be ascertained. (See Art. XIV-20.)

14. Composition of the Particles. Although the results of a chemical analysis combined with a knowledge of the mineral content of a fine aggregate is sometimes helpful in determining its value, too great importance is often attached to the chemical analysis of sands. Some experimenters have believed that a very high silica content should be demanded in specifications for fine aggregate. Doubtless a sand which consists principally of hard, tough, and non-porous grains of quartz is superior to a soft, calcareous sand, provided other characteristics are similar. Nevertheless there are many good sands and a variety of suitable broken stone screenings having comparatively low silica contents which make mortars of high strength.

Inasmuch as the strength of the mortar or concrete depends upon the strength of the aggregate as well as the strength of the cement, the grains of sand or screenings should, at least, equal the cement in strength. Since the resistance of cement paste to attrition and abrasion is small, the resistance of mortar to such influences is largely dependent upon the hardness and toughness of the aggregate. Consequently, whenever high resistance to abrasion is desired the particles of the aggregate should be so hard that they cannot be readily scratched with a pocketknife. If the aggregate is very porous it is likely to withdraw water from the cement during the hardening. This results in the formation of a weak layer of paste surrounding the grains.

From a consideration of the above facts, it is, therefore, evident that the presence of a large proportion of hard, tough, dense minerals which are not readily attacked by atmospheric conditions is a favorable indication of the quality of an aggregate. If porous, the aggregate should be thoroughly soaked with water before mixing with cement.

Some of the more desirable mineral constituents are quartz, dolomite, and hornblende. Among the objectionable are mica, talc, iron pyrites, shale, limonite, ochre, hematite, and the absorbent types of chert. Most of these weather badly under freezing and thawing, as shown by R. R. Litehiser before the National Sand and Gravel Association in 1938. Siliceous dolomitic limestone, opal, and opaline chert should not be used with a high alkali cement because of the possibility of alkali-aggregate reactivity.

15. Gradation of the Sizes of the Particles. Experiments have indicated that mortars made from fine sands are less dense and strong than those made from coarse sands. This is probably due to two causes: first, the difficulty of coating very fine particles of sand with cement particles of like size; and second, the larger percentage of voids in the mixture of fine sand and cement. Experiments have also shown that the most effective gradation of the sizes of the particles depends upon the richness of the mix and the maximum size of the aggregate.

A good conception of the gradation of the sizes of aggregate particles is afforded by mechanical analysis diagrams coupled with values of the *fineness modulus, m* (see Fig. 4 and Table 2). Whereas the fineness mod-

TABLE 2

Sieve No.	Diameter Opening (In.)	PERCENTAGE COARSER THAN SIEVE FOR AGGREGATE					
		Sd 13	Sd 1	Sd 21	Sg 4	Sg 11	Sg 12
4	.187	0	0	0	0	0	0
8	.094	20	5	0	60	5	20
16	.047	55	12	7	78	48	32
30	.0232	77	45	16	84	66	52
50	.0117	92	78	73	90	77	67
100	.0059	99	84	84	95	87	80
Fineness modulus (m).		3.43	2.24	1.80	4.07	2.83	2.51
Gradation.		Coarse	Medium	Fine	Coarse	Medium	Fine

ulus per se gives no indications of gaps in grading, it is the best of the simple indices thus far devised for measuring grading. For studies of the effects of particle interference, reference should be made to the work of C. A. G. Weymouth (*Proc. ASTM*, Vol. 38, Pt. 2, p. 354).

The results of strength tests of mortars made of these fine aggregates are given in Table 1, Chapter XV. Sand Sd 1 of medium gradation is preferable to either of the other sands for making concrete of usual proportions but inferior to sand Sd 13 for making a strong mortar. Sand Sd 13, on the other hand, would produce a harsh working concrete unless a high content of cement were used. Sand Sd 21 is too finely graded to make the most efficient concrete or mortar. Beach sands are often graded like it. Coarse sands like Sd 13 are rarely found.

Broken stone screenings should not contain over 10 per cent of dust passing a No. 100 sieve nor more than 25 per cent of particles passing a No. 50 sieve. Large amounts of crusher dust are especially objectionable when the screenings are to be used for tops of floors or sidewalks, since mortars containing large percentages of dust are likely to wear badly.

16. Voids and Specific Weight. Two other criteria of the worth of sands and screenings are afforded by the percentage of voids and the specific weight. Usually, for fine aggregates of like chemical and mineral constitution, those with the lowest percentage of voids or the highest specific weight are the most desirable, since less cement will be required to fill the unoccupied space in such aggregate. However, due to differences in gradation, two sands which contain the same percentage of voids may produce mortars differing considerably in density and strength. For instance, comparing a fine and a coarse sand containing the same proportion of voids, the coarse sand will produce the stronger mortar.

Since even a small percentage of moisture tends to hold apart the grains and increase the voids, the moisture content exercises a very important influence upon the percentage of voids and the specific weight. For

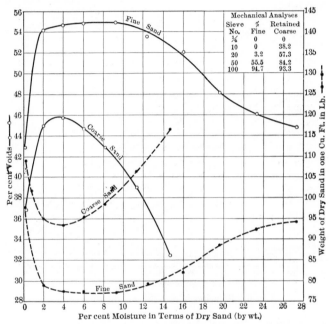

Fig. 5. The effects of moisture on the voids and specific weight of a fine and a coarse sand.

examples examine Fig. 5, which shows the effect of the percentage of moisture upon the voids and specific weights for a fine and a coarse sand. The curves in the diagram serve to illustrate the importance of making the determinations on material containing the per cent moisture ordinarily present in field operations, if the results are to be employed in the field. If, however, a comparison of different sands is to be made determinations should also be conducted upon dried aggregate.

To facilitate the computation of the percentage of voids from the specific weights, the diagram in Fig. 6 is provided. Since a knowledge of the specific gravity of the aggregate is necessary in order to use this diagram the following average values are given for sands: Quartz, 2.65; dolomitic sands, 2.65–2.75; calcareous sands, 2.60–2.70. A rough average value for all sands is 2.65. For specific gravities of stones, see Art. VII-18.

For good sands the percentage of voids generally lies between 28 and 35. The corresponding weights per cubic foot range from 120 to 105 lb. In screenings, on account of the angular shape of the particles, a somewhat higher range in the percentage of voids is to be expected. Screenings of good quality should not, in general, contain over 38 per cent voids.

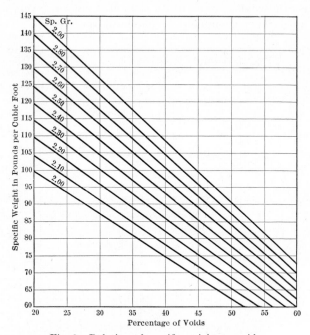

Fig. 6. Relation of specific weight to voids.

17. Mortar Tests. By far the most valuable indices of the efficiency of a fine aggregate are given by the strength and yield tests of mortars made with a cement of known properties.

Usual procedure in determining quality of fine aggregate is to compare the strength of an Ottawa sand mortar with the strength of a similarly made mortar of the given sand. In practice, however, there is considerable difference in the kind of test, the grading of Ottawa sand, proportions and consistency of mix, and method of procedure specified.

Where a flow table is not available the following method may be used: Proceed in the standard manner indicated in Art. XII-7 and mix a batch of 500 or 600 gm of mortar. Cover with a bowl. Proceed in like manner with a batch of the same proportions containing the given sand or screenings. In estimating the required amount of water for the latter batch, it should be remembered that natural sand or screenings will generally require 10 to 50 per cent more water than standard sand, and that the percentage of water required varies with the proportion of fine material in the aggregate. Two or three trials will ordinarily suffice to obtain the consistency which appears and feels like that of the standard sand mortar.

For comparing the strength of the given sand with that of Ottawa sand, the following procedure is suggested. Use Ottawa sand, about half standard and half run of mine, with a fineness modulus between 2.3 and 2.5. Use a water-cement ratio of 0.60 by weight for both sands. If six 2-in. cubes are to be made from one batch, 600 gm of cement and 360 gm of water should be placed in a pan and allowed to stand for 1 min and then mixed into a smooth paste. Enough of the Ottawa sand, or of the surface-dry given sand, should then be mixed with the paste until a flow of 100 ± 5 per cent is obtained with ten $\frac{1}{2}$-in. drops in 10 sec. At least 3 cubes of each kind of sand should be tested at 3 and 7, or at 7 and 28, days.

The following mortar test is suggested as an inexpensive test to predict the strength of concrete which can be made with a given sand. Mold and cure in standard manner five 2- by 2- by 9-in. mortar prisms of the given sand. Test at 3 or 7 days first as beams under center loading; then test the halves as modified cubes (Art. III-16). For these tests a fixed water-cement ratio, 0.5 by weight, should be used. A considerable amount of testing by P. J. Hunt, C. D. Matthias, J. L. Shipman, and E. C. Wagner at the University of Wisconsin, 1936, indicated that this procedure has merit in predicting either the compressive strength or the modulus of rupture of gravel concrete of the same water-cement ratio and age as the mortar.

The yield test on a mortar is often made to ascertain both the yield and the density. The density is a more reliable index of the mortar strength than is the voids in the fine aggregate. In general, the density of a 1:2 or 1:3 mortar, by weight, made with well-graded sand and mixed to standard consistency used in cement testing will lie between 0.70 and 0.75; the yield will generally vary between 1.08 and 1.20 for similar mixes, being greater for the richer mix (Art. XII-38).

CHARACTERISTICS AND PROPERTIES OF COARSE AGGREGATE

18. Requirements for Coarse Aggregate. Any stone or gravel which possesses the strength of neat cement is sufficiently strong for use as an aggregate. In hardness, however, there is a considerable range permissible, depending upon the kind of construction. In floors, pavements, and other surfaces subjected to considerable wear and upon which no top dressing is placed, a uniformly hard and tough coarse aggregate which will show less than 30 per cent loss in the Los Angeles rattler test (Art. VII-23) is desired. For other constructions extreme hardness is not essential provided the aggregate shows a rattler loss under 40 per cent.

The coarse aggregate should also be free from loam, clay, vegetable or organic matter, and other injurious substances previously mentioned under fine aggregates. More than 1 per cent of shale is objectionable. The permissible limit for clay lumps and for coal and lignite should be 0.25 per cent by weight. Soft fragments should not exceed 2 per cent by weight.

Preferably, the particles of the aggregate should be approximately cubical or spherical in form. Flat, disc-shaped pieces and long, thin, wedge-like particles are objectionable since they cannot be so closely compacted as the cubical or rounded stones. To secure a good bond between the mortar and the coarse aggregate, the cleavage planes of broken stone and the surfaces of gravel particles should be uneven and rough. Very porous particles must be saturated with water before mixing with cement.

In a well-graded coarse aggregate 95 per cent or more should pass the sieve of maximum permissible size of opening, 30 to 70 per cent should pass the sieve of half that size of opening (the mean sieve), and not over 10 per cent should pass the No. 4 sieve. The maximum permissible size of aggregate depends upon the type of construction, but it rarely exceeds 2½ in. in diameter. The maximum diameter of particle should not exceed one-fifth of the minimum width of form. In reinforced work it should not be larger than three-fourths of the clear spacing of reinforcing.

The aggregate should be resistant to freezing and thawing action if it is to be used in exposed locations in northern climates. If no service record for the aggregate is available, an accelerated sodium or magnesium sulfate test may be made. (See Art. 9.) The maximum weighted average loss after 5 cycles should not exceed 15 per cent. Where large temperature variations are likely, it is desirable that the coefficient of thermal expansion of the coarse aggregate should approximate that of the mortar.

For economical production of both fine and coarse aggregate, pit-run gravel should contain 50 per cent or over of coarse aggregate.

Measured loose, the voids in well-shaped broken stone range between 45 and 50 per cent; if uniformly varying in gradation, between 40 and 50 per cent. For loosely measured gravel varying from ¼ in. to 1½ in. in diameter the voids vary from 35 to 40 per cent. In dry well-graded pit-run gravel, voids run under 28 per cent. When rodded in measuring, the voids will be approximately 4 to 5 per cent less than the above data.

19. Characteristics and Properties of Broken Stone. The broken stones commonly used for coarse aggregate are trap rock, granite, dolomite, limestone, and sandstone. Trap rock, on account of its hardness, toughness, high resistance to fire, and great strength, is an excellent coarse aggregate. The granites also furnish a very good material for coarse aggregate. Both of these classes of rock are very desirable in road or floor construction, or on surfaces which are subjected to considerable abrasion. Often, however, these hard igneous rocks crush into elongated particles which cannot be closely compacted. Consequently maximum density cannot be secured in the concrete or mortar into which they are made. When such aggregates have very smooth cleavage planes, the mortar will not strongly adhere to the surfaces and the resulting concrete will be deficient in strength. In spite of these objections, however, these rocks form the most valuable class of crushed aggregates.

Crushed dolomite and limestone are extensively used for coarse aggregate. Although softer than the granites and traps, the dolomites and hard limestones make concrete which is as strong as, and which resists fire better than, concrete made of granite. Usually limestone concrete wears more uniformly than concrete made of igneous rocks. Soft limestone is often very porous, and unless thoroughly wetted before mixing will weaken the strength of the surrounding mortar by absorbing water from it while the hardening process is going on. Limestones frequently contain large quantities of very fine dust which, in wet weather, coat the surfaces of the stones. If there is a large proportion of this dust in the coarse aggregate, and if a fine sand is being used, it may be necessary to screen out the dust in order to secure a concrete of high strength. However, if the sand is coarse, allowance may be made for this dust in proportioning.

TABLE 3. PERCENTAGES OF VOIDS AND WEIGHTS PER CUBIC YARD OF CRUSHED LIMESTONE (Baker) *

Locality in Illinois.	Size of Stone.	Per Cent Voids.		Weights in Lb. per Cu.Yd.			
				Wagon Loads.		Car Loads.	
		By Pouring in Water.	From Specific Gravity.	At Crusher.	After Hauling ½ Mile or More.	At Crusher.	After Hauling 75 Miles or More.
Chester....	⅜-in. scr.	40.9	46.8				
Chester....	¾-in. scr.	43.0	45.6	2442	2797	2546	2850
Chester....	2-in. to ¾-in.	46.6	46.6	2344	2582		
Chester....	3-in. to 2-in.	46.1	45.1	2367	2569	2348	2545
Joliet......	½-in. scr.	42.2	47.1	2303	2533	2659	2905
Joliet......	2-in. to ½ in.	47.9	46.2	2315	2480	2386	2592
Joliet......	3-in. to 2-in.	47.5	46.1	......	......	2361	2553
Kankakee..	⅜-in. scr.	39.6	46.1	2430	2697		
Kankakee..	1¼-in. to ⅜-in.	45.7	44.7	2325	2546		
Kankakee..	2¼-in. to ⅜-in.	44.3	42.9				
Kankakee..	2¼-in. to 1¼-in.	46.2	43.4				

* Each value of per cent voids represents a number of tests in which size of vessel varied from 0 7 cu.ft to 27 cu.ft. and the height of drop of materials varied up to 20 ft. Percentages of absorption (by weight) for these limestones were Joliet, 0.64; Kankakee, 1.84; Chester, 1.01. Average values of specific gravity were Joliet, 2.71; Kankakee, 2.61; Chester 2.57.

The stronger and more dense sandstones make a satisfactory coarse aggregate, but the soft varieties together with the shales and, slates should not be used. The latter are likely to be deficient in strength and to consist of particles which are improperly shaped for making dense concrete.

Table 3 contains a summary of voids and specific weight tests conducted by Professor I. O. Baker.* These data show the effect of hauling in wagon or car in compacting these aggregates. The data in Table 4

TABLE 4. VOIDS AND SPECIFIC WEIGHTS OF COARSE AGGREGATES

Kind of Aggregate.	Range in Sizes.	Specific Gravity.	Weight per Cu.ft. (Lb.)	Per Cent Voids.	Authority.
Trap.............	¼-in. scr.	2.90	98.1	46.5	W. E. McClintock
Trap.............	1½-in. to ½-in.	2.90	90.0	50.2	W. E. McClintock
Trap.............	3-in. to 1½-in.	2.90	93.5	48.1	W. E. McClintock
Quartzite........	¼-in. scr.	2.67	92.8	44.3	M. O. Withey
Quartzite........	1½-in. to ¼-in.	2.67	86.4	48.1	M. O. Withey
Granite.........	¼-in. scr.	2.62	95.0	41.8	M. O. Withey
Granite.........	¾-in. to ¼-in.	2.62	86.5	47.0	M. O. Withey
Granite.........	1¼-in. to ¼-in.	2.62	88.9	45.6	M. O. Withey
Granite.........	2-in. to ¼-in.	2.62	84.7	48.1	M. O. Withey
Granite.........	1-in. to dust	2.58	95.3	40.9	U. S. Geol. Sur.
Limestone.......	1-in. to dust	2.49	97.7	37.1	U. S. Geol. Sur.
Gravel..........	1-in. to ¼-in.	2.45	102.4	33.0	U. S. Geol. Sur.
Gravel..........	1½-in. to ¼-in.	2.77	110.5	36.0	M. O. Withey
Gravel (Pit-run).	{ 1½-in. to dust { 51% < ¼-in.	2.77	125.9	27.0	M. O. Withey
Gravel (Lake)....	1-in. to No. 10	2.75	112.5	34.4	M. O. Withey
Gravel..........	⅝-in. to ¼-in.	2.70	105.0	37.7	M. O. Withey
Gravel..........	1¼-in. to ¼-in.	2.70	102.4	39.2	M. O. Withey
Cinders.........	{ 1¼-in. to dust { 37% < ¼-in.	1.53	47.0	50.7	U. S. G. S.
Bank slag.......	3/16-in. scr.	......	117.0	......	Carnegie Steel Co.
Bank slag.......	1-in. to ½-in.	......	67.0	......	Carnegie Steel Co.
Bank slag.......	2½-in. to 1-in.	......	72.0	......	Carnegie Steel Co.
Machine slag....	2-in. to 1-in.	......	96.0	......	Carnegie Steel Co.

have been compiled from various reports. One can compute voids or specific weight of a given aggregate if either of them and the specific gravity (Art. VII-18) are known.

On account of the tendency of the stone to separate from concrete when a uniform size of coarse aggregate is used, it seems preferable to use graded mixtures. Furthermore, with graded mixtures the voids in the aggregate are less than in aggregate of uniform size, and concrete made

* *Bull.* 23, Univ. Ill. Eng. Expt. Sta., 1908.

of the graded mixtures is fully as strong and dense as that made of the one-size coarse aggregate. On the other hand, it is doubtful if the uniformly varying gradation often advocated is superior to other gradings differing considerably from it. For example, in Fig. 7 compare the range in gradings for crushed limestone between $\frac{7}{64}$- and $2\frac{1}{4}$-in. sieves ($\frac{1}{8}$- and $2\frac{1}{2}$-in. round openings), all of which Goldbeck * found to have approximately equal voids, with curve U for crushed stone varying uniformly in gradation over the same range in sizes. However, to conserve workability the omission of intermediate sizes should be avoided. Reasonable toler-

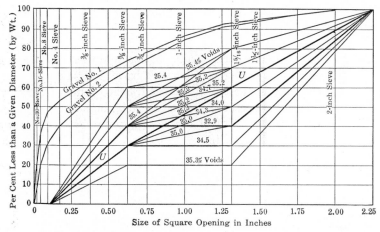

Fig. 7. Sieve analysis curves for typical pit-run gravels and for broken stone.

ances in gradation, such as suggested in Art. 18, will yield low-void aggregates and lessen costs.

Since stronger and denser concrete can be made from broken stone well graded from $2\frac{1}{2}$ in. down to $\frac{1}{4}$ in. than from similar material less than 1 in. in size, the use of rather large coarse aggregate is often economical. When such coarse aggregate is used, uniformity in the grading in successive batches will be conserved by screening the coarse aggregate into two sizes and measuring them separately prior to mixing. Such procedure will promote uniformity in the workability, strength, and watertightness of the concrete.

20. Characteristics and Properties of Gravels. The statements previously made in regard to the mineral composition of sands apply equally well to gravels. For concrete pavement subjected to heavy traffic all particles should be of uniform hardness. They should not be scratched by the knife. Somewhat softer material may be employed in making con-

* From *Crushed Stone J.,* Sept., 1928. Voids are for rodded volumes. For loose volumes voids were about 1.1 times the voids in Fig. 7.

crete for constructions where strength is the only requisite. Gravels containing considerable proportions of disintegrated rock, pebbles coated with soft limestone, clay, or loam should be avoided. Organic matter even in small percentages is very objectionable. Such impurities are often present in gravels obtained from pits in which the overlaying material is covered with leaves and decayed timber. It is possible, however, to remove loam, clay and organic material by thorough washing.

The particles composing the gravel should be approximately round; flat, disc-shaped particles are undesirable since the latter do not compact into as dense mixtures as the former.

Pit-run gravel generally contains too much material passing a $\frac{1}{4}$-in. sieve. Since the gradation of sizes in material from a given pit is often quite variable, as shown by curves for gravel No. 1 and No. 2, Fig. 7, is difficult to maintain a uniform quality of concrete when pit-run material is used. Hence, whenever considerable gravel is to be used, better concrete and economy in the use of cement will be promoted by screening the pit-run into two or more sizes and recombining in proportions desired in making concrete. Gravel coarse aggregate should conform to requirements suggested in Art. 18.

Boulders of hard, dense rock may often be economically employed, especially in massive walls, abutments and dams, provided the interstices are thoroughly filled with concrete composed of smaller stones. It is desirable to keep such large rocks back from the surfaces of the work since thin outside shells of concrete sometimes spall off, especially if they are poorly bonded and are subjected to frost action.

The voids and specific weights of a number of gravels differing in gradation are given in Table 4. Average values of specific gravity for the different classes of gravel commonly found are approximately the same as the values given for sands in Art. 16.

21. Broken Stone and Gravel Compared. On account of the spherical shape of its particles gravel makes a more fluid and dense concrete than does broken stone. Furthermore, gravel concrete requires less tamping or puddling than concrete made of broken stone in order to expel entrained air and thoroughly compact the mixture. Considering mixes of concrete of like cement contents and workabilities, those made with well-graded crushed limestones or slags usually exhibit higher cross-bending strengths than concretes made of equally well-graded gravels. On the whole, if equal care is taken in grading the particles of aggregate, gravel concrete seems to be more impervious to water than broken stone concrete. One of the main advantages in using broken stone for concrete is the possibility of securing a product which is of fairly uniform composition.

22. Miscellaneous Aggregates. Slag has been used to some extent both as fine and as coarse aggregate. It is an efficient aggregate for fireproofing. For concrete aggregate molten slag from the furnace is run into pits, or onto suitable banks, where it air cools into a dense, hard mass. It is then excavated, crushed, and screened into desired sizes. Slag sand is the finely crushed material passing a No. 4 sieve. Slag coarse aggregates which are sufficiently hard, tough, and durable for highway pavements should weigh not less than 70 lb per cu ft, by rodded volume.

Tailings from zinc and lead mines have been considerably used in Missouri and southwestern Wisconsin for concrete aggregate. The chief objection to these aggregates is the presence of pyrites, which causes rust-like spots on the surface of the concrete.

Metallic aggregates have been used for special purposes. Cast-iron and lead aggregates have been used in counterweights for bridges. Sized and graded iron particles have been embedded in concrete surfaces while the concrete was still in a plastic state to make floor surfaces, about $\frac{1}{8}$ in. thick, that are highly resistant to impact and abrasion.

CHARACTERISTICS AND PROPERTIES OF LIGHTWEIGHT AGGREGATES

23. Lightweight Mineral Aggregates. The use of lightweight aggregates has been increasing because of their many desirable properties such as light weight, good heat and sound insulation, nailability, and satisfactory strength properties for the intended uses. Lightweight aggregates are usually under $\frac{3}{4}$ in. in size and frequently under $\frac{3}{8}$ in. They are apt to be harsh working, and additions of admixtures or fine natural sands may be necessary to overcome this undesirable property. Despite the fact that most lightweight aggregates are more costly than sand and gravel aggregates and that lightweight structural concrete requires a higher cement content for a given strength, lightweight structural concrete is economical in multistory buildings and long-span bridges because of savings due to changes in design and construction practices.

The lightweight aggregates may be classified as natural, by-product, and processed aggregates. The natural aggregates are taken from volcanic deposits, crushed, sized, and graded. These aggregates include various forms of pumice and scoria which usually weigh between 30 and 60 lb per cu ft.

The by-product aggregates include cinders, and the various metallurgical slags which are expanded by treating with controlled quantities of water. The cinders should be the residue from the high temperature combustion of coal or coke, should be hard and vitreous, practically free from sulfur, iron oxide, and combustible substances. Cinders usually weigh between 50 and 70 lb per cu ft. The expanded slag aggregates sold under such trade names as Waylite, Celocrete, Foamed Slag, and Superock usually weigh between 40 and 70 lb per cu ft.

The processed aggregates are made by subjecting raw materials to specific heat treatments to produce expanded or bloated lightweight aggregate characteristics. Expanded shales and clays weighing between 40 and 70 lb per cu ft are made by heating raw shale or clay to incipient fusion, cooling, and crushing. An important aggregate of this type is sold under the trade name of Haydite. Certain volcanic glasses expanded under heat produce highly porous and extremely lightweight aggregate, usually weighing between 6 and 12 lb per cu ft, called Perlite. Another extremely lightweight aggregate sold as Zonolite is made by heating a micaceous mineral for a few seconds to a temperature of about 1800°F. Its specific weight is about the same as that of Perlite.

Perlite and Zonolite are used for their very light weight and insulating characteristics. In loose granular state, they may be used as insulation fill in walls and on roofs of buildings. When they are mixed with water and a cementing agent, they may be used for insulating and acoustical plasters, insulating concrete roof fill, insulating structural roof slabs, acoustical tile, and other similar items.

Pumice, expanded shale or clay, cinders, and expanded blast-furnace slag may also be used for insulating floor and roof fill concrete, but produce a heavier and less insulating concrete. These aggregates are also used to make masonry units, various precast units, and structural monolithic concrete.

24. Miscellaneous Lightweight Aggregates. Many other materials such as grog, coke breeze, and sawdust have been used as lightweight aggregates in concrete. Sawdust has sometimes been used because it is cheap. Concrete made with it is light in weight, low in heat conductivity, resilient, may be easily cut after it has hardened, and will hold nails and screws. Various types of sawdust made from maple, yellow birch, hemlock, Douglas fir, white pine, and spruce have been used to make sawdust concrete. In order to avoid unsatisfactory results it is desirable to test the sawdust in a mortar. Various recommendations for processing sawdust include aging for periods up to 1 year, presoaking periods of at least 5 min, and washing for 24 hours. The processing period is usually followed by a drying period so that in mixing, the cement and the sawdust may be dry mixed before the water is added. A 1:3 mixture, by volume, of cement to sawdust with just enough water to produce good workability may be expected to have a 28-day compressive strength of 200 psi. If greater resistance to abrasion is required, additions of sand may be made. Some use has also been made of various mineralized sawdusts.

Making Mortar and Concrete

1. Introduction. When using concrete and mortar in construction the engineer is placed in the position of a manufacturer who fabricates a finished structural product from several raw materials. It is, therefore, necessary that he should be thoroughly cognizant of the properties of the constituent materials and the methods of handling them in order that a satisfactory product will result. In view of this consideration and in view of the great number of concrete constructions now being built, we shall pay considerable attention to the important factors which enter into the making of mortar and concrete.

It will be appreciated that very often the ideal conditions hereinafter mentioned cannot be attained in practice: Old cement must sometimes be used; only a fine-grained sand is attainable; the gravel is dirty or is of decidedly variable gradation and cannot be economically screened; a very wet consistency must be used on account of difficulties encountered in placing the concrete; or no care can be given to providing suitable curing conditions. Very often such undesirable conditions may be offset, to a large extent, by increasing the proportion of cement in the mixture. Many times it will be found economical to use local material of poor quality in a rich mixture rather than to ship in a superior sand or gravel and use a lean mix. Then, too, there is often a wide variation in the finished concrete, due to methods of handling. Changes in consistency may easily produce variations of 100 per cent in strength, and the methods of mixing and placing adopted by different concerns may also be responsible for as wide variations in properties. All of these facts emphasize the necessity of testing samples of concrete, made under the conditions of practice, before deciding upon the proper mixture to use; and also, they point out the importance of testing the product as used in the work. The procedures for securing, preparing, and testing specimens of hardened concrete are given in ASTM *Standard* C42.

DEFINITIONS

2. Mortar. A mixture of sand, screenings, or similar inert particles with cement and water which has the capacity of hardening into a rock-like mass is called mortar. In general the maximum size of the inert particles in mortars is less than $\frac{1}{4}$ in.

3. Concrete. A mixture of crushed stone, gravel, or similar inert material with a mortar is called concrete. The maximum size of inert particles in concrete is variable but is ordinarily under 2 in. Rubble concrete is made by embedding a considerable proportion of large boulders or blocks of stone in concrete.

4. Yield is used in two senses: (a) to indicate the ratio of the volume of mortar or concrete to the loosely measured volume of aggregate in the mix; (b) to indicate the volume of mortar or concrete in cubic feet which can be made with a sack of cement. In either sense it is useful in estimating quantities of material for making a given volume of concrete or mortar.

The volume of the concrete produced from a given batch may be obtained by placing and compacting all the concrete in a calibrated can, placing a loosely fitting plunger fastened to the lower end of a graduated piston rod on top of the concrete, and reading the volume on the piston rod opposite a fixed index.

The volume of concrete, in cubic feet, produced per batch may also be calculated after the specific weight of the concrete has been determined by dividing the total weight, in pounds, of all constituents in the batch by the specific weight, in pounds per cubic foot.

When the volume is known, the yield as it is most commonly used in the field, cubic feet of concrete per sack of cement, may be calculated by dividing the volume of concrete, in cubic feet, by the number of sacks of cement in the batch. The details of the test procedures may be found in ASTM *Standard* C138.

5. Absolute Volume. When a cubic foot measure is loosely filled with material, such as cement or aggregate, the apparent volume is 1 cu ft. This apparent volume is composed of the solid volume, or absolute volume of the material, plus the voids between the particles. The absolute volume, or the volume the material would occupy if there were no voids, may be determined by dividing the weight of the air-dry material, in pounds, by the product of the unit weight of water, 62.4 lb per cu ft, and the bulk specific gravity. When saturated surface-dry aggregates are used, the weight of the aggregate should be divided by the product of the unit weight of water and the bulk specific gravity of the aggregate (saturated surface-dry basis). Obviously the absolute volume of the material in the measure would increase if the weight of the material were increased because of greater compaction.

Two related terms frequently used are porosity and void ratio. Porosity may be defined as the ratio of the void space in a given apparent volume of material divided by the apparent volume, and expressed as a percentage. Void ratio may be defined as the ratio of the void space in a given apparent volume of material divided by the absolute volume of the solid material.

6. Density * is the ratio of the absolute volume of the solid particles of cement plus aggregate to the volume of the resulting mortar or concrete. If c, s, and g represent the absolute volumes of cement, sand, and gravel, respectively, in a unit volume of concrete, the density $= \rho = c + s + g$. If the specific gravities of the cement and aggregate are known, then the density of a mix may be computed as follows: Let $V =$ volume of mix; W_c, W_s, and $W_g =$ the weights of the cement, air-dry sand, and air-dry gravel, respectively; K_c, K_s, and $K_g =$ the bulk specific gravities of the cement, sand, and gravel, respectively; $W_w =$ the weight per cubic unit of water. Then

$$\rho = \frac{1}{W_w V} \left[\frac{W_c}{K_c} + \frac{W_s}{K_s} + \frac{W_g}{K_g} \right]$$

Experiments have shown that the density of a mortar or concrete is a measure of its strength and imperviousness.

THE PROPORTIONING OF MORTARS AND CONCRETES

7. The Principles of Proportioning. The fundamental object in proportioning concrete or mortar mixes is the production of a durable material of requisite strength, watertightness, and other essential properties at minimum cost. To attain this end, careful attention must be given to the selection of cement, aggregate, and water in accordance with preceding principles, and to the following considerations:

1. The mix must be workable so that it can be placed and finished without undue labor.†

2. Since cement is the most costly ingredient in the mix, the proportion used should be as small as is consistent with the attainment of desired properties.

3. Within wide limits, experiments have shown:

(a) The strength and degree of watertightness of mixes, having like constituent materials, density, and workability, increase with the cement content.

---

* Note that this definition differs from that usually given in treatises on mechanics by excluding the mass of the water. The term solidity ratio, adopted in *Tech. Paper* 58 of the National Bureau of Standards, is more exact.

† There is no simple method for measuring workability which is entirely satisfactory. Usually the slump, or flow, of the mix is specified, but either is really a criterion of consistency. The ease with which a mix can be worked and surfaced

(*b*) With the cement content, materials, and workability all constant, the strength and degree of watertightness increase with the density of the mix.

(*c*) For usual methods of placement, the strength and degree of watertightness of well-cured concrete and mortar are greatest when the mix is plastic (has a slump of approximately 2 in). Drier mixes, although frequently as strong, are likely to be porous unless compacted by pneumatic rammers or electrically driven vibrators. Increasing the water content beyond that required for plasticity causes the strength to decrease rapidly.

(*d*) Concrete with 3 to 6 per cent, by volume, entrained air made by using an air-entraining cement or by adding air-entraining admixtures is more resistant to freezing and thawing action and also to scaling due to the use of salt for ice removal than concrete made with regular cement and without air-entraining admixtures.

In addition to the above, the following statements appear to be justified by the results of experience and tests:

(*e*) To proportion concrete for the maximum resistance to fire, a porous non-combustible aggregate of high specific heat together with cement sufficient to provide the requisite strength should be thoroughly mixed and placed with as little ramming as possible to produce a porous concrete.

(*f*) In proportioning concrete or mortar which is to be subjected to freezing temperatures shortly after placement, a minimum amount of water and a quick-setting cement should be used. (Art. X-7.)

(*g*) Concrete for road construction should be made from a carefully graded, hard tough aggregate bound together with as small a proportion of rich mortar as is consistent with the required workability, strength, and imperviousness. In locations where resistance to freezing and thawing is required, the concrete should have from 3 to 6 per cent of entrained air.

The principal schemes used in scientific proportioning of mixes are based upon relationships between properties and ratio of cement to voids in the mix, or on the relationship between properties and the ratio of water to cement in the mix.

8. The Measurement of Proportions. The most accurate method of measuring proportions is to weigh the required quantities of each material. This may be done whether the proportions are based upon volumes or weights. This method is being extensively used in road construction and in many central mixing and in central proportioning plants. It is

with a trowel affords a rough index of workability. Unfortunately, personal equation and experience exert a powerful influence in such determinations.

also widely used in large building construction, but in small building construction the less accurate method of measuring proportions by volumes is frequently used. The chief inaccuracies in volumetric measurement arise from the wide variations in the bulk of the fine aggregate due to small changes in its moisture content and faulty methods of filling measuring devices. If a careful check is maintained both on the measures and methods of filling, much of the error in volumetric measurement can be obviated. Cement is usually measured by the bag, assuming that each bag contains 1 cu ft or 94 lb. More accuracy is obtained by weighing the cement also.

9. Arbitrarily Selected Proportions. A method of proportioning frequently used for small jobs is based upon arbitrary selection. In specifying proportions for mortars it is common practice to call for 1:2, 1:3, or 1:4 parts of cement to parts of fine aggregate, depending upon the quality of mortar demanded. In proportioning concrete by this method, the engineer, guided by experience and a knowledge of the requirements for the structure, assumes a mortar of given proportions and selects a proportion of stone such that the voids in the stone, as measured at the job, will be 15 to 25 per cent less than the volume of the mortar. Such methods or proportioning may give very fair results when used by a man experienced in judging aggregate, but in the hands of a person inexperienced in their use a poor mix or a waste of cement is likely to result.

10. Proportions Based on Voids. A great variety of rules for proportioning based upon the principle of filling the voids in the aggregate with cement have been formulated. There are two main reasons why such rules are not accurate. First, the problem of wetting the aggregate and bringing it into the same state of compactness which it assumes in the concrete or mortar is very difficult of solution; second, the general assumption that the particles of cement will fit into the void spaces in aggregate is fallacious, especially if particles passing a No. 50 sieve are present in the aggregate.

More satisfactory methods of mix design have been developed from the relation of the strength to the cement content and density of the mix. Thus Talbot and Richart * evolved a scientific and reliable method of mix design based upon a knowledge of the following factors:

1. The relation of strength of concrete to the cement-void ratio.

2. The relation of voids in mortar used in the concrete to the water content of the mortar.

3. The relation of the voids in the mortar to the ratio of the absolute volumes of sand and cement contained in the mortar.

* *Bull.* 137, Eng. Expt. Sta., Univ. Ill.

This method is fundamentally sound and accurate but it requires the determination of more experimental data than does the water-cement ratio method which follows.

11. Proportioning by the Water-Cement Ratio Method. In 1918 Abrams * established the validity of the following simple but very valuable law:

For placeable mixes made from durable aggregates the strength depends upon the net ratio of the mixing water to the cement. The net ratio is based upon the amount of water free to combine with the cement when setting begins. The water-cement ratio has been commonly computed by volume, but the weight ratio is handier in designing mixes.

Later it was shown that the water-cement ratio (x) bears a direct linear relation to the ratio of the volume of cement plus voids to the volume of cement $[(v + c)/c]$.† Hence it follows that this law expresses in an inverse manner the previously stated principle that the strength depends upon the ratio of the cement to the space in the concrete unoccupied by aggregate. The advantage of this law is its simplicity and its comparative independence of other variables. Success in the application of this method depends upon the care taken (a) in selecting materials; (b) in obtaining proper placeability with the use of minimum amount of cement; (c) in determining accurately the relation of the water-cement ratio to the desired property for the materials at hand; (d) in controlling the measurement of materials, especially the cement and water, at the job. The procedure is illustrated by the steps in the solution of the following typical example in which it is assumed that selection of materials has been made:

EXAMPLE. A concrete pavement is to be built in a northern climate. In order to resist frost action and to withstand traffic and other conditions, the concrete is to be made with a compressive strength of 4000 psi at 28 days. For workability a 2-in. slump is desired. The materials required per cubic yard of concrete, and their proportions, are to be determined.

The available coarse aggregate is a dolomitic gravel, all of which passes a 1½-in. sieve, 40 per cent passes a ¾-in. sieve, and all is held on a No. 4 sieve. The available sand is of good quality; it passes a No. 4 sieve and has a fineness modulus of 2.7. The specific weight of the gravel containing 1.5 per cent moisture and measured loose is 102 lb per cu ft; the specific weight of the sand measured loose with 3 per cent moisture, the normal content in stock pile, is 92 lb per cu ft. Costs are: cement, $4.00 per barrel (376 lb net); sand, air-dry, $2.25 per ton; gravel, air-dry, $2.50 per ton.

Solution. In order to determine the proper water-cement ratio (x) one may enter Abrams' curve between compressive strength (C) and the water ratio (Abrams' C-x curve in Fig. 1) with the given strength and find x. Then a paste may be made with

---

* *Bull.* 1, Structural Materials Laboratory, Lewis Institute.

† Report of Com. C-9, *Proc. ASTM,* Vol. 27, Part I, p. 370.

the given water-cement ratio (x) and, by trial, sand and gravel may be added to that paste until the desired workability is obtained. From the quantities used the mix proportions may be determined. The procedure is satisfactory for small jobs when the materials are of good quality. On large jobs or on work where the aggregates are unknown, it is best to find by trial the C-x curve for the available materials.

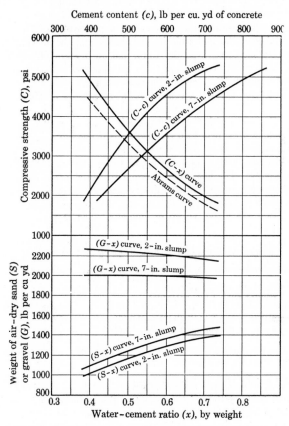

Fig. 1. Chart for designing concrete mixes using the strength-water-cement ratio relationship.

For the materials of this problem the strength-water ratio $(C$-$x)$ curve shown in Fig. 1 was constructed as follows:

Four values of the water ratio (x) were selected to cover the range in concrete strength likely to be used. For the mix of lowest water ratio a paste consisting of 25 lb of cement and 10 lb of water was thoroughly mixed and several additions of *air-dry* sand and gravel were made. In such procedure the endeavor was to use as much coarse aggregate and as little sand as possible, thereby promoting economy. On the other hand, if too little sand was used the mix became harsh and unworkable. Hence, if the mass, when worked with the trowel, appeared too harsh, more sand was added; or, if it appeared oversanded, more stone was added. Finally after the sand and gravel additions amounted to 30 and 82 lb, respectively, the slump was tested and found to be 1½ in. Since the absorption of the sand (for determination, see Art. XIII-5) was 0.6 per cent and of the gravel 0.4 per cent, the water absorbed by both was 0.5 lb. Hence the water free to combine with cement was $10 - 0.5 = 9.5$ lb, and $x = 9.5 \div 25 = 0.38$. The specific weight of the concrete was determined, and then the batch was made into three 6 by 12-in. cylinders in accordance with standard procedure. Similarly, the three other batches were made and molded into cylinders. On important work the number of batches should be doubled to reduce errors. After curing 1 day in molds and 27 days in moist air all cylinders were broken and the strength-water ratio (C-x) curve plotted (Fig. 1).

From the weights of the materials in each batch and the specific weights of the resultant concretes the cement, air-dry sand, and air-dry gravel contents were computed. These data made possible the plots for concrete with a 2-in. slump of the strength-cement content (C-c) curve, the water-cement ratio vs. weight of air-dry sand (S-x) curve, and the water-cement ratio vs. weight of air-dry gravel (G-x) curve.

Entering the C-x curve with $C = 4000$ psi, x is found to be 0.47. Entering the C-c curve for 2-in. slump with $C = 4000$ psi, the cement content c is found to be 540 lb per cu yd of concrete. From the S-x and the G-x curves for a 2-in. slump the weights of air-dry sand and gravel are found to be 1110 and 2220 lb per cu yd of concrete, respectively. The net water is equal to $540 \times 0.47 = 254$ lb per cu yd of concrete. The water absorbed by the air-dry aggregates is equal to $2220 \times 0.004 + 1110 \times 0.006 = 16$ lb per cu yd of concrete, and the total water to be added is then equal to $254 + 16 = 270$ lb per cu yd of concrete. The cost per cubic yard of the concrete is equal to

$$\tfrac{540}{376} \times 4.00 + \tfrac{1110}{2000} \times 2.25 + \tfrac{2220}{2000} \times 2.50 = \$9.77$$

The allowances for moisture in the sand and gravel per cubic yard of concrete are:

Sand weight with 3% moisture		1143 lb
Gravel weight with 1.5% moisture		2253 lb
Net water required	254 lb	
Excess water in sand 1110 (0.03 − 0.006)	− 27 lb	
Excess water in gravel 2220 (0.015 − 0.004)	− 24 lb	
Water to be added		203 lb
Cement		540 lb
Total weight of materials per cu yd		4139 lb

On a one-sack basis, with moist aggregates, the proportions by weight are obtained by dividing each of the above quantities by $540 \div 94 = 5.74$. Hence, with 1 sack of cement there would be required 199 lb of sand, 393 lb of gravel, and 35.4 lb of water. By volume, measured loose, the proportions would be $1:\tfrac{199}{92}:\tfrac{393}{102} = 1:2.16:3.85$ with 4.25 gal of water per sack of cement. The proportions by weight, air-dry aggregates, would be 540:1110:2220 or 1:2.05:4.11.

Trial of the above mix in a mixer might reveal deficiencies in working qualities or it might indicate that slightly less sand and more gravel could be economically used.

For many types of building construction more workable mixes than those just determined and more fluid consistencies are desirable. Hence the ratio of sand to total aggregate should be increased somewhat and the proportion of aggregate to paste reduced. For certain members the larger sizes of the coarse aggregate should be eliminated. To design mixes for such conditions the C-x curve for the materials is not appreciably changed but new C-c, S-x, and G-x curves should be determined. Data for these can be obtained by trial without performing strength tests. In Fig. 1 are shown such additional curves for a 7-in. slump, using the materials of the previous problem with coarse aggregate gradation unchanged.

To facilitate the use of this method, the slumps (adapted from Table 4 of the 1940 Joint Committee Report on Recommended Practice and Standard Specifications for Concrete and Reinforced Concrete), sand ratios, and moisture contents suggested by the Portland Cement Association in *Design and Control of Concrete Mixtures* are tabulated in Table 1.

TABLE 1. USEFUL DATA FOR DESIGNING CONCRETE MIXES

Recommended Slumps for Various Types of Construction

	Slump in Inches [1]	
Type of Construction	Maximum	Minimum
Reinforced foundation walls and footings	5	2
Plain footings, caissons, and substructure walls	4	1
Slabs, beams, and reinforced walls	6	3
Building columns	6	3
Pavements	3	2
Heavy mass construction	3	1

Recommended Proportions of Aggregates

	Ratio of Fine [2] to Total Aggregate on Basis of Dry, Compact Volumes, Measured Separately	
Maximum Size of Coarse Aggregate, Inches	Minimum	Maximum
⅜	0.55	0.70
¾	0.40	0.60
1 and over	0.30	0.50

Approximate Amounts of Free Water in Aggregates [3]

Very wet sand	6 to 8 per cent by weight
Wet sand	4 per cent by weight
Moist sand	2 per cent by weight
Moist gravel or crushed stone	1½ per cent by weight

Approximate Absorption of Air-Dry Aggregates

Ordinary sand	0.5 to 1 per cent by weight
Gravel and crushed limestone	0.5 to 1.5 per cent by weight
Trap rock and granite	0.3 to 0.5 per cent by weight
Porous sandstone	7.0 per cent by weight

[1] When high-frequency vibrators are used, the values given should be reduced about one-third.

[2] The finer the sand, the lower will be the percentage required.

[3] The amount of free water carried increases with the fineness of the aggregate.

XIV-10 Materials of Construction

Since aggregates in air-dry condition absorb water, allowance for absorption should be made when they are used in that condition. The absorption may be approximated by the method outlined in Art. XIII-5. The values in Table 1 may be used in absence of test data.

On important work moisture determinations should be run several times a day. When moisture-content determinations are not made, the approximate values in Table 1 may be assumed.

12. American Concrete Institute Standard Recommended Practice for the Design of Concrete Mixes.* Where data such as shown in Fig. 1 are not available for given materials, the determination of proper mix proportions may be most readily obtained by first selecting a trial mix that will approach the final proportions as closely as possible and then adjusting the trial proportions on the job. Initial trial mixes may be determined by following the procedure recommended by the American Concrete Institute.

The six factors in this recommended procedure are:

(*a*) Select the proper water-cement ratio to satisfy requirements for strength and durability. If data for specific conditions are not available, see Table 5 and Fig. 13, Chap. XV.

(*b*) Choose on the basis of job conditions the proper slump, and set limits on the maximum variation allowed. (See Table 1.)

(*c*) Determine on the basis of job conditions the maximum size of coarse aggregate.

(*d*) Estimate the minimum percentage of sand for proper workability. (See Table 2.)

(*e*) Estimate the required amount of water. (See Table 2.)

(*f*) Compute the trial mix proportions. These proportions should be adjusted on the job to obtain the required concrete.

In order to illustrate the method of computation, a trial mix will be designed for the following typical example:

EXAMPLE. Concrete to be used for thin reinforced slabs and beams not exposed to the weather is to be designed. The concrete should have a compressive strength of 3500 psi at 28 days and a slump of 5 in. The air-dry coarse aggregate is a dolomitic gravel with a maximum size of ¾ in. The air-dry natural sand has a maximum size of ¼ in. and has a fineness modulus of 2.85. Both aggregates have a bulk specific gravity of 2.65 (saturated surface-dry basis). The sand absorbs 0.5 per cent water and the gravel absorbs 1.0 per cent water, based on air-dry weight. Type I Portland cement is to be used.

Solution. Step 1. Refer to the compressive strength vs. water-cement ratio curve if available for the given materials, or to published curves such as those given in

* *Proc. Am. Concrete Inst.,* Vol. 41, June 1945, p. 651.

TABLE 2.   APPROXIMATE SAND AND WATER CONTENTS PER CUBIC
YARD OF CONCRETE [1]

Based on aggregates of average grading and physical characteristics in mixes having
a w/c of about 0.57 by weight or 6½ gal per sack of cement; 3-in. slump; and natural
sand having an F.M. of about 2.75.

| Maximum Size of Coarse Aggregate, inches | Rounded Coarse Aggregate | | | Angular Coarse Aggregate | | |
| | Sand, per cent of total aggregate by absolute volume | Net Water Content per Cubic Yard | | Sand, per cent of total aggregate by absolute volume | Net Water Content per Cubic Yard | |
		pounds	gallons		pounds	gallons
½	51	335	41	56	360	44
¾	46	310	37	51	335	40
1	41	300	36	46	325	39
1½	37	280	34	42	305	37
2	34	265	32	39	290	35
3	31	250	30	36	275	33
6	26	220	26	31	245	29

Adjustment of Values in Table 2 for Other Conditions

| Changes in Conditions Stipulated in Table 2 | Effect on Values in Table 2 | |
	Per cent sand [2]	Unit water content [2]
Each 0.05 increase or decrease in water-cement ratio	±1	0
Each 0.1 increase or decrease in F.M. of sand	±½	0
Each 1-in. increase or decrease in slump	. . .	±3%
Manufactured sand (sharp and angular)	∓3	+15 lb
For less workable concrete, as in pavements	−3	−8 lb

[1] Taken from *Am. Concrete Inst. Standard* 613–44, *Am. Concrete Inst. J.*, June 1945.

[2] (+) indicates an increase and (−) a decrease corresponding to the conditions stated
in the first column.

Fig. 13, Chapter XV, to determine the water-cement ratio. From the curves in Fig. 13, the ratio may be taken as 0.85 by volume or 0.57 by weight.

Step 2. From Table 2 the sand content may be obtained as 46 per cent of the total aggregate by absolute volume, and the net water content as 310 lb per cu yd. Both of these values must be corrected because of differences in various conditions for the trial mix compared to those assumed in Table 2. The sand content should be increased ½ per cent because the fineness modulus of the given sand is 0.10 higher than the assumed value, and should be 46.5 per cent. The net water should be increased 6 per cent because the slump of the trial batch is to be 2 in. greater than the assumed value, and should be 328.6 lb.

Step 3. The cement content may then be calculated from the equation

$$\text{Cement content} = \frac{\text{Net water content (lb/cu yd)}}{\text{Water-cement ratio (by weight)}} = \frac{328.6}{0.57} = 576 \text{ lb/cu yd}$$

Step 4. The absolute volume of the cement and water may then be calculated from:

$$\begin{aligned}\text{Absolute volume} \atop \text{(cement and water)} &= \frac{\text{Net water (lb/cu yd)}}{62.4} + \frac{\text{Cement content (lb/cu yd)}}{\text{Specific gravity} \times 62.4} \\ &= \frac{328.6}{62.4} + \frac{576}{3.15 \times 62.4} = 8.20 \text{ cu ft per cu yd of concrete}\end{aligned}$$

Step 5. The absolute volume of the total aggregate in a cubic yard of concrete is equal to 27 − the absolute volume of water and cement = 27.00 − 8.20 = 18.80 cu ft per cu yd of concrete.

Step 6. The absolute volume of sand in a cubic yard of concrete is equal to the per cent of sand times the absolute volume of the total aggregate = 0.465 × 18.80 = 8.74 cu ft per cu yd of concrete.

Step 7. The absolute volume of the gravel in a cubic yard of concrete is equal to the absolute volume of the total aggregate minus the absolute volume of the sand = 18.80 − 8.74 = 10.06 cu ft per cu yd of concrete.

Step 8. The weight of the surface-dry sand per cubic yard of concrete is equal to the product of the absolute volume of the sand, the specific gravity of the sand, and the specific weight of water. In this problem it is equal to 8.74 × 2.65 × 62.4 = 1445 lb per cu yd of concrete.

Step 9. The weight of the surface-dry gravel is equal to the product of the absolute volume of the gravel, the specific gravity of the gravel, and the specific weight of water. In this problem it is equal to 10.06 × 2.65 × 62.4 = 1665 lb per cu yd of concrete.

Step 10. The weight of air-dry sand and gravel and the total water are then calculated.

$$\begin{aligned}\text{Air-dry sand} &= 1445/1.005 = 1438 \text{ lb per cu yd} \\ \text{Air-dry gravel} &= 1665/1.01 = 1649 \text{ lb per cu yd} \\ \text{Total water} &= 328.6 + 7 + 16 = 351.6 \text{ lb per cu yd}\end{aligned}$$

Step 11. The dry-weight proportions are then:

$$576:1438:1649 \quad \text{or} \quad 1:2.50:2.86$$

The water to be added is 6.88 gal per sack of cement.

The proportions obtained by this method should be used to make a trial batch of concrete on the job since it is frequently necessary to make adjustments in consistency and in the fine-coarse aggregate ratio. The proportions obtained in Step 11 above will usually give a slightly over-sanded mix, and in certain instances this is necessary. However, in the interests of economy, the sand content should be kept as low as possible without adversely affecting the workability. Adjustments of batch weights are frequently necessary because of the variable water content of the aggregates.

13. Air-Entrained Concrete. All concrete made with normal Portland cement contains some incidentally entrapped or natural air, usually varying between $\frac{1}{2}$ and 2 per cent. This air occurs in relatively large bubbles, is poorly distributed, and does not significantly affect the workability and durability of the concrete. The entrained air intentionally added, usually between 3 and 6 per cent of the volume of the concrete, consists of millions of uniformly distributed minute globules. Entrained air in concrete greatly improves resistance to freezing and thawing, and also resistance to surface scaling of pavements which is due to the use of various salts to melt ice coatings in the winter months. Air entrainment reduces bleeding and segregation, and increases workability and homogeneity. An increase in the yield along with the increase in workability due to air entrainment permits the use of lower sand and water contents than those used in concrete mixes which do not contain entrained air. Some reductions in strength due to air entrainment may be expected, especially in the richer mixes, but these reductions may be largely offset by changes in mix design which take advantage of smaller sand and water contents.

Entrained air may be produced in concrete by the use of gas-generating agents or by the use of foaming agents. The usual procedure in concrete is to use foaming agents, which include fatty acids, detergents, fatty alcohols, resins, and resinates. Materials widely used for this purpose are sold as Darex Vinsol resin, and N-Tair (see Art. IX-2). The air-entraining agents should not accelerate or retard the time of set of the cement. They should not increase the normal shrinkage of mortar or concrete under air storage conditions or the expansion under moist storage. In addition, the agent itself (not the air entrained by it) should have no harmful effect on the strength properties of the mortar or concrete.

Air may be entrained in concrete in two ways. In the first, an air-entraining cement, Type IA, IIA, or IIIA, which contains a small amount of an interground air-entraining agent, may be used; and in the second, plain Portland cement is used and the necessary amount of the air-entraining agent is added at the concrete mixer. Each method has certain advantages and disadvantages. When an air-entraining cement is used, it is possible that the air content of the concrete made with it may not be within the required limits. If the air content is too high, it may be necessary to use a proper blend of plain and air-entraining cements; and when it is too low it may be necessary to provide additional air-entraining agents at the mixer. Some changes in the air content may also be made by adjusting the mix proportions and changing the mixing procedure. Under usual conditions, the amount of air will increase as the sand content is increased, as the consistency is increased, as the temperature decreases, and as the richness of the mix is decreased; the air content is also dependent on the type of mixer, length of mixing period, and method of placement. The amount of entrained air may be fairly well controlled when the second method is used, but this involves handling an additional material on the job.

Regardless of the method used for entraining air, the actual air content of the concrete should be checked by either the gravimetric or the pressure method. The gravimetric method requires that the actual unit weight of the concrete be carefully determined and that the weights and specific gravities of all constituents be accurately known. The air content may then be calculated from the relation:

$$\text{Per cent of air} = \frac{(\text{Theoretical unit weight-Actual unit weight}) \times 100}{\text{Theoretical unit weight}}$$

The theoretical unit weight may be obtained by dividing the total batch weight by the sum of the absolute volumes of the individual constituents. The details of this test may be found in ASTM *Standard* C138.

The pressure method is a simple application of Boyle's law, and the test procedure consists essentially of taking a known volume of concrete at atmospheric pressure and determining the reduction in volume due to an increase in pressure. It is assumed that the reduction in volume is due solely to the compression of the air in the concrete. Air contents determined in this manner must usually be corrected for the air contained within the aggregate particles. After the correction is once known for given aggregates, it need be only occasionally checked.

Since air in concrete tends to increase yield and workability and to reduce strength, air-entrained concrete is usually designed to have a smaller sand-total aggregate ratio and less water than similar concrete without entrained air. The actual adjustments to be made depend on the required air content and on whether the mix is to be designed for given strength, given water-cement ratio, or given cement content. The suggested adjustments that follow are essentially those recommended by the Portland Cement Association in *Design and Control of Concrete Mixtures*. They are approximate but accurate enough for the design of the first trial batch. Further changes as required should be made on the job. In order to illustrate the method, the mix designed in Art. 12 for concrete without entrained air is redesigned for an air content of 4½ per cent.

Design for Given Strength. The proportions determined in Art. 12 were 576 lb of cement, 1445 lb of surface-dry sand, 1665 lb of surface-dry gravel, and 328.6 lb of water, or 94 lb of cement, 236 lb of sand, 272 lb of gravel, and 6.43 gal of water. In order that the air-entrained concrete will have the same strength as the designed concrete without air, the water content per sack of cement should be reduced ¼ gal for each per cent of entrained air, and the sand content per sack of cement should be reduced 10 lb for each per cent of entrained air. For the given problem, the water should be reduced 4½ × ¼ or 1.12 gal per sack, and the sand should be reduced 4½ × 10 or 45 lb per sack. The adjusted mix should then consist of 94 lb cement, 191 lb of sand, 272 lb of gravel, and 5.31 gal of water. Concrete mixes adjusted in this manner should have the required strength but will require higher cement contents, especially in the rich mixes.

Design for Given Water-Cement Ratio. In this case, the coarse aggregate should be increased about 5 per cent for each per cent of entrained air. For the given problem, the gravel should be increased 0.05 × 4½ × 272 or 61 lb. The adjusted mix should then consist of 94 lb of cement, 236 lb of sand, 333 lb of gravel, and 6.43 gal of water. Concrete mixes adjusted in this manner will have slightly lower strengths and cement contents compared to the plain concrete.

Design for Given Cement Content. In this case, the sand may be reduced about 5 lb per sack of cement for each per cent of entrained air. The reduction in water content per sack of cement depends on the richness of the mix and varies from ¼ gal per sack for each per cent of entrained air for very lean mixes to no change for the richest mixes. Assuming the given mix as intermediate, the water may be decreased 4½ × ⅛ or 0.56 gal per sack, and the sand may be decreased 5 × 4½ or about 22 lb. The adjusted mix should then consist of 94 lb of cement, 214 lb of sand, 272 lb of gravel, and 5.87 gal of water. This method provides mixes that have the same cement content as those made with plain cement, but the air-entrained concrete will usually have lower strength. The strength decreases are small for lean concrete (may even be slight increases), but are significant for rich concrete.

14. Proportions for Different Constructions. The mixes listed in Table 3 are satisfactory when good materials and workmanship are used. Proportions marked * refer to natural cement mortars. For ease in laying, the Portland cement (C) in masonry mortars is often tempered with 25 to 50 per cent of quicklime paste or hydrated lime (L). Compressive strength values are for moist curing at 70°F. Allowance for effects of other temperatures can be made from information in Art. XV-42. For influence of different curing conditions see Fig. XV-9 and Table XV-7.

TABLE 3

Mortar for

Laying masonry:	Proportions by Volume
In exposed or wet locations..................................	$1 : 2$ to $1 : 3$
In exterior walls of buildings.............................	$\left\{\begin{array}{l} 1C : 1L : 6S \\ 1* : 2 \text{ to } 1* : 3 \end{array}\right.$
Filling joints in sewer pipe...............................	$\left\{\begin{array}{l} 1 : 0 \text{ to } 1 : 2 \\ 1* : 0 \text{ to } 1* : 1 \end{array}\right.$
Surfaces of floors and sidewalks...........................	$1 : 1$ to $1 : 2$
Waterproof linings...	$1 : 0$ to $1 : 2$
Cement bricks and blocks...................................	$1 : 2\frac{1}{2}$ to $1 : 4$

	Desired Compressive Strength at 28 Days (Lb.-In.²)	Water-Cement Ratio		Proportions by Volume
		By Weight	Gallons per Sack	
Concrete for				
High early strength in pavements; strong columns, beams, and slabs; or for structures very severely exposed......	5500	0.40	$4\frac{1}{2}$	$1 : 1 : 2$ to $1 : 1\frac{1}{2} : 3$
Walls, dams, piers, pavements, and other structures requiring high strength or watertightness; or for structures severely exposed...................	4500	0.50	$5\frac{1}{2}$	$1 : 1\frac{1}{2} : 2\frac{1}{2}$ to $1 : 2 : 3\frac{1}{2}$
Walls, dams, piers, reservoir linings, exposed to weather in northern climate. Watertight structures, pipes, tanks, sewers, pavements, and thin members exposed to frost action.............	3800	0.55	6	$1 : 1\frac{1}{2} : 3$ to $1 : 2\frac{1}{4} : 4$
Walls, dams, piers, reservoir linings, exposed to weather in southern climate. Basement walls or thin structural parts subjected to moderate exposure......	3000	0.60	$6\frac{3}{4}$	$1 : 2 : 3$ to $1 : 2\frac{1}{2} : 4$
Enclosed structural members, piers, retaining walls, foundations, and footings protected from alternate wetting and drying and from severe weather..	2200	0.65	$7\frac{1}{2}$	$1 : 2\frac{1}{4} : 3\frac{1}{2}$ to $1 : 3 : 5$
Mass concrete requiring little strength and well protected.................	1800	0.75	$8\frac{1}{2}$	$1 : 2\frac{1}{2} : 4\frac{1}{2}$ to $1 : 3\frac{1}{2} : 6$

15. Interpretation of the Meaning of Proportions. Sometimes it becomes necessary to substitute a pit-run gravel or other mixed aggregate when the specifications call for separate measurement of the fine and coarse aggregate. Since such substitution often causes disagreement, it should be provided for in the specifications. To illustrate, consider a 1:2:4 mix of cement, sand, and gravel measured by volume. It has been erroneously argued many times that the equivalent proportions with pit-run gravel are 1:6, whereas volume measurements of 2:4 mixture of sand and gravel will generally show that about 1:5 or even a richer proportion is the proper equivalent. Furthermore, unless the pit-run material is well graded, it is likely that the quality of the substituted mix will be inferior to the specified even though the equivalent ratio of cement to aggregate is used.

16. Quantities of Materials Required for 1 Cubic Yard of Mortar and Concrete. The values given in Table 4 are computed from the results of

TABLE 4. YIELD IN MORTAR FOR DIFFERENT PROPORTIONS OF AGGREGATES BASED ON LOOSE MEASUREMENTS OF VOLUME *

All aggregates passed a $\frac{1}{4}$-in. sieve and were air dry.   Plastic consistency

No.†	Per Cent Voids	Per Cent (by Wt.) Passing Sieve				Yield for Mix			
		10	30	50	100	1 : 2	1 : 3	1 : 4	1 : 5
S ‡......	37.0	100.0	0	0	0	1.18	1.11	1.08	1.07
Sd1......	36.5	86.4	39.0	9.1	2.8	1.18	1.08	1.03	1.01
Sd2......	35.2	81.2	61.4	34.5	9.7	1.25	1.15	1.10	1.07
Sd3......	38.2	91.9	39.7	13.7	1.2	1.22	1.11	1.06	1.03
Sd4......	39.8	100.0	95.8	62.5	8.6	1.30	1.15	1.09	1.04
Sd5......	45.3	100.0	99.8	67.6	5.7	1.22	1.09	1.03	0.99
Sd7......	36.6	67.7	25.9	11.2	2.2	1.19	1.07	0.99	0.95
Sd8......	36.4	82.0	55.3	16.1	1.9	1.21	1.09	1.95	1.01
Sd9......	36.0	66.8	13.9	4.9	1.4	1.14	1.03	0.98	0.95
Sd10.....	27.9	69.7	34.0	17.4	6.5	1.26	1.14	1.05	0.96
Sd11.....	35.0	72.0	23.8	4.3	0.5	1.21	1.08	1.01	0.99
Sg1......	42.0	62.8	35.5	25.1	13.0	1.13	1.01	0.93	0.88
Sg3......	39.0	64.0	28.0	19.5	13.8	1.15	0.99	0.92	0.88
Sg4......	40.0	69.0	32.6	23.8	15.9	1.15	1.01	0.93	0.88
Tg1......	43.6	34.6	15.4	11.5	7.5	1.07	0.97	0.89	0.84

* Weight per cubic foot of cement was taken at 100 lb.
† Sd =sand; sg =screenings; Tg =zinc mine tailings.   ‡ Standard Ottawa sand.

yield tests on 15 different sands and screenings.* All these aggregates were in air-dry condition at the time of test. It will be appreciated that the values will not apply to all mixes with equal accuracy, since the kind of cement, per cent moisture in aggregate, gradation of sizes, and percentage of particles passing a No. 100 sieve will considerably influence the yield. The greatest variations in yield are produced by variations in the moisture content in the aggregate. If the per cent moisture is known allowance for such variations may be made by using the information in Fig. XIII-5 in connection with the yields in Table 4.

* *Proc. ASTM*, Vol. 13, p. 834.

For common mixes and aggregates the volume of concrete can be very closely estimated from the sum of the absolute volumes of the dry materials and the water. With lean mixes and also with porous aggregates such estimates will be smaller than the actual volumes of concrete. The following statements of this principle are useful:

$$S = \frac{27}{0.5 + x' + \dfrac{W_s}{62.5K_s} + \dfrac{W_g}{62.5K_g}} \tag{1}$$

$$S = \frac{27}{0.5 + x' + s(1 - v_s) + g(1 - v_g)} \tag{2}$$

Here S = the number of sacks of cement per cubic yard of concrete.
x' = the volume of water in cubic feet per sack of cement.
W_s = pounds of surface-dry fine aggregate per sack of cement.
W_g = pounds of surface-dry coarse aggregate per sack of cement.
K_s and K_g = bulk specific gravities of fine and coarse aggregates, respectively (saturated surface-dry).
s = number of volumes of fine aggregate per sack of cement.
g = number of volumes of coarse aggregate per sack of cement.
v_s and v_g = voids in fine and coarse aggregate, respectively, as measured on job.

In using either of these equations the excess moisture in the aggregates should be included in computing x'.

EXAMPLE. Calculate the materials required for 200 cu yd of 1:2:3 (by vol) concrete. The water-cement ratio is 6 gal per sack of cement. The sand contains 3 per cent and the gravel 1 per cent of excess water. The weights per cubic foot measured loose at the job are sand 95 lb and gravel 102 lb. Bulk specific gravities are sand 2.65 and gravel 2.70.

By formula 1: $x' = 6 \div 7.5 = 0.8$, $W_s = 2(95 \div 1.03) = 185$ lb, and $W_g = 3(102 \div 1.01) = 303$ lb; hence

$$S = \frac{27}{0.5 + 0.8 + 185 \div (62.5 \times 2.65) + 303 \div (62.5 \times 2.70)} = 6.41 \text{ sacks}$$

Sand, moisture included, per cubic yard of concrete = $6.41 \times 2 \times 95 = 1215$ lb. Gravel, moisture included, per cubic yard of concrete = $6.41 \times 3 \times 102 = 1960$ lb. Water to be added per cubic yard = $6.41 \times 0.8 \times 62.5 - 1215 \times (0.03/1.03) - 1960 \times 0.01/1.01 = 265$ lb.

By formula 2: the voids may be measured, or, from data above,

$$1 - v_s = \frac{95 \div 1.03}{62.5 \times 2.65} = 0.557 \quad \text{and} \quad 1 - v_g = \frac{102 \div 1.01}{62.5 \times 2.70} = 0.599$$

hence $$S = \frac{27}{0.5 + 0.8 + 2 \times 0.557 + 3 \times 0.599} = 6.41 \text{ sacks}$$

If purchased on a surface-dry basis there would be required for 1 cu yd of concrete 0.59 ton of sand and 0.97 ton of gravel. If sold damp and loose by the cubic yard the sand required is 1215 ÷ (27 × 95) = 0.48 cu yd, and the gravel is 1960 ÷ (27 × 102) = 0.71 cu yd. Values of specific gravity for common aggregates may be found in Art. XIII-16 and VII-18. Errors of 0.1 in the assumed value will not greatly affect the computed quantities. Voids may be readily computed by entering Fig. 6, Art. XIII-16, with weight of surface-dry sand in a cubic foot and bulk specific gravity.

17. Simplified Methods of Calculating Quantities. A simple method of determining quantities of materials for a given volume of concrete depends on the knowledge of the specific weight of the mixed concrete. If this value is known from previous work, or if it can be estimated from the known properties of the materials to be used, satisfactory results will be obtained. With usual aggregates and concrete mixtures this value may be expected to vary between 148 and 154 lb per cu ft, and for air-entrained concrete the value may be estimated about 5 lb per cu ft lower. Average values may be assumed at 150 and 145 lb per cu ft.

If, for example, it is required to determine the amounts of cement, air-dry sand, air-dry gravel, and mixing water to make 1 cu ft of plain concrete of proportions 1:2:4, by weight, and with a water-cement ratio of 0.50, by weight, the first step is to select a specific weight value. The weight of the cement per cubic foot of concrete may then be calculated as 20 lb by dividing the specific weight of the concrete, 150 lb per cu ft, by the sum of the parts by weight, 7.5. The weights of all constituents per cubic foot of concrete are: cement 20 lb, air-dry sand 40 lb, air-dry gravel 80 lb, and net water 10 lb. If the absorption factors for the air-dry aggregates are known, the water of absorption may be easily calculated; and if the aggregates have excess water, the free water in the aggregate may be calculated as in Art. 11.

18. Checking Proportions of Fresh Concrete. It is desirable at times to check the proportions of the concrete delivered to a job, or the proportions of concrete placed in various locations to ascertain the amount of segregation. A method for the analysis of fresh concrete given by W. M. Dunagan [*] is fairly rapid and gives good results if carefully used. The method with some slight modifications follows:

Step 1. Select a representative sample of the fresh concrete weighing about 4 kg and weigh it in air to the nearest 0.5 gm. If the yield and the quantities of materials for a given volume of concrete are to be determined, the specific weight of the concrete sample should also be determined.

Step 2. Determine the weight of the concrete sample immersed in water to the nearest 0.5 gm.

Step 3. Place the sample on a No. 4 sieve which is nested on a No. 100 sieve, and wash the sample until all the cement and the silt associated with the aggregate have been washed through.

* *Bull.* 113, Iowa State College.

Step 4. Determine the weight of the coarse aggregate, material retained on the No. 4 sieve, immersed in water. Then add the fine aggregate retained on the No. 100 sieve to the coarse aggregate and obtain the weight of the combined aggregate immersed in water.

Step 5. Determine the immersed weight of the fine aggregate by subtracting the immersed weight of the coarse aggregate from that of the combined aggregate. Also, determine the immersed weight of the cement by subtracting the immersed weight of the combined aggregate from that of the concrete sample.

Step 6. Correct the immersed weights of the fine aggregate and the cement to take into account the silt associated with the fine aggregate. The amount of the correction may be obtained by multiplying the immersed weight of the fine aggregate by the silt correction factor. The correction should be added to the immersed weight of the fine aggregate and subtracted from that of the cement.

Step 7. The weights of the cement, surface-dry sand, and surface-dry gravel may then be calculated from the equation

$$W = w \frac{\text{(Specific gravity)}}{\text{(Specific gravity} - 1)}$$

In this equation, W is the required weight, w is the immersed corrected weight of the cement, sand, or gravel, and the specific gravity for the aggregates is the bulk specific gravity on a saturated surface-dry basis.

Step 8. The weight of the net water may then be calculated by subtracting the sum of the weights of all solid constituents obtained in Step 7 from the weight of the original sample in air.

After the weights of the constituents are known, the proportions may be calculated.

19. Checking Proportions of Hardened Concrete. The problem of checking on the proportions of a hardened concrete is a difficult one, and a satisfactory solution may be impossible under certain circumstances. It is far better to provide adequate supervision on the job at the time the concrete is placed to see that the proper proportions and methods are being used than to attempt any checking of the hardened concrete. Proportions of the fresh concrete at the time of placement can be easily obtained in accordance with the method given in Art. 18.

There is a strong tendency to attribute poor concrete performance largely to the use of a poor cement or to the use of less cement than required. Both of these factors are important, and either or both may be the basic cause, but probably more frequently one or more of the following may be largely responsible: poorly graded aggregates, dirty aggregates, unsound or friable aggregates, contaminated materials, excess mixing water, poor proportions, insufficient mixing, unsatisfactory transportation and placement procedures, and lack of proper curing. In addition, failure of concrete may be due to entirely different causes such as poor structural design or poor foundations.

When all the materials used in a concrete are available, a check on the cement content of the hardened concrete may be made in accordance with the method given in ASTM *Standard* C85. The method is not applicable, however, to hardened concrete that contains aggregates or admixtures that liberate soluble silica under the test conditions. The method essentially consists of crushing and pulverizing a sample, more than 10 lb, of the hardened concrete to a fineness of approximately 150 to 200 mesh. A representative sample is then dried and subjected to a specified chemical test procedure to determine the silica content. The soluble silica content of the aggregates used should be determined and subtracted from the value found for the concrete to give the amount due to the cement. The percentage of cement may then be calculated by dividing the corrected percentage of silica in the concrete by the silica of the cement used, or by the average value 0.2175 if the value for the cement is not known. When the materials used in a given concrete are not known, the value of this test is questionable.

20. Testing the Quality of Concrete. Auxiliary tests on the aggregate are of assistance in making a selection of the proper aggregate, and the use of proper methods of proportioning tends toward economy in cement, but the value of these tests and schemes can only be ascertained by tests on the concrete itself. In making such tests, the sampling and proportioning of the materials, the method of mixing, the placing and the curing conditions for the specimens should all be controlled so that the test pieces will in every way represent the concrete to be used in construction. Workability tests and strength tests are the chief control tests made on concrete.

The workability of concrete is judged by visual examination, and by various tests such as slump, flow, and bleeding. Visual examination provides a great deal of information to experienced individuals. Estimates of the slump and bleeding may be quickly made, and the mix may be judged as harsh, or oversanded. The cohesiveness or the ability of the mixture to stick together, and the workability under a trowel may be obtained by simple operation. The slump, or consistency test, is made by placing the freshly made concrete in three layers in a frustum of a cone (top diameter 4 in., bottom diameter 8 in., and altitude 12 in.) placed on a metal base. Each layer is puddled 25 times with a bullet-pointed rod. After the last layer has been rodded, the surplus concrete is struck off, the mold is withdrawn vertically, and the subsidence or slump of the top of the mass is measured. Complete details for the slump and flow tests are given in ASTM *Standards* C143 and C124. The test for bleeding (ASTM Des. C232) consists essentially of taking freshly made concrete and placing it in a ½ cu ft container to a height of 10 in. The container should be weighed, covered, and placed on a level floor and zero time then recorded. The water rising to the top of the concrete, bleeding water, should be drawn off at 20-min intervals for a period of

3 hours and measured in a graduate. The bleeding water may then be expressed as a percentage of the net mixing water.

For testing the compressive strength of concrete a cylinder with ratio of diameter to height of 1:2 is good practice (see Art. III-16). The diameter of the mold should be at least three times and preferably four times the maximum diameter of the aggregate. With aggregate between $\frac{3}{4}$ in. and 2 in. in maximum diameter, a 6 × 12-in. cylinder is generally used. For tests of concrete with larger sizes of aggregate 8 × 16 and 10 × 20-in. cylinders are used. Standard methods for making and testing compression specimens are given in ASTM *Standards* Des. C31, C39, and C192.

Transverse tests of concrete afford a good means of determining quality, especially in concrete pavement construction. By use of the modified cube test, Art. III-16, the compressive strength can also be obtained from the beam ends. Methods of mixing, molding, curing, and testing are given in ASTM *Standards* Des. C78–38. It is essential that non-absorbent molds be used. Beams should be molded in two equal layers. Each layer should be puddled with a $\frac{5}{8}$-in. rod, 25 strokes per square foot of top surface. The sides of each layer should be surfaced with a mason's trowel. The top of a beam should be struck off flush with the top of the mold with a trowel. Evaporation of moisture from the top surface should be prevented by placing the beam in a moist closet or by covering the top with a wet canvas until the molds are stripped. For concrete made with aggregate having maximum diameter of $\frac{3}{4}$ to $1\frac{1}{2}$ in., a beam 4 × 6 in. in cross section can be used; for concrete of aggregate under 2 in. in size, a beam 6 × 6 or 6 × 8 in. in cross section is satisfactory. The span length for the beam should not be less than twice and preferably not less than three times the depth of the beam.

Loading beams at the third points of the span produces a wider distribution of the maximum fiber stress than a center loading or a cantilever loading. For third-point loading, the length of span is immaterial * when the length is over twice the depth, but for the center loading and especially the cantilever loading the effect of span length is noticeable. The cantilever loading gives the highest modulus of rupture and the third-point loading the lowest. The discrepancy for short spans may amount to 30 per cent. Hence it is necessary to specify the method of loading for transverse tests on concrete. A suitable machine for field testing is described in Art. II-11. Owing to the presence of shrinkage strains in the top surfaces, it is well to subject top fibers to tensile stress in making beam tests. The relation of modulus of rupture from beam tests to the tensile and compressive strength of concrete is considered in Art. XV-16.

* See Report of Research Director of Portland Cement Associaton, 1928.

When using either strength test as a criterion of quality, there should be made at least 3 specimens for each variable covered. For high early strength concrete, tests at 1, 2, or 3 days are made, but for ordinary mixes 7 and 28 days are the more common test ages. In some road constructions, beam tests are run at frequent intervals in order to determine the proper time for opening the road to traffic. When the durability of concrete is in question or the effect of curing is to be ascertained, tests should run over much longer periods of time.

For certain purposes, abrasion, absorption, fire, or freezing tests of concrete are made (see Chapters VIII and XV for types of tests used).

MIXING, PLACING, AND CURING

21. Principles of Proper Mixing. The first consideration in mixing either mortar or concrete should be to bring all materials into a homogeneous mixture of uniform consistency in the minimum amount of time and without waste. Whatever method of mixing is used, in order to insure that in the completed batch each grain of aggregate will be coated with cement paste, the aggregate and cement should be dry mixed for a short time. The object of this dry mixing is to distribute evenly the cement throughout the mass and to prevent it from balling up when the water is added. Since the time of mixing may be somewhat shortened if dry sand is employed, it may be economical on large jobs to cover the storage pile. On the other hand, a porous aggregate should not be allowed to completely dry since it will absorb water from the cement paste and adversely affect the hardening properties of the mix. Instances in which this action has caused a failure of the structure have been recorded.

The question of the proper consistency largely depends upon the character of the work. At the present time variations from a dry consistency which will barely show moisture under heavy ramming to a soupy mix which can be spouted into the molds are in use. The general practice in this country is to employ a wet mix which will readily flow for nearly all reinforced concrete construction. In European countries practice favors a somewhat drier consistency. The effects of different consistencies on the properties of mortar and concrete are discussed in Art. XV-5, 13, and 30.

22. Hand Mixing. Mortar can be hand mixed most satisfactorily in a tight wooden or sheet-metal box. For a 3- or 4-wheelbarrow batch a box 4 × 8 ft with sides 8 or 10 in. high is convenient. The sand is spread in a layer of uniform thickness over the bottom of the box and covered by a similar layer of cement, or if the batch is large the cement may be sandwiched between equal layers of sand. The dry materials are then thoroughly mixed by hoe or by shovel until the mass is of uniform appearance.

If shovels are employed the men should work in pairs, partners facing each other on opposite sides of the box. Beginning at one end and working toward the other, both men shovel simultaneously into the pile, giving each shovelful a flip which scatters the material as it falls. The entire pile should be given at least three turns in this manner. A long crater is next formed in the pile and filled with water. The batch should then be given at least three more turns with the shovels.

Mixing by hoe is not so effective as by shovels, if two or more men are available. If the hoe is employed, water is generally added at the end of the box, the dry mix is rapidly drawn down into it, and the whole mass vigorously worked until the consistency is uniform.

For hand mixing of concrete, a tight platform somewhat larger than the mortar box is desirable, and the mixing should be done with shovels. The following method is rapid and conserves labor: The sand is spread in a layer 4 to 6 in. thick at one end of the platform and covered with the proper proportion of cement. These materials are then given three turns and the mixture formed into a wide crater into which the stone or gravel is dumped. The predetermined amount of water is then poured over the gravel, and the edges of the pile gradually turned in to absorb the water. The whole mass is then given three or more turns until it is of uniform consistency.

For mixing small batches of three to five 6 × 12-in. test cylinders, a 3½ × 5-ft tray of No. 16 gage galvanized iron with its edges rolled upward about 3 in. is convenient. The procedure for mixing outlined above is satisfactory, but the dry sand and cement should be mixed at least six turns and the wetted batch ten turns.

23. Machine Mixing. Most concrete is now mixed by machine. Although there are a great many designs and forms of mixers, they may all be separated into two classes—batch mixers and continuous mixers. In the operation of a batch mixer a definite charge of materials is mixed and discharged before another batch is admitted. The other type of mixer receives and discharges material continuously.

In general, concrete made in a batch mixer is more uniform than the product of the continuous mixer for the following reasons: All portions of the charge are mixed together in the batch machine, whereas in the continuous mixer product the uniformity of successive portions depends upon the regularity of the feeding device. Furthermore, in most types of continuous mixer the time of mixing is too short for thorough work, whereas in the batch machine the mixing period can be regulated as desired.

In selecting a mixer, special attention should be given not only to the initial cost of the machine but also to other factors which vitally affect the quality of the product, efficiency, cost of operation and maintenance, such as: (1) time required to produce a homogeneous mix; (2) waste in charging and discharging; (3) rapidity of charging and discharging; (4) ease in cleaning; (5) durability of mechanical parts; (6) capacity of the power drive; (7) visibility of charge during mixing; (8) accuracy of water-feeding device; (9) uniformity in quality of discharge; (10) completeness of the discharge. In general the capacity of a batch mixer should be a little greater than can be handled by the gang employed.

In mixing with batch mixers it is desirable to have the sand, cement, and coarse aggregate intermingle as much as possible as they are gradually chuted into the mixer in order to cut down time in the mixer. A small amount of water should precede the dry materials, and then it should be continuously admitted in such manner that the blades and drum are washed and the water is well distributed through the mass. Usually admission of water is continued until after all other materials are in the drum. Experiments with small mixers on wet concrete have shown that the 28-day compressive strength of the concrete is improved from 5 to 15 per cent by increasing the time of mixing from 30 sec to 10 min, but the gain in strength after mixing 5 min was small. Premixing of the cement and water does not affect an increase in strength. For producing uniform and impervious concrete, mixes cured only a few days require more mixing than those cured a month; lean mixes require longer mixing than rich mixes; dry mixes require longer periods than wet mixes; and mixes with find sand require more time than those with coarse sand.

For mixers of 1, 3, and 5 cu yd capacity, the Bureau of Public Roads tests * indicate that there is no material gain in strength obtained by extending the time of mixing concrete of 1- to 6-in. slump beyond 1 min. They indicate also that with the largest mixers there is a considerable addition of fine material owing to attrition as the mixing period is increased from 1 to 4 min. At the Grand Coulee Dam † the total time required for mixing was 3 min with ¾ min allowed for charging and discharging the 4 cu yd mixers.

Ready-mixed concrete is now extensively used. This commodity is produced either (a) by a central mixing plant and hauled to the job by trucks equipped with agitators (air-entrained concrete is frequently transported by specially designed dump trucks), or (b) by a central proportioning plant and a transit mixer which operates during conveyance to the job. Tests by S. C. Hollister ‡ indicate that there is little effect on

* *Public Roads*, July 1928, and Nov. 1934.

† *Eng. News-Record*, Jan. 23, 1936, p. 119.

‡ *Proc. Am. Concrete Inst.*, Vol. 28, 1932, p. 405.

compressive strength due to variations in time of transit mixing from 40 turns of the drum up to a period of 90 min. The concrete in Hollister's tests had 5 sacks of cement per cubic yard and varied from 1 to 7 in. in slump. Since the slump decreased markedly during the longer periods of mix, it is evident that workability is the principal limitation on time of mixing in such operation.

If full advantage is to be taken of the properties of drier mixes which now can be so effectively placed by vibration, either longer time must be allowed in mixing such batches with present mixers, or special mixers must be designed to handle the drier concrete.

24. A Comparison between Machine- and Hand-Mixed Concretes. If a sufficient number of turns is employed, concrete can be as well mixed by hand as by machine. However, the cost of such thorough work prohibits its use in practice. With the practiced methods of hand mixing it is not possible to secure as homogeneous mixtures as with machine mixing. This non-homogeneity of the hand-mixed material is especially noticeable when the permeability of the concrete is tested.

In a series of tests at the University of Wisconsin on forty-eight 10- by 24-in. cylinders of concrete, made in proportions varying from 1:1:2 to 1:4:8, by volume, with crushed limestone coarse aggregate, the relative strengths of hand- and machine-mixed concretes were determined. In making the hand-mixed specimens the cement and sand were turned twice dry; the cement, sand, and stone, twice dry; the whole mass was then wetted and given three more turns. The machine-mixed concrete was turned for 1 min dry and 2 min wet in a No. 0 Smith batch mixer running at 26 rpm. In order to obtain a medium consistency, the machine mixes required an average of 9.2 per cent water and the hand mixes took an average of 9.9 per cent water, by weight of dry materials.

As a result of the extra water and lack of mixing in the hand mixes, the average ratios of the strengths of specimens of machine-mixed concrete to the strengths of the hand-mixed averaged as follows: 1:1:2 mix, 1.38; 1:2:4 mix, 1.25; 1:3:6 mix, 1.33; and 1:4:8 mix, 1.07.

25. Handling and Transporting Concrete. From the standpoint of securing good concrete after placement, certain fundamental principles should be borne in mind in handling the concrete.

For conveying concrete, wheelbarrows and two-wheel carts are commonly employed on small jobs, whereas elevators with gravity chutes, cars, belt conveyors, and buckets handled by cranes or cableways are used on large structures. For lining tunnels, concrete is often transported by compressed air or pumped through a pipe line. In using wheelbarrows or carts, attention should be given to minimizing the length of haul not only for the sake of economy in labor but also to prevent separation of the ingredients in the wheelbarrow due to jarring. The spouting of concrete by gravity requires a very wet, soupy mixture, unless a high pitch is employed; consequently the strength and density of the product suffer when this method is used. Whatever system is employed, the number of changes from one conveying vessel to another should be minimized in order to avoid waste of mortar due to slopping.

Ready-mixed concrete is transported in mixer or agitator trucks, and air-entrained concrete is frequently hauled in non-agitating trucks. Flat-bottom trucks with wide tailgates are not considered satisfactory for this purpose except under the most favorable conditions. Specially designed non-agitating trucks with rounded corners, deflector plates, and with a maximum discharge angle of 90° have been used to transport air-entrained concrete over distances up to 10 miles without harmful segregation or bleeding. The distance that such trucks can be used depends on the characteristics of the concrete, the atmospheric conditions, the design of the truck, and the condition of the roadway.

In locations where space is limited, such as bridges, tunnels, piers, and other structures, concrete has been pumped through steel pipes 6 to 8 in. in diameter at power costs usually less than 2 cents per cu yd. In operation of the pump the concrete is drawn from the hopper into the cylinder on the back stroke of the piston, and is then pushed into the pipe line on the forward stroke. Pumpcrete machines of various capacities are available up to a maximum of 65 cu yd of concrete per hour of operation. Concrete having a slump of ½ to 6 in. has been satisfactorily pumped, but a 3- to 4-in. slump usually gives the best results. The maximum horizontal distance that concrete can be pumped is about 1000 ft, and the maximum vertical distance is about 175 ft. In calculating pumping resistance, each 90° bend is considered equivalent to 40 ft of horizontal straight pipe, each 45° bend as 20 ft, and each vertical foot as equivalent to 8 horizontal ft.

For placing concrete under water, some method must be used which prohibits the separation of the cement or mortar from the stone. This is sure to occur if the concrete is poured into open water; the stone, sand, and cement will be found in layers one above the other in the order named. Wherever possible the work should be enclosed in a coffer-dam to avoid wave action and prevent currents about the structure. Enclosed buckets holding ½ cu yd or more, which can be lowered to the bottom and emptied without the contents being subjected to the wash of the water, have been successfully used to deposit concrete in depths of 200 ft. In this method a dry consistency is employed and care is taken to create as little disturbance as possible in raising and lowering the bucket.

A tremie, or pipe with a flared top and of sufficient length to reach bottom, is often used to deposit concrete under water. Commonly a battery of tremies is effectively centered over the work.   Then each tremie is kept filled with concrete as it is gradually raised.

In the construction of foundations for the San Francisco-Oakland Bay Bridge, concrete with 6 sacks of cement per cu yd, 50 per cent of the aggregate sand, and a water-cement ratio of 0.85, by volume, was used. At 1 month the compressive strengths of cores cut from this subaqueous concrete average 3562 to 3954 psi. (See *Proc. Am. Concrete Inst.*, Vol. 33, pp. 346–351.)

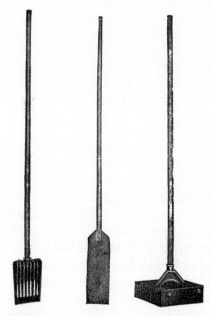

Fig. 2.   Facing and tamping irons.   (*a*) Gridiron tamper for facing side walls. (*b*) Flat-faced tamper.   (*c*) Grid tamper for floors or walks.   (Ransome Concrete Machinery Co.)

26. Placement of Mortar and Concrete.   Mixtures of dry consistency should be placed in layers not over 8 in. thick. Wet concrete can be placed in much thicker layers, depending upon the consistency and width of the cross section. Dry concrete should not be allowed to fall more than a few feet, since the coarse aggregate is likely to become separated from the mortar. When concrete must be poured from a considerable height, it is desirable to use an inclined chute both to avoid separation of ingredients and to avoid excessive pressure on forms.[*]

In placing concrete of 2- to 6-in. slump, use of the spading and facing tools shown in Fig. 2 will improve the appearance of vertical surfaces. For placing concrete of 1-in. slump or less in sidewalks or floors, the grid tamper is useful. Pockets in thin walls and columns can be avoided by puddling a wet mix with long rods.

Vibrators.   The internal, electrically driven vibrators, Fig. 3, are effective devices for uniformly consolidating concrete in walls, columns, beams, or other units.   External vibrators are usually applied to horizontal surfaces like floors or pavements or to the compaction of concrete products in molds.   Pavement slabs have been successfully compacted by vibrating a cylindrical tube supported by and in front of the finishing machine in the roll of concrete formed at the strike-off device.   Vibration of forms or of reinforcing has not met with favor in this country.

[*] See discussion in *Eng. Record,* Vol. 59, p. 279.

Fig. 3. Types of vibrators. Sizes: (1) 1⅛ by 21 in.; (2) 1⅞ by 18 in. (with flexible shaft); (3) 2¼ by 20 in.; (5) 6½ by 18½ in., wt 96 lb (2 men required). (4) External vibrator, ½ hp motor. Speeds: (1) 12,000 rpm; others 3500 to 5000 rpm. (Electric Tamper and Equipment Co.)

In most of the vibrators a displacement of 0.03 to 0.09 in. from mean position is caused by revolving an eccentric weight at a speed in excess of 3500 rpm. Using an internal vibrator with a spud $2\frac{3}{4}$ in. in diameter, weighing 24 lb, running at 6000 rpm, and an eccentric moment of 2.3 in-lb, it is possible to consolidate concrete of zero slump into a plastic mass within a radius of 12 in. of the vibrator in 20 to 30 sec. With concrete of $\frac{1}{2}$-in. slump the time requirement is about one-half. The energy required to consolidate zero-slump concrete is approximately 1500 to 3000 ft-lb per cu ft; for $\frac{1}{2}$-in. slump, the energy required is one-fourth as much.

Vibrators are most effectively used on relatively dry mixes, preferably with slumps less than 2 in. Their use makes it possible to reduce sand contents down to 28 to 35 per cent of the total aggregate weight and to place more harshly graded mixes than with hand methods.*

Vibration causes some expulsion of entrained air, but the amount is small under average job conditions. If under certain conditions a large decrease in the air content is expected, the original mix design should be altered to provide a larger initial air content.

The strength properties of partially set concrete that has been re-vibrated are usually improved by this action. Care should be taken, however, to avoid disturbing reinforcing bars that project from partially hardened concrete that does not become plastic under additional vibratory action.

Strong concrete and early form removal have been attained in certain house constructions by applying a partial vacuum to a wet concrete after placement. Thus the fluidity of the concrete is effectively used in placing; then the excess water, harmful in hardening, is removed before setting occurs. (See *Proc. Am. Concrete Inst.*, Vol. 34, p. 305.)

In sidewalk and floor construction it is best to roughen and clean the base before it has hardened and apply the topping immediately. Committee 802 of the American Concrete Inst. recommended the following topping: Make a mix of 1 part cement, 1 part coarse sand with not more than 10 per cent passing a No. 50 sieve, and $1\frac{1}{2}$ to 2 parts of gravel or crushed stone ranging from $\frac{1}{4}$ to $\frac{3}{8}$ in. in size. Use $4\frac{1}{2}$ to 5 gal of water per sack of cement, a 2-min mixing period, and a consistency as dry as can be screeded. If necessary, a small change can be made in the coarse aggregate proportion. After this topping mixture has been screeded to proper level, it should be floated with a wood float until a small amount of mortar is brought to the surface for finishing purposes. Then it should stand for 30 to 45 min to prevent an excess of fine particles coming to the surface when it is troweled. Steel troweling should then be done until the surface is smooth and free from defects.

* See *Proc. Am. Concrete Inst.*, Vol. 31, pp. 527–551; Vol. 32, p. 445. See also *Proc. Highway Research Board,* Vol. 15, p. 217; Vol. 16, p. 193; Vol. 17, pp. 279–327.

The Cement Gun. An apparatus which is being considerably used for applying a coat of mortar or grout to large surfaces is the cement gun. The essential feature of this machine is a vertical tank into which the mixture of sand and cement is admitted through a bell hopper. At the lower end of the tank is placed a horizontal wheel which is provided with radial arms to sweep the dry mortar under an outlet pipe. The dry mortar is driven out of the tank by means of air pressure which also serves to operate an air motor that turns the distributing wheel. From the outlet the mix is driven through a flexible hose, which may be of any length up to 200 ft, to a nozzle. As the mixture is shot through the latter it is tempered with sufficient water to produce a plastic mortar and is then deposited at high velocity in the form of a spray on the surface of the work. For mobility the machine is mounted on a truck.

In 1936 tests on 1:3, 1:4, and 1:5 mortars placed in fifty-three 3- by 3- by 28-in. prisms by a cement gun were made for a thesis by R. D. Culbertson and L. J. Deno at the University of Wisconsin. Their data show that there was little difference in the average strengths of these mixes after placement by the gun. After 7 days of damp curing and 21 days in the air of the laboratory, the moduli of rupture of individual specimens of gunite ranged from 629 to 1030 psi, and the compressive strength (modified cube method) ranged from 4750 to 11,110 psi. Other tests show such mortars have high density. (*Concrete*, Vol. 9, p. 26.) The cement gun has been used for facing dams, for reinforcing old sewers, for placing a protective coating of mortar around structural steel in buildings and tunnels, for lining tunnels, and for repairing the walls of furnaces and coke ovens.

27. Joining Old and New Work. Whenever watertight concrete is desired, pouring should be carried on continuously * or a watertight joint † must be provided (see Fig. 4). On less important structures the surface of the old work should be roughened thoroughly, cleaned of all laitance and dirt with wire brushes, saturated with water, and then allowed to dry until the surface will absorb water from the fresh mortar or concrete. For roughening the surface of old work, dilute hydrochloric acid is effective, but it should be entirely washed off before bonding.

A vibrator is a valuable aid in bonding fresh concrete or mortar to old work. In 1936 at the University of Wisconsin a series of 428 flexural tests on 6- by 6-in. beams tested over a 16-in. span were made by J. E. Liebmann and R. E. Stiemke to determine the bond of fresh concrete to hardened concrete (*Proc. Highway Research Board*, Vol. 16, p. 193). In-

* Examples in erecting stand pipes, *Concrete Cement Age*, Dec. 1913; Feb. 1914.
† For examples of joints, see Rept. of Com. E-8, *Proc. Am. Concrete Inst.*, Vols. 24 and 25.

cluded variables in these tests were 3 water-cement ratios, 3 slumps, both high early strength and Portland cement, vertical and horizontal joints, two ages at bonding and two ages of bonding, vibration, and hand placement, and condition of the surface.

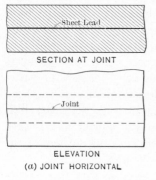

SECTION AT JOINT

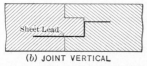

ELEVATION
(a) JOINT HORIZONTAL

(b) JOINT VERTICAL

Fig. 4. Methods of making watertight joints.

All specimens were cast in tight forms and moist cured until tested. Surfaces to be bonded were cast against clean plywood. In bonding specimens with vertical joints, an external vibrator was used for 10 sec or less per specimen; for bonding on horizontal joints a 1¾-in. internal vibrator was used for 15 to 20 sec per specimen. Beams were made with two joints 9 in. apart and tested with a joint under a center load over a 16-in. span. Reported bond values are computed moduli of rupture.

The following are some of the more important conclusions obtained from these tests. Brushing or grouting of the hardened surfaces had no appreciable effect on the bond of the high-strength concrete of 0.47 w/c, by weight. Allowing the surfaces to be bonded to dry for 3 days in the laboratory air effected a 15

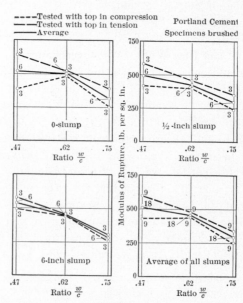

Fig. 5. The effect on bond of position of beam in testing.

to 25 per cent increase in bond over that obtained when surfaces were dried 1 day. Aging 2 days or 28 days prior to bonding produced no effect on the 28-day bond strength. Changes in consistency from 0- to 6-in. slump affected the bond strength little, if the water-cement ratio was constant. The 28-day bond strength of high early strength concrete was 10 to 20 per cent higher and more uniform than that developed by Portland cement concrete. The bond of the latter increased approximately 30 per cent between 7 and 28 days.

For concrete of 0.47 w/c the bond modulus of rupture in a series of 108 tests averaged over 500 psi with a minimum of 338 psi. The average ratio of bond to normal modulus for this series of tests was 0.67. Figure 5 shows the effect of the water-cement ratio on bond and also the superiority of the bond at the top fibers in vertical joints. With horizontal joints there was less range in bond, although the average bond was about the same as in vertical joints. With cement content constant, the bond obtained with vibration was over 40 per cent greater than that obtained by hand puddling.

28. Forms. To prevent leakage of water and a loss of fine mortar, the forms should be made as rigid and nearly watertight as possible. This feature should be given very careful attention when thin, watertight sections are being constructed. If smooth surfaces are desired, plywood or tongued and grooved lumber planed on one side should be used. Oiling the forms diminishes warping and shrinkage and reduces labor in removing them. Collapsible steel molds or wooden forms covered with galvanized iron are economical for repeated use.

The pressure of unset concrete against forms depends on the depth of fresh concrete, the consistency and richness of the mix, the rate of pouring, the temperature, and the method of compacting in the forms. The tests reported by F. R. Shunk in 1908 (*Eng. News*, Vol. 62, p. 288) have been widely publicized, but tests by H. G. Roby (*Civil Eng.*, Vol. 5, p. 163, March, 1935) indicate that Shunk's values are much too large for certain conditions.

Roby made his tests by accurately measuring the deflection of a calibrated steel plate 6 in. wide and $\frac{7}{16}$ in. thick, supported on knife edges 28 in. apart. This plate was placed at the bottom of a form 2 ft 6 in. square by 15 ft high. The aggregates were sand and gravel of good quality. Mixing was done in a small batch mixer, and the concrete was placed in 1-ft layers with the ordinary amount of puddling and spading. Thirty-one complete tests were made. Three mix proportions, $1:2:3\frac{1}{2}$, normal, $1:1\frac{1}{4}:2\frac{1}{4}$, rich, and $1:2\frac{1}{2}:5$, lean, were used, each with a 7-in. slump; also a normal mix with a 3-in. slump was included. The effects of temperature and rate of placing on the maximum form pressure for the normal, $1:2:3\frac{1}{2}$ mix, as determined by Roby are shown in Fig. 6. For

the rich mix, the maximum pressure at a pouring rate of 4 ft per hour
and a temperature of 60° to 70°F was 1000 lb per sq ft, or 42 per cent more
than for the normal mix. The lean mix under similar conditions developed
pressures 10 to 15 per cent less than the normal mix, and the dry mix 20
to 25 per cent less.

When vibration is used to compact a dry mix, the pressures on the forms
will reach a fluid intensity of 150 lb per sq ft, if the rate of placement is
rapid. Two tests by T. E. Stanton
(*Concrete*, Jan. 1937, p. 5) indicate
that vibrated concrete of 2-in. slump
will maintain such pressure up to
heights of 4 to 7 ft.

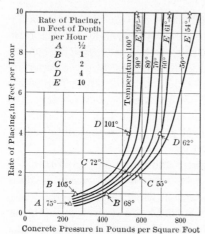

Fig. 6. Relation of pressure exerted by
fluid concrete on forms to rate of filling.
(H. G. Roby, *Civil Eng.*, Vol. 5, p. 163.)

The time at which forms may be
removed depends upon the rate of
hardening of the cement and the temperature of the air. The best index
of the proper time for removal of
forms is afforded by a series of tests
on small beams or cubes made and
cured under the same conditions as
the structure. Forms should never be
removed until the concrete will support 150 per cent of its working unit
stress. In warm weather, wall forms
not over 10 ft high can be removed in
2 or 3 days, but, in the spring and fall when the temperature at night
drops to 30° or 40°F, 4 to 7 days should be allowed (see also Art. XV-42).

29. Joints. Owing to the shrinkage which takes place when concrete
sets in air (see Art. IX-31 and XV-25), and the volume changes which
occur due to variations in temperature, provision for contraction and expansion joints should be made.

In two-course sidewalks it is good practice to make joints $\frac{1}{16}$ to $\frac{1}{8}$ in.
wide, every 4 to 6 ft. Such joints should extend through both surface coat
and base. In concrete pavement constructions and in unreinforced walls,
joints are placed from 30 to 50 ft apart.* The width of the joint now used
is quite variable, depending upon the type of construction, position of
joint, thickness of concrete, and conditions surrounding the construction.
The width of joint varies from a plane of separation for contraction to
$\frac{1}{2}$ in. or more for expansion. In thin members where the moisture changes
are felt throughout the mass, wider joints will be more necessary than in
thick sections. Expansion joints are commonly filled with a poured

* See Specifications for Concrete Roads, Streets and Alleys adopted by Second
National Conference on Concrete Road Building.

bituminous mastic or prepared felt and are provided with dowels to maintain alignment. In many cases construction joints are sealed with metallic plates to prevent the entrance of debris.

The tongued and grooved joint shown in Fig. 4 is impervious and also serves to preserve alignment when used in a vertical wall. A strip of sheet lead, bent as shown, permits free articulation of the joint. Provision for such joints should be made at all angles in order to avoid cracks due to settlement, contraction, or expansion.

30. Curing. No part of the process of making good mortar or concrete is more important than thorough curing. It is also one of the operations most frequently neglected. Dusty floors, loose surface coats on sidewalks and pavements, weak concrete blocks, leaky conduits and pipes illustrate defects frequently caused by improper curing. The effects of premature drying on the strength and permeability of concrete are discussed in Art. XV-32.

Curing concrete consists of keeping the concrete moist and warm during the period after placement so that hydration of the cement can take place. The temperature range considered most desirable with ordinary curing methods is 70° to 90°F. The length of the curing period depends on such variables as atmospheric conditions, characteristics of the concrete, importance and expected use of the concrete, and special job considerations.

In warm weather the essential principle is to keep the work damp for a period of 1 to 2 weeks subsequent to pouring. Rich mixes do not require so long a time for curing as lean mixes and are less affected by premature drying. Wet mixes suffer less than those of dry consistency when improperly cured. If provision cannot be made for wetting the work, the forms should be left on long enough to insure proper curing.

The following methods of curing yield good results: sprinkling two or three times a day when not exposed to the sun, covering with burlap saturated twice a day, covering with a 2-in. layer of damp sand, earth, or sawdust wetted once a day, impounding a shallow pool of water over the surface of the work. Of these methods, the wet-sand treatment is very effective for pavements and floors over a wide range of conditions. In arid regions where water for curing is difficult to obtain the U. S. Bureau of Reclamation has found that 2 coats of asphalt emulsion or coal tar cutback applied to the surface of the concrete within an hour after finishing are effective in retaining sufficient water for curing purposes. Seal coat curing compounds are also available as colorless or white pigmented coatings. They should be applied immediately after the finishing of the concrete. Waterproof papers are frequently used on horizontal surfaces. These papers should be strong enough to withstand normal abrasive action on the job, and should be non-staining. The seams between adjacent sheets should be carefully sealed.

Concrete blocks, brick, and tile can be given 70 per cent of their normal 28-day strength by subjecting them to properly controlled wet steam curing at temperatures of 125°F for 15 hours. Menzel's tests (*Proc. Am. Concrete Inst.*, Vol. 32, p. 51) indicate that by curing in saturated steam at 350°F (120 psi) the full 28-day moist-cured strength of concrete units can be made available in 24 hours. He found that steaming was most efficient if begun 5 to 8 hours after molding and continued for 8 hours.

31. Protection against Freezing. In cold weather, concrete should be protected from freezing until it has secured hard set. The effects of freezing on the properties of cements, mortars, and concretes are discussed in Art. IX-33, XV-42, and XV-44. Some of the ways of preventing freezing will be briefly considered.

Tests on small 8-in. walls poured in 2-in. plank forms at a temperature of 10°F have shown that concrete will set before freezing begins provided the temperature of the concrete is above 70°F when it is poured. This temperature may generally be maintained by heating the mixing water alone. If necessary, the aggregates may be heated by building fires in large iron pipes running through the piles of sand and stone. Dolomitic and calcareous sands, however, may be injured by overheating in this manner. Furthermore, this method does not distribute the heat uniformly throughout the aggregate. Steam in radiators, or steam allowed to escape through perforated pipes placed at the bottom of the aggregate pile, is a better source of heat. Heating concrete above 150°F should be avoided because it may produce weaker concrete.

After placement the concrete can be kept warm by covering it with a couple of feet of straw or hay, or a heavy layer of sawdust may be employed. Since these materials mix with the surface to some extent, their use is often objectionable.

For heating buildings in the process of construction, salamanders or box stoves are often used. Exposed walls and floors have been heated by placing a covering of canvas or building paper a few inches from the surface of the concrete and running steam pipes between the covering and work. Special protection should be given to corners, footings, surfaces of thin members, and all parts where heat will be rapidly dissipated. The liberal use of thermometers properly placed and read frequently during the first 24 hours after pouring will provide information with regard to the need of additional heat. Minimum temperatures should not be less than 40°F in large masses and 50°F in smaller members. After 24 hours the heat generated by chemical activity aids in maintaining proper temperatures for continuing the process, but all work should be maintained at 40° to 50°F for at least 72 hours after pouring. Precaution should be taken when a structure is being heated to keep the air saturated with moisture in order to prevent too rapid drying of the hardening concrete.

See also papers by R. B. Young and W. Schnarr on manufacture and protection of concrete in cold weather in *Proc. Am. Concrete Inst.*, Vol. 30, pp. 279 and 292.

Tempering the mixing water with salt or calcium chloride solutions to lower the freezing point of concrete is a practice to be condemned, especially if the work is reinforced. Either of these ingredients weaken the concrete and decrease the resistance of reinforced concrete to corrosion. (See Art. XV-53.)

32. Painting Concrete. Paints used on concrete surfaces include Portland cement paint, which is a water-dilutable paint with cement as the principal binder; Portland cement-and-oil paints, which consists of ground Portland cement and color pigments in an oil vehicle such as linseed, soybean, China wood, and other drying oils; oil paints which consist of white lead and color pigments in an oil vehicle; and paints which consist of such materials as gums, resins, and synthetic plastics dissolved in suitable solvents.

Portland cement paints have been widely used and are recommended for use on exterior and interior concrete surfaces except floors and other surfaces subjected to mechanical abrasion. The two most important ingredients in these paints are Portland cement and hydrated lime, and other constituents usually included are hygroscopic salts, water repellents, carbonates, and opaque and color pigments. These paints should be applied to clean damp concrete surfaces, and each coat should be dampened as soon as possible after painting. Two coats of paint having a consistency of rich cream are usually applied, with a period of at least 24 hours between coats.

The oil paints form impermeable films and should not be used on walls subject to moisture on the opposite side. These paints should be used on concrete that has been allowed to dry for at least 2 months after the initial curing period. The concrete should be clean and should be given a neutralizing wash consisting of about $2\frac{1}{2}$ lb of zinc sulfate crystals per gallon of water or 2 lb of magnesium fluosilicate per gallon of water. After the neutralizing wash has been allowed to dry, the concrete surface should be given a primer coat before the regular oil paint is applied.

Special and proprietary paints should be applied in accordance with the manufacturer's directions.

The Physical Properties of Mortar and Concrete

1. Introduction. In this chapter we shall consider the effects of various elements and conditions which greatly influence the properties of mortar and concrete, such as strength and elastic properties, permeability to water, absorption, thermal properties, and the durability. In most cases the results given are from laboratory experiments; and it should be kept in mind that only by exercising the utmost care in selecting, proportioning and mixing materials and in the placement and curing of the concrete will it be possible to secure similar results under the conditions of practice. Also it must be recognized that many of the results represent only a limited range of variables, and deductions should not be made for conditions lying without this range.

STRENGTH OF MORTARS

2. Effect of Proportion of Cement on Mortars. The result of Feret's * tests on mortars made from fine, medium, and coarse sands (Fig. 1), show, in a general way, the effect of the proportion of cement on strength. Each tension value is the average from 25 briquets; each compression result represents 5 cubes 2.8 in. on a side; each transverse value was averaged from tests on 15 prisms, 0.8 × 0.8 in. in cross section, loaded at the center of a 3.9-in. span; and each shear test represents the average obtained from 15 halves of the transverse specimens. The latter were tested as cantilevers with the load applied close to the support. All mixes were of plastic consistency. The test pieces were cured in water for 5 months before testing.

The influence of age upon the strength of water-cured mortars made from several of Wisconsin sands and screenings is illustrated in Fig. 2. Information concerning the aggregates used in these mortars is given in *Proc. ASTM*, Vol. 13, p. 834.

3. Effect of Character of Fine Aggregate on Mortars. From a large number of tests by the U. S. Geological Survey (*Bull.* 331), the results in Table 1 have been drawn. Mechanical analysis diagrams for several of

---

* *Bull. soc. encouragement ind. nat.*, 1897, p. 1593; article by R. Feret, chef du laboratoire des ponts et chaussées.

these fine aggregates may be found in Fig. 4, Chapter XIII. These tests show in a rough way that the density and strength of mortars made of the same class of aggregates decrease as the proportion of fine grains in the aggregate increases. In strength, the mortars made of stone screenings are slightly superior to sand mortars.

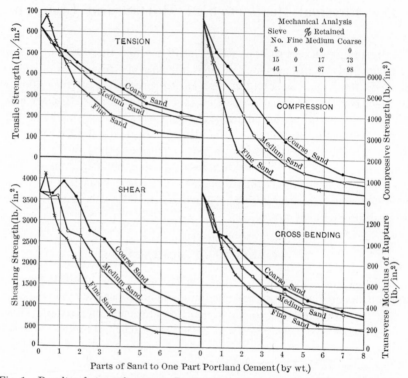

Fig. 1. Results of strength tests on Portland cement mortars of different proportions made from fine, medium, and coarse sands (Feret).

From a series of tests on approximately 115 natural sands which were reported in *Tech. Paper* 58,* the relation between density (ρ) and the average compressive strength (S_c) of 2-in. cubes of 1:3 mortar was $S_c = 26,500\rho - 15,750$. Practically all the strengths were within 30 per cent of the values given by this equation. In these tests a mixture of several brands of cement, a plastic consistency, hand tamping with moderate pressure, and water storage were used. Variables in these factors as well as the character of the grains of fine aggregate will affect the constants in equations like the above.

4. Experiments on Mortars with Artificially Graded Sands. One of the most exhaustive researches on the effects of granulometric composi-

---

* By Wig, Williams, and Gates of the National Bureau of Standards.

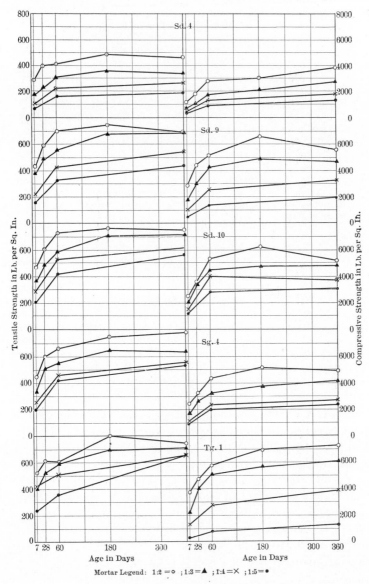

Fig. 2. The effect of age on the strengths of water-cured mortars made with Portland cement. (Each point represents 3 or 4 tests.)

TABLE 1. EFFECT OF GRADATION OF SIZES OF PARTICLES OF AGGREGATE ON STRENGTH, DENSITY, AND YIELD OF 1:3 MORTARS OF PORTLAND CEMENT

(U. S. Geol. Survey, *Bull.* 331)

Aggregate No.	Per Cent Retained on Sieve No.				Per Cent Voids.	Yield.	Density.	Strength at 180 days in Lb. per Sq.In.		
	10	30	50	100				Tensile.	Compressive.	Transverse.
Sd. 13.......	31	77	93	99	28.9	1.21	.754	668	7183	1314
Sd. 16.......	40	79	95	99	29.7	1.20	.760	605	7108	984
Sd. 19.......	27	70	92	98	26.9	1.19	.789	773	6719	
Sd. 20.......	23	64	83	97	28.0	1.16	.794	670	6200	
Sd. 11.......	32	63	80	94	36.0	1.13	.730	708	5067	1272
Sd. 10.......	6	33	73	95	31.6	1.18	.743	488	4639	
Sd. 1.......	3	43	79	84	32.5	1.18	.742	415	3677	1056
Sd. 21.......	1	17	80	99	40.9	1.05	.700	380	2892	
Sd. 15.......	1	5	39	93	40.5	1.13	.676	331	2633	792
Sg. 4.......	74	85	90	94	36.0	1.08	.755	939	8644	1602
Sg. 6.......	68	82	86	88	33.1	1.11	.760	750	8048	1326
Sg. 10.......	50	78	88	92	31.8	1.11	.763	767	7394	1218
Sg. 3.......	35	57	73	85	37.0	1.09	.733	809	6500	1410
Sg. 12.......	31	66	79	87	35.1	1.13	.733	717	6193	1446
Sg. 7	47	82	91	94	36.1	1.07	.756	677	5279	1206
Sg. 21.......	6	28	47	70	41.0	1.14	.655	683	3948	
Sg. 11.......	10	69	54	80	42.1	1.12	.709	543	3757	918

tion of sands has also been conducted by Feret. In an important series of tests he used sands graded as follows: Large grains G (0.2 to 0.08 in.), medium grains M (0.08 to 0.02 in.), and fine grains F (0.02 to 0 in.). In analyzing results he plotted points representing the proportions of the three sizes on equilateral triangular diagrams, the distance from any side representing the percentage of grains marked at the opposite vertex. The contour lines were then drawn through the points which corresponded to mortars of the same density, strength, etc. A comparison of Fig. 3 and 4 show the similarity of the contours in the density and strength diagrams of 1:3 mortars and indicates that the maximum strength and density obtain when about five-sixths of the sand is composed of the coarse grains with fine grains constituting the principal portion of the remainder. From his experiments,* Feret drew the following conclusions:

1. With cement varying between 10 and 30 per cent of the weight of sand, the strongest mortar for any given percentage of cement was always

* *Ann. ponts et chaussées,* Mar. 1890, July 1892, Aug. 1896.

obtained from a proportion of coarse sand equal to twice the weight of the cement plus fine sand.

2. It requires about twice as much cement mixed with a given quantity of sand to produce a mortar of given strength when fine sand is used as it does with coarse sand.

3. The weight of cement per cubic yard of mortar of a given strength is about twice as much for fine sand as for coarse sand, with the ordinary mixtures.

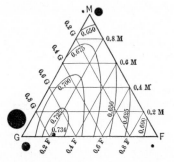

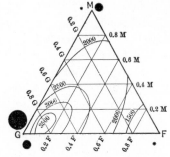

Fig. 3. The effect of the gradation of the sizes of sand grains on the densities of mortars of 1:3 proportions (by weight). (The range in actual size of grain corresponding to a given letter is represented by the pair of circles at each apex in the diagram.)

Fig. 4. The effect of the gradation of the sizes of sand grains on the compressive strength of 1:3 Portland cement mortars after storing 1 year in fresh water.

4. The cost per cubic yard of coarse-sand mortar of a given strength (such as is found for the ordinary ratio $1c:3s$), is only about 75 per cent of the cost of fine-sand mortar of the same strength, even when the coarse sand costs six and one-half times as much as the fine sand (coarse sand $1.30, and the fine sand $0.20 per cubic yard).

Feret also declared * that "for all series of plastic mortars made with the same cement and of inert sands, the resistance to compression after the same time of set under identical conditions is solely a function of the ratio $\dfrac{c}{e+v}$ or $\dfrac{c}{1-(c+s)}$, whatever may be the nature and size of the sand the proportions of the elements—sand, cement, and water—of which each is composed." In the above law e and v represent the volume of the water and air voids, respectively; the other symbols are defined in Art. XIV-6. He derived the following relations for compressive strength:

$$S_c = j\left[\frac{c}{1-(c+s)} - 0.1\right] \quad \text{and} \quad S_c = k\left(\frac{c}{1-s}\right)^2$$

* *Bull. soc. encouragement ind. nat.*, 1897, p. 1604.

in which S_c = unit compressive strength in pounds per square inch and j and k are constants. His results indicated a value of $k = 26,000$ psi. These equations with modified constants have been found to hold in other tests.*

5. Effect of Proportion of Mixing Water on Strength of Mortars. In general, increasing the percentage of mixing water beyond that required to form a placeable mix lowers the density and strength of the mortar. The proportionate effect on strength is greatest at early ages.

In Reinke's tests † the ratios of the tensile strengths of eighteen 1:3 mortars, taking 12 per cent of water for normal consistency, to the strengths of 12 like mortars requiring 14 to 15 per cent averaged 3.9:1, 1.6:1, and 1.5:1 at 3, 7, and 28 days, respectively. Hence it follows that the water required for a given consistency and mix is a rough index of the strength of mortars made of clean, durable sands. The Report of the Director of Research of the Portland Cement Association shows that the strength-water-cement relation for mortars is similar to that for concretes.

6. Effect of Mica on Strength of Mortar. Experiments by W. A. Willis ‡ on 1:3 mortars show that small percentages of mica decrease the tensile strength considerably. An addition of $2\frac{1}{2}$ per cent of mica served to reduce the strength at 7 days 11 per cent; by adding 20 per cent of mica the strength at the same age was decreased from 180 to 40 psi. Feret also found that mica adversely affected the compressive strength. The observed effects are probably due to the weakness of the mica and to the decrease in density resulting from its presence.

7. Effect of Hydrated Lime on Strength of Mortars. Tests by E. W. Lazell, § Table 2, show that replacement of less than 15 per cent of the cement by hydrated lime does not decrease the tensile strength of 1:3 mortars. The result of E. S. Wheeler (*Rept. Chief Eng., U. S. A.*, 1896, p. 2823) are confirmatory. W. E. Emley and S. E. Young ¶ found that both tensile and compressive strengths of 1:3 mortars of slush consistency were adversely affected by the substitution of only 5 per cent of either high-calcium or dolomitic hydrate, if the specimens were cured in water or exposed to the weather. However, the loss in compressive strength was small for replacement of less than 25 per cent of cement by hydrate. (See also *Proc. ASTM*, Vol. 35, Pt. 2, p. 426.)

8. Adhesion of Mortars and Concretes. Tests by E. Candlot for the French Commission show that the normal adhesion block of Art. XII-36 is a satisfacory specimen, but results are much affected by the character of the surface. Some results of tests on various substances by Wheeler in which 1- by 1- by $\frac{1}{4}$-in. discs were placed transversely in the minimum

---

* *Proc. ASTM*, Vol. 13, p. 852.   § *Proc. ASTM*, Vol. 8, p. 418.
† *Proc. ASTM*, Vol. 13, p. 797.   ¶ *Proc. ASTM*, Vol. 14, p. 339.
‡ *Eng. News*, Feb. 6, 1908.

TABLE 2. THE EFFECT OF THE INCLUSION OF HYDRATED LIME ON
THE TENSILE STRENGTH OF 1:3 MORTARS OF PORTLAND CEMENT
AND STANDARD SAND (LAZELL)

Per Cent Cement Replaced by Hyd. Lime.		0	5	10	15	20	25	30	100
Method of Curing.	Age in Days.	Tensile Strengths in Lb. per Sq. In.							
In air, specimens moistened once a week	7	209	203	205	209	133	112	141	10
	28	266	258	255	245	203	170	225	44
	90	286	289	295	297	197	117	177	55
	180	382	312	304	281	229	211	219	53
	270	607	545	441	499	441	397	342	136
	360	630	456	513	642	553	444	327	168
In water after 3 days in air	7	206	157	189	239	237	173	173	
	28	278	311	364	264	268	259	268	
	90	441	389	419	372	374	314	281	
	180	358	321	341	278	260	207	253	
	270	390	301	308	279	268	250	232	
	360	426	336	311	322	299	260	231	

NOTE—Each value represents five tests.

section of a briquet are shown in Fig. 5. He found the adhesion of mortar
to cut stone was not increased by roughening the surface. For sawn
limestone the adhesion of neat to 1:2
mortars was 30 to 40 per cent of the tensile strength of the mortar. Retempering
reduces adhesive strength somewhat but
lessens shrinkage in setting.

Tests on the adhesion of mortars to
brick by L. A. Palmer, National Bureau
of Standards, *RP* 683, indicate that the
suction rate of the surface and the
strength, plasticity, and the retentivity
of the mortar all vitally affect adhesion.
A mortar containing 2 parts lime putty
to 3 parts Portland cement to 12 parts
of good mason's sand by weight, having
a flow of 80 to 100 per cent (Art. XII-
34), will usually develop at 28 days a
tensile adhesion of 50 to 100 psi when

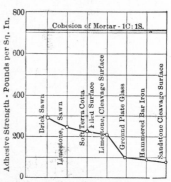

Fig. 5. Adhesive strength of Portland cement mortar, $1C:1S$, 28
days old, to different substances,
and the cohesive strength of the
mortar itself. (Wheeler, *Rept.
Chief Eng., U. S. A.,* 1895, p. 3019.)

properly joined to brick having a suction rate between 5 and 30 gm per
brick per min (Art. VIII-18).

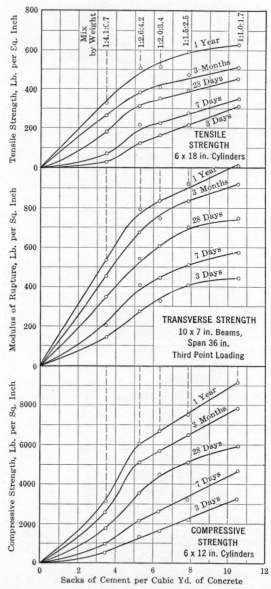

Fig. 6. The effect of cement content on the strength of concrete (*Rept., Director of Research, Portland Cement Assoc.*, 1928, Series 210). Each point represents 5 or more tests. Materials, Elgin sand and gravel graded from 0 to 1½ in. Fineness modulus of mixed aggregate = 5.5. Flow = 200.

The adhesion of concrete or mortar to plain round steel bars as rolled varies inversely with the ratio of length of bedment (l) to diameter (d). For a ratio of l/d of 25 and concrete of 3000 to 5000 psi compressive strength, the average adhesion is about 500 psi; for l/d of 50, the adhesion approximates 300 psi. For cold-rolled bars or bars with polished surfaces, the adhesion is 40 per cent less; and for square or flat bars, about 25 per cent less than for round bars with mill surface.*

STRENGTH OF CONCRETE

9. Effect of Proportion of Cement on Strength of Concrete. With materials, consistency, and density constant, the strength of concrete increases with the proportion of cement in the mix until the strength of the cement or aggregate, whichever is the weaker, is reached. The data in Fig. 6 represent tests on moist-cured, workable concretes having the same consistency (flow of 200 and slump of 4 to 6 in.) and made from the same aggregate mixture, 38 per cent sand and 62 per cent gravel. The curves show the normal relations of strength to cement contents for these conditions. Owing to the excess of sand in the richer mixes, their densities were lower than those of the leaner mixes. This fact accounts in part for the downward droop of the upper right portions of the strength-cement-content curves. For workable mixes of drier consistencies, the corresponding curves would be higher and for those of wetter consistencies the curves would be lower. The influence of vibration in placement on the properties of concrete is well shown in Fig. 3, Art. X-9, and in Art. XIV-27.

10. The Increase in Strength of Concrete with Age. For moist-cured concrete mixed with about 6 gal of water per sack of cement, the Report of the Director of Research of the Portland Cement Association, 1928, provides a large number of tests, including different aggregates from which the percentages of 28-day strengths were developed at various ages, as

TABLE 2A

Type of Test	Age at Test				
	3 Days	7 Days	28 Days	3 Months	1 Year
Compression............	35	59	100	135	161
Flexure...............	53	71	100	126	143
Tension...............	46	68	100	121	150

* For further information on adhesion and bond see *Bull.* 71, Eng. Expt. Sta., Univ. Ill., and *Proc. Highway Research Bd.*, Vol. 17, p. 150.

shown in Table 2A. These data show that flexural strength is gained most rapidly and the compressive strength least rapidly as age increases.

Studies of a large amount of test data by W. A. Slater (see *Proc. ASCE*, Jan. 1925) indicate for moist-cured concrete that the relation of the 28-day compressive strength (S_c') to the 7-day strength (S_c) is given by

$$S_c' = S_c + 30\sqrt{S_c}$$

Figure 7 contains strength-age curves for 1:4 mixes, by volume, made of different aggregates. The cement content was approximately constant,

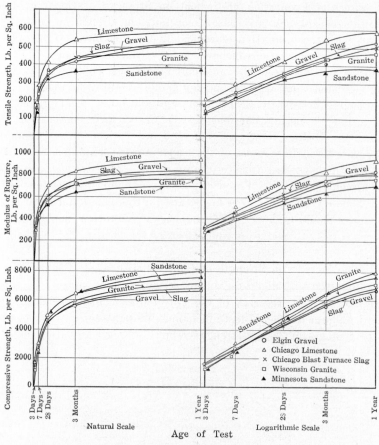

Fig. 7. Strength-age relationships for moist-cured 1:4 concrete made of different coarse aggregates (*Rept., Director of Research, Portland Cement Assoc.*, 1928).

6.3 sacks per cu yd. In each mix 38 per cent of the aggregate, by weight, was Elgin sand ($m = 3.0$). The remainder was coarse aggregate of which 100 per cent passed a 1½-in. sieve and 74 per cent passed a ¾-in. sieve.

The net water-cement ratio ranged from 0.76 to 0.80, by volume, and the flow was 200. These and other data show that for ages up to 1 year moist-cured concrete increases in strength approximately as the logarithm of the age.

A series of experiments on the effect of age on the strength of concrete cylinders cured in three different ways was described in *Proc. Am. Concrete Inst.,* Vol. 27, p. 547. The Atlas cement for these tests was mixed

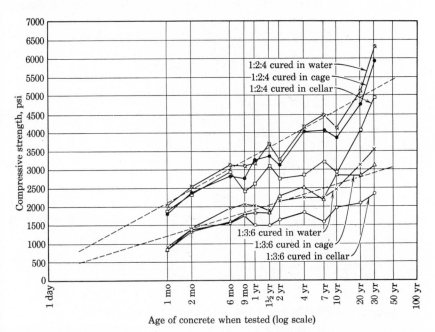

Fig. 8. Effect of age on the compressive strength of limestone concrete. (University of Wisconsin tests made in summer of 1910. See *J. Am. Concrete Inst.,* Feb. 1943.)

and stored in an airtight tank; the proportions, amount of water, time of machine mixing, and storage in molds were each made constant for the entire series of tests. Specimens from each batch of concrete were distributed throughout the various ages so that the five results for any given test period are representative of different batches of concrete. The coarse aggregate was a limestone ranging from ¼ to 1¼ in. in size. It contained 48 per cent of voids measured loose. The sand passed a ¼-in. sieve; 38 per cent passed a No. 30, and 3 per cent passed a 100 mesh. It contained 34 per cent voids. Figure 8 shows the strength-age relationships for these mixes over a 30-year period. The compressive strengths of specimens cured in water or out of doors increased approximately with the logarithm of the age, whereas those cured in the drier cellar had lower strengths. Present evidence shows that the strength-age relationships for concretes made of low-heat cements may resemble the foregoing, but those relationships for present-day normal and high early strength cements will exhibit maxima within a few years.

The effect of various curing conditions on the strength-age relation of concrete is shown in Fig. 9. As previously noted, the best strengths are obtained for concrete that is continuously moist cured, and the poorest strengths are obtained for concrete that is continuously air cured. The curves also show that concrete strengths will rise sharply if moist curing

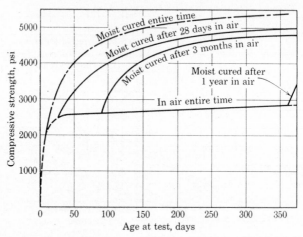

Fig. 9. Effect of curing condition on compressive strength. (Portland Cement Association.)

is resumed after a drying period. The curves were obtained from tests of relatively small specimens that were easily resaturated and consequently responded rapidly to moist curing. In the field, resaturation of large concrete structures after long periods of drying is difficult, and such structures should be moist cured continuously until the desired quality has been obtained.

The strength-age relationship for concrete is also greatly affected by the temperature, especially during the days immediately after mixing. Curing at temperatures only slightly above the freezing point of water adversely affects the strength, as shown in Art. 42. Freezing and thawing of concrete is harmful, especially at an early age. The harmful effect on strength of a single freezing and thawing cycle at an early age may be largely overcome by favorable curing after the cycle, but several cycles of freezing and thawing at an early age cause permanent strength reductions.

The strength-age relation also depends on the type of Portland cement, as is shown in Table 2B, from *Design and Control of Concrete Mixtures*

TABLE 2B

Compressive Strength—Per Cent of
Strength of Normal Portland
Cement Concrete

Type of Portland Cement	3 days	28 days	3 months
1. Normal	100	100	100
2. Modified	80	85	100
3. High early strength	190	130	115
4. Low-heat	50	· 65	90
5. Sulfate-resistant	65	65	85

published by the Portland Cement Association. The values are for moist-cured concrete.

11. Effect of Density on the Compressive Strength of Concrete. If the kind of cement and the proportion of cement per unit volume of concrete

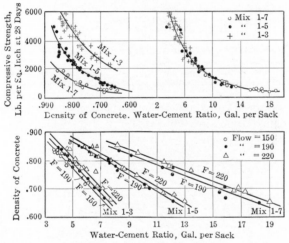

Fig. 10. Interrelationships between density, strength and water-cement ratio for gravel concrete. (*Rept., Director of Research, Portland Cement Assoc.,* 1928.)

are maintained constant and if the consistency, shape of aggregate particles, age, and method of curing the concrete are the same, the strength will increase with the density. These relationships are well established in Fig. 10.

12. Effect of Size of Coarse Aggregate on Compressive Strength. With the largest particles not over 6 in. in diameter, it may be stated that the larger the maximum size of the aggregate the denser and stronger will be the concrete, provided other influencing factors are eliminated. The change in strength with the increase in maximum size of aggregate is most marked for diameters under 1 in. The tests of Fuller and Thompson * on 1:9 concrete, which illustrate the latter statement, are shown in Table 3. The beams used in these tests were $6 \times 6 \times 72$ in. and the

TABLE 3. EFFECT OF VARIATION IN THE MAXIMUM SIZE OF COARSE AGGREGATE ON THE STRENGTH AND DENSITY OF PORTLAND CEMENT CONCRETE (FULLER and THOMPSON)

| Proportion, by weight. | MATERIAL.* | | Character of Mixture. | AVERAGE DENSITY. | | | AVERAGE MODULUS OF RUPTURE AT 90 DAYS, IN LB. PER SQ.IN. | | | AVERAGE COMPRESSIVE STRENGTH AT 140 DAYS, IN LB. PER SQ.IN. | | |
	Stone.	Sand.		2¼-in. Stone.	1-in. Stone.	½-in. Stone.	2¼-in. Stone.	1-in. Stone.	½-in. Stone.	2¼-in. Stone.	1-in. Stone.	½-in. Stone.
1 : 9	J. Park	J. Park	Ideal	0.851	0.810	0.767	257	226	208	1342	950	915
1 : 9	"	"	Natural	0.821	0.798	0.768	211	171	162	980	879	821
1 : 9	"	"	Uniform Aggregate	0.832	0.797	0.769	257	229	180	1350	950	890
1 : 9	Cowe* Bay	Cowe Bay	Various	0.859	0.847	0.853	243	246	189	1486	1402	1231
1 : 9	J. Park	Cowe Bay	"	0.872	0.818	0.784	291	273	207	1798	1585	1185
			Averages	0.847	0.814	0.788	252	229	189	1391	1153	1008
			Ratios	1.00	0.96	0.93	1.00	0.91	0.75	1.00	0.83	0.72

* Jerome Park stone was a crushed mica schist, the sand was screened from the crusher-run material. Cowe Bay material consisted of gravel and sand.
    NOTE.—A soft mushy consistency was used in all tests. Aggregates were well graded.
    The ideal mixture was graded in accordance with a fixed sieve analysis curve.

spans were 60 and 30 in. The compression tests were made on prisms from the beams, approximately $6 \times 6 \times 19$ in., which were capped on each end with neat cement.

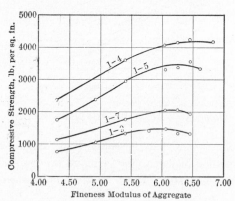

Fig. 11. Effect of fineness modulus of aggregate on strength of concrete (Abrams). Each point represents 5 tests of 6×12-in. cylinders; slump = ½ in.; age = 28 days; aggregate was sand and pebbles graded up to 1¼ in. in diameter.

Tests by Abrams, Fig. 11, show that the strength of concrete of a given consistency increases with the fineness modulus of the mixed aggregate,

* *Trans. ASCE,* Vol. 59, p. 115.

provided the limits of workability are not exceeded. The peaks of the curves in Fig. 11 indicate that coarser gradings, as evidenced by higher fineness moduli, may be permitted in rich mixes like 1:4 than in lean mixes like 1:9. Figure 12 shows relation of compressive strength to fineness modulus when the maximum size of aggregate ranges up to 2 in.

If there are no large gaps in the grading of the aggregate particles, the fineness modulus of the mixed aggregate is of assistance in estimating the workability of mix. Experience has shown that it is not practicable to

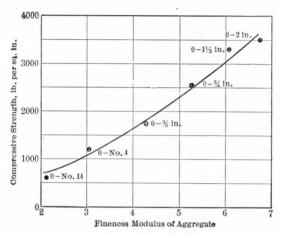

Fig. 12. Effect of gradation of aggregate on strength of concrete (Abrams). Each point represents 5 tests on 6 × 12-in. cylinders of 1:5 proportions at 28 days. Aggregate was sand and pebbles. Slump = ½ in.

increase the fineness modulus beyond certain limits shown in Table 4. These limits depend upon the character and maximum size of aggregate, the richness of the mix, and the use for the concrete.

In the construction of large dams by the U. S. Bureau of Reclamation, many tests were made on concrete containing aggregate up to 9 in. in diameter (see paper by R. F. Blanks and C. C. McNamara, *Proc. Am. Concrete Inst.*, Vol. 31, p. 280, 1935; Vol. 32, p. 234). The results showed an increase of 16 per cent in the strength of concrete per barrel of cement used due to a change in maximum size of gravel from 1 to 3 in. and an increase of 29 per cent due to a change from 1 to 6 in. The fineness moduli of the aggregates passing the 3-in. and 6-in. openings were 7.83 and 8.25, respectively, and their dry-rodded void contents 31.8 and 29.1 per cent.

13. Effect of Proportion of Water on Strength of Concrete. For a given cement content, the greatest strength at an early age can be secured from a concrete of dry consistency in which there is only sufficient water for perfect hydration of the cement. Such concrete requires heavy ramming or vibration to make it homogeneous and dense. A somewhat wetter

Materials of Construction

TABLE 4. MAXIMUM PERMISSIBLE VALUES OF FINENESS MODULUS OF AGGREGATES. (ABRAMS)

For *mixes* other than those given in the table, use the values for the next leaner mix. For *maximum sizes* of aggregate other than those given in the table, use the values for the next smaller size.

This table is based on the requirements for *sand-and-pebble or gravel* aggregate composed of approximately spherical particles, in ordinary uses of concrete in reinforced concrete structures. For other materials and in other classes of work the maximum permissible values of fineness modulus for an aggregate of a given size is subject to the following corrections:

(1) If *crushed stone* or *slag* is used as coarse aggregate, *reduce* values in table by 0.25. For crushed material consisting of unusually flat or elongated particles, *reduce* values by 0.40.

(2) For *pebbles* consisting of *flat particles*, reduce values by 0.25.

(3) If *stone screenings* are used as fine aggregate, *reduce* values by 0.25.

(4) For the top course in *concrete roads*, or other work requiring a smooth finish, *reduce* the values by 0.25. If finishing is done by *mechanical means*, this reduction need not be made.

(5) In work of *massive proportions*, such that the smallest dimension is larger than 10 times the maximum size of the coarse aggregate, *additions may be made* to the values in the table as follows: for ¾-in. aggregate, 0.10; for 1½-in., 0.20; for 3-in., 0.30; for 6-in., 0.40.

Sands with fineness modulus lower than 1.50 are undesirable as fine aggregate in ordinary concrete mixes. Natural sands of such fineness are seldom found.

Sand or screenings used for fine aggregate in concrete must not have a higher fineness modulus than that permitted for mortars of the same mix. Mortar mixes are covered by the table and by (3) above.

Crushed stone mixed with both finer sand and coarser pebbles requires no reduction in fineness modulus provided the quantity of crushed stone is less than 30 per cent of the total volume of the aggregate.

| Size of Aggregate. | PROPORTIONS (BY VOLUME). AGGREGATE: CEMENT. | | | | | | | | |
	1	2	3	4	5	6	7	9	12
Mortars Sieve No.									
0–28	2.25	2.00	1.85	1.70	1.60	1.50	1.40	1.30	1.20
0–14	3.00	2.70	2.50	2.30	2.15	2.05	1.95	1.85	1.80
0– 8	3.80	3.40	3.10	2.90	2.75	2.65	2.55	2.45	2.40
0– 4	4.75	4.20	3.90	3.60	3.45	3.30	3.20	3.05	2.95
0– 3*	5.25	4.60	4.30	4.00	3.80	3.65	3.55	3.45	3.35
Concretes In.									
0–⅜	5.60	5.05	4.70	4.40	4.20	4.05	3.95	3.85	3.80
0–½*	6.05	5.45	5.10	4.80	4.60	4.45	4.35	4.25	4.20
0–¾	6.50	5.90	5.50	5.20	5.00	4.85	4.75	4.65	4.60
0–1*	6.90	6.30	5.90	5.60	5.40	5.25	5.15	5.00	5.00
0–1½	7.35	6.70	6.30	6.00	5.80	5.65	5.55	5.40	5.35
0–2.1*	7.75	7.10	6.70	6.40	6.20	6.05	5.95	5.80	5.75
0–3	8.20	7.55	7.15	6.85	6.60	6.50	6.40	6.25	6.20
0–4½*	8.65	7.95	7.55	7.25	7.00	6.90	6.80	6.65	6.60
0–6	9.10	8.40	8.00	7.65	7.45	7.30	7.20	7.05	7.00

* Half sieves; not used in computing fineness modulus.

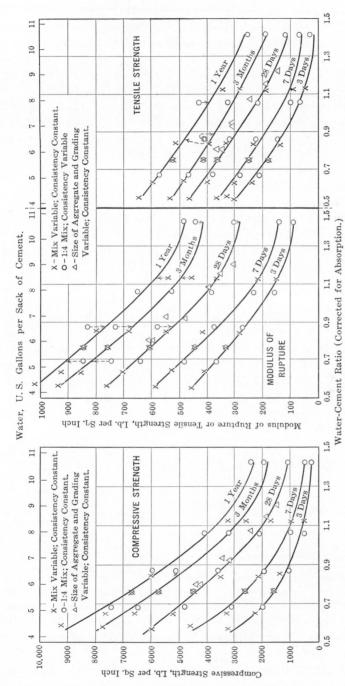

Fig. 13. Relationships between compressive, flexural, and tensile strengths of moist-cured concrete and the water-cement ratio (*Rept. Director of Research, Portland Cement Assoc., 1928*). Compression and tension tests on 6 × 12-in. cylinders; flexure tests on 10 × 7 × 38-in. beams. Aggregate, Elgin sand and gravel.

consistency, slump 1 to 2 in., is much more workable and furnishes approximately as high strength. If the cement content is maintained constant and the proportion of mixing water is increased the strength decreases.

As previously mentioned (Art. XIV-11), Abrams demonstrated that for workable mixes the strength of concrete is an inverse function of the water-cement ratio, regardless of the cement content. Figure 13, from the Report of the Research Director of the Portland Cement Association, 1928, shows the relationships between the water-cement ratio and the compressive strength, tensile strength, and modulus of rupture for concrete made of sand and gravel and tested at the ages indicated. Each point represents 5 tests. It will be observed from Fig. 13 that the relationship is independent of cement content, consistency, and size and grading of aggregate. Abrams' original diagram, *Bull.* 1, Structural Materials Research Laboratory, Lewis Institute, covered a somewhat wider range in water-ratio and mix proportions for 28-day compressive strengths, but lacked in other respects the scope of Fig. 13.

Evidence that for workable mixes the water-ratio relationship covers the effects of variables in density, cement content, and consistency is well shown in Fig. 10 by the plotting of the data of the various relationships into the single water-ratio curve.

Variations in quality of cement, in the structural characteristics of the aggregate, and in curing conditions affect the water-ratio strength relationship. Hence it is desirable in important work to secure this relationship for the materials and conditions on the work. The data in Table 5, taken from the curves of Fig. 13, are representative of the effect of the water ratio on the early strength of concrete.

TABLE 5.   REPRESENTATIVE STRENGTHS FOR DIFFERENT WATER-CEMENT RATIOS *

WATER-CEMENT RATIO			COMPRESSIVE STRENGTH, POUNDS PER SQUARE INCH		MODULUS OF RUPTURE, POUNDS PER SQUARE INCH		TENSILE STRENGTH, POUNDS PER SQUARE INCH	
By Volume	By Weight	Gallons per Sack	7 Days	28 Days	7 Days	28 Days	7 Days	28 Days
0.60	0.40	4.5	4000	5700	550	725	330	440
0.80	0.53	6.0	2300	4000	410	580	230	340
1.00	0.66	7.5	1300	2600	280	430	140	240
1.20	0.80	9.0	800	1600	180	325	80	170

* From Report of the Director of Research of the P. C. A.. 1928.

14. Effect of Air Content on Strength of Concrete. Concrete made with air-entraining Portland cement or concrete containing entrained air produced with the aid of an air-entraining agent usually has lower strength than corresponding concrete made with normal Portland cement. The reduction in strength depends on the amount of the entrained air, the richness of the mix, and the age of the concrete when tested.

If air is added to a concrete batch, without any adjustment for increased yield and decreased water requirement, the compressive strength will be reduced about 5 per cent for each per cent of added air within usual limits. In practice, however, it is quite probable that the water content of the air-entrained concrete will be decreased to give the same slump as the normal concrete, and the sand content will also be decreased to compensate for the increased yield. These changes permit the air-entrained concrete to be designed for the same slump and the same cement content as the corresponding normal concrete. Mix design methods are discussed in Art. XIV-13.

Results from a comprehensive test program reported in ASTM *Bull.* 163 are given in Table 6. In this program, the results for four different cement types made with and without an interground air-entraining agent are compared. Two brands of Type I and Type II, and their corresponding air-entraining cements were used. Each plain cement and its companion air-entraining cement were made into concrete with a nominal cement content of 4.5 sacks per cu yd and a slump of 5 in., and concrete with a nominal cement content of 6.0 sacks per cu yd and a slump of 3¼ in. The reductions in the water-cement ratios for the lean concretes with entrained air compared to the lean concretes without entrained air were much greater than the reductions for the rich concretes with entrained air compared to the rich concretes without entrained air. The reductions are reflected in the strength data which show that the largest reductions in strength were generally obtained with the rich mixes. The larger strength decreases for the rich mixes show the great need for carefully controlling the air contents of these mixes. The strength data also show that strength losses were usually small, or were even slight increases for the lean concrete, at an age of 7 days, but that they increased as the age of the concrete at test was increased. The maximum percentage decrease in compressive and flexural strength due to air entrainment in these tests was 15 per cent.

It should be noted that, although decreases in concrete strength due to air entrainment are obtained, concrete durability is increased. Both field and laboratory tests have conclusively shown that the entrainment of 3 to 6 per cent air greatly increases resistance to freezing and thawing and also to surface scaling due to the use of calcium chloride for ice removal in the winter months.

15. Tensile Strength of Concrete. In general, the tensile strength of concrete varies between one-eighth and one-twelfth of its compressive

TABLE 6. MIX PROPERTIES AND STRENGTH RESULTS FOR CONCRETE MADE WITH DIFFERENT TYPES OF PLAIN AND AIR-ENTRAINING CEMENTS

| Cement | | Properties of Fresh Concrete | | | | | | Strength Test Results, psi (Moist Curing) | | | | | | |
| | | | | | | | | Compressive Strength, 6 × 12-in. cylinders | | | | Flexural Strength, 4 × 6 × 24-in. beams | | |
Manufacturer	Type	Cement Content, sacks per cu yd	Slump, in.	Sand, per cent by weight of total aggregate	Net [a] Water-Cement Ratio, gal per sack	Specific Weight, lb per cu ft	Net Air Content (Pressure Meter), per cent	7 days	28 days	6 mo	10 mo or 1 yr [b]	7 days	28 days	6 mo
B	I	4.46	5.3	44	7.98	149.6	1.5	1770	3305	4530	4920	425	627	809
B	IA	4.50	4.8	40	6.71	145.0	6.0	1730	3225	4215	4585	403	544	761
B	I	5.97	3.4	39	5.65	151.5	1.3	3210	5150	6345	7360	572	682	985
B	IA	6.00	3.4	35	5.12	147.9	4.1	3000	4320	5745	6375	504	676	846
C	I	4.49	5.0	44	7.74	148.6	1.5	1895	3370	4635	5105	461	611	744
C	IA	4.49	4.9	40	6.62	143.0	6.1	2140	3280	4635	4885	457	585	705
C	I	6.00	3.2	39	5.49	150.7	1.6	3535	5420	6895	7615	622	783	953
C	IA	6.01	3.2	35	5.04	147.5	4.0	3520	5110	6645	6835	515	708	862
D	II	4.49	5.0	44	7.77	150.3	1.2	1650	3080	5055	5525	397	597	813
D	IIA	4.49	5.3	40	6.70	144.7	5.9	1620	3080	4585	5345	380	542	838
D	II	6.00	3.4	39	5.39	151.8	1.2	3130	5060	6990	7545	569	710	933
D	IIA	5.98	3.5	35	5.05	148.5	3.9	2885	4530	6275	7375	563	735	887
E	II	4.45	5.1	44	7.79	148.8	2.3	1875	3155	4835	5075	390	569	810
E	IIA	4.48	5.0	40	6.73	145.0	5.5	1900	3215	4695	4780	415	556	771
E	II	6.00	3.2	39	5.36	151.7	1.8	3670	5170	7095	8010	594	709	963
E	IIA	5.98	3.4	35	5.06	148.7	3.8	3110	4540	6365	6770	526	700	842
A	III	4.50	4.8	44	7.59	149.2	1.4	2950	4250	5255	5555	568	674	789
A	IIIA	4.52	5.0	40	6.90	145.6	4.6	3070	3870	4765	4805	560	653	732
A	III	6.01	3.4	39	5.57	151.1	1.3	4610	5900	7115	7365	664	760	971
A	IIIA	6.03	3.4	35	5.19	148.3	3.1	4320	5230	6365	7315	646	748	923
F	IS	4.46	5.0	44	7.81	149.4	1.2	1735	3235	5235	5670	398	610	865
F	IS-A	4.46	4.4	40	6.78	145.3	5.4	1745	3515	5160	5520	370	553	766
F	IS	5.98	3.3	39	5.53	151.6	1.1	3280	5550	7230	7585	556	748	969
F	IS-A	5.98	3.1	35	5.23	149.4	2.6	3175	5020	6710	6450	533	713	895

[a] Total water added minus water absorbed by aggregates.
[b] Results for cements from manufacturers C, E, and F are 1-year results; all others 10 months.

strength. Besides the affecting conditions discussed under compressive strength tests, imperfections in the fabrication of specimens, the tensile strength and surface characteristics of the aggregate and the method of gripping and loading greatly affect the tensile strength of concrete. Owing to the influence of these factors the results of tension tests are generally less uniform than those obtained in compression.

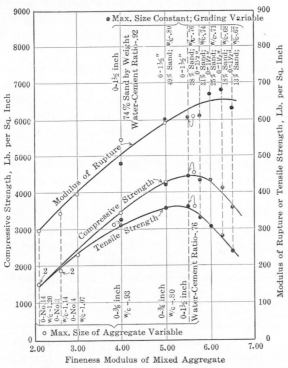

Fig. 14. Effect of size and grading of aggregate on the strength of moist-cured 1:4 concrete (*Rept., Director of Research, Portland Cement Assoc.*, 1928). Aggregate, Elgin sand and gravel; flow, 200 per cent; age 28 days.

The effects of cement content, age, and water ratio on the tensile strength of moist-cured gravel concrete are well illustrated in Fig. 6 and 13. Figure 14 from the Report of the Research Director of the Portland Cement Association illustrates the effect of grading on the tensile strength of concrete. In a general way the tensile strength increases as the fineness modulus is increased, or the grading is made coarser, until the coarseness causes the mix to become harsh in working. The maximum permissible degree of coarseness depends upon the same factors that govern the compressive strength; see Table 4.

The tensile strength is also affected by the character of the surface of the aggregate and its tensile strength. Figure 7 shows that the tensile strength of the concrete made of Chicago limestone was approximately 20 per cent greater than that made of Elgin gravel or slag, 25 per cent stronger than that of Wisconsin granite, and 40 per cent stronger than the concrete of Minnesota sandstone.

A convenient form of specimen for use in tension tests on concrete * is a 6- by 18-in. cylinder. In the tests at the Portland Cement Association laboratory, each end of such cylinder was gripped in a section of steel tubing which had been slit into quadrants and attached to heavy end plates. To each quadrant was riveted a piece of channel with flanges extending radially outward. The tubing was lined with leather $\frac{1}{8}$-in. thick to provide a uniform friction grip on the test pieces. Each grip was squeezed against a specimen over a 5-in. length by tightening bolts inserted in the outstanding flanges of the channels. The load was applied to the grips by two heavy bolts, one for each grip, which passed through the heavy end plates. Each bolt was provided with a spherical seated nut at each end.

16. The Transverse Strength of Concrete. The effects of cement content, age, water ratio, and kind of coarse aggregate on the modulus of rupture of concrete are well shown in Fig. 6, 7, and 13. Figure 14 shows the effect of changing the grading of the aggregate on the modulus of rupture. It will be noted that somewhat coarser gradings can be more effectively used in the production of high flexural strength than in securing maximum compressive or tensile strength.

Like the tensile strength, the modulus of rupture appears to be affected by the shape, character of the surface of the aggregate, and its tensile strength, as shown in Fig. 7.

For moist-cured concrete of well-graded limestone or gravel having a water ratio of 0.80, by volume, or 6 gal per sack of cement, the ratio of the modulus of rupture to the compressive strength approximates the following values: at 7 days $\frac{1}{5}$, at 28 days $\frac{1}{7}$, and at 1 year $\frac{1}{8}$. A large amount of data in the Report of the Research Director of the Portland Cement Association indicates that for moist-cured concrete of Elgin gravel—mix, age, grading and consistency being included variables—the modulus of rupture $S_m = 200 + 0.09S_c$, when S_c, the compressive strength, is between 1500 and 9000 psi.

The continued growth in strength of concrete over a 1-year period depends to a large extent upon the amount of moisture given the specimens during curing. The adverse effect on strength of a dry curing condition is more pronounced as the age of the specimen increases. The flexural strength does not appear to be affected as seriously by dry curing

* For descriptions of other types of test pieces see Mills, *Cornell Civil Eng.*, Vol. 19, p. 106; Talbot in *Bull.* 1, Univ. Ill., Eng. Expt. Sta.; Withey in *Bull.* 197, Univ. Wis.

as the compressive strength. Relative strengths based on damp curing are given in Table 7.*

TABLE 7. THE EFFECT OF CURING CONDITIONS ON STRENGTH OF 1:4 CONCRETE

Curing	Coarse Aggregate	RELATIVE STRENGTHS OF CONCRETE IN PER CENT							
		Compressive Strength				Modulus of Rupture			
		7 Days	28 Days	3 Months	1 Year	7 Days	28 Days	3 Months	1 Year
Under wet burlap; tested damp	....	100	100	100	100	100	100	100	100
Air of laboratory; tested dry.	Gravel	90	84	75	65	84	77	78	75
	Limestone	101	85	80	62	95	86	90	87
Air of laboratory; tested wet.	Gravel	91	65	54	49	101	110	96	81
	Limestone	102	62	61	53	110	110	107	98
Air of laboratory; sodium silicate coated, tested as cured.	Gravel	98	89	76	65	101	90	87	76
	Limestone	104	75	72	61	91	85	84	87

17. The Shearing Strength of Concrete. Failure of concrete in pure shear is a rare occurrence. When this term "shear failure" is applied to the diagonal failure in the web of a concrete beam it is misleading, for the cause of such failure is a tensile stress resulting from the combining of tensile and shearing stresses. On account of the difficulty of producing a pure shear stress but few tests have been made. The usual method of making such tests is to support the specimen as a cantilever or fixed beam and apply the load as closely as possible to the supports. Frequently encircling envelopes are placed at each support and around the span portion to prevent bending of the test piece.

Fig. 15. Morsch's shear specimen.

In E. Mörsch's *Eisenbetonbau* (translation by E. P. Goodrich), Chapter III, the theory is advanced that the shearing strength of concrete (S_s) is the geometric mean of its tensile (S_t) and compressive strength (S_c), $S_s = \sqrt{S_t \times S_c}$. .Mörsch's results obtained from tests on $7 \times 7 \times 16$-in. prisms loaded as indicated in Fig. 15 are in accordance with this theory. However, since in these tests the concrete cracked in tension before the full shearing strength was developed, one is led to believe that the computed values of shear are much too low. Mörsch also tested the torsional strength of solid concrete cylinders 10.24 in. in diameter by 13.38 in. long and hollow cylinders of the same outside measurements with an internal diameter of 5.9 in. The proportions were 1:4 gravel concrete, and the ages of the solid and hollow specimens 3 months and 2 months, respectively. The modulus of rupture in torsion (see formula

* From Series **171**, *Rept., Director of Research, Portland Cement Assoc.*

17 in Art. I-23) for 4 solid cylinders averaged 243 psi, for 3 hollow cylinders 126 psi. All specimens fractured on helicoidal surfaces. Tensile tests on like hollow sections gave a strength of 133.8 psi. Apparently the torsional strength is equal to the tensile strength if the specimen is dimensioned so that the intensity of the shearing stress is approximately the same over the entire cross section. Mörsch also reports results of tests on slotted beams reinforced in the tension fibers so that failure in horizontal shear along a small portion of the neutral plane was produced. Here again it seems certain that diagonal tension must have largely influenced the results.

The results of shearing tests on 5-in. cylinders of concrete made at the Massachusetts Institute of Technology under the direction of C. M. Spofford * are digested in Table 8. In these tests the end and center portions of the cylinders were tightly clamped so that bending action was made small. The results indicated such an abnormally high ratio of shearing to compressive strength that one is led to believe frictional resistance must have been induced at the planes of fracture. Specimens cured in water for 1 month appear to be slightly stronger in shear than those cured in air.

A very comprehensive series of tests by Talbot † included punching tests on plane plates, on recessed plates, and on plates reinforced and recessed as shown in Table 8. The punch used was a cylinder $5\frac{7}{8}$ in. in diameter, which acted through the specimens against a die 6 in. in diameter. Talbot reported that the reinforced recessed plates were the most satisfactory of the types of specimen used in the punching tests. He also used short-beam test pieces restrained at the end in a device like the Johnson shear tool (Art. II-15) and applied the load across the span uniformly but without restraining the center portion of the beam.

The existing data indicate that the shearing strength of concrete lies between 40 and 60 per cent of the compressive strength.

18. The Effect of Fatigue on Concrete. The resistance of plain concrete to fatigue deserves consideration in many structures but particularly in pavements. Tests of concrete 6 months, or more, in age under loads rapidly repeated for 2,000,000 cycles indicate that the fatigue strength (Art. XXXII-14) of air-dry concrete in compression or in bending is approximately 50 to 55 per cent of the corresponding strength under loading progressively applied to failure. Tests of mortars saturated with water indicate that the fatigue strength is only about 40 per cent of the strength of air-dry mortar under progressive loading. Hatt ‡ states that

---

* See Reid's *Concrete and Reinforced Concrete Construction*, p. 198.

† *Bull.* 8, Univ. Ill. Eng. Expt. Sta.

‡ For further data see *Bull.* 34, Eng. Expt. Sta., Purdue Univ.; also *The Fatigue of Metals*, by Kommers and Moore.

TABLE 8. SUMMARY OF RESULTS OF SHEAR TESTS ON BROKEN STONE CONCRETE MADE AT UNIVERSITY OF ILLINOIS AND MASSA-CHUSETTS INSTITUTE OF TECHNOLOGY

Mix by Vol.	Stored in.	No. Tests.	Strength in Lb. per Sq.In in		Ratio Shear* Compr.	Form of Specimen.
			Shear.	Compression.*		
		UNIVERSITY OF ILLINOIS TESTS. AGE 2 MONTHS.				
1 : 3 : 6	Air	9	679	1230	0.55	
1 : 3 : 6	Water	7	729	1230	0.59	Plain Plate
1 : 3 : 6	Damp Sand	4	905	2428	0.37	
1 : 2 : 4	"	5	1193	3210	0.37	
1 : 3 : 6	Air	17	796	1230	0.65	
1 : 3 : 6	Water	5	879	1230	0.71	Recessed Plate
1 : 3 : 6	Damp Sand	4	1141	2428	0.47	
1 : 2 : 4	"	5	1257	3210	0.39	
1 : 3 : 6	Air	4	1051	1230	0.86	
1 : 3 : 6	Damp Sand	4	1821	2428	0.75	Reinforced Rec.Pl.
1 : 2 : 4	"	5	2145	3210	0.67	
1 : 3 : 6	Damp Sand	4	1313	2428	0.54	4×4×12 in. beams restrained at ends
1 : 2 : 4	"	6	1418	3210	0.44	
		TESTS AT MASS. INST. OF TECH. AGE 1 MONTH.				
1 : 2 : 4	Air	......	1310	2070	0.63	5×15 in. cylinders
1 : 2 : 4	Water	......	1650	2620	0.63	restrained at ends
1 : 3 : 5	Air	......	1240	1310	0.94	and loaded over
1 : 3 : 5	Water	......	1120	1360	0.82	span $5\frac{7}{16}$ in. long
1 : 3 : 6	Air	......	1180	950	1.25	by a half cylinder
1 : 3 : 6	Water	......	1120	1270	0.88	bearing.

* Illinois specimens were 6-in. cubes; M.I.T. specimens were 5 × 18-in. cylinders.
NOTE.—In Illinois tests limestone passed 1-in. mesh. Trap rock passing 1½-in. ring was used at M.I.T.

beams reinforced with small percentages of steel mesh show an increase of about 13 per cent in strength and 7 per cent in extension as compared to similar plain beams when subjected to repeated loadings.

19. Resistance of Concrete to Wear. In *Bull.* 10, Structural Materials Research Laboratory, Abrams gives results of wear tests on about 10,000 8 × 8 × 5-in. concrete blocks. These blocks were tested in groups of 10 in a Talbot-Jones rattler. In testing, the blocks were wedged securely to form the lining to the rattler drum and were subjected to the abrasion and impact of a 200-lb charge of cast-iron balls while the machine ran 1 hour at 30 rpm. Wear was measured by loss in weight, but expressed as depth lost in inches.

Abrams found that the quality of the concrete was the most important factor which affected the resistance to wear. He found that the wear (W) decreased with the compressive strength of the concrete (S_c) and could be expressed by the relationship $S_c = A/W^n$, in which A and n are constants depending on quality of concrete and method of test. For one series of 300 tests he reports $A = 2230$ and $n = 1.07$. For concrete of the type used in road construction, his tests show that the resistance to wear increases directly with the compressive strength. From his tests Abrams concluded that the quality of the aggregate did not have as potent an effect on the amount of wear as the water-cement ratio or proportion of cement.

The experience of one of the authors in conducting several hundreds of similar wear tests on slabs 8 by 20 by 4½ in. in a modified brick rattler has demonstrated that, with a properly proportioned mix of well-graded materials, the uniformity of wear and the amount of wear are both considerably affected by the quality of the aggregate. A concrete of tough angular crushed dolomite will in most cases wear less, and more evenly, than a like concrete made of pebble aggregate. The two main reasons for this difference are the greater uniformity of the crushed stone in strength and toughness and the better bond which it affords the mortar.

20. The Strength of Lightweight Concrete.* On account of its fireproofing properties and its light weight, cinder concrete is considerably used for floor construction and for a fireproofing shell around beams and columns. The strength of cinder concrete is decidedly variable and is greatly influenced by the strength, granulometric composition, and absorptive properties of the cinders. Table 9 shows the results of tests made by various experimenters. The results of the tests by the U. S. Geological Survey show that consistency has but little effect on the compressive or transverse strength of cinder concrete. From the latter tests on 6-in. cubes and 8 × 11-in. beams on a 12-ft span, the ratio of the compressive strength to the transverse modulus of rupture averages 9.8:1 for concrete 6 months old. It will be noted that this ratio is considerably larger than the corresponding value for gravel or broken stone concrete.

Lightweight concrete is also made from such aggregates as pumice, scoria, coke, expanded shales or clays, expanded slags, Perlite, and ver-

* See also Title No. 45-37, Vol. 20, May 1949, *J. Am. Concrete Inst.*

TABLE 9. THE COMPRESSIVE STRENGTH AND SPECIFIC WEIGHT OF
CINDER CONCRETE

No. Spec.	Mix by Vol.	Con-sistency	Age in Months	Com-pressive Strength, Lb. per Sq. In.	Specific Weight, Lb. per Cu. Ft.	Type of Specimen	How Cured	Authority
3	1 : 1 : 3	Dry	1	1466	112.1			
3	1 : 1 : 3	Dry	3	2001	110.4			
3	1 : 2 : 3	Dry	1	1098	115.2			
3	1 : 2 : 3	Dry	3	1634	112.8			*Tests of*
3	1 : 2 : 4	Dry	1	904	111.2	12-in.	Air	*Metals.*
3	1 : 2 : 4	Dry	3	1325	107.9	cubes		1908
3	1 : 2 : 5	Dry	1	769	108.8			
3	1 : 2 : 5	Dry	3	1084	105.3			
3	1 : 2 : 6	Dry	1	529	107.6			
3	1 : 2 : 6	Dry	3	788	103.5			
3	1 : 2 : 5	Wet	1	1081		8×16-in.	Moist	
3	1 : 2 : 5	Medium	1	1201		cyl.	air	
3	1 : 2 : 5	Damp	1	1118				U.S.
3	1 : 2 : 5	Wet	3	1764	116.5			Geol. Sur.
3	1 : 2 : 5	Medium	3	1819	115.6			*Bull.*
3	1 : 2 : 5	Damp	3	1726	112.5			No. 344.
3	1 : 2 : 5	Wet	6	2021	113.9			
3	1 : 2 : 5	Medium	6	2203	114.3			
3	1 : 2 : 5	Damp	6	1945	113.7			
10	1 : 2 : 5		1	407		8×16-in.	Air	
10	1 : 2 : 5		2	701	107	cyl.		
10	1 : 2 : 5		6	933				
10	1 : 2 : 5		1	818				Strehan and
10	1 : 2 : 5		2	1254	107			Perrine
10	1 : 2 : 5		6	1744				in
10	1 : 2 : 5		1	980				*Engr.* *News*
10	1 : 2 : 5		2	1035	109			Vol. 70
10	1 : 2 : 5		6	1478				p. 722
10	1 : 1 : 5*		1	507				
10	1 : 1 : 5		2	662	100			
10	1 : 1 : 5		6	754				

(Consistency not stated. Concrete taken from 4 buildings in N. Y. City.)

* Hand-mixed, the other batches of this group were machine-mixed.

miculite, Art. XIII-23. The properties of concretes made with these aggregates may vary over a wide range, depending upon the specific aggregate used, the mix proportions, the manufacturing methods, and the intended use. Properties usually desired include good strength, low specific weight, good durability, good fire resistance, good sound absorption, low volume change, low thermal conductivity, low water absorption, and good nailability. It is obviously impossible to get the optimum values for all properties in any one concrete, but the properties in any case are a compromise because an increase in certain properties is usually gained at the expense of others. For example, under comparable circumstances, an increase in the specific weight of the concrete will cause an increase in strength but a decrease in nailability and a decrease in insulating ability.

Lightweight concretes are frequently harsh, and consequently admixtures and additions of fine natural sands are used to overcome this difficulty. In order to obtain satisfactory mixing, most lightweight aggregates are first mixed with water before the cement is added. In the case of vermiculite and Perlite, however, the water, cement, and the admixture are mixed before the aggregate is added.

Lightweight concrete may be considered in terms of its intended use. *Structural concrete* is used for buildings, bridges, and ships where a reduction in weight without much sacrifice in strength is necessary. This type of concrete should have about the same workability characteristics as ordinary plastic concrete. A higher cement content for a given strength is usually required for the lightweight concrete. *Precast concrete* masonry units for wall and partition construction are made from comparatively dry mixes placed by means of vibrators and tampers. Masonry units should be lightweight and have good strength and insulating properties. The *insulation* type concrete is used for such things as insulating concrete roof fills, insulating structural roof slabs, acoustical tile, acoustical plasters, and other similar items. This type of concrete is very light weight and has excellent insulating properties, but its strength is usually low.

A comparison of the range in properties for heavy structural concrete and the three different types of lightweight concrete is given in Table 10.

Haydite has been used to make concrete ships. Crushed to pass a $\frac{3}{16}$-in. screen, the fine aggregate weighed about 70 lb per cu ft and the coarse aggregate which passed a $\frac{5}{8}$-in. screen and was retained on a $\frac{3}{16}$-in. screen weighed 45 lb per cu ft. Mixed in $1:\frac{2}{3}:1\frac{1}{3}$ proportions by volume with about 22 per cent of water, by weight of dry materials, this concrete had a slump of 8 to 10 in. and weighed when green 114 lb per cu ft. At 28 days the compressive strength averaged above 4000 psi (*Eng. News-Record*, Vol. 82, p. 802). Other tests on cylinders of 1:6 Haydite concrete which had been subjected to temperatures between 1500 and 1800°F for 5 hours showed that the compressive strength, 2835 psi,

TABLE 10.   USUAL RANGE IN PROPERTIES FOR HEAVY AND
LIGHTWEIGHT CONCRETES

Type of Concrete	Specific Weight, lb/cu ft	Compressive Strength, psi	Modulus of Elasticity, 1000 psi	Heat Conductivity K [1] (Btu)
Heavy structural	145–155	2000–5000	2000–5000	6.0–10.0
Lightweight structural	80–120	2000–5000	1500–2500	2.0–4.0
Masonry units	75–100	1000–2000	700–1400	. . . .
Insulation or fill	20–75	50–800	40–600	0.7–2.0

[1] Btu per square foot per hour per °F per inch of thickness.

was reduced about 55 per cent by exposure to these high temperatures (see *Eng. News-Record*, Vol. 87, p. 765; see also paper by Richart and Jensen, *Proc. ASTM*, 1930).

THE ELASTIC PROPERTIES OF MORTARS AND CONCRETES

21. General Characteristics of the Elastic Curves. As Fig. 16 shows, the stress-deformation curves for cement and concrete resemble those for other brittle materials like cast iron, brick, and stone. Carefully made experiments fail to disclose a limit of proportionality or an elastic limit. Compression tests indicate, however, that after several applications of stresses less than one-half the ultimate strength of concrete the set becomes momentarily constant. On account of the occurrence of set for low intensities of stress, the true elastic stress-deformation curve for these materials may differ considerably from the gross deformation curve. Bach, in finding the true elastic curve in compression, repeatedly applied and released each load until the set at zero load became constant. By subtracting the set from the total deformation the elastic deformation for a given load was determined. Although the true elastic curve is of importance in considering the change of shape of concrete after removal of stress, the total unit deformation due both to the initial imposition of load and to the further yielding with time are the more important factors in arriving at a measure of stress from strain either in plain or reinforced concrete. The *increase* in unit strain caused by the *sustained* application of a unit stress of unity is called the *plastic flow*. Methods of estimating strains due to sustained stress are given in Art. 23.

22. Calculation of the Modulus of Elasticity. Since mortar and concrete have no elastic limit, the modulus of elasticity must be the slope

of the stress-deformation curve at zero stress. For mixes which have a
stress-deformation curve of sharp curvature near the origin, the initial

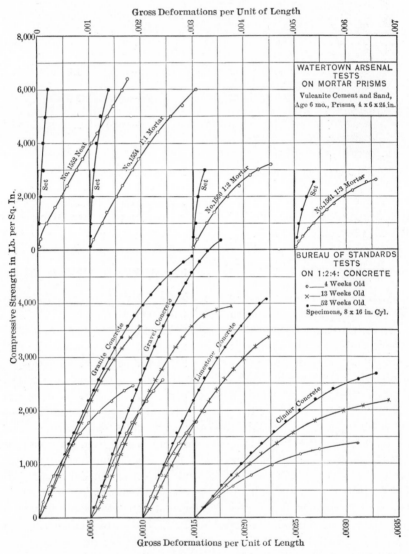

Fig. 16. Stress-deformation diagrams for mortars and concretes in compression
(*Tests of Metals*, 1904. *Tech. Paper* 2.)

modulus of elasticity E is of little value, except for comparing the stiffness of different concretes; since, for all finite values of unit stress S or
unit deformation ϵ, $E\epsilon > S$ and ($S/E < \epsilon$, as may be seen from Fig. 17.
For such curves the slope of a secant drawn from the origin through a

point corresponding to a working unit stress is useful in determining stresses from strains accompanying momentary working loads. Also, in reinforced concrete design the use of the secant modulus considerably shortens the computations without undue sacrifice of accuracy.

Professor Bach's studies of true elastic curves led to an exponential equation for unit deformation in compression, $\epsilon = KS_c^m$, in which K and m are constants, depending upon the material. Mörsch * gives the following equations of the true elastic curve for $1:2\frac{1}{2}:5$ sand and gravel concrete and $1:2\frac{1}{2}:5$ sand and broken stone concrete, $\epsilon = S_c^{1.14}/5,676,100$ and $\epsilon = S_c^{1.16}/9,190,500$, respectively.

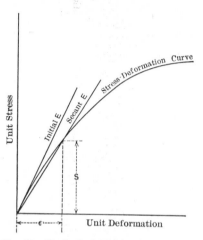

Fig. 17. Method of finding the (secant) modulus of elasticity, $E = S/\epsilon$.

Professor Talbot † developed a formula for the elastic curve in compression, based upon the theory that the stress-gross-deformation curve for concrete is a parabola. His formula is $S_c = (1 - \frac{1}{2}q)E_c\epsilon$, in which q is the ratio of ϵ (the unit deformation for S_c), to the ultimate unit deformation, and E_c is the initial modulus.

23. Values of the Modulus of Elasticity of Mortars and Concretes. Table 11 shows values of the moduli of elasticity of neat cement and concretes compiled from the sources mentioned. The modulus increases with the density, and to some extent with age, if specimens are water cured. Mörsch's results show that the moduli for wet mixes are less than for dry mixes of the same proportions. For lean mixes of the same aggregate, the modulus like the strength increases with the proportion of cement; but the variation is small for proportions richer than $1:2$, in the case of mortar, or $1:1\frac{1}{2}:3$, in the case of concrete.

The stiffness of the aggregate affects both the elasticity and the strength of concrete. Large differences between the stiffness of the mortar and aggregate must promote non-uniformity of stress under load and undoubtedly account for the low early strengths of concretes made from certain granites and trap rocks.

From 3500 tests of concrete in which mix, grading, water ratio, and type of aggregate were variables, Walker concluded that the initial modulus of elasticity (E_i) and the tangent modulus at $\frac{1}{4}$ ultimate (E_{25}) varied within limits with the compressive strength (S_c) thus: $E_i = 33,000S_c^{5/8}$ and $E_{25} = 66,000S_c^{1/2}$.

* *Eisenbetonbau*, p. 22 (trans).
† *Bull.* 14, Eng. Expt. Sta., Univ. Ill.

TABLE 11.   MODULI OF ELASTICITY FOR NEAT CEMENT, MORTAR AND CONCRETE

No. Spec.	Mix, by Volume	Age, in Months	Method of Curing	Consistency	Aggregate	Dimensions of Spec., in Inches	Modulus of Elasticity, Pounds per Square Inch		Range of Stress (Lb./In.^{2})	Authority
							Tension	Compression		
3	1 : 1.8 : 1.2	3	....	Dry / Wet	Sand and Gravel <0.8 in.	7×7×29	3,380,000 / 2,950,000	3,650,000 / 3,160,000	0–552 C. / 0–44 T. elastic def.	Mörsch
3	1 : 2.4 : 1.6	3	....	Dry / Wet			3,410,000 / 3,140,000	3,200,000 / 2,630,000		
21	1 : 2 : 4	1	Moist } Air	Medium	Sand and Cinders	8×16 in. cyl.	....	1,610,000	Initial E	Bureau of St'ds Tech. Paper No. 2
21	1 : 2 : 4	12						2,110,000		
21	1 : 2 : 4	1			Sand and Granite	8×16 in. cyl.		4,290,000		
21	1 : 2 : 4	12						4,770,000		
21	1 : 2 : 4	1			Sand and Gravel	8×16 in. cyl.		4,600,000		
21	1 : 2 : 4	12						5,390,000		
21	1 : 2 : 4	1			Sand and Limestone	8×16 in. cyl.		3,590,000		
21	1 : 2 : 4	12						4,550,000		
5	Neat	1	Moist } Air	Flow200	Sand and Gravel <1½ in.	6×12-in. cyl.	....	2,510,000	Secant 0 to ¼ Ult.	Walker, Bull. No. 5 Structural Materials Research Laboratory
	1 : 0.3 : 0.8							3,150,000		
	1 : 0.7 : 1.6							4,500,000		
	1 : 1.0 : 2.8							4,510,000		
	1 : 1.4 : 3.2							4,120,000		
	1 : 1.7 : 4.0							4,310,000		
	1 : 2.4 : 5.7							4,030,000		
	By Weight				Sd. + Gl.	Cylinders	Comp. Str.			
13	1 : 2.4 : 7.0	1	Moist } Air	3-in. Sl.	< 9 in.	36×72 in.	3090	5,100,000	Initial E	Boulder Dam Bureau of Reclamation Proc.A.C.I., Vol.31,p.280
14	1 : 2.4 : 6.4	1		3-in. Sl.	< 6 in.	24×48 in.	3020	5,200,000		
6	1 : 2.5 : 4.9	1		3¾-in. Sl.	< 3 in.	24×48 in.	3250	5,100,000		
9	1 : 2.4 : 3.3	1		5-in. Sl.	<1½ in.	24×48 in.	3400	4,720,000		
155	1 : 2.4 : 3.3	1		5-in. Sl.	<1½ in.	6×12 in.	4050	5,400,000		

In *Bull.* 90, Eng. Expt. Sta., Ames, Iowa, J. W. Johnson reports 750 tests on modulus of elasticity in tension and in compression. His data indicate that the modulus in tension is in most cases slightly less than in compression, but for design purposes they may be considered equal.

Plastic Flow. From the studies of J. R. Shank * it appears that for ordinary concrete of Portland cement and common aggregates loaded in air at 28 days, the plastic flow (y) in millionths (in./in.) per 1 psi is approximated by $y = 0.13x^{1/3}$, where x is the time the load is sustained in days up to 1 year. For maximum effect due to sustained load, increase the value at 1 year by 27 per cent. For similar concretes in water the plastic flow is about half as much; the equation is $y = 0.089x^{1/4}$. Hence the effective value of the modulus of elasticity (E_y) for calculation of stresses may be approximated for a sustained load by $E_y = E_c/(1 + E_c y)$, in which y would be calculated for the duration of the load. In the present state of our knowledge, for ordinary concretes in air under usual working stresses of long duration, E_y will not be far from 1,000,000 psi, and 1,500,000 psi for strong lean vibrated concrete.

24. Poisson's Ratio for Concrete. Under compression the unit lateral expansion of concrete is about one-sixth to one-twelfth of the unit strain in the direction of the applied forces for the ordinary range of working stress. The ratio increases with the richness of the mix and is influenced by the other factors which affect the magnitude of the modulus of elasticity. Values of Poisson's ratio in compression found by Talbot (*Bull.* 20, Univ. Ill.) varies between 0.1 and 0.16 for working loads on 1:2:4 concrete 60 days old. Withey (*Bull.* 466, Univ. Wis.) found, for stresses at one-fourth the ultimate strength on concrete 2 months old, the following values: for 1:3:6 mix, 0.08; for 1:2:4 mix, 0.11; for 1:1¾:3¼ mix, 0.18; for 1:1⅓ mortar, 0.16.

25. Expansion and Shrinkage Due to Variations in Moisture Content.† Concrete will shrink upon drying and expand upon wetting, independent of any changes due to temperature or load. Shrinkage may take place from the beginning while the mass is still plastic and will continue until the concrete is thoroughly dry.

The behavior during the plastic state is the same as that of any inert powdered material mixed with water, the shrinkage that develops being a consolidation of the mass which takes place as water is lost.

Shrinkage during the hardened state occurs chiefly in the cement paste and depends upon the amount of paste in the mix and the quantity of water lost.

---

* *Proc. Am. Concrete Inst.,* Vol. 32, p. 149; also Vol. 33, p. 123.

† Prepared by M. B. Lagaard from tests conducted in the Research Laboratory of the Portland Cement Association.

Shrinkage during the plastic state can be obviated by preventing the loss of water from the mass, either through evaporation from the surface or through absorption of water by the aggregates, forms, or other media. Shrinkage during the hardened state can be kept to a minimum by the proper selection of the mix.

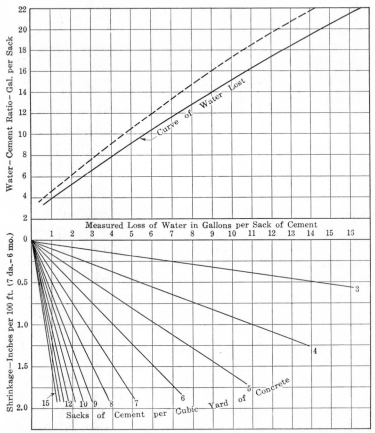

Fig. 18. Interrelationship of shrinkage, loss in weight, cement content, and water-cement ratio. (Lagaard.)

The relationship between the quantity of water lost, the cement content of the mix and the shrinkage, is shown in the lower diagram of Fig. 18. The relationship between quantity of water lost and the water-cement ratio is shown by the upper diagram. These diagrams are based on tests which included concretes and mortars, using sand and gravel aggregates, with the cement content varying from 3 to 15 sacks per cu yd. The specimens were 5 × 5 × 17 in., and all the mixes were workable. The curing consisted of an initial period of 7 days in the moist room followed by 6 months in air at 70°F and 50 per cent relative humidity. This condition of curing resulted in almost complete drying, as was shown by forced drying in an oven at 120°F at the end of this period, which produced very little additional loss in weight. The diagram therefore represents about the maximum shrinkage that may be expected.

To use the diagram in predicting the shrinkage of any mix for these conditions, determine the water-cement ratio and the number of sacks of cement in 1 cu yd of concrete. From a point on the upper curve, representing the water-cement ratio, proceed vertically to the radiating line in the lower diagram representing the number of sacks of cement in 1 cu yd of concrete. The shrinkage can then be read directly from the scale at the left.

For other conditions of exposure, it will be necessary to estimate the probable position of the curve of water lost for the expected condition of drying, and determine the shrinkage on the basis of the new curve. The dashed curve shows the water lost from these same specimens at the age of 28 days, representing 1 week in the moist room and 3 weeks in air at 50 per cent relative humidity and 70°F. This will help in estimating the probable position of the curve of water lost for other conditions, but consideration must be given to the mass of concrete involved and the opportunity for drying out. The shrinkage in larger masses in outdoor exposure may be as little as $\frac{1}{5}$ the maximum values determined from the diagram. In thin sections, subject to the direct rays of the sun or in artificially heated buildings, the maximum possible shrinkage indicated by these curves may be developed.

THE PERMEABILITY AND ABSORPTION OF MORTAR AND CONCRETE

26. Discussion of Terms. Water may enter a porous body through capillary attraction, it may be forced in under pressure, or it may be introduced by a combination of pressure and capillary attraction. The character and size of the minute canals connecting the pores with one another and with the exterior of the body are apparently the factors which determine the rate of flow into the body. By absorption is meant the drawing in of water by capillary attraction. All cement mixtures absorb water to some extent. When the size and arrangement of the canals are such as to permit water to flow through the substance it is said to be permeable. The rate of absorption depends upon the size, upon number of pores connected with the surface of the body, and upon the size and character of the connecting ducts; the permeability depends upon the character and size of the minute passageways leading through the body; consequently there can be no relation between these properties.

With hydrostatic heads of 100 ft, tests have been made which indicate that neither Portland cement paste nor mixtures made from it are absolutely impervious. Nevertheless, there is abundant evidence which shows that concrete and mortar can be made so impermeable that no leakage or dampness is visible on the surface opposite the water pressure. Apparently, even when the humidity is high, the frictional resistance to flow prevents the water from leaving the free surface of such material at a rapid enough rate to escape evaporation. Concrete or mortar similar to the above will hereafter be frequently referred to as impermeable or impervious. The approximation in such a statement should be remembered.

27. Objectives and Methods of Testing Permeability. Although the principal objective in permeability testing is to find the watertightness of the concrete, such tests often have little direct relation to the imperviousness of the structure due to presence of cracks and poor joints. On the other hand, the test is useful in determining the corrosive effects of percolating waters which leach out the free lime and gradually attack the lime in the tricalcium silicate. It can also be used to measure the relative efficiencies of cements and their rates of hydration.

Two methods of measuring permeability are in use. In one, the water passing out of the specimen is measured; in the other, the quantity entering is determined. The first method does not require as elaborate apparatus as the second, but is inaccurate when the leakage is small due to evaporation losses. The second method necessitates the use of a calibrated water gage for measuring the flow and air pressure to force the water into the specimens. Corrections due to temperature changes are also necessary when the flows are small. Measurements made by the latter method may include both the water absorbed and the water passing through the specimen, depending on the method of curing.

Figure 19 shows three forms of specimen which, more or less modified, have been used in many important experiments. The type illustrated in Fig. 19a is the simplest, most easily made and readily attached to the testing apparatus; but the path of flow is neither restricted to a definite volume of concrete, nor is the area of the opening in the casting sufficient for the testing of concrete made from large aggregate.

Figure 19b illustrates the form of mortar test piece used by the U. S. Bureau of Standards. Similar specimens 18 in. in diameter were used in testing concrete. This type of test piece requires expensive castings and gaskets. If the flow into the specimen is to be measured, it is probable that difficulty in securing a tight joint at the gasketed surfaces will be experienced when high pressures are used.

The specimen shown in Fig. 19c has been successfully used in many tests at the University of Wisconsin. In the form shown, the cross section exposed to pressure is ½ sq ft in area and the volume is ¼ cu ft. Curing

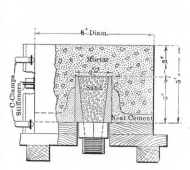

(a) Sectional elevation of mortar permeability specimen, not suitable for concrete (University of Wisconsin).

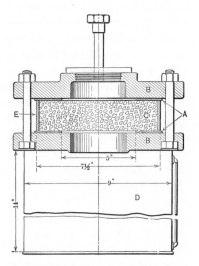

(b) Sectional elevation of Bureau of Standards specimen. (A, A = rubber washers; B, B = cast-iron top and bottom of holder; C = specimen; D = retainer for leakage; E = wrought-iron pipe.)

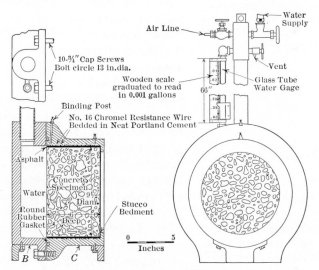

(c) Specimen used for testing permeability of concrete to water at the University of Wisconsin.

Fig. 19. TYPES OF PERMEABILITY SPECIMENS.

conditions may be varied and tests repeated at different time intervals on the same specimen. Specimens are cast in simple cylindrical molds cured as desired; then, with part C rotated 90° to the right of position shown, they are bedded in neat gypsum on the circular shelf of the casting. After the plaster has dried for a half hour, the ⅜-in. annular space around the specimen is filled with Crystal Steep Roofing Asphalt. The bonnet, B, is then bolted to the casting, the tube filled with water, and pressure up to 100 psi can be applied by means of an automatically controlled air pump. Readings of flow into the apparatus are taken at regular time intervals on the water gage and leakage from the face of the specimen noted. The resistance wire is used to heat the casting during the sealing process and in releasing the specimen after test.

In the tests for Boulder Dam, the U. S. Bureau of Reclamation engineers adopted an 18- by 18-in. cylindrical specimen, which was sealed with axis vertical in a manner similar to that shown in Fig. 19c, and pressures up to 400 psi were applied.

In making permeability specimens, homogeneity is a prime requisite. Laitance and excess mortar should be removed by a wire brush from the faces of specimens within 24 hours after casting. Molds must be watertight. Care must be exercised to insure watertight seals in testing.

28. The Effect of the Proportion of Cement on Permeability. Data from tests show that the flow through concrete or mortar decreases with the increase in proportion of cement, provided that the density is constant. Plastic neat cement and 1:1 mortar linings 2 in. or over in thickness may be considered impervious under heads less than 100 ft, provided that the mortar is not cracked by overstressing. If made of bank sands of good quality, 1:2 mortars of plastic consistency will, in general, show no leakage under a like pressure. With well-graded sands impervious mortars of 1:3 and 1:4 proportions may be secured. Figure 20 (*Proc. ASTM*, Vol. 13, p. 835) well shows the effect of the proportion of cement upon the permeability of mortars made of fine (Sd 4), medium

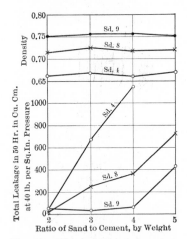

Fig. 20. The influence of proportion of cement on the permeability of mortar made from fine (Sd 4), medium (Sd 8), and coarse (Sd 9) sands.

(Sd 8), and coarse (Sd 9) sands. The experiments were made on specimens like Fig. 19a. The properties of these sands may be found in Table XIV-4.

Extensive tests at the University of Wisconsin are reported in *Trans. West. Soc. Eng.*, Vol. 19, p. 833; *Eng. Bull.* 1245; *Eng. Reprint* 22 and 41. These data show that hand-puddled concrete made with well-graded gravel or broken stone less than 1½-in. in size, and with a slump of 2 to 4 in., can be made impermeable to heads under 100 ft by using 5½ to 7 sacks of cement per cu yd, provided the thickness is 1 ft or more. For heads of 10 ft or less, properly made mixes with 4 sacks per cu yd can be made watertight. By using mixes of 0 to ½-in. slump and internal vibration in placing, mixes can be made watertight under 100 ft head with only 4 sacks of cement per cu yd.

29. Effects of Density and Water-Cement Ratio on Permeability. With the same cement content the permeability of concrete or mortar increases as the density decreases. This is most marked in lean mixes.

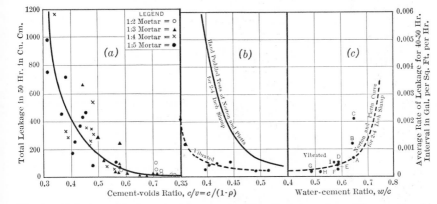

Fig. 21. Relation of leakage to (*a*) cement-void ratio for mortars, (*b*) cement-void ratio for concrete, (*c*) water-cement ratio for concrete. Pressure, 40 psi.

From the results of numerous tests on sand mortars, Feret concluded that most impermeable mortar for any given proportion of cement will be obtained when the percentage of fine sand (*F*) plus cement equals the percentage of coarse sand (*G*). This grading, he also found, produced the maximum strength and density (Art. 4). Mortars made from fine sand he found more impervious than those containing large grains (*G*) only.

Figure 21 shows the relation of leakage to the cement-void ratio for certain of the Wisconsin mortar and gravel concrete tests. Figure 21*a* and *b* indicate the effect of the cement-void ratio on the leakage of the leaner mortars and concretes. Figure 21*b* illustrates the superior watertightness of the zero-slump concrete specimens 6 in. thick placed by vibration, to that of the 2- to 4-in. slump, hand-puddled mixes. None of the specimens with flows of 0.0005 gal/sq ft/hour, or less, exhibited visible leakage. Watertightness, as measured by invisible leakage under a 100-ft head for a thickness of 1 ft, is indicated as obtainable for mixes with $w/c = 0.5$, or less, by weight, in Fig. 21c and in Fig. 3, Chapter X. These diagrams also indicate the superior watertightness of the concretes made of the finely ground, high early strength cements and the Portland-puzzolan cement.

For hand-puddled concrete made of gravel under $1\frac{1}{2}$ in. in size and a good sand, $m = 2.7$, Norton and Pletta's tests at the University of Wisconsin show that the highest degree of watertightness was obtained with the mixed aggregate graded to m-values of 5.2, 5.5, and 5.8 for the 1:4, 1:5, and 1:6 mixes, by volume, respectively. For the vibrated mixes made of the same aggregates, Fig. 21b, the values of m ranged from 5.7 to 5.9, and the cement contents from 2.9 to 3.8 sacks per cu yd. For the 2.9-sack mixes represented by points A, B, and C, the sand-to-gravel ratios were 0.30, 0.32, and 0.34, and the values of m, 5.9, 5.8, and 5.7. These data indicate the pronounced influence of grading on the density and watertightness of lean mixes.

30. The Effect of Consistency on Permeability. With hand placing, a dry mix leads to pin holes and heavy leakages, especially with lean concretes. The use of excess water reduces density and increases flow. A slight excess of water produces far less leakage than a similar deficiency, even in a mix as rich as $1:1\frac{1}{2}:3$. For most hand-placed concrete, the minimum slump which can be successfully used varies from 2 to 6 in., depending upon the richness of the mix, size of aggregate, intricacy of reinforcing, width of forms, and amount of puddling. With vibrated concrete, slumps of 0 to 1 in. can often be used effectively on massive constructions, and rarely need the slump exceed 2 in.

31. Permeability Coefficients. From the high-pressure permeability tests of the U. S. Bureau of Reclamation[*] in connection with Boulder and other dams, A. Ruettgers, E. N. Vidal, and S. P. Wing established several useful coefficients based on the application of D'Arcy's law, $Q/A_c = K_c H/L$, to flow of water through concrete. By repeatedly testing specimens under different pressures and other specimens differing in thickness, they demonstrated that the quantity of water (Q) flowing in a given time was proportional to the ratio of the head (H) to the percolation length, or thickness of specimen (L). Hence the *permeability coefficient* (K_c) represents the unit rate of discharge in cubic feet per second due to a head of 1 ft acting on a specimen of 1 sq ft cross section and 1 ft thick.

From their tests using measured rates of inflow after flows of 250 hours or more, and their studies of existing data, they evolved the diagrams shown in Fig. 22. In Fig. 22a, K_c has the aforesaid significance.

[*] *Proc. Am. Concrete Inst.*, Vol. 31, p. 382; Vol. 32, p. 230, p. 378.

Dividing K_c by the absolute volume of the paste in the mix, the equivalent of $1-s-g$, gives the coefficient K_p. By comparing values of K_p found by different experimenters for the same w/c ratios, a measure of the corrosive action of the percolating water can be had.

The Density Coefficient. Dividing K_c by the volume of mixing water per unit volume of concrete furnished the coefficient K_v. K_v is directly proportional to the mean velocity of the percolating water and is a more

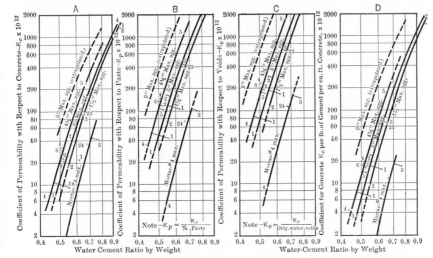

Fig. 22. Coefficients of permeability of concrete. (*Proc. Am. Concrete Inst.*, Vol. 31, p. 395.)

sensitive measure than K_c of the influence of the water-cement ratio and coarseness of the aggregate on the pore formation.

The Corrosion Coefficient. The coefficient K_c per pound of cement per cubic foot of concrete is a direct measure of the relative life of the concrete, since it measures the rate of corrosion due to percolating water.

These experimenters also furnished evidence to show that there was little effect on strength due to a removal of 20 per cent of the lime content by corrosive action of the percolating water, but a removal of 33 per cent entailed an 11 per cent strength loss. In order to produce a removal of half the lime they estimated that a percolation of 35 cu ft of water would be required for each pound of cement in the concrete mass, assuming water as corrosive as distilled water.

In addition to the foregoing, the bureau's tests indicated that the major factors affecting the permeability of their vibrated gravel concrete of 2- to 4-in. slump was the water-cement ratio and the maximum size of aggregate (Fig. 22). Their analysis indicates that water percolated through (a) intersand voids above the settled cement paste which increased rapidly in size for values of the water-cement ratio greater than 0.4 to 0.5, by weight; (*b*) minute voids in the cement paste which depended for size upon the state of the chemical reaction; and (*c*) voids under the coarse aggregate particles, caused by settlement of the mortar and depending upon the size of the aggregate and the water-cement ratio. Tests on neat cement pastes furnished higher K_c and K_p values than concretes with $1\frac{1}{2}$-in. aggregate or mortars. This shows that the watertightness of the neat paste is improved by additions of properly graded aggregates which break up interconnected pores in the paste.

Their tests indicated that Boulder Dam mass concrete containing 9-in. gravel and 1 barrel of low-heat cement per cu yd is so impermeable that the flow through its pore structure is negligible.

In this very informative report are also included permeability coefficients and classes of permeability for various materials as listed in Table 12. An increase in the classification number of unity indicates an increase in impermeability of ten times.

TABLE 12.   TABULATION OF TYPICAL PERMEABILITY COEFFICIENTS
FOR VARYING MATERIALS

Coefficient represents quantity of water in cubic feet per second, per square foot of surface exposed to percolation, passing through one foot of substance with one foot head. $Q = \dfrac{K_c H}{L}$

Material	$K \times 10^{12}$		Class
Granite specimen	2—	10	12
Slate specimen	3—	7	12
CONCRETE and MORTAR, w/c 0.5—0.6	1—	300	12—10
Breccia specimen	20—		11
CONCRETE and MORTAR, w/c 0.6—0.7	10—	650	11—10
Calcite specimen	20—	400	11—10
CONCRETE and MORTAR, w/c 0.7—0.8	30—	1,400	11— 9
Limestone specimen	30—	50,000	11— 8
CONCRETE and MORTAR, w/c 0.8—1.0	150—	2,500	10— 9
Dolomite specimen	200—	500	10
CONCRETE and MORTAR, w/c 1.2—2.0	1,000—	70,000	9— 8
Biotite gneiss in place, field test	1,000—	100,000	9— 7
Sandstone specimen	7,000—	500,000	9— 7
Cores for earth dams	1,000—1,000,000		9— 6
Slate in place, field test	10,000—1,000,000		8— 6
Face brick	100,000—1,000,000		7— 6
CONCRETE, unreinforced canal linings, field test	100,000—2,000,000		7— 6
*Steel sheet piling—junction open 1/1000″ with $\frac{1}{2}$″ of contact—18″ sections	500,000—		7
*CONCRETE, restrained slabs with $\frac{1}{4}$ to $\frac{1}{2}$% reinforcing —30° Temp. change	1,000,000—5,000,000		6
Water bearing sands	1,000,000,000		3

* Flow through 1 ft. length of crack, 1 ft. deep, $Q = 60,000 \dfrac{H}{L} D^3$

32. Effect of Curing on Permeability. Proper curing is of the utmost importance if impermeable concrete or mortar is to be secured. Premature drying adversely affects the imperviousness of lean mixes much more than that of the rich mixes. The imperviousness of lean mixtures properly cured for 3 weeks may be entirely destroyed by drying at 120° to 150°F. These facts are evident from the previously mentioned tests at Wisconsin. Also the increase in percolation is roughly in proportion to

the weight lost in drying. The Bureau of Reclamation tests show that
the percentage of percolation after various lengths of moist curing varied
as follows: after 20 days 300, 30 days 200, 60 days 100, 270 days 50.
These influences are more important in structures under 6 in. or 1 ft in
thickness, since atmospheric drying causes little moisture withdrawal beyond a depth of 2 or 3 in. from the surface.

33. Other Conditions Affecting Permeability. The watertightness of
concrete will also vary with the fineness of the cement, the character of
the aggregate, the quality of the percolating water, time of mixing, and to
some extent with the direction of flow.

The influence of fineness of cement is evident in the data of Fig. X-3.
With hand placement, angular or flat particles of aggregate are less easily
compacted than rounded particles.

The watertightness of the concrete will also be affected by the porosity
of the aggregate. A rapid flow is likely to increase with water of high pH
content due to a more rapid leaching of the lime from the cement and to
decrease if the percolating water contains sediment or bacteria which will
plug the pores of the concrete. A low flow may gradually diminish due
to the deposition of lime carbonate in the pores of the concrete.

The Wisconsin tests showed that the amount of mixing markedly influenced the watertightness of hand-puddled lean mixes such as 1:9, by
weight, but affected the watertightness of the rich mixes much less.

With hand-puddled concrete the Wisconsin tests showed greater permeability when the pressure was normal to the direction of pouring than when
parallel to that direction. In the Bureau of Reclamation tests on vibrated
concrete the percolation was the same in either direction.

34. The Absorption of Concrete and Mortar. A proper method of
testing the absorptive properties of concrete or mortar is yet to be determined. By drying these substances at temperatures above 120° to 150°F,
the imperviousness is greatly reduced, and consequently water will penetrate farther into such material than it would into undried concrete.
Nevertheless, the method of conducting the absorption test ordinarily
employed for other porous materials is generally used in testing mortar
and concrete.

A series of tests on the absorption of 1:2, 1:4, 1:6, and 1:8 mortars
made from three different sands is reported in *Tech. Paper* 2. The test
pieces were 2-in. cubes. They were stored in a damp room between testing periods. Before testing they were dried for several days at a temperature of 212° to 230°F. After cooling they were immersed in water to a
depth of 3 in. They were periodically weighed until they gained less than
$\frac{1}{20}$ of 1 per cent per day; the test was then stopped.

The experiments show that the absorption generally decreases with age,
the greatest change occurring in the first two months. Mortars of damp

consistency absorbed more than those of quaking consistency. Mortars made of coarse sand were somewhat less absorptive than those made of fine sands. The absorption, in general, decreased with the increase in richness of mix. The results show, however, that some factor, probably porosity, exercised a more important influence than the proportion of cement. Slag sand mortars, on account of the porosity of the aggregate, absorbed much more water than either the fine or coarse sand mortars.

Absorption tests made at the University of Wisconsin on mortars varying in richness from 1:2 to 1:5 have shown that those made from screenings and fine sands generally absorb more water than those made of better graded material. Mortars of 1:2 to 1:4 proportions made of good materials and properly cured ought not absorb more than 10 per cent of water after 48 hours' immersion. Well-made concrete of dense aggregate should not absorb more than 6 per cent of water under the same conditions.

35. Waterproofing Materials. For a number of years attempts have been made to discover washes and compounds which will waterproof concrete and mortar. In general, tests seem to show that if proper attention is given to proportioning, mixing, and curing these compounds are not needed to secure impermeable concrete for heads under 100 ft. Furthermore, if good materials are procurable at average prices it is questionable if the extra expense involved in the use of such compounds will not be greater than the cost of additional cement required for watertightness. It must also be understood that any beneficial results accruing from the use of these compounds cannot offset poor workmanship or improper curing. Furthermore, if the concrete cracks neither a properly made mix nor the use of such washes or compounds is effective. When there is probability of cracking, expansion joints should be used or a waterproof elastic membrane forming an integral part of the wall should be employed.

Waterproofing compounds may be divided into two classes: integral mixtures, those which are added before the concrete is mixed; and surface washes, those which are applied after the work is finished. The integral mixtures may be inert, simply void fillers such as finely ground clay or hydrated lime; or they may be active by virtue of compounds which they form during the hardening of the cement or by their repelling action toward water—the soap and alum combination, for example. The coatings comprise seven classes. These are: (1) water solutions of inorganic salts, such as magnesium fluosilicate, zinc sulfate, and sodium silicate; (2) water suspensions of pore-filling substances, such as iron filings or casein in ammonia; (3) soap solutions with an evaporable solvent which react with the hydrated lime to fill the pores; (4) combinations of solutions in successive applications which react chemically and fill the pores, such as the soap and alum process and the sodium sulfate, barium chloride combination; (5) solutions of solid hydrocarbons in oil or paraffin, such as Minwax; (6) bituminous coatings such as the asphalt emulsions; and (7) miscellaneous, such as cement and mortar grouts. For reports on surface coatings, see *Proc. Am. Concrete Inst.*, Vol. 28, p. 209, and Vol. 30, p. 1.

36. Effect of Hydrated Lime on Permeability. On account of the plasticity and easy working qualities which hydrated lime imparts to cement mortars, and since it also decreases segregation, it has been considerably used as a waterproofing compound. It may be mixed with the cement in proportions less than 15 per cent without producing loss in strength of concrete. Numerous tests on mortars and concretes have indicated that its use decreased permeability.[*] With a 60-psi water pressure, S. E. Thompson's tests [*] indicated that additions of 8, 12, and 16 per cent of hydrated lime in terms of the weight of the cement gave watertight concrete for 1:2:4, 1:2½:4½, 1:3:5 proportions, respectively. The concrete was made of run-of-crusher hard conglomerate rock below 2 in., with dust removed. All the sand passed a ¼-in. mesh, 26 per cent passed a No. 40 sieve, and 4 per cent passed a No. 100 sieve. Specimens of the type shown in Fig. 19a were used, the thickness of wall subjected to flow was 8 in., and leakage through the specimens was caught and weighed. Thompson contended that hydrated lime paste is a more efficient void filler than Portland cement paste, since the volume of the former is about 2¼ times that of the latter.

Tests of lean concrete made by J. L. Davies [†] on cylinders 8 in. long, 6 in. in diameter, showed that the rate of flow was decreased by replacing 20 per cent of the cement, by weight, with high-calcium lime. The results with dolomitic lime were not so satisfactory. Davies used mixtures varying from 1.1:3:6 to 1.3:3:6 by weight and pressures of 40 and 80 psi. From a study of his results and the cost per cubic yard of the different concretes based on New York City prices, it does not appear that such use of lime is economical.

Tests by E. W. Lazell [‡] and by the U. S. Bureau of Standards [§] show that the replacement of 10 per cent of the cement with hydrated lime increases the imperviousness of 1:3 and 1:4 mortars.

37. Effect of Finely Ground Clay on Permeability of Mortars. R. H. Gaines [¶] made a number of tests on 1:3 mortars in which he replaced 10 per cent of Cowe Bay sand with finely ground clay. Under pressures

[*] *Proc. ASTM*, Vol. 8, p. 500.
[†] *Eng. News*, Vol. 68, p. 866.
[‡] *Proc. ASTM*, Vol. 6, p. 341.
[§] *Tech. Paper* 3, by R. J. Wig and P. H. Bates.
[¶] *Eng. News*, Sept. 26, 1907.

of 80 psi he found no leakage for test pieces containing the clay, although the normal specimens leaked considerably. Davies also made tests on the efficiency of finely ground clay for waterproofing concrete, but he concluded that this method also was not economical.

38. Other Integral Mixtures. The large number of commercial compounds available as integral waterproofing materials may be classified on the basis of their compositions into groups such as: calcium chloride in water; calcium chloride and various stearates in water; soaps consisting chiefly of ammonium or sodium stearate in water; alum and soap; hydrated lime and soap; finely divided filler materials such as diatomaceous silica, lime, and clay; heavy oil; and cellulose and wax in an ammoniacal copper solution. The value of many of these materials in reducing permeability of concrete is open to question. Tests made by C. H. Jumper [*] indicate that the finely divided fillers and the heavy oils were the most effective.

39. Waterproofing by Surface Washes. Between 1924 and 1933 tests on the waterproofing efficiency of 21 surface washes covering the 7 classes enumerated were made at the University of Wisconsin by C. L. Neumeister and G. W. Washa. The specimens were of the type shown in Fig. 19c. Specimens initially permeable were chosen, and their flows determined immediately prior to treatment under a pressure of 40 psi over the 40- to 50-hour interval. They were then treated with a surface wash in accordance with the recommended procedure and again tested for flow. The efficiency of a treatment was based on the ratio of the difference between flow before and after treatment to the initial flow. The efficiency for a given wash was calculated from 3 or 4 such tests.

Of the washes in the first six classes, colorless Minwax had the highest efficiency, 72 per cent. After a 2-year exposure out of doors it exhibited an efficiency of 44 per cent. Four coats of asphalt emulsion had an efficiency of 71 per cent, but it was not available at the time the exposure tests were run. This material is very easy to apply. Most of the washes showed severe losses in efficiency due to the 2-year exposure.

Neat cement and 1:1 and 1:2 grouts containing sand passing a No. 20 sieve were also tested. Three coats of each of these washes were applied at intervals of 10 to 12 hours. After this they were kept moist under damp burlap for various lengths of time up to 7 days. The efficiency of the washes improved with the length of the curing period, and there was a marked increase in the efficiency of the specimens cured 7 days as compared to those cured only 3 days. The 1:1 grout exhibited an efficiency of 88 per cent and the lowest flow after treatment of any of the washes tested. The 1:2 grout was next with an efficiency of 72 per cent. The efficiency

[*] *Proc. Am. Concrete Inst.*, Dec. 1931.

of the neat cement wash was only 65 per cent. None of these cement washes were run in the exposure tests.

40. Waterproof Membranes. Absolute imperviousness can be secured by the use of several layers of fabric like the better grades of roofing felt cemented to the work by hot asphalt or coal tar washes. To prevent deterioration it is well to cover the alternate layers of pitch and felt with a protective layer of concrete or mortar.*

41. Surface Hardeners. The surface of an improperly cured floor can be hardened and rendered less dusty by the application of water solutions of either aluminum sulfate or sodium silicate. Prior to either treatment the floor must be thoroughly cleaned, scrubbed, and allowed to dry completely.

If aluminum sulfate is used, a 15 per cent solution should be prepared a few days in advance of treatment in order to dissolve the sulfate completely. The quantity required may be estimated at 1 gal per 100 sq ft. Apply 3 coats with a mop or soft brush at 24-hr intervals, allowing each to dry thoroughly.

If commercial sodium silicate is applied, it should be thinned with four times its weight of water. One gallon of this solution will cover about 200 sq ft. Three applications should be made, and each one should be thoroughly brushed into the surface for several minutes. After each coat has dried it should be carefully washed and again dried before the next application is made.

THE EFFECTS OF TEMPERATURE ON MORTAR AND CONCRETE

42. The Effects of Low Temperatures on the Hardening of Concrete. An extensive investigation of the effects of low temperatures on the strengths of concrete made with normal and with high early strength Portland cements at the Portland Cement Association laboratory was reported by A. G. Timms and N. H. Withey in *Proc. Am. Concrete Inst.*, Vol. 30, p. 159, and Vol. 31, p. 165. A mixture of 4 brands of normal cements and 2 different high early strength cements were used. Aggregates were Elgin sand and gravel passing a ¾-in. sieve. Workable mixes of 2- to 6-in. slump containing 4½, 6, and 9 gal of water per sack of cement were made with each cement. Four 3- by 6-in. cylinders cast and puddled in standard manner were made in paraffin-treated cardboard molds for each test condition. Prior to low-temperature exposures, specimens were given a preliminary curing in the uncovered molds for the

---

* For further information concerning methods of waterproofing concrete, see *Proc. Am. Concrete Inst.*, Vol. 19, p. 294, and Vol. 20, p. 641.

Results of tests on concrete waterproofed by fabrics may be found in *Bull.* 336, Univ. Wis.

periods indicated in subsequent diagrams. Specimens were removed from cold storage when 1, 3, 7, or 28 days old. Subsequent to cold-temperature exposure, certain specimens were stripped of their molds and cured at warm temperatures in air at 50 per cent humidity for various periods.

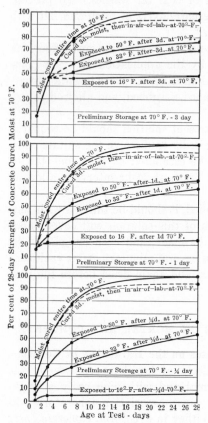

Fig. 23. Relative strength of concrete as influenced by storage temperature. $w/c = 0.8$ by vol.; slump 3 to 5 in.

Molds and materials were brought to the casting temperature indicated before the specimens were molded. All specimens were soaked 1 to 3 hours in water at 70°F, immediately before testing.

Figures 23 and 24, taken from the Timms and Withey report, show relations useful in design. In Fig. 23 is shown the relative strength of concrete with a water content of 6 gal per sack placed at 70°F for ¼, 1, or 3 days and then treated as indicated. Specimens exposed at 16°, 33°, and 50°F were in uncovered cardboard molds in a cold room. The concrete represented was of excellent quality. Its w/c, by weight, was 0.53, and its compressive strength moist-cured at 70°F for 28 days was about 5200 psi. This figure shows the marked retardation in hardening suffered by concrete when placed at low temperatures.

Further data given in the report show that practically the full potential strength of a concrete subjected to such low temperatures can be developed provided it is *kept saturated* during the warming period, but warming in an atmosphere at 50 per cent relative humidity was not a satisfactory procedure.

Figure 24 is an aid in designing concrete placed in cold weather but subjected to 50°F curing temperature. In the upper four diagrams the design strength, given by the upper dash lines, is *based* on concrete cured in molds 1 day then moist at 70°F, whereas in the lower four diagrams the design strength is *based* on water curing at 72°F after removal of molds. The solid lines represent the relative strengths of concrete given the preliminary storage at normal temperatures, then in air, or water, at 50°F. The dashed lines indicate strengths for concrete after preliminary storage of 1 day in air at 50°F, followed by storage in air or water at 50°F.

As an example of the use of Fig. 24, assume that the relative 7- and 28-day strengths of concrete made of normal cement and subjected to curing at 50°F in air are wanted in terms of the 7-day normal strength.

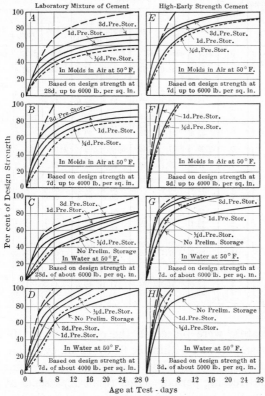

Fig. 24. Relative compressive strength of concrete stored at 50°F based on wet curing at 70°F.

From the dotted curve in diagram B the respective ratios are 0.5 and 0.8. Hence the estimated 28-day strength of concrete cured in air at 50°F is 80 per cent of the 7-day strength normally cured.

In *Proc. ASTM*, Vol. 37, p. 306, H. H. Scofield reports freezing tests made at Cornell University on 1500 specimens. These tests show the effect of immediate and delayed freezing on the strength, stiffness, and permeability of concretes and mortars made from 6 types of cement. His data on the effect of immediate freezing are given in Table 13. Cement No. 1 was normal Portland; No. 2, a high early strength Portland; No. 3, a waterproofed Portland; and No. 4, a high-alumina cement. Specimens

Materials of Construction

TABLE 13.   EFFECT OF IMMEDIATE FREEZING ON THE STRENGTH OF CONCRETE.   (SCOFIELD)

Actual compressive strength in pounds per square inch is given for all normal (0-days frozen) results.
Ages given are for moist curing periods after frozen period.

| Cement | Slump, in. | Frozen Period, days | Compressive Strength of Previously Frozen Concrete as Percentage of the Strength of the Normal Concrete at the Same Age | | | | | | | | | |
| | | | 1 : 2 : 3 Concrete | | | | | 1 : 3 : 5 Concrete | | | | |
			7 days	28 days	1 yr.	4 yr.	Average, per cent	7 days	28 days	1 yr.	4 yr.	Average, per cent
No. 1	2	0	2387	4180	6773	6787	100	1502	2777	4045	4665	100
		1	61.6	55.1	64.4	67.8	62.2	40.2	43.2	55.5	55.4	48.6
		7	57.6	51.0	55.6	64.3	57.1	38.5	37.4	53.4	51.7	45.2
No. 2	2	0	4000	4996	6370	7040	100	3075	3690	4815	4596	100
		1	50.0	61.7	57.0	58.4	54.8	54.0	67.7	63.1	71.8	60.6
		7	44.2	56.7	60.5	53.8	53.8	42.3	56.9	59.4	58.7	54.3
No. 3	2	0	1750	3055	4335	4567	100	1090	1990	3760	3061	100
		1	44.6	48.5	73.4	77.2	60.9	51.4	50.2	70.3	76.0	62.3
		7	52.0	51.7	72.2	65.7	60.4	50.4	49.2	60.0	77.7	58.7
No. 1	6	0	2300	3677	6046	5685	100	1118	2033	3433	4063	100
		1	48.8	51.2	55.1	67.7	55.7	37.2	37.0	44.4	50.6	42.8
		7	47.5	50.1	54.7	63.1	53.8	33.7	37.2	43.7	45.1	39.9
No. 2	6	0	3605	4630	5572	5692	100	2390	3290	3990	3656	100
		1	38.4	46.0	51.3	55.2	47.7	50.6	57.1	50.9	57.1	53.9
		7	36.9	43.5	52.8	56.3	47.4	43.0	43.4	50.0	61.0	49.3
No. 3	6	0	1750	3160	4725	5291	100	990	1770	3250	3005	100
		1	45.7	57.9	70.9	65.3	58.7	51.1	57.7	52.9	59.9	55.4
		7	46.8	49.7	55.7	60.0	53.5	48.0	50.9	50.6	57.9	51.8
No. 4	6	0	4970	4922	5755	5872	100	2775	2780	3538	2788	100
		1	87.7	97.7	88.5	101.0	93.7	69.0	70.0	65.4	68.5	68.2
		7	85.0	97.0	97.4	92.7	93.0	70.3	77.3	81.0	72.7	75.3
No. 1	9	0	1840	3047	5123	4738	100	825	1453	2640	2950	100
		1	53.0	54.7	60.5	71.1	60.6	49.0	49.3	52.1	62.6	53.2
		7	38.7	52.0	51.3	64.7	51.7	39.7	46.0	46.8	54.4	46.7

frozen immediately were placed in the cold room at 10°F as soon as molded.   The temperature within the 6- by 12-in. cylinders reached 32°F in 3 to 4 hours and 10°F in about 12 hours.   All specimens were moist cured after the freezing period.   Each result represents at least 3 tests. These data show that concrete of Portland or high early strength Portland cement loses from 40 to 60 per cent of its potential strength and stiffness when frozen immediately.   Varying the length of the freezing period had little effect.   The dryer mixes of 2-in. slump suffered somewhat less than the wet mixes, especially at the early ages.   The influence of freezing in increasing permeability was marked, especially at the early ages and for specimens frozen 7 days.   Here again the leaner mix was most affected. The high-alumina-cement concrete developed much higher percentages of its potential strength and stiffness and exhibited no leakage after freezing.

Scofield's data on effect of delayed freezing showed that the full potential strength of the 2-in. slump mixes could subsequently be developed by moist curing, provided the concrete was given 24 to 48 hours in room-dry conditions prior to freezing.   For the wet mixes of 9-in. slump, 3 or

4 days of such preliminary curing were required before freezing in order to avoid injury. His data indicated that moist-cured specimens required longer precuring than air-cured specimens in order to avoid permanent injury by freezing.

Several alternate freezings and thawings prior to hardening are more injurious than continuous freezing. A few tests by W. C. F. Rath in a thesis in 1906 at the University of Wisconsin indicate that the greatest injury was done to the cements then used when the intervening thawing periods were 4 to 6 days apart.

43. The Rate of Cooling of Concrete Setting at Low Temperatures. A number of tests on rapidly cooled concrete wallettes were made by O. A. Bailey and F. D. Bickel at the University of Wisconsin in 1915. The wallettes were 30 by 24 by 6 or 12 in. They were cast in 1½-in. pine forms in a refrigerator at temperatures about 10°F. The wallettes were cast with a dividing partition of galvanized iron so that 12- by 12- by 24-in. prisms could be removed and tested. Data on 1:2:4 gravel concrete of medium consistency made with several Portland cements indicated that such concrete placed in 2-in. plank forms with top covered will set before it freezes, provided the temperature of the concrete at pouring is 100°F, the wall 6 in. or more thick, and the outside temperature 0°F, or above.

Methods of calculating temperature changes in setting and hardening concrete, and of evaluating the accompanying stresses, are discussed by R. W. Carlson in *Proc. Am. Concrete Inst.*, Vol. 34, pp. 89 and 497.

44. Alternate Freezing and Thawing Tests on Hardened Concrete. Although thus far no fixed procedure has been adopted for measuring the resistance of masonry materials to freezing and thawing, progress has been made (see Rept. of Committee on Cements, *Proc. Highway Research Board*, 1936; also *Rept. of Building Research Board*, 1927 and 1928).

Among the influential factors are (1) the criterion to use in judging the effects of the test, (2) method of immersion of specimen, (3) rate of lowering temperature through the freezing point, (4) method and rate of thawing, (5) number of cycles required as a criterion. The following procedure has been used successfully at the University of Wisconsin.

Make and cure in accordance with standard methods 3 to 5 prisms for each condition to be tested. These can be tested as beams, then broken as modified cubes in compression, and, if desired, used for expansion and loss in weight measurements prior to testing for strength. For concrete 6- by 6- by 18-in. and for mortars 2- by 2- by 9-in. prisms are satisfactory specimens. Soak specimens 24 hours prior to freezing and support with top surface as molded down in trays of water 1 in. deep. The trays should be cooled at such a rate that the recorded temperature at the center of a prism will drop from 32°F to 15°F in not less than 3 hours and not more than 5 hours. After freezing, thaw them 1 hour in water at 70°F. Repeat for 100 cycles; make determinations of differences in strength, weight, etc., between the normally cured and the frozen-and-thawed specimens. Standardize condition of specimens by soaking them in water prior to making such determinations. See also ASTM *Standards* C290, 1, 2, and C310.

Figure 25 shows the effects of 150 cycles of freezing and thawing on 6- by 6- by 18-in. prisms of excellent vibrated concrete tested as suggested. Concretes with water-cement ratios above 0.54 exhibited marked reductions in modulus of rupture due to freezing and thawing.

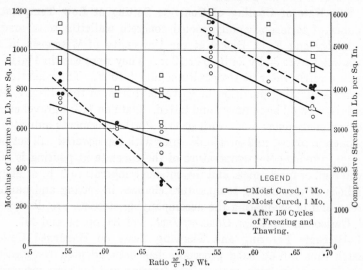

Fig. 25. Effect of freezing and thawing on the strength of concrete made of crushed dolomite. (*Proc. Am. Concrete Inst.*, Vol. 35, p. 553.)

After 100 cycles of such test, durable concrete should have a modulus of rupture not less than 80 per cent of that of similar unfrozen concrete.

45. Measuring Damage Due to Freezing. A method involving the periodic determination of the fundamental transverse frequency of concrete beams to determine the damage caused by freezing and thawing is widely used. The method is simple and permits determination of the damage done by each cycle of freezing and thawing on each specimen.

After initial curing, the specimens, usually 3- by 4- by 16-in. beams, are immersed in water for 24 hours. They are then surface dried, and their initial fundamental transverse frequencies are determined. This is done by supporting each specimen at its nodal points, subjecting it to forced vibrations of varying frequency at its center, and determining the fundamental or resonant vibration by means of a pickup unit that is placed against the concrete surface and is actuated in the plane of vibration. The vibratory motion of the pickup unit is amplified and then indicated on a meter. At resonant frequency of the beam a peak value of the amplified pickup motion is obtained.

The sonic or dynamic modulus of elasticity may be calculated for a prism after the fundamental transverse frequency is known from the equation

$$E = \frac{1.42L^4Tpf^2}{d^2}$$

where E = dynamic modulus of elasticity, psi.
   L = length of specimen, in.
   d = dimension of specimen in direction of vibration, in.
   p = specific weight, lb per cu ft.
   f = fundamental transverse frequency, kc per sec.
   T * = correction factor dependent on the ratio of the radius of gyration to the length, and on the value of Poisson's ratio. If Poisson's ratio is assumed as $\frac{1}{6}$, the value of T is 1.23 for d = 3 in., and 1.40 for d = 4 in.

As freezing-and-thawing action damages a concrete specimen, its fundamental transverse frequency and its dynamic modulus of elasticity are reduced. Freezing and thawing is usually continued until the dynamic modulus of elasticity has been decreased to 70 per cent of the value at zero cycles or until 200 cycles have been reached without such a reduction in the dynamic modulus of elasticity.

Reagel † has shown that decreases in the dynamic modulus of elasticity due to freezing and thawing may be closely correlated with decreases in modulus of rupture and gives the following formula for predicting decreases in modulus of rupture:

$$R = 6E^{0.6}$$

where R = percentage reduction in modulus of rupture.
   E = percentage reduction in dynamic modulus of elasticity.

46. The Effect of Adulterants in Lowering the Freezing Point. Small percentages of salt or calcium chloride dissolved in the mixing water serve to lower the freezing point of the mix and thereby permit hardening at temperatures lower than 32°F. With some cements the use of small percentages of salt appears to diminish the strength; with others the reverse is true. So far as published results show, the use of a 10 or 12 per cent (by weight) solution of common salt has rarely decreased the long-

* For complete discussion see *Proc. ASTM*, Vol. 45, p. 846.
† *Freezing and Thawing Tests of Concrete*, Proc. *Highway Research Board*, Vol. 20, pp. 587–597, 1940.

TABLE 14. THE EFFECT OF CALCIUM CHLORIDE AND SODIUM CHLORIDE ON THE COMPRESSIVE STRENGTH OF 1 : 2 : 4 CONCRETE

Materials:—Atlas cement, good pit sand weighing 108 lb. per cu.ft., and limestone passing a $1\frac{1}{4}$-in. mesh and weighing 90 lb. per cu.ft.

Consistency:—Wet.

Storage:—Normal specimens stored in air one day, in water 13 days. Low-temperature specimens, placed out of doors or in a refrigerator immediately after molding, remaining frozen until tested.

Testing:—Each result represents tests on 4-in. cubes. Specimens were embedded in blotting paper on a spherical bearing block.

PER CENT SALT.		SPECIMENS CURED AT ROOM TEMP.				SPECIMENS CURED AT LOW TEMP.			
CaCl₂	NaCl.	Temp. of Batch at Mixing, ° F.	Compressive Strength in Lb. per Sq.In. at			Temp. (in °F.) at Mixing.		Compressive Strength in Lb. per Sq.In. at	
			14 Days.	60 Days.	360 Days.	Batch.	Out of Doors.	14 Days.	60 Days
0	0	52	1910	3010	3580	52	13	213	427
0	6	52	1684	2620	2895	51	13	482	685
0	9	65	1525	2385	3055	51	13	680	942
0	12	68	1270	2060	2485	51	13	813	1192
0	15	58	1335	2220	2740	42	13	614	1060
2	0	59	1920	3220	3740	41	17	420	466
4	0	60	2105	3510	3880	44	17	444	564
6	0	60	1725	3280	3670	55	18	349*	367*
8	0	61	1510	3070	3155	46	1	286*	334*
10	0	61	1655	3025	3330	46	1	234*	348*
2	6	59	1600	2650	3150	52	15	817	992
2	9	63	1695	2590	3100	52	15	848	1185
2	12	64	1420	2440	2805	41	7	690	1045
2	15	60	1320	2350	2725	38	7	583	801
4	6	56	1685	2550	2960	52	21	785	914
4	9	58	1550	2390	2965	51	20	755	926
4	12	58	1710	2935	3680	45	15	766	1215
4	15	55	1245	1880	2410	45	15	713	1200
6	6	60	1310	2475	2575	43	20	680	988
6	9	54	1305	2370	3025	38	20	480	850
6	12	54	1345	2420	......	52	21	505	615
6	15	52	1380	2415	......	52	21	527	863
8	6	60	1120	2075	2490	51	21	390	580†
8	9	58	1135	2085	2445	50	30	487	654
8	12	60	1110	1995	2525	52	30	402	589
8	15	59	1550	2605	2940	44	14	535	658†

* Badly disintegrated.
† Edges were spalled to some extent.

time strength over 25 or 30 per cent, and in most cases the weakening in final strength is much less. The use of salt in reinforced concrete should be prohibited, since in damp locations it may cause rusting of the steel. A common rule for the use of salt is: add 1 per cent of salt to the mixing water for each degree Fahrenheit below 32.

Tests by H. E. Pulver and S. E. Johnson * at the University of Wisconsin, on the effects of calcium and sodium chloride solutions on the strength of 1:2:4 concrete subjected to freezing conditions, are abstracted in Table 14. The combination of 2 per cent calcium chloride with 9 per cent sodium chloride gave the best results of any of the salt solutions under freezing temperatures. Since calcium chloride alone greatly hastens the set, its employment in the field will require very rapid handling during pouring.

47. Resistance of Concrete and Mortar to High Temperatures. Observations after conflagrations like the San Francisco, Baltimore, and Chelsea fires have shown that concrete possesses a high resistance to fire. Many examples have been cited of concrete buildings which were left standing alone in fire-swept areas of these cities.

A series of 215 tests on concrete-block walls 5½ by 6 ft and of 4-, 8-, and 12-in. thickness were made at the Portland Cement Assoc. laboratory and reported by C. A. Menzel in *Proc. ASTM,* Vol. 31, Pt. 1, p. 607, and *Proc. Am. Concrete Inst.,* Vol. 29, p. 113. Excepting the size of wall, the fire tests on 165 of the walls were made in accordance with the requirements of *Tentative American Standard A2–1926.* The program included 9 types of aggregate and variables in grading, cement content, type of block, mortar, workmanship, and use of plaster.

Machine-tamped units were moist cured 5 days, then aged 2 weeks in laboratory until laid. In most of the tests a 1 Portland cement:0.15 hydrated lime:3 sand mix, by dry rodded volume, was used. The walls were tested at ages of 45 to 60 days. Walls were first loaded to 240 psi of gross area and measurements of deformations and deflections taken. During the fire test the walls were exposed on one face and loaded with 80 psi on gross area. In most tests the fire exposure extended for 1¼ hours for 4-in. walls, 3 to 3½ hours for 8-in. walls, and 5 to 6½ hours for 12-in. walls. Measurements were made of both furnace and block temperatures by 33 thermocouples and 9 thermometers. The average temperatures of the furnace after ½, 1, 3, and 6 hours approximated 1540°, 1700°, 1920°, and 2140°F.

Since only one wall failed under load during the fire test, the evaluation of performance was based on the time required for the average temperature on the unexposed face to exceed by 250°F its initial temperature, or

* *Concrete Cement Age,* Vol. 3, p. 256.

the maximum at any point to exceed the initial value by 325°F. After the fire exposure, the walls cooled under the load of 80 psi for 24 hours and were then progressively loaded to failure.

In one series of Menzel's tests the cement content was held at 4.3 lb per block, and the grading of the aggregate was changed so that values of the fineness modulus (m) ranged from 2.0 to 4.75. Results showed a marked increase in strength of both units and walls after fire as m was raised up to the values shown in Table 15. On the other hand the fire-

TABLE 15. FIRE ENDURANCE AND STRENGTH OF WALLS OF DIFFERENT CEMENT CONTENTS. (MENZEL)

Walls 8 in. thick made with 3-oval-core blocks.
Descriptions of aggregates used are given in notes accompanying Table 16.

Fineness Modulus	Mix by Volume	Cement Content		Average Weight of Air-Dry Block, lb.	Fire Endurance Period, minutes	Ultimate Strength, lb. per sq. in. Gross Area		Ratio of Wall Strength to Original Strength of Unit, per cent
		Block per Sack	Lb. per Block			Block Before Fire Exposure	Wall After Fire Exposure Indicated	
CALCAREOUS SAND AND GRAVEL AGGREGATES								
4.50	1 : 14.0	40.0	2.35	46.4	133	920	270 (3 hr.)	29
4.50	1 : 11.0	30.0	3.13	48.5	135	1160	310 (3 hr.)	27
4.50	1 : 7.0	19.0	4.95	51.1	142	2440	560 (3 hr.)	23
4.50	1 : 5.0	14.3	6.58	51.6	149	2300	550 (3 hr.)	24
4.50	1 : 4.0	11.1	8.45	52.4	154	3350	615 (3 hr.)	18
4.50	1 : 3.0	9.3	10.10	52.4	162	3550	750 (3 hr.)	21
SILICEOUS SAND AND GRAVEL AGGREGATE "A"								
4.25	1 : 14.0	38.5	2.44	44.5	a	725	a	a
4.25	1 : 7.5	21.2	4.42	46.4	118	1810	480 (3 hr.)	26
4.25	1 : 3.0	9.3	10.10	49.6	137	4075	855 (3 hr.)	21
HAYDITE AGGREGATE								
3.25	1 : 10.0	29.1	3.23	26.8	160	750	256 (3½ hr.)	34
3.25	1 : 8.0	23.6	3.98	27.8	174	1000	445 (3½ nr.)	44
3.25	1 : 7.0	21.1	4.45	28.2	178	1120	358 (3½ hr.)	32
3.25	1 : 5.0	15.3	6.15	30.0	194	1575	580 (3½ hr.)	37
3.25	1 : 3.0	9.8	9.60	32.8	221	2100	770 (4 hr.)	37

a This wall failed at 93 minutes of fire exposure under the working load of 80 lb. per sq. in. of gross area and was withdrawn from the furnace at 94 minutes. Readings of temperatures on the unexposed surface which were continued indicated that an average rise of 250° F. was attained at 114 minutes and the maximum rise of 325° F. at 122 minutes. Had the exposure to fire been continued for about 20 minutes longer, it is estimated that the average temperature rise of 250° F. would have been attained about 5 minutes earlier or at 109 minutes.

endurance period was about 15 per cent longer for the blocks containing the most fine material. The data in Table 15 show that there is an increase in endurance period, strength of unit, and wall after exposure with increase in cement content, although it does not appear that more than 4.5 to 5 lb of cement per block of the type tested would be effectively used. Table 16 presents data showing the relative endurance of walls made of various aggregates. The fire endurance expressed in minutes per

TABLE 16. INFLUENCE OF AGGREGATE ON FIRE RESISTANCE OF WALLS.
(MENZEL)

Walls 8 in. thick made with 3-oval-core block.
Description of aggregates:

Siliceous Sand and Gravel (B): A highly siliceous aggregate (85 per cent silica in form of quartz) containing very little calcareous material. Particles range from regular to irregular in shape but generally with well-rounded edges and hard smooth surfaces.

Siliceous Sand and Gravel (A): A somewhat more siliceous aggregate than aggregate (B) (95 per cent silica in form of flint and chert). Particles very irregular with both sharp and slightly rounded edges and both polished and pitted surfaces.

Calcareous Sand and Gravel: A typical calcareous aggregate containing about 40 per cent calcium carbonate, 30 per cent magnesium carbonate, and less than 15 per cent quartz. Particles range from regular to irregular in shape but generally with well-rounded edges. Surfaces varied from smooth, slippery texture to a rough porous pitted type with neither type predominating.

Crushed Limestone: Typical of crushed calcareous stone of dolomitic variety containing roughly 50 per cent of calcium carbonate, 30 per cent magnesium carbonate, and with less than 5 per cent quartz. Particles very irregular in shape with slightly rounded sharp edges. Surfaces were somewhat slippery to the touch and slightly porous.

Crushed Common Brick: Typical of the fine and coarse low fusing porous burned clay aggregate produced by crushing common brick. Particles very irregular in shape with sharp rough edges and rough pitted surfaces.

Crushed Fire Brick: Typical of the fine and coarse highly refractory porous burned clay aggregate produced by crushing broken pieces of fire brick and other shapes of similar refractory material. Particles very irregular in shape with very rough edges and deeply pitted exceedingly rough surfaces.

Haydite: A light, porous, aggregate material prepared by burning shale to incipient fusion and crushing and grading the resulting clinker. Particles irregular in shape with slightly rounded sharp edges and slightly rough porous and pitted surfaces. Unless otherwise noted the Haydite aggregate used in this and other groups of tests came from the same source.

Air-Cooled Blast Furnace Slag: Typical of the slag discharged from blast furnace and brought from the molten to solid form by cooling in air.

Soft Coal Cinders: Typical of the porous clinkerous ash resulting from the high temperature combustion of soft coal in the modern power plant. It contained about 12 per cent of combustible material principally in the form of coke and to a minor extent as soft coal. Particles irregular in shape with both sharp and well-rounded edges and both glossy and rough pitted porous surfaces.

Coke Breeze: This material consists of screenings ranging from dust to ⅜ in. of the highly porous product commonly used as fuel known as coke. It consists almost entirely of carbon (ash 12 to 14 per cent) and is the product remaining after the hydrocarbon gases have been distilled from soft coal in the manufacture of gas. Particles irregular in shape with slightly rounded sharp edges and rough deeply pitted exceedingly porous surfaces.

Aggregate			Mix by Volume	Cement Content		Average Air-Dry Weight, lb.		Fire Endurance Period, minutes	
Type	Fineness Modulus	Unit Weight, lb. per cu. ft.[a]		Blocks per Sack	Lb. per Block	Per Block	Per sq. ft. of Wall	Wall	Per lb. per sq. ft. of Wall
Coke Breeze................	3.50	49	1 : 7.5	21.2	4.44	23.5	29.0	110	3.79
Siliceous Gravel A.........	3.50	115	1 : 7.5	21.8	4.30	45.2	53.2	124	2.33
Siliceous Gravel B.........	3.70	113	1 : 8.3	22.5	4.18	46.7	54.9	129	2.35
Crushed Fire Brick........	3.50	91	1 : 7.5	21.9	4.29	36.8	43.8	145	3.21
Calcareous Gravel.........	3.50	120	1 : 7.8	22.4	4.20	46.6	54.8	150	2.74
Crushed Limestone........	3.50	120	1 : 7.8	21.7	4.33	49.0	57.4	158	2.75
Soft Coal Cinders.........	3.25	79	1 : 7.0	20.6	4.56	33.9	40.6	163	4.01
Haydite...................	3.50	67	1 : 7.0	21.2	4.43	27.6	33.5	168	5.01
Crushed Common Brick.....	3.50	77	1 : 7.5	21.6	4.36	32.3	38.8	175	4.51
Air-Cooled Slag...........	3.50	102	1 : 7.5	22.0	4.25	41.1	48.7	193	3.96

a Based on dry rodded 0 to ⅜-in. aggregate graded to fineness modulus indicated.

pound per square foot of wall surface shows the advantages of the lighter-weight materials based on fire resistance. On the other hand, as evidenced by data in Table 15, in order to produce a given wall strength a higher cement content must be used with the lighter-weight aggregates.

The increased strength obtained by bedding both face shells and transverse webs in mortar as compared to bedding face shells alone is well shown in Table 17 from Menzel's tests. His tests showed that a half inch of gypsum plaster applied to either face of an 8-in. block wall increased the fire-endurance period 30 per cent. If applied to both faces, the in-

TABLE 17. STRENGTH OF WALLS LAID UP WITH DIFFERENT TYPES
OF MORTAR JOINTS

Block units made from aggregate graded from 0 to ⅜ in. and from mixes ranging from 1 : 5 to 1 : 14 by volume of cement to dry rodded volume of aggregate. Walls laid up with 1 : 3 Portland cement mortar plus 15 per cent hydrated lime by volume of cement.

Type of Mortar Bed Construction	Application of Mortar at Horizontal Joints	Type of Aggregate	Ratio of Wall Strength after Fire Exposure Indicated to Original Strength of Unit, Per Cent		Improvement in Wall Strength with Full Mortar Bedding over Face Shell Bedding, Per Cent	
			Before Fire	After Fire	Before Fire	After Fire
Face Shell Bedding	Face Shells Only	Haydite	55	36 (3½ hr.)	..	..
		Calcareous	55	28 (3 hr.)	..	..
		Siliceous	55	22 (3 hr.)	..	..
Full Bedding	Face Shells and Transverse Webs	Haydite	70	49 (3½ hr.)	27	36
		Calcareous	70	43 (3 hr.)	27	53
		Siliceous	70	36 (3 hr.)	27	64

crease was 60 per cent. Plaster also appreciably increased the wall strength after fire exposure. Tests of units of various designs indicated that the length of the fire-endurance period was closely related to the weight per square foot of wall surface. An increase of 50 per cent in that weight doubled the fire-endurance period. There was little effect on wall strength after exposure to fire, owing to the presence of coke and coal in soft coal cinders up to 33 per cent by weight of the cinders. Filling the cells of the units with sand, Haydite, or granulated slag increased the fire-endurance period two and one-half times.

Menzel's tests demonstrate that the expansion in the 6-ft height of walls averaged ⅙ to ⅛ in. for walls made with cinders, blast-furnace slag, coke breeze, brick, and Haydite; ³⁄₁₆ to ⅜ in. for walls with limestone, calcareous sand, and gravel; and ⁵⁄₁₆ to ⁹⁄₁₆ in. for walls with highly siliceous sand and gravel. They all bowed towards the fire and were thus eccentrically loaded during the test to destruction. The moduli of elasticity for the walls prior to test ranged from 200,000 to 750,000 psi; after exposure, from 100,000 to 300,000 psi on gross area. For 8-in. walls the modulus after exposure was about 40 per cent of the initial value. The high strengths of these walls after the fire test are heartening evidence of the resistance of this type of construction to fire. The linear relation of the strength of walls after exposure to strength of unit is also a most important contribution.

In the foregoing tests it should be noted that only the exposed face shell of the units became heated to 1000°F. Tests by I. H. Woolson (*Proc. ASTM*, Vol. 5, p. 335, and Vol. 7, p. 404) on 4-in. cubes of 1:2:4 concrete showed that limestone concrete heated throughout to a temperature of 1250°F lost half its strength and that trap rock concrete was so injured at a temperature of 1700°F. Woolson's tests showed that the modulus of elasticity of concrete of either trap rock or limestone was reduced 60 per cent by heating to 500°F. At 1500°F the modulus was only a tenth of the normal value.

48. The Coefficient of Expansion of Concrete and Mortar. Table 18 contains values of the linear coefficient of thermal expansion of concrete for atmospheric ranges of temperature. The coefficient for concrete approximates the weighted mean of the coefficients of the neat cement and aggregates. An average for common mixes is 0.0000055 per °F.

49. Other Thermal Properties. Tests by C. L. Norton [*] on the specific heat of various mixtures of concrete gave the results in Table 19. In these tests he employed Regnault's method of mixtures, using an ordinary double calorimeter.

Norton also determined the coefficient of thermal conductivity (K) for concrete. $K = Qd/[(t_1 - t_2)As]$ in which Q = the quantity of heat flowing through a plate whose area = A and thickness = d; s is the time of flow; and t_1 and t_2 the temperatures on the hotter and cooler sides of the plate, respectively. His results for various types of concrete appear in Table 20. It will be noted that the conductivity of cinder concrete is only about 40 per cent that of stone concrete.

Although concrete is superior to the metals and natural stones, it must not be considered a first-class insulating material. At room temperatures it is greatly surpassed as a heat insulator by asbestos, mill shavings, powdered magnesia, mineral wool, hair felt, pulverized cork, and hair cloth; and at high temperatures it is inferior to such substances as asbestos, infusorial earth, and powdered magnesia. The protective value of concrete lies in a high resistance to fire coupled with a fairly low conductivity and high strength.

Woolson also determined the rate of flow of heat into different classes of concrete when the exposed face of the block was subjected to a temperature of 1500°F. His measurements were made by Le Châtelier pyrometers placed at distances of ½, 2, 3, 4, 5, 6, and 7 in. from the exposed faces of rectangular prisms 8 in. deep and 7¼ × 13½ in. in elevation. After 1 hour at the above temperature the records obtained on single specimens of 1:2:5 cinder, 1:2:4 gravel, and 1:2:4 trap rock concrete are shown in Fig. 26.

In certain tests Woolson embedded ¾-in. bars in the axes of 8 × 8 × 36-in. concrete blocks. These blocks were of similar proportions and ingredients to those mentioned above. The bars were cut longer than the blocks and projected from either 8 × 8-in. face. One 8 × 8-in. face was gradually heated to 1700°F, and measurements of the temperature at different points along the bar were made. After 1 hour at the above temperature a point on a bar 2 in. from the exposed face of the prism had a temperature of only 700° to 1000°F; a point 5 in. from the surface

[*] *Proc. Nat. Assoc. Cement Users,* Vol. 7, p. 78.

TABLE 18.   LINEAR COEFFICIENT OF EXPANSION OF CONCRETE AND MORTAR AT NORMAL TEMPERATURES

Mix.	Aggregate.	Coefficient per °F.	Authority.	Reference.
1 : 0	....	.0000070	Keller	
1 : 2	Pit gravel	.0000056	Keller	*Tonind'z't'g*, No. 24,
1 : 4	Pit gravel	.0000058	Keller	1904
1 : 8	Pit gravel	.0000053	Keller	
1 : 2 : 4	Sand and limestone	.0000055	Pence	*Jour. W. S. E.*, Vol. 6,
1 : 2 : 4	Sand and gravel	.0000054	Pence	p. 549
1 : 4½	Quartz	.0000066		
1 : 4½	Sandstone	.0000065	Davis and Troxell	*Proc. Am. Conc. Inst.*, Vol. 26, p. 438
1 : 4½	Gravel	.0000060		
1 : 4½	Granite	.0000053		
1 : 4½	Basalt	.0000048		
1 : 4½	Limestone	.0000038		

TABLE 19. · THE SPECIFIC HEAT OF CONCRETE.   (NORTON)

Range of Temp. ° F.	1 : 2 : 5 Stone Concrete.	1 : 2 : 4 Stone Concrete.	1 : 2 : 4 Cinder Concrete.
72 to 212	0.156	0.154	
72 to 372	0.192	0.190	0.180
72 to 1172	0.201	0.210	0.206
72 to 1472	0.219	0.214	0.218

TABLE 20. · THE COEFFICIENT OF THERMAL CONDUCTIVITY OF CONCRETE.   (NORTON)

Temperature of Hot Side of Plate in Degrees.		Mixture.	Coefficient in Calories per 1 Deg. C. per Sq.Cm. per Cm. per Sec.	Coefficient In B.T.U. per 1 Deg. F. per Sq. Ft. per In. Thick per 24 Hr.
C.	F.			
35	95	Stone 1 : 2 : 5	0.00216	150
50	122	Stone 1 : 2 : 4		
		not tamped	0.00110 to 0.00160	76 to 114
50	122	Cinder 1 : 2 : 4	0.00081	56
200	392	Stone 1 : 2 : 4	0.0021	146
400	752	Stone 1 : 2 : 4	0.0022	153
500	932	Stone 1 : 2 : 4	0.0023	160
1000	1832	Stone 1 : 2 : 4	0.0027	188
1100	2012	Stone 1 : 2 : 4	0.0029	202

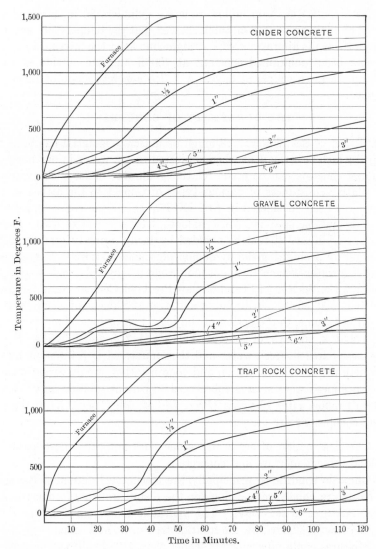

Fig. 26. The thermal conductivity of concrete. (Woolson, *Proc. ASTM,* Vol. 7, p. 406.)

reached 400° to 500°F; a point 8 in. from the surface attained the temperature of boiling water. These tests and others indicate that 2 in. of good concrete affords ample protection to embedded steel against fire.*

* For the calculation of the rate of flow of heat into concrete and other materials reference may be made to Ingersoll and Zoebel's *The Mathematical Theory of Heat Conduction, with Engineering and Geological Applications;* also *Eng. News,* Vol. **70,** p. 866.

A few experiments * on hollow concrete cylinders 36 in. inside diameter, 36 in. high, and 6 to 8 in. thick showed that the temperature gradient through the walls approximated a straight line after the internal temperature had been maintained constant at 700°F and the outside at room temperature for a couple of days. A 1:2:4 concrete made of limestone was used.

THE DURABILITY OF CONCRETE

50. Effect of Sea Water. Although no masonry material has been developed which is permanent when subjected to sea water in our northern latitudes, concrete can be made relatively durable under such exposure. The relative resistances of various types of cement to the attack of sea water have been considered in Art. IX-36. In marine concrete, durable materials must be used and dense, smooth, hard surfaces secured. Segregation and laitance should be avoided by using properly graded aggregates and by prohibiting sloppy or non-placeable mixtures. For exposed surfaces, a water-cement ratio not more than 0.8, by volume, is suggested.

In 1896 the Society of Scandinavian Portland Cement Manufacturers subjected 3500 2.8-in. mortar cubes and over 100 blocks of concrete, each 1 cu yd in volume, to the action of the sea. Proportions of mortars were neat, 1:1, 1:2, and 1:3, of concrete 1:1:2⅞, 1:2:4, and 1:3:5⅛. Specimens were cured in fresh water and then immersed in 5 different localities where the severity of action and concentration of salt varied widely. Some specimens were always submerged; others at midtide only. From Poulsen's report after 10 years (*Proc. IATM*, 5th Congr., XI_4), the following conclusions are drawn:

1. Chemical action of sea water alone does not cause destruction of Portland cement mortars and concretes.

2. Climatic conditions, principally the mechanical action of the tides and frost, are chiefly responsible for the disintegration of concrete and mortar mixtures in sea water. The hydraulic lime from Teil was especially adversely affected by the midtide treatment at Vardo.

3. Mixtures containing mortars leaner than 1:2 should not be used in maritime construction.

4. From the tests on graded mixtures, sands for marine concrete should contain from one-third to two-thirds of particles passing a No. 30 sieve.

A valuable set of experiments on the effect of sea water on concrete was begun in 1909 by the Aberthaw Construction Co. of Boston. Twenty-four piers 16 ft × 16 in. × 16 in. were suspended from a wharf in Boston harbor so that both the effect of continued submergence below low water

* Thesis by Melin and Pulver, University of Wisconsin, 1910.

and the action of the tides could be observed. Crushed trap rock, 98.25 per cent of which was between $1\frac{1}{2}$ and $\frac{1}{4}$ in. in diameter, and a good bank sand, 52 per cent of which passed a No. 30 sieve, were the aggregates. Portland cements of high-, medium-, and low-alumina contents, iron-ore cement, and slag Portland cement were used. One pier of 1:3:6 proportions was made with 10 per cent of the cement replaced by hydrated lime, another with 5 per cent of pulverized clay, and, in a third, waterproofing with a soap and alum solution was tried. The mixes were 1:1:2, $1:2\frac{1}{2}:4\frac{1}{2}$, and 1:3:6. Most of the concrete was of quaking consistency, although wet and dry mixes were also made. The specimens were well cured before submergence. After 11 years a careful examination of the piers indicated:

1. In the untreated specimens which were eroded on the surface most of the action occurred between the high and low watermarks.

2. The erosion in such cases was most pronounced on the faces and sides of the specimens.

3. Evidence of the superiority of any one type of Portland cement is not furnished by an 11-year exposure.

4. Mixes containing hydrated lime or soap and alum were badly attacked throughout their submerged length, the pulverized clay mix was in fair condition.

5. 1:3:6 mixes are too lean even when very well mixed and of proper consistency.

6. A wet or a quaking consistency is much superior to a dry consistency, the 1:1:2 mixtures of wet consistency having withstood the attack very well (see *Eng. Record*, Vol. 69, p. 344).

Evidences of chemical attack of the Baltic Sea on the cement in large rubble concrete blocks of $1:2\frac{1}{2}:7$ proportions were reported by W. Czarnowski in *Proc. IATM*, 6th Congr., XVII[1]. Although the alumina contents of the cements were normal, $6\frac{1}{2}$ per cent, analyses of material from the interior of the blocks after 11 years' exposure showed that a liberation of lime from the cement and an absorption of magnesia and sulfur trioxide had taken place.

R. J. Wig and L. R. Ferguson wrote a valuable report based on examination of many structures situated along the coasts of continental United States (see *Eng. News-Record*, Vol. 79, pp. 532, 641, 689, 737, and 794). Their investigations may be summarized as follows:

1. Well-made plain concrete is durable in sea water provided it is properly placed and protected from erosion and abrasion. Plain concrete structures in northern latitudes are exposed to much more severe conditions than those built on the southern coasts.

2. The aggregate should be composed of tough particles so graded as to produce a hard, dense concrete. Enough water should be used to produce a placeable mix. Excess water is very harmful. Sea water can be used in gaging plain concrete, but should not be used when the work is reinforced and exposed to the air. In placing, great care must be taken to make the forms tight. Seams and porous spots must be avoided. If subjected to erosion or abrasion, surfaces above the low-water line must be protected. Walls and piers may be faced with stone. Piles may be protected by wooden fenders.

3. Reinforced concrete, when used above mean-tide level, is likely to disintegrate through corrosion of the reinforcement unless the latter is galvanized or protected by a considerably thicker shell of concrete than is now the current practice. Corrosion of reinforcement proceeds more rapidly in structures of the southern coasts than in those farther north where the water is colder.

51. Effect of Alkali Water. In regions where alkali is present in the soil and ground waters, trouble has been experienced due to the disintegration of concrete and masonry structures. Waters running through such soil may contain as much as 1 per cent of alkali salts, the most destructive of which are the sulfates of magnesium and sodium, and the carbonate of sodium. Examinations of structures show that the most pronounced action occurs in portions of the masonry which are subjected to alternate wetting by the alkali solutions and drying by the air. Laboratory tests have shown that alkali salt crystals, which form very slowly, if at all, during the period of immersion, grow rapidly when the degree of saturation of the solution is increased by desiccation, and cause stress in the surrounding structure. If such crystals find lodgment in the surface of a porous substance, their expansion will break off portions of the material and gradually cause disintegration. When concrete or mortar is continuously submerged in alkali water the action is not marked.

Experiments have shown (see Art. IX-36) that certain cements, high in silica and low in C_3A, make concrete more resistant to alkali attack than others. Such cements in rich dense mixes should be used in alkali regions. When concrete conduits are used for alkali waters precautions must be taken both in placing and curing to secure a dense hard surface. If the concentration of alkali salts in the water is greater than 0.1 per cent, protective fabric coatings should be used, or suitable underdrainage should be provided to carry the alkali water away from the structure.

Many examples of the destructive action of alkali waters are cited in *Bull.* 69 of Montana Agricultural College; *Bull.* 132 of Colorado State Agricultural College, *Trans. ASCE*, Vol. 67, p. 572; *Tech. Papers* 12, 44, 95, 217, and 307, National Bureau of Standards; also *Bull.* 89, Engr. Expt.

Sta., Ames, Iowa. See also *Bibliography on Sulfate Resistance of Portland Cements, Concretes, and Mortars* by Miller, Manson and Chen, Paper 78, University of Minnesota, *Misc. Jour. Ser.*

52. The Effect of Sewage on Concrete. Whether concrete or mortar can be used in sewer constructions depends upon the character of the sewage. There are concrete sewers which have been in successful operation for many years, but there are also published accounts of others which have failed. If the sewage is of such nature that a strong odor of hydrogen sulfide is evolved, sulfuric acid will be formed with sufficient strength to attack the lime compounds of the concrete and produce disintegration.

Barr and Buchanan * assert that the hydrogen sulfide is formed both by the bacterial decomposition of the sulfur-containing proteins, and related compounds, and by the reduction of sulfates in the water supply. They found that the escaping hydrogen sulfide which is dissolved by the moisture on the walls above the sewage is oxidized, not alone by the air, but also by bacterial action. Examinations of septic tanks by these investigators showed that a soluble sulfur (SO_4) content in the raw sewage equal to 427 ppm was sufficient to produce disintegration in a concrete dosing chamber. The disintegration of concrete sewers due to the above action always takes place above the water level. In the septic tanks investigated the action was particularly noticeable on the insides of the roofs. (See also *Eng. Record*, Vol. 61, p. 633.)

Acid effluents from pickling baths, wastes from creameries, or other acid wastes should not be discharged into concrete sewers until effectively diluted. For an example of the destructive action of pickling acid, see H. C. Webster's report on failure of the 29th St. sewer in Milwaukee, Wisconsin.

53. Electrolysis of Concrete. The disintegrations of certain reinforced-concrete structures have apparently been due to electrolytic action of stray currents from neighboring power circuits. Studies of such action have been made by a number of investigators all of whom report that, under certain conditions, the integrity of a structure may be endangered. Probably the most exhaustive study of electrolysis in concrete has been made by the National Bureau of Standards; its report is rendered in *Tech. Paper* 18, by Rosa, McCullum, and Peters. In these experiments over 400 specimens of the type shown in Fig. 27 were tested under voltages varying from 0 to 70. The test pieces were made of $1:2\frac{1}{2}:4$ concrete of Portland cement, sand, and broken stone. They were cured under damp sand after removal from

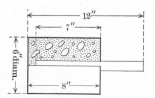

Fig. 27. Type of specimen used in electrolysis tests.

* *Bull.* 26, Iowa State College.

molds for a period of 20 days, then they were placed in a damp closet
until tested. The age of specimens when the tests were begun varied from
a few days to about 1 year. The voltage was maintained continuously on
some specimens for a period of over 1 year. Several different brands of
cement were used, but the results showed no great difference in efficiency
of corrosion for the normal American Portland cements. White Portland
cement was inferior to the normal brands in resisting corrosion.

The conclusions of these investigators may be partially summarized
as follows:

1. Plain concrete is not affected by stray currents unless power lines
are grounded in it.

2. A potential gradient of approximately 60 volts per foot was required
to cause destruction of the test pieces when the current flowed from the
steel anode into normal wet concrete. With dry concrete the voltage
required to produce disintegration was much higher.

3. The resistance of normal wet concrete rises rapidly with the length
of time of passage of the current.

4. The use of salt in the mixing water is to be condemned, since it
increases the conductivity of the concrete and thereby accelerates the
corrosion of the reinforcement.

5. The splitting of the concrete surrounding a steel anode is caused by
the oxidation of the steel. The volumetric increase of the steel due to
oxidation was sufficient in a certain specimen to produce a radial stress
of approximately 4700 psi.

6. For a given number of ampere-hours and a given temperature, the
amount of corrosion is independent of the current strength.

7. When the current flows for some time from the concrete to a steel
cathode, the concrete is softened to a depth of $\frac{1}{4}$ in. or more around the
reinforcement and the bond is destroyed.

8. Softening at the cathode occurs under much lower potential gradients
than does the anode effect. Since in practice the steel may often be the
cathode, danger from such effect is greater than from the anode effect.

9. The passage of the electric current from the concrete into the steel
causes a gradual concentration of sodium and potassium near the cathode.
When these alkalies are concentrated, their attack is sufficient to soften
the concrete and weaken the bond.

10. The danger from stray currents in practice, although well worthy
of consideration, has been much overestimated.

11. By encasing concrete which is in contact with water in waterproof
membranes, its resistance may be increased and the danger from electrolysis diminished. The electrical resistance of concrete foundations
may also be materially increased by surrounding them with a shell of
granite masonry.

12. Direct-current power circuits in concrete structures must be insulated from the ground. Pipe lines should be provided with insulating joints where they enter and leave a structure and lead-covered cables should be isolated from the concrete.

13. When the metal within a building is insulated with respect to metal without, it may well be interconnected but it should never be grounded.

54. Specific Resistance of Concrete to Electricity. Measurements of the specific resistance by the above investigators for mortars and concretes made of river sand and crushed trap rock gave the results in Table 21 (from National Bureau of Standards). The specimens were 9 months

TABLE 21.   THE SPECIFIC RESISTANCE OF CONCRETE AND MORTAR
TO ELECTRICITY.   (*Technologic Paper* No. 18)

Proportions...............	Neat	1 : 2	1 : 4	1 : 2 : 3	1 : 2½ : 4	1 : 3 : 5	1 : 4 : 7
Resistance, in ohms per cm.³	3500	2300	2100	6300	8000	8200	9900

old and had been soaked for 3 months previous to the test. Similar tests on granite and limestone rocks showed that limestone has six or eight times, and granite about a hundred times, the resistance of the concrete tested. Consequently the character of the aggregate as well as the age, proportions, and moisture content will greatly affect the specific resistance of concrete.

55. Effect of Various Substances on Concrete and Protective Treatments, Where Required.[*] Concrete of a suitable quality must be assumed in a discussion of the effect of various substances on concrete, and protective treatments. In general, this means a properly proportioned, carefully placed, and well-cured concrete resulting in a watertight structure. This requires:

1. Low water-cement ratio, not to exceed 6 gal of mixing water per sack of Portland cement.

2. Suitable workability, to avoid mixes so harsh and stiff that honeycomb occurs, and those so fluid that water rises to the surface.

3. Thorough mixing, at least one minute after all materials are in mixer, or until mix is uniform.

4. Proper placing, spaded or vibrated, to fill all corners and angles of forms without segregation of materials—avoid construction joints.

5. Adequate curing, protection by leaving forms in place, covering with wet sand or burlap, and sprinkling. Concrete to be kept wet and above 50°F for at least the first week. Not to be subject to hydrostatic pressure during this period.

Many solutions, such as brines and salts, which have no chemical effect on concrete, may crystallize upon loss of water. It is especially important that concrete

[*] This article is reproduced from *Concrete Information* No. ST4, courtesy Portland Cement Association.

subject to alternate wetting and drying of such solutions be impervious. When the free water in the concrete is saturated with salts, the salts crystallize in the concrete near the surface in the process of drying and this crystallization may exert sufficient pressure to cause surface scaling. Salt solutions corrode steel more rapidly than plain water. In structures which are to be subject to frequent wetting and drying by these solutions, it is essential to provide impervious concrete and sufficient coverage over the steel, and it may be advisable to provide some surface coating such as sodium silicate, linseed oil, or one of the varnishes as an added precaution.

Surface Treatments. Materials are available for almost any degree of protection required on concrete. The best material to use in a given case will depend on many factors in addition to the substance to be protected against. These include concentration of solution, temperature, taste and odor, and abrasive action. High temperatures usually accelerate any possible attack and therefore better protection is required than for normal temperatures. Bituminous materials soften at elevated temperatures, may even melt and become ineffective. Grades are available for a fairly wide temperature range and manufacturers should be consulted as to grade required for given conditions. Where taste or odor is important it should be determined whether proposed treatment will be satisfactory. As a rule, thin coatings are not so durable as heavier coatings, where there is considerable abrasion.

The more common treatments are indicated in Table 22, the numbers corresponding to the descriptions given below. For most substances, several treatments are suggested. These will provide sufficient protection in most cases, but any of the other treatments designated by a number higher than the highest shown would be equally suitable and often may be advisable. In making a selection, economy should be considered as well as the factors discussed above. Where continuous service over long periods is desirable it may be more economical to use the more positive means of protection rather than those of lower first cost which may be less permanent.

Protective coatings usually require dust-free, surface-dry concrete for satisfactory application.

1. *Magnesium fluosilicate or zinc fluosilicate:* The treatment consists of two or more applications. First, a solution of about 1 lb of the fluosilicate crystals per gal of water is used. For subsequent applications about 2 lb of crystals per gal of water is used. Large brushes are convenient for applying on vertical surfaces, and mops on horizontal areas. Each application should be allowed to dry; after the last one has dried, the surface should be brushed and washed with water to remove crystals which have formed. The treatment hardens the surface by chemical action and makes it more impervious. Fluosilicates are available from chemical dealers.

2. *Sodium silicate* (commonly called water glass): This is quite viscous and must be diluted with water to secure penetration, the amount of dilution depending on the quality of the silicate and permeability of the concrete. Silicate of about 42.5° Baumé gravity diluted in proportions of 1 gal with 4 gal of water makes a good solution. It may be applied in two or three or more coats, allowing each coat to dry thoroughly. On horizontal surfaces it may be poured on and then spread evenly with brooms or brushes. Scrubbing each coat with water after it has hardened provides a better condition for application of succeeding coats. For tanks and similar structures, progressively stronger solutions are often used for the succeeding coats.

3. *Drying oils:* Boiled or raw linseed oil may be used, but the boiled oil dries more rapidly. China wood oil or tung oil and soybean oil are also effective. Applied hot, better penetration is secured. The oil should be applied immediately after heating, however, as it will become more viscous if allowed to stand. Two

or three coats may be applied, allowing each to dry thoroughly before the next application. Diluting the oil with turpentine, up to a mixture of equal parts, gives better penetration for the first coat. The concrete should be well cured and seasoned before the first application. The oil is sometimes applied after the magnesium fluosilicate treatment, providing a good coating over a hardened surface.

4. *Cumar:* Cumar is a synthetic resin soluble in xylol and similar hydrocarbon solvents. A solution consisting of about 6 lb of Cumar per gal of xylol with ½ pint boiled linseed oil makes a good coating. Two or more coats should be applied. Concrete should be fairly dry. The Cumar should be powdered to aid dissolving. It is available in grades from dark brown to colorless, and sold through paint and varnish trades.

5. *Varnishes and paints:* Any varnish can be applied to dry concrete. High-grade varnishes of the spar, China wood oil, or Bakelite types and synthetic resin paints and coatings, or paints consisting largely of chlorinated rubber or synthetic rubber give good protection against many substances. Two or more coats should be applied. Some manufacturers can provide specially compounded coatings for certain conditions.

6. *Bituminous or coal tar paints, tar, and pitches:* These are usually applied in two coats, a thin priming coat to insure bond and a thicker finish coat. Finish coat must be carefully applied to secure continuity and avoid pin holes. Surface should be touched up where necessary.

7. *Bituminous enamel:* This is suitable protection against relatively strong acids. It does not resist abrasion at high temperatures. Two materials are used, a priming solution and the enamel proper. The priming solution is of thin brushing consistency and should be applied so as to completely cover, touching up any uncoated spots before applying the enamel. When primer has dried to slightly tacky state, it is ready for the enamel. The enamel usually consists of a bitumen with a finely powdered siliceous mineral filler. The filler increases the resistance to flowing and sagging at elevated temperatures, and to abrasion. The enamel should be melted and carefully heated until it is fluid enough to brush. The temperature should not exceed 375°F. When fluid it should be mopped on quickly, as it sets and hardens rapidly.

8. *Bituminous mastic:* This is used chiefly for floors on account of the thickness of the layer which must be applied, but some mastics can be troweled on vertical surfaces. Some mastics are applied cold. Others must be heated until fluid. The cold mastic consists of two compositions—the priming solution and the body coat or mastic. The primer is first brushed on. When the primer has dried to a tacky state, a thin layer—about $\frac{1}{32}$ in.—of the mastic is troweled on. When this has dried, successive $\frac{1}{32}$-in. coats of the mastic are applied, until the required thickness has been built up. The mastic is similar to the primer but is ground with sufficient asbestos and finely powdered siliceous material fillers to make a very thick, pasty, fibrous mass.

The hot mastics are somewhat similar to the mixtures used in sheet asphalt pavements, but contain more asphaltic binder so that when heated to fluid condition they can be poured and troweled into place. They are satisfactory only when applied in layers 1 in. or more in thickness. When ready to lay, the mixture usually consists of about 15 per cent asphaltic binder, 20 per cent finely powdered siliceous mineral filler, and the remainder is sand graded up to ¼-in. maximum size.

9. *Vitrified brick or tile:* These are special burnt clay products which possess high resistance to attack by acids or alkalies. They must, of course, be laid in mortar which is also resistant against the substance to which they are to be exposed.

A waterproof membrane and a bed of mortar are usually placed between the brick or tile and concrete. Some of the acid-resistant cements are melted and poured in the joints. Only materials suitable for the conditions should be used and the manufacturer's directions for installation must be followed. Silica brick and cement are not resistant to hydrofluoric acid and the hydroxides, but special brick and cement for these substances are available.

10. *Glass:* May be cemented to the concrete.

11. *Lead:* May be cemented to the concrete with an asphaltic paint.

12. *Sheets of synthetic resin, rubber, and synthetic rubber:* Thin sheets of synthetic resin, rubber, or synthetic rubber resistant to many acids, alkalies, and other substances are available. These are cemented to the concrete with special adhesives.

TABLE 22

Acids

Material	Effect on Concrete	Surface Treatment [1]
Acetic	Disintegrates slowly.	5, 6, 7
Acid waters	Natural acid waters may erode surface mortar, but usually action then stops.	1, 2, 3
Carbolic	Disintegrates slowly.	1, 2, 3, 5
Carbonic	Disintegrates slowly.	2, 3, 4
Humic	Depends on humus material, but may cause slow disintegration.	1, 2, 3
Hydrochloric	Disintegrates.	8, 9, 10, 11, 12
Hydrofluoric	Disintegrates.	8, 9, 11, 12
Lactic	Disintegrates slowly.	3, 4, 5
Muriatic	Disintegrates.	8, 9, 10, 11, 12
Nitric	Disintegrates.	8, 9, 10, 11, 12
Oxalic	None.	None
Phosphoric	Attacks surface slowly.	1, 2, 3
Sulfuric	Disintegrates.	8, 9, 10, 11, 12
Sulfurous	Disintegrates.	8, 9, 10, 11, 12
Tannic	Disintegrates slowly.	1, 2, 3

Salts and Alkalies (Solutions) [2]

Carbonates of Ammonia Potassium Sodium	None.	None
Chlorides of Calcium Potassium Sodium Strontium	None unless concrete is alternately wet and dry with the solution, when it is advisable to treat with	1, 3, 4
Chlorides of Ammonia Copper Iron Magnesium Mercury Zinc	Disintegrates slowly.	1, 3, 4
Fluorides	None except ammonium fluoride.	3, 4, 5

TABLE 22.—*Continued*

Salts and Alkalies (Solutions)—*Continued*

Material	Effect on Concrete	Surface Treatment [1]
Hydroxides of Ammonia Calcium Potassium Sodium	None.	None
Nitrates of Ammonia	Disintegrates.	8, 9, 10, 11, 12
Calcium Potassium Sodium	None.	None
Potassium Permanganate	None.	None
Silicates	None.	None
Sulfates of Ammonia Aluminum Calcium Cobalt	Disintegrates.	6, 7, 8, 9
Copper Iron Manganese Nickel Potassium Sodium Zinc	Disintegrates; however, concrete products cured in high-pressure steam are highly resistant to sulfates.	1, 3, 4

Petroleum Oils

Heavy oils below 35° Baumé [3]	None.	None
Light oils above 35° Baumé [3]	None—require impervious concrete to prevent loss from penetration, and surface treatments are generally used.	1, 2, 3, 5, 9
Benzine Gasoline Kerosene Naphtha	None—require impervious concrete to prevent loss from penetration, and surface treatments are generally used.	1, 2, 3, 5, 9
High-octane gasoline		12

Coal-Tar Distillates

Alizarin Anthracene Benzol Cumol Paraffin Pitch Toluol Xylol	None.	None

TABLE 22.—*Continued*

Coal-Tar Distillates—*Continued*

Material	*Effect on Concrete*	*Surface Treatment* [1]
Creosote Cresol Phenol	Disintegrates slowly.	1, 2, 5, 9

Vegetable Oils

Cottonseed	No action if air is excluded. Slight disintegration if exposed to air.	None 1, 2, 5, 9
Rosin	None.	None
Almond Castor China wood [4] Coconut Linseed [4] Olive Peanut Poppy seed Rape seed Soybean [4] Tung [4] Walnut	Disintegrates surface slowly.	1, 2, 5, 9
Turpentine	None—Considerable penetration.	1, 2, 5, 9

Fats and Fatty Acids (Animal)

Fish oil	Most fish oils attack concrete slightly.	1, 2, 3, 5, 9

Foot oil
Lard and
  lard oil
Tallow and
  tallow oil
	Disintegrates surface slowly.	1, 2, 3, 5, 9

Miscellaneous

Alcohol	None.	None

Ammonia water
  (ammonium
  hydroxide)
	None.	None

Baking soda	None.	None
Beer	Beer will cause no progressive disintegration of concrete, but in beer storage and fermenting tanks a special coating is used to guard against contamination of beer.	Coatings made and applied by Turner Rostock Co., 420 Lexington Ave., New York, and Borsari Tank Corp. of America, 60 E. 42nd St., New York

TABLE 22.—*Continued*

Miscellaneous—*Continued*

Material	*Effect on Concrete*	*Surface Treatment* [1]
Bleaching solution	Usually no effect. Where subject to frequent wetting and drying with solution containing calcium chloride provide	1, 3, 4
Borax, boracic acid, boric acid	No effect.	None
Brine (salt)	Usually no effect on impervious concrete. Where subject to frequent wetting and drying of brine provide	1, 3, 4
Buttermilk	Same as milk.	3, 4, 5
Charged water	Same as carbonic acid—slow attack.	1, 2, 3
Caustic soda	None.	None
Cider	Disintegrates (see acetic acid).	5, 6, 7
Cinders	May cause some disintegration.	1, 2, 3
Coal	Great majority of structures show no deterioration. Exceptional cases have been coal high in pyrites (sulfide of iron) and moisture showing some action but the rate is greatly retarded by deposit of an insoluble film. Action may be stopped by surface treatments.	1, 2, 3
Corn syrup	Disintegrates slowly.	1, 2, 3
Cyanide solutions	Disintegrate slowly.	7, 8, 9, 10, 12
Electrolyte	Depends on liquid. For lead and zinc refining and chrome plating use	7, 8, 9, 10, 11
	Nickel and copper plating.	None
Formalin	Aqueous solution of formaldehyde disintegrates concrete.	5, 9, 10, 11, 12
Fruit juices	Most fruit juices have little if any effect as tartaric acid and citric acid do not appreciably affect concrete. Floors under raisin seeding machines have shown some effect, probably due to poor concrete.	1, 2, 3
Glucose	Disintegrates slowly.	1, 2, 3
Glycerine	Disintegrates slowly.	1, 2, 3, 4, 5, 9
Honey	None.	None
Lye	None.	None
Milk	Sweet milk should have no effect, but if allowed to sour the lactic acid will attack.	3, 4, 5
Molasses	Does not affect impervious, thoroughly cured concrete. Dark, partly refined molasses may attack concrete that is not thoroughly cured. Such concrete may be protected with	2, 5, 9

TABLE 22.—*Continued*

Miscellaneous—*Continued*

Material	Effect on Concrete	Surface Treatment [1]
Niter	None.	None
Sal ammoniac	Same as ammonium chloride—causes slow disintegration.	1, 3, 4
Sal soda	None.	None
Saltpeter	None.	None
Sauerkraut	Little, if any, effect. Protect taste with	1, 2
Silage	Attacks concrete slowly.	3, 4, 5
Sugar	Dry sugar has no effect on concrete that is thoroughly cured.	None
	Sugar solutions attack concrete.	1, 2, 3
Sulfite liquor	Attacks concrete slowly.	1, 2, 3
Tanning liquor	Depends on liquid. Most of them have no effect. Tanneries using chromium report no effects. If liquor is acid, protect with	1, 2, 3
Trisodium phosphate	None.	None
Vinegar	Disintegrates (see acetic acid).	5, 6, 7
Washing soda	None.	None
Whey	The lactic acid will attack concrete.	3, 4, 5
Wine	Many wine tanks with no surface coating have given good results but taste of first batch may be affected unless concrete has been given tartaric acid treatment.	For fine wines the concrete has been treated with 2 or 3 applications of tartaric acid solution. (1 lb tartaric acid in 3 pints water.) Sodium silicate is also effective. In a few cases tanks have been lined with glass tile.
Wood pulp	None.	None

[1] Treatments indicated provide sufficient protection in most cases but any of the other treatments designated by a number higher than the highest shown would be equally suitable and often may be advisable. See discussion.

[2] Dry materials generally have no effect.

[3] Many lubricating and other oils contain some vegetable oils. Concrete exposed to such oils should be protected as for vegetable oils.

[4] Applied in thin coats the material quickly oxidizes and has no effect. Results indicated above are for constant exposure to the material in liquid form.

Portland Cement Products

1. General. Since about 1910 building blocks, brick, drain tile, and sewer pipe made of Portland cement mortar or concrete have come into general use in construction. The use of these products has been especially large in regions where good aggregates and cement are obtainable at reasonable rates, and in regions where the cost of clay products is large due to freight charges. Furthermore, the wide distribution of suitable aggregates, the small cost of plant equipment, and the possibility of using unskilled labor are factors which have made these industries popular sources of investment for the man with little capital. These factors have had both a good influence and a bad influence on the growth of cement-product industries. They have been of advantage in promoting the widespread use of cement products, but great harm has been done the industries by the large quantity of poor material which has been turned out by incompetent manufacturers.

CONCRETE BLOCKS AND BRICK

2. Merits of Concrete Blocks. By using hollow blocks it is possible to secure wall constructions which will be fireproof, dampproof, and of low heat conductivity without sacrificing the strength of the structure. Concrete blocks can be made true in shape and dimensions and of such size that the maximum efficiency can be secured in laying a wall. In the latter respect they have a decided advantage over brick.

3. Types of Blocks. Figure 1 shows several types of blocks now on the market. All blocks except the one shown in Fig. 1d are 8 in. high. The block shown in Fig. 1a is much used in $8 \times 8 \times 16$-in. and to a less extent in $8 \times 10 \times 16$-in. and $8 \times 12 \times 16$-in. sizes. Occasionally blocks of this shape, $8 \times 12 \times 24$ in., are demanded, but they are heavy to lay. Blocks like Fig. 1b are also considerably used in $8 \times 8 \times 16$-in. sizes. For backing up brick or other facing material the narrow $8 \times 4 \times 16$-in. block of Fig. 1c finds use. The block of Fig. 1d in $5 \times 8 \times 12$-in. size is light and is favored by some because of the double air space.

4. Methods of Manufacture. Concrete blocks are most economically made from a mixture of fine and coarse aggregate, although many good blocks are made without any aggregate larger than $\frac{1}{4}$ in. in diameter.

If coarse aggregate is used, all of it should pass a ⅝-in. mesh and be retained on a ¼-in. mesh. Gravel is preferable to broken stone because of the greater fluidity and density which it gives to concrete. In other respects the aggregates and cement should conform to the recommendations and specifications found in Chapters XIII and XII, respectively.

A natural aggregate for block and tile manufacture should be graded so that about one-third to one-half is coarse aggregate between No. 4 and ⅜-in. sieves with the remainder a well-graded fine aggregate passing a No. 4 sieve. The fineness modulus can be built up to the values shown in Table XV-15, for the various types of aggregates. Although these

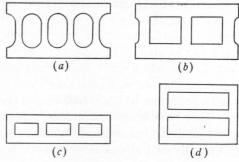

(a)   (b)

(c)   (d)

Fig. 1. Common types of concrete blocks.

data from Menzel's tests show that blocks of good strengths can be made in proportions as lean as 1:14, tests by Copeland and Carlson (*Proc. Am. Concrete Inst.*, Vol. 32, p. 485) show that walls made with blocks of 1:6 mix and leaner leaked in the rain test unless given two coats of paint on the exposed wall face. Therefore, if impervious units are desired, it seems unwise to use a mix leaner than 1:5 by volume. For severe exposures, blocks 1 month old should have crushing strengths of 2400 psi of net cross section. If faced blocks are made, the aggregate should be well graded and durable and the mix should not be richer than 1:2½ or 1:3 to insure against crazing. Machine mixing is preferable to hand mixing. With lightweight porous aggregates, premixing with water for 2 or more minutes is an effective way of eliminating too rapid withdrawal of water from the paste.

Blocks are commonly consolidated in power tamper machines, although some hand-tamped units are still made. The vibrating table provides an effective means for producing dense units of relatively dry mixes. Excellent machines using this process are now on the market. Inasmuch as a deficiency in the amount of mixing water will cause a marked increase in the permeability of a block, it is of the utmost importance that all the water which the block can hold and still retain its shape after the mold is removed should be used. The use of an excessively dry mixture has been responsible for a great many poor blocks.

Blocks of slush consistency are poured into iron molds. By this process it is possible to secure a very dense block with a minimum amount of labor in molding, but it requires a very large outlay in molds.

No portion of the process of manufacture of concrete products is of more importance than proper curing. Advantageous ways of securing well-cured blocks are discussed in Art. XIV-30.

5. The Testing of Blocks. There are three rough field tests which can be made to determine the quality of concrete blocks: (1) the ring emitted when struck with a hammer; (2) the rapidity with which a dry block will absorb a bit of water poured upon its face; (3) the ease with which it can be scratched with a knife. A strong dense block will give a clear metallic ring, show little absorption, and cannot be cut with a knife.

The most important laboratory tests, compressive strength and absorption, are usually made in accordance with ASTM *Standard* C140 or *Federal Specification* SS-C-621. Freezing and thawing tests and volume change tests are sometimes made on masonry units, and fire tests, heat transmission tests, sound absorption and sound transmission tests, strength tests, and permeability tests are made on masonry walls.

Five blocks are usually required for the strength and absorption tests. The blocks as received are weighed in air and are then saturated by immersing in water for 24 hours, and are then weighed in air and completely submerged in water. They are then dried to constant weight in an oven at 100° to 115°C. From the information obtained the absorption is calculated in per cent on the dry-weight basis and also as pounds of absorbed water per cubic foot of concrete. The moisture content of the block at the time of delivery expressed as a percentage of the total absorption is also usually calculated. The maximum average absorption allowed in specifications varies between 14 and 16 lb per cu ft. The maximum moisture content at the time of delivery is specified as 40 per cent. This requirement is made in an attempt to have only reasonably dry block placed in the wall so that unsightly cracking of the wall at a later date due to shrinkage of the block caused by air drying may be prevented.

The compressive strength tests may be performed on the blocks that have been tested for absorption and moisture or on another set of five. Before test the blocks are capped with a mixture consisting of 1 part of Portland cement (by volume) and 1 part of plaster of Paris mixed with enough water to give a paste of soft consistency. The average compressive strength of load-bearing block based on the gross area depends on the exposure conditions and also on the minimum face-shell thickness. Blocks with a minimum face-shell thickness of $1\frac{1}{4}$ in. used in exterior walls below grade and in exterior walls above grade without any protection are required to have a minimum compressive strength of 1000 psi. Similar blocks used above grade and protected by suitable waterproofing treatment are required to have a minimum strength of 700 psi. Blocks with a face-shell thickness between $\frac{3}{4}$ and $1\frac{1}{4}$ in. are usually required to have a minimum strength of 1000 psi under all exposure conditions. Non-load-bearing blocks used for interior partitions, as backing for exterior walls, or as fireproofing in skeleton-frame buildings are required to have a minimum compressive strength of 350 psi.

A comprehensive series of tests on compressive strength, absorption, freezing and thawing, volume change, and thermal expansion of concrete blocks made with Haydite, limestone, Pottsco, sand and gravel, Superock, and Waylite aggregates has been reported by K. F. Wendt and P. M. Woodworth in the November 1939 *J. Am. Concrete Inst.* On the basis of the tests performed they recommended that a minimum compressive strength of 1000 psi of gross area for load-bearing units would insure reasonably satisfactory behavior under severe exposure conditions.

The important factors that affect the strength of masonry walls have been determined from a considerable amount of test work and observation in the field. These factors include (a) strength of block, (b) characteristics of block such as design and size, (c) strength of mortar, (d) bond between mortar and block, and (e) various construction details such as thickness of mortar joint, completeness of mortar bed, and quality of workmanship. From tests made at the University of Illinois and the Portland Cement Association it appears that the strength of concrete-block walls laid up with a full bed of 1:1:6 Portland cement-lime or stronger mortar averages about 55 per cent of the strength of the block. When face-shell bedding instead of full bedding is used the value is decreased to about 42 per cent.

Well-made concrete masonry walls, especially those built up with lightweight aggregate block, have good resistance to fire. Tests to determine this property of load-bearing walls involve placing the masonry wall under the maximum working load and at the same time subjecting one side of the wall to high temperatures, up to 2300°F in the manner as specified by ASTM *Standard* E119, and noting the performance of the wall during the fire test. In some cases the wall may be subjected to the action of a hose stream immediately after the fire test and then subjected, within 72 hours, to the dead load plus twice the imposed maximum working load. Walls are considered to pass the fire-endurance test if they do not allow passage of flames or gases hot enough to ignite waste, and if the temperature of the unexposed surface does not exceed 250°F. If the hose stream test is used the wall in addition should not allow the passage of the stream, and it should carry the load previously mentioned at the end of the test. Concrete masonry walls 8 in. thick are usually rated as 2- to 4-hour fire-retardant walls.

Masonry walls made with 8-in. lightweight block have coefficients of heat transmission (U) between 0.30 and 0.40 Btu per sq ft per hr. These values will be decreased if the wall is plastered or if rigid insulation is used or if the cores of the blocks are loosely filled with lightweight aggregate. Under the best conditions the coefficient is usually reduced to a value slightly below 0.15 Btu per sq ft per hr.

Sound absorption tests of unpainted masonry walls made with lightweight block indicate that they efficiently absorb sound, with an average absorption factor of about 50 per cent of the incident sound at each reflection. Wood and plaster surfaces usually have factors less than 5 per cent. Such masonry walls are also effective in reducing sound transmission through the walls.

An excellent test of the imperviousness of a given concrete block wall can be made as follows: A wall 4 blocks long and 4 or 5 courses high is laid in neat cement mortar. A perforated pipe is suspended horizontally a few inches from the face and near the top of the wall. The pipe is then connected with a garden hose and the blocks subjected to a miniature shower. Observations should be made from time to time on the condition of the back of the wall. In tests made at the University of Wisconsin, walls of one-piece dry-process blocks wet through in many instances within an hour or two. Two-piece dry-process blocks and blocks of slush consistency withstood the test for several days.

6. Concrete Brick. In localities where a good coarse sand is found and cement is cheap, brick may be made of cement mortar which can successfully compete with clay building brick. One of the merits of concrete brick is the true shape. Furthermore it is possible to make special shapes and sizes to exact dimensions almost as cheaply as the standard sizes.

For body brick an economy may be effected by adding coarse aggregate to the mix. The same considerations should obtain in determining proportions for concrete brick as for concrete blocks. Mortar or concrete for brick making should have a strength of 1800 psi at an age of 1 month when tested in the form of a prism or cylinder with a height equal to twice the diameter. Good concrete brick 1 month old should have a modulus of rupture under transverse test of 450 psi, half brick, at the same age bedded flatwise, should have a compressive strength of 2500 psi. Good concrete brick should not absorb more than 6 per cent of water. The methods of testing used for clay brick can be applied to concrete brick.

CEMENT DRAIN TILE AND SEWER PIPE

7. The Advantages of Cement Pipe. Besides having the advantages common to other cement products cement pipe possess two additional merits. They can be made true to form and of circular, oval, or any desired cross section. Furthermore, it is possible, by regulating the thickness of the shell or by reinforcing with steel, to make the pipe strong enough to withstand the pressure due to any superimposed ditch filling. Indeed, reinforced pipe are being used for pressure conduits.*

8. Method of Manufacture. Portland cement of standard quality and a well-graded sand containing a large proportion of coarse particles are generally used for making the smaller sizes of tile or pipe. The proper proportions vary with the nature of the aggregate. For ordinary bank sands it is not safe to use a mix leaner than 1:3. With exceptionally good aggregate the proportions may be increased to 1:4. If the tile is to be laid in an alkali soil, only the best of sands should be used and the proportions should not be leaner than 1:3.† In making the larger sizes of drain tile and sewer pipe, it is good practice to employ concrete having a maximum size of coarse aggregate not over one-third of the thickness of the pipe wall. The mix should contain sufficient mortar so that a dense product can be secured. Proportions may vary from 1:2:3 to 1:2½:4, depending on the nature of the fine and coarse aggregates. The use of pit-run gravel or run of crusher stone should not be permitted on account of the variation in the gradation of the aggregate.

In mixing, both machine and hand methods are used. Either is satisfactory when properly done (see Art. XIV-22 and XIV-23), but the machine mixing is far more economical. The consistency of the mix should be as wet as possible without interfering with the immediate removal of the molds. When the proper consistency is employed a web-like marking will be produced on the surfaces of the pipe. This is entirely lacking on products made from dry mixes.

In the larger plants the tile or pipe are filled and tamped by machines, of which there are two main types—the spiral-tamping machines and packer-head machines. In the former the mold is centered upon a horizontal table revolving about a vertical axis, and the mix is spouted into it. Tamping is accomplished by blows from a slender plunger which is moved up and down four or five hundred times a minute while the tile is being revolved. In some machines the plunger is held by a friction grip so that its length can be automatically shortened as the mold is filled without changing the intensity of the blow.

---

* The description of a long 36-in. pipe line under 70 ft head may be found in *Eng. News,* Vol. 68, p. 248.

† See *Tech. Paper* 44, National Bureau of Standards, entitled Investigation of the Durability of Cement Drain Tile in Alkali Soils.

With the packer-head machines the molds have no inner lining and are stationary. The packer head revolves about a vertical central axis and also has an up-and-down motion. The head itself consists of a smooth cylindrical iron disc about 4 in. long and of the same diameter as the inside of the tile. It is surmounted by a set of adjustable radial vanes. In operating, the head is run to the bottom of the mold and the feeding spout opened. As the head is raised the material is forced outward against the mold by centrifugal force and the interior of the tile is finished by the troweling action of the outer portions of the vanes and the disc.

Tamping machines operate more slowly than the packer-head devices, but they produce a more uniform pipe. For these reasons cement drain tile are generally made by the packer-head method; cement sewer pipe are made by tamping machines.

The method of curing outlined in Art. XIV-30 should be followed if good results are to be secured. Nearly all plants now expose the tile to an atmosphere of wet steam for at least 36 hours, the temperature being kept above 70°F. The steam should be saturated so that condensation is in evidence on the walls of the curing chamber and on the product. Dry steam even at a high temperature will generally do more harm than good. After steam curing the pipe or tile should not be subjected to a temperature below 40°F before they are 2 weeks old. To secure an impervious product it is necessary to sprinkle the pipe twice a day for at least 1 week after removal from the steam, especially if the weather is warm and the humidity low.

9. The Testing of Cement Pipe. The rough field tests mentioned in Art. VIII-14 may also be used to determine the quality of drain tile or sewer pipe. Many plants and most laboratories make absorption and crushing tests to ascertain quality. Both of these tests are made in the same manner, as described in Art. VIII-18 and VIII-20. Fragments of cement drain tile or sewer pipe should not absorb over 8 per cent of water, by weight. Table VIII-10 shows the bearing strength per lineal foot which the different sizes and classes of drain tile and sewer pipe should carry. A method for making freezing tests on drain tile appears in Art. VIII-23.

Good concrete sewer pipe should be capable of carrying an internal water pressure of 15 psi for 15 min when subjected to test (see ASTM specifications).

MISCELLANEOUS CONCRETE PRODUCTS

10. Poles, Posts and Piles are also cast or formed by centrifugal processes out of concrete. In most cases these forms must be reinforced to withstand flexure. The material is well adapted to use in posts and poles, but reinforced piles exposed to sea water are likely to suffer from corrosion of the reinforcement in the sections above high-water level. Reinforced concrete railroad ties have also been tried but without much success, the material being too brittle for such purposes.

11. Cast Stone and Other Forms. *Cast Stone.* Since World War I a considerable impetus has been given to the manufacture of artificial stone produced from Portland cement and specially prepared aggregates for facing and trim on buildings and other structures. Cast stone usually is made either from a relatively dry mix and tamped into molds (dry tamped stone) or from a mix which will flow sluggishly into place in the molds (wet cast stone). Sand, plaster of Paris, glue, wood, or steel molds are used for various kinds of products. Sand or plaster molds may be used to effect a reduction in the water-ratio of the mix prior to hardening. Beautiful shades and textures are evolved from combinations of white cement, colored aggregates, and mineral pigments. The finished surface is commonly produced by cutting, by etching with an acid, or by rubbing on a revolving cast-iron table.

Tests on specimens from 58 varieties of cast stone made by Tucker and Walker of the U. S. Bureau of Standards (see *Proc. Am. Concrete Inst.*, Vol. 29, p. 501) show that over half of the samples exhibited crushing strengths of 5000 to 8000 psi and, after drying to constant weight at 110°C and soaking 24 hours in distilled water at 21°C, absorptions of 5 to 8 per cent. Many of the stronger samples were in good condition after being subjected to 300 cycles of freezing.

Other Forms. On account of the readiness with which concrete can be cast and molded it forms an inexpensive material out of which the artist creates a great variety of handsome ornamental forms for the decoration of structures. Artistic urns, fountains, benches, and pieces of statuary molded out of concrete adorn many of our lawns, parks, and drives.

12. Precast Concrete Structural Units. Advantages of precast floor and roof concrete construction over similar cast-in-place construction include elimination of forms, greater speed of erection, shorter waiting period after erection, and less protection required under severe weather conditions. A large number of methods and products are available, and many of them are covered by patents.

Precast concrete joists such as shown in Fig. 2a are usually made 8 to 12 in. deep and are used for spans of 16 to 24 ft. The usual spacing of the joists is 27 to 33 in. The joists are reinforced with tension and compression longitudinal steel bars and with steel stirrups connected to the longitudinal steel. After the joists are properly positioned, a reinforced-concrete floor slab, usually 2 or 2½ in. thick, may be cast in place over the joists, or reinforced precast concrete slabs may be set and leveled on a bed of mortar placed on top of each joist. The edge and end joints are then filled with mortar or grout. Exposed joint ceilings are usually

painted, and the floor surface may be covered with wood, terrazzo, linoleum, carpet, or asphalt tile.

Several types of patented precast floor and roof slabs are available.
The Flexicore slab is usually 6 in. deep, 12 in. wide, and up to 22 ft 6 in.
long. The top side is not quite as wide as the bottom side so that when
the slabs are placed in position a mortar key, Fig. 2b, is obtained by
placing mortar in the space between adjacent slabs. Each slab has longitudinal compression steel bars, prestressed tension steel bars, and steel

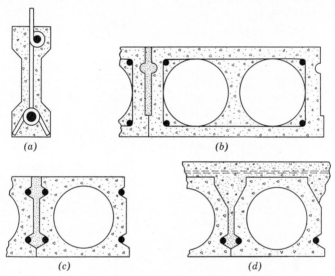

Fig. 2. Precast concrete structural units.

stirrups. The two parallel longitudinal cores, which account for about
50 per cent of the volume, are obtained by placing two inflated flexible
rubber tubes in the mold and placing the concrete around them. After
the concrete has hardened sufficiently the tubes are deflated and withdrawn. The cores are used to accommodate service pipe and conduit.
The ceiling surface of the slab may be painted or plastered, and the floor
surface may be covered with any of the usual materials such as linoleum,
asphalt tile, terrazzo, and wood.

Prestcrete floor and roof slabs consist of an assembly of precast concrete units. The units are made in 3-ft lengths on a concrete pipe machine
and are of two types, Fig. 2c and 2d, known as "standard" and "tee."
The ends are ground to provide uniform bearing between units. The required length of slab to provide spans up to 24 ft is made by placing the
necessary number of units end to end and thrust plates at each end of
the slab. The reinforcing steel rods placed in the "V" notches are
threaded at the end and extend through the end thrust plates. The assem-

bly of the slab is completed by tightening the nuts on the rods against the thrust plates. This procedure places the concrete in compression and allows the steel to be prestressed to the desired amount. The completed slab has the required length, is about 10 in. wide and 8 in. deep, and has one longitudinal core. The top surface of the slab is not as wide as the bottom surface so that a mortar key may be formed between slabs after they are positioned. Where heavy loads and long spans are involved, the "tee" type section is used. Ceiling and floor treatments are similar to those previously discussed.

Metals and Their Ores

1. Metallurgy Defined. Metallurgy may be defined as the art of extracting metals from their ores, and their subsequent adaptation to the uses of man. As a division of engineering practice, the field is intermediate between those of the mining geologist and engineer, who exploit nature's deposits and take out the ores of value, and of the civil, electrical, and mechanical engineers, who are concerned with the fabrication of the metal into the finished structure or machine.

As implied in the definition, the field of metallurgy is broadly divisible into two parts: the recovering of the metal from the comparatively crude or complex forms in which it is taken from the ground; and the further manipulation or treatment of the metal, relatively pure or otherwise, to fit it to withstand best the varying conditions of service. To the user of materials the latter is in general the more interesting and important division of the art.

2. The Metals of Construction. The metals used in considerable quantities in engineering construction are comparatively few in number: iron, copper, lead, zinc, and aluminum may be considered as the primary; and tin, nickel, antimony, silicon, manganese, vanadium, chromium, magnesium, molybdenum, and tungsten as the important secondary metals. The first five are usually the base metals in materials of construction, and are essential in engineering practice; the secondary metals are usually not so essential, or have their principal use because of their modifying influence when alloyed with the metals of the primary division.

3. The Utility of the Metals in Construction. The utility of any metal depends upon its adaptability and workability and upon its cost. The two first named are functions of the physical properties of the material; the cost depends upon the abundance and accessibility of the metal, its form of occurrence, and the ease of extraction and treatment. The properties of importance in metals for construction purposes are: tenacity, elasticity, ductility, malleability, hardness, specific gravity, fusibility, viscosity, color, corrodibility, expansibility, conductivity (electric and thermal), magnetic quality, electric potential, and frictional quality.

Iron is by far the most important of the metals used in engineering construction. It is very abundant in nature, which fact, together with the accessibility of the deposits and the comparatively low cost of extraction, makes it a cheap metal. The value is about 2 cents per pound in the form of pig iron, which may be considered as the raw material for the manufacture of the shapes used in construction. Production in the United States in 1951 reached upwards of 70 million net tons per year. This is about one-half the yearly production of the world. Pure iron is relatively soft, very ductile, and of moderate tensile strength—40,000 to 50,000 psi. The specific gravity is 7.9, and the melting point 1539°C. The ready corrodibility of iron in the atmosphere and otherwise is a disadvantage; and in many places it is used only because its cheapness, coupled at times with advantageous properties, is a factor sufficient to offset the inevitable decay. Iron possesses magnetic properties superior to many other metals, and it would therefore find extensive use in certain fields, regardless of the development of substitutes for many of its present uses. Iron owes its greatest utility to the fact that it alloys freely with other elements, and its inherent properties are markedly altered and improved for varying conditions of service. Practically all the iron used in engineering construction has purposely had added to it varying proportions of different elements, and it will therefore receive consideration with the alloy group.

Copper is a very important metal. The United States in 1950 produced about 720,000 net tons, approximately 33 per cent of the world's output. Consumption of copper in this country in 1950 was about 1,600,000 net tons. Approximately 50 per cent was used by wire mills, 47 per cent by brass mills, and the remainder by chemical plants, secondary smelters, and foundries. Copper is soft and ductile, its specific gravity is 8.9, and the melting point 1083°C. Its relatively high cost, about 22 cents per pound, limits its use to those places where its inherent advantages make its employment necessary. Copper is especially immune to corrosion in the atmosphere, and has an exceptionally high electric conductivity, being slightly surpassed only by silver. It alloys very freely with other metals, particularly zinc and tin, to form brass and bronze.

Lead is of service in the arts because of its softness, ductility, plasticity, low fusion point, and non-corrodibility. It has very low strength, a specific gravity of 11.3, and melts at 327°C. It is a metal of moderate cost, varying from 6 to 18 cents per pound in different years. Production in the United States in 1950 was 430,000 short tons, or about 25 per cent of that of the world. About 4 per cent of the lead consumed was made into white lead and oxides; 33 per cent was used in storage batteries; 8.0 per cent for red lead and litharge; 11 per cent for cable covering; 10 per cent for tetraethyl fluid; 12 per cent for bearing metal, type metal, solder, and foil; and 2.5 per cent for ammunition.

Zinc is a metal of low tensile strength—7000 to 8000 psi—and is rather brittle. It becomes sufficiently ductile at about 100° to 150°C to be rolled into sheet form. The specific gravity is 7.1 and the melting point 420°C. The cost varies normally from 8 to 17 cents per pound. United States production in 1950 was about 625,000 short tons, or about one-fourth of the world's total. The property which renders the metal most useful is its resistance to atmospheric attack. About 8 per cent finds outlet as sheet zinc, and 50 per cent for the galvanized protective surface of steel sheets, tubes, wire, and shapes. Zinc forms with copper the useful alloy brass, and about 15 per cent of the total consumption is for that purpose. Miscellaneous uses in die castings, alloys, and otherwise account for the remaining 27 per cent.

Aluminum has many useful properties and is becoming increasingly more important. Most aluminum is used where light weight is essential, either in the pure form or alloyed with moderate amounts of other metals, which confer added stiffness or other useful properties without great increase of specific gravity in the resultant metal. It is non-corrodible in the atmosphere, has good color, is easily workable, has good strength and ductility, and is especially serviceable because of its low specific gravity and high electric conductivity. The specific gravity is 2.71 and the melting point 657°C. The tensile strength is about 17,000 psi in the cast form and 35,000 psi when drawn into wire. Production in the United States for 1950 was about 720,000 short tons, over 40 per cent of the world production. The price of virgin aluminum ingot in 1950 was 18 cents per pound. Consumption of aluminum in 1949, based on shipments of aluminum ingot and mill products by the Aluminum Co. of America, was as follows: building products 18 per cent, transportation 18 per cent, power transmission 8 per cent, household appliances 7 per cent, cooking utensils 6 per cent, machinery 4 per cent, shipments to fabricators for future processing 25 per cent, and miscellaneous 14 per cent.

The secondary metals are used mainly in mixture with the iron, copper, lead, or zinc, to alter or improve their normal properties. Considerable proportions of the nickel, and tin, however, are employed to form ornamental or rust-resistant coatings for objects made from the other metals, especially iron.

4. Ores. One of the important divisions of the field of metallurgy is the winning of the metals from their ores. The ore is the form in which the metalliferous mineral occurs in the earth, and from which it may be commercially extracted. The metal which it is sought to recover may be present in the native or metallic form, but usually exists as a compound of the metal with other elements; associated with the metalliferous mineral is a varying amount of earthy matter, called the gangue.

The following are the most important chemical combinations in which the more common metals are found:

Oxides or hydrated oxides	Iron, copper, aluminum, tin
Sulfides	Copper, lead, zinc, nickel
Carbonates	Lead, zinc, iron, copper
Native	Copper (silver, gold)
Silicates	Zinc
Chlorides	Lead, magnesium

5. Economic Value of Deposits. Whether or not a metalliferous deposit is an ore depends upon economic considerations. The commercial feasibility of recovery depends upon:

1. *Nature of the Metal.* The more valuable the metal to be recovered, the greater the extremes to which one may go in such recovery, and still show a profit in the operation.

2. *Richness of the Deposit.* The greater the percentage of metal present in the deposit, the more feasible is the prospect of extraction, other things equal. A deposit with 50 per cent of iron content is high grade; one with 30 per cent is lean. Copper ores, on the other hand, vary from 5 to 1 per cent in the largest workings of the United States. The average amount of gold recovered from gold ores in the United States in 1950 was about 0.28 oz per ton.

3. *Association.* Two or more metals may be associated in an ore, and recovery of both will show a net profit, whereas if the separate metals were alone in their individual proportions extraction would not be feasible. Very great values in silver are recovered in lead extraction from certain ores, although the percentage content is so low in many cases as to be apparently negligible. Most of the nickel is obtained from ores where it is associated with sufficient copper to warrant recovery of both metals. Certain iron ores have an added value conferred by the association of nickel or manganese. Again the association may not be of a metallic nature, but may, even as part of the gangue material, save additions in the extraction process, and in consequence warrant the treatment of otherwise too lean ores. Thus the lime associated with some European and southern United States ores enhances their value. On the other hand, foreign substances of a detrimental nature may be present in the deposit, and either destroy the possibility of economical recovery or so increase the costs of the operation as to lower the grade of an otherwise rich ore. High phosphorus in iron ores and the high titanium content of many of the iron deposits of New York are instances in point.

4. *Situation.* Geographical location with respect to facilities for transportation, and accessibility to smelting centers and markets for their products are factors for consideration. Immense deposits of rich iron ores in Brazil are practically untouched at the present time because of transportation difficulties and costs. Again, location of the deposit with respect to ground surfaces, as determining the methods and cost of mining, is an

item in the determination of its value. Finally, extent of the deposit, both as to total quantity and character of distribution, is an important factor. To warrant exploitation, an iron deposit must have large tonnages in sight in a bedded form of considerable thickness. The more valuable the metal, the more feasible it becomes to take out the mineral occurring in veins, pockets, or streaks.

5. *State of the Art.* Cheaper methods of extraction may be developed which will show a profit in the recovery of metals from ores of too lean a character to be treated by present-day methods; or such processes may eliminate some element now detrimental. Also as the high-grade ores become exhausted it becomes necessary to draw upon sources of supply of less rich character, or at more remote or inaccessible places. Research on beneficiation of the low-grade ore and taconite in the Lake Superior region is expected to provide a commercial means of utilizing the immense deposits of these materials.

6. Preparation of Ores for Extraction of Metals. After the ore has been mined, it is usually necessary to prepare it for the extraction process, by some method of ore dressing or concentration. The object is to get rid of some harmful constituent or some of the gangue material by a method depending upon different physical or chemical properties than those of the extraction operation, and accomplishing the result in a more effective and economical manner. Naturally the greater the intrinsic value of the metal to be recovered, the greater is the amount of ore dressing which can be employed, other things being equal. On account of the fact that it is usually more feasible to extract the metal at a place favorably situated with respect to fuel, etc., and remote from the mine mouth, elimination of a considerable portion of the gangue at the mine will minimize transportation of such useless material, and such saving will often more than repay the cost of concentration aside from the advantages resulting from a material more favorable for extraction.

Concentration methods usually begin with a crushing and sizing of the ore to a point as close as economical considerations will warrant, to the theoretical limit of mechanical disintegration of the useful mineral from the gangue. Varying physical or chemical characteristics of the two are the basis for the separation. Washing with water will carry away clays or substances which will form an emulsion or go into solution. Specific gravity differences will permit a separation by flotation in water, oil, etc., usually by some means of controlling its velocity of flow or pulsation. Magnetic separation is often of value, particularly when iron minerals are present.

7. Principles of Extraction of Metals. Metallurgical extraction methods are divisible into two groups: Wet methods involve solution of the metal sought, and recovery by precipitation; although useful in some fields, particularly gold and silver, they are relatively unimportant in the metallurgy of the metals used in engineering construction. Dry methods predominate; these are usually called smelting, and are effected with the aid of heat. After the ores have been properly prepared for treatment, the smelting operation consists essentially of a reduction of the metal from its chemical combination in the mineral, a fusion of the metal and the gangue as slag, with recovery of the metal. The result may be obtained in one operation and furnace; or it may require several to properly fit the metal for use in the arts.

The chemical reactions involved in the recovery of the metals in smelting are mainly oxidation with air, metallic oxides, and carbon dioxide; and reduction by means of carbon, carbon monoxide, hydrogen, sulfur, or certain metals.

Heat is often employed preliminary to smelting, to effect a change in the chemical nature of the mineral or ore, without fusion or reduction to the metallic form. Drying, calcination, or roasting involve driving off the moisture, the dissociation of hydrates or carbonates with elimination of water or carbon dioxide, and the removal of sulfur by oxidation and volatilization as sulfur dioxide.

CHAPTER XVIII

Reduction of Iron from Its Ores

1. The Economic Importance of Iron and Steel. The iron and steel industry has had its principal development in the United States and Europe. Production of pig iron in recent years is shown in Table 1.

TABLE 1. QUANTITY AND VALUE OF PIG IRON PRODUCED IN LEADING COUNTRIES OF THE WORLD

Country	1905		1915		1950	
	Long Tons	Millions of Dollars	Long Tons	Millions of Dollars	Long Tons	Millions of Dollars
United States	22,992,000	382	30,384,000	401	59,200,000	2770
Germany	10,814,000		11,604,000		9,550,000	
Great Britain	9,593,000		8,794,000		9,600,000	
France	3,028,000		4,675,000		9,300,000	
Russia					19,100,000	

Production in Russia has grown rapidly and now exceeds that of Great Britain. In addition, Belgium, Japan, India, Canada, Luxembourg, and Australia produce considerable pig iron. By far the greater proportion of pig iron produced in the United States is made from domestic ores, although there is a considerable tonnage of ore imported from Chile, Sweden, Canada, Brazil, Venezuela, and Algeria to supply seaboard furnaces. Germany is largely dependent upon iron ores obtained from beyond her borders. Her chief supplies are from the Lorraine fields, extending into Luxembourg, Belgium, France, and Germany. Great Britain has important deposits of iron ore on her northeast and northwest coasts, but obtains about one-third of her supply from foreign fields.

2. The Native Sources of Iron Ores. Iron ores are mined in many states of the United States. There are three great producing districts: Lake Superior, centering about the head of that lake in Minnesota, Michigan, and Wisconsin; southern, chiefly in Alabama, near Birmingham; and eastern, largely in Pennsylvania, New York, the Adirondacks region, and New Jersey. Additional tonnage is obtained from Wyoming, Utah, California, Tennessee, and New Mexico. The Lake Superior district produces about four-fifths of the annual tonnage of this country. Southern ores are smelted largely in the vicinity of the mines. New York ores find outlet locally and in eastern Pennsylvania furnaces; almost all the Lake Superior ore is shipped from 600 to 1000 miles to smelting centers. The greatest proportion is sent to lower Lake Erie ports for transshipment by rail to furnaces in the Pittsburgh district; a considerable tonnage is smelted in the region centering about Chicago.

The production of pig iron in the United States in 1951 was about 70,000,000 net tons. This production broken down on a geographical basis was as follows: Pennsylvania 29 per cent, Ohio 20 per cent, Chicago area 20 per cent, eastern United States 14 per cent, southern United States $8\frac{1}{2}$ per cent, western United States $4\frac{1}{2}$ per cent, and Michigan and Minnesota 4 per cent.

3. Classes of Iron Ores and Their Characteristics. The ores of iron are classed according to the iron mineral which is predominant. They are, in the order of theoretical percentage of iron content in the mineral:

Magnetite. Fe_3O_4. 72.4 per cent iron. It is steel gray to black in color, very hard, and strongly magnetic. Magnetite is not a very prominent ore in the United States, but is mined to a considerable extent in Pennsylvania and New York. There are large tonnages in New York which are not exploited at the present time because of associated titanium, which causes difficulty in smelting. Magnetite is the important ore of Sweden, where it is of high purity.

Hematite. Fe_2O_3. 70 per cent iron. It is red to brown in color, and occurs in some deposits in a hard, lumpy condition, whereas in others it is soft and of fine texture. Hematites form the principal ores of the United States; the ore of Lake Superior and much of that of the South is of this character. Hematites are also important in the west of England, Spain, Cuba, Chile, and Africa. Immense deposits of high-grade ore exist in Brazil, but have not been exploited to any extent as yet because of transportation difficulties.

Limonite. $2Fe_2O_3 + 3H_2O$. 59.9 per cent iron, 14.5 per cent water of combination. This is a hydrated hematite, is soft and of a yellow color. It becomes red hematite by dehydration at high temperature. By partial dehydration, ores of brown color, called brown hematites, result. These are prominent in the southern deposits of the United States, and in the Minette district on the German-French border. Limonites are important in the Cuban deposits.

Siderite. $FeCO_3$. 48.3 per cent iron, 41.4 per cent CO_2. Also called spathic ore. The principal deposits are in Germany and Austria, in Wales and the northwest district of England. Normally the ore is hard and stonelike with a gray color, but is often associated with clay or carbonaceous matter, and in the latter case the color is black or streaked with black. Carbonate ores were formerly important in Pennsylvania.

Although iron silicates and sulfides are plentiful in nature, they are of no importance at the present time as ores.

Iron ores occur in all conditions in nature, from hard ores requiring blasting, to soft ores which can be mined directly with steam shovels. Successfully mined deposits are often thousands of feet below the surface of the ground, and again may be so close to the surface as to be capable of open-cut mining after a variable amount of stripping of top soil.

The relative production of the various iron ores in the United States during recent years is given in Table 2.

TABLE 2.   PRODUCTION OF IRON ORE IN THE UNITED STATES

	1905		1915		1950	
Kind of Ore	Long Tons	Per Cent	Long Tons	Per Cent	Long Tons	Per Cent
Hematite [1]	37,568,000	88.3	52,227,000	94.1	104,400,000	83.2
Brown ore [2]	2,547,000	6.0	1,489,000	2.7	8,400,000	6.7
Magnetite	2,390,000	5.6	1,807,000	3.2	12,900,000	10.1
Carbonate	22,000	0.05	3,500			
Total	42,527,000	100.0	55,526,500	100.0	125,700,000	100.0

[1] Anhydrous sesquioxide.   [2] Hydrated sesquioxides.

4. Elements Associated with Iron Ores.   Typical analyses of iron ores, except for the oxygen combined with the iron, are given in Table 3.

TABLE 3.   TYPICAL COMPOSITIONS OF IRON ORES

	Natural Chemical Composition, per cent						
Source of Ore	Fe	P	Mn	SiO_2	Al_2O_3	CaO + MgO	H_2O
Marquette Range, Minn.	56.8	0.14	0.08	15.5	1.25	1.00	0.9
Mesabi Range, Minn	52.5	0.04	0.52	11.5	1.55	0.48	7.9
Mesabi Range, Minn.	47.5	0.07	1.43	6.1	0.85	0.57	16.8
Mesabi Range, Minn.	50.8	0.06	0.64	6.0	1.90	0.50	13.3
Alabama	37.0	0.30	0.15	15.0	3.25	15.10	—
New York [1]	67.0	0.15	0.40	2.9	1.00	2.00	—

[1] Concentrate

The iron content in different ores varies considerably; values range from 30 per cent to upwards of 50 or even 60 per cent. The Lake Superior ores are very rich; those of the South are comparatively lean. Many ores, and this is true of certain of the southern deposits, have the disadvantage of the lean iron content offset to a degree by the association of lime, alumina, and silica in proper proportions to be self-fluxing, thereby forming suitable slags without purchase of the necessary flux (usually limestone) to insure fluidity. The gangue is earthy material, of which the principal constituents are usually silica and alumina. Increasing amounts of such gangue lower the value of the ore by decrease of iron content and corresponding increase of handling, fuel, and flux costs per ton of pig iron. Alkalies or basic constituents may have the offsetting advantage of decreasing the amount of flux required in smelting. Sulfur and phosphorus are always present in varying degree in iron ores. Up to 1 per cent of sulfur may be successfully removed to the required limits in blast-furnace smelting, but requires increased fuel and flux; thus increasing sulfur lowers the value of the ore. Phosphorus, on the other hand, is eliminated only by special processes in the refining of the crude blast-furnace product to steel; the necessity of such selection of a more costly method means that phosphorus content greater than 0.05 per cent in an ore carrying 50 per cent of iron has a marked effect in lowering the value. Phosphorus of 0.001 per unit of iron is the limiting content dividing iron ores into the two great divisions of Bessemer and basic. All good steel must not exceed 0.10 per cent in phosphorus content; the elimination of any excess costs money; and the presence of such excess in the ore lowers the grade.

5. Preliminary Treatments for Iron Ores. Iron ores usually undergo no treatment preliminary to smelting, except carbonates, which are calcined to drive off the carbon dioxide. Sulfur in excess of that suitable for economical smelting can be lowered by roasting and volatilization as sulfur dioxide. Much of the magnetite mined in New York is crushed and treated by magnetic separation, whereby a considerable proportion of the non-magnetic gangue and phosphate constituents are removed, and twofold enrichment in grade is the result. Washing of the brown ores of the South is practiced to remove excessive clay, and this method is also used for certain of the Lake Superior ores. Drying of ores is often necessary; elimination of excessive moisture results in increased smelting economies, and in addition the cost of drying may be more than compensated for by the saving in freight charges on the water content. Agglomeration of fine ores by briquetting with binders of slag, tar, etc., and nodulizing or sintering by partial fusion, are being successfully practiced. The employment of these methods is chiefly in the utilization of flue dusts formed in blast-furnace operation.

6. Fundamental Principles of Extraction of Iron. The fundamental chemical principles in the extraction of iron from the ores are very simple. Heating the ores in the presence of a reducing agent (usually carbon or carbon monoxide) will result in the formation of carbon monoxide or carbon dioxide, liberated as a gas, and metallic iron. Reduction of red oxide of iron, Fe_2O_3, by carbon monoxide will begin at temperature as low as 200°C, and proceed by progressive formation of Fe_3O_4, FeO, and Fe. Reduction to metallic iron is practically complete at temperatures as low as 800°C very much below the fusion point of iron, which melts at 1539°C when pure, and may have its fusion point lowered to 1100°C by the presence of associated elements or impurities.

7. Ancient Methods of Extraction. This ready reducibility of iron oxide to metallic iron at moderate temperatures was the basis of the ancient methods of manufacture with apparatus of the simple hearth or forge type, resembling a crude blacksmith's forge, and with such forced draft only as could be obtained from bellows, in many cases hand operated. A small charge of ore together with the necessary charcoal for fuel and reduction were heated for a sufficient time to effect reduction of the iron to a pasty mass. Ores of a minimum of associated gangue material were selected, much of which could be eliminated by combination with iron oxide to form a slag of fairly low fusion point, but necessarily with considerable loss of iron in the slag. The resultant mass of spongy iron, with its entrained slag, was taken from the forge and hammered to a rough bloom or bar. Much of the slag was thus eliminated by pressure; but, just as it is impossible to eliminate all of the moisture from a sponge by squeezing, so it was impossible to squeeze out all the slag. The product of the forge was a malleable material with varying amounts of occluded slag which was extended by forging into long filaments; a product identical in physical structure with the wrought iron of more modern times.

8. Direct and Indirect Methods of Producing Ductile Ferrous Metals. Since for the larger part of the iron which is used in the arts, some degree of its inherent malleability and ductility are desired, any process of manufacture whereby the product is obtained in this condition in a single operation represents the ideal. The "direct process" still makes its appeal to the inventor; actually, however, the amount of product so produced is negligible in a consideration of the annual tonnage. Unfortunately, such processes have many disadvantages: intermittent character, inefficient types of furnace, high labor costs, and large losses of iron in the slag; especially because detrimental impurities such as sulfur and phosphorus are only removed, or most economically so, in processes which bring the products to fusion, and where slags of special composition and volume can be formed. "Direct" methods have given way today to the so-called "indirect," whereby the malleable end product of greatest use in the arts is the result of a two-step operation: a preliminary smelting producing a relatively crude pig iron, and subsequent refining or conversion of this into steel of the desired composition and properties for various uses.

The most efficient furnace is a shaft type where the fuel and charge to be treated are in direct contact; where these solid materials can be charged at the top and descend by gravity to the base of the stack; where in this descent they may meet a countercurrent of ascending gases, formed from the combustion of the fuel near the bottom of the shaft; and, finally, where uninterrupted operation is made possible by fusion of all the products and their withdrawal from the furnace at will in the molten condition. By attainment of suitable temperatures and character of slags, the latter may be easily separated from the iron in the molten condition, due to the different densities and lack of mutual solubility.

9. The Development of the Blast Furnace. The modern blast furnace, which embodies all the above characteristics, is the result of evolution and development. The first shaft-type furnaces were designed primarily for more efficient and economical operation; the product was malleable material, removed intermittently in the unfused condition. With higher temperatures resulting from increased height of stack and better blast, the spongy mass of iron absorbed carbon from the fuel, and its fusion temperature was lowered from 1539°C to between 1100° and 1200°. This was below the working temperature of the furnace, and the result was a molten product; but the absorption of carbon up to the limit of saturation of the temperature changed the product from a malleable material to a brittle and relatively weak cast iron, while at the same time there was elimination of slag because of liquation in the fused condition. The era of this development was about A.D. 1400 to 1500. The limited demand for a malleable product, however, practically nullified the advantages of the method until the birth of the puddling process in 1784 gave a refining on a scale commensurate with the capacity of the shaft type of furnace.

10. Description of a Modern Blast Furnace. In the early part of the eighteenth century, the blast furnace for the manufacture of pig iron was a square masonry stack, with four tuyeres near the base for the introduction of cold blast furnished by a crude blowing equipment. Its dimensions were about 10 ft across by 30 ft high, and production was from 30 to 40 tons of pig iron per week with a consumption of 3 tons of fuel per ton of iron. The furnace was usually placed at the side of a hill, so that materials of the charge could be hauled by team to the level of the top.

Important events in the development of the blast furnace have been the substitution of coke for charcoal at the beginning of the eighteenth century, and the invention of the steam engine in the latter part of that century; both of these made possible larger furnaces, more rapid driving, and less restriction in location of plant. Hot blast was introduced in the early part of the eighteenth century, and with the resulting increase of temperature of the hearth, there was an increase in furnace production per unit of capacity, with decrease of fuel consumption. Closing of the top of the furnace enabled the top gases to be collected and utilized for blast heating, boiler firing and the like.

Modern developments have been chiefly of a mechanical nature—enlargements of capacity, the adoption of the circular steel shell with brick lining, evolution of furnace lines as dictated by experience and by the changing character of the available ores; and most especially, in the installation of mechanical handling appliances to eliminate hand labor to the greatest degree, and make for larger output and more economical operation.

A late development in blast-furnace operation consists of using an air blast with an oxygen content slightly over 30 per cent, by volume, instead of the normal 20.8 per cent. This oxygen enrichment is believed to result in (1) decreased heat removal from the furnace by the gas, (2) decreased volume and velocity of the gas, causing a decrease in the flue dust problem, and (3) faster combustion of the coke and higher hearth temperatures.

The modern blast furnace has a daily capacity from 100 to 1500 tons; 1000 tons may be considered fairly standard. Fuel consumption is approximately 1 ton of coke per ton of iron—it varies from 1700 to 3500 lb according to character of ore and details of practice. Furnace diameters are from 15 to 28 ft at the base, and the height is from 60 to 100 ft.

A section of a modern blast furnace is given in Fig. 1. It is of the vertical shaft type, of two cone frustums, with their bases together, and resting upon a short cylindrical lower section. The long, gradually outward-flaring portion furnishes the shaft for the descent of the charge for the absorption of heat from the ascending current of gases, and for the step-by-step reduction of the ore to metallic iron. This operation begins shortly below the top, and is practically completed by the time the charge reaches the part of the furnace of greatest diameter. The outward flare is to take care of the increasing volume of material due to any swelling of the charge, and to allow of easy descent without danger of sticking. The lower frustum, called the "bosh" of the furnace, is the hottest part and forms the zone of fusion. There is a rather sharp flare of the walls inwards in the descent in accordance with the diminished volume of material in this zone. Also this bosh angle tends to promote arching, thus supporting the charge column, and to contract the base of the furnace to the diameter needed for the crucible and for penetration of the blast. The lower cylindrical portion is the crucible, or hearth, and serves as a reservoir for collection of the iron and slag between the periodic taps.

The upper shaft of the furnace is of steel-plate construction and sets upon a "mantle ring" in turn supported by 8 to 12 columns. This portion is lined with firebrick to a thickness of 4 to 5 ft in thick-wall furnaces. A newer development is the thin-wall furnace with artificially cooled upper shaft walls 9 to 18 in. thick. The bosh zone in general is of brickwork from 2 to 3 ft thick, and without a metal shell. Support is furnished by a series of heavy steel bands, and several rows of "bosh plates" through which water is circulated are set in the brickwork to assist it in withstanding the high temperature of the fusion zone. The crucible is surrounded by a heavy jacket of segmental steel castings, and has a firebrick lining about 3 ft thick.

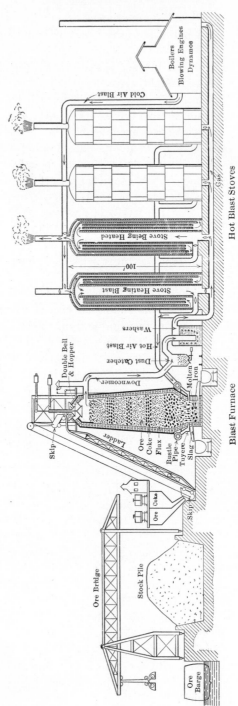

Fig. 1. Diagrammatic sketch showing scheme of operating a blast furnace.

The blast is introduced through 8 to 18 tuyeres, or nozzles, made of bronze or copper, and water cooled; these are connected by suitable pipes to the large blast main surrounding the furnace and connected with the stoves and blowing engine. At the lower level of the crucible is the tap hole, from which the pig iron is run into sand beds or large ladles. Just below the tuyeres is a "cinder notch" through which the slag accumulated between taps of iron can be flushed. Near the top of the furnace are one or two openings for the escape of the gases. These gases are led by a pipe to the stoves, boilers, and other points of consumption. The top of the stack is closed by a conical bell and hopper; in the most modern furnaces this is double, to prevent escape of gas which would occur during the lowering of a single bell in charging. Old furnaces were charged by hand buggies taken to the top by an elevator. Modern construction is an inclined bridge up which skips are hauled and automatically dumped after being filled at pits at the base of the furnace.

Typical dimensions of a modern blast furnace of 1000 tons daily capacity are: crucible, diameter 24 ft, bosh, 26 ft, bell, 14 ft, height, 90 ft. Such a furnace would require daily about 3500 tons of charge material— ore 2000 tons, coke 1000 tons, flux 500 tons. This material is charged at the top in alternate layers as required to keep the furnace full. The molten iron is tapped off every 5 hours and cast into pigs of 150 lb weight or taken away in ladle cars for conversion into steel. The slag, which may be of greater total weight than the iron, floats on top of the iron, and is flushed off at intervals and usually dumped as waste material either molten or after water granulation. Some of the slag finds outlet in cement making, for road ballast, and for various other uses.

11. Accessories to the Blast Furnace. The top gases are combustible. They contain carbon monoxide diluted with much carbon dioxide from the reduction of the ore and decomposition of the limestone, and large volumes of nitrogen derived from the air of the blast. This gas is freed from dust to varying degrees by dust catchers, scrubbers, and washers, and used in part for heating the blast; the rest is available for power purposes. The air blown into the furnace is preheated to about 500 to 600°C by four stoves, Fig. 1. For the 1000-ton furnace noted above each stove would be about 20 ft in diameter and 100 ft high, consisting of a steel shell lined with firebrick and containing a combustion chamber and a heat-absorbing chamber of firebrick checker work. The stoves operate on the regenerative principle—combustion of the gas for 1 hour results in sufficient heat absorption to enable each stove to heat the entire cold blast for ½ hour. With four stoves per furnace, one heats the air, usually two are on gas, and the fourth is held in reserve.

Besides the accessories used in heating and cleaning the blast, power is needed for ore handling and for pumping the enormous quantities of water used for cooling. Also, 4500 to 5000 hp is required for supplying the 70,000 cu ft of air required per minute for a 1000-ton furnace. Blast pressure is about 18 psi.

12. The Essential Reactions in Extracting Pig Iron. The underlying chemical principle in the extraction of iron from its ores is comparatively simple. The ores are oxides in the natural state, or converted to oxides by preliminary roasting or calcination. The problem involves reduction of an oxide (ore) by a reducing agent (C) with the aid of heat (combustion of C). The ideal reaction would be:

$$2Fe_2O_3 + 3C = 4Fe + 3CO_2$$

requiring 36 units of carbon to yield 224 units of iron, or a ratio of 6 iron to 1 reducing agent. In addition to the above, there would be needed the heat required for continuance of the above reaction, since that furnished by the combustion of carbon to carbon dioxide is only $\frac{3}{4}$ of the quantity necessary to dissociate the oxygen from the union with the iron. Also, if the resultant iron is to be fused, together with the associated gangue of the ore, still more fuel would be required. Actually the conditions in the blast furnace result in variation from the reaction cited above. The ore and coke are charged together at the top of the furnace, and descend slowly through the shaft in contact. No combustion of the fuel takes place until it reaches the air supply at the tuyere zone, where intense heat generation results. The products of combustion pass rapidly up the stack, giving up heat to the charge in their ascent and causing a temperature gradient in the furnace from 1600°C in the tuyere zone to 200–300°C at the top of the furnace. The carbon dioxide formed at the tuyeres undergoes almost immediate change to carbon monoxide in the presence of the large coke bed, and as such passes upwards through the stack. As a gas, it has great penetrating power; furthermore it will begin to reduce iron oxide at temperatures as low as those of the blast-furnace top, and will practically complete the reaction at temperatures at which solid carbon begins to act. Consequently, although the ore and carbon are in contact, with ores of reasonably porous texture, the reduction may be considered as effected through the agency of the carbon monoxide. The ideal reaction is:

$$Fe_2O_3 + 3CO = 2Fe + 3CO_2$$

Under these conditions there would result 112 units of iron for each 36 units of carbon, or a ratio of 3 to 1. Unfortunately, conditions of chemical equilibrium govern the approach to the ideal which can be obtained, and experience indicates that, with the temperatures, pressures, and materials prevailing in the blast furnace, the ratio of carbon monoxide to carbon dioxide is usually about 2 to 1. The blast-furnace reduction of iron may be typified approximately as follows:

$$Fe_2O_3 + 9CO + 17.1N = 2Fe + 6CO + 3CO_2 + 17.1N$$

The result is a production of 112 units of iron with the consumption of 108 units of carbon, or an approximate ratio of 1 to 1. The combustion of the 108 units of carbon to carbon monoxide in the tuyere zone results in sufficient heat generation to fuse the iron and slag, and in the surplus heat needed to complete the reactions in the upper zones of the furnace. Passing from the shaft is a gas which has considerable combustible value because of the high carbon monoxide ratio, but which is diluted by the carbon dioxide and particularly by the large volumes of inert nitrogen accompanying the oxygen in the air blast.

The simple equation of reduction given above is complicated by the successive stages taking place in the zones of descent, by the changes accompanying varying physical conditions in charge and atmosphere, and by the reversibility of reactions and conditions of chemical equilibrium as influenced by mass relations.

In actual blast-furnace practice fuel ratios are subject to considerable variation with varying richness of ore and coke and details of furnace construction and operation. From 1400 to 2300 lb of coke and from 600 to 1100 lb of limestone per ton of pig iron is about the range for modern furnaces working on Lake Superior ores. The averages in pounds per ton of pig iron for constituents of the charge in the blast furnaces of the United States are as follows:

Coke	1800
Limestone	800
Ore	3400
Cinder, etc.	400

In Fig. 2 is given a diagrammatic representation of the typical reactions of the blast furnace, together with the weights of the several materials making up the charge and the products. These are based upon a dry ore containing 60 per cent iron, coke containing 87 per cent carbon, pure limestone, pig iron with 4 per cent carbon and 1 per cent silicon, and a tunnel head gas of 1 part carbon dioxide to 2 parts carbon monoxide by volume. Beginning at the upper left corner of the diagram and following the sequence of figures to the right, one observes how the ore, coke, and limestone are affected as they gradually move downward in the furnace, also how the gases are transformed as they pass upward through the charge.

13. The Reduction of Impurities in Iron Ores. Besides reducing iron ore to the metallic state, the blast furnace causes a variable reduction of the constituents of the gangue, flux, or fuel, and an absorption of the liberated metalloids by the iron, to its benefit or detriment. By regulation of temperature and slag characteristics, the blast-furnace manager has a considerable degree of control over certain of these. Carbon is taken up from the fuel in the fusion zone in fairly fixed amounts of 3½ to 4 per cent. The percentage varies with the amounts of other elements in the iron; silicon decreases total carbon; manganese increases it. Whatever phosphorus is present in ore or fuel is readily reduced to the elemental form and absorbed by the iron. It cannot be controlled under the reducing conditions of the blast furnace, and appears in the iron to the full extent to which it may be present in the charge. The presence of phos-

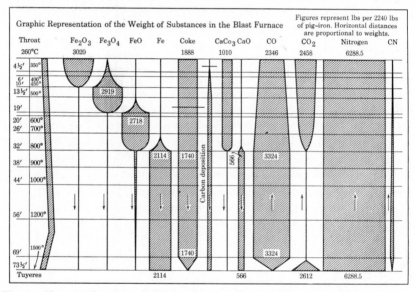

Fig. 2. Changes that occur in a blast-furnace charge. (From Campbell's *Manufacture and Properties of Iron and Steel.*)

phorus is detrimental in steel-making irons, and in cast irons, except where considerations of fluidity supersede those of strength.

Manganese is present to varying extent in the ores of iron. Part of it is reduced and appears in the iron, the amount varying with the quantity in the ore and running conditions in the furnace. For ordinary grades of pig iron, control of furnace conditions is not regulated by manganese consideration; the relative amounts in iron and slag are the result of conditions determined by elements more vitally affecting quality.

In ordinary grades of pig iron silicon is desired in fairly fixed percentages, varying from 0.75 to 3.5 per cent according to use. With increasing temperature in the hearth zone, there is increasing tendency for reduction of SiO_2 by carbon; offsetting this is the strong affinity of lime or other bases to unite with SiO_2 to form silicates. Such silicon as is set free in the metallic state is absorbed by the iron; unreduced SiO_2 forms part of the slag. High silicon in the pig iron results from high temperatures of running (usually the accompaniment of higher fuel ratios). Slags of high basicity, that is with the lime or other strongly basic flux held to a maximum, tend to retard the liberation of silicon.

Sulfur is an undesirable element in most iron and steel, in amounts exceeding about 0.10 per cent. And since the amount present in ores of a blast-furnace charge may approach 1 per cent, and since the removal of sulfur is best effected under reducing conditions, its elimination by proper control of blast-furnace conditions is a most important function of operation. As iron sulfide it is absorbed by the iron; as calcium sulfide it will be dissolved by proper slags; elimination from the pig iron depends largely upon the formation of calcium sulfide. Excess of lime above the amount needed for complete satisfaction of the silica (neutralization of acid by base) together with high temperature, favor the reduction of lime (CaO), in which case the free calcium will take hold of any sulfur to form calcium sulfide, which is soluble to limited extent in the hot, limey slag. Low sulfur pig iron is the result of high-temperature furnace operation with high-lime (basic) slags of sufficient quantity to insure solution of all of the calcium sulfide formed before the saturation limit is reached.

14. Grades of Pig Iron. Analyses of typical grades of pig iron are given in Table 4. It will be noted that the carbon content is not given. Although it is the most important element in cast irons, its percentage is

TABLE 4

	Composition, per cent			
Product	Si	S	P	Mn
Foundry pig iron				
(A) Northern low-phosphorus	1–5	<0.05	0.30–0.50	0.50–1.25
(B) Northern high-phosphorus	1–5	<0.05	0.50–0.70	0.50–1.25
(C) Southern	1–5	<0.05	0.70–0.90	0.25–0.75
Malleable pig iron	1.25–2.25	<0.05	0.10–0.19	0.40–1.0
Low-phosphorus pig iron	0.50–3	<0.035	<0.035	<1.25
Intermediate low-phosphorus pig iron	1–3	<0.05	0.036–0.075	<1.25
Gray forge	1.2–1.75	<0.05	0.1–0.35	0.5–1.0
Puddling iron	0.75–2.5	<0.05	0.1–0.5	0.5–1.0
Acid pig, Bessemer	1–2.25	<0.045	0.04–0.1	0.5–1.0
Acid pig, open-hearth	1–1.5	<0.045	<0.05	0.5–2.5
Basic pig, open-hearth	<1.5	<0.05	0.11–0.90	0.4–2.0
Basic pig, Bessemer	0.5–1.0	<0.20	1.9–2.5	1.5–2.5

$<$ = below or less than.

fairly constant—3.5 to 4.5 per cent—in pig iron, and is largely governed by the amounts of other elements, as noted heretofore.

Foundry irons are intended for the manufacture of iron castings. Softness and soundness are desired with reasonable strength. Increasing the silicon content promotes the formation of graphitic carbon, and thus tends to increase softness. Sulfur promotes formation of combined carbon, and tends to increase hardness. High phosphorus decreases strength but increases fluidity and therefore is of value in the manufacture of thin castings, stove plate, etc. Foundry pig irons are of higher grade (and value) with increasing silicon and decreasing sulfur content. Gray forge iron is a lower or off grade of foundry pig, often used in puddling.

Malleable pig iron is intended for the production of malleable cast iron. Silicon is held within restricted limits to insure a hard white casting which will be subsequently converted to the proper soft gray texture by annealing. Phosphorus is kept low because of strength considerations, but not too low to destroy fluidity in casting.

Acid Bessemer pig iron has a silicon content sufficiently high for the fuel requirement of the acid Bessemer steel-making process. Phosphorus must be below the limiting amount for a satisfactory steel when the acid Bessemer or the acid open-hearth methods are used.

Basic pig irons are intended for steel making by basic processes in which phosphorus can be removed. Economic slag conditions necessitate low silicon. In the basic Bessemer method high phosphorus is needed for its fuel value; it is not essential in the basic open-hearth method.

15. Slags. Blast-furnace slags will in general have a silica plus alumina ($SiO_2 + Al_2O_3$) content about equal to the lime plus magnesia ($CaO + MgO$), and these four constituents will form about 96 per cent of the total slag. Typical analyses will show SiO_2, 25 to 50 per cent; Al_2O_3, 5 to 20 per cent; CaO, 25 to 50 per cent; MgO, 0 to 25 per cent.

Manufacture of Wrought Iron and Steel

1. Introduction. Of the total annual production of iron and steel in the United States, about 85 per cent is steel and the remainder cast iron. Although direct production of the steel from the ore is feasible, and seemingly would be advantageous, in view of the proportionate magnitude of its consumption, economic considerations have determined that present practice should reduce practically all the ore to the form of crude pig or cast iron, as one step in the manufacturing process; then convert this product into steel by refining or purification as the second step. Typical analyses of crude and finished product are shown in Table A.

TABLE A

	C	Si	S	P	Mn
Pig iron.............	3.5–4	1–3	0.03–0.12	0.05–1.0	0.50–1.0
Steel...............	0.10–0.75	0.05–0.20	0.03–0.07	0.03–0.10	0.30–0.75

Service requirements of strength and ductility necessitate the reductions of the amounts of the elements in the pig iron, in particular the carbon, silicon, and at times the phosphorus, to the lower limits prescribed by experience.

2. The Purification of Pig Iron. Oxidation is the essential chemical principle upon which processes for the conversion of pig iron into steel are based. It is usually considered that a part of the iron is oxidized first and that subsequent oxidation of the impurities is largely performed by FeO rather than by gaseous oxygen. The actual processes, however, are complex, and the principal reactions in Table B are consequently given in the simplest form.

Oxygen will unite with silicon to form SiO_2, and manganese to form MnO, both of which products are insoluble in the molten iron, and, because of lower specific gravity, will rise to the top as slag. The silica (SiO_2) will in turn unite with the manganese oxide (MnO), or any other basic constituent, such as iron oxide (FeO) or lime (CaO), to form stable silicates of a more fusible character than the constituent radicals. Carbon will oxidize to carbon monoxide (CO) (or to CO_2 at times), which will

TABLE B

Reactions.	Calories of Heat Generated.	
	Per Kg. of Metal.	Per Kg. of Oxygen.
$Si + O_2 = SiO_2$	6428	5625
$Mn + O = MnO$	1653	5681
$C + O = CO$	2430	1823
$Fe + O = FeO$	1173	4106
$P_2 + O_5 = P_2O_5$	5703	4562

bubble through the bath and escape as a gas. The relative order of affinity for oxygen is about as given in Table B. After the silicon, manganese, and carbon have been eliminated, some iron will oxidize to FeO, a very small proportion of which is soluble in the molten iron; the greater part, however, rises to the top of the bath and becomes a basic constituent of the slag. Phosphorus will oxidize freely to the gas P_2O_5: but, under the conditions prevailing in the steel-making operation, this element will not be eliminated unless it is locked up in the stable form of calcium phosphate $3CaO \cdot P_2O_5$. To accomplish this end, lime additions to the bath are necessary, and form the essential feature of the basic process, which will be discussed more fully in Art. 10 and 14.

The oxygen needed in the reactions may be obtained from the air; or by adding Fe_2O_3 to the bath, in which case the oxygen is seized by the silicon, manganese, or carbon, and the liberated iron becomes part of the resultant steel. A significant feature in the tabulation of reactions in Table B is the heat liberation accompanying each. All the elements which it is desired to eliminate from the iron have a fuel value, in most instances greater than that of carbon itself. With proper details of combustion these fuel values may be utilized not only to supply the heat dissipated during the interval of refining a molten bath of cast iron, but in addition to furnish the increment of heat needed to raise the temperature the several hundred degrees necessary to insure fluidity in the final steel. To illustrate: A ton of coal may be burned so slowly and inefficiently that there will be barely appreciable liberation of heat and a maintenance of temperature hardly sufficient to insure continuous ignition and combustion. On the other hand, by rapid combustion with forced draft in an efficient type of furnace, heat liberation and temperature are such that iron or other refractory substances may be melted. The total quantity of heat is in both instances the same; temperature rise is the result of rapidity of generation and effectiveness of utilization. If oxidation of the elements in a bath of pig iron is sufficiently rapid, temperature rise may result; if slow, rate of heat generation may not equal that of its dissipation, and fuel from other sources may be required to keep the bath molten.

THE MANUFACTURE OF WROUGHT IRON

3. History. Modern steel-making methods were preceded by the puddling process, invented by Cort in 1784, improved by Hall in 1830, and persisting to the present day, although puddling went into the background with the inception of the Bessemer process and the "Age of Steel," in 1856. Puddled iron is today about 2 per cent of the annual output of iron and steel.

4. Methods of Manufacture. The puddling operation is carried out in a reverberatory furnace with rather small hearth and large grate area to

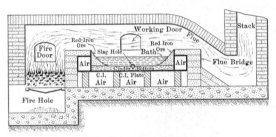

Fig. 1. Principle of puddling furnace.

insure the working temperature desired. A longitudinal section of such a furnace is given in Fig. 1.

The furnace has a dish-shaped hearth consisting of a cast-iron bottom plate on which is fused about 2 to 3 inches of protecting cinder, essentially oxide of iron. The sides and ends are lined with iron ore. Side doors are provided for handling the charge and product, and for rabbling the bath during the refining operation. The furnace has a low-hanging arched roof of refractory brick. The fuel is usually bituminous coal, preferably of low sulfur percentage and of high volatile content to insure a long flame. Heating of the bath is accomplished entirely by the temperature of the gases and by their combustion over its surface. The products of combustion escape to a stack, necessarily at high temperature. To save some of the heat, waste-heat boilers are often installed above the furnace, and the furnace gases pass through the boiler flues before they enter the stack. Natural draft is used, and there is no preheating of the air used for combustion.

The capacity of puddling furnaces ranges from 300 to 1500 lb per heat; in general about 600 lb. Pig iron of white or mottled grade, and known as forge or mill iron, is charged on the banks of the hearth, together with some old slag or iron oxide to furnish a slag blanket for the bath, and to serve as the basic constituent of the new slag and as oxidizing agent in the refining.

A single heat takes about 1½ hours. After melting of the charge, iron oxide additions are rabbled into the bath and serve to remove practically all the silicon and manganese and some of the phosphorus into the highly basic iron silicate slag thus formed. Carbon is next oxidized to carbon monoxide, and in bubbling through the bath causes much boiling and agitation. These operations take up somewhat over two-thirds of the time of the heat. With elimination of carbon and close approach to purity, the fusion point of the charge becomes raised from about 1200°C to 1500°C. The furnace temperature, high enough to melt down the pig iron and keep the charge molten during the greater part of the time of refining, is not sufficiently high to fuse the refined product, and it solidifies to a pasty mass, which can be worked into balls of a weight of a couple of hundred pounds. These balls are removed from the furnace dripping with slag, which is fluid at the finishing temperature. This fluid slag is largely removed by an eccentric roller squeezer, and the bloom thus formed is rolled into flat "muck bars" about ¾ by 3 in. to 6 in. in cross section.

The results of the conversion operation are shown in Table C.

TABLE C

	C	Si	S	P	Mn
Pig iron.............	3.5 –4.25	1–2	0.03–0.10	0.50–1.00	0.25–1.00
Wrought iron........	0.02–0.10	0.10–0.20	0.01–0.06	0.05–0.20	Tr.–0.10

Considerable of the silicon, phosphorus, and manganese in the wrought iron is associated with the 2 to 3 per cent of occluded slag which is not removed in the squeezer. The slag contains 60 to 80 per cent of the oxides of iron, 15 to 30 per cent of silica, together with the oxides of manganese and phosphorus.

Further density and homogeneity are imparted to the iron by hot rolling of the muck bars. Thus *refined bar iron* is made by cutting muck bars into equal lengths, stacking them parallel in rectangular piles, binding with wire, and rolling to size. Scrap bars of wrought iron of length equal to the muck bars may also be included within the pile, but no steel is permitted. *Double-refined iron* is made entirely of muck bars which are twice piled and rerolled with all bars in the final pile of length equal to the pile. In plates and sheets the ductility and strength in the transverse and longitudinal directions can be made more uniform by rolling in both directions. The methods of rolling wrought-iron shapes are similar to those given in Chapter XX.

Aston's Process for making wrought iron, put into operation at the A. M. Byers Co. plant in 1930, is a less expensive method of producing high-grade wrought iron than the puddling process. In this process pig iron is continuously melted in cupolas and tapped into ladles, where it is desulfurized. It is then purified in a Bessemer converter and poured at a controlled rate into a ladle containing an iron silicate slag. The slag is made in an open-hearth furnace from iron oxide and siliceous materials. Owing to the lower temperature of the slag, the iron is rapidly solidified into pasty particles and also freed of gases. The particles agglomerate in the bottom of the ladle into a 3- or 4-ton sponge ball impregnated with slag. The sponge ball is then squeezed in a press which ejects the excess slag and welds the ball into a bloom. Subsequently the bloom is rolled into desired shapes.

5. Kinds of Wrought Iron and Their Uses. In addition to the types of pure wrought iron previously mentioned there are some that may contain additions of steel scrap and some that contain alloys. *Fagoted iron* is hot rolled from box piles, the outsides of which are formed from muck bars or soft-steel plates and the interior of scrap wrought iron or soft steel. *Busheled iron* is made in much the same way as muck-bar iron excepting that the metal charges is wrought-iron scrap, steel scrap, or a mixture of both. *Alloy wrought iron* may contain nickel, molybdenum, or copper, or combinations of these elements. Additions of nickel up to $3\frac{1}{2}$ per cent will increase substantially the elastic limit and tensile strength. Copper may be added to increase the corrosion-resistant properties.

Because of its desirable qualities wrought iron is in considerable demand for blacksmith stock, welded pipe, tubing and casing, roofing sheets, crane chain, staybolt iron, and as a base for certain high-grade tool steels.

STEEL MAKING

6. Classes of Processes. The prominent present-day steel-making processes are as follows:

Bessemer or pneumatic $\begin{cases} \text{Acid} \\ \text{Basic or Thomas-Gilchrist} \end{cases}$

Open-hearth or Siemens-Martin $\begin{cases} \text{Acid} \\ \text{Basic} \end{cases}$

Electric furnace

The distinctive difference between Bessemer and open-hearth processes is essentially one of type of apparatus to effect the conversion; the acid and basic methods, adaptable to either type of equipment, differ in the chemical reactions involved, and in the resultant character of refining and elimination which may be effected.

The fundamental difference of acid and basic processes is the type of slag; in the former, slags of acid character, that is, high in SiO_2, or with the silica unsatisfied, are formed. And since any unsatisfied silica in the slag would tend to reach saturation by attacking any bases with which it might come into contact at high temperature, the refractory lining of the furnace is made of acid material (silica, ganister, mica schist, etc.) to prevent scouring. With acid slags there is no absorption and holding of phosphorus which might tend to be oxidized during refining. The acid process will not eliminate phosphorus.

The basic process provides basic slags, usually by lime additions in sufficient quantity to more than satisfy the silica and to have the basic constituents predominate. This can only be insured by lining the furnace with basic refractories (magnesite, dolomite, etc.) since any excess base would tend to neutralize itself by scouring an acid lining with which it might come in contact at high temperature. With excess of lime in the slag, phosphorus after oxidation to P_2O_5 unites with such lime to form the stable phosphate $3CaO \cdot P_2O_5$, which in turn is absorbed by the slag. The basic process will eliminate phosphorus; likewise by proper conditions of working, there is a slight oxidation of sulfur, and some further elimination as calcium sulfide.

The Bessemer Process

7. Principle of the Process. The Bessemer process was introduced in 1856. It depends upon the essential principle of sufficiently rapid oxidation of the elements—Si, Mn, and C—which it is desired to remove from the iron, to keep an initially molten bath fluid throughout the whole of the refining operation, and deliver a molten product. In such a case, because of lack of mutual solubility and differences of specific gravity, the slag separates from the steel by flotation, and the steel (unlike wrought iron) is free from this constituent.

8. The Converter. A cross section of the Bessemer vessel is shown in Fig. 2. It consists of a steel shell in three detachable sections—bottom, body, and nose. The body section is cylindrical; the nose tapers to a relatively small opening, in order to conserve heat, prevent excessive ejection of metal and slag, and to provide for proper handling of metal in charging and pouring. The nose section may be concentric with the body axis, or set eccentrically. The several sections are held together by means of stirrups and wedges, in order that they may be readily separated in spite of heat and slag accumulations. The shell is supported on trunnions, one of which is hollow to allow of the blast being kept on regardless of the position of the converter. A pipe leads from the hollow trunnion to the wind box at the bottom of the vessel. The converter is tilted by means of a pinion mounted on the trunnion, and rotated by a hydraulically operated rack.

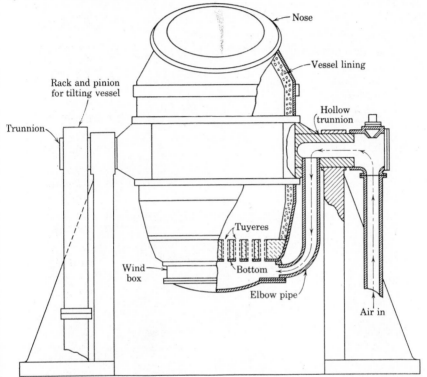

Fig. 2.   A Bessemer converter.   (From *The Making, Shaping and Treating of Steel*, 6th Ed., U. S. Steel Corp.)

Bessemer vessels are built in sizes from ½ ton to 30 tons capacity per heat; in general 10 to 30 tons represents the customary steel works size. In acid working, the body and nose are lined with a 12-in. thickness of rammed ganister, or blocks of mica schist or other siliceous material. The bottom section is a pan, with rammed silica lining about 2 ft thick. In this bottom are set 15 or 20 silica refractory tuyeres, each provided with a dozen or more holes from ½ to ⅝ in. in diameter. A clay joint is made in keying the bottom to the body, to prevent leakage of metal. The body lining lasts for 10,000 to 20,000 heats, or a period of several months. The bottom is worn away in 20 to 25 blows, or a period of 5 or 6 hours. This is due to the fluxing action of the iron oxide formed at the bottom immediately upon entrance of air through the tuyeres. Facilities are provided for rapid change of bottoms. Figure 3 shows the method of charging and operating a converter.

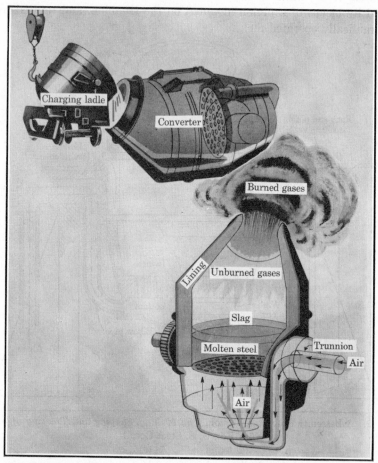

Fig. 3. Operation of a Bessemer converter. (American Iron and Steel Inst.)

9. The Acid Bessemer Process. The charge for the converter must be molten. The pig iron may be melted in cupolas, but is now usually brought in ladle cars from large mixers or reservoirs of 200 to 600 tons capacity, the mixer in turn taking its hot metal from the blast furnace. In this way there is no confusion or delay in working because of the large casts of the blast furnace at 6-hour intervals, and the relatively small charge requirements of the converter at 15-minute intervals. Also, irregularities of composition of the different blast-furnace casts are equalized for the

Bessemer heats. In charging, the converter is tilted to a horizontal position, and the hot metal charge poured in; the blast is then put on, the vessel turned upright, and the heat blown. The blast pressure is about 20 to 25 psi in bottom blowing, and the metal is kept out of the small tuyere openings by this pressure.

The time of blowing is about 12 minutes; for the first few minutes silicon and manganese are chiefly oxidized, and form slag. During this interval there are iron sparks and slag ejections, but no real flame. Then carbon begins to oxidize in the converter to carbon monoxide, and burns at the nose of the vessel to carbon dioxide with a flame which increases in intensity, and is accompanied by the roaring boil of the bath as the gases go through it and agitate it. After several minutes, the flame flickers and drops, a sign to the blower that the carbon is practically burnt out of the bath. With the drop of the flame, the converter is turned down, the blast is cut off, and the metal is cast after the proper additions have been made.

In American practice, the blow is continued until practically all the silicon, manganese, and carbon of the bath have been eliminated. During the interval, iron oxide is formed, and, in the absence of the above elements, there is no chance for its reduction to metallic iron at the end of the blow, and a small proportion remains dissolved in the iron of the bath. Also, there is saturation of the bath in dissolved gases. A heat poured in this condition would result in rotten steel unsuitable for rolling or forging. The remedy is deoxidation with ferrosilicon and manganese alloy (ferromanganese or spiegeleisen) added while teeming the steel into the pouring ladle. The silicon and manganese rob the iron of its oxygen, and separate as oxides (insoluble in the bath of steel) into the slag. The manganese, also, if in sufficient quantity, unites with sulfur to form manganese sulfide (MnS), which remains in the ingot but in a form less conducive to red shortness or brittleness at a red heat than that resulting from iron sulfide. Final "killing" or quieting of the heat is effected by treatment with small amounts of aluminum thrown into the ingot mold during casting. The manganese alloys, which carry several per cent of carbon, serve also as recarburizers to bring the carbon content of the steel to the amount required by the specifications for varying character of service. The extent of conversion is about as shown in Table D.

TABLE D

	C	Si	S	P	Mn
Pig iron	3.5 –4	1–1.25	0.05	0.09	0.50–1.75
Steel	0.10–0.60	0.05–0.20	0.05	0.10	0.30–0.50

The silicon and manganese values in the steel are the amounts of these elements remaining alloyed with the iron, in excess of the requirements for deoxidation. Carbon is added to the limits of specifications; sulfur and phosphorus are not removed during conversion, and are in the steel in greater amount than in the pig-iron charge, because of concentration due to the conversion loss during blowing.

The carbon in the pig iron is in fairly constant amount as it comes from the blast furnace; the manganese content is largely a characteristic of the iron ore used. Silicon, being the essential fuel in converting, is held to close limits; below 1 per cent there is liability of cold heats, while with rapid and efficient blowing a silicon content much in excess of this amount only tends to prolong the heat and introduce difficulties through too high temperature during the blow.

During the heat there is a conversion loss of 8 to 10 per cent; 5 to 6 being accounted for by the silicon, manganese, and carbon removed; the remainder consists of a loss of iron, some because of sparks and splashing, but principally as iron oxide taken up by the slag to supply its deficiency in basic constituents. The amount thus required varies with the quantity of metalloids removed from the bath, with the composition of the slag, and with the amount of scouring of the bottom. No slag-forming constituents are added during the heat. The quantity of slag formed is about 150 lb per ton of steel made, and has a composition approximately SiO_2, 50–70 per cent, FeO, 10–25 per cent, MnO, 10–30 per cent.

10. The Basic Bessemer Process. The basic process was adapted to Bessemer working in 1876 by Sydney Thomas and Thomas Gilchrist. In basic Bessemer practice the vessel is the same as that used for acid working except for the lining of dolomite or magnesite to resist scouring by the basic slag. This lining is rammed into place with a tar binder. Phosphorus removal is effected during the blow by oxidation to the pentoxide (P_2O_5) and subsequent formation of calcium phosphate $3CaO \cdot P_2O_5$, which becomes a constituent of the slag. The necessary lime is added to the converter before and during the heat. Silicon, manganese, carbon, and phosphorus are eliminated in about the order named, and the period of blow is from 15 to 20 minutes.

Typical conversion is as shown in Table E.

TABLE E

	C	Si	S	P	Mn
Pig iron..........	3.5 –4	0.5–1.0	0.05	2–3	1–1.5
Steel.............	0.10–0.60	0.20	0.04	0.05–0.10	0.30–0.50

The necessary heat is obtained during the blow from the oxidation of the silicon, manganese, carbon, and phosphorus. The silicon, however, must be kept low, because of its acidity and the increased lime needed to flux it. The deficiency in heat value thus resulting, together with the extra amount required to bring the high lime additions to slag fusion temperatures and to supply the increased radiation losses during a longer period of blow, are supplied by the phosphorus. The suitable pig iron is therefore one having a phosphorus content of 2 to 3 per cent, and is obtained from the ores of special districts, notably in Germany. Basic Bessemer working is not practical in the United States, although many of our southern ores are suitable. The conversion losses are from 12 to 17 per cent, about 9 or 10 per cent of which is accounted for by the metalloids eliminated. The slag weight will be 400 to 500 lb per ton of steel, with a percentage composition of SiO_2, 5–15; P_2O_5, 15–20; CaO, 40–45; MgO, 0–10; FeO, 5–20; MnO, 5. Because of their high content in phosphoric acid, basic Bessemer slags have value as a fertilizer after pulverizing.

11. The Tropenas Converter. A modification of the standard bottom-blown converter used in steel works is the side-blown vessel of which the Tropenas converter is a type. The air is introduced through the side of the vessel at the surface of the bath under a pressure of 3 to 5 lb. These converters have a capacity of $\frac{1}{2}$ to 2 tons per heat, and are used chiefly for the manufacture of steel castings, where hot steel free from occluded gases is particularly desirable. The lessened agitation of the bath in side blowing favors the latter, although accompanied by increased conversion loss and time of blowing. By allowing part of the tuyeres to deliver free air above the surface of the bath, the initial carbon monoxide is burned to carbon dioxide, and the full calorific value of each unit of carbon (C to CO_2 gives 97,200 calories against 29,160 produced in burning C to CO) is utilized within the body of the converter and the temperature of the bath raised thereby. The molten metal is obtained from cupolas, and must have a silicon content of 2 per cent or upwards in order that sufficient heat may be generated in the small vessel to maintain fluidity.

THE OPEN-HEARTH PROCESSES

12. Essential Features and the Development of the Processes. The fundamental distinction of the open-hearth process as compared with the Bessemer is the relatively slow rate of oxidation of the impurities; so slow that the heat of reaction is insufficient to keep the bath fluid during conversion, and additional heat from outside sources becomes necessary to insure completion of refining and final fluidity of the steel and slag. Of necessity any coal or coke used as fuel must be in a compartment of the furnace separate from that of the bath, to enable desired oxidation reactions to be carried out. Combustion of coal in a separate grate box will hardly give the high temperature required for fusion of the finished steel, as was noted in discussion of the puddling furnace. The inception of the open-hearth process was marked by the invention of the gas producer by Sir William Siemens in 1862, the utilization of the gas to obtain high temperatures by preheating of the gas and air required for combustion by regeneration, and the development of these principles and their application to the furnace and methods for refining of the steel between the years 1862 and 1868. Siemens' method was the use of all pig-iron charges, with iron ore as the agent to supply the necessary oxygen. About the same time the application by Pierre Martin of the Siemens furnace to the manufacture of steel by dilution of pig iron with scrap, and subsequent refining, caused his name to become identified with the development of the open-hearth process; it is still known in Europe as the Siemens-Martin process.

13. The Open-Hearth Furnace. The modern open-hearth furnace is built in capacities of 15 to 300 tons per charge and may be stationary or tilting, the stationary being the more usual. The smaller sizes are used mainly for the manufacture of steel castings, with usual capacities of 15 to 25 tons. The furnace hearth consists of a shallow steel pan, supported by foundation arches, and lined to a thickness of about 2 ft, with brickwork over which are successive layers of refractory sintered into a continuous bottom. For acid practice, this bottom is made of silica brick and sand; for basic working, of magnesite brick and crushed magnesite or dolomite with tar binder. Figure 4 shows a diagrammatic sketch of a stationary open-hearth furnace. Figure 5 shows a transverse section through an open-hearth plant.

A 60-ton furnace has hearth dimensions of about 40 ft in length by 15 ft wide, with a depth of metal of 18 to 24 in. Length is limited largely by necessity of high and uniform temperature throughout the bath; width by necessity of effective patching of bottom; too great a depth means inefficient treating of a charge which must be heated entirely from the top surface.

The furnace is enclosed on sides and top by walls and a low-hanging arched roof of silica brick, secured by buckstays and tie rods. Above the hearth there is no contact with slag; therefore there is no necessity for using the more expensive and mechanically weaker magnesite bricks, even in basic practice. Charging is done through doors at one side of the furnace; in the middle of the opposite side the bottom slopes to a tapping hole. The level of bath and charging floor is usually at sufficient height above the pouring floor to permit ladles to be set under the tapping spout without the necessity of deep ladle pits. This arrangement also permits

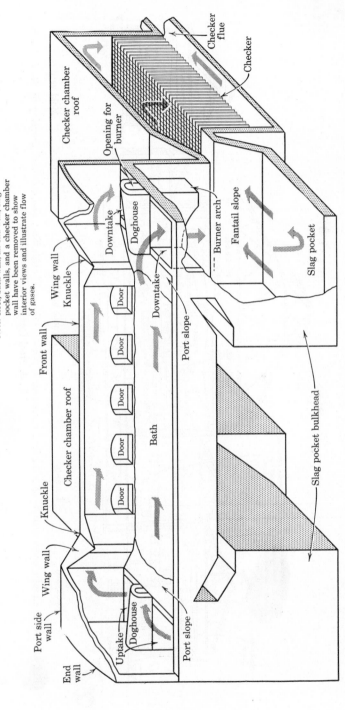

Note: Roof, back wall, an end wall, slag pocket walls, and a checker chamber wall have been removed to show interior views and illustrate flow of gases.

Fig. 4.   Diagrammatic sketch of an open-hearth furnace.   (From *The Making, Shaping and Treating of Steel*, 6th Ed., U. S. Steel Corp.)

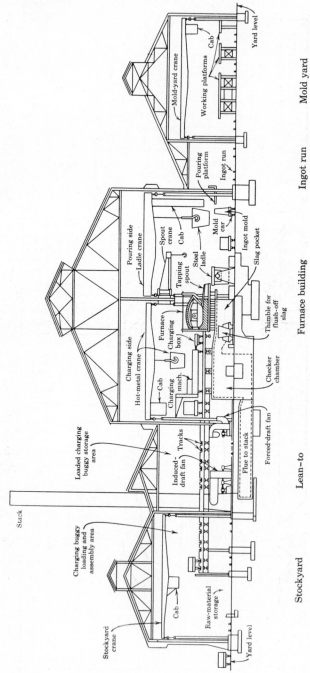

Fig. 5. Diagrammatic cross section of a modern open-hearth plant. (From *The Making, Shaping and Treating of Steel*, 6th Ed., U. S. Steel Corp.)

flues, valves, and regenerators to be placed in accessible positions under the charging platform.

At each end of the furnace are separate uptake flues for the gas and air used for combustion, and ports to direct them into the furnace for proper mixture and combustion. The uptake flues lead into heat-storing or "regenerator" chambers, one each for gas and air at each end of the furnace. These chambers are usually built under the charging floor, and are filled with built-up rows of a checker work of silica brick, so piled as to allow of fairly free passage of the gases, and yet present a large surface of contact for heat absorption and extraction. Between the regenerator chamber and the single stack for each furnace is a set of flues and hydraulically operated valves by which the combustion gases and waste gases can be led to and from either end of the furnace, and reversed periodically as desired. Natural draft is employed.

Producer gas is the customary fuel, although natural gas has played a very important part in American practice, and crude oil, pulverized coal, and tar have been used. For fuels other than producer gas only the air required for combustion is preheated, and no regenerators are required for the fuel. In the use of producer gas, both gas and air are heated prior to combustion. The fuel and air ignite at the ports at one end of the furnace, and burn in their passage over the surface of the bath of metal, escaping at the other end at high temperature, approximately that of the furnace itself. Passing on their way to the stack through the regenerator chambers at that end of the furnace, these hot gases give up a large part of their heat to the brick checker work. This brickwork stores up a large quantity of heat and in an interval of about 20 minutes has attained a high temperature. The direction of flow of gases is now reversed, and combustion is at the opposite end of the furnace hearth. The entering gas and air, passing through the hot regenerator chambers, absorb their stored-up heat, and reach the ports at a temperature of 1000°C. The temperature attained in the furnace is now greater than that due to direct combustion of the fuel and air, by an increment dependent upon the heat stored up in these gases. The waste gases in turn give up their heat to the cooler regenerators at the opposite side of the furnace. The periodic reversals at intervals of 15 to 20 minutes permit the necessary temperature to be maintained. The slag pockets shown in Fig. 4 are used to trap oxides in the form of a fine dust that is carried by the hot gases that have passed over the charge.

14. Conversion by the Open-Hearth Furnace. Usual open-hearth practice is with basic bottoms; in the United States the relatively small tonnage of acid steel is used largely in castings.

The charge may be cold or molten; in the latter case there is some saving of fuel and time. Also, since the success of the process does not depend upon the fuel value of the elements in the burden, the latter may vary widely in composition. Usually the charge is a mixture of pig iron and steel scrap; increase of the scrap effects partial refining of the bath by dilution.

The reactions are virtually the same as in Bessemer working; an oxidation of the silicon, manganese, and carbon; and in basic practice, an elimination of phosphorus by oxidation and union with lime. The rate of reaction is, however, very slow, and heats require from 6 to 12 hours, usually about 10 hours for basic heats of 80 to 100 tons each. The oxidizing agent is iron ore; by interaction the oxygen of the ferric oxide (Fe_2O_3) unites with the metalloids and is eliminated as gas or slag; the liberated iron in turn becomes a part of the bath. With ore additions it is possible, therefore, to practically offset the conversion loss due to elimination of metalloids, and to keep it to 5 per cent or less. Basic open-hearth slags in the United States rarely carry sufficient phosphoric acid to warrant their use as fertilizer; this is due to the moderate phosphorus content (0.20 to 1 per cent) in the charge. Control of the heat is by fracture tests of samples and by chemical analyses of same; the heat is tapped under controllable conditions. Ferromanganese and ferrosilicon additions are made to the ladle on tapping, and aluminum may be thrown into the ingot mold as in Bessemer practice.

After each heat the furnace bottom is patched by shoveling in crushed and calcined dolomite, which frits into place at the working temperature. The lining and bottom are good for 3 to 6 months of service, when shutdown for repairs and rebuilding is necessary.

15. Comparisons of Bessemer and Open-Hearth Processes. Factors of advantage and disadvantage in the Bessemer and open-hearth processes are as follows:

Bessemer	Open Hearth
Rapid conversion—10 to 20 min.	Relatively slow conversion—6 to 12 hours.
Relatively small heats—1 to 30 tons.	Relatively large heats—15 to 300 tons.
Small plant cost per unit of output.	Heavy plant cost per unit of output.
All fuel is in charge.	Extra fuel—50 lb of coal per ton-hour.
Oxygen obtained from blown air.	Oxygen obtained from iron oxide.
Charge must be molten.	Charge may or may not be molten.
Little liberty in composition of charge.	Much liberty in composition of charge.
Control entirely in skill of operator.	Accurate control of product.
Heavy conversion loss—10 to 15 per cent.	Small conversion loss—0 to 5 per cent.
Simplicity of operation.	Operation more complex than Bessemer.
Steel considered to be inferior.	Steel considered to be superior.

About 90 per cent of the steel production in the United States is obtained through the basic open-hearth process, and the remaining 10 per cent chiefly from the acid Bessemer and the electric furnace. Comparative productions in the United States, Germany, and Great Britain are given in Table 1.

TABLE 1.   TONNAGE OF STEEL INGOTS AND CASTINGS PRODUCED BY VARIOUS PROCESSES IN LEADING COUNTRIES

(In Thousands of Long Tons)

	1913			1937			1951
Process	United States	Germany	Great Britain	United States	Germany (Ingots only)	Great Britain	United States
Acid Bessemer	9,546	153	1,049	3,450	....	233	{ 4,370
Basic Bessemer	....	10,460	552	....	7,840		{ ....
Acid open-hearth	1,255	374	3,811	500	225	2,260	700
Basic open-hearth	20,345	7,470	2,252	45,773	10,650	9,677	82,500
Crucible	121	....	....				
Electric furnace				846 [1]	658 [1]	452 [1]	6,370 [1]
and other	34 [1]	....	....				
Total	31,301	....	....	50,569	19,373	12,622	93,940

[1] Principally from electric furnaces.

16. The Decline of the Bessemer Process. In spite of the simplicity of the Bessemer process and its many other features of seeming advantage over the open-hearth method, the former has been steadily forced into the secondary position in this country. This is largely due to the gradual increase in the phosphorus content of available ores; the difficulty of securing ores of Bessemer grade has caused a spread of price between this and grades suited for basic working sufficient to make the open-hearth method economically attractive. In addition there is the advantage of greater yield in conversion, and the better reputation for quality which open-hearth steel holds in the opinion of users. Bessemer steel finds its principal outlet in pipes and tubes, wire and wire rods, plates and sheets, and free-machining steels. Practically all structural steel has for years been of open-hearth grade.

17. The Duplex Process. The dearth of steel scrap required in open-hearth operation, the possibility of conserving existing Bessemer plants and of combining the advantages of converter operation with the elimination of phosphorus are reasons which have led to the successful use of the duplex method at several plants. A heat is blown to virtual elimination of silicon and manganese, and partial removal of carbon. It is then transferred to a basic open-hearth furnace, where the phosphorus is eliminated and the heat slowly finished to the desired quality. In certain plants electric furnaces are being used for the finishing operations in the duplex combination with the Bessemer converter. The duplex method effects a marked saving in the time necessary for treatment in the open-hearth furnace.

OTHER PROCESSES

18. The Electric Furnace. Various types of electric furnaces are used in super-refining steel and in purifying cast iron. In 1945 there were about 700 electric furnaces in the United States and the production of electric steel was approximately 3,500,000 net tons.

Electric furnaces are used in iron foundries to melt iron for castings, or to take the molten iron from a cupola and keep it at the desired temperature while the composition is adjusted by means of various additions. Furnaces with an acid lining are widely used in steel foundries to melt high-quality steel for castings. Basic-lined furnaces are usual for making high-grade steel ingots from either solid or molten metal. The solid metal charge consisting of carefully selected steel scrap is melted and may be refined under a reducing slag or by a combination of an initial oxidizing and a final reducing slag. The molten metal charge may come from the basic open-hearth furnace or from the Bessemer converter.

The two types of electric furnaces used are the arc-resistance (Heroult) type in which the current arcs from the positive electrode to bath and then arcs or is conducted from the bath to negative electrodes; and the high-frequency induction type in which the bath of metal forms the closed secondary circuit in a step-down transformer. Three-phase alternating current is generally used in these furnaces.

Heroult furnaces have nominal capacities of from 1 to 100 tons with transformer capacities varying between 1000 and 24,000 kva. On account of its efficiency and adaptability the Heroult furnace is used more than any other electric furnace for refining steel. Figure 6 shows a schematic cross section of a Heroult electric arc furnace with a typical acid lining (left) and basic lining (right). In the larger furnaces three-phase current is used and three electrodes made of graphite or amorphous carbon are set over the bath on the apices of an equilateral triangle. The time required for refinement of the metal depends on many factors but is about 1 to $1\frac{1}{2}$ hours when molten metal is charged and about three to four times as long when cold metal is charged.

The high-frequency induction furnaces have capacities ranging between $\frac{1}{2}$ to 5 tons. In these furnaces the solid charge is placed in refractory crucibles that are surrounded by water-cooled electric conductors carrying a high-frequency alternating current. Frequencies used vary between 500 and 60,000 cycles per sec, but a value of about 1000 cycles per sec is considered most practical in steel production. As the high-frequency current passes through the conductor a secondary current in the charge is generated by electromagnetic induction and causes the charge to melt.

About 1 hour is required to melt the smaller charges and 1½ hours to melt the larger charges.

The principal advantages of the electric furnace in melting iron or steel are: (1) rapidly available heat; (2) the possibility of securing any desired temperature, thus providing a means of removing impurities and occluded gases without perturbation of the bath; (3) no contamination of charge

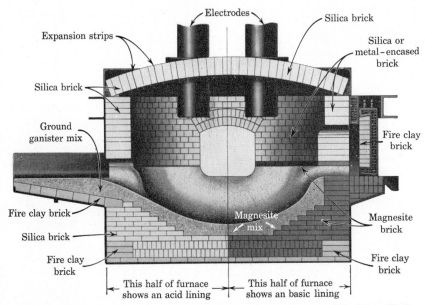

Fig. 6.   Schematic cross section of a Heroult electric arc furnace. (Harbison-Walker Refractories Co.)

as may be the case with other fuels; and (4) excellent control. The basic-lined Heroult furnace is adapted to double refining of the charge under oxidizing or reducing slags. In the usual procedure the charge is melted and refined under an oxidizing slag; then the slag is removed and a reducing slag is added under which refinement is completed. Under these conditions the amounts of phosphorus, sulfur, and oxygen can be almost eliminated. Also, very small or no losses of alloying elements are sustained in the production of alloy steels.

The many advantages of the electric furnace are offset to some extent by the higher cost of electricity as a source of heat energy over the usual fuels such as coal, fuel oil, and gas. The cost of electricity for operating the larger Heroult electric furnace is about two to three times the cost of fuel for the open-hearth furnace under comparable conditions.

The electric furnace produces only about 5 per cent of the total tonnage of steel made in the United States, but its importance is far greater than the tonnage indicates. The electric furnace produces nearly all the stainless constructional alloy steel and special alloy steels used in the chemical, automotive, aviation, machine-tool, and food-processing industries.

19. Minor Processes Used in Making Steel. The cementation process was the only known method of making steel until A.D. 1500. The process is still used in England for making cutlery and tools but has never found favor in America. The well-established fact that wrought iron packed in charcoal and heated to a bright red will absorb carbon and form a solid solution with it is the basic principle of the process.

The crucible process was invented in A.D. 1740 by Daniel Huntsman of Sheffield, England. The process consists in melting wrought iron together with charcoal and a little ferromanganese in a small barrel-shaped vessel called a crucible. In America, steel scrap occasionally forms a portion of the charge and ferrosilicon is added just before drawing the crucibles. For very superior grades of steel Sheffield makers charge cementation steel instead of wrought iron. Various alloy steels are also made by this process. Thus ferrochromium and ferrotungsten are added to the charge in making chrome and tungsten steels, respectively.

CHAPTER

XX

Manufacture of Iron and Steel Shapes

1. Essentials in the Production of Shapes. Iron and steel finds outlet in engineering construction in shapes produced either by casting or some form of mechanical working. In the former operation, the metal is melted and poured into molds made in sand or other suitable refractory substance; fluidity of metal is necessary, and it may be cast iron, steel, or malleable cast iron. Mechanical working of the metal, however, results in improved physical quality, and, where this is essential, the required shape is produced by forging or rolling. For the latter operations malleability, at least while hot, is essential, and consequently cast iron is not suitable. Intricate or special shapes are produced by direct forging; or, where numerous pieces of the same form are required, by drop forging with dies. By far the greatest tonnage of shapes required in engineering construction is of certain standard sections, uniform in cross section throughout a length which is, in general, relatively much greater than the cross section. Rolling mills can produce such shapes in quantity at a speed much greater and a cost much lower than any method of forging or casting.

2. Ingots. Steel intended for rolling or forging is cast into ingots. These vary in shape and size, but in rolling-mill practice are usually square or rectangular in cross section. Common cross-sectional dimensions vary between 15 and 35 in., and the length varies between 5 and 8 ft. The molds are made of cast iron and are usually from 3 to 5 in. thick. The big-end-down mold is the most widely used because of its economy, but the big-end-up hot-top mold is becoming more important because of the superior quality of its product. The big-end-down ingot mold is set upon end on an iron bottom plate, either stationary upon the casting floor, or on cars to enable prompt removal of the ingots after pouring. The mold has a gradual taper in cross section from bottom to top, to facilitate freeing of the ingot. Steel is poured into the open top of the ingot mold from a large ladle, with nozzle and stopper at the bottom, and is handled by a crane. When the steel has solidified sufficiently, the mold is stripped from the ingot by lifting the mold; or in case of sticking, by forcing downwards upon the ingot with a plunger at the same time that the ingot mold is lifted. A better but more expensive method of casting ingots by bottom pouring is shown in Fig. 1.

In the big-end-down molds freezing progresses inward from the sides and faster from the top than from the bottom surface, resulting in a large and deep central shrinkage cavity in the ingot, called a pipe. In order to decrease the depth of the pipe some ingots are cast in big-end-up molds as in Fig. 1. Progressive freezing in these molds takes place up from the

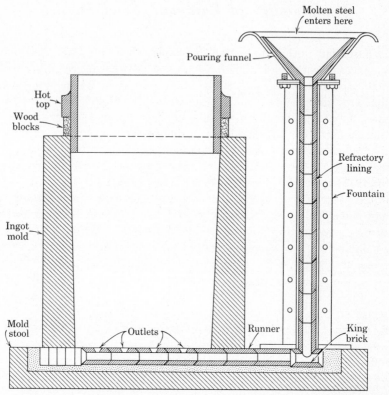

Fig. 1. Mold assembly for bottom pouring. (From *The Making, Shaping and Treating of Steel,* 6th Ed., U. S. Steel Corp.)

bottom and in from the sides because of the smaller volume of metal near the bottom and because these molds have thicker bottom walls. The depth of the cavity may be further decreased and a better-quality ingot obtained by using a refractory hot top with the big-end-up mold. The metal in the hot top is the last to solidify and consequently contains a large amount of the impurities and most of the shrinkage cavity. These ingots are removed from the molds by means of tongs that are applied to the hot-top section.

The following defects are present to some degree in all ingots: *pipes, blow-holes, segregation, slag,* and *ingotism.* Blow-holes result from entrapped gases and from the solidification of certain impurities which shrink more than the iron in cooling. Segregation of the impurities is caused by the rejection of impurities by the exterior as it solidifies and also by the differences in density, the impurities being lighter than iron. These defects are idealized in Fig. 2. Slow cooling of an ingot from a very high temperature causes ingotism, a very coarse crystalline structure. Removal of the head of the pipe, most of the slag, and much of the segregated metal can be made by cutting off, or "cropping," the upper portion of the ingot. The undesirable effects of blow-holes and ingotism can be greatly reduced by proper heat and mechanical treatment. Surface defects such as slivers due to tears, scabs due to the solidification and oxidation of metal splashes on the mold wall, and cracks due to improper molding conditions are not usually serious and can be easily detected and chipped out.

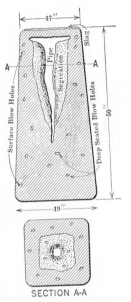

Fig. 2. Defects in ingots.

Plain-carbon steels produced as previously described are known as rimmed steels, semi-killed steels, or killed steels, according to the amount of gas evolved during solidification. *Rimmed* steels are only partially deoxidized low-carbon steels that evolve a considerable amount of gas during solidification. In this process a solid rim of clean metal is rapidly formed next to the mold while the core which solidifies more slowly is porous and has segregated impurities. This type of steel is used where an excellent surface of the finished product is desired and is widely used for deep drawing. *Semi-killed* steels are deoxidized more completely than rimmed steels but still give off a small amount of gas during solidification. Structural steels containing less than 0.25 per cent carbon are generally treated in this manner. *Killed* steels are deoxidized by such materials as ferrosilicon and aluminum to the point where there is no evolution of gas and the molten metal remains quiet in the mold. Most steels containing more than 0.25 per cent carbon are treated in this manner.

3. Heat Treatment of Ingots. Rolling or forging of the ingot immediately after stripping is not satisfactory. If the outside is at proper temperature, the inside is so hot that the fluid interior is likely to squirt out when pressure is applied; if the interior is at rolling temperature, the exterior is too cold.

A uniform temperature of the proper degree is obtained by inserting the ingots in soaking pits and holding them there until required for rolling.

These pits are gas-fired furnaces equipped with regenerators for conserving the heat of the waste gases. This procedure also provides a regular supply of ingots to satisfy the continuous requirements of the mill, despite the intermittent delivery of the furnace; and no confusion, in case of accident or delay at either mill or furnace, will result.

4. General Method of Rolling Shapes.* When an ingot is inserted between two revolving rolls it is drawn through them in the direction of rotation, and at the same time there is downward and upward pressure upon the metal, and a pull in the direction of travel, which results in a reduction of thickness, a slight increase in width, and a material increase

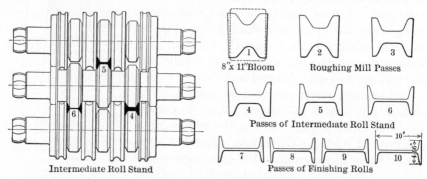

Fig. 3. Typical roll passes in forming a 10-in. I-beam. (Illinois Steel Co.)

in length. A pair of simple rolls would in a single pass reduce an originally square bar to a rectangular one of even thickness equal to that of the distance between the rolls; the width, on the other hand, is slightly greater than the original, and of somewhat irregular and bulging outline, due to the downward pressure without side restraint. By a second pass through the same rolls, this time edge on, a square bar is obtained of dimensions equal to the distance between rolls, and of increased length in proportion to the amount of reduction of original section. By successive passes through rolls of varying distances of separation, or by adjusting the center distance of a single pair of rolls, and by quarter turning, or edging the piece as required, a square or rectangular bar of uniform cross section may be rapidly produced.

Or, the same result may be obtained in rolls of fixed center distance, which have grooves turned in their surfaces of proper dimensions for the successive reductions. Again, by varying the character of the grooves, a wide variety of cross sections can be produced. Figure 3 illustrates

* For further study see *Ferrous Metallurgy*, Vol. 2, by E. J. Teichert, and *The Making, Shaping and Treating of Steel*, by J. M. Camp and C. B. Francis, U. S. Steel Corp.

types of rolls used in forming I-beams. It also shows the shapes assumed by a bloom as it is gradually reduced to an I-beam.

5. Rolling Mills. Rolling mills have been developed from the original type with a single pair of rolls, or two-high stand. Such an arrangement has a limited capacity, since succeeding passes are made only by sending the piece back idle over the roll stand, with consequent loss of time and heat. The three-high mill has been adopted for the rolling of most standard shapes. It consists of three rolls with their axes in the same plane, and so driven that, by passing the bar through the lower pair in one direction, and through the upper pair on the return, reduction is obtained in both directions. For sections of great weight requiring very heavy mills with rolls of large diameter, the lift from lower to upper passes becomes impracticable; but rolling in each direction is accomplished by reversal of rotation of the two-high stand after each pass. In rolling rods or other shapes of very great lengths, there is much loss of time and cooling of the piece, even in three-high mills, if each pass is begun only after completion of the preceding one. By looping the rod back through the next pass as soon as the entering end comes through the rolls, several reductions may be effected simultaneously on the same rod, with great saving in time and heat. The capacity of the "looping mill" may be obtained by the "continuous mill." In this case the several stands of two-high rolls are set in tandem, and properly geared to speed up successive passes to take care of the increased length of bar resulting from each reduction. The "universal mill" has a set of small rolls with their axes vertical; by varying the center distances of horizontal and vertical sets of rolls, a great variety of flat sections can be produced without multiplicity of rolls. Four-high mills are used for rolling sheet and strip.

Rolling mills have undergone much development, with resultant increase of output and elimination of hand labor. Heavy material is fed into the rolls by geared roller tables, and these tables in turn are made of the lifting, tilting, or transfer type to raise the bars from lower to upper passes or transfer them to others in different stands of the same mill train. The power required for driving varies from a few hundred to several thousand horsepower; heavy mills are usually driven by direct connection to steam engines, while electric motors have had much application for smaller mills, and especially for auxiliary equipment. The output of mills varies greatly. With light sections such as thin sheets and strips it may be as low as 10 tons per 24 hours; certain mills will produce 4000 tons of billets or rails in the same period.

Most standard sections—rails, I-beams, channels, angles, round and square bars, etc.—are produced in three-high mills with rolls of fixed center distances and grooved to the special shapes.

Ingots are usually rolled into rectangular or square forms known as blooms, having a minimum cross-sectional area of 36 sq in. or billets having a maximum cross-sectional area of 36 sq in. and a minimum cross-sectional dimension of 1½ in.

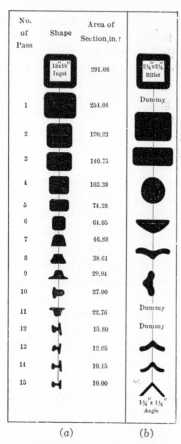

No. of Pass	Shape	Area of Section, in.²
	18"x18" Ingot	291.08
1		254.04
2		190.23
3		140.75
4		103.38
5		74.28
6		64.05
7		46.88
8		38.61
9		29.94
10		27.00
11		22.76
12		15.80
13		12.05
14		10.15
15		10.00

(a)   (b)

Fig. 4. Changes of shape in rolling (a) a 100-lb rail; (b) a 1¼ × 1¼-in. angle. (*Iron Age*, Vol. 92, pp. 968 and 1037.)

The successive passes through the rolls from ingot or billet to finished section are given in Fig. 4 for typical shapes. In the design of the successive passes, the aim is to effect not only the reduction with maximum speed and efficiency, but at the same time to so shape the grooves or turn the bar that work will be done uniformly upon all sides of the piece. Speeds of travel through the rolls range from 60 ft per min for ingots to 600 ft per min in the finishing pass.

Specialized lines of manufacture include plates, sheets, pipe, and wire.

6. Plates. Plates are flat-rolled products at least ¼ in. thick when the width is 6 to 48 in. and at least 3/16 in. thick when the width exceeds 48 in. Plates are rolled from slabs which are more than twice as wide as they are thick. The slabs are heated before rolling in gas- or oil-fired furnaces. Some plates are rolled on universal mills and are produced with the required thickness and width. Other plates are rolled on three-high mills and after reduction to the required thickness are straightened, cooled, and sheared to the correct width and length. Rolled plates may be obtained up to 14 in. in thickness and up to 204 in. in width. Maximum lengths are available up to 125 ft, depending on other dimensions.

7. Sheet and Strip. Thin, flat, rolled pieces of steel usually under ¼ in. thick and more than 12 in. wide are called sheet, and pieces less than 12 in. wide are called strip. Steel for sheet and strip production is first rolled into slabs that may range up to 8 in. in thickness, 64 in. in width, and 216 in. in length. The slabs are reheated to temperatures between 2000° and 2400°F and are then sent through a scale-breaker two-high mill, after which they are subjected to a descaling water spray. Then the slabs are sent through four roughing stands, each of which is a four-high mill. After the front and back ends of the material are sheared, it is sent through a second scale-breaking mill and descaling water spray. The material is then sent through 6 four-high finishing mills. Finally, the rolled product is coiled or sheared to required length. The speed of the steel in a continuous strip mill may be as high as 2400 ft per min, depending on the thickness of the finished product. Rolling of slabs 5 in. thick, 30 in. wide, and 210 in. long to strip $\frac{1}{16}$ in. thick and 1400 ft long takes about 3 min.

8. Pipes. Pipes or tubes may be seamless, electric welded, lap welded, or butt welded. Seamless tubes are made by piercing a round billet while it is being distorted by a set of special skew rolls; or by gradually pressing a plate into a closed end cup or tube. These hollow billets are drawn (hot or cold) to size over a mandrel and through dies. The principal outlet is for boiler tubes, standard pipe, line pipe, casing, drill pipe, mechanical tubing, etc., where maximum strength and lightness are desired.

Lap-welded tubes are made from skelp, a flat strip rolled to proper thickness and of a width equal to the circumference of the pipe plus the lap, Fig. 5. The edges of the skelp are slightly beveled or scarfed to prevent too great an excess of metal at the lap. Up to 12 in. in diameter, bending to circular form is done by drawing the heated skelp through a bell-mouthed die; larger sizes are formed by putting the plate sidewise through a set of three bending rolls. The formed pipe is then heated to welding temperature and passed through a pair of rolls with grooves, corresponding to the outside diameter of the pipe. The roll pressure is resisted by a mandrel or ball on the inside of the pipe, which is mounted between the rolls and on the end of a long rod. The pipe is then sized in grooved rolls and finished and straightened with a pair of skew rolls. Lap-welded pipe is used for boiler tubes and for steam and hydraulic piping to withstand high pressure and is made in diameters $1\frac{1}{4}$ to 30 in.

Butt-welded pipe is made from skelp which is welded along the butt joint without lap. The strips are heated to welding temperature, then drawn from the furnace through a bell-mouthed die, Fig. 5, which curls the strip to a circular form and forces the edges together with sufficient

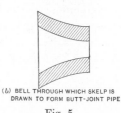

(1) SKELP WITH SCARFED EDGES

(2) SKELP ROUGHLY FORMED INTO PIPE

(3) WELDING BY ROLLING

Roll

Mandrel

Pipe

Roll

(a) WELDING LAP-JOINT PIPE

(b) BELL THROUGH WHICH SKELP IS DRAWN TO FORM BUTT-JOINT PIPE

Fig. 5.

pressure to effect a continuous weld. The pipe is finished by being passed through a pair of grooved sizing rolls. Butt-welded pipe is made in sizes from ⅛ to 4 in. in diameter; it is used for gas and water pipe and miscellaneous purposes where not subjected to great pressure.

9. Wire. Rods are rolled in looping or continuous mills to about ¼ or ⅜ in. in diameter, coiled into bundles, and pickled in acid to remove scale. Further reduction is effected by cold drawing through dies of high-carbon steel. The drawbench consists of the drawplate and a power reel for pulling the wire through and coiling. Successive reductions may be made on individual benches; or by multiple drawing, in which case the coil is reeled only after reduction in several dies. A power reel is provided between each pair of plates around which the wire is given a couple of turns. After several reductions the wire becomes hard and brittle because of overstrain, and must be annealed before drawing can be continued. Speed of drawing is from 75 to 750 ft per min, depending on size and hardness of wire; reduction is from 20 to 25 per cent per hole.

10. Forging and Pressing. Whereas it is only possible to roll members of uniform cross section and for every change in cross section it is necessary to provide a special set of rolls, forging provides a means of securing fine-grained, strong and tough parts of almost any required design. Forging requires little expense for special tool equipment but, on the other hand, on account of the length of time consumed does entail a much heavier fuel and labor charge than rolling. Since in forging the part is more completely under the control of the operator it is possible to finish it at just the right heat and to diminish the intensity of the blows in a manner suited to securing a fine-grained product. The effect of the hammer blow, however, is not deep seated; consequently the process is best adapted to sections under 2 or 3 in. in thickness.

Small forgings may be made directly from ingots or from rolled bars. Ingots for small forgings are usually square or rectangular in form, those for large parts are cast in hexagonal sections with fluted surfaces. The latter type of ingot is less likely to crack in cooling than a square section. After cropping the remainder of the ingot is brought to a light red heat in a non-oxidizing flame and taken to the forge. Since the interior of a large ingot is often under high tensile stress due to cooling strains, reheating must be done at a very slow rate in order to avoid cracking. Often, with ingots weighing many tons, 1 or 2 days is required for reheating.

When the parts are of small size and the required number is small, reduction of the ingot or bar is accomplished by the hand hammer or sledge on the smith's anvil. If a large number of small parts are wanted, *drop forgings* are made. They are formed between dies which are attached to the anvil and head of a steam hammer. In shaping intricate parts approach to final form is gradually made through the use of a number of sets of dies. Drop forgings are very commonly used in making various types of levers, wrenches, small connecting rods and crank shafts. They are superior to steel castings in quality on account of the mechanical work done upon them; but, unless large quantities are wanted, they are more expensive due to high cost of dies.

Large forgings are reduced from the ingot under double-acting steam hammers which range in capacity up to 30 or 40 tons and are capable of striking 100 to 300 blows per minute. The ingot is clamped to a very heavy bar, called a porter bar, which is slung in an endless chain in such a manner that the forging may be pushed backward or forward under the hammer, or rotated as desired. In making heavy shafting it is good practice to bore out the central portion of the ingot before reheating, thus rendering it easier to heat and reducing the probability of cracking. When the ingot is forged, a long bar fitted with a head like a torpedo, called a mandrel, is thrust into the hole and kept under the hammer. As the ingot is revolved and hammered on the outside the mandrel acts as an anvil on the interior. In this manner the metal of the hollow section is rendered much more compact and uniform in structure and properties than is possible with a solid section. Forging is usually stopped when the color becomes a dull red. If further forging is required the part is again reheated to a bright red.

Pressing. Armor plate, cannon tubes, heavy shafting, and other thick heavy masses of steel requiring mechanical treatment are most effectively worked under heavy hydraulic presses. The action of the press is much deeper than that of the steam hammer or the rolling mill. Furthermore, the press effects a reduction in size of large parts more quickly than the steam hammer. Presses range in capacity from 500 to 14,000 tons and are operated under pressures of 800 to 8000 psi.

Stamping. In this process relatively thin metal blanks are forced to take the outline of a die by mechanical or hydraulic presses. Stamping presses are used for making such articles as coins, key blanks, builders' hardware, bottle tops, brass novelties, rivets, washers, and gear blanks. Stamping is also widely used in the manufacture of automobile fenders and bodies. In this low-cost continuous operation the steel is worked until it strain hardens almost to the breaking point before it is annealed.

11. Casting Steel. Steel castings are most effectively used for intricate parts which cannot be rolled or forged and which must possess high strength and toughness; also when the required number of parts is small and the cost of equipment prohibits rolling or forging. With proper care in manufacture, castings can be made having strength equal to the rolled or forged product but somewhat inferior in ductility and toughness.

Steel castings are made from metal smelted by the crucible, Bessemer, open-hearth or electric-furnace process. For small- and medium-size castings of the very best grade, the electric furnace, or the electric furnace in conjunction with an acid Bessemer converter or basic open-hearth furnace, is superior to all other processes. It is, however, less adaptable to a wide variety of work than the crucible process, which is commonly used for very small castings of all grades and qualities. For the production of very large castings and for obtaining a large tonnage of standardized castings of medium size with continuous operation, the acid open-hearth furnace is very efficient and turns out an excellent product. The basic open-hearth process shares the same field of production, but makes castings somewhat inferior in quality and less costly than those from the acid open hearth. For intermittent operation and a variable tonnage demand, the acid Bessemer process is well adapted. Baby converters of the Tropenas type are often used where the output is small. The quality of acid Bessemer castings is in general inferior to that which can be obtained from the other processes.

Patterns for steel castings are commonly designed with an allowance of ¼ in. per ft for shrinkage. The castings are formed in green sand or dry sand molds which are made in much the same way as those used for cast iron. With steel castings, however, a good deal of care must be exercised to properly vent both molds and cores, to provide adequate gates for rapid filling of the mold, and to install a sufficiency of properly placed risers in order that the interior of heavy sections may be kept full of hot metal until the whole is frozen. Chills are sometimes used to hasten solidification during pouring and reduce blow-holes.

Steel may also be cast by various modifications of the centrifugal casting method. The molten steel may be poured into a metal die or sand-lined metal form that rotates about its axis, or it may be poured into a feed gate at the center of rotation from which it is forced into the mold cavities.

Owing to the great shrinkage of steel in cooling, intricate castings, or those which vary considerably in cross-section, must be separated from the mold as soon as the metal has solidified in order to prevent cracking. After the castings have been cooled slowly under sand or in a heated furnace the sprues are broken or cut off and the surfaces are freed from sand.

Steel castings which are to be subjected to heavy stresses should always be annealed at a temperature above the upper critical point (Art. XXV-8). Annealing not only removes internal shrinkage stresses but also refines the grain and renders the casting stronger, tougher, and more ductile. The toughness of castings of uniform section can be considerably increased by quenching in oil and reheating to a temperature just below the critical range.

12. Protective Coatings for Steel Sheet and Strip. Since steel corrodes readily when exposed to weathering, or when used underground or underwater, or when exposed to various acids and salts, it is necessary that sheet, strip, and small objects be coated with some material to prevent or inhibit this undesirable action. Both metallic and non-metallic coatings are used for this purpose.

The more important metals used for coating steel include tin, zinc, terne metal, aluminum, chromium, lead, silicon, copper, nickel, and bronze. These metals may be applied to the steel surface by dipping the steel into a molten bath of the coating material, by impregnating the steel surface with the protective coating, by spraying the protective coating, by cladding, by fusion welding, and by electroplating.

The hot-dip process used to secure coatings of zinc, tin, terne metal, lead, and aluminum is the most widely used. In this process the carefully cleaned steel is immersed in a molten bath of the coating until the desired thickness has been obtained. When zinc is used as the coating material the process is known as galvanizing; when tin is used it is known as tinning. Steel plate dipped into a molten bath consisting of from 12 to 50 per cent tin and 88 to 50 per cent lead is known as terne plate. Impregnation of the steel surface with aluminum, silicon, chromium, or zinc is accomplished by heating the steel and the necessary coating materials in intimate contact to high temperatures dependent on the process and coating used. Spray coatings are usually applied by melting and atomizing the coating metal, in wire form, by an oxyacetylene flame, and by projecting the atomized metal at high speed by means of compressed air against the steel surface. Copper-clad steels are made by heating the steel in a closed container, from which air has been excluded, to a temperature slightly higher than the melting point of copper, casting the molten copper around the steel, and then hot rolling the product. Aluminum-clad steels are made by placing the clean steel sheet between two sheets of aluminum, hot rolling the three sheets, and annealing. Nickel and nickel alloys are also used as cladding metals. Gas welding, metal-arc welding, or atomic hydrogen arc-welding may be used to deposit satisfactory weld metals onto the steel surface. Among the many metals that may be used to provide coatings for steel by the electroplating process are nickel, chromium, copper, tin, lead, silver, zinc, and cadmium.

Rust-preventive compounds that provide barriers to moisture are used to protect steel. Some of the more important of these are paints, lacquers, varnishes, enamels, petroleum greases and oils, and phosphate coatings. Vitreous enamels fused to properly prepared steel surface are also used to protect steel.

13. Powder Metallurgy. The production of metallic objects from metal powders that are compressed and heated (sintered) is another metal-forming process that is important under certain conditions. It is used in the production of parts made with refractory (heat-resistant) metals such as tungsten and molybdenum, parts made of very hard materials such as the cemented carbides, porous metallic parts which may have non-metallic additions or that may be oil impregnated, machine parts, clad parts, and electrical and magnetic parts. This method is used where certain desired properties cannot be obtained by other methods and to eliminate machining operations.

Most of the metal powders required for the process are made by the oxide reduction process, atomization, electrodeposition, and various milling methods. The particles are angular, irregular, or spherical in shape, usually vary in size between the No. 8 and No. 325 sieves, and may be graded to obtain satisfactory size distributions. The powders are then mixed to obtain a homogeneous material, during which time alloying powders, lubricants, and volatilizing agents may be added. Compression of the mixed powders is usually carried out at room temperatures in mechanical or hydraulic presses that have maximum capacities between 10 and 1000 tons. Compacting pressures may range between 10 and 100 psi. The formed parts are removed from the dies and are placed in sintering furnaces heated by gas, oil, or electricity. The sintering temperature depends on the material, varying between 1500° and 2000°F for iron products and usually exceeding 5000°F for the refractory materials. The

TABLE 1. TONNAGE OF PRINCIPAL IRON AND STEEL PRODUCTS OF THE UNITED STATES FOR 1951 [1]

Class and Kind	Thousands of Net Tons
Total hot-rolled products	81,911
Plates	9,677
Sheets	22,192
Strip	3,971
Strip and sheet for cold reduced black plate and tinplate	6,989
Cotton ties and baling bands	77
Merchant bars	10,677
Concrete bars	2,085
Structural shapes	6,348
Sheet piling	270
Rails	1,854
Long splice bars and tie plates	695
Skelp	4,384
Blanks or pierced billets	4,448
Wire rods	6,231
Rolled forging billets	1,377
Rolled-steel car wheels	386

[1] *Statistical Report* of the American Iron and Steel Institute, 1951.

time for most products varies between 15 and 90 min. Reducing, non-oxidizing, or hydrogen atmospheres are usually used during the sintering period. Subsequent to sintering, the product may be impregnated with oil or low-melting-point alloys, re-pressed, resintered, or machined.

The tensile properties of metals made by this method are usually not as good as those of wrought metals because of the relatively porous structure. Ultimate tensile strengths for iron containing 0.3 per cent carbon may vary between 30,000 and 40,000 psi, depending upon the density of the product. Ductilities and impact strengths are similarly low.

14. Statistics. In 1949 the total steel production in the United States was about 78,000,000 net tons, about 81 per cent of production capacity. In 1953, production was up to about 111,000,000 net tons. About 80 per cent of the 1951 production was used for hot-rolled products, as shown in Table 1.

Formation and Structure of Alloys

ALLOYS IN GENERAL

1. Reasons for Making Alloys. In general, the properties desired in a metal to be used in engineering construction are not embodied to the best advantage in any single metal, and recourse is had to the mixing of two or more metals to attain the desired end. Such combinations of metals or metallic substances are classed as alloys, and they form one of the most important subdivisions of metallurgy.

2. Mixtures. The properties of alloys are influenced not only by the nature and proportions of the components, but also by the character of the mixture. The constituents may form a simple mixture, coherent, of course, but existing in the mass as distinct individuals. The properties of such a mixture are in large measure an average of those of the components, and vary with the relative proportions; this general relation may be modified by the relative adhesion of unlike particles as compared with the cohesion of the like constituents, and by the degree of fineness of the aggregate as affected by the nature of the components and physical conditions of manufacture. An important example in the iron-carbon alloys is pearlite, a mixture of ferrite, pure iron, and cementite, iron carbide.

3. Chemical Compounds. In extreme contrast to the above, the components may have such a degree of affinity that they unite in atomic proportions to form a chemical compound, a new unit substance in which the individuality of the constituents is lost, and which may have physical properties distinct from and unrelated to those of the components of the alloy. Intermetallic compounds play an important role in the consideration of alloys, the carbide Fe_3C being of especial influence on the properties of steel.

4. Solid Solutions. The above-mentioned conditions represent the extremes or end relations in the possible degrees of miscibility of the constituents of alloys. Between is the wide gap in which the components are mutually soluble to the extent that they become blended into a homogeneous unit with loss of visible evidence (even microscopic) of isolation of particles, and yet where there is not that absolute loss of individuality which accompanies chemical union in atomic proportions. Solid solutions are important factors in the study of alloys; the resultant properties may differ in varying degrees from those of the components, according as the order of solubility approaches that of definite chemical union as a new compound. In the iron-carbon alloys, austenite, a solid solution of carbon in gamma iron, is an important example.

Constituents of an alloy may be only partially soluble; that is, solid solutions may result from addition of either component to the other up to certain limits of saturation, beyond which there results a simple mixture between these saturated solid solutions. Again, an intermetallic compound may form a simple mixture or a solid solution with the components of the mixture, or with a second compound of different atomic proportions in the same series of constituents.

5. Methods of Making Alloys. Alloys may be made in various ways; those of greatest importance in the manufacture of materials for engineering construction are made by fusion of the constituents and solidification after mixture, and by diffusion, where the body metal is in the solid state, and the diffusing material is solid, liquid, or gas. The fusion method is most common and is employed where uniformity of material is desired throughout the entire section; the diffusion method is chiefly of value in imparting a surface differing in composition and properties from those of the body material proper. In the formation of alloys by fusion, complete solubility of the constituents in the liquid state is usually desired; otherwise differences of specific gravity of the components will result in liquation and consequent irregularities of composition throughout the mass. But the solubility of metals is a function of temperature, pressure, and particularly of the state of the constituents. Thus, although there may be perfect miscibility while fusion exists, solidification may result in a solubility which is complete, partial, or nil. Perfect homogeneity of liquid is no criterion of structure in the solid; the solid may be homogeneous or heterogeneous—a solid solution or a simple mechanical mixture. Furthermore, the degree of miscibility, or especially the limit of saturation, being a function of the temperature, may alter by diffusion with changes of temperature below that of solidification. Diffusion in the solid state is, however, comparatively slow, and it is only by the maintenance of relatively high temperatures for long periods of time that alterations of structure occur. Such alterations are not usual in customary service.

6. Allotropy. Certain metals while in one state, such as the solid, undergo at definite temperatures reversible changes in some of their physical properties which are usually accompanied by changes in the crystal structure. Such changes are called "allotropic." A solid alloy, which has as one of its constituents a metal exhibiting allotropy, may undergo transition in passing through the temperature normal for such allotropic change. Iron undergoes allotropic modifications in the solid state, and these are of extreme importance in heat-treatment processes.

7. Crystalline Structure of Metals. By means of X-ray analysis it has been shown that the atoms in metals are arranged so as to form minute crystals of regular geometrical outline. In metal crystals there are commonly found three simple atomic arrangements, known as face-centered cubic, body-centered cubic, and hexagonal close-packed. In the face-centered cubic arrangement there is one atom at each corner of the cube and one atom at the center of each face (Fig. 1a). The body-centered cubic arrangement has atoms at each corner and one atom at the geometrical center of the cube (Fig. 1b). In the hexagonal close-packed

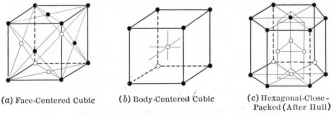

(a) Face-Centered Cubic   (b) Body-Centered Cubic   (c) Hexagonal-Close-Packed (After Hull)

Fig. 1. Common atom arrangements in metals.

arrangements (Fig. 1c), an atom is located at each prism corner and at alternate prism centers.*

Solidification from a melt, in the case of a single, pure metal, will be by formation of numerous small definitely formed crystals in those parts of the melt which have reached the freezing temperature, which is a constant for the single metal. Each crystal is made up of many aligned unit cells, Fig. 1, having some commonly shared atoms. Upon these crystals as nuclei others will build as solidification progresses, attaching themselves regularly with crystal faces together, and making up aggregates, each of which has a resultant orientation of axes of crystallization dependent upon the purely accidental position of its nucleus in the melt. As solidification approaches completion, there will be interference to further growth along lines of contact between different aggregates, and, with complete solidification, a single pure metal will consist of a large number of grains, with irregular boundaries resulting from the contact lines of the individual crystalline aggregates which constitute the several grains. A typical structure of this character is shown in Fig. 2. Although the structure, the strength, and other properties are those of the single metal, variations may result from differences in average size of grains. This in turn may be influenced by cooling conditions which affect the number and

* For further study see *The Science of Metals*, by Zay Jeffries and R. S. Archer; *Structure of Metals*, by C. S. Barrett; *The Physics of Metals*, by F. Seitz.

distribution of nuclei of crystallization. Variations in properties may also be caused by differences in the relative cohesion along the contact faces of the crystals making up the individual grains, as compared with that along the boundaries or contacts between the separate aggregates or grains.

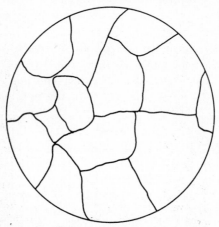

Fig. 2.   Microstructure of a pure metal.

8. Effects of Solubility Relations in Alloys. When two or more metals are mixed to form an alloy, solubility relations have great influence upon the progression of freezing and the structure of the resultant alloy. If the relations of the constituents are such that chemical combination results, and the amounts are of proper atomic proportions, solidification will progress in a manner entirely similar to that of a single pure metal. An intermetallic compound is essentially a unit substance; it will freeze at constant temperature, and it must exhibit a homogeneous structure consisting of a mass of grains, each composed of an aggregate of uniform crystals.

With relations of solubility other than that of chemical combination, solidification proceeds selectively, and is almost always spread over a range of temperature. Materials in a given state resist conditions which tend to change that state. In the case of a single substance, this takes place by sacrifice of part of the mass, which in freezing liberates its latent heat of solidification and thus, by a tendency to hold up the normally falling temperature, tends to keep the remainder of the mass in a liquid condition. With two or more metals in mixture, there is the possibility of resistance to change of state by liberation of heat during freezing of a portion of the mass, as noted above for a single metal; in addition there is the added possibility of sacrifice of some portion of the mass, which differs in composition from the body material in the direction of a higher temperature of freezing. Thus there is enrichment, by such selective freezing, of the remaining portion of the melt in the direction of a composition of lower temperature of solidification, and a resistance thereby to the external conditions tending to promote solidification.

The structure of the alloy will be influenced by its method of freezing and the solubility relations; the former is, however, a function of the latter, and thus relations of solubility of the solidified constituents of the alloy are governing factors in the final structure. Assuming complete solubility in the solid, freezing will proceed by progressive selection, and will be spread over a range of temperature, as noted above. However, the assumed condition of solid solution implies that initial heterogeneity, because of progressive selection, should be effaced by diffusion, and the resultant alloy should, therefore, exhibit a homogeneity of structure of the granular type characteristic of the single pure metal or the intermetallic compounds. But interdiffusion of solid particles is likely to be relatively slow; thus, by rapid cooling of the alloy through and below the freezing range, opportunity for such blending to a homogeneous mass may be checked to a greater or lesser degree, and a heterogeneity, varying throughout the individual grains from the composition of the first frozen particle to that of the last, may result in the solid alloy.

With solubility nil between the constituents of an alloy, resulting structure must be heterogeneous. Freezing from the melt will be by selection, with solidification of that one of the constituents which will, by its elimination, progressively enrich the melt in composition towards that of lowest freezing point. This first portion to freeze will have an opportunity to solidify with considerable definiteness and regularity with respect to its crystal form, and without interference between the individuals, since there is freedom for movement in the remaining liquid. This liquid is finally forced to composition of lowest and final freezing temperature—the so-called eutectic temperature and composition, and constant for a particular alloy—when it will solidify and occupy such space as may remain between the particles making up the portion frozen during selection. Again, however, because of lack of solubility between the solid constituents, the eutectic portion must separate into its individuals on solidification and in itself must be heterogeneous.

9. Methods Used to Determine Constitution Diagrams. In order to construct constitution diagrams for alloys, it is necessary to secure considerable experimental information and to interpret it in accordance with the principles of the phase rule. Some of the more important methods used to secure such data are: thermal analysis, microscopic examination, X-ray diffraction, magnetic and dilatometric measurements. The thermal methods are probably the most important. They are based upon the principle that changes in state of a substance are accompanied by change in its internal energy content, which is manifested by an absorption or liberation of heat. A body without transitions in the temperature range will absorb heat from surroundings at higher temperature, or radiate heat to surroundings at lower temperature, with perfect regularity, and a graphical representation, plotted as a function of temperature and time, will show an approximately logarithmic curve without breaks from smoothness or regularity. Should there be a change of state within the temperature range of investigation, the accompanying absorption or liberation of heat will cause a deviation from the normal law of heating or cooling, and such transition will be manifested by a jog or break from the normal curve extending over a time interval equal to that of heat absorption or liberation due to the transition. A familiar example of the above is the arrest of temperature during melting or freezing of a single pure substance.

By inserting a sensitive pyrometer into a molten alloy of any desired composition, and noting the temperature-time variations during normal cooling and solidification to atmospheric temperature, a "cooling curve" may be plotted which will be a record of the internal condition of the particular alloy within the temperature range employed. Changes of state and allotropic changes will be indicated by breaks from a smooth curve for intervals of temperature and of time corresponding to such transitions.

10. Cooling Curves. Explanation of the construction of constitution diagrams will be presented simply by means of the ordinary temperature-

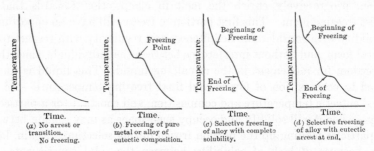

Fig. 3. Typical cooling curves.

time curves, such as shown in Fig. 3a to d. The freezing of a single pure metal, an intermetallic compound, or the eutectic portion of an alloy which solidifies at constant temperature, introduces the arrest illustrated in Fig. 3b, over a time interval corresponding to the liberation of the heat of solidification. In an alloy where the freezing is selective, the progressive shift of composition distributes the process over a range of temperature. For complete solubility in the solid, shown in Fig. 3c, the progressive solidification of particles which are solid solutions of two or more constituents, and the blending of these into a homogeneous unit as freezing proceeds, results in gradual approach of the break in the cooling curve to the normal with progressive elimination of the liquid portion. Where solubility is nil between the solid constituents, selective freezing introduces a break similar to that of the solid solution type while such selection proceeds. But since the solid portion now consists of one pure substance alone, the shift in composition of the liquid is to a portion—which may be the other constituent of a two-component mixture, but is usually some fixed, intermediate mixture of the two—which solidifies at constant temperature. The form of cooling curve is shown in Fig. 3d. For the particular metal under investigation, a cooling curve which exhibits freezing over a range of temperature without arrest at constant temperature denotes complete solubility in the solid; where freezing is spread over a range of temperature with final solidification at a constant temperature, solubility is nil between the solid constituents, or the composition is beyond the saturation limits of an alloy of partial miscibility; with constant freezing only, the metal is a single pure substance, an intermetallic compound, or the eutectic mixture of an alloy with solubility nil or partial between the two components.

BINARY ALLOYS WITH LIQUID SOLUBILITY PERFECT, SOLID SOLUBILITY NIL

11. Significance of the Freezing-Point Diagram. Many cooling curves such as that shown in Fig. 3d can be obtained for alloys of progressively

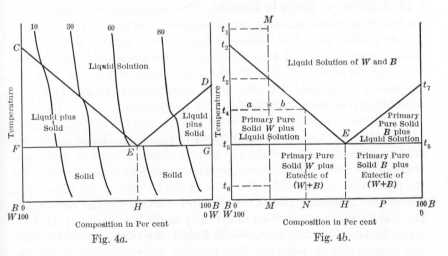

Fig. 4a.   Fig. 4b.

varying composition and can be drawn on one diagram. Then, if lines are drawn through the critical points as shown in Fig. 4a, the constitution diagram for the two given components is obtained. Composition of the two components, W (white) and B (black), is indicated on the horizontal axis, and temperature on the vertical axis. The line CED indicates commencement of solidification and is called the liquidus; the line FEG indicates completion of solidification and is called the solidus. The region above the line CED is a liquid solution of W and B; everything below the line FEG is completely solidified. The region between the two lines is the freezing range and contains both solid and liquid.

That solubility is nil in the solidified alloy is indicated by the fact that the line FEG, marking the completion of solidification, extends completely across the diagram. Thus, whatever may be the composition of the alloy chosen in the series W-B, completion of solidification will always be at a constant temperature F-G; and this, in turn based upon interpretation of experiment, and particularly upon the deductions of the phase rule, is evidence of a lack of solid solubility between the components W and B.

The solidification temperatures of W and B are at C and D, respectively. A feature of interest is that, upon addition of W to B, or B to W, freezing begins at progressively lower temperatures with each addition of the second element, until finally a composition H is reached at the intersection of CE and ED, which has the lowest freezing temperature of any alloy of the series, and one which is usually below that of either of the constituent metals. This marks the so-called "eutectic point" of composition and temperature, which is constant for the particular alloy series, but need not be, in fact usually is not, at a composition of definite atomic proportions of the components.

12. Behavior of Alloys in Freezing. Two important rules applying to the two-phase portions of constitution diagrams will now be considered.

Rule 1 states that, if a horizontal line is drawn through a point x of definite composition and temperature in a two-phase field, such as the solid plus liquid field of Fig. 4b, the intersections of this line with the boundaries of the field will give the compositions of the two phases in equilibrium with each other at the given temperature.

Rule 2 provides information as to the relative amounts of the two phases present at any temperature within the two-phase field. To determine the relative proportions by weight of the two phases present at any given temperature draw a temperature horizontal and note where it intersects the boundaries of the field. The ratio of the weights of the two phases is equal to the inverse ratio of the distances from the vertical corresponding to the average composition of the alloy to the boundaries of the field.

On the horizontal line indicated in Rule 1, the relative weights of the two phases, such as solid and liquid in Fig. 4b, are represented by the lengths of the horizontal line from the given point x to the liquidus and to the solidus lines, respectively. This relationship may be seen to be qualitatively true by noting that as the temperature decreases the length of the line representing the relative weight of the solid increases while that representing the relative weight of the liquid remains the same. Hence the ratio of solid to liquid is shown to be increasing, as it obviously should be.

In discussing the changes that take place in an alloy of composition M, Fig. 4b, as it cools from the liquid state to room temperature, it is assumed that the cooling rate is slow enough for equilibrium conditions to be maintained at all times. This alloy at a temperature t_1 is a homogeneous liquid solution of W and B and will remain so until the temperature has dropped to t_3, at which point freezing must begin. According to Rule 1 the first particle that freezes out of solution must be pure W. As the temperature falls, more of the W component freezes out, while the liquid becomes richer in component B. Investigation of the conditions at temperature t_4 shows that the solid particles freezing out are W, while the composition of the liquid is represented by N. Application of Rule 2 at this temperature indicates that the ratio of solid weight, W, to liquid weight, W plus B, is given by b/a. From t_4 to t_5 more W continues to freeze while the liquid composition approaches the eutectic E. At a constant temperature of t_5 the last residual liquid of composition H solidifies to form the eutectic while the primary pure W does not undergo any change. The eutectic formed is a mixture of W and B crystals, each definitely visible at high magnification under the microscope. From t_5 down to room temperature there is no further change, and the resultant alloy has a heterogeneous structure of large primary W crystals plus eutectic areas, which as previously indicated are themselves heterogeneous.

The mechanism of cooling of an alloy of composition P is similar to that of the alloy just discussed, except that the primary solid that freezes out is now pure B instead of pure W. In the solid plus liquid range, more and more pure B freezes out as the temperature drops while the liquid composition gradually approaches the eutectic. At a constant temperature of t_5 the residual liquid again freezes to form the eutectic. The final structure in this case would consist of large primary B crystals plus the eutectic of W and B. The eutectic alloy, composition H, will not freeze on cooling until the temperature t_5 is reached. At this constant temperature complete solidification will take place and a structure entirely eutectic will be formed. It should be noted that, regardless of alloy composition, final freezing always takes place at temperature t_5.

If a fast-cooling rate is used instead of the slow rate assumed, the resulting structure will be finer in both primary crystals and eutectic, but there will be little change in the relative amounts of each. A fast-cooling rate will also tend to reduce segregation of the primary crystals.

13. Structures of Alloys of Perfect Liquid Solubility—Solid Solubility Nil. An alloy structure of definite type will accompany the method of solidification outlined above. Assuming W to crystallize as cubes, such a portion of this constituent as solidifies during the period of primary selective freezing will make up a ground mass of white cubes, being free to build up on the cubical nuclei of initial crystallization because of the relative mobility of the remaining liquid portion during the temperature range of selective crystallization. The eutectic, on the other hand, will occupy the space remaining after the interval of primary crystallization, but will exist in this area as a composite granular or lamellar structure of white and black particles. For all alloys on the W side of the eutectic proportions, W will be the excess substance, exhibiting primary crystal-

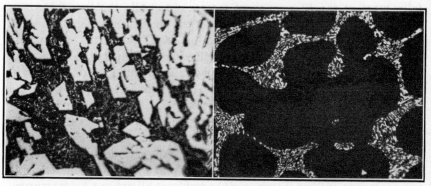

Fig. 5a. Photomicrograph of an alloy of lead (B) and antimony (W) containing 60 per cent lead. Cubes of excess antimony in a eutectic of lead and antimony are shown ($\times$250). (R. A. Ragatz.)

Fig. 5b. Photomicrograph of an alloy of antimony (W) and lead (B) containing 95 per cent lead. Note the oval black areas of lead surrounded by the eutectic network ($\times$250). (R. A. Ragatz.)

lization; while all of the B constituent will appear in the eutectic. The relative proportion of primary constituent W and eutectic will depend upon the initial composition of the alloy; the more rich it is in W, the less will be the relative quantity of eutectic.

A typical structure is shown in Fig. 5a. The white cubes of W, exhibiting various polygonal shapes depending upon the purely chance form of orientation and distribution of the cubes, and the plane of cutting of the section, are imbedded in a granular white and black eutectic of relatively finer state of aggregation of both W and B.

All alloys on the B side of the eutectic proportions (B is in this case called the excess substance, regardless of the particular weight relations) will exhibit a structure of black aggregates of regular outlines due to primary crystallization, together with a composite black and white granular or lamellar eutectic, the latter similar in all respects to that characteristic of the W-rich alloys described previously. The typical structure is shown in Fig. 5b, assuming B to form aggregates of oval form.

Should the initial alloy be of eutectic composition, there will be no primary crystallization of either W or B. The structure will be entirely eutectic of either granular or lamellar type (see Fig. 6 and 7).

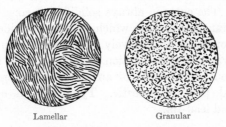

Lamellar   Granular

Fig. 6.   Lamellar and granular types of eutectic structure.

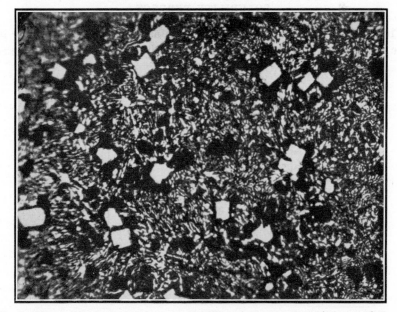

Fig. 7.   Photomicrograph showing eutectic alloy of 13 per cent antimony and 87 per cent lead ($\times$250).   (R. A. Ragatz.)

14. Summary for Alloys with Solid Solubility Nil.   To summarize, binary alloys of the type where solubility is complete in the liquid state, and nil in the solid, are characterized by the presence of a eutectic throughout the series.   All intermediate alloys, therefore, solidify at temperatures lower than those of the two constituent metals, except for the unusual limiting case where the eutectic point is at the end of the series coincident with the constituent metal of lowest freezing temperature. Freezing is spread over a range of temperature and is rigidly selective throughout the series, with primary crystallization of that component which is in excess of the eutectic proportions. The eutectic occupies the areas remaining after primary crystallization, and its quantity is inversely proportional to the distance of the particular alloy from the eutectic composition. The eutectic always solidifies at constant temperature, is always of constant proportions, which are only coincidentally of atomic ratios, and is a composite of relatively finer state of aggregation than the excess metal of primary crystallization. All alloys of the series are heterogeneous throughout, and consist of an excess substance, which may be either pure metal, plus the eutectic. Typical alloys of this series are lead-antimony and lead-tin.

BINARY ALLOYS WITH LIQUID SOLUBILITY PERFECT, SOLID SOLUBILITY PERFECT

15. Typical Constitution Diagram. The assumption of a solubility in the solid state, which is complete throughout the entire alloy series, implies

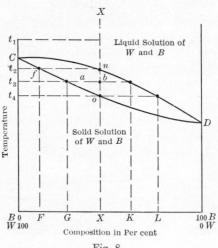

Fig. 8.

of necessity perfect homogeneity of structure. Experimental evidence, however, indicates selectiveness during freezing, with consequent heterogeneity which is effaced only after solidification.

A typical constitution diagram is given in Fig. 8, plotted in the customary manner as a function of temperatures for ordinates against composition abscissas for two components W (white) and B (black). The liquidus and solidus, as determined by transition points noted on cooling curves taken for various compositions within the series, are given by the lines CnD and CoD respectively. The region above the liquidus will be a homogeneous liquid solution of W and B. Between the two lines is the region of selective freezing containing both liquid and solid solutions of W and B.

16. Behavior of a Typical Alloy in Freezing. Again cooling is assumed slow enough for equilibrium to obtain at all times. For an alloy of composition X, Fig. 8, freezing will begin when the temperature falls to t_2. Rule 1 indicates that the composition of the first frozen crystal is represented by F. Since there is complete solubility in the solid state, this particle will be a homogeneous blend, a solid solution of W and B, which has no tendency to split up into its constituents.

As the temperature drops to t_3 the composition of both solid and liquid is constantly changing and more crystals are being formed. At t_3 application of the two rules indicates that the composition of all the solid is represented by G, that of the liquid by K, and that the ratio of solid weight to liquid weight is given by b/a. Because of the solubility in the solid state the crystals formed during the drop in temperature from t_2 to t_3 tend to diffuse into a homogeneous unit and to draw enough B from the liquid to enrich the resultant blended solid to composition G at t_3.

Freezing continues as the temperature drops from t_3 to t_4, resulting again in constantly changing liquid and solid compositions and an increasing amount of solid. If, as has been assumed, diffusion of the solid particles has kept pace with their crystallization from the melt, solidification will be complete at t_4. The last liquid portion just before complete solidification will have the composition L. The solidified alloy will be a homogeneous light gray solid, and will have a composition X, which is identical to that of the original liquid. After complete solidification no further change will take place from t_4 down to room temperature.

Should diffusion in the solid fail to keep pace with the rate of crystallization, freezing will not be completed until the melt has reached a composition between n and D; the last frozen particle will in this case have a composition between o and D. And because of lack of diffusion of the solid particles, the resultant alloy will exhibit a heterogeneity in the individual grains, progressively shading in color from the lighter gray of a nucleus of W-rich material of composition somewhere between f and o, to a relatively darker gray of the last freezing portions of B-rich material of composition between o and D. The extreme or limiting condition, provided no diffusion in the solid resulted, would be a nucleus corresponding to the first frozen material f, shading progressively to B, marking the boundaries of the individual grains. But in all cases, the structure should exhibit a mass of grains, similar to that of a pure metal (Fig. 2), with each grain a crystalline aggregate having the homogeneity of a solid solution under ideal conditions, but actually approaching this only to the degree that diffusion in the solid has effaced the heterogeneity resulting from selective freezing.

Attainment of homogeneity depends upon the characteristics of the constituent metals, and upon the condition of cooling. Since diffusion in the solid is relatively much slower than in the liquid state, slow cooling at temperatures just below the solidification range is rather an essential condition to promote homogeneity; rapid solidification and cooling to normal temperatures, on the contrary, promote heterogeneity of the characteristic shading-off type discussed above.

17. Summary for Alloys of Perfect Solid Solubility. To summarize: binary alloys of the type having complete solubility in both liquid and solid states solidify by a process of selective freezing. This is not rigid, however, and the heterogeneity of structure resulting from such selection is effaced by diffusion, under ideal conditions of cooling; the final alloy is then a solid solution with homogeneity of structure. The so-called "onion peel" type of structure may result if cooling conditions are such that there is not complete effacement of the heterogeneity of selective crystallization. All alloys of the series must freeze over a range of temperature, and there can be no solidification at constant temperature corresponding to the eutectic of alloys of the immiscible type. Typical alloys of this type are iron-manganese and antimony-bismuth.

BINARY ALLOYS WITH LIQUID SOLUBILITY COMPLETE, SOLID SOLUBILITY PARTIAL

18. Typical Constitution Diagram. Partial solubility in the solid state implies perfect miscibility, with accompanying homogeneity of structure, at either or both ends of the series, up to particular limits of saturation.

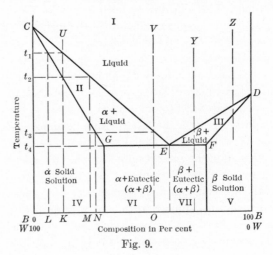

Fig. 9.

Beyond these limits, there must be separation of the constituents, and heterogeneity of structure. The relations are a combination of the two types previously discussed.

The conventional Greek letters are used as names of the solid solutions in the typical constitution diagram shown in Fig. 9. There are seven characteristic areas: I, the molten solution; II and III, the regions of selective crystallization containing α solid solution plus liquid and β solid solution plus liquid, respectively; IV and V the regions of solid solubility, α and β solid solutions, respectively; VI and VII, the regions beyond the saturation limits containing α solid solution plus the eutectic, and β solid solution plus the eutectic, respectively. The limits of solid solubility are marked by the eutectic line GEF; that is, the presence of a eutectic is evidence of final solidification at constant temperature and composition, and of consequent separation, in accord with the deductions of the phase rule, into the distinct constituents.

19. Behavior of Typical Alloys in Freezing. An alloy of composition U will solidify entirely in accord with the method outlined for complete solubility. Freezing will start when temperature t_1 is reached, and the composition of the first solid crystal forming will be L. The solid freezing out of solution is neither pure W nor pure B, but a solid solution of both rich in W, which is called α solid solution. As the temperature drops, the composition of both liquid and solid is constantly changing, and more solid is freezing out. The composition of the last portion of liquid just before complete solidification at temperature t_2 is M. If a very slow rate of cooling has been maintained, the heterogeneity of the final structure due to the selective crystallization through the freezing range will be effaced by diffusion of the solid particles. The final structure at t_2 and down to room temperature will be a homogeneous solid solution of composition K and of light gray color due to the preponderance of white constituent W. The above discussion will hold for any alloy in the composition range $B0$ to G.

The above reasoning will hold, likewise, for the solidification of an alloy of composition Z. β solid solution, rich in the black constituent B, will freeze out, however, instead of the α solid solution, and the composition of the solidified alloy will be Z. The final structure in this case will be considerably darker than the U alloy because of the large amount of B present. As indicated in Fig. 9, the final structure for all alloys between F and $100\ B$ will be β solid solution.

An alloy V will begin to freeze at temperature t_3, with separation of the first frozen particle of α solid solution with a composition N. As the temperature drops the composition of both liquid and solid is constantly changing, and more solid continues to freeze out. At t_4, assuming a very slow rate of cooling through the freezing range, diffusion of the solid particles plus extraction of sufficient B from the melt has resulted in a completely homogeneous solid solution of composition G. The last residual liquid at t_4 has the composition E, and final solidification proceeds at constant temperature accompanied by immediate separation of the solid constituents of the eutectic. Owing to partial solid solubility, the eutectic will not be a composite of the two pure components W and B, but will consist of a heterogeneous mixture of particles of W saturated with B, and B saturated with W; in other words, of a granular or lamellar composite of α solid solution, composition G, and β solid solution, composition F.

The final structure will therefore consist of a primary aggregate of composition G—a solid solution exhibiting its particular definiteness of crystallinity—together with a eutectic occupying the remaining area, and composed of a composite mixture of particles of composition G and F, each a saturated solid solution. The structure is heterogeneous, and is characteristic of all alloys between G and E; the differences between these alloys being in the quantitative proportions of primary substance with respect to eutectic, the amount of the latter increasing from 0 to 100 per cent as the composition of the particular alloy varies from G to E.

Alloys of composition between E and F solidify in a manner similar to those just discussed. The excess substance of primary crystallization is, however, a saturated solid solution of composition F, which will structurally exhibit its particular definiteness of crystalline habit. The eutectic will be identical in composition with that resulting in alloys from G to E; that is, a heterogeneous composite of two saturated solid solutions G and F. The quantity of eutectic will vary from 0 to 100 per cent as the composition of the original alloy is shifted from F to E.

Should the original alloy be of eutectic proportions E, solidification will not begin until the temperature has dropped to t_4. It will then proceed at this constant temperature, with accompanying separation of the two constituents G and F to form the characteristic granular or lamellar composite, making up the entire structure.

If a fast-cooling rate is employed, instead of the slow one which has been assumed, the α and β solid solutions will be heterogeneous instead of homogeneous. The composition from point to point will vary instead of being the same. Also, a fast-cooling rate will result in the presence of some eutectic in the alloys between $B0$ and G, and from F to 100 B.

20. Summary for Alloys with Solid Solubility Partial. To summarize, binary alloys of the type where solubility is complete in the liquid state, and partial in the solid, are characterized by a eutectic for part of the series, and this eutectic marks the limits of solubility in the solid. Freezing is selective throughout the series. It is not rigidly so within the limits of saturation, and the heterogeneity of selective crystallization should be effaced by diffusion in the solid, and homogeneous alloys should resu'.t. Beyond the limits of solubility, the heterogeneity cannot be effaced by diffusion, and the resultant alloys consist of an excess substance of primary crystallization, plus a eutectic. The excess substance is a saturated solid solution, of either component of the series saturated with the other, depending upon the composition of the particular alloy with respect to that of the eutectic. The eutectic is a composite of the two components of the alloy series, each saturated with the other, and is always of the same composition for the particular series. All alloys of compositions within the limits of solubility are structurally homogeneous, provided cooling conditions have enabled diffusion to complete itself. Beyond the limits of solubility, the structure is heterogeneous.

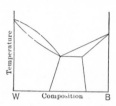

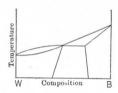

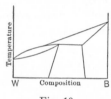

Modifications in the form of solidification diagram for alloys of this type of partial solubility, are given in Fig. 10. The differences involved are only in details of progress of solidification, and not in the character of structure resulting. The reader is referred to treatises on metallography for detailed discussion of these modified forms.

Fig. 10.

Typical alloys of this class are those of aluminum and zinc, copper-silver, and cadmium-mercury.

BINARY ALLOYS WITH AN INTERMETALLIC COMPOUND

21. Complexity Due to Metallic Compounds. Additional complexity is introduced into the study of alloys by the possibility of formation of chemical compounds between the constituents.

If an intermetallic compound, for example, of the atomic proportions W_1B_1, forms in the alloy series W-B, this compound is a homogeneous, unit substance, and usually is unlike the constituent metals in its melting point or general physical properties. It enters into alloying relations with W on the one hand, and B on the other. Virtually, therefore, W and B no longer have simple relations with one another; the series becomes a duplex one of W with W_1B_1 and W_1B_1 with B. There is a duplex set of solubility relations, each independent of the other. Figure 11 illustrates such a series, in which W_1B_1 and W have a completely miscible relation in the solid state, whereas W_1B_1 and B form heterogeneous alloys because of lack of solubility in the solid. No alloys of the series will have free W

and free B together. A second compound W_2B_2 would make the couples of the complete series $(W$-$W_1B_1)$, $(W_1B_1$-$W_2B_2)$, $(W_2B_2$-$B)$, each in reality a binary series independent with respect to the others. The simplest method of treatment of a binary alloy with intermediate chemical compounds is to break the series into its component groups, and to consider each as a simple binary alloy having one of the three fundamental types of solubility relations discussed heretofore.

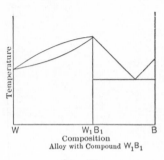

Composition

Alloy with Compound W_1B_1

Fig. 11.

TERNARY ALLOYS

22. General Discussion of Ternary Alloys. The determination of the necessary cooling curves, microscopic data, and X-ray data required to develop a constitution diagram when more than two alloys are involved is an extremely arduous task. Also, graphical representation of the data becomes complex or even impossible. It is possible, for ternary alloys, to represent the composition relations by means of triangular coordinates. Each apex of the equilateral triangle represents 100 per cent of one of the three components, and the amounts of the three components represented by any point within the triangle must add up to 100 per cent. A point X within the triangle corresponds to a ternary alloy of a definite composition given by the lengths of the three lines drawn through X parallel to the sides of the triangle. Temperatures are plotted on axes that are perpendicular to the triangular composition plane, and the resultant constitution diagram then takes the form of a space model in three dimensions.

Because of the difficulty of working with space models, information is usually obtained from vertical and horizontal sections and sections parallel to one of the sides of the solid. A satisfactory method of analyzing ternary and other more complicated alloys is to consider first the binary relationships of the two most important constituents, and subsequently to deal with the modifying influences of the various secondary elements.

Constitution of Iron and Steel

1. History of Iron and Steel. The exact date that iron was first used by man is not known, but archaeological research has established the fact that it has been in use for about 4000 years. Wrought-iron blades have reportedly been found in one of the pyramids and beneath the base of a sphinx in Egypt. The ancient Hebrews and Assyrians used iron products about 1400 B.C., and the ancient Romans made considerable use of iron in making their instruments of war. The process of manufacturing the early wrought iron consisted simply of heating iron ore and fuel to produce a spongy mass which was then taken out and forged. A major advance in the production of wrought iron was the Catalan forge, originated in 1293 in Spain. In this furnace the ore and fuel were placed in a hearth and were subjected to an air blast that entered the furnace through tuyeres near the bottom.

Cast iron was known in China in the years 200 to 1100, and there is also some evidence of cast-iron statuary made by the ancient Romans. The iron makers of central Europe in 1350 first succeeded in making iron that would melt in the furnace and could be cast. The process was introduced into England about 1500 and into America about 1619.

Two methods of making steel, the cementation and crucible processes, were known to have been used by the ancients. The Damascene swords made by the Moslems in the Middle Ages and by the Japanese during the years 500 to 1500 were made with steel produced by these methods. The Wootz steel of India and the famous steels of Toledo, Spain, were also made by these methods. Until 1856 when the Bessemer process was patented the crucible and cementation methods were the only known methods used to produce steel. The Bessemer process was the dominant process for many years before it lost much of its popularity to the open-hearth process which was developed during the years 1860 to 1870. Electric melting furnaces began operating in 1878 on a limited basis, but produce about 8 per cent of the steel made today. The great importance of steel to our modern economy is evident by the fact that production during the first half of the twentieth century has been about 2½ billion tons.

DEFINITIONS FOR DIFFERENT FERROUS METALS

2. Cast Iron. The general term "cast iron" includes gray, white, mottled, malleable, alloy, and ductile cast iron. Cast irons are alloys of iron, carbon, and silicon that usually contain 2.0 to 4.5 per cent carbon, 0.5 to 3.0 per cent silicon, and also some sulfur and phosphorus.

Gray cast iron is relatively soft and machinable, has most of its carbon in the form of graphitic flakes, and has a gray to black fracture. It is considered by many people as a material having a steel matrix (0.10 to 0.90 per cent carbon as iron carbide) in which from 1.5 to 3.5 per cent carbon in the form of graphite flakes is distributed. It is the most widely used cast metal.

White cast iron is hard, brittle, non-ductile, and has almost all the carbon in the combined form (Fe_3C). It is cast as an intermediate product in the production of malleable cast iron, and to form a thin hard layer on the surface of a softer casting to provide high surface hardness. In the latter case it is known as chilled iron because it is cast against metal chills which carry the heat away rapidly. It has a white fracture.

Mottled cast iron is intermediate between gray and white cast iron.

Malleable cast iron is cast iron which is cast as white cast iron and is made malleable by heat treatment in which substantially all the combined carbon is converted to nodules of graphite called temper carbon. Malleable cast iron usually contains from 2 to 3 per cent carbon (in temper-carbon form) and from 0.7 to 1.5 per cent silicon. The structure of malleable cast iron consists of a matrix of ferrite with scattered nodules of graphite. In the United States the castings are packed in an inert material during the heat-treating cycle and very little carbon is removed. The final product is known as *black heart* malleable cast iron, because of the black color of its fracture. In Europe the castings are packed in an oxidizing material during the heat-treating cycle, and under these conditions most of the carbon is oxidized and eliminated. This material has a white fracture and is known as *white heart* malleable cast iron. A modified form of malleable cast iron called *pearlitic malleable cast iron* is made by incompletely graphitizing the combined carbon of the original white cast iron or by reheating the graphitized metal.

Alloy iron is cast iron to which chromium, nickel, molybdenum, copper, or other elements have been deliberately added to change or augment the properties available with normal compositions.

Ductile cast iron is relatively soft and machinable, has higher strength and stiffness than gray cast iron, and under certain conditions also has a substantial amount of ductility. Most of the carbon is in the form of spheroidal graphite obtained by introducing small amounts of magnesium

or a magnesium-containing agent into the iron. Structurally it is similar
to gray cast iron except that its graphite is in spheroidal form instead of
in flake form.

3. Pig Iron. This material is considered separately, even though it is
a cast iron, because it is of little direct interest to the engineer. It may
be defined as the product of the blast furnace which has been cast into
pigs. The name also applies to molten cast iron which is about to be
cast into pigs, or is in a condition in which it could readily be cast into
pigs.

4. Wrought Iron. Wrought iron is a malleable ferrous metal aggre-
gated from solidifying particles of refined metallic iron with which, without subsequent fusion, are uniformly mixed minute particles of ferrous
silicate slag. Wrought iron is the only ferrous material that contains
siliceous slag. It usually contains from 1 to 3 per cent slag, by weight,
and such a small amount of carbon (about 0.02 to 0.10 per cent) that it
does not harden usefully when suddenly cooled. The slag in physical
association with the iron is present as fibers, about 250,000 per sq in.,
which extend in the direction of rolling. Wrought iron is made by either
the puddling or the Aston process.

5. Steel. Almost all steel now being made in the United States is the
product of the basic open-hearth, acid Bessemer, or electric furnaces.
Steel may be considered as a commercial alloy of iron and carbon, having
less than 2.0 per cent carbon, less than 1.6 per cent manganese, less than
0.6 per cent silicon, and small amounts of sulfur, phosphorus, and other
elements. Steels having more than 0.30 per cent carbon harden usefully
on rapid cooling; steels with less carbon do not. *Carbon steels* are steels
which owe their distinctive properties chiefly to the carbon as distinguished from the other elements they contain. *Alloy steels* are steels
which owe their distinctive properties chiefly to some element or elements other than carbon, or jointly to such other elements and carbon.

6. Ferroalloys. This type of alloy may be defined as iron with such
large additions of some element or elements other than carbon that it
is used primarily as a vehicle for introducing that element in the manufacture of iron or steel.

COMPOSITION AND CONSTITUTION

7. Composition of Iron and Steel. Chemical composition of typical
forms of iron and steel products finding utility in connection with engineering construction are given in Table 1. The much-used SAE and
AISI numbers for designating steels are described in Art. XXIV-15.

While commercial forms of iron and steel have in general several elements associated with the iron, and each of these has some effect on the

Materials of Construction

TABLE 1. TYPICAL COMPOSITIONS OF IMPORTANT FERROUS METALS

METAL.	Composition in Per Cent (Iron Omitted).								
	C	Si	Mn	S	P	Ni	Cr	Va	Ti
Ingot iron (pure)	.01–.02	<.01	.01–.02	.01–.02	<.01				
Boiler plate	.10–.20	.05–.15	.30–.50	<.05	<.05				
Structural steel	.15–.25	.05–.25	.30–.50	.04–.06	.04–.10				
Structural steel (electric)	.15–.25	.05–.25	.50–.80	<.02	<.02				
Axles and shafts	.30–.40	.05–.25	.40–.80	<.06	<.05				
Vehicle springs	.90–1.0	.05–.25	.25–.50	<.05	<.05				
Rails	.40–.70	<.20	.60–1.0	<.06	<.10				
Carbon tool steels	.50–1.5	.10–.30	.10–.50	<.03	<.03				
Steel castings	.15–.40	.20–.35	.50–1.0	<.05	<.06				
Cast-iron castings	2.5–4.0	.70–2.5	.40–1.0	<.12	.20–1.2				
Nickel steel (structural)	.30–.45	.05–.25	.60–.70	<.05	<.05	3.5–4.0			
Manganese steel	1.0–1.3	.30–.80	11–14	......	<.06				
Transformer (silicon) steel	.05–.10	4.0–4.3	.10–.15	<.06	<.05				
Vanadium steel	.25–.50	.10–.25	.80–.90	<.05	<.05			.15–.25	
Titanium rail steel	.40–.80	.05–.10	.80–1.0	<.05	<.05				.10–.20
Nickel-chrome steel	.20–.40	<.10	.30–.60	<.05	<.05	1.2–4.0	.60–2.0		
Chrome-vanadium steel	.20–.60	.10–.25	.50–.80	<.04	<.04		.80–1.1	.15–.25	W
High-speed steels *	.60–.80	.15–.40	0–2.0	<.03	<.03		3.0–5.0	.50–2.0	13–19
18-8 Stainless Steel	<.20	.50–1.0	<.50	<.045	<.045	7–10	17–20		
Low Alloy High Strength Steels								Cu	
Cor-ten	.10	.50–1.0	.10–.30	<.05	.10–.20		.50–1.5	.30–.50	
Yoloy	.05–.25	<.30	.....	<.05	<.05	2.0		1.0	
Jal-ten	<.35	.....	1.3–1.7	<.05	<.04			<.40	
Cromansil	.10–.45	.60–.90	1.0–1.4	<.05	<.05		.40–.60		

* Some high-speed steels also contain 3 to 5 per cent of cobalt.

physical properties, it is customary to consider the material as essentially an alloy of iron and carbon, the inherent properties of which are modified by the other associated elements.

8. Determinations of Constitution of Iron and Steel. The pioneer attempts at grouping the iron-carbon series into a constitution diagram were made by Sauveur, in 1896, and Roberts-Austen, in 1897. In 1900, Roozeboom constructed a diagram based upon experimental data and interpreted in accordance with the phase rule. The data were accurately redetermined and somewhat elaborated by Carpenter and Keeling, in 1904. Since that time many investigators have striven to determine the iron-iron carbide constitution diagram. Among the later diagrams are those presented by Honda, Daeves, and Epstein. The most accurate and widely used constitution diagram is that given in the latest edition of the *Metals Handbook*.

9. Critical Temperatures. Iron is a relatively complex element. Between its freezing point of 1539°C and normal temperatures, it exhibits transition points at 1400°, 910°, and 768°C. Iron exists in three allotropic states from room temperature up to the freezing point. Alpha iron existing below 910°C has a body-centered cubic lattice, gamma iron existing between 910° to 1400°C has a face-centered cubic lattice, and delta iron existing between 1400° and 1539°C has a body-centered cubic lattice. There is, however, a slight break in the cooling curve at the critical temperature of 768°C and a loss or gain of magnetism by the iron when heated above, or cooled below, that temperature. The transition from alpha to gamma iron at 910°C is accompanied by a change in the crystallographic form of the iron, which, in turn, affects the solubility relations of the iron and carbon, and, therefore, has a most vital bearing upon the structure and physical properties. The critical temperatures in the vicinity of 768° and 910°C are called the A_2 and A_3 points, respectively. Owing to lag in reaction, they are somewhat higher on rising temperature than if recorded on cooling curves; the designations Ac_2 and Ac_3 are used for the former, and Ar_2 and Ar_3 for the latter. In the iron-carbon alloys there are two other important critical temperatures, A_0 at 210° and A_1 at 723°C. A_0 is important because it is the temperature at which there is a reversible magnetic transformation in the iron carbide; the importance of A_1 is indicated in Art. 11.

10. Definitions. Iron forms with carbon a compound having formula Fe_3C, technically classified as cementite, and often called iron carbide or combined carbon. It contains 6.67 per cent of carbon and 93.33 per cent of iron, and is extremely hard and brittle; in fact the hardest constituent of steels, about 6 to 6½ compared with 4 to 5 for iron in Mohs' scale.

In metallographic nomenclature the carbonless iron is called ferrite.

Carbon in the form of small flakes or nodules that are mechanically mixed with the iron is called graphite.

Austenite is a solid solution of carbon in gamma iron. Maximum solubility of 2.0 per cent carbon occurs at 1130°C.

Pearlite is a mechanical mixture of ferrite and cementite containing 12 per cent cementite and 88 per cent ferrite.

11. The Iron-Iron Carbide Constitution Diagram. For purposes of discussion it is best to consider the alloying relations between iron and cementite (Fe_3C) as the constituents of the binary series. For each 1 per cent of carbon there is 15 per cent of Fe_3C formed, and the limit of the series will be at 6.67 per cent carbon, or 100 per cent of the Fe_3C. A simplified constitution diagram is shown in Fig. 1. The melting point of pure iron is taken as 1539°C; that of cementite is not known, since it has not been isolated in mass, and it undergoes decomposition before fusion. It is not material to the discussion, however, since the useful range of composition does not exceed 5 per cent of carbon content.

In representing the simplified form of the constitution diagram the three omissions listed below have been made, none of which is believed to be of major importance in the discussion of ordinary iron-iron carbide alloys: (1) the A_0 line at 210°C; (2) the region at eutectoid temperature and carbon less than 0.025 per cent, in which there is a slight solubility of carbon in alpha iron; (3) the peritectic region at 1400° to 1539°C.

Consider first only that part of the diagram above 1130°C. It is typical of complete solubility of iron and carbon in the liquid condition, with partial solubility in the solid, at least at the iron end of the series. Addition of either constituent to the other lowers the freezing point of the alloy to a eutectic temperature and composition E of 1130°C and 4.3 per cent carbon (64.5 per cent Fe$_3$C), respectively. The limit of solid solubility is at S, that is, 2.0 per cent of carbon, or 30 per cent of cementite, at 1130°C; this solubility decreases, however, with further lowering of temperature as is indicated by the slope of the line PS.

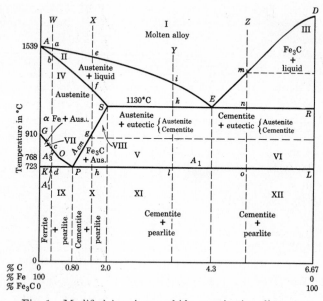

Fig. 1. Modified iron-iron carbide constitution diagram.

Consideration of the diagram below 1130°C indicates a complexity resulting from the change in solubility relationships. At 1130°C gamma iron will have a maximum of 2.0 per cent carbon in solution, whereas the maximum amount of carbon dissolved in alpha iron, at 723°C, is approximately 0.025 per cent (not shown in Fig. 1). The breaking down of the austenite, because of the changing solubility relationships, occurs in a manner analogous to that of a molten alloy whose solid solubility is nil. The slope of the line GOP indicates that the presence of carbon in solid solution lowers the transformation temperature of gamma iron to alpha iron. The slope of the line SP indicates that the solubility of carbon in gamma iron decreases as the temperature is decreased. The point P, called the eutectoid to distinguish it from the eutectic at E, occurs at a temperature of 723°C and a carbon content of 0.80 per cent. The vertical line through S separates the steel region, 0 to 2.0 per cent carbon, and the cast-iron region, 2.0 to 6.67 per cent carbon.

12. Behavior of Typical Alloys in Cooling. Examination of the iron-iron carbide constitution diagram shows that it can be broken up into three regions. The transformations in the cast-iron region, 2.0 to 6.67 per cent carbon, follow in a manner similar to those of Art. XXI-12. The changes from the molten alloy to solid solution austenite, 0 to 2.0 per cent carbon, occur in manner similar to those which take place for any two materials soluble in both liquid and solid states (Art. XXI-16). The transformations in the solid state for the steels from solid solution austenite to ferrite plus pearlite, or to cementite plus pearlite, are analogous to those which occur in two materials soluble in the liquid state but insoluble in the solid state (Art. XXI-12). The changes which take place on cooling will be discussed for four typical alloys.

Discussion of changes on cooling for alloy W, Fig. 1, will be typical of all the hypoeutectoid steels (0 to 0.80 per cent carbon). As alloy W is cooled through the molten region no change takes place until the temperature a at the intersection with the liquidus AE. The first solid to form is austenite, with a carbon content that can be determined by drawing a horizontal line through a until it intersects the solidus AS. As the temperature falls, freezing continues, and both the solid austenite and the liquid become richer in carbon. Freezing will be complete when the temperature has dropped to b. The resultant solid, with a cooling rate slow enough to allow uniform diffusion, will be a homogeneous solid solution, austenite, containing the same amount of carbon as the liquid alloy W. The austenite suffers no change until the temperature drops to c at intersection with GOP. Here the precipitation of primary ferrite begins. As the temperature is decreased from c to d, more primary ferrite is precipitated, and the austenite consequently becomes richer in carbon, reaching finally the eutectoid composition P at 723°C. At 723°C, the austenite splits up into the eutectoid mixture of ferrite and cementite, which is called pearlite, but the primary ferrite remains unchanged. There is no further phase change with further cooling. The final alloy will have a heterogeneous structure consisting of primary ferrite plus pearlite (see Fig. 3b, 3c, 3d, and 3e). The proportion of pearlite to ferrite will depend on the carbon content of the alloy, reaching 100 per cent for a carbon content of 0.80 per cent. The final structure of the eutectoid alloy will be completely pearlitic, as is shown in Fig. 3f and 4.

The changes on cooling of alloy X are typical of the hypereutectoid steels, 0.80 to 2.0 per cent carbon. Freezing begins at temperature e, with separation of austenite, and is completed at temperature f. The mechanism of solidification between e and f is similar to that discussed previously for alloy W. There is no change in the austenite as it cools from f to g. At g the first particle of primary Fe_3C is precipitated out of solution. As the temperature drops from g to 723°C, more primary Fe_3C is precipitated, and the austenite becomes poorer in carbon, reaching finally the eutectoid composition P. Again at 723°C the residual austenite changes to pearlite, while the primary cementite undergoes no change. There is no phase change due to further cooling, and the final structure is heterogeneous, consisting of primary cementite plus pearlite (Fig. 3g). The proportion of primary cementite will increase and that of pearlite will decrease as the carbon is raised above 0.80 per cent.

Iron-carbon alloys of more than 2.0 per cent carbon have a heterogeneous structure after solidification at 1130°C. Alloy Y typifies the hypoeutectic cast irons, containing from 2.0 to 4.3 per cent carbon. Solidification begins at i with separation of austenite from the liquid and is completed at k. Meanwhile the carbon content of the austenite increases to 2.0 per cent and that of the liquid increases to 4.3 per cent. At 1130°C, the primary saturated austenite remains unchanged, while the liquid solidifies to form the eutectic, a mixture of cementite and saturated austenite. As the temperature cools from 1130°C to 723°C, cementite is precipitated out of the primary austenite and also out of the austenite in the eutectic, leaving less carbon in solution, as is indicated by the line SP. At 723°C, the residual austenite has reached the eutectoid composition, and breaks down into pearlite. There is no further phase change down to room temperature. In outline form the alloys between 2.0 and 4.3 per cent undergo transitions as follows:

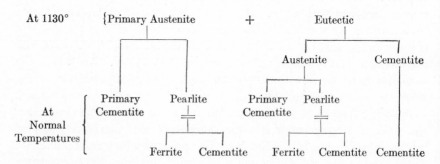

Thus at ordinary temperatures, two constituents only, the cementite and ferrite, are present; yet there is complexity of structure because the cementite may have five degrees of aggregation due to the selective separation, while the ferrite may have two—that in the pearlite from decomposed primary austenite and that in the eutectic.

An alloy of the eutectic composition of 4.3 per cent carbon will undergo transition in accordance with that part of the diagrammatic scheme above referring to the eutectic.

Hypereutectic cast irons, like Z, have a structure immediately after solidification of primary cementite plus a eutectic of saturated austenite and cementite. The proportion of this eutectic decreases with increase of carbon above 4.3 per cent. All the cementite remains stable upon lowering the temperature to normal; the austenite, however, undergoes progressive transition, first by primary separation of cementite, and finally, at 723°C by formation of pearlite. The diagrammatic representation is as follows:

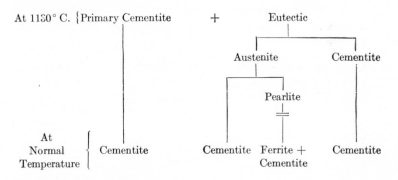

The cementite may have four degrees of aggregation; the only ferrite is that found in the pearlite formed from transition of the austenite of the original eutectic.

13. The Formation of Graphite. Silicon is always associated with the commercial alloys of iron and carbon. In steel the proportion of silicon is small and its influence is chiefly confined to the mitigation of structural defects; but in cast iron, where it is present in larger proportions, silicon exerts an influence both on the solubility of carbon in iron and on the stability of cementite in cooling.

With 1 to 3 per cent of silicon and slow cooling the percentages of carbon required for saturation and for the eutectic are less than for a pure carbon-iron alloy. Therefore, points S and E of the constitution diagram are shifted to the left by additions of silicon. In the alloys having more carbon than the eutectic, the cementite of region III is very unstable under the above-mentioned conditions and readily breaks up into graphite and ferrite while cooling through region VI. In alloys of less carbon than eutectic composition the cementite of region V decomposes quite easily. Cementite liberated by cooling austenite in regions V and VI breaks up less readily, and that in the pearlite of regions XI and XII is decomposed with difficulty. With the rate of cooling and carbon content constant, the proportion of graphite will vary with the percentage of silicon. If the silicon content and rate of cooling are constant graphitization will increase with the percentage of carbon. Again, if the composition remains constant more carbon will be freed by slow cooling than by rapid cooling.

Thus, depending on the proportion of silicon and the rate of cooling, a high-carbon alloy may have any one of the following constitutions:

1. Cementite plus pearlite.
2. Cementite plus pearlite plus graphite.
3. Pearlite plus graphite plus ferrite.
4. Graphite plus ferrite, which is the only stable constitution but is also very rare.

14. Structures in Iron-Carbon Alloys. Figure 2 gives in diagrammatic form the structural relations of the iron-carbon series. For 0.27 per cent of carbon, the relative proportions of the constituents will be two-thirds excess ferrite and one-third pearlite; for 0.54 per cent carbon, one-third ferrite and two-thirds pearlite; for 0.80 per cent carbon, all pearlite. Above 0.80 per cent carbon, cementite becomes the excess constituent of primary separation. An alloy of 2.0 per cent carbon will consist

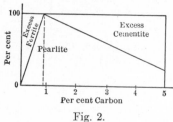

Fig. 2.

of 20.4 per cent excess cementite and 79.6 per cent pearlite; with 3.73 per cent of carbon, the structure will show one-half cementite and one-half pearlite. The pearlite is in all cases of constant composition, 88 per cent of ferrite and 12 per cent of cementite; and the total ferrite or cementite in the alloy will be that constituting the excess substance—either ferrite or cementite alone—plus the amount in the pearlite.

Typical microstructures of the iron-carbon series are given in Fig. 3 and 4. The etching has been with picric acid solution; this reagent does not attack cementite, and ferrite in mass but very slowly. Therefore, they retain the mirror-like reflecting surface of the polished specimen and appear white in the photographs. However, it does attack the ferrite of the pearlite, probably because of its fine state of division and the electrolytic action set up with the closely associated cementite. Consequently, since the ferrite constitutes 88 per cent of the pearlite, and the latter is usually in such a fine state of aggregation that under lower magnification (150 diameters or less) its separate constituents are not revealed, the

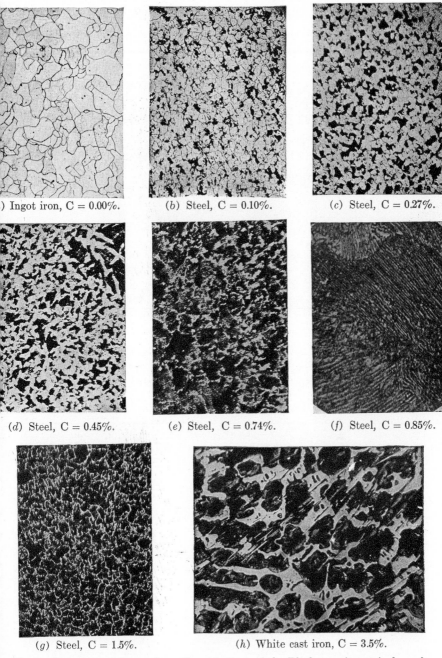

(a) Ingot iron, C = 0.00%. (b) Steel, C = 0.10%. (c) Steel, C = 0.27%.

(d) Steel, C = 0.45%. (e) Steel, C = 0.74%. (f) Steel, C = 0.85%.

(g) Steel, C = 1.5%. (h) White cast iron, C = 3.5%.

Fig. 3. Structures of iron-carbon alloys slowly cooled. Black constituent in b, c, d, e, g, and h is pearlite; white is ferrite in b, c, d, and e, cementite in g and h. In f is shown lamellar pearlite; here the black is ferrite and the white is cementite. Figure 3a by Ragatz; Fig. 3f by Tinsley; others by Aston. Magnification in f, ×1000; in others, ×70.

pearlite is apparently entirely etched, and then appears black in the photograph, due to the dispersion of the light by the roughened surface.

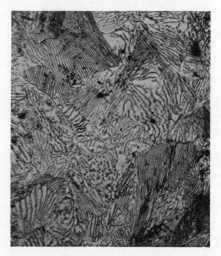

Fig. 4.   Lamellar pearlite (×1000).   (Sauveur and Boylston.)

Higher magnifications (500 to 1500 diameters) reveal the composite nature of the pearlite; see Fig. 4.   The black constituent is the ferrite and the white, cementite.

CHAPTER XXIII

Properties of Wrought Iron

1. Structure. Under the microscope wrought iron is seen to consist of grains of ferrite more or less surrounded by filaments of slag. In the cross-sectional view of Fig. 1a the slag inclusions appear as dark rounded patches of variable size, whereas in the longitudinal section, Fig. 1b, their thread-like nature is evident. The amount of slag in the iron depends upon the character of materials charged into the furnace, upon the work

(a) (b)

Fig. 1. Photomicrographs of wrought iron. (a) Section transverse to direction of rolling; (b) Section parallel to rolling. Magnification about $\times 50$. (Sauveur and Boylston and A. M. Byers Co.)

received by the puddle ball, and upon the amount of hot work done in shaping the iron. The size of the ferrite grains depends upon the time the metal is held at temperatures above the critical range and upon the temperature from which it cools. High temperatures and long soaking periods favor large grains. Rapid cooling and continued hot working of the iron while it is above the recalescence point effect small grain size. To secure maximum fineness of grain the hot work should not cease until the temperature has fallen to about 700°C. The ductility and toughness of the iron are rendered high by removing the slag and by making the grain size as fine as possible without causing permanent distortion of the grains.

When a wrought-iron bar of uniform section is ruptured in the ordinary tensile test it generally exhibits an irregular fibrous fracture (Fig. III-6). The fibrous character of the wrought-iron fracture is also shown in Fig. 2.

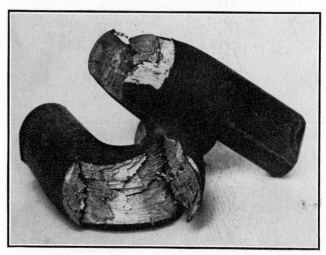

Fig. 2. Fibrous structure of wrought iron. (A. M. Byers Co.)

2. Composition. Wrought iron has a low carbon content, usually varying between 0.02 and 0.10 per cent. Higher amounts of carbon may indicate incomplete refining or may indicate that steel scrap had been used in piling.

Good wrought iron contains less than 0.10 per cent manganese, and frequently the amount may be less than 0.06 per cent. Higher manganese contents may also indicate incomplete refining or adulteration by the use of steel in piling. The low manganese content of wrought iron provides a chemical means of differentiating between wrought iron and low-carbon steel.

The silicon content is usually between 0.10 and 0.20 per cent, practically all of which is in the slag. Silicon contents outside this range may indicate an improper amount of slag, poor distribution of the slag, or a slag of an improper composition.

Phosphorus in wrought iron is associated partly with the iron and partly with the slag. It is usually present in amounts varying between 0.08 and 0.16 per cent. High phosphorus contents are undesirable because they promote brittleness at low temperatures.

Sulfur is not desirable in wrought iron because it promotes red shortness. The sulfur content is generally kept below 0.035 per cent.

Alloying elements used in wrought iron include nickel, copper, and molybdenum. Additions of nickel from 1½ to 3½ per cent have been most common and produce substantial increases in the elastic limit and tensile strength. Nickel is also beneficial in preventing reductions of impact strength at subzero temperatures. Copper may be added to increase corrosion-resistance properties.

The slag content of wrought iron ordinarily varies between 1 and 3 per cent by weight and generally averages about 2 per cent. A typical slag may contain about 70 per cent FeO, 15 per cent SiO_2, and minor amounts of Fe_2O_3, CaO, Al_2O_3, MnO, P_2O_5, Cu, and S.

3. Mechanical Properties. The properties of wrought iron are essentially those of pure iron with allowance for the effects of the amount, character, and distribution of the incorporated slag. Wrought iron has directional properties due to the distribution and to the thread-like character of the slag. Some degree of equalization of the directional properties is being accomplished with development of rolling procedures.

The *tensile strength* of wrought iron along the grain varies between 45,000 and 55,000 psi. With a given material it is greater in small rods and thin plates than in large bars and thick sections. The tensile strength of wrought iron across the grain, transverse to the direction of rolling, generally ranges from 60 to 85 per cent of the strength along the grain. The yield point is also greatly influenced by the thickness of section and varies between 23,000 and 40,000 psi as the size of section is decreased from 2 to ⅜ in. When tested in the direction of the fibers the percentage of elongation in 8 in. normally varies between 10 and 35 per cent, and the reduction in area usually averages about 50 per cent more than the elongation.

The *compressive strength* of wrought iron, like that of other ductile metals, must be regarded as the yield point. At this stress the material buckles out of shape and failure follows if the specimen has appreciable length. Thin sections which receive more work during rolling are stronger than thick sections. Compressive strengths of short sections ¼ to ⅝ in. thick may be expected to vary between 40,000 and 30,000 psi.

The *shearing strength* of wrought iron varies greatly with respect to the direction of the applied forces. The shearing strength across the thickness of a wrought-iron plate, either with or across the grain, is about 80 per cent of the tensile strength. If the external forces are parallel to the plane of the plate, and are applied on faces perpendicular to the plane of the plate, the shearing strength is about the same as the tensile strength. If the external forces are parallel to the plane of the plate, and are applied on faces parallel to the plane of the plate, the shearing strength is slightly less than half the tensile strength.

The *modulus of elasticity* of wrought iron lies between 25,000,000 and 29,000,000 psi for either tension or compression. It is slightly increased by cold work. The modulus of elasticity in torsion is approximately 11,000,000 psi.

4. Other Properties of Wrought Iron. Since wrought iron consists essentially of pure iron and an iron silicate slag, its properties are similar to those of pure iron except as modified by the amount and distribution of the slag. Wrought iron is generally considered to have good welding properties (Art. 6) and good resistance to corrosion, especially to the type called pitting.

The excellent service record of many wrought-iron units exposed for long periods of time to various conditions indicates that wrought iron has superior resistance properties. Some of this behavior may have been due to the presence of small amounts of corrosion inhibitors, such as copper, but many examples of excellent corrosion resistance are available for wrought iron that does not contain any inhibitors. While wrought iron may rust as much as steel under some circumstances, it is generally agreed that the slag fibers act as a barrier against corrosive action and cause it to spread over the surface rather than to pit or penetrate deeply.

It is also claimed, on the basis of actual service records, that wrought iron has superior resistance to shock and vibratory loading and that it is exceptionally tough. It appears difficult to make such claims for class superiority of wrought iron over low-carbon steel in view of the variations of the quality of these materials and also in view of experimental performance. Experimental evidence shows that low-carbon steel of good quality has more capacity for absorbing the energy of a single blow and that under repeated stress wrought iron is weaker than low-carbon steel. Results of impact tests on slotted bars, however, indicate that good wrought iron when overstrained retains as high resistance to impact as soft steel similarly overstrained.

5. Methods of Distinguishing Wrought Iron from Soft Steel. Often the mechanical properties as revealed by the tension test are ample to differentiate steel from wrought iron. Generally wrought iron exhibits lower elastic limit, ultimate strength, and elongation than steel and a very much less reduction in area. The fracture is jagged and fibrous, whereas that of steel is cup-cone and finely crystalline, or silky. The nick-bend test (Art. III-47) serves as a determinator if the iron has a pronounced fibrous fracture. Compression tests on short prisms of wrought iron and steel generally furnish indications of metal texture.

Resistance to corrosion is another basis of distinguishing between these metals. The ends of small rods are turned or filed smooth and suspended for about a half hour in a solution of 1 part hydrochloric acid, 3 parts sulfuric acid, and 9 parts water. After immersion steel will be found to have been evenly attacked, whereas wrought-iron specimens show ridges parallel to the axis of the specimen. The ridges are slag filaments which resist the attack of the acid much better than the intervening grains of iron.

The manganese content of wrought iron is usually less than 0.05 per cent, whereas for steel it is above 0.30 per cent. Hence a chemical analysis furnishes a means of identification. Of all methods, the detection of slag filaments by the microscope is the most positive means of identification of wrought iron.

6. The Welding of Wrought Iron. One of the most valuable properties of wrought iron is the facility with which portions of it may be united by squeezing or hammering while at a high heat. This characteristic renders the iron very useful to the smith. The property is due to the high plasticity of the iron throughout a considerable range of temperature extend-

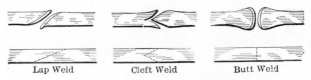

Lap Weld   Cleft Weld   Butt Weld

Fig. 3. Common types of welds.

ing below a white heat. However, if the iron parts are heated to such temperatures in the presence of much air, their surfaces soon become coated with a film of iron oxide. Consequently it is difficult to bring the welding surfaces into perfect contact. To avoid imperfect cohesion it is necessary that the central portions of the surfaces in the weld be first brought together so that the oxide forming at the joint may be expelled outward and not entrapped as the seam is closed under the hammer. The evil effects of the oxide may be greatly reduced by using borax or other flux which acts as a solvent of the oxide and renders it more easy to expel from the joint. Moreover, by maintaining a thick fire in which most of the oxygen is combined with carbon, or by heating the parts in a muffle it is possible to considerably reduce the amount of slag formed. One of the advantages of electric welding lies in the fact that no air blast is employed, and by having the parts in contact during the heating period, air is largely excluded from the welding surfaces and hence little oxide is formed there.

Figure 3 shows the common types of welds and the shapes of the parts prior to welding. After the parts have been shaped and upset as required by the work in hand, they are reheated, if necessary, and then rapidly hammered until the metal is below a red heat. This hot work reduces the grain size and renders the metal at the weld more ductile and tough. Inasmuch as there is likely to be overheated metal on either side of the joint which has not been properly worked during the welding, it is best to anneal welds and thus secure uniformity in structure and properties of the metal in the vicinity of the joint.

Wrought iron may be welded by the usual methods used for mild steel. In pressure welding, the parts to be joined are heated in a forge, by an oxyacetylene flame or by a localized electric current, to a plastic state and forced together under pressure. In fusion welding, the abutting edges may be fused or fused metal from an external source may be added. The heat required for fusion may be supplied by any one of the following methods: combustion of a fuel gas and oxygen; oxyacetylene flame; carbon arc; metal arc; atomic hydrogen arc; or by a chemical reaction between iron oxide and finely divided aluminum known as the Thermit process.

Properly made welds in wrought iron have ultimate tensile and yield strengths that are equal to or usually greater than those of the parent material.

7. Wrought-Iron Chain. Wrought iron is well suited for the manufacture of chain, since it is easily welded and has good resistance to impact, bruising, and corrosion. Wrought-iron chains are proof tested to loads about twice the safe working load before they are used to increase their stiffness and to make them behave elastically up to loads well above the safe working loads. Proof testing also discovers any poor welds that the chain may have. The safe working loads for $\frac{1}{2}$-, 1-, $1\frac{1}{2}$-, and 2-in. trade-size chains are about 4250, 17,000, 35,600, and 63,300 lb, respectively. The actual material size is $\frac{1}{32}$ in. larger than the given trade size. A complete tabulation of weights and dimensions, as well as safe working loads, is given in ASTM *Standard* A56. Since wrought-iron chains are subject to embrittlement at low temperatures, their impact strength at 32°F is only about one-half that at normal temperatures, and decreases rapidly at lower temperatures.

In use the rubbing action of the links against one another causes work hardening which may result in failure under impact or repeated loads. It is therefore desirable to subject the chain to periodic annealing. This heat treatment consists of heating the chain to a temperature between 1350° and 1375°F and holding for a period of $\frac{1}{2}$ to 2 hours, depending on the size of the chain links. It is then uniformly cooled in air to room temperature. After annealing the chain should be again proof tested.

Effect of Composition on the Properties of Steel

1. Principal Factors Influencing Properties of Steel. Properties of steel may be varied over a wide range by control of the three important factors: (1) chemical composition, (2) heat treatment, and (3) mechanical work. Composition bears a vital relation to the constitution of the metal and through structure has a most important bearing on physical properties. In considering composition the effects of the major elements present in all steels—iron, carbon, silicon, manganese, sulfur, and phosphorus—must be understood. The effects of specific alloying elements, singly or in combination, such as nickel, chromium, vanadium, molybdenum, tungsten, cobalt, and titanium, must be evaluated in the design of special-purpose or special-property steels. Heat treatment may be influential (*a*) in altering the solubility relations of the constituents, (*b*) in changing the crystallization either with respect to form or degree of aggregation, (*c*) in introducing or relieving internal stresses in the metal. Mechanical work may be hot or cold; it has an effect (*a*) in altering the form of the crystalline aggregate, (*b*) in introducing internal stresses. Although, for the sake of simplicity, these influences are studied separately, it should be kept in mind that combinations of all of them, in general, affect the properties of the final steel product.

CARBON

2. Importance of Carbon in Steel. The marked changes in structure produced by the additions of small percentages of carbon to pure iron are discussed in Chapter XXII. Indeed, it is the presence of these small quantities of carbon which makes it possible to secure the high degrees of hardness and strength that differentiate steel from ingot iron or wrought iron. The great importance of small additions of carbon is clearly shown by the fact that for fully annealed steels, up to about 0.80 per cent carbon, an increase of carbon of $\frac{1}{100}$ of 1 per cent (one point of carbon) strengthens the steel by approximately 1000 psi. On the other hand, the addition of carbon to iron decreases the malleability and ductility of the metal and reduces its permeability to magnetic forces.

The constitution diagram, Fig. XXII-1, shows that for a carbon content above 2.0 per cent there is always a heterogeneity of structure with separation of cementite at temperatures below 1130°C. When the carbon content is below 2.0 per cent, it is possible to have all the carbon or cementite in solid solution in the iron at some temperature below fusion. The limit of solid solubility at 2.0 per cent carbon marks the theoretical dividing line between steel and cast iron, the cast iron being non-malleable at any range of temperature.

3. The Physical Characteristics of Ferrite and Cementite. Regions IX to XII of the constitution diagram referred to above show that slowly cooled steels and cast iron consist of pure iron (ferrite) and iron carbide (cementite), a portion or all of the ferrite and cementite always being intimately associated in the eutectoid, pearlite. Ferrite is relatively soft, ductile, malleable, and tough, and has low strength. Cementite, on the contrary, is extremely hard, brittle, and non-malleable at any temperature. It is to be expected, therefore, that the relative properties of these two constituents, together with the nature of the association and degree of aggregation, will determine the physical properties of steels and cast irons. In fact the strengths of normal carbon steels of less than eutectoid composition are in direct ratio to the percentage of pearlite, whereas in the hypereutectoid steels the strengths diminish slightly as the excess cementite increases.

4. The Influence of the Carbon Content on the Strength of Steel. The essential relations between carbon content and the strength of steel containing less than 1.4 per cent carbon are shown in Fig. 1 and 2. It should be noted that the tensile strength and the yield point increase to a maximum for steels of approximately eutectoid composition. This is probably due to the relatively intimate mixture and the fine state of aggregation of the constituents of the pearlite. With a decrease or increase of carbon the ferrite or cementite, respectively, becomes an excess substance forming a grain network which has a weakening influence on the metal.

The data in Fig. 1 and 2 show that the tensile strength of hot-rolled steel bars varies from 55,000 psi for 0.10 per cent carbon to 150,000 psi for 1.0 per cent carbon. The tensile strengths of the annealed bars are appreciably lower for a given carbon content. The tensile strength of the hot-rolled bars appears to reach a maximum value for a carbon content between 1.0 and 1.2 per cent, whereas annealed steel bars appear to reach their maximum strength at eutectoid composition.

Since the relation between tensile strength (S_t) and the points of carbon (C) for hot-rolled steel with carbon contents less than 1.00 per cent is approximately linear, the relation may be expressed by the equation

$$S_t = 45,000 + 1000C$$

The proportional limit and the yield point of steel in tension, like the ultimate strength, increase with the carbon content, but at a lower rate.

The ratio of the yield point to the ultimate strength usually runs between 0.60 and 0.70 for low- and medium-carbon steels and between 0.50 and 0.60 for high-carbon steels. The yield point in high-carbon steels is much less pronounced than in low- or medium-carbon steels.

The ultimate compressive strength of steel in very short prisms is not well defined. In members with l/r above 100, column action is present, but in fairly short prisms with l/r between 20 and 50 the compressive

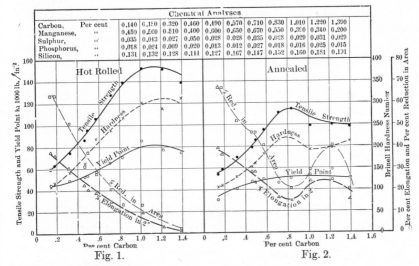

Fig. 1.   Fig. 2.

Fig. 1.   The influence of carbon on the mechanical properties of hot-rolled steels (Nead).   Diameter of specimens, 0.505 in.; gage length = 2 in.

Fig. 2.   The influence of carbon on the mechanical properties of annealed steels (Nead).   Annealing temperatures were those recommended by ASTM, which were slightly higher than those shown in Fig. XXV-10.

strength is practically equal to the yield point. The compressive strength of steel increases directly with the carbon content up to 1 per cent carbon in approximate accord with the relation $S_c = 30,000 + 550C$. Since the yield points of steel in tension and compression are nearly identical, it is possible to make an approximate determination of the compressive strength from the results of a tensile test.

The shearing strength of steel as determined from transverse shear or torsional tests also increases with the carbon content for carbon contents up to about 1 per cent. The ratio of the shearing strength to the tensile strength is approximately 0.80 for low- and medium-carbon steels, but decreases as the carbon content increases to about 0.60 for high-carbon steels.

5. The Influence of the Carbon Content on Other Properties of Steel.
The modulus of elasticity of steel is nearly the same for tension and com-

pression, and for either stress it is practically independent of the carbon content. It is likely to be slightly higher on a second loading than on the first loading. The available experimental data indicate that the modulus of elasticity in tension or compression generally lies between 29,000,000 and 31,000,000 psi and averages about 29,500,000 psi.

The modulus of elasticity in shear (modulus of rigidity) determined from torsional tests usually varies between 11,500,000 and 12,500,000 psi. An average value of 12,000,000 psi is frequently used.

The ductility and plasticity of steel as measured by the per cent elongation and the per cent reduction in area, respectively, decrease markedly as the carbon content is increased (Fig. 1 and 2). Since ductility is much influenced by variations in heat treatment and by the gage length, it is not possible to give an accurate equation between carbon content and ductility.

The static toughness of steel as measured by the energy of rupture obtained from the area under a tensile stress-strain curve shows little significant change up to a carbon content of about 0.40 per cent, after which it decreases rapidly with increasing carbon. Toughness as determined from impact tension tests shows, in general, the same trend as determined from the static tensile tests. However, results obtained from Charpy and Izod tests show that notch sensitivity decreases most rapidly as the carbon content increases up to about 0.40 per cent, and that further decreases in notch sensitivity with higher carbon contents are not as great.

The elastic toughness of steel as measured by the modulus of resilience determined from the area under the tensile stress-strain curve up to the proportional limit increases as the carbon content increases up to approximately eutectoid proportions. Tests have shown that the harder steels with a higher proportional limit are better suited to withstand repeated stress or a succession of light blows.

6. Influence of Carbon on the Stress-Strain Diagram. The effects of carbon on the tensile properties of steel are well shown by the changes in the shape of the stress-strain diagram. Thus, in Fig. 3, the increases in the proportional limit and ultimate strength and the accompanying decreases in the elongation with increasing amounts of carbon cause the diagrams to increase in height and decrease in width. The horizontal portion of the curve for low-carbon steel which follows the drop in the load after the yield point has been passed disappears in the diagrams for the high-carbon steel. The downward slope of the portion of the stress-strain curve beyond the ultimate stress accompanying necking becomes less pronounced in the high-carbon steels and disappears in the diagrams of the very high-carbon steels which break without necking. The entire area under the curve, representing the energy of rupture, does not vary significantly until the carbon content exceeds about 0.40 per cent, after which it decreases rapidly with increasing carbon content.

Chemical Analyses, %				
C	Mn	Si	S	P
0.19	1.00	0.12	0.027	0.023
0.49	0.75	0.22	0.026	0.014
0.64	0.66	0.15	0.037	0.032
0.90	0.41	0.18	0.028	0.022

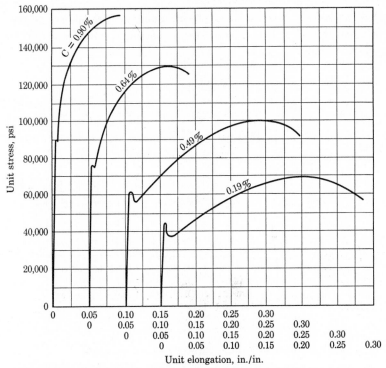

Fig. 3.   Tension stress-strain diagrams of hot-rolled steel bars.

7. The Range in Composition of Structural Steels.   Practically all steels used in engineering construction in the normal or annealed condition are of less than eutectoid proportion (0.80 per cent carbon).   The carbon content is the result of experience whereby the proper combination of strength, elasticity, hardness, and workability have been obtained to fit the material for the particular service.   Increased tenacity and elastic strength are gained at the sacrifice of ductility and softness.   In structural steels, boiler plate, and the like, where some increase of strength is desirable, provided there is not too great loss of ductility and softness, a carbon content of about 0.20 per cent is customary.   The tensile strength is thereby increased by about 15,000 psi (from 45,000 to 60,000) without material loss of the ductility and softness so essential to the requirements for manufacture and service. In steel rails there is little fabrication of the finished product and the stresses are heavy shocks at intermittent periods. Hardness is essential for wear, and high strength and elasticity are necessary to enable rails to withstand the loads and recover alignment; yet ductility cannot be sacrificed to the extent of dangerous brittleness. The carbon content of rails varies from 0.50 to 0.90 per cent, the larger amounts having been introduced in special cases, particularly in heavy sections and where the steel has the minimum of phosphorus, sulfur, or other associated detrimental elements, which lower ductility without adding much strength.

TABLE 1

CLASSIFICATION BASED ON			Per Cent Carbon.	Tensile Strength (lb./in.^{2}).	Per Cent Elongation in	
Usage.	Hardness.	Manufacture.			8 in.	2 in.
Rivets and Welding......	Extra soft	O. H.	0.08–0.15	45– 55,000	30	
Tubing and Pressed Metal	Extra soft	O. H.	0.08–0.15	45– 55,000	30	
Screw stock............	Mild or Soft	O. H. / Bess.	0.10–0.20	55– 65,000	25	
Boiler plate............		O. H.	0.10–0.20	55– 65,000	25	
Structural.............		O. H. / Bess.	0.15–0.25	60– 72,000		
Structural.............	Medium	O. H.	0.20–0.35	65– 75,000	22	
Machine..............	Medium	O. H.	0.20–0.30	60– 70,000	23	
Car axles..............	Medium hard	O. H.	0.40–0.55	75–100,000	..	12–15
Rails and Tires........	Hard	O. H.	0.50–0.90	90–130,000	..	10–12
Springs................	Extra hard	O. H.	0.85–1.05	125–150,000	..	8–10

Table 1 shows classifications,* approximate composition, and mechanical properties of some of the more important steels used in construction. Carbon contents for tool steels are given in Chapter XXVII.

EFFECTS OF PRINCIPAL IMPURITIES OF STEEL †

8. General Effects. As noted in Chapter XIX, it is not feasible under present practice to remove impurities entirely in making either iron or steel. Therefore, the final product always contains, besides iron and carbon, small percentages of the metallic impurities—silicon, manganese,

* See also SAE classification system, Art. 15.
† For a discussion of the effects of impurities on steel, see *The Making, Shaping and Treating of Steel,* U. S. Steel Corp., and *Metals Handbook,* Am. Soc. Metals.

sulfur, and phosphorus—together with lesser amounts of the oxides of silica, manganese, and iron, silicates of manganese and iron, and some occluded gases. Occasionally very small percentages of copper, nickel, chromium, vanadium, molybdenum, tin, and arsenic are also present. In well-made steel the total amount of these impurities generally ranges between 0.2 and 1.0 per cent and their resultant effect on the constitution of steel is often very small. Of the common impurities, phosphorus and sulfur are injurious elements present in the ore which cannot be eliminated in the process of manufacture, whereas most of the silicon and manganese are introduced to improve the metal. The non-metallic impurities are objectionable substances which find their way into the steel during the process of refining.

9. Effects of Silicon. Silicon, probably in the form of iron silicide, forms solid solutions with iron in all proportions up to 20 per cent. It is often added to molten metal to remove oxygen and diminish blow-holes. In the carbon steels silicon rarely exceeds $\frac{1}{2}$ of 1 per cent and in structural steels it is generally under $\frac{1}{4}$ of 1 per cent. With such small proportions of silicon the microscope reveals no peculiarities in constitution. Silicon up to 1.75 per cent appears to increase both ultimate strength and elastic limit without decreasing ductility.* Silicon increases the hardness of steel and is about one-third as effective as carbon in increasing hardness.

On account of the marked tendency of silicon to prevent solution of carbon in iron (Art. XXII-13) it is necessary to avoid prolonged heating at high temperatures in treating steels having high silicon and carbon contents. Instances have been recorded where steel castings have been ruined by soaking for a long time at a temperature considerably above the recalescence point, the combined carbon being thus transformed into graphite and the casting thereby greatly embrittled. However, with normal percentage of silicon and good heat treatment graphite is not present in steel.

10. Effects of Phosphorus. When present in the low proportions common to steel, phosphorus exists in a solid solution of iron phosphide (Fe_3P) and iron. Howe maintained that the presence of phosphorus in ferrite makes the ferrite more mobile when it is slowly cooling through the transformation range. This mobility results in the banding of the ferrite into thin rods or layers which, upon etching, are revealed as light-colored lines, called ghost lines. Such formations, of course, render the metal less homogeneous.

In wrought iron much of the phosphorus content is held in the slag fibers in the form of iron phosphate. As a constituent of the slag its effect is probably less detrimental than as a phosphide in the ferrite.

* The properties of silicon steels are discussed in Chapter XXVII.

Although the ductility of low-carbon steel may be slightly decreased by the presence of 0.3 to 0.5 per cent phosphorus, the yield point, ultimate strength and hardness are increased. Resistance to shock is, however, markedly reduced by such high percentages of phosphorus. Tests on low-carbon steels show that toughness is adversely affected (i.e., the metal is rendered cold short) by 0.1 per cent phosphorus and very much decreased by 0.2 per cent of this element. The evil effect on toughness appears to be more pronounced in high-carbon than in low-carbon steels.

Although it is very probable that many failures have been erroneously ascribed to a high phosphorus content which, if all facts were known, were traceable to other causes, yet a due regard for the tendency to produce cold shortness requires that phosphorus be kept low in steel. At present the maximum percentage limits are: for inferior grades of structural steel 0.1, for best grades of structural steel 0.05, and for tool steels 0.02.

11. Effects of Sulfur. Sulfur readily combines with iron to form iron sulfide (FeS) which, when present in iron or steel, has a tendency to segregate and form brittle networks at the grain boundaries. On account of its low melting point, iron sulfide causes a lack of cohesion between adjacent grains of the metal when it is heated above a red heat. Such brittleness at high temperatures is termed red shortness. Since red shortness makes steel or iron hard to roll or forge, it is a serious defect in the metal from the standpoint of the manufacturer. Manganese sulfide has a much higher melting point than iron sulfide and does not render ferrous metals red short. Therefore, inasmuch as manganese has a very powerful affinity for sulfur, it is possible to relieve red shortness by adding sufficient manganese to the molten metal to combine with the sulfur. Theoretically the ratio of manganese to sulfur should be 1.7:1 in order to form manganese sulfide (MnS) and completely satisfy sulfur. Levy contends, however, that even if manganese is present in sufficient quantities to form the sulfide some iron sulfide will still remain and will be found mixed with the manganese sulfide. Since manganese sulfide also segregates and forms brittle masses, more or less rounded in castings and elongated in mechanically worked pieces, it appears that either sulfide causes a lack of homogeneity.

If sufficient manganese is present to prevent red shortness there is little evidence that sulfur in quantities less than 0.15 per cent exercises any appreciable effect on the mechanical properties of structural steel. For screw stock a high sulfur content (0.10 to 0.15 per cent) is commonly specified, since chips of such metal crumble without curling and the stock threads nicely. There appears to be a feeling, even though there is little direct evidence to support it, that percentages of sulfur too small to produce red shortness in rolling may develop invisible flaws in the finished

metal. Specifications for steel, therefore, stringently limit sulfur to practically the same amounts as phosphorus.

12. Effects of Manganese. Manganese is one of the main elements of
the recarburizers used in manufacturing steel. Through its strong affinity for oxygen and sulfur, manganese acts as a cleanser of the molten
metal by withdrawing much of these undesirable impurities into the slag.
When more manganese is present than is required to satisfy sulfur and
oxygen, the excess manganese forms the carbide, Mn_3C, which is associated with cementite. If present in this form manganese acts as a
hardener. In carbon steels the manganese content is generally under
1 per cent and ordinarily runs about 0.3 to 0.6 per cent. Tests show that
manganese, when under 1.0 per cent, hardens steel slightly, the average
increase in hardness due to an increase of 0.1 manganese being about 4.0
on the Brinell scale. Intermediate-manganese steels with amounts of
manganese varying between 1.0 and 1.9 per cent are used for various
structural purposes and also as a substitute for low-alloy steels containing important amounts of nickel.

In high-carbon steels manganese increases the solubility of carbon in
iron and hinders the precipitation of graphite in cooling.

13. Effects of Other Metallic Elements. In addition to the metallic
elements previously discussed many others may be present in carbon
steels, usually in relatively small quantities. Some, such as aluminum
and titanium, are purposefully added for deoxidation and grain-size control. Lead may be added to low-carbon steel to improve machinability.
Some elements, such as arsenic, tin, and antimony, are present in small
amounts in the ores and are not removed in the manufacturing process.
Others, such as nickel, copper, molybdenum, chromium, and vanadium,
may have been introduced by the use of alloy-steel scrap during melting
and refining. The small amounts of these elements introduced by the
scrap increase hardenability (see Chapter XXVII). In some instances
where ductility is important, as in deep drawing, this effect may be
harmful.

Aluminum in relatively small controlled amounts is considered desirable
because it acts to refine the grain and to decrease the susceptibility to
strain aging. Since aluminum tends to promote graphitization, it is not
desirable in steels for high-temperature service. Copper in small amounts
seems to increase resistance to corrosion. Tin is undesirable in steels to
be used for deep drawing because it increases hardness and reduces
toughness.

14. Effects of Oxygen, Hydrogen, and Nitrogen in Steel. The average
amount of oxygen present in ordinary carbon steels is probably less than
0.015 per cent. Most of it is usually present as an oxide or silicate.
Elongated oxide inclusions are partially responsible for directional prop-

erties of steel. Oxygen in steel is also believed to be one of the elements responsible for aging of steel.

The amount of hydrogen in steel is small, probably less than 0.005 per cent. Even in very small quantities, hydrogen has an embrittling effect on the properties of steel. Hydrogen is one of the important factors in the development of internal cracks, known as flaking. Such cracks may occur in steel during the cooling period following rolling or forging.

TABLE 2. SOCIETY OF AUTOMOTIVE ENGINEERS AND AMERICAN IRON AND STEEL INSTITUTE NUMBERING SYSTEM [1]

Type of Steel	Range in SAE Numbers	Range in AISI Numbers
Carbon steels		
Plain carbon (C <0.06–1.05, P <0.04%)	1006–1095	C1005–C1095
Plain carbon (C <0.08– <0.13, P 0.07–0.12%)	—	B1006–B1010
Plain carbon (C 0.43–0.80, P <0.05%)	—	D1049–D1075
Free cutting (C <0.08–0.55, S <0.33%)	1109, 1114–1151	C1106–C1151
Free cutting (C <0.13, S <0.33, P 0.07–0.12%)	1111–1113	B1111–B1113
High manganese (Mn 1.60–2.10%)	1320–1340	1320–1340
Nickel steels		
3.25–3.75% Ni	2317–2345	2317–2345
4.75–5.25% Ni	2512–2517	2512–2517
Nickel-chromium steels		
1.10–1.40% Ni, 0.55–0.90% Cr	3115–3150	3115–3150
3.25–3.75% Ni, 1.40–1.75% Cr	3310–3316	3310–3316
Molybdenum steels		
0.20–0.30% Mo	4017–4068	4017–4068
0.15–0.30% Mo, 0.40–1.10% Cr	4119–4150	4130–4150
0.20–0.30% Mo, 0.40–0.90% Cr, 1.65–2.00% Ni	4317–4340	4317–4340
0.15–0.30% Mo, 1.40–2.00% Ni	4608–4640	4608–4640
0.20–0.30% Mo, 3.25–3.75% Ni	4812–4820	4812–4820
Chromium steels		
0.20–0.75% Cr	5045, 5046	5045, 5046
0.70–1.20% Cr	5115–5152	5120–5152
0.40–1.60% Cr	50100–52100	50100–52100
Chromium-vanadium steels		
0.70–1.10% Cr, <0.10% Va	6150	6120–6152
Special alloy steels		
0.40–0.70% Ni, 0.40–0.80% Cr, 0.15–0.25% Mo	8615–8660	8615–8660
0.40–0.70% Ni, 0.40–0.60% Cr, 0.20–0.30% Mo	8720–8750	8720–8750
1.20–2.20% Si, 0.50–1.00% Mn	9255–9262	9254–9262
3.00–3.50% Ni, 1.00–1.40% Cr, 0.08–0.15% Mo	9310–9317	9310–9317
0.30–0.60% Ni, 0.30–0.50% Cr, 0.08–0.15% Mo	9437–9445	9437–9445
0.40–0.70% Ni, 0.10–0.25% Cr, 0.15–0.25% Mo	9747–9763	9747–9763
0.85–1.15% Ni, 0.70–0.90% Cr, 0.20–0.30% Mo	9840–9850	9840–9850

[1] Complete chemical compositions of all steels are given in the SAE *Handbook* and in the *Metals Handbook*. Compositions of wrought stainless steels, heat-resisting alloys, and heat-resistant castings are also given in the *Metals Handbook*.

Flaking may be prevented by slow cooling after rolling or forging to allow the hydrogen opportunity to diffuse out of the steel. This slow cooling period, now standard in the manufacture of rails, has largely eliminated the "transverse fissure" type of failure.

Usually less than 0.005 per cent of nitrogen is present in steel. It is another element believed to have an important role in the aging of steel. Nitrogen is an effective surface-hardening agent when, in the form of ammonia, it is placed in contact with the hot surface of solid steel for the required length of time.

15. Society of Automotive Engineers and American Iron and Steel Institute Numbering Systems for Steels. These organizations have adopted standard numeral index systems by which it is possible to designate with four or five figures the names and the percentages of the important elements in steels. The first figure indicates the name or names of the important alloying element. The second figure for alloy steels usually shows the percentage of the most important alloying element. The last two or three figures generally designate the approximate carbon content. For example, 1015 indicates a plain carbon steel with 0.13 to 0.18 per cent carbon; 2335 indicates a nickel steel with 3.25 to 3.75 per cent nickel and 0.33 to 0.38 per cent carbon; 3140 designates a nickel-chromium steel with 1.10 to 1.40 per cent nickel, 0.55 to 0.75 per cent chromium, and 0.38 to 0.43 per cent carbon; 52100 signifies a chromium steel with 1.30 to 1.60 per cent chromium and 0.95 to 1.10 per cent carbon. Table 2 provides information as revised in 1947.

Heat Treatment of Steel

1. The Importance of Heat Treatment. The wide variety of products made of steel and the wide range of their required properties indicate that versatility is one of the outstanding advantages of steel. Initial control of the properties may be obtained by careful consideration of the chemical composition. In plain carbon steels control is exercised principally through the carbon content, and in alloy steels through control of the type and amount of the alloying elements used. Control of the composition does not end the possibilities of controlling the properties, because of the very significant changes available through mechanical work and heat treatment. The properties of steel can be controlled and changed at will by various heat treatments. A steel of given composition may be made soft, ductile, and tough by one heat treatment, and the same steel may be made relatively hard and strong by another. Heat treatment affects the nature, amount, and character of the metallographic constituents.

Some of the principal purposes of heat treatment are (*a*) to increase properties such as strength, ductility, hardness, and toughness; (*b*) to relieve internal stresses and strains; (*c*) to refine the grain; (*d*) to remove gases; (*e*) to normalize steel after mechanical or heat treatment. Selection of the proper heat treatment to obtain the best properties of a steel for a specific use requires a good understanding of the principles of heat treatment.

2. Effects of Heating above the Critical Range. On heating steel past the critical range of temperature, there is a structural change from an aggregate of ferrite and cementite to a homogeneous solid solution. This transition effectively destroys all preexisting crystallization, not only as to type of aggregate, but of size as well.

Referring to the constitution diagram, Fig. XXII-1, it will be noted that so long as a steel of carbon content 0 to 2.0 per cent is not heated above Ac_1 (723°C) there will be no change in the structural relations of the iron and the cementite.* With rise of temperature above this critical point, however, formation of austenite will begin and proceed to a degree dependent upon the carbon content of the steel and the temperature at-

---

* On account of lag in reaction the change takes place at Ac_1 which is slightly higher than Ar_1, the temperature of transformation on cooling.

tained above the critical one. Solution of all of the pearlite is completed immediately the temperature exceeds Ac_1.

For hypoeutectoid (below 0.80 per cent carbon) or hypereutectoid (above 0.80 per cent carbon) steels the solution of the excess ferrite or cementite, respectively, proceeds with each degree of temperature rise above Ac_1, but is not completed until the temperature reaches the upper transition limit, marked by GP and PS, respectively, corresponding to the particular carbon content of the steel under treatment. In other words, the austenitic state in a steel of eutectoid composition (0.80 per cent carbon) is entirely brought about by heating to or just above the constant critical temperature of transition; a steel of other carbon content necessitates a range of temperature which is greater the farther the carbon content is removed from 0.80 per cent. The temperature necessary to accomplish complete solution of the cementite is higher the more the steel varies either way from eutectoid proportions. The transition, as noted heretofore, is the result of allotropy in the iron; cementite is only slightly soluble in alpha iron, but is completely soluble in gamma iron, within the saturation limits marked by region IV in the constitution diagram.

3. Effects of Cooling from above the Critical Range. There will be progressive aggregation of the austenite into grains which increase in size with rise of temperature, up to the fusion stage. That grain size which is attained as a result of the maximum temperature reached during heating will be retained during the cooling of the steel to ordinary temperatures, and, although the transition from the austenitic to the pearlitic (or some intermediate) form will take place during the critical temperature range, the final structure will exhibit such coarseness of texture as was inherent in the austenite when cooling began. Coarseness of grain is a function of temperature rise above the critical point Ar_3 and of the time at that temperature; but diminution of grain is not an accompaniment of temperature fall.

Rate of cooling through and somewhat below the transition zone influences the final structure, however; (1) the reversion from austenite to ferrite-cementite requires time for its completion, and, the quicker the cooling for a given composition, the less complete is the transition, and the more nearly the final product approaches austenite in structure and properties; this is treated more fully in the discussion of tempering of steel; (2) the ferrite-cementite aggregate, particularly the pearlitic portion, will have opportunity for greater coalescence of like to like, the slower the cooling.

The grain size obtained by heating steel into the austenitic field, the austenitic grain size, cannot be readily seen at high temperatures, but it may be observed after the steel has been cooled to room temperature. In the case of hypoeutectoid carbon steels, this may be accomplished by slowly cooling the steel during the initial part of the transformation in order to reject the proeutectoid ferrite in the form of a thin network to the grain boundaries. The same method may be used for hypereutectoid steels, but for these steels the rejected proeutectoid carbide outlines the grain boundaries. The austenitic grain size in eutectoid carbon steels may be observed by incompletely hardening these steels so that the outer portions are hardened or martensitic, and the inner portions are unhardened or pearlitic. Etching the area between the hardened and unhardened portions will show dark-etching finely divided pearlite grain boundaries surrounding light-etching martensite (an unstable decomposition constituent found in rapidly quenched steel).

A standard classification of the austenitic grain size in steels is given in ASTM Des. E19. In this classification, the grain size number (N) varies between 1 and 8 as the mean number of grains (M) per square inch observed under a magnification of 100 varies between 1 and 128 in accordance with the equation $M = 2^{N-1}$.

Grain growth in carbon steels heated well above the transformation temperature may be controlled by the additions of aluminum to molten steel during the manufacturing process. The amount of aluminum added to control grain growth and to deoxidize the steel does not usually exceed 0.20 per cent and is frequently less than 0.10 per cent.

With like constitution it appears to be generally true that ductility, strength, toughness, resistance to fatigue, and resistance to quenching cracks increase with decreasing grain size. Fine-grained steels are generally desired for the reasons given, but under certain conditions coarse-grained steels are preferred. Coarse-grained steels machine more easily and harden more deeply than fine-grained steels and are less apt to have soft areas on the surface of carburized-and-quenched steel.

4. Application of Isothermal Transformation Diagrams of Steel. Investigations of constant-temperature (isothermal) transformations of austenite at temperatures below A_3 and A_{cM} were started by E. C. Bain and E. S. Davenport in the United States Steel Corp. research laboratories. These important investigations from which the transformation-temperature-time (TTT) or S-curve were developed have helped provide a better understanding of the heat treatment of steel. Such curves are now available for plain carbon and many alloy steels.

Determination of the S-curves for steel of a given composition, such as shown in Fig. 1, involves quenching a large number of small specimens in a molten lead or salt bath maintained at a constant temperature. These specimens are held in the bath for different times varying between $\frac{1}{2}$ and 100,000 sec to allow various amounts of austenite to transform to ferrite and cementite. The specimens are then removed from the batch, quenched in cold brine to be certain that all untransformed austenite is changed to martensite, and examined under a microscope to determine the amount of austenite that has transformed. The upper portion of Fig. 1 shows that for a transformation temperature of 700°F the transformation started at 3.5 sec and was completed after about 550 sec. The lower portion of Fig. 1 has been plotted from the results of many tests carried out at

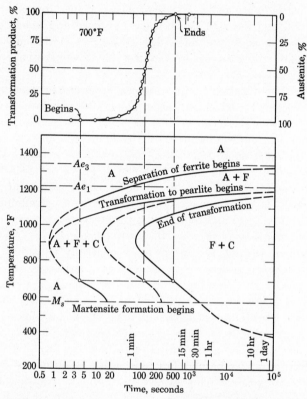

Fig. 1. Isothermal transformation curve at 700°F (top) and its relation to the complete diagram (S-curve) for a 0.45 per cent carbon low-nickel steel. (Research Laboratory, U. S. Steel Corp.)

various transformation temperatures. The horizontal lines Ae_1 and Ae_3 on the diagram represent the A_1 and A_3 equilibrium temperatures, respectively. The light dashed line gives the time required for 50 per cent of the transformation to take place.

Above the knee of the curve, approximately 900°F for Fig. 1, the first step in the isothermal transformation in hypoeutectoid steels is the separation of proeutectoid ferrite. In hypereutectoid steels, the proeutectoid cementite separates out; in eutectoid steels pearlite separates out. For the hypoeutectoid steel of Fig. 1 at any transformation temperature between 900°F and Ae_1 the ferrite separation is followed after some time by the separation of ferrite and cementite in pearlitic form, and after an additional period the transformation is completed and a combination of ferrite and cementite is obtained as the final structure.

In order that isothermal transformations take place at temperatures below the knee of the curve, it is necessary that the steel be rapidly quenched to the desired temperature so that it passes through 900°F in less than about 0.7 sec. Isothermal transformations at any temperature between the M_s line and 900°F proceed with increasing time from austenite to a combination of austenite, ferrite, and cementite and finally to a combination of ferrite and cementite known as Bainite. This structure is formed only by isothermal transformation and consists of finely dispersed ferrite and cementite.

Steel that is to transform at temperatures below the M_s line must also be rapidly quenched so that the time-temperature cooling curve passes to the left of the knee. When cooled in this manner to temperatures below the M_s line, some of the austenite is converted to martensite. Between 400°F and the M_s line the austenite not converted to martensite is finally transformed to ferrite and cementite. Below 400°F essentially all the austenite is converted to martensite in the quenching operation.

Under usual conditions, steels are not made to transform at a given temperature but the transformations take place while they are being cooled at a desired rate. However, the isothermal transformation diagrams are useful to show what takes place under various cooling conditions. In Fig. 2, the line GF marks the beginning of transformation from austenite to pearlite for a eutectoid carbon steel, and the beginning of the change from austenite to martensite is shown by the line MN. The figure also shows the relation of various cooling rates to these lines. Slowly cooled steels start to transform after 1000 sec at a temperature of 700°C to coarse pearlite, and transformation is completed at a lower temperature and after some time has elapsed, in essential accord with the complete S-curve. Steels cooled at a medium rate start to transform after approximately 70 sec at a temperature about 670°C to a medium pearlite. Steels that are slowly quenched transform in a shorter period and at a lower temperature to fine pearlite. Steels that are rapidly quenched so that they pass to the left of the knee at F transform to martensite.

Figure 2 clearly indicates that as the cooling rate increases the transformation temperature decreases, the time required for the transformation to start decreases, the final structure is finer, and that a completely martensitic structure is obtained only when the cooling curve passes to the left of F.

Hypoeutectoid or hypereutectoid steels show similar changes but in addition precipitate excess ferrite or cementite from the austenite before the transformation to pearlite takes place. Increasing the cooling rate for such steels also lowers the A_3 and A_{cM} temperatures. Most alloying elements retard the transformation rate, and the knee of the S-curves is moved to the right. Consequently, alloy steels are more easily hardened

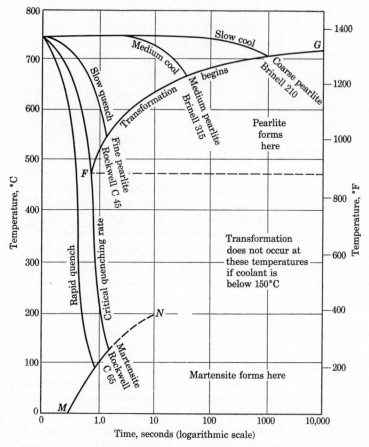

Fig. 2. Relation of constant-temperature transformation rates to ordinary cooling rates for 0.80 per cent carbon steel. (Bain, *Trans. Am. Soc. Steel Treating*, Vol. 20, 1932, p. 390.)

because drastic quenches are not necessary in order that the cooling curve pass to the left of the knee.

5. Microstructure of Heat-Treated Steels. Steel is a versatile material because its properties can be varied over a wide range by subjecting it to various heat treatments. These property changes are due to structural changes in steel brought about by heat treatment and are all fundamentally due to the fact that carbon is soluble in gamma iron and is essentially insoluble in alpha iron. The solid solution of carbon in gamma iron existing in steel above 723°C is called austenite and is shown in Fig. 3.

Austenite may have from a trace to 2.0 per cent carbon, along with other elements as manganese and nickel in the solution. At room temperatures it is not present in the usual carbon steels, because it is impossible to cool it rapidly enough to prevent transformations from taking place. However, addition of sufficient amounts of the alloying elements manganese, nickel, tungsten, etc., either lower the critical temperature

Fig. 3. The microscopic structure of austenite, ×500. (From *Suiting the Heat Treatment to the Job*, U. S. Steel Corp.)

Fig. 4. Microstructure of martensite, ×2500. (From *Suiting the Heat Treatment to the Job*, U. S. Steel Corp.)

or slow down the rate of transformation and thus allow retention of austenite. The physical properties of austenite vary with the carbon content. Strength and hardness are increased and ductility is decreased as the carbon content is increased.

If austenite is quenched rapidly so that transformation takes place below 450°F, martensite, a supersaturated solid solution of carbon in alpha iron, is obtained (Fig. 4).

In order that martensite be formed it must be quenched fast enough so that the cooling curve passes to the left of the knee of the S-curve and is made to transform at temperatures below 450°F. Figure 5 shows the relation between transformation time and transformation temperature and the transformation product. The figure shows that martensite transforms almost immediately when the transformation temperature falls below 450°F, and that as the temperature falls from 450° to 200°F an increasing amount of martensite is formed. The transformation from austenite to martensite is substantially complete when the steel is quenched to room temperature.

The structure, composition, and properties of martensite depend primarily on the carbon content and the rate of quench. Martensite has an acicular structure and is very hard, strong, and brittle. It is the principal constituent of hardened carbon steels and the cause of their great hardness. The primary cause of the hardness of martensite is believed to be

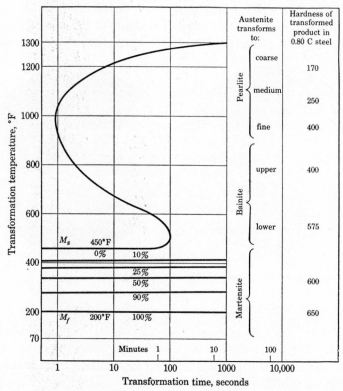

Fig. 5. Time required by austenite in transforming at different temperatures. (From *Suiting the Heat Treatment to the Job*, U. S. Steel Corp.)

due to the precipitation of submicroscopic particles of carbon as iron carbide from the gamma solid solution and the presence of these particles in the alpha-iron lattice where they act as keys to prevent slip.

When austenite is slowly cooled in a furnace, the necessary time for complete transformation is available and the final structure is lamellar pearlite. In hypoeutectoid steels the excess ferrite will be present along with the pearlite, and in hypereutectoid steels the excess cementite forms grain boundaries surrounding the pearlitic areas. The structure of eutectoid steels will be completely pearlitic and, as shown in Fig. 6, will consist of more or less parallel plates of cementite in ferrite. The pearlitic structure will vary from coarse to fine, depending on the temperature at which the transformation takes place. Coarse pearlitic structures result when the austenite is made to transform between 1200° and 1300°F, and fine

pearlitic structures result when transformation takes place around 1000°F, as shown in Fig. 5. It is also evident from Fig. 5 that the time required for the transformation to coarse austenite is much greater than that required to produce fine pearlite.

When steel is quenched at a rate fast enough so that the cooling curve passes to the left of the knee of the S-curve and is then made to transform at some constant temperature between 450° and 900°F (isothermal transformation) an acicular type structure called bainite is obtained. Bainite is a mechanical mixture of ferrite and cementite and has a micro-

Fig. 6. The microscopic structure of pearlite, ×2500. (From *Suiting the Heat Treatment to the Job,* U. S. Steel Corp.)

structure suggestive of martensite (Fig. 7a and 7b), but shows evidence of cementite, which is not present in martensite. A bainite structure is considered to provide a high degree of toughness.

       (a)   (b)

Fig. 7. The microscopic structure of bainite, ×2500. a, Partial; b, complete. (From *Suiting the Heat Treatment to the Job,* U. S. Steel Corp.)

The previous discussion has shown that very slowly cooled austenite transforms to a lamellar structure; that rapidly quenched austenite transforms to an acicular structure, martensite; and that austenite, which is rapidly quenched to a temperature between 450° and 900°F and allowed to transform at a constant temperature within that range, transforms to bainite. It should also be noted that, once a transformation product has formed from austenite at some temperature, that product when further cooled to a lower temperature will not transform to the product characteristic of the lower temperature. Pearlite, for example, formed above 900°F will not form martensite when cooled below 450°F.

Fig. 8. A 1.1 per cent carbon steel quenched from 900°C, reheated to 600°C, and quenched. ×150. (Sauveur and Boylston.)

Since steels that are rapidly quenched to obtain a martensitic structure have poor ductility and toughness and may have high internal stresses and strains, it is necessary to reheat them to some temperature below the critical range and cool (temper them). This procedure reduces internal stresses and strains, improves ductility and toughness, and decreases the strength, especially when the reheat temperature is relatively high. These changes in properties are due to the fact that martensite is not highly stable and will revert to a more stable structure if given the opportunity. Reheating martensite provides that opportunity, and the new structure formed is granular, with increasingly coarser carbide particles as the reheating temperature is increased. Figure 8 shows the granular structure of tempered martensite.

While many metallurgists prefer to refer to all structures obtained by reheating martensite as tempered martensite, some prefer to use the names troostite and sorbite. Troostite is a mixture of very fine particles of cementite and ferrite obtained by reheating martensite to a temperature between 200° and 400°C. Sorbite is also a mixture of ferrite and cementite, but contains fairly coarse cementite particles. It is obtained by reheating martensite to some temperature above 400°C, but below the lower critical temperature.

Martensite reheated for prolonged periods at temperatures just below the lower critical temperature will have a spheroidized structure, shown in Fig. 9. This structure is still a mixture of ferrite and cementite, but the cementite is present as small rounded particles set in a matrix of ferrite.

6. Heating and Cooling Steel. Heating should be by gradual approach to the desired temperature, and the object should be held at this temperature for a sufficient time to reach a uniform condition throughout and to permit phase equilibrium to be established. Control of the heating rate through the transformation range is especially important in order to avoid cracking due to uneven expansion. The specific treatment will vary with the amount of carbon and other constituents in the steel, with the size of the object, and with the

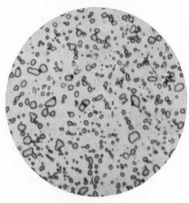

Fig. 9. The microscopic structure of spheroidite, ×1000. (From *Suiting the Heat Treatment to the Job*, U. S. Steel Corp.)

relations of hardness, strength, ductility, toughness, and machinability desired in the final product.

During the heating stage the steel should be protected from oxidation and decarburization of the surface. This is generally accomplished by heating the steel in non-oxidizing controlled atmospheres or in salt or deoxidized lead baths. Oxidation and the resultant scaling are undesirable where accurate size or good surface characteristics are required. Decarburization is especially harmful when the steel is to be subjected to fatigue stress.

Cooling of steel from the desired temperature is usually performed in air, brine, water, oil, or molten metal. When the cooling is rapid, it is called quenching. Liquids are most frequently used because of their excellent heat-transmission properties. Quenching in brine extracts the heat most rapidly. Quenching in water is about 50 per cent as effective as quenching in brine, and quenching in oil is about one-third as effective as quenching in water. Cooling in air is relatively slow. The effectiveness of quenching in a given medium may be greatly increased by agitating either the cooling medium or the steel part being cooled. Quenching oils are most frequently used in heat-treating operations because their action on the steel is less severe than water or brine quenching and the end products are apt to be freer of internal stresses and quenching cracks.

Very rapid cooling, especially of steel products having irregular form, may produce high internal stresses, which in turn may cause warping and cracking. These internal stresses caused by quenching are due to (1) contraction due to cooling, (2) expansion during transformation, and (3) large temperature gradients between the surface and the center. Shrinkage cracking may be avoided by choosing the proper steel, by avoiding abrupt changes in section and notches in the design and manufacture of the product, by heating slowly through the transformation range, and by cooling only as rapidly as necessary to secure the desired structure and properties.

7. Mass Effect in Heat Treatment. A small steel rod $\frac{1}{2}$ in. in diameter, 1 ft long, and a large steel shaft 5 in. in diameter and 4 ft long cool at different rates when subjected to the same quenching conditions. In cooling the small steel rod the ability of the quenching medium to carry the heat away from the surface is the most important factor, and it is quite probable that the surface and the center of the rod have nearly the same hardness after quenching. In cooling the large steel shaft the ability of the quenching medium to carry heat away from the surface is also important, but another factor, probably even more important, is the rate at which the heat diffuses from the center to the surface. The steel shaft, because of the time lapse involved in getting all the heat to flow from the center to the surface, will be harder at the surface than at the center. It is thus entirely possible to have a hard martensitic structure on the surface of a large shaft and a soft pearlitic structure at the center. In the regions between the surface and the center the structure will be partly martensite and partly fine pearlite. When a more uniform hardness and structure are required from center to surface it is necessary to use an alloy steel of greater hardenability.

8. Annealing. The primary objectives of annealing are to (1) refine the grain structure, (2) soften the metal, (3) remove internal stresses, (4) change ductility, toughness, electrical and magnetic properties, and (5) to remove gases. The most common annealing procedure, full annealing, consists of heating hypoeutectoid steel to above the critical temperature, holding it for sufficient time at that temperature to allow complete solution of the carbon and the alloying elements, and then allowing it to cool very slowly down to room temperature. Desirable heating temperatures for annealing, hardening, and normalizing are given in Fig. 10. The schematic representation of this heat treatment is shown in Fig. 11. It should be noted that transformation takes place above the knee of the curve and that the final structure consists of ferrite and pearlite.

Isothermal annealing consists of heating the material above the critical range, holding the steel at that temperature for the required time, cooling rapidly to a predetermined temperature near the top of the isothermal transformation diagram, and holding for the time required to produce

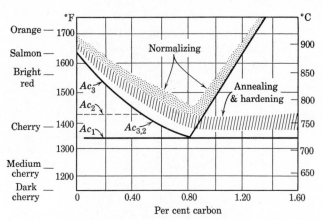

Fig. 10. Temperature for normalizing, annealing and hardening carbon steels. (From *Metals Handbook,* 1948, p. 661.)

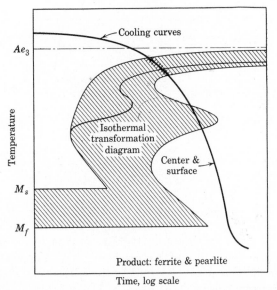

Fig. 11. Schematic transformation diagram for full annealing. (From *USS Carilloy Steels,* U. S. Steel Corp.)

complete transformation, as shown schematically in Fig. 12. The end structure is again ferrite and pearlite, but it is claimed that a more uniform structure is obtained with this method of annealing and that the desired properties may be obtained in a shorter time.

In process annealing the steel is heated to a temperature below the critical range, but high enough to obtain strain recrystallization, and then cooled in any manner. The exact heating temperature depends on the composition of the steel and the amount of work that it has received, but it is frequently between 550° and 650°C. In stress-relief annealing the steel is heated below the critical range and below the strain recrystal-lization temperature for a period long enough to remove internal stresses

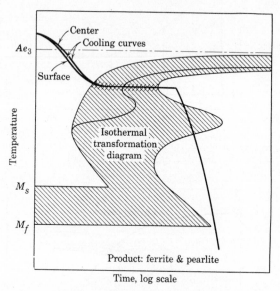

Fig. 12. Schematic transformation diagram for isothermal annealing. (From *USS Carilloy Steels*, U. S. Steel Corp.)

resulting from such manufacturing processes as welding, flame cutting, and machine straightening. Spheroidize annealing is performed to break up the plate-like carbides into spheroidal form, shown in Fig. 9. This structure is produced by heating the steel to slightly below or above the lower critical for a period long enough to spheroidize the carbides and then cooling to room temperature. It is most frequently used in medium- and high-carbon steels to improve machinability. Patenting consists of heating alloys having an iron base above the critical range and then cool-ing below that range in air or molten lead which is held at a temperature between 455° and 510°C. This process is used principally in the manu-facture of wire and cable.

9. Normalizing. Normalizing consists of heating steel to a temperature above the critical range and cooling in air. The purpose of this heat treat-ment is to refine the grain structure resulting from rolling, forging, or other manufacturing processes. It is used on large forgings or castings which have not been quenched and tempered, and also as a preliminary treatment before quenching and tempering in order to reduce distortion and to allow solution of carbides and alloying elements. Normalizing is regarded as a corrective treatment and not as a strengthening heat treatment. This treatment is schematically shown in Fig. 13, and it should be noted that the final structure contains ferrite, pearlite, and bainite.

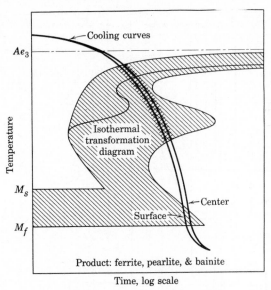

Fig. 13. Schematic transformation diagram for normalizing. (From *USS Carilloy Steels*, U. S. Steel Corp.)

10. Hardening. This heat treatment consists of heating the steel above the upper critical temperature, for hypoeutectoid steels, holding at that temperature until phase equilibrium has been established, and then quenching rapidly to produce a martensitic structure. As previously stated, the quenching medium is usually brine, water, or oil, depending on the desired cooling rate. The objective of this treatment may be to secure a given hardness to a desired depth in the steel, but in most instances the hardening treatment may simply be considered as a starting point from which better combinations of desired properties may be secured by subsequent heat treatment. Fully hardened steels are not suitable for most commercial uses because they are hard and brittle and have poor toughness.

The terms hardness and hardenability should not be confused. Hardness is resistance to deformation and is most commonly measured in Brinell, Rockwell, or Shore hardness machines. Hardenability is the depth to which a steel will harden and is usually measured in inches. A plain carbon and an alloy steel, for example, may have the same surface hardness after quenching, but, if the plain carbon steel has hardened to a depth of ⅛-in. below the surface whereas the alloy steel has hardened to a depth of ½-in., the alloy steel has greater hardenability.

11. Hardenability of Steel. The capacity of steel to harden as it cools from some temperature above the critical range to room temperature,

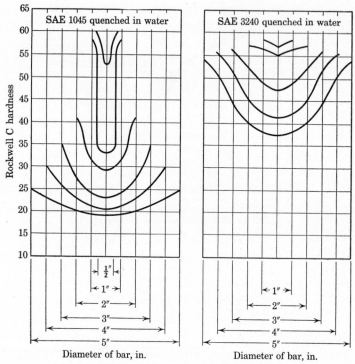

Fig. 14.　Hardness distribution in various sizes of quenched round bars.　(From *USS Carilloy Steels,* U. S. Steel Corp.)

known as hardenability, depends on the homogeneity and the grain size of the transforming austenite and also on the composition of the steel.

The best method of determining hardenability consists of quenching bars of different sizes from the proper temperature in the required hardening bath, cutting the hardened specimens in half, and determining the hardness gradient from the surface to the center. The information obtained may then be plotted as shown in Fig. 14. The curves show that the greatest hardness is obtained at the surface and the least at the center, that the smaller bar sizes have steeper hardness gradients, and that the center hardness decreases as the bar size increases. Comparison of the curves shows that SAE 3240 steel bars have greater hardness than similar size bars of SAE 1045 steel. The greater hardenability of the SAE 3240 steel is explained by the fact that the knee of the S-curve for this steel is farther to the right than that for the SAE 1045 steel. Similar curves for these steels quenched in oil would show the same general relationships but would be lower down, especially those for the SAE 1045 steel, because of the slower quenching rate.

A rapid and quite reliable test to determine hardenability developed by W. E. Jominy and A. L. Boeghold is given in ASTM *Standard* A255–48T. The test consists of heating a steel specimen 1 in. in diameter and 4 in. long to the proper quenching temperature, and then, with the specimen held in a vertical position in a fixture, cooling by means of a water column directed against the bottom end until the entire specimen is cold. Hardness measurements are then taken at $\frac{1}{16}$-in. intervals, starting at the quenched end, on two ground flat surfaces 180° apart and are plotted as ordinates against the corresponding distances from the quenched end as abscissas to obtain the end-quench hardenability curve. Such curves for various types of steels show that the plain carbon steels are shallow hardening because the hardness decreases rapidly as the distance from the quenched end increases, whereas low-alloy steels of the same carbon content are usually deeper hardening as shown by the more gradual decrease in hardness as the distance from the quenched end increases.

The Jominy bar quenched in the manner previously described has cooling rates that vary from about 600° per sec on the quenched face to less than 5° per sec at the other end. A large amount of work has been done by Jominy and others to correlate the results of the end-quench bar with the results obtained by quenching round bars of various sizes in various mediums. This work has shown, for example, that a $\frac{1}{2}$-in. round bar quenched in agitated cold water has about the same cooling rate at its center, 600° per sec, as the quenched end of the Jominy bar; that the cooling rate at the center of a 4-in. round bar quenched in oil is about the same as that at the other end of the Jominy bar; and that the cooling rate at the center of a 2-in. round bar quenched in oil or that at the center of a 3-in. round bar quenched in water is about the same as that on the Jominy bar at a distance of $\frac{3}{4}$ in. from the quenched face. Curves are available which correlate the cooling rates of the various points on the Jominy bar with those on the surface, at the center, and at intermediate points of round bars quenched in oil or water. By using these curves and the end-quench hardenability curve for a given material, it is possible to estimate the hardness at any point in a given round bar of the same material quenched in oil or water; or, if the end-quench curves are known for plain carbon and various low-alloy steels, it is possible to select the proper type of steel that will have a required hardness at any point in a round bar of given size that has been quenched in oil or water.

Hardenability specifications are frequently designated by a code such as $J_{50} = 6$ which means that the given steel should have a minimum Rockwell hardness of C50 at a distance of $\%_{16}$ in. from the quenched end of the Jominy bar.

12. Tempering. A plain carbon steel that has been hardened is in a metastable condition of equilibrium. If this hardened steel is reheated to some temperature below the critical range, a more stable condition will

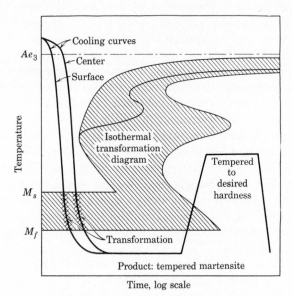

Fig. 15. Schematic transformation diagram for quenching and tempering. (From *USS Carilloy Steels*, U. S. Steel Corp.)

be obtained. A low reheating temperature will begin the precipitation of the carbides from the unstable supersaturated alpha iron of the martensite, and with increasing temperatures the precipitation continues, followed by diffusion and coalescence. As previously stated, a long reheating period just below the critical temperature will produce a spheroidized structure.

Since hardened steels do not usually have the combination of properties desired for specific uses, modification is effected by tempering. Tempering consists of reheating a previously hardened steel to a temperature below the critical range and cooling as desired. A schematic representation of quenching and tempering, Fig. 15, shows that the final product is tempered martensite. The reheating temperature to be used depends on the final properties desired in steel. As this temperature is increased the internal stress, hardness, and strength will decrease, and the ductility and toughness will increase. If good strength and hardness are desired, the steel is usually reheated to less than 400°C. If greater ductility and toughness are required, the steel is reheated to a temperature between 400° and 600°C. Tempering at around 600°C produces a steel that has excellent toughness and shock resistance.

13. Austempering. This heat treatment consists of heating the steel above the critical range, quenching in a medium maintained at constant temperature in the range of bainite formation (about 450° to 750°F), and holding at that temperature until transformation is complete. The initial

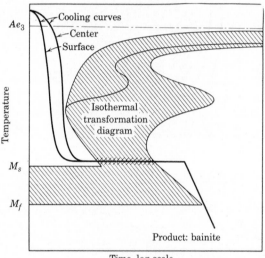

Fig. 16. Schematic transformation diagram for austempering. (From *USS Carilloy Steels,* U. S. Steel Corp.)

quenching, as shown in Fig. 16, must be rapid enough to prevent the formation of pearlite in order that the final structure be completely bainitic. This method is restricted to small sizes, about 0.50 in. thick, because all pearlite formation must be avoided. The maximum size may be somewhat increased when alloy steels are used. The advantages of this treatment are the elimination of a separate tempering treatment and better ductility and tougness than tempered martensite for a given hardness.

14. Martempering. This method consists of heating the steel above the critical range, holding it at that temperature until the structure is completely austenitic, cooling rapidly to a temperature slightly above that at which martensite starts to form, holding it at that temperature for a period long enough to equalize the temperature throughout the section, and then cooling slowly in air through the temperature range in which martensite is formed. This is immediately followed by a tempering operation as shown in Fig. 17. It is claimed that air cooling from just above the martensite formation range results in a very small temperature differential between the surface and the center of the steel, and that martensite occurs at a fairly uniform rate throughout. Consequently residual stresses are minimized and distortion and hardening cracks are reduced.

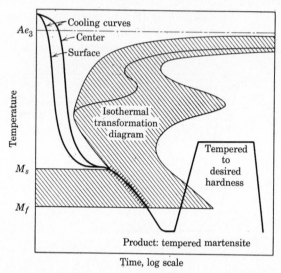

Fig. 17. Schematic transformation diagram for martempering. (From *USS Carilloy Steels*, U. S. Steel Corp.)

15. Properties of Heat-Treated Steels. Full annealing usually decreases hardness, strength, and resistance to abrasion, and increases ductility and machinability. Figure 18 shows the effect of annealing on the properties of hot-rolled carbon-steel bars. In addition to showing that annealing decreases strength and hardness and increases ductility, the curves show that the properties of high-carbon steels are much more affected by annealing than those of low-carbon steels. The strength and hardness of normalized steels are generally slightly higher and the ductility is lower than the values for full-annealed steel bars of the same carbon content.

Effects of quenching and tempering on the properties of steel are given in Fig. 19–22. The effect of varying reheat temperatures on the hardness of water-quenched steels of different carbon contents is given in Fig. 19, and similar data for small steel specimens quenched in oil are shown in Fig. 20. A comparison of these curves shows that water-quenched specimens are much harder than oil-quenched specimens of like composition and size. The high hardness of the water-quenched specimens decreases with very low reheat temperatures; the hardness of the oil-quenched

specimens remains unaffected until the reheat temperature is raised above
350°C.

The influence of tempering on the ultimate strength and yield point
of oil-quenched steels is shown in Fig. 21.   These curves show that the

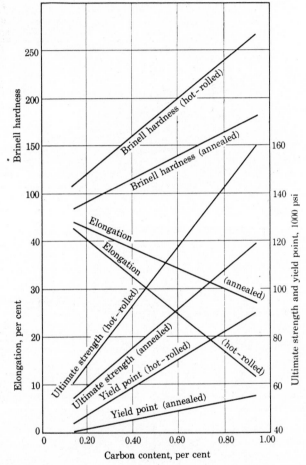

Fig. 18. Effect of annealing on the properties of hot-rolled steel bars.   (Diameter
½ in.)

ultimate strength and yield point are not materially affected by tempering at temperatures below 400°C.   There is, however, a marked decrease
in these properties with higher tempering temperatures.   It is also evident
that the effects are most pronounced for the high-carbon steels.   The
effects of tempering temperature on the properties of three grades of steel
are shown in Fig. 22.   It is again evident that the properties of low-carbon

steels are not greatly changed by heat treatment and that the properties of high-carbon steels are greatly affected. Low tempering temperatures

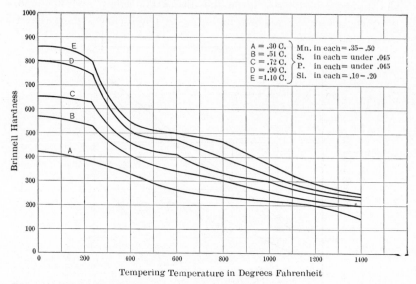

A = .30 C. Mn. in each = .35 − .50
B = .51 C. S. in each = under .045
C = .72 C. P. in each = under .045
D = .90 C. Si. in each = .10 − .20
E = 1.10 C.

Fig. 19. Effect of tempering on the hardness of water-quenched spring steels.
(Tinsley.)

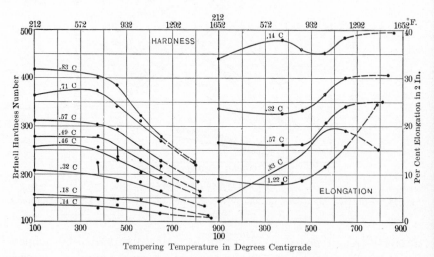

Fig. 20. The effect of tempering on the hardness and elongation of oil-quenched steels. (Nead.)

which may be used to reduce internal stresses due to quenching do not produce great changes in mechanical properties. Large changes are obtained with higher tempering temperatures. The curves for energy of

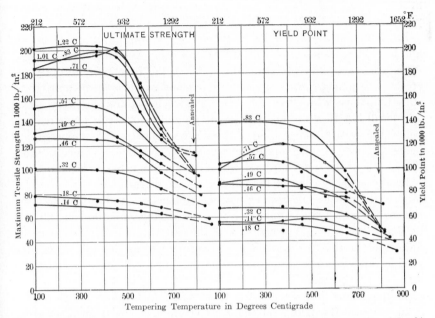

Fig. 21. The effect of tempering on the strength of oil-quenched steels. (Nead.)

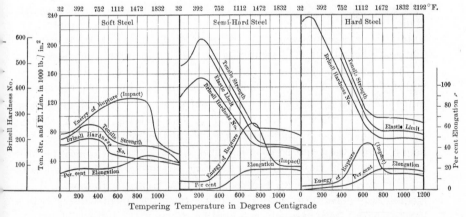

Fig. 22. Effects of tempering on the mechanical properties of three grades of steel. (Grard.) Impact tests were made on notched specimens.

rupture in impact show that the low-carbon steels are toughest and that maximum toughness in each steel was produced by tempering at a temperature slightly below the critical range.

For temperatures below 400°C the energy of rupture of the semi-hard and hard steels is low and constant. Again when the annealing temperatures are reached in the tempering process the toughness abruptly decreases. It appears, therefore, that the quenched steels in the martensitic state and those which have been tempered below 400°C are very strong and hard, but they do not possess the toughness of steels tempered just below the critical range. Steels that are quenched and tempered just below the critical range are tougher and have greater resistance to shock than steels of the same hardness which have a fine pearlitic structure.

In any consideration of the effect of heat treatment on the properties of steel the effect of mass must not be overlooked. As the distance from the surface of a large section increases the cooling rate and generally the hardness and strength decrease and the ductility increases. Available data indicate that for a given quenching method as the size of the steel product increases the strength and hardness decrease and the elongation increases. The mass effect appears to be more important when very rapid quenching methods and low tempering temperatures are used.

16. Surface-Hardening Methods. Certain steel parts such as armor plate, safes, plowshares, special types of gears, pinions, and bearing surfaces must combine toughness with a high resistance to indentation or abrasion. Large surfaces, as in safes, armor plate, and plowshares, are made by sandwiching tough soft-steel plates between hard plates and rolling the combination together at a welding heat. Then the exterior plates are heat-treated to secure the desired hardness and toughness.

Case hardening consists in forming a hard surface on a wrought iron, malleable cast iron, or low-carbon steel part by heating above the critical range (900–950°C) while the part is surrounded by a medium rich in carbon. The surface metal should not contain initially over 0.2 per cent carbon. For a heavy case the metal is held at the high temperature 1 to 8 hours. After the required case has been formed, the parts may be heat treated in several ways. If a hard surface is wanted and toughness is of small moment, the objects may be withdrawn from the furnace and immediately plunged into cold water or oil. Such treatment will result in a hard case, but both case and core will be coarsely crystalline. If toughness is important, the objects should be cooled below the critical range, then heated above the upper critical point for the core (900°C), and quenched. This procedure hardens and refines the grain in the core but makes the case coarse grained. By reheating to a temperature just above the critical range of the case (775° to 825°C) and again plunging in water or oil, the core will be annealed, the case hardened, and its grain refined.

Manganese, tungsten, chromium, and molybdenum steels are readily case hardened; but those of nickel, silicon, and aluminum are less susceptible.

Among the substances used for packing materials are granulated bone, wood charcoal, burnt leather, a mixture of 2 parts barium carbonate to 3 parts wood charcoal, potassium cyanide, and gases rich in carbon monoxide, such as illuminating gas. Granulated bone is the base of most of the packings used in this country. Although the rate of penetration of carbon is slower with wood charcoal than with burnt leather or the barium carbonate and charcoal mixture, yet it gives good satisfaction when a deep case is required. The potassium cyanide compounds quickly produce thin uniform cases, but evolve poisonous gases which render them dangerous.

The thickness of the case varies from 0.02 to 0.2. Ordinarily the case wanted is less than 0.1 in. thick. Best results are obtained when the carbon content of the case is slightly above the eutectoid ratio (0.9 to 1.0 per cent). There is very little absorption of carbon when the temperature is held below Ac_1. Above that point the rate of penetration increases with the temperature and decreases with the time of exposure.

Nitriding of certain steels will produce a case hard enough to scratch glass (900–1100 Brinell) and high in resistance to atmospheric corrosion. The operation is conducted on steels containing appreciable percentages of aluminum, vanadium, or nickel combined with chromium or molybdenum. Parts to be nitrided are loosely packed in gas-tight boxes, which are heated, under careful control, to between 500° and 600°C. While they are thus heated, ammonia gas is circulated through the boxes for 2 to 90 hours. Parts are then slowly cooled in the furnace. The case depth is usually less than 0.03 in. (see *Trans. Am. Soc. Steel Treating*, Vol. 16, No. 5, 1929. See also Chapter XXVII).

Two useful developments in methods of heating surfaces are provided by *flame hardening* and *induction hardening*. In the former the oxyacetylene torch is used to heat the surface and quenching is accomplished by application of water spray or compressed air. Induction hardening is most readily applied to cylindrical surfaces like crankshafts. It is accomplished by sending a high-frequency current with high amperage and low voltage through inductor blocks which surround but do not contact the object to be hardened. These blocks, acting like the primary coil of a transformer, induce a current in the object which is thus quickly heated through hysteresis and eddy current losses. Quenching is done by a water spray passed through the inductor blocks.

Effect of Mechanical Work
on the Properties of Steel

1. Types of Mechanical Work. Steel products are made by casting molten refined steel of suitable composition into the desired form or by mechanically working steel from the ingot through many intermediate forms to the desired product. Mechanical working involves many stages of hot working and may or may not include eventual cold working. The specific temperature dividing the fields of hot and cold work is arbitrarily defined as that temperature below which spontaneous recrystallization does not take place while the steel is being worked.

The most important methods of hot working steel are hot rolling, hammer forging, hydraulic and mechanical press forging, and hot extrusion. Miscellaneous hot-working methods include hot spinning, hot deep drawing, hot flanging, and hot bending. Many steel products with less than 0.35 per cent carbon, such as structural shapes, sheet plate, strip, pipe, and tubes, are hot worked to their final form. Medium-carbon steels containing between 0.35 and 0.70 per cent carbon are hot worked into rails, forgings, and high-strength wire; and high-carbon steels containing between 0.70 and 1.30 per cent carbon are hot worked into tools, cutlery, and springs. Heat treatment after hot working is seldom used with low-carbon steels, whereas high-carbon steels are always hardened and tempered. Heat treatment of medium-carbon steels depends on the properties and use of the product.

The principal methods of cold working steel are cold rolling, cold drawing, and cold extrusion. These various cold-working methods are used to provide increased strength, accurate dimensions, and bright and scale-free surfaces. Thin sheet and small-diameter wire are most economically produced by cold-working methods. Steel bars, plate, strip, and tubes are also cold worked. These products may be used in the cold-worked condition or they may be annealed after cold working.

2. Effect of Hot Work on Structure. The grains of an ingot are usually coarse and fragile due to slow solidification from the melt. In order to obtain the desired form of product and to refine the grain structure, the ingot is heated above the critical temperature and hot worked. The temperature at which steel is hot worked depends on the specific circumstances and requirements in each case because of two contradictory factors. Hot working is easier at higher temperatures when the metal is hotter and more plastic, but a fine-grain structure, usually required, is obtained by working or at least finishing at a temperature just above the critical.

When steel is heated above the critical temperature there is a complete obliteration of the existing grain structure and a formation of recrystallized austenite grains. These grains increase in size with temperature rise above the critical temperature and with time at such temperatures.

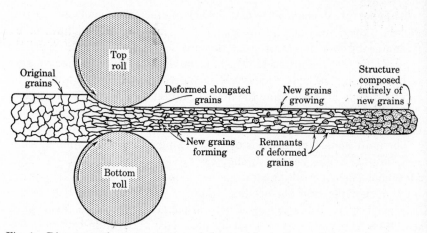

Fig. 1. Diagrammatic representation of the combined effects of the mechanisms of hot rolling and recrystallization on the grain structure of steel. Grain size is shown much exaggerated for clarity. (U. S. Steel Corp.)

The size and character of the grains attained in the austenitic zone is not destroyed during the cooling to normal temperatures. Hot working distorts the grains and flattens them in the direction of the applied pressure. Within the austenitic range, however, the steel will recrystallize into a mass of grains of symmetrical character and approximately equal in size to the dimensions determined by the distortion. These grains will in turn grow into an aggregate of larger symmetrical grains in conformance with the temperature and time conditions. If, therefore, as is usual in hot working, distortion and reduction of grain size within the austenitic temperature range is accompanied by a gradual decrease of the temperature of the steel, the resultant grain is finer than the original because of the combination of mechanical reduction and low finishing temperature. Heavy mechanical reductions and finishing temperatures just above the critical result in a fine-grained structure generally considered to have better properties than coarse-grained steel of the same chemical composition. A diagrammatic sketch showing the effect of hot working on the grain structure is shown in Fig. 1.

Hot-worked steel must be slowly cooled after working in order to avoid internal ruptures that result from fast cooling rates. The required rate of cooling depends on the composition of the steel and on the size of the product. Alloy steels are more susceptible than plain carbon steels and large sections are more susceptible than small sections to internal ruptures caused by fast cooling. The microstructures of hot-rolled mild steel sectioned in the direction of rolling and across the direction of rolling are shown in Fig. 2 and 3.

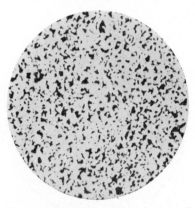

Fig. 2. Hot-rolled mild-carbon steel sectioned in the direction of rolling, ×100. Note fine pearlite and ferrite and moderately banded structure. (Republic Steel Corp.)

Fig. 3. Hot-rolled mild-carbon steel sectioned across the direction of rolling, ×100. Note uniform distribution of ferrite and pearlite in the plane. (Republic Steel Corp.)

Even after hot rolling, steel still retains a slightly elongated structure and has better mechanical properties in the longitudinal direction than in the transverse direction. The elongated structure is believed to be due to the presence of microscopic non-metallic inclusions that are elongated and form fibers when the steel is hot worked and also to banding caused by slight differences in chemical composition.

3. Effect of Cold Work on Structure. Cold working as previously stated takes place at temperatures that are low enough to prohibit spontaneous recrystallization. In modern reduction mills much cold working is carried out at room temperatures but higher temperatures are also used where required. When steel is cold worked the pearlite and ferrite grains are elongated in accordance with the applied forces, and the elongation remains because of lack of mobility of the steel at such temperatures. Cold working results in increased density, hardness, and brittleness, and produces an internally strained condition in the steel. If cold working is continued the internal stresses and strains become very high and ultimately may cause failure of the steel.   Figure 4 shows the microstructure of an annealed low-carbon steel, and Fig. 5 shows the microstructure of the same steel after it had been subjected to a 77 per cent cold reduction.

If large reductions are required it is usually necessary to relieve the excessive hardness and internal stress due to cold work by annealing above the recrystallization temperature to restore essentially original structure and properties.   After such treatment the steel may again be cold worked, and the process of cold working and annealing may be repeated until the desired reduction has been obtained.   In wire drawing,

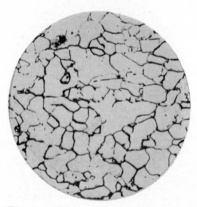   

Fig. 4.   Microstructure of annealed low-carbon steel, ×100.   (Republic Steel Corp.)

Fig. 5.   Microstructure of low-carbon steel after 77 per cent cold reduction, ×100.   (Republic Steel Corp.)

for example, several passes through the dies makes the steel so brittle that annealing is necessary to restore ductility and insure further reduction without rupture.   The effect of cold drawing and annealing at 600°C on the microstructure of soft-steel wire is shown in Fig. 6.

4. Effect of Work on the Mechanical Properties of Steel.   The properties of hot-worked carbon steel depend on the composition of the steel (Chapter XXIV), the dimensions of the cross section, the amount and the direction of the reduction, the finishing temperature, and the rate of cooling after working.   The beneficial effects of hot working steel are readily apparent, since a comparison of mechanical properties shows that the properties of hot-worked steel are generally superior to those of cast steel of the same chemical composition.

Hot working small sections of steel results in approximately the same improvement of the properties throughout the section.   As the size of section increases the properties of the steel on and near the surface are improved more than those of the steel near the center because the action of hot work is not as effective near the center as it is near the surface

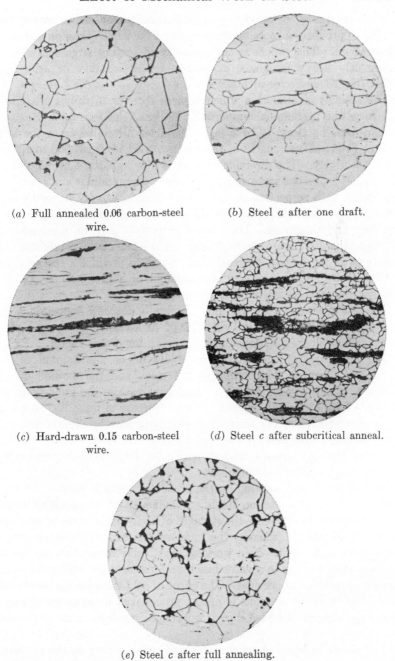

(a) Full annealed 0.06 carbon-steel wire.

(b) Steel a after one draft.

(c) Hard-drawn 0.15 carbon-steel wire.

(d) Steel c after subcritical anneal.

(e) Steel c after full annealing.

Fig. 6. Effect of cold work and annealing on the structure of low-carbon steel wire. Longitudinal sections. Magnification ×500. (From *The Making, Shaping and Treating of Steel*, 6th Ed., U. S. Steel Corp.)

and because the effect of cooling after working plus possible further heat treatment produces a more uniform effect on the small- than on the large-size sections. This points to the necessity of forging large shafts under enormously heavy hammers, or, better, the desirability of using only hollow-forged shafts for such service.

The amount of reduction which a piece receives in rolling materially influences the mechanical properties. Bullens,* for example, cites tests of bars ranging from ½ to 3 in. in diameter all rolled from the same ingot. The tensile strengths of these bars varied from 137,000 to 100,000 psi, respectively. The direction of work is also important because of the directional properties imparted to the steel. Longitudinal and transverse specimens, with respect to the direction of work, usually have the same ultimate and yield strengths, but the longitudinal specimens have better ductility and toughness. Directional properties may be minimized by changing the direction of work during the hot reduction. Finishing temperatures as low as possible, just high enough to produce a recrystallized structure, are desirable from the standpoint of a fine-grained structure and associated good mechanical properties.

The rate of cooling after working is generally not very important except in deep-drawing sheet, small sections of high-carbon steel, and alloy-steel sections where air hardening may be an important factor.

The properties of cold-worked steel depend on the amount of cold work, the chemical composition of the steel, and the method of cold working. Cold working causes a marked increase in the yield point and ultimate tensile strength of steel, a large decrease in ductility, and a decrease in toughness. The modulus of elasticity may be slightly raised by cold working. However, if the reductions due to cold working are very large the internal stresses induced may adversely affect the strength as well as the ductility and toughness.

The effect of cold working on the tensile strength is greater for high-carbon than for low-carbon steels. A reduction of 70 per cent in area may be expected to increase the strength of high-carbon steel of small size by about 75,000 psi, whereas the increase for low-carbon steel may be only about 50,000 psi. Cold working drastically reduces the elongation of plain carbon steels to a value less than 5 per cent for cold-work reductions greater than 10 per cent. The effect of cold work on the mechanical properties of heavy sections is not as pronounced because the grains at the center are not distorted during working as much as those at and near the surface.

The curves in Fig. 7 show the effects of cold drawing on the properties of two alloy steels. These steels show the same general effects of cold working as plain carbon steels, but the decrease in ductility is not as great.

* *Steel and Its Heat Treatment*, p. 229.

The effect of heating subsequent to cold drawing on the mechanical properties of SAE 4615 steel is shown in Fig. 8. The effect of cold drawing on the properties of hot-rolled steel is again evident. Generally the effect of reheating on the mechanical properties is not very marked until the lower critical temperature is reached at which temperature the strength and hardness decrease sharply and the ductility increases. Reheating cold-worked steel to above the recrystallization temperature restores the original structure and properties.

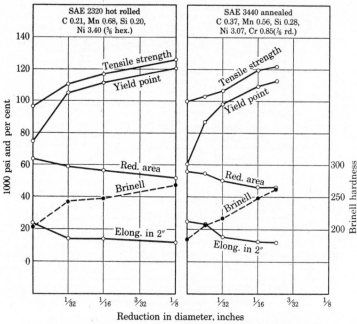

Fig. 7. Effect of cold drawing on the properties of hot-rolled 2320 and annealed 3440 steels. (International Nickel Co.)

All the various methods of cold working stress the metal beyond its proportional limit, and each method produces a particular kind of overstrain. In general, it may be said that overstraining a bar, in a certain direction, say tension, will raise the tensile yield point to the overstraining load and will increase the ultimate tensile strength. The magnitude of the effect on the ultimate will depend upon the amount of overstrain. The proportional limit is greatly lowered immediately after overstrain, but recovers more or less with time and may eventually rise above its original value. If the overstrained bar is put under the opposite kind of stress (compression) the yield point and the proportional limit of the bar are lowered, and may even vanish if the period of rest after overstrain is small. The effect of tensile overstrain on tensile properties appears to be greatest in the direction of overstrain and least at right angles to it. Tensile overstrain effects the greatest increase in the compressive proportional limit and ultimate strength in directions normal to the overstrain.

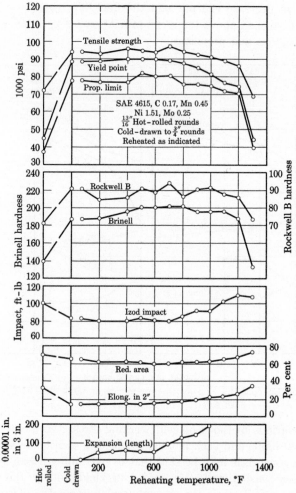

Fig. 8. Effect of heating subsequent to cold drawing on the mechanical properties of an SAE 4615 steel. (International Nickel Co.)

The stress-strain diagrams in Fig. 9 provide a comparison of the properties of hot-rolled and cold-drawn SAE 1035 steel.

5. Aging of Carbon Steels. Aging of steel may be defined as a spontaneous increase in hardness at room temperature in steels that have been previously quenched or strained. The process may be accelerated by heating the steel slightly above room temperature. The increase in hardness is assumed to be due to the disintegration of supersaturated solutions of nitrogen, carbon, and oxygen in ferrite. There appears to be some doubt whether oxygen itself causes aging or exerts a secondary influence on the amounts of carbon and nitrogen required to cause aging.

Quench aging, which is common in low-carbon steels, is believed to be due chiefly to the precipitation of carbon, probably as iron carbide, after

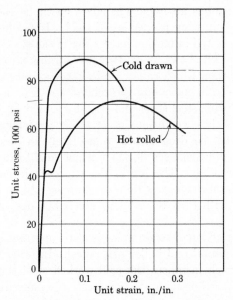

Fig. 9. Stress-strain diagram of hot-rolled and cold-drawn SAE 1035 steel.

quenching. Quench aging above room temperature increases hardness more rapidly than room-temperature aging, but results in a lower final hardness. The maximum quench-aging effect, obtained with steels having a carbon content of about 0.04 per cent, is an increase of about 60 in the Brinell hardness number. Quench aging may be greatly reduced by drastically deoxidizing the steel with aluminum or aluminum and titanium. Quench aging is relatively unimportant from a practical consideration since low-carbon steels are only rarely quenched.

Strain aging, important in low-carbon steels, is believed to be due chiefly to the precipitation of nitrogen, probably as iron nitride, after straining steel beyond its proportional limit. The effect of strain aging on hardness of steel is somewhat less than that due to quench aging, but strain aging is believed to cause greater brittleness. The tensile strength of ordinary mild steel is greater and the ductility is less at 400°F, blue heat, than at ordinary room temperatures. This is believed to be due to rapid precipitation and aging at this elevated temperature. Confirmation of this hypothesis is afforded by the fact that non-aging steels do not show this pronounced increase in strength and decrease in ductility. The room-temperature toughness of ordinary steels that are worked in the blue-heat region or are worked at room temperature and subsequently are heated at temperatures in this blue-heat region is greatly decreased. The undesirable effects due to strain aging may be greatly reduced by using an aluminum-killed fine-grained steel.

Strain aging also has an important effect on the stress-strain characteristics and deep-drawing properties of steel. Hot-rolled, annealed, or normalized steels tested in tension have a jog in the stress-strain curve at the yield point which shows up as stretcher strains during drawing and stamping of sheet and which causes undesirable surface roughness. The jog in the stress-strain curve and the related stretcher strains are eliminated in deep-drawing steel sheet and strip by a light final cold roll after hot rolling. Since these conditions favor strain hardening it is necessary that the steel sheet be deep drawn immediately in order to avoid increased hardness and decreased ductility which might cause failure in the deep-drawing operation. The jog in the stress-strain curve along with the tendency to form stretcher strains on drawing and an increased hardness may return with time to ordinary steels but does not return with non-aging steel.

The embrittling action of strain aging is also important around punched rivet holes in structural and boiler plate steel. In order to avoid severe notch effects in such instances the cold-worked steel should be reamed out after punching. Non-aging steels increase resistance to embrittlement under these circumstances.

PROPERTIES OF WIRE AND WIRE ROPE

6. Properties of Wire. The quality of wire is determined from tension, torsion, cold-bend, wrap, fatigue, and hardness tests. If a complete tensile stress-strain curve is obtained it provides the essential information. The ultimate strength, proportional limit, and ductility may be read directly and the toughness may be roughly estimated from the area under the curve. The per cent elongation is not only an index of ductility, but also a valuable criterion of the wearing quality of the wire when made into rope. The cold-bend test is usually made by clamping one end of the wire between jaws having a radius of $\frac{1}{8}$ in. or equal to the diameter of the wire, and bending the projecting portion back and forth through an angle of 180° until failure occurs. The number of bends required for rupture constitutes a measure of ductility and capacity to undergo cold work. The wrapping test, a measure of ductility and of the adherence of surface coatings, is commonly made on bare or zinc-coated iron and steel wire. Wire may be required to withstand without failure wrapping six complete turns in a close helix on a mandrel having a diameter twice that of the wire. Torsion tests with constant tension imposed are made on a gage length of 8 in. The number of turns withstood under constant tension constitutes a measure of ductility and uniformity. Fatigue tests are made when information on the life of the wire under alternating bending stresses is desired.

The strength and ductility of wire depend upon the chemical composition, the nature of the drafting practice, the heat treatment, and the diameter of the finished wire. Annealed iron wire has a tensile strength of 50,000 to 60,000 psi. The same material, hard drawn with a diameter of ⅛ in., has a strength of 70,000 to 80,000 psi, and when drawn to a very fine wire it may have a strength of 100,000 psi. Cold-drawn, high-carbon steel wire has a strength of 170,000 to 225,000 psi in sizes between 0.2 and 0.3 in., and a strength of 300,000 to 480,000 psi for wire having a diameter of less than 0.10 in.

7. Properties of Wire Rope. Wire rope is made by twisting 7 to 61 wires into strands and then twisting 3 to 18 such strands into a rope. Common wire rope is twisted from 6 strands each of which consists of 7 to 37 individual wires. Wire ropes are made from ¼ to 2¾ in. in diameter and bridge cable up to 36 in. in diameter. In ordinary rope the strands are twisted in the opposite direction to the twist of the wire in the strands; but in rope which must have high abrasion resistance both wires and strands are twisted in the same direction. Where great flexibility is desired the rope is provided with a hemp core, or, if the wear is not great a larger number of wires may be used in the strands. Various types of wire rope with a wide range in properties are available. Iron rope (0.05–0.15% carbon) is soft and low in strength and is used for passenger elevators, and transmission of power. Traction rope (0.20–0.50% carbon) is used chiefly for traction elevators. Mild plow steel rope (0.65–0.80% carbon) is generally used for tool drilling in oil fields and for drilling water wells. Plow steel rope (0.65–0.80% carbon) because of its good strength and toughness is used where conditions are fairly severe. Improved plow steel rope (0.70–0.85% carbon) is used where high strength and abrasion resistance are required, as for scraper, dredge, and rigging ropes, and heavy cranes.

For the fixed lines in aerial cableways where very great wearing resistance is wanted, a rope with a smoother surface is sometimes used. One of the two common types is the steel-clad wire rope in which each strand is spirally wound with flat steel strips. The other is the locked-wire rope in which the surface layer is made of wires drawn to such a shape that they interlock when twisted about the rope and form a true cylindrical surface. Flat ropes are also used for hoisting purposes.

The strength of wire rope is difficult to obtain from short specimens because of the small stretch of the wires and the non-uniformity in stretch due to variation in the rigidity with which they are held. A fairly satisfactory method of gripping the ends follows: A length of 5 ft or more should be marked off on the rope, and two sets of four servings (or windings) with black iron wire should be made at each end of the marked length, as shown in Fig. 10a. The rope should be cut at the

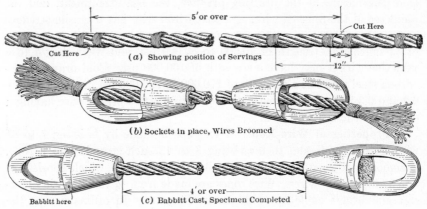

Fig. 10. Method of socketing wire rope.

marks by means of a cold chisel, and the servings will prevent unraveling. Conical sockets may now be slipped over the ends of the rope, the outer servings removed, and the wires broomed as shown in Fig. 10b. If there is a hemp core it should be cut back to the inner servings. The wires are cleansed by dipping in gasoline followed by hot caustic potash. After cleaning, the wires should be dipped in zinc chloride and thoroughly tinned in the molten babbitt used to fill the socket. The sockets can then be pulled over the cable ends and the babbitt poured into the socket in such a manner as to completely fill it. Alloys used with success at the University of Wisconsin are: lead, 83 per cent; tin, 7 per cent; antimony, 10 per cent; also lead, 60 per cent; tin, 30 per cent; antimony, 9 per cent, and bismuth, 1 per cent. Both of these melt below 550°F. Government specifications require the use of zinc cast at a temperature below 830°F. After socketing, the specimen is ready for the testing machine.

In long wire ropes on a straight pull the strength of the rope may be taken as about equal to the average strength of the individual wires if these are all of about the same ductility and ultimate strength. If the wires differ greatly in ductility, the ultimate strength of the rope is the average resistance of the wires at that percentage of elongation which corresponds to the total elongation of the least ductile samples. It is common to assume the rope to have 85 per cent of the total strength of the wires when tested individually. The total area (a) of the wires in a rope may be calculated from the following: Ordinary rope with hemp core, $a = 0.46d^2$; ordinary rope with steel core, $a = 0.50d^2$; locked wire rope, $a = 0.74d^2$, where d = diameter of rope. The weights in pounds per lineal foot (w) of the same ropes may be estimated by the following equations: $w = 1.58d^2$, $w = 1.70d^2$, and $w = 2.5d^2$, respectively. A factor of safety of 5 is commonly used in figuring working loads, but, for passenger elevators and conditions where failure in the rope may endanger life, the factor should be increased to 8. The modulus of elasticity of wire rope after several loadings usually is between 14,000,000 and 16,000,000 psi of metal in cross section. Values for initial loading are about half the above.

Alloy Steels

BY PHILIP C. ROSENTHAL [*]

1. Definition and Structure. Alloy steels are steels containing one or more elements selected from a group which includes manganese, chromium, nickel, molybdenum, silicon, vanadium, copper, phosphorus, tungsten, titanium, boron, and cobalt. These steels are usually made in basic open-hearth or electric-arc furnaces, or in the case of highly alloyed steel may be made in high-frequency electric induction furnaces.

Chapters XXIV and XXV explain how it is possible to obtain a wide range in properties of plain carbon steels by varying the carbon content or heat treatment to alter the amount and manner of distribution of the iron carbide (cementite) in the steel. No greater complexity of structure occurs in most alloy steels, and phases foreign to plain carbon steels appear only when considerable amounts of the alloys are added. Even then, the effects of these additions can often be discussed in terms of their effect on the iron-iron carbide equilibrium diagram. *The important fact remains that for alloy steels of moderate alloy content (5%) carbon is still the basic alloying element in steel, and the effects of the other elements should be considered primarily from the standpoint of how they affect the amount and distribution of the carbide.* Effects of secondary importance are the strengthening of ferrite by certain alloys in solution and/or a change in the composition of the cementite from Fe_3C to a more complex carbide by certain elements.

2. Reasons for Adding Alloys. Three important reasons for alloy additions are:

1. To increase the hardenability of steel. This is by far the most important effect in those steels containing up to about 5 per cent total of alloying elements. The greatest tonnage of alloy steels is produced for this purpose. Since hardenability is involved, sufficient carbon must be present to take advantage of the added hardenability conferred by the alloys. Therefore, the carbon content of these steels usually ranges from 0.30 to 0.50 per cent (except for the low-carbon carburizing grades to which a superficial layer of high carbon is given during the carburizing

[*] Professor of Metallurgy, University of Wisconsin.

process). The steels in this group are usually heat treated by quenching and tempering, for it is only in this way that the added expense of the alloys can be justified through the better combination of properties that is obtained.

2. To strengthen the steel when it is to be used without special heat treatment. Whereas the preceding type of alloy steel represents a heat-treatable grade, the steels that fall in this category are designed specifically for constructional purposes. Since the major requisites of constructional steels such as plates, sheets, angles, beams, are low cost and ease of fabrication by welding and forming, both the alloy content and carbon content are restricted. Thus, the total alloy addition seldom exceeds 3 per cent, and the carbon content is rarely over 0.15 per cent. Alloying elements that strengthen the ferrite are important to this group. These steels are often referred to as "low-alloy, high-strength steels," or "mild-alloy steels."

3. To confer some special property such as
    a. Machinability. The so-called "free-machining" steels fall in this group.
    b. Good cutting ability. Tool steels and high-speed steels; graphitic steels.
    c. Corrosion resistance. Stainless steels.
    d. Heat and oxidation resistance. Stainless steels and irons.
    e. Wear resistance.
    f. Low-temperature toughness.
    g. Nitriding qualities.
    h. Permanent magnetism.
    i. Electrical permeability.

In these steels carbon may range from a low value of a few hundredths of 1 per cent to over 1.0 per cent, depending on the particular purpose, and the alloy content may vary from a few per cent to the point where it becomes large enough to remove the alloy from the steel classification.

3. Effect of Alloys on Eutectoid Composition and Temperature. One effect resulting from alloy additions which is of little significance as far as mechanical properties is concerned, but which is of importance in establishing the proper heat-treating temperatures, is the change in the eutectoid carbon content and temperature. It has been shown [*] that all the common alloying elements lower the carbon content of the eutectoid. With the exception of manganese and nickel, they also raise the eutectoid temperature. These effects are considered to be largely additive algebraically; consequently it should be possible to select a combination of alloys

---

[*] E. C. Bain, *ASM,* 1939, p. 312.

that would have little effect on the critical temperature. However, no particularly useful purpose would be served by such a selection.

HARDENABLE ALLOY STEELS

4. Basis of Classification. Prior to World War II, alloying elements used in steel were classified principally on the basis of their effects on such properties as strength, ductility, or toughness, or on other physical property changes. However, no systematic evaluation of the effects of these elements on hardenability had been made and the merits of one particular grade of alloy steel was considered to depend upon the intrinsic benefits contributed by those elements that were used. This method of evaluation has now been largely superseded by one based on hardenability. Nevertheless, the past development of alloy steels on an essentially trial-and-error approach resulted in a substantial fund of useful knowledge of their properties, and a standardization of analyses and grades that led to the SAE and later the AISI series of classification (Art. XXIV-15).

5. Hardenability and Importance of Carbon. The advent of the hardenability concept provided a tool whereby the alloy steels could be compared quantitatively; and work by M. A. Grossmann and others revealed the previously obscured principle that the major role of the alloying elements in this type of alloy steel was their effect on hardenability.

For a full understanding and appreciation of this important relationship, it is first necessary to emphasize that the carbon content of the steel still determines the basic properties of the steel. This is apparent from Fig. 1, which shows that, despite the alloy content of the steel, its basic hardness on quenching, and hence its other mechanical properties also, is controlled by the carbon content.

As mentioned in Art. XXV-4, the only major contribution furnished by the alloying elements, although a very important one, is that they determine the ease with which the full hardness of the steel can be realized. Thus, a 0.40 per cent plain carbon steel in a given section size might have to be quenched drastically in water or brine solution to assure a martensitic structure before tempering, whereas an alloy steel might provide that same structure with a less severe quench in oil or even by an air cool.

The practical application of this effect is best expressed in terms of the end-quench test, and Fig. 2 shows how a variation in the alloy content of steels of the same carbon content shifts the end-quench curves without altering appreciably the maximum hardness value obtained at the quenched end of the bar. A steel such as 4640 shown in this figure would, on the basis of the evidence, be expected to harden to a greater depth in

a given cross section than a steel of lesser hardenability such as 1040 or
1340. Also, steel 4640 would require a less severe quench to obtain a
given quenched microstructure than steel 1040. A comparison of the
hardenabilities of a number of AISI steels appears in the table on page
501, *ASM Handbook*, 1948 edition.

Grossmann and others early in World War II demonstrated that each
alloying element contributed a specific hardenability effect to steel. In
order to determine a numerical evaluation of this effect, the hardenability

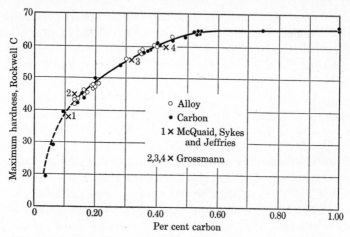

Fig. 1. The maximum hardness obtainable in steel by rapid cooling is a function
of the carbon content rather than of alloying elements. (From Burns, Moore, and
Archer, *Trans. ASM*, Vol. 26, March 1938, p. 14.)

contributed by a given percentage of the element was divided by the base
hardenability of the steel.* The result was a "multiplying factor," which
indicated the increase in hardenability that could be obtained by that
percentage of the alloying elements. Investigations of this type were
carried out for many of the alloying elements, and results for a few more
common elements are plotted in Fig. 3.

Grossmann and his associates further found that the hardenability of
an alloy steel containing several alloying elements could be approximated
by multiplying the base hardenability factors for the respective elements
that appeared in the steel. A correction for the grain size of the steel
also is necessary since grain size influences the hardenability. Thus, the
hardenability of any steel can be established by calculation. Although
a calculation of this type can be made to determine the hardenability of
an alloy steel, the results represent only a first approximation, and a

* The method whereby the hardenability can be expressed numerically is given in
the original papers by Grossmann; also in the *ASM Handbook*.

hardenability test such as the Jominy end-quench test (Art. XXV-11) should still be made.

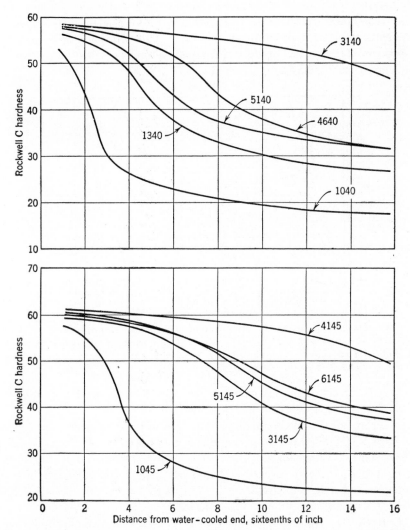

Fig. 2. Variation in alloy content of steels with the same carbon content shifts the position of the end-quench curves without appreciably changing the maximum hardness reading at the quenched end. (W. E. Jominy, *Metal Progress*, Vol. 38, Nov. 1940, p. 685.)

Rather than serving to determine the hardenability of a steel, the hardenability calculation is perhaps more useful in demonstrating a way to best utilize the alloys. Thus, because of the multiplying effect, calculations can be made to show that the most effective way to use the alloys is to use a small amount of several elements rather than a large amount of a single element. Recognition of this principle resulted in tremendous strides in conservation of alloying elements and in the development of alloy combinations, utilizing to the fullest extent the residual alloying elements that often occur in steel scrap. The "National Emergency" (N.E.) or "triple-alloy" steels which appeared during World War II were developed on this basis.

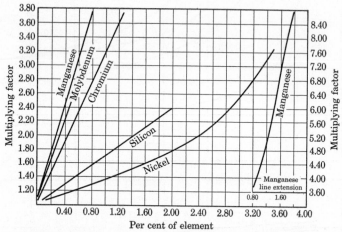

Fig. 3. Multiplying factors for a number of the alloying elements used in steel. These factors indicate that, of those elements shown, manganese is most effective and nickel least effective in contributing to hardenability. (From *The Making, Shaping and Treating of Steel*, 6th Ed., U. S. Steel Corp.)

6. N.E. Steels. These steels made use of residual quantities of nickel, chromium, manganese, and molybdenum that appeared in much of the steel scrap, but the maximum amount of each of these elements that could be used was limited. In other words, a more economical utilization of these elements was realized with no sacrifice in hardening quality. These steels proved to be so successful that many have become popular in the industry and accepted as standard. (See Table V, p. xxi, *Steel and Its Heat Treatment*, by Bullens, Vol. III, 1949.)

7. H Steels. Since the hardenability investigations emphasized that the most important function of the alloys was to increase hardenability, it was recognized that cost savings could be made if the steel producers were required to meet certain hardenability specifications rather than chemical specifications. Thus, if a steel user was interested in securing a steel of a given hardenability range, this could be obtained by selecting a combination of elements that might not necessarily fall in a given chemical specification, but would, nevertheless, meet a hardenability specification. If, for instance, a manufacturer found that a particular heat was low in chromium, he could compensate for this by raising the manganese content above the normally allowable limits and thus obtain the required hardenability. A list of so-called H steels may be found in Table VI, p. xxiii, *Steel and Its Heat Treatment*, by Bullens, Vol. III, 1949.

8. Boron Steels. Another important development occurring during the World War II era was the use of small boron additions ($<0.005\%$) to gain an increase in hardenability. The boron is added as an iron-boron alloy or as a complex alloy containing deoxidizing elements. This small addition of boron contributes a marked increase in hardenability, making it possible to reduce the content of other alloying elements. A considerable savings in the expensive alloys is therefore made possible by using boron-treated steels. A listing of boron steels is given in a *Metal Progress* Data Sheet of June 1952, page 96B. Boron apparently increases hardenability without appreciably changing any other characteristic of the steel. It is found to be decreasingly effective as the carbon content increases and has virtually no effect on steels of 0.80 per cent carbon or more. It differs from other alloying elements in that it does not change the temperature at which the steel forms martensite during rapid cooling (Art. XXV-5).

9. Interrelationship of Properties. It has previously been stated that the major role of alloying elements is to affect hardenability, and any other effects are of minor consequence. Hence, one should expect similar properties in the various alloy steels when they are placed on a common basis of comparison. Such a common basis would be similar carbon contents and similar hardnesses. Similar heat-treating cycles would not be a basis for this comparison since it will be seen from evidence presented later that not all the steels temper to the same hardness at the same temperature. Figure 4 gives Patton's studies of the interrelationship of properties of quenched and tempered steels of a variety of compositions and with carbon ranging from 0.30 to 0.50 per cent. It is apparent that a knowledge of one property permits a close estimation of other mechanical properties. It must be emphasized that these comparisons are made on fully quenched and tempered steels. If such comparisons were made between steels of the same hardness but differing in the type of microstructure producing that hardness (pearlite vs. tempered martensite), the correlation would not be so good, particularly with respect to ductility and toughness. There is also more scatter in property correlations at high hardnesses than at low.

The comparison is also valid only when made between samples tested in a given direction relative to the rolling direction of the steels. Thus data by Herres and Jones in *Metal Progress*, Sept. 1946, p. 462, show that longitudinal specimens for a given strength are superior in impact resistance and ductility to transverse specimens.

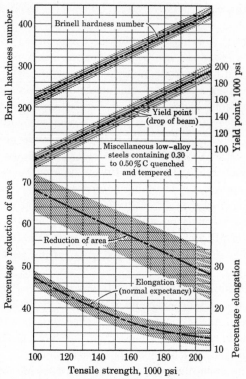

Fig. 4.   Interrelation of mechanical properties of quenched and tempered low-alloy steels. (From *ASM Handbook*, 1948, Fig. 10, p. 458.)

10. Quench Cracking and Martensite Formation Temperature. When steels transform from austenite to martensite or to ferrite and pearlite, there is a volumetric expansion of the metal. If steels are quenched rapidly, this expansion takes place first at the outside of the piece and later in the interior. The result of this sequence of dimensional changes is the development of considerable internal stress as indicated in Art. XXV-5 and XXV-6. It is possible that residual tensile stresses of considerable magnitude may develop in the steel, and, if these are not relieved by plastic flow (strain), they may exceed the strength of the steel and produce a crack.

As Fig. XXV-2 shows, the martensite transformation is temperature dependent. This temperature dependency has been found to be controlled by the composition of the steel, certain alloys lowering the start of the martensite transformation temperature more than others. Studies have revealed the relative effect of the alloys on this temperature, and some of the results are given in Table 1.

TABLE 1.   EFFECT OF CARBON AND OF ALLOYING ELEMENTS ON THE M_s TEMPERATURE

Element	Effect per Percentage of Element		Element	Effect per Percentage of Element	
	°C	°F		°C	°F
Carbon			Molybdenum	−10	−18
(0.20–0.90%)	−350	−630	Tungsten	−5	−9
Manganese	−40	−72	Silicon	0	0
Vanadium	−35	−63	Boron	0	0
Chromium	−20	−36	Cobalt	+15	+27
Nickel	−17	−31	Aluminum	+30	+54
Copper	−10	−18			

Compiled by Hollomon and Jaffe in *Ferrous Metallurgical Design*, John Wiley & Sons, 1947.

These data show that carbon is by far the most important element in determining quench-crack susceptibility. For that reason carbon must be definitely restricted where cracking may be encountered, as in welded structures or heat-treated parts of non-uniform shape. The effect of alloying elements in lowering the M_s temperature is of considerably lower magnitude. Cobalt and aluminum raise the M_s temperature. Boron apparently has no effect.

11. Tempering Alloy Steels. As with plain carbon steels, the tempering of alloy steels results in decreased hardness and strength and increased ductility and toughness. Typical data showing these trends are frequently published by steel manufacturers to permit an estimation of the tempering temperature that will be needed to obtain a given set of properties. Actually the softening effect is time dependent as well as temperature dependent, but temperature is the more important of the two variables. Typical tempering curves are given in Fig. 5 for a 4140 steel. For effects of treatments on other sizes of bars, see reference.[*]

The effects of tempering may also be indicated by plotting hardness data taken on Jominy end-quench bars tempered at several temperatures, Fig. 6. By using the determined cooling rates for bars differing in diameter from the 1-in. round Jominy standard, the hardness and other mechanical properties can be ascertained, as exemplified in the table in Fig. 6. Information of this type is useful in indicating the heat treatment required to achieve the desired properties.

[*] From *Alloy Steel Reference Book*, 3rd Ed., by Ryerson, pp. 240 and 241.

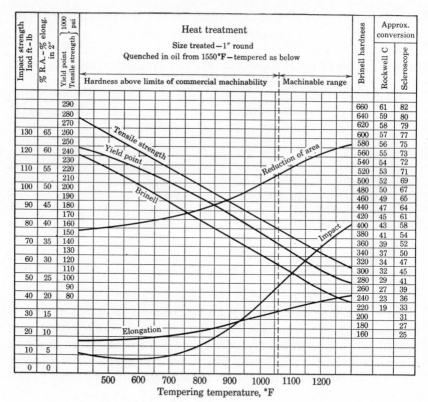

Fig. 5. Typical property changes resulting from tempering AISI 4140 steel. (From *Alloy Steel Reference Handbook,* 3rd Ed., by Ryerson, p. 240.)

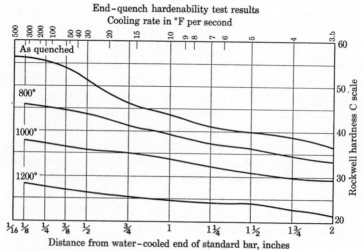

Fig. 6. The effect of tempering on the hardness of end-quench specimens of AISI 4140 steel. (From *Alloy Steel Reference Handbook,* 3rd Ed., by Ryerson, p. 241.)

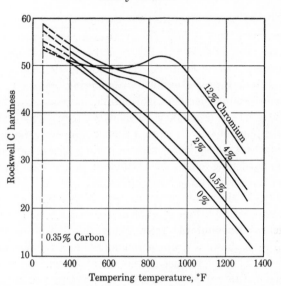

Fig. 7. The effect of chromium on the tempering rate of 0.35 per cent carbon steel, tempered for 1 hour at the indicated temperatures. (From *The Making, Shaping and Treating of Steel*, 6th Ed., U. S. Steel Corp.)

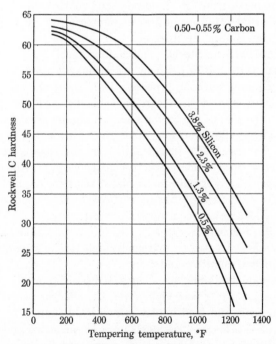

Fig. 8. The effect of silicon on the tempering rate of 0.50 per cent carbon steel, tempered for 1 hour at the indicated temperatures. (From *The Making, Shaping and Treating of Steel*, 6th Ed., U. S. Steel Corp.)

Although it has been shown that the carbon content determines the as-quenched hardness, this is not strictly true for tempered steels. Hence a set of curves such as shown in Fig. 5 or 6 is not applicable to all alloy steels of the same carbon content. The alloying elements tend to retard the normal softening processes during tempering, and in case of the so-called carbide-forming elements, chromium, molybdenum, or vanadium, may even introduce a secondary hardening effect. This means that an alloy steel will customarily require a higher tempering temperature or a longer holding time at temperature to obtain a given hardness. Curves showing the hardening effect of chromium, a carbide former, and of silicon, a ferrite former, in the tempering process are given in Fig. 7 and 8. It is apparent that chromium accounts for a higher hardness at the higher tempering temperatures than is evident for the steel containing silicon.

12. Brittleness Encountered from Tempering. The curve for impact strength in Fig. 5 shows a drop in toughness at a temperature of about 500° to 600°F. The exact cause of this is not known, but it accounts for the avoidance of this range in normal heat-treating practice.

Alloy steels cooled slowly from the tempering temperature of 1100°F or above are likely to lose most of their toughness when tested at room temperature or below. The critical temperature range accounting for this so-called "temper-brittleness" is about 850° to 1100°F. The brittleness can be avoided by rapid cooling after tempering or by using about 0.3 per cent molybdenum in the steel.

13. Alloy Carburizing Steels. Those alloy steels that fall in the carbon range of about 0.10 to 0.20 per cent are ordinarily used for superficially hardening by the carburizing process. The use of alloy additions gives somewhat better control than can be achieved with the plain carbon steels. Thus, the core of the carburized part can be given higher hardenability through the alloy addition. This gives a stronger core and a better backing for the case. The hardenability of the case is also increased, which assures a proper microstructure after heat treatment. Ferrite-forming elements such as silicon or nickel tend to lower the maximum carbon content of the case, whereas carbide-forming elements like chromium or molybdenum exert an opposite effect.

14. Ultra-High-Strength Steels. Aircraft applications find uses for steels that are heat treated to extremely high tensile strengths, although this results in low ductility and toughness. No standard specifications for these steels are available, but a suggested set of properties is: ultimate tensile strength, 256,000 psi; yield strength, 192,000 psi; elongation in 2 in., 11.0 per cent; and Izod impact strength, 14 ft-lb.

To obtain these properties the steels must be quenched and tempered at 400° to 600°F. Steels that have been considered for these applications include AISI 8740, 8745, 4330, 4340, "HyTuf" (0.25 C, 1.35 Mn, 1.50 Si,

2.0 Ni, 0.40 Mo), "Super HyTuf" (0.40 C, 1.5 Mn, 1.9 Si, 1.4 Cr, 0.25 V, and 0.30 Mo), and "Super TN-2" (0.38–0.43 C, 0.7–1.0 Mn, 0.5–0.7 Si, 1.30–1.60 Cr, 2.0–2.4 Ni, 0.4–0.6 Mo) * (all of these compositions are in per cent).

15. Other Factors. The preceding information suggests an interchangeability between alloy steels provided they have the same hardenability. Although this is essentially correct, there are certain other factors which may be instrumental in accounting for the selection of one steel over another. Some of these factors are:

1. Alloy steels may have the same hardenability as measured by the end-quench test, but they may react differently when used in an actual part. This deviation from predicted results has not been fully explained, is not marked in the majority of cases, and does not detract from the usefulness of the hardenability concept. However, it points to the need for close observation of results and may occasionally be responsible for the rejection of a particular alloy steel although it meets all other requirements.

2. Manufacturing problems may be involved. Thus, a steel manufacturer may have available a source of scrap which lends itself better to the production of one particular alloy grade. Again, the cleanliness of the steel or its formability, machinability, or weldability may differ enough to give preference to one steel over another.

3. Heat-treating problems may determine the selection of an alloy. Some alloys may have carbides that are more difficult to take into solution during austenitizing. Again, the differences in tempering behavior mentioned earlier may account for the preference for one grade over the others. This is particularly true if the tempering temperature may introduce the problem of temper brittleness.

4. Relative costs or availability are always important factors.

Final selection of a hardenable alloy steel will therefore be made primarily on the basis of hardenability and secondarily on one or several of the other minor factors that have been enumerated. Although the largest tonnages of these alloy steels appear in wrought products, many can also be produced as castings, usually with some slight modification in composition to improve casting characteristics.

CONSTRUCTIONAL ALLOY STEELS

16. High-Strength Structural Steels. Plain carbon steels of relatively low carbon content suit the needs for the majority of those applications

* *Metal Progress,* Vol. 63, May 1953, p. 95.

where ordinary plates, sheets, bars, T-beams, angle irons, and other constructional shapes are concerned. The increased demand for weight savings, particularly in transportation fields, has created a need for constructional steels of higher strengths (50,000 psi yield strength) and corrosion resistance without too much sacrifice in formability or weldability, and it is for these purposes that the high-strength, low-alloy steels have been developed. They are normally furnished in the hot- or cold-rolled, annealed, or normalized condition, and are intended for use without further heat treatment.

Uses for these steels include railroad-freight and passenger-car bodies, farm-machinery parts, mine cars, power shovels, ship plate, bridge construction, and transmission towers.

17. Fundamental Characteristics of High-Strength Steels. The important characteristics required in addition to high strength are good resistance to corrosion, good formability, good weldability, good toughness, and resistance to fatigue.

Strength. The finely distributed carbides in these steels are undoubtedly the major source of strength, but the carbon content must be restricted to assure weldability, and strength is also achieved through the use of alloying additions which strengthen the ferrite. The relative order of potency of elements in increasing strength and the percentages normally used is as follows: *

Carbon	0.10 to 0.13	Silicon	0.05 to 0.75
Phosphorus	0.03 to 0.12	Copper	0.10 to 0.90
Molybdenum	0.10 to 0.25	Chromium	0.0 to 0.85
Manganese	0.20 to 1.20	Nickel	0.0 to 1.80

Of the elements listed, molybdenum and chromium are carbide-stabilizing elements, and manganese is mildly so. The other elements are referred to as ferrite strengtheners. In the absence of sufficient carbon, elements such as chromium and molybdenum dissolve in the ferrite and thereby also serve as ferrite strengtheners. A comparison of the various elements strictly on the basis of what they do when in solution in ferrite is given in Fig. 9. Phosphorus is included here because it serves as a definite alloying element in some of the steel compositions and should, for this purpose, not be considered as an impurity. It can only be used to good advantage, however, when the carbon content is low.

Corrosion Resistance. If the higher strengths exhibited by these alloys permit reductions in section size, it is imperative that such reductions are not accompanied by a decreased service life through rusting. Hence, a corrosion resistance superior to that of plain carbon steels is necessary.

* From *ASM Handbook,* 1948 Ed., p. 534.

That such added atmospheric corrosion resistance has been obtained is
indicated by Fig. 10.

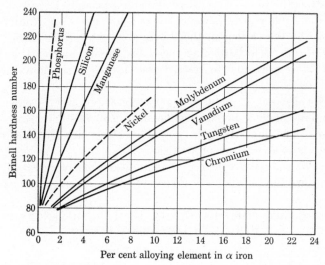

Fig. 9.   The relative effectiveness of the alloying elements as ferrite strengtheners.
(From *The Making, Shaping and Treating of Steel*, 6th Ed., U. S. Steel Corp.)

It is seen that the alloy steels suffer a much lower weight loss from
atmospheric corrosion than a typical low-copper structural steel. Copper
and phosphorus have been found to contribute good atmospheric corrosion
resistance.

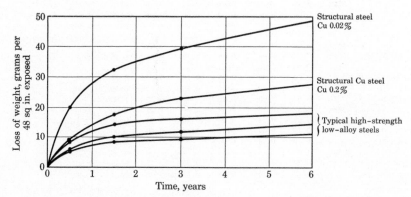

Fig. 10.   Comparative weight losses by atmospheric corrosion for structural and
high-strength steels. (From *The Making, Shaping and Treating of Steel*, 6th Ed.,
U. S. Steel Corp.)

Formability. More force is required to deform a high-strength steel
than a plain carbon steel of the same thickness, but since the high-strength

steels can generally be used in thinner sections this differential in formability is largely nullified.

High-strength steels also have greater springback after forming. Despite these differences, however, these alloy steels are readily formed hot or cold by the various methods available to the steel fabricator.

Weldability. Weld hardening correlates closely with carbon content; therefore, it is necessary to restrict the carbon to the limits indicated earlier.

Other Properties. In addition to the foregoing properties, other properties of interest include notch toughness, fatigue resistance, and abrasion resistance. The high-strength, low-alloy steels are superior to plain carbon steels in these three properties.

Compositions and Properties. Compositions of representative high-strength, low-alloy steels * are given in Table 2, and a comparison of

TABLE 2.   COMPOSITION RANGES OF SOME REPRESENTATIVE HIGH-STRENGTH LOW-ALLOY STEELS

Composition, per cent

Type	C	Mn	P	S	Si	Cu	Ni	Cr	Other Elements
Mn-Cu	0.25	1.10	0.045	0.05	0.30	0.20	—	—	—
	Max	1.60	Max	Max	Max	Min			
Mn-Ni-Cu	0.25	1.40	0.045	0.05	0.25	0.30	0.50	—	—
	Max	Max	Max	Max	Max	0.60	1.00		
Mn-Cu-P	0.15	0.90	0.08	0.04	0.10	0.30	Resid.	Resid.	—
	Max	1.40	0.13	Max	Max	Min			
Mn-Ni-Cu-P	0.20	1.25	0.10	0.05	0.30	0.60	1.00	—	Mo 0.10 Max
	Max	Max	Max	Max	Max	Max	Max		
Si-Cr	0.08	0.50	0.04	0.05	0.60	Resid.	Resid.	0.50	Zr 0.05-0.15
	0.15	0.75	Max	Max	0.90			0.65	
Si-Cu-Mo-P	0.12	0.15	0.08	0.05	0.35	0.35	—	—	Mo 0.16-0.28
	Max	0.40	0.15	Max	0.75	0.60			
Cu-Ni-Mo-P	0.12	0.50	0.05	0.05	0.15	0.95	0.45	—	Mo 0.08-0.18
	Max	0.90	0.12	Max	Max	1.30	0.75		Al 0.12-0.27
Cu-Ni-Cr-Si-P	0.12	0.50	0.08	0.05	0.10	0.50	0.25	0.40	—
	Max	1.00	0.12	Max	0.50	0.70	0.75	1.00	
Ni-Cu-P	0.15	0.60	0.05	0.05	—	0.75	1.50	—	—
	Max	Max	0.10	Max		1.25	2.00		
Ni-Cu-P	0.12	0.50	0.04	0.04	0.10	0.50	0.60	—	—
	Max	0.75	0.07	Max	Max	0.70	0.90		
Ni-Cu-Mo	0.12	0.50	0.04	0.05	—	0.50	0.50	—	Mo 0.10 Min
	Max	1.00	Max	Max		1.00	1.10		
Cr-Si-Ni-Cu-P	0.12	0.20	0.07	0.05	0.25	0.25	0.65	0.50	—
	Max	0.50	0.15	Max	0.75	0.55	Max	1.25	

their properties * with those of structural carbon steel is given in Table 3. The steels are sold under various proprietary trade names, including Cor-ten, Man-ten, Cromansil, Yoloy, and Hi-steel.

* From *The Making, Shaping, and Treating of Steel,* 6th Ed., U. S. Steel Corp., Tables 107 and 108, p. 1295.

TABLE 3.   COMPARATIVE PROPERTIES AND ENGINEERING DATA FOR TWO STRUCTURAL CARBON STEELS AND A TYPICAL HIGH-STRENGTH STEEL

Mechanical Properties in Thicknesses $\frac{1}{2}''$ and Under	Typical High-Strength Steel	Structural Carbon Steel	
		ASTM A-7 for Bridges and Buildings	ASTM A-113 for Railroad Cars
Yield Point, psi	50,000 Min	0.5 T.S. 33,000 Min	0.5 T.S. Min
Tensile Strength, psi	70,000 Min	60,000 to 72,000	50,000 to 65,000
% Elongation in 2″	22 Min [1]	—	—
% Elongation in 8″, $\frac{3}{16}''$ and Heavier [2]	$\dfrac{1,500,000}{\text{T.S.}}$	$\dfrac{1,500,000}{\text{T.S.}}$	$\dfrac{1,500,000}{\text{T.S.}}$
Cold Bend	180° $D = 1T$	180° $D = \frac{1}{2}T$	180° flat
Resistance to Atmospheric Corrosion (Comparative)	4 to 6	1 (or 2 with copper 0.20% Min)	1 (or 2 with copper 0.20% Min)
Modulus of Elasticity	28/30,000,000	28/30,000,000	28/30,000,000
Endurance Limit (as Rolled), psi	42,000	28,000	26,000
Charpy Impact, Keyhole Notch, (as Rolled—Room Temp., Average) ft-lb	40	25	30
Coefficient of Expansion per °F 70° to 200°F	0.0000063	0.0000063	0.0000063

[1] For material lighter than 8 gage, the per cent elongation in 2″ is 20% min.
[2] For material under $\frac{5}{16}''$ to $\frac{3}{16}''$ inclusive, in thickness or diameter, reduce elongation 1.25% for each decrease of $\frac{1}{32}''$ below $\frac{5}{16}''$.

SPECIAL STEELS

18. Free-Machining Steels. Steels designed specifically for machining are listed in the *ASM Handbook*. This property is attained in two ways: Either the continuity of the metallic structure is broken up by having an above-average number of non-metallic inclusions; or the metal itself is made more brittle so that it forms short chips instead of long curls during machining.

Additions of sulfur above the normal limit of 0.05 per cent but not exceeding 0.33 per cent (together with sufficient manganese to form MnS) represents the usual way of breaking up metal continuity. The excessive amount of MnS that appears in the microstructure causes the chips to break into small pieces, permitting an increase in the speed of machining. Lead additions are also used to achieve free-machining properties.

The other approach for gaining good machining qualities is to embrittle the ferrite by additions of phosphorus above normal limits. Table 4 gives a relative rating of the machinability of a number of AISI steels.

19. Tool Steels. Steels classified as tool steels are put to a large variety of uses. Some tools are designed primarily for cutting purposes; others, such as cold chisels, must resist battering action. Each use requires a different set of properties. All tools must resist wear, but the battering

TABLE 4. RELATIVE MACHINABILITY OF CERTAIN AISI STEELS [1]

Steel	Per Cent	Steel	Per Cent	Steel	Per Cent
C 1016	73	B 1112	100	A 4140	61 [2]
C 1019	73	B 1113	135	A 4145	57 [2]
C 1022	70	C 1113	103	A 4340	51 [2]
C 1040	55	C 1117	85	A 4615	64
C 1045	51	C 1118	82	A 8617	64
C 1050	48	C 1137	73	A 8620	61
		Mod. C 1144	79	A 8640 (0.04S)	55 [2]
		C 1217	130	A 8640 (0.07S)	70 [2]

[1] G. D. Boyer in *Product Eng.*, Vol. 18, Jan. 1947, p. 81.
[2] Annealed and cold drawn.

tools need high resistance to compression together with some toughness. Die blocks used in forming operations require essentially the same properties and may also require heat resistance. Cutting tools sacrifice toughness in favor of wear resistance and cutting ability. Toughness would certainly be desired here too, but, because these properties are essentially determined by the carbon content, one cannot be had without a sacrifice of the other. Some cutting tools maintain their good qualities while operating at a red heat.

Because the primary requisite of tool steels is to cut or punch other hard materials, the carbon content is generally not less than 0.5 per cent and may exceed 1.5 per cent. Carbon in the form of Fe_3C or complex alloy carbides provides the hardness and cutting qualities. The basic microstructure of a finished tool steel may be described as tempered martensite containing spheroidized carbides dispersed in this matrix. The size and amount of these carbides may vary from none to a fairly large amount, depending on whether toughness or cutting action, respectively, are required. When the tool steel is supplied by the mill, these carbides are in a spheroidized condition, somewhat similar to that shown in Fig. XXV-9. This structure is relatively soft, and the steel can be cut or worked to its final shape. To harden the tool steel for subsequent use, it is heated above the critical range to dissolve part of these carbides in the austenite and then quenched to form martensite. The degree of solution of the carbides is determined by the time and temperature of holding. Careful control of this part of the heat-treating cycle is necessary because too much solution of the carbides may result in cracking during quenching or may produce a steel which may not have good cutting action because of a deficiency of dissolved carbon and alloys in the austenite. Thus, although the metallurgy of tool steels is basically the same as that of plain carbon steels, a rather delicate balance exists between composition, austenitizing temperature and time, and tempering temperature. Despite the fact that alterations in the heat treatment can be used to alter the number of carbides in the matrix, control of properties must still be obtained principally by altering the carbon content. Thus, when toughness is desired, carbon is low (around 0.5 per cent), whereas when good cutting is needed, and toughness can be sacrificed, the carbon is raised to a higher level.

There are many modifications in compositions of tool steels and their heat treatment, and only a brief survey can be given here. The alloy steels used range from ordinary AISI type steels to complex, highly alloyed compositions.

A classification covering the composition and treatments for carbon, "non-deforming," shock-resisting, hot-work, high-speed, and certain miscellaneous types of tool steels may be found in the *ASM Handbook*, 1948 Ed., pp. 656 and 657.

Except for the lower-carbon steels requiring toughness, such ferrite-strengthening elements as silicon and nickel are not used to any great extent. Instead, elements such as chromium, molybdenum, and tungsten are important alloys. Manganese is also used, and, because of its marked contribution to hardenability, it is an important part of a class of tool steels referred to as "non-deforming" type.

The non-deforming tool steels have sufficient carbon and alloy content so that they retain some austenite after quenching. Then, during tempering, this austenite decomposes. Since austenite expands on transforming, whereas martensite contracts when it is tempered, it is possible, through a close control of composition, austentizing temperature, and tempering temperature, to heat-treat a tool steel of this type with very little dimensional change. The advantage of this is that the steel can be practically finished to the desired shape before heat treating.

Steels that are used for working at elevated temperatures and that border the high-speed steel type, in addition to carbon, contain elements such as chromium, molybdenum, tungsten, and vanadium in various combinations. The alloy content of the steel may be high enough so that it hardens to martensite on air cooling. Such is a so-called "air-hardening" steel.

"High-speed" steels are a class that can retain a good cutting edge while operating at a red heat. A popular analysis is the 18–4–1 type which contains 18 per cent tungsten, 4 per cent chromium, 1 per cent vanadium, and 0.70 per cent carbon.

The structure typical of an 18–4–1 high-speed steel is shown in Fig. 11, and the effects of tempering on certain properties of this steel are illustrated in Fig. 12. The other steel illustrated in Fig. 12 is one containing 6 per cent tungsten, 5 per cent manganese, 2 per cent vanadium, 4 per cent chromium, and about 0.85 per cent carbon. Austenitizing temperatures of these steels range from 2200° to 2400°F. Molybdenum can be used to replace all or part of the tungsten; not, however, without introducing decarburization difficulties during heat treatment.

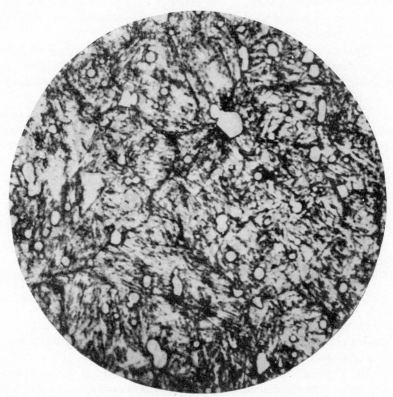

Fig. 11. Photomicrograph of 18–4–1 type high-speed tool steel. Etched with 6 per cent nitric acid in alcohol, ×2000. Hardened at 2380°F for 30 sec in a salt bath; tempered at 1040° (30 min in salt bath); 55.5 Rockwell C. (J. V. Emmons.) (From *Steel and Its Heat Treatment,* by Bullens, Vol. III, 1949, p. 555.)

For a comparison of the behavior of tool steels, refer to the table on Classification and Approximate Compositions of Tool Steels, p. 656, and the table on Approximate Comparison of Principal Types of Tool Steels, p. 659, in the *ASM Handbook* (1948 Ed.).

Certain tool steels can be heat treated to contain free graphite in their microstructure. These so-called "graphitic steels" contain about 1.5 per cent carbon and such elements as manganese, silicon, molybdenum, tungsten, aluminum, nickel, and chromium. Trade names include Graph-sil, Graph-mo, Graph-tung, Graph-al, and Graph-M.N.S. They have excellent machinability in the annealed condition, because of the graphite, and can be heat treated to serve as shock- or wear-resisting tools such as die blocks.

Hard carbide particles, such as tungsten, tantalum, or titanium carbides, bonded together with a metallic bonding agent, such as cobalt, constitute

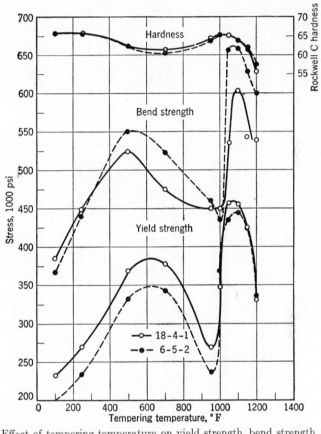

Fig. 12. Effect of tempering temperature on yield strength, bend strength, and hardness of 18–4–1 and 6:5:2 tool steels. Tempering time was 1 hour. (From *Steel and Its Heat Treatment,* by Bullens, Vol. III, 1949, p. 557.)

another type of tool material that is worthy of mention. These are used for drawing dies, extrusion dies, and other cold- and hot-working applications, as well as for cutting operations. Tools made from these so-called "sintered" or "cemented" carbides can be operated at higher speeds than ordinary cutting tools.

20. Corrosion-Resisting Steels. Chromium is the most important addition to steel for corrosion resistance. Other elements are also used, but usually in connection with chromium. The other elements include nickel, silicon, manganese, molybdenum, and aluminum as shown in Table 5.

TABLE 5. AISI NUMBERS AND DATA FOR CORROSION- AND HEAT-RESISTING STEELS

[Prepared by the Research Division of Rustless Iron and Steel Corp. (April, 1945)]

	GROUP A (MARTENSITIC)	GROUP B (FERRITIC)	GROUP C (AUSTENITIC)
	Straight Chromium; Hardenable	Straight Chromium; Non-Hardenable	Chromium-Nickel; Non-Hardenable
Type numbers	501, 502, 403, 405, 410, 414, 416, 420, 420-F, 431, 440-A, 440-B, 440-C, 440-F.	430, 430-F, 442, 443, 446.	301, 302, 302-B, 303, 304, 308, 309, 310, 316, 321, 347.
Chemical analysis	Chromium 4.0 to 13.5% with up to 0.15% carbon, or chromium 12 to 18% with carbon 0.15 to 1.20%. Most types contain molybdenum, up to 0.60%. Some contain nickel up to 2.50%, or sulfur or selenium up to 0.40%. Magnetic.	Chromium over 14% to 27% with carbon not over 0.35% (generally 0.15% or less). One type contains up to 1.25% copper, one sulfur or selenium up to 0.40%. Magnetic.	Chromium 16 to 26% and nickel 6 to 22%. Carbon from about 0.05 to 0.25% (generally less than 0.15%). May contain molybdenum, columbium, titanium, sulfur or phosphorus and selenium. Non-magnetic.
Heat treatment	Harden by air or oil quenching to 350 to 620 Brinell, depending on carbon and chromium content. Can be drawn back to develop a wide range of mechanical properties. (Brinell 140 to 600.)	Do not harden significantly. Should be annealed by cooling rapidly from around 1500°F for maximum toughness and good corrosion resistance. (Brinell 140 to 190.)	Do not harden by heat treatment, but can be hardened by cold work to high hardnesses. Should be annealed by cooling rapidly from 1800° to 2050°F for maximum softness and corrosion resistance. (Brinell 140 to 185.)
Toughness	High bend toughness and good notch toughness when properly heat treated. Generally lose some notch toughness when tempered from about 750° to 950°F, or when exposed to low temperatures.	High bend toughness, but notch toughness may be low depending on composition and heat treatment. Overheating lowers toughness; additions of nitrogen increase it. Notch brittleness disappears at elevated temperatures.	Unusually high toughness, unaffected by notches. Retains toughness down to liquid-air temperatures. Exposure at 800° to 1600°F may impair toughness of non-stabilized types.
Structural changes at high temperatures	Not subject to excessive grain growth. Grains may be refined by heat treatment. Mechanical properties not impaired by prolonged exposure to temperatures up to 1400°F, and structural changes negligible. Low-chromium alloys contain molybdenum to prevent temper brittleness.	Types especially low in carbon and high in chromium are susceptible to marked grain growth when heated for long periods over 1650°F. Grain growth is reduced by nitrogen in alloy.	Austenitic alloys precipitate carbides at grain boundaries when heated to or cooled slowly through the range of 900° to 1650°F, becoming susceptible to intergranular corrosion and losing some toughness. This is controlled by very low carbon content, or by addition of titanium or columbium.
Strength at elevated temperatures	Creep strength much superior to plain carbon steels up to 1200°F. Retain tensile properties to 750°F.	About same creep strength as Group A. Load-carrying properties are low at temperatures over 1300°F.	Excellent creep strength up to 1200°F, which is further enhanced by molybdenum or columbium. Load-carrying ability superior to Groups A and B.

Hot-working qualities	Readily forged, rolled, or pierced from 2350° to 2000°F. High-carbon types should be preheated and worked at lower temperatures, and low carbon and free-machining types worked at higher temperatures. Air-hardening characteristics may call for slow cooling after forging.	Readily forged, rolled, or pierced. Should not be overheated or soaked long, to avoid grain growth. Usual forging temperature around 2200°F. Finish around 1450°F to refine grain. Alloys do not air harden significantly.	May be forged, rolled, and in most cases pierced. Usual working temperature 2250°F, but free-machining type with sulfur may require higher temperatures. May be water quenched after working without harm.
Cold-working qualities	In annealed condition the cold metal can be easily drawn, rolled, upset, bent, formed, coined, or deep drawn. High-carbon and free-machining types are more difficult to work. Work-harden slowly, like carbon steels.	Well adapted to all types of cold work. The alloy with 17% chromium is especially suited for forming and deep drawing. Alloys work-harden slowly, like carbon steels.	Can be readily cold worked by drawing, rolling, upsetting, forming, deep drawing, etc. Work-harden rapidly, compared to carbon steels, and may be cold drawn or rolled to high tensile strengths.
Machinability	Machining rates of regular types are about 50% of Bessemer screw stock; free-machining types up to 80% (with high-speed or carbide tools). Tools and work should be rigidly mounted. Suitable for automatic screw machining.	Machining rates and tooling practices similar to Group A. Suitable for automatic screw machining. Sulfur-base oils recommended for Groups A, B, and C. Tools should be honed for maximum production.	Machining rates of regular types are about 40% of Bessemer screw stock; free-machining types up to 75% (with high-speed or carbide tools). Tapping, threading, and drilling require reduced speeds.
Riveting	Suitable for cold rivets. Hot riveting above about 1450°F not recommended because of air-hardening properties.	Suitable for cold rivets. Hot riveting requires care to avoid brittleness; rivets should be driven at 1425°F into chamfered holes.	Excellent for cold and hot rivets. Hot rivets may be driven at any temperature over 1600°F.
Welding properties	May be welded with gas or electric arc, or by resistance. Preheating and post-annealing generally desirable to avoid cracking. Use of austenitic electrodes will minimize the latter.	May be welded with gas or electric arc, or by resistance. Anneal to reduce embrittlement alongside welds. Use small electrodes and low currents to minimize grain growth.	Eminently suited for all welding methods. Weld does not air harden and is very tough. Weldments subject to severe corrodents require post-annealing unless very-low-carbon alloys or columbium- or titanium-stabilized types are used.
Corrosion resistance	Increases with chromium content; inferior to Groups B and C. Resists weather, water, steam, and mild corrodents when chromium exceeds 11.5%. High-carbon types (over 0.15%) should be used after hardening and stress relief (below 800°F).	Better than Group A. Excellent for interior trim. Resistant to many chemicals and food products. Extremely resistant to nitric and other oxidizing acids.	Generally better than Group B, especially in reducing and organic acids. Molybdenum aids resistance to sulfite liquors and pitting attack in chlorides. Resistant to most ordinary corrosive agents in domestic and industrial use.
Scaling resistance	Increases with chromium content. Generally useful for continuous service up to 1200°F, and in some atmospheres up to 1500°F.	Excellent resistance to destructive scaling up to 2100°F, depending on chromium content. Resistant to oxidizing and reducing gases. Presence of sulfur lowers maximum useful temperature.	Excellent where high strength is required in combination with resistance to destructive scaling. High silicon improves resistance to scaling. High-chromium, low-nickel types resist sulfurous (oxygen-free) gases best.

TABLE 6. MECHANICAL PROPERTIES OF CHROMIUM STAINLESS STEELS AND CHROMIUM-NICKEL AUSTENITIC STEELS (KRIVOBOK)

Principal Elements, %	Treatment or Number	Tensile Strength in 1000 psi	Yield Point in 1000 psi	Elongation in 2 in., %	Reduction in Area, %	Izod Impact, ft-lb	Brinell Hardness	Influence of Heat Treatment and Cold Work on Mechanical Properties
Cr 11.5 to 14.0 C 0.12 Max	Annealed	65 to 85	35 to 45	40 to 25	65 to 55	120 to 60	140 to 160	Properties modified by heat treatment or cold work
	Heat treated[1]	100 to 200	65 to 175	30 to 10	60 to 25	120 to 10	250 to 275	
	Cold rolled[1]	135 to 150	100 to 125	10 to 5			220 to 250	
Cr 16.0 to 20.0 C 0.12 Max	Annealed	75 to 90	40 to 55	30 to 20	55 to 40	5 to 75		Slightly modified by heat treatment, modified by cold work
	Cold rolled	90 to 190	65 to 130	20 to 2	40 to 20	30 to 2		
Cr 25.0 to 30.0 C 0.30 Max	Annealed	75 to 95	45 to 60	30 to 20	60 to 50	Very low	140 to 180	Modified by cold work only
	Cold rolled	85 to 175	55 to 135	25 to 2	50 to 20	Very low	150 to 250	
Cr 17.0 to 19.0 Ni 7.0 to 9.5 C 0.07 to 0.11	304[2]	80 to 115	35 to 45	40 to 65	55 to 65	70 to 110	135 to 250	Can be modified by cold work
Cr 24.0 to 26.0 Ni 19.0 to 21.0 C 0.25 Max	310[2]	90 to 110	40 to 60	45 to 55	50 to 60	100 to 120	145 to 210	Can be modified by cold work

[1] 35 per cent reduction in thickness.
[2] Steels 304 and 310 quenched from 2100°F to render them austenitic. No. 304 is widely used to resist corrosion, No. 310 is highly resistant to corrosion and sealing at high temperatures.

Chromium is beneficial because it renders the steel passive; i.e., the steel is more noble in oxidizing environments than its position in the electrochemical series of the elements would normally indicate.

There are three major classes of chromium-bearing steels:

I. Hardenable or martensitic type: 11 to 14 per cent chromium, 0.12 max carbon.

II. Ferritic type: 16 to 30 per cent chromium, 0.30 max carbon.

III. Austenitic type: 17 to 26 per cent chromium, 7 to 21 per cent nickel, 0.02 to 0.25 per cent carbon.

The AISI type numbers, compositions, and principal uses of these steels * are given in Table 5. Room-temperature properties of some of these steels † are given in Table 6. In the hardenable type, the combination of carbon and chromium produces an air-hardening composition which can subsequently be tempered. This is also known as the "cutlery" grade of stainless. The ferritic type has sufficient chromium and low enough carbon so that it does not pass through the austenite field at any temperature. The austenitic type, on the other hand, does not generally exhibit ferrite because of the austenite-stabilizing effects of nickel.

The martensitic-type steels are principally used for resistance to atmospheric oxidation and to mildly corrosive chemicals. The ferritic irons or steels are fairly weak at high temperature, but are extremely resistant to oxidation and strongly oxidizing solutions. The austenitic variety, which includes the popular "18–8," has better strength at elevated temperatures and is easier to fabricate. Its corrosion resistance toward oxidizing conditions is excellent, but it is not so resistant to sulfur-containing atmospheres as the ferritic type. The 18–8 type is also susceptible to a grain boundary attack if cooled slowly through the 800° to 1200°F temperature range. Such attack can be prevented by fast cooling through this range. However, in large structures that are fabricated by welding, such rapid cooling is not feasible. Then the columbium- or titanium-bearing stainless steels (Types 347 and 321) must be employed. The additions of either of these elements prevent intergranular attack.

Nickel and its alloys are also used for corrosion resistance, but these fall out of the realm of steels because of their high nickel content. Chemical composition of these alloys ‡ is given in Table 7. In addition to corrosion resistance, some of these alloys are used for their high-temperature properties, or high electrical resistivity.

21. Steels for High-Temperature Service. In the design of steels for high-temperature services many factors of little consequence at room-

---

* Data Sheet from *Metal Progress*, Vol. 47, May 1945, p. 936B.
† From *Modern Steels, ASM*, 1939, pp. 308 and 311.
‡ From *ASM Handbook*, 1948 Ed., Table 1, p. 1029.

TABLE 7.   NOMINAL COMPOSITIONS AND USES OF CERTAIN
NICKEL ALLOYS

Material	Nominal Composition, per cent	Principal Uses
Nickel	99+ Ni	Electronic, protective coatings
Monel	67 Ni, 30 Cu, 1.5 Fe, 1 Mn	High strength plus corrosion resistance
80 Ni, 20 Cr	80 Ni, 20 Cr	Heating elements
Inconel	80 Ni, 15 Cr, 5 Fe	High strength, high corrosion and oxidation resistance.
60 Ni, 15 Cr	60 Ni, 15 Cr, 25 Fe	Heating elements
Hastelloy	53–62 Ni, 19–32 Mo, 0–17 Cr, 0–5 W, balance Fe	Corrosion resistance in HCL and certain other chemicals

temperature operation become increasingly more important.   Factors that must be given consideration are:

1. Thermal expansion.   Operation over a temperature range will cause dimensional changes of considerable magnitude.   If the design involves both ferritic and austenitic materials this is of even greater importance because of the differences in thermal expansion of these two types of steel.

2. Thermal conductivity.   This property varies widely for the different steels, being about one-half as high in the high-chromium steels as in the constructional alloy steels.

3. Modulus of elasticity.   This property drops with temperature, the degree of change being dependent on whether the steel is austenitic or ferritic.

4. High-temperature fatigue.

5. Creep.

6. Spheriodization of the carbides.

7. Aging effects.

8. Oxidation.

9. Effect of cyclic temperature changes.

10. Embrittlement due to long-time temperature exposure.

11. Decarburization.

12. Carburization or graphitization.

In the ferritic steels of relatively low alloy content, molybdenum is the outstanding element for high-temperature strength.   The beneficial effects of molybdenum and other alloying elements on the creep resistance of steel is shown in Fig. XXXI-12.

At higher alloy levels are the chromium-bearing steels of about 12 per cent chromium and higher.   The higher chromium steels, however, are usually fortified with nickel for strength to throw them into the austenitic classification. A comparison of a broad range of analyses * is given in Fig. 13 so far as creep rate is concerned. Although this does not present the only basis for comparison, it does give some idea of the approximate resistance of the various alloys.

New heat-resisting alloys are constantly being developed. Some are iron-base, but others may have other elements as the base metal. One alloy with an iron base of considerable prominence contains 16 per cent

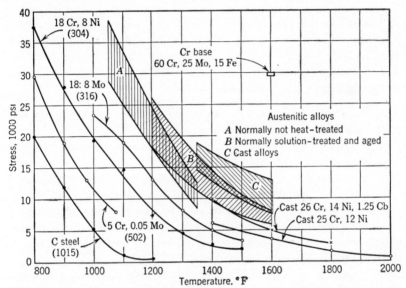

Fig. 13.   Stress required to produce a creep rate of 0.0001 per cent per hour in various alloys. (From *Steel and Its Heat Treatment,* by Bullens, Vol. III, 1949, p. 469.)

chromium, 25 per cent nickel, and 6 per cent molybdenum. The future holds promise for other high-temperature materials using combinations of metals with carbides, borides, and nitrides.

A good thumbnail sketch of the various stainless-steel alloys is also given in Table 5. This table includes data relative to corrosion resistance as well as heat resistance. For both the corrosion- and heat-resisting alloys, it should be remembered that both wrought and cast alloys of basically similar compositions are often produced. In some instances, the alloys are preferably cast because of their resistance to deformation at elevated temperature.

22. Steels for Low-Temperature Service. Steels increase in strength, and lose ductility, as the temperature is decreased. In ferritic steels this results in a sudden drop in toughness at around room temperature or

* From *Steel and Its Heat Treatment,* by Bullens, Vol. III, 1949, Fig. 244, p. 469.

below and one of the problems in design of steel compositions is to lower this so-called "transition temperature." Lack of knowledge concerning this effect has resulted in many failures, outstanding of which was the loss of many Liberty ships fabricated during World War II.

The austenitic steels do not show this sudden drop in toughness and are recommended where toughness down to extremely low temperatures is desired. Among the factors that increase low-temperature toughness of ferritic steels are:

1. Deoxidation with aluminum.
2. Use of fine grain size.
3. Quenching and tempering to produce tempered martensite instead of pearlite and ferrite.
4. Low carbon content.
5. Low hardness.

Most low-alloy, high-strength steels are superior to carbon steels at low temperatures. Low-carbon constructional steels containing nickel up to 8½ per cent have been used for low-temperature service. A low-manganese steel has been used for ship plate.

23. Wear-Resisting Steels. Any tool steels or ordinary steel used in service where frictional wear is encountered is actually a wear-resisting steel. Carburized or nitrided steels or steels given other hard coatings are also wear resistant. There is, however, a special class of wear-resisting steels where the wear comes from abrasion and battering action rather than from gradual attrition characteristic of lubricated parts. This special class of steels is used in ball mills, dipper-bucket teeth, jaw-crusher liners, or any other application where impact and abrasion occur. The outstanding steel for this type of service is austenitic Hadfield's manganese steel containing about 13 per cent manganese. This steel apparently obtains its good resistance by transforming to a hard wear-resistant structure under the impulse of the cold-working action it receives during use. This action is so pronounced that it is difficult to machine or fabricate this steel except by grinding or casting. Other work-hardenable austenitic steels can be employed, but their cost is usually higher than that of the manganese steel.

24. Nitriding Steels. Although AISI chromium-molybdenum steels, free of aluminum, can be used for this purpose, aluminum is a desired part of the composition because of the hardness of the case conferred by aluminum. Compositions of certain nitriding steels are given in Table 8.

25. Permanent Magnet Steels. Permanent magnetism is promoted by having a highly stressed or two-phased structure. In such steels carbon is fairly high, between 0.6 and 1.0 per cent. Other elements that are used include manganese, chromium, tungsten, cobalt, and molybdenum.

TABLE 8.[1] COMPOSITIONS OF NITRIDING STEELS

Steel	Composition, per cent		
	C	Cr	Mo
Nitralloy 135 (type H)	0.20–0.30	0.90–1.40	0.15–0.25
Nitralloy 135 (type G)	0.30–0.40	0.90–1.40	0.15–0.25
Nitralloy 135 modified (aircraft spec.)	0.38–0.45	1.40–1.80	0.30–0.45
Nitralloy N (3½% Ni)	0.20–0.27	1.00–1.30	0.20–0.30
Nitralloy 230 (Alamo)	0.25–0.35	....	0.60–1.00
Nitralloy EZ (0.15 to 0.25% Se) type G with selenium for machinability	0.30–0.40	1.00–1.50	0.15–0.25

Note. All steels contain 0.85 to 1.20 per cent aluminum, 0.20 to 0.40 per cent silicon, and 0.40 to 0.70 per cent manganese, except Nitralloy EZ which contains 0.50 to 1.10 per cent manganese.

[1] From *ASM Handbook*, 1948 Ed., Table 1, p. 697.

Magnetic alloys that are not really steels contain aluminum, nickel, and cobalt. "Alnico" is the trade name for this group.

26. Magnetically Soft Steels (High Permeability). For transformer stock, magnetic properties opposite to those needed for permanent magnets are necessary. Very soft, unstrained ferrite is required. A silicon steel with low carbon, manganese, and other impurities is a popular variety. Silicon will vary in such steels from 2.75 to 4 per cent. Special iron-nickel alloys, not classified as steels, also have been developed for this purpose. These include the *Permalloys* (40 to 55 per cent nickel), *Hypernik* (50 per cent nickel) which is especially heat treated, and *Perminvars* (iron-cobalt-nickel alloys).

27. Other Metals for Special Purposes. *Invar,* an alloy of iron with 36 per cent Ni and 0.50 per cent C, has a coefficient of expansion of only 0.000001 per °C. It is most useful in making steel measuring tapes and bars, clock pendulums, and struts in aluminum automobile pistons. *Superinvar,* containing 31 per cent nickel and 5 per cent cobalt, has zero expansion near room temperature. Alloys of 53 per cent nickel with iron have the same coefficient of cubical expansion as glass and are used for glass-to-metal seals. Alloys of iron with 17 per cent nickel, 11 per cent chromium, or 23 per cent nickel, 5 per cent chromium, are used with Invar as components of bimetallic strips for temperature controls.

Cast Iron and Malleable Cast Iron

CAST IRON

1. Importance of Cast Iron. On account of cheapness, strength, ease with which it may be melted and cast into more or less intricate shapes, ease of machining, high damping capacity, and ease with which its hardness may be varied, cast iron is the most used of the cast metals employed in engineering constructions and machines. It is extensively fabricated into water pipes, cylinders, car wheels, agricultural machinery, stoves, hardware, machine frames, bed plates, and column bases; and to a less extent for columns, grate bars, ornamental castings, pipe fittings, and agricultural implements. Further uses are indicated in Table 1. Where toughness is necessary cast iron is displaced by the more expensive malleable cast iron or by the still more costly cast steel. Again in constructions where the metal must withstand corrosion, brasses, bronzes and other alloys, all of which are very much more expensive than cast iron, displace it.

As an indication of the great use of cast iron, we note that in 1950 approximately 16.5 million short tons of steel scrap and pig iron were used in cupolas, and about 1.5 million tons were used in air furnaces to manufacture gray-iron castings.

MANUFACTURE OF CAST IRON

2. Remelting of Pig Iron. Although pig iron from the blast furnace is sometimes molded into final form, most of the pig iron used for castings is remelted before being molded into final shape. Remelting is necessitated by the variability in the pig iron run from a given furnace, by the difficulty of adjusting the composition of the molten iron, and by the necessity of mixing different grades of pig iron in order to secure the desired grades of castings.

Most gray iron used in machine parts is remelted in the cupola; most of the white iron used in making malleable cast iron is remelted in the air furnace. The air furnace and the cupola are also sometimes used in a duplex operation. Some use has also been made of small open-hearth furnaces and considerable use of electric furnaces to remelt pig iron for high-grade cast iron and malleable cast iron.

The function of the remelting furnace is simply to produce homogeneity in the charge which has been proportioned with reference to the use of the product. Changes between the average composition of the metal charged and that of the castings are, in general, small although sometimes important.

3. Materials Charged. Compositions of the pig irons commonly used in smelting cast iron are given in Art. XVIII-14. In many parts of the country the chemical analysis of the pig iron serves as means of grading it and purchase is made on this basis. Generally the silicon content is specified and the sulfur limit prescribed. Some foundrymen still rely on the character of fracture exhibited by the pig iron as a criterion of composition. Special pig irons containing high percentages of silicon, the Scotch irons and ferrosilicons, are sometimes added to soften the iron; others containing high percentages of manganese, ferromanganese, for example, are used as hardeners.

Besides pig iron, from a tenth to a half of the metal charged consists of the foundry scrap from previous heats and whatever old machinery or cast iron the foundrymen can purchase. All this heterogeneous mass is termed scrap. On account of variability in its composition the proportion of scrap is generally less than 25 per cent of the metal charged when the best grades of castings are being made.

Coke is the fuel most commonly used in the cupola, bituminous coal in the air furnace. Under favorable conditions with large furnaces the ratio of fuel to iron is about 1:8 or 1:10 for the cupola and 1:4 for the air furnace.

A flux consisting of crushed limestone or other form of lime carbonate is usually added in very small amounts to slag off the earthy impurities and reduce the sulfur content of the cast iron.

4. The Cupola is a sort of small blast furnace. It consists of a vertical cylindrical steel shell of nearly uniform diameter lined with firebrick. Figure 1 shows an elevation of a cupola. At the bottom is placed the well, which extends upward a short distance to the level of the tuyeres. At the bottom of the well is located the tap hole, and opposite to it some distance above the bottom is the slag hole. The tuyeres are placed in one or two circumferential rows. Air at a pressure of 1 psi or less is served to the tuyeres through the wind box which surrounds the hearth. Above the tuyeres, in order, are the superheating, melting, and preheating zones, and the stack which contains the charging doors. Cupolas vary in internal diameter up to 10 ft. The common sizes are from 4 to 6 ft in diameter with their charging doors 12 to 25 ft above the hearth bottom. Cupolas of these sizes will run from 10 to 20 tons of metal per hour.

In operating a cupola, kindling is first placed on the hearth and a thick layer of coke on top of it. Alternate layers of pig iron mixed with scrap and layers of fuel are then dumped in until the stack is filled to the level of the charging door. If flux is used it is charged immediately after each

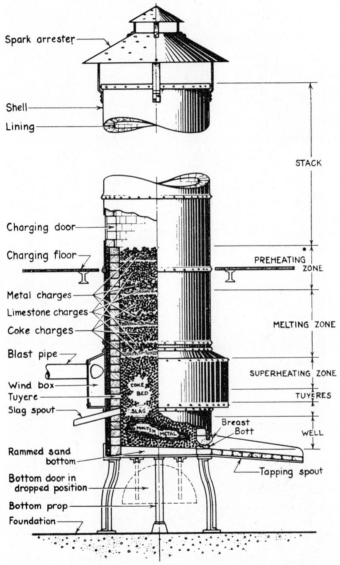

Spark arrester

Shell

Lining

STACK

Charging door

Charging floor

PREHEATING ZONE

Metal charges

Limestone charges

MELTING ZONE

Coke charges

Blast pipe

SUPERHEATING ZONE

Wind box

Tuyere

TUYERES

Slag spout

COKE BED

SLAG

Breast

Bott

WELL

MOLTEN METAL

Rammed sand bottom

Bottom door in dropped position

Tapping spout

Bottom prop

Foundation

Fig. 1. Cupola. (From *Foundry Work,* by Doe.)

layer of coke. After the fire has been kindled and the bed of fuel well ignited the blast is turned on, and in about 10 minutes molten iron trickles from the tap hole. The tap hole is then closed with a plug of fire clay. As the slag accumulates it runs off through the slag hole, and from time

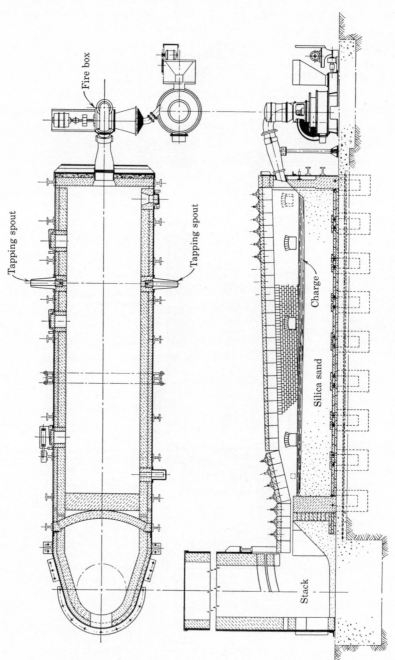

Fig. 2. Air furnace. (Whiting Corp.)

to time the iron is tapped into a large ladle. Ordinarily cupolas are charged and discharged several times a day, but at some plants they are run continuously for several days. The necessity of repairing the lining at frequent intervals prohibits long runs.

During the melting process small amounts of iron, manganese, and 0.2 to 0.3 per cent of silicon are oxidized, while 0.05 to 0.10 per cent of sulfur and, under certain conditions, a little carbon is absorbed from the fuel.

5. The Air Furnace. A horizontal section through an air furnace is shown at the top of Fig. 2, and a vertical section is shown at the bottom. Between the fire box at one end and the stack at the other is a shallow rectangular hearth served by doors in the side. The tapping spouts are located near the fire-box end. Modern air furnaces ordinarily use pulverized coal, oil, or gas for fuel and range in capacity from 5 to 40 tons.

Before the charge is introduced into the furnace the bottom of the hearth is covered with a layer of sand; then the scrap and pig iron are placed upon it. As the flame and hot gases pass through the melting chamber they heat the walls and roof of the furnace. The charge is melted principally by the heat radiated from the roof and side walls of the furnace and partly by the hot gases which sweep over the hearth. During the melting process the bath is rabbled occasionally with iron bars to promote uniformity in melting and in composition. If much slag forms on the bath it is partially skimmed off to raise the temperature and promote oxidation of the carbon and silicon. In order that the top metal, which is the hottest, may be run from the furnace, tapping is done through a set of holes placed at different elevations in the hearth. The usual rate of producing iron with the air furnace is 3 to 4 tons per hour.

6. Comparison of Cupola and Air-Furnace Processes. The cupola process is quicker, cheaper in installation and in operation; the metal is hotter and more uniform in temperature—conditions which mean much in casting; the loss of metal through oxidation is also less than in the air furnace. On the other hand the air furnace produces a larger quantity of high-grade iron at a single tapping. The metal in the air furnace, not being in contact with the fuel, absorbs neither sulfur nor carbon. The air-furnace process is under better control and permits better regulation in the composition of the iron. In neither process, however, has there been a successful attempt at utilization of the latent heat in the escaping gases.

MOLDING

7. Patterns of the castings are made either of wood coated with shellac, or of metal. Wood is largely used when only a few castings are desired. When the number of castings is to be great, brass or aluminum patterns are employed to avoid imperfections likely to be found in the castings, due to damaging of wooden patterns. If a number of castings of similar shape are to be made it is customary to join several patterns in such way that they may be poured simultaneously. Such patterns are said to be gated. Patterns are always made larger than the casting to allow for contraction in cooling. For ordinary gray cast iron an allowance of ⅛ in. per ft is a common rule. White cast iron and steel shrink double this amount; brass and copper about 50 per cent more; and lead and zinc two and one-half times as much as gray cast iron. The fundamental considerations in designing a pattern are: (1) make the pattern of such shape that it may be removed from the sand without damaging the mold; if of intricate shape it may be necessary to make the pattern in two or more parts; (2) use fillets of large radius at all sharp angles and corners and thus avoid planes of weakness arising from the crystallization of the metal; * (3) avoid joining heavy and light sections wherever possible, since these parts, cooling at unequal rates, will be highly stressed at their junction (if such design is necessary some provision should be made for rapidly cooling the heavy section); (4) when possible avoid shapes where the ends of the casting will be rigidly held by the mold and contraction stresses or checking will thus be produced in the intermediate parts of the casting.

8. Cores. When it is necessary to make a hollow casting some sort of core is used. This is located in proper place in the mold by projecting fins which rest in core prints that are made by corresponding projections of the pattern. If the core is of such size or shape that it cannot be held in place by core prints, iron supports called chaplets are placed in the mold. Generally cores must be so made that they will offer little resistance to shrinkage of the metal and will not burn onto the iron. They are commonly molded of dry sand mixed with flour, molasses, linseed oil or patented compound and baked in an oven. Sometimes green sand cores are used. When it is particularly necessary to avoid all stressing of the casting, cores are made with centers of crushed coke or of pipe wound with hay rope, the outside being of sand. Cores are vented to permit the escape of gases generated in pouring.

9. Materials for Molds. Not only must the material composing the mold retain the metal and give it a smooth and true surface but it must also be sufficiently porous to allow the escape of air and gas. Sand is the most refractory cheap material for this purpose. A good molding sand generally contains not less than 80 per cent silica, 5 to 10 per cent of

---

* When a metal cools the crystals form perpendicularly to the surfaces. If a corner is left sharp there will be a plane of separation between crystals bisecting the angle at the corner. Since the cohesion across these planes is less than in the crystals, a pronounced weakness is thus produced. By rounding the corners, interlocking of the crystals is promoted and a stronger, more homogeneous casting is obtained.

alumina, and about 1 per cent of an organic binder. The higher the temperature of the molten metal, the more refractory must the sand be. Consequently the silica content must be higher for steel than for cast-iron castings. Some alumina and binder, however, are needed to furnish requisite cohesiveness. Small proportions of magnesia, lime, and iron oxide are also usually present. More than 2 or 3 per cent of the carbonates is objectionable owing to the gas formed in calcination of them; and metallic oxides render the sand less refractory. Another important factor which affects the cohesiveness and the porosity of molding sand is the gradation in sizes of particles. The smoothness of the surface of the casting is also affected by the fineness of the sand grains. Therefore, molding sand is generally screened through a 20-mesh sieve, the gradation in sizes below that opening being determined by the work in hand.

Parting sand is a highly refractory sand which cannot be rendered cohesive by the addition of water.

Facing materials are shaken over the pattern or surface of the mold to prevent the sand from being burnt and to make the castings leave the mold freely, thus preserving a bright surface and avoiding expense in cleaning. Fine soft coal, graphite, charcoal, and talc are among the substances which are mixed with six to fifteen times as much fine molding sand to make facings.

Loam is the name for a soil carrying a high content of siliceous sand, considerable clay, and more or less decayed vegetable and animal matter. The term is also used to designate artificial mixtures made of sand and clay with some sawdust or rye meal.

10. Molds. The kind of castings and the number, size, and shape determine the character of the molds. The common types of molds are green-sand, dry-sand and loam molds. Besides these, cast-iron molds are considerably used when a permanent type of mold is desired.

Green-Sand Molds. The pattern is surrounded by a flask of wood or cast iron which serves to hold the sand in place. Generally the flask consists of two, sometimes three or more, rectangular frames of equal size which may be doweled or locked together to form a bottomless box. In molding many simple objects, half the pattern is bedded in the lower frame, called the drag, and the other half is covered by the upper part of the flask, called the cope. The procedure is to place the drag on a mold board bottom side up with the pattern or portion of the pattern resting on the mold board. Molding sand moistened with sufficient water to render it coherent is rammed about the pattern and several small vent holes are punched through to the pattern. A bottom board is put over the drag and the drag is turned over. The remainder of the pattern is inserted and a bit of parting sand is sifted over the top of the drag, the pattern being kept clean. Next, the cope is put in place and plugs for the runner * and riser * are properly located. Molding sand is tamped about the pattern and vents provided. The plugs are then withdrawn, the cope carefully lifted, and gates from plugs to pattern are cut. A draw spike is attached to the pattern, and tapped until the pattern can be removed. After the loose sand has been removed a facing may be smeared on the surfaces of the mold; the cope is then placed on top of the drag and locked in position for pouring.

Green-sand molds are much used, especially for articles of like shape, because they can be rapidly made at low cost. When there is a large demand for a certain type of casting, molding machines are frequently used.

Dry-Sand Molds are fashioned in iron flasks in much the same way as those of green sand. A rather coarse loamy sand is used, and the molds are dried at 300° to 400°F. After the mold is baked, the surface is generally coated with a wet mixture of graphite, or charcoal with clay. Such molds are strong, will withstand hard usage, and, if properly vented, produce sound smooth castings. Dry-sand molds are well adapted for the production of cylinders, rolls, engine beds, and other heavy castings where the pressure of the metal is great, or where a smooth wall of uniform thickness must be obtained.

Dry-sand molds are likely to be somewhat distorted during drying and cause heavier shrinkage stresses in castings than green-sand molds. On the other hand, castings made in dry-sand molds are more sound, smoother, and freer from inclusions of sand and dirt than those cast in green sand.

Loam Molds are used principally for very large castings which are bounded by surfaces of revolution. Castings of heavy engine cylinders and flywheels are generally made in loam molds. The outer casing of the mold is ordinarily built of brick, sometimes of iron. To the interior of this casing dampened mixtures of loam are plastered. The surface of the mold is generated by revolving a sweep, the end of which is fashioned in conformity with the surface desired for the casting. The mold is then baked and faced. Owing to the rigidity of loam molds, provision is made during the fabrication to permit rapid destruction of certain parts immediately after the casting is poured in order that the latter may contract freely.

Much of the manual work required in the production of molds has been eliminated by automatic machinery. Molding machines range in size from

---

* A runner is the canal through which the molten metal is poured. It is provided with a basin at the top and a hole at the bottom connecting with the mold called a gate. A riser is a vertical canal leading from the mold to the top of the cope. It serves to vent the mold, to supply metal as the casting cools, and to carry off dirt.

those used for ramming a mold 12 in. wide by 14 in. long to the large machines that ram, roll over, and remove the pattern for molds 6 ft wide by 12 ft long.

11. Chills. Surfaces of castings which are subjected to heavy wear are made hard by rapidly cooling them in chills. Chills consist of pieces of cast iron which form the surface of the mold in contact with the part of the casting to be hardened. Sticking of the iron to the chills is prevented by coating the latter with shellac and plumbago or with a thin film of light oil. To avoid explosions resulting from contact between the molten

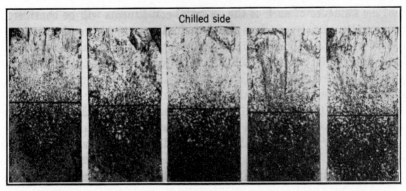

Fig. 3.   Chilled test pieces showing variable chill depth.   (Assoc. of Manufacturers of Chilled Car Wheels.)

metal and the chill, it is necessary to heat the latter to 300° or 400°F before pouring. The treads of car wheels and the bearing surfaces of rolls are cast against chills. Changes in composition due to chilling are explained in Art. 14. Figure 3 shows the effect of chilling on structure. The depth in inches of white iron produced by chilling is termed chill.

12. Cleaning Castings. Flasks are removed as soon as the castings have solidified, but the pieces are generally allowed to remain in the sand until cool. Sand and dirt adhering to the surfaces of the castings are removed by tumbling, by pickling in acid, or by sand blasting. Tumbling is done in a device similar to that used in testing the toughness of paving brick. It can only be successfully employed on sturdy regular-shaped pieces. Tumbling also produces a hard skin on the castings. Pickling is used on fragile or intricate castings and on pieces which must be machined. Dilute solutions of hydrochloric or sulfuric acid are often used for pickling, but they attack the iron. Hydrofluoric acid in a 5 per cent solution is more efficacious since it attacks the sand. Sand blasting and hydro blasting are effective means of cleaning heavy work.

COMPOSITION AND CONSTITUTION

13. The Principal Constituents. As in the carbon steels, the five main impurities in cast iron are carbon, silicon, sulfur, phosphorus, and manganese. They constitute from 5 to 8 per cent of cast iron, by weight. In addition to these elements, in making alloy cast irons one or more of the following elements is added: nickel, chromium, molybdenum, vanadium, titanium, and copper.

Since the properties of cast iron depend principally upon the proportion of the different impurities and the combinations which they form in the iron, the influence of each of the essential constituents will be considered. Owing to the variety of forms and combinations in which carbon is found in cast iron, the influence of this element is of the most importance in determining the properties and the value of the iron. The three main types of cast iron—gray, white, and mottled iron—owe their characteristics and properties to variations in the form of carbon content.

14. Carbon in Cast Iron. The proportion of carbon in cast iron generally lies between $2\frac{1}{2}$ and 4 per cent by weight. Carbon occurs in two forms—either free as graphite, or chemically combined with the iron as iron carbide (Fe_3C). When the carbon is free, the proportion of the volume of the metal occupied by the graphite globules or flakes, due to its specific gravity being much less than that of iron, is about 3.2 times as much as the percentage by weight. Therefore the spaces occupied by the flakes of graphite aggregate 8 to 13 per cent of the bulk of the iron. When the carbon is combined with the iron, the volume of the iron carbide formed is fifteen times the percentage of the combined carbon.

The amount of carbon which the molten iron will retain in solidifying depends upon the composition of the iron. Again the proportion of the carbon which is retained in combined form is influenced greatly by the presence of other elements and by the rate of cooling. Additions of manganese and chromium increase the solubility of carbon in iron and promote carbide stability. On the other hand, additions of silicon or aluminum reduce the solubility of carbon in iron and promote the formation of graphite. Rapid cooling tends to cause combined carbon, slow cooling furthers increase in graphite. When the composition is properly adjusted it is possible to retain the carbon as carbide of iron by rapid cooling or to precipitate it by slow cooling.

The process of inoculating cast irons to obtain improvement in mechanical properties and in structure has become increasingly important. These materials added to the molten cast iron, usually in the ladle, effectively change the structure with only slight changes in chemical composition. Inoculants such as ferrosilicon and various proprietary materials are graphitizing inoculants. Other types such as chromium are carbide stabilizers. Inoculants when properly used in carefully controlled cast iron are a valuable aid in the production of high-quality castings.

If in cooling the carbon is largely precipitated, more or less uniformly in the form of graphite flakes, the iron is soft and presents a dull gray fracture. This is *gray cast iron.* When the carbon is retained in com-

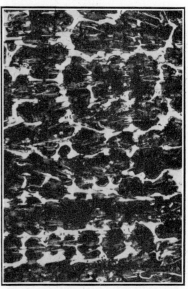

(a) Gray cast iron. The structure consists of graphite flakes, lamellar pearlite, and phosphide eutectic, steadite, ×750. (L. F. Porter.)

(b) White cast iron. The white constituent is cementite and the dark one is pearlite, ×150. (R. W. Heine.)

Fig. 4. Photomicrographs of gray and white cast irons.

bined form, the cast iron is very hard and brittle; and the silvery white fracture has led to the name *white cast iron.* In some irons the major portion of the carbon is retained in the combined form while a lesser part is precipitated as graphite. Such irons exhibit a white fracture spotted with dark gray patches and are termed *mottled cast irons.* Photomicrographs of gray and white cast irons appear in Fig. 4.

From the foregoing it follows that irons containing large amounts of manganese or chromium are likely to be permanently white while those having a high silicon content are gray. With proper adjustment in composition, cast iron may be rendered white by cooling rapidly or gray by cooling slowly from the molten state.

The proportion of carbon and its form influence more or less most of the physical and mechanical properties of cast iron. The initial and final solidification temperatures vary with the composition. The initial solidification temperature is lowered by increasing the carbon or silicon contents and may vary between 2066° and 2500°F. The final solidification temperature varies between 2066° and 2100°F. Shrinkage varies inversely as the carbon content, but white iron shrinks nearly twice as much as gray iron. The specific weight of gray iron increases with the decrease

Name of matrix	Low carbon steel	Medium carbon steel	High carbon steel	White cast iron
Name of the cast iron i.e., of the whole	Very open gray or very graphitic cast iron		Close gray cast iron	Mottled cast iron · White cast iron

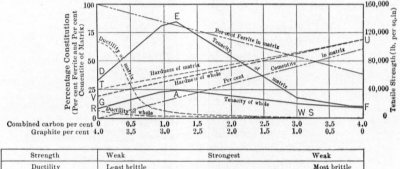

Strength	Weak		Strongest	Weak
Ductility	Least brittle			Most brittle
Hardness	Softest		Soft · Harder	Hardest
Be cause of its — Strength and ductility	the iron is suited to uses in which it will have to undergo or resist	shock	moderate shock the iron is suited to most engineering purposes	no shock unless metal is strongly supported
hardness		much machining in preparation but little abrasion in use	moderate machining in preparation not excessive abrasion in use	no machining in preparation, much abrasion in use

Fig. 5. Influence of carbon on constitution and properties of cast iron. (Howe.)

in carbon content and varies from 425 to 450 lb per cu ft. White cast iron is heavier than gray because of the chemical combination of the carbon and weighs in the vicinity of 475 lb per cu ft.

The influence of the proportion of combined carbon on the constitution and mechanical properties of cast iron containing 4 per cent of carbon is idealized in Howe's diagram in Fig. 5.* Other factors constant, the tenacity of the whole varies with the proportion of pearlite in the matrix and is a maximum, as in normally cooled steels, when the matrix contains 1.2 per cent carbon. The hardness varies with the proportion of cementite in the matrix. The diagram also shows the influence of combined carbon on machining qualities, properties, and general uses of cast iron. Irons

* *Proc. ASTM,* Vol. 2, p. 252.

with total carbon contents of 2.75 to 3.25 per cent are preferred to the one illustrated because the weakening influence of the graphite is less, the strengthening effect of the matrix is greater, and the castings can be made more sound and free from defects.

Mechanical properties of cast irons are affected not only by the proportion of graphite but also by the size and dispersion of the flakes. The tenacity and toughness of cast irons containing fine, rounded, graphite particles uniformly dispersed, are superior to the same properties for similar irons with coarse flakes. Hence melting at high temperatures (above 1500°C), which is attended by obliteration of existing non-metallic nuclei, effectively reduces the size of flakes and thus promotes superior mechanical properties.

15. Silicon in Cast Iron. Next to carbon, silicon exercises the most important influence on the properties of cast iron. It combines with the iron, forming iron silicide, which in turn is dissolved in the ferrite. The proportion of silicon in cast iron usually runs between 0.5 and 3.0 per cent, although certain special castings for acid containers are made with a much higher silicon content. Silicon in small percentages increases the fluidity of the molten iron, decreases blow-holes and increases the density of castings. Silicon also reduces the solubility of carbon in iron. According to Wust and Peterson, each percentage of silicon throws out of solution 0.27 per cent carbon; consequently, by decomposing the hard cementite, silicon acts as a softener and also decreases shrinkage. However, when present in excess of the amount required to decompose cementite, the direct hardening influence of iron silicide becomes noticeable; and with 5 or 6 per cent of silicon the iron is hard and has a mirror-like fracture. In short, by varying the silicon content the foundryman exercises a most important control over a wide range in the properties of cast iron.

The combined influence of carbon and silicon upon the structure of cast iron is well illustrated in Fig. 6 for small specimens cast in sand molds. Cast irons with compositions in area I cool with no dissociation of iron carbide. These cast irons are hard and brittle, have a white fracture, and have a structure of pearlite plus excess cementite. Cast irons with compositions in area IIa cool with considerable dissociation of the iron carbide and have a structure consisting of a matrix of pearlite plus excess graphite. As cast irons with compositions in area IIb cool, most of the iron carbide dissociates and the resultant structure is that of a 0.20 to 0.50 per cent carbon steel plus graphite. Cast irons with compositions in area III cool with almost complete dissociation of the iron carbide, and the resultant structure is made up of ferrite and graphite. The cast irons with compositions in areas II, IIb, and III have a gray fracture. Those in area II are strong, and those in area III are relatively weak.

Coyle related the carbon and silicon contents of small cast-iron specimens cooled in sand molds to the tensile strength as shown in Fig. 7.

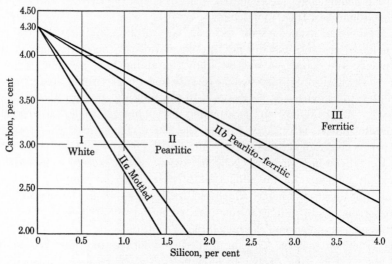

Fig. 6.   Constitutional diagram of cast iron.   (Maurer.)   (*Proc. ASTM*, Vol. 29, p. 88.)

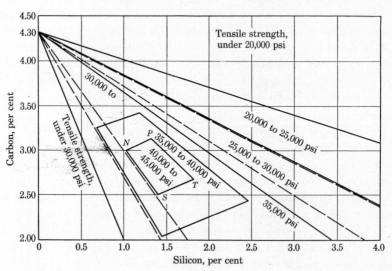

Fig. 7.   Constitutional and strength diagram of cast iron.   (*Proc. ASTM,* Vol. 29, p. 88.)

From this diagram it appears that the most favorable composition on the basis of tensile strength is approximately 2.50 to 3.25 per cent total carbon and 1.00 to 2.00 per cent silicon.

Since composition and cooling rate materially influence the mechanical properties of cast iron it is desirable to use some method for predicting properties that takes these factors into account. One such method, shown in Fig. 8, employs a log-log relationship. The properties of gray cast iron

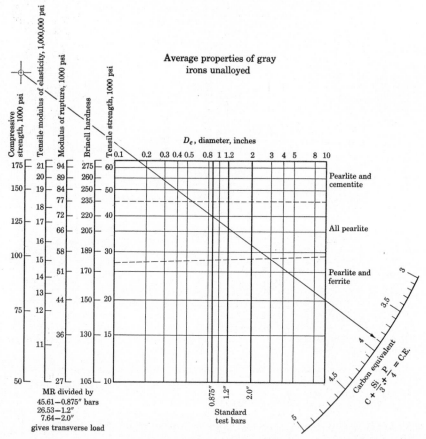

Fig. 8. Tensile strength of unalloyed gray irons as affected by the carbon equivalent and section size. (Composition and Properties of Gray Iron by R. Schniedewind and R. G. McElwee, *Trans. Am. Foundrymen's Soc.*, Vol. 58, p. 328.)

are related to the carbon equivalent, defined as $\%C + \%Si/3 + \%P/4$, and the size of bar. The carbon equivalent (C.E.), arrived at experimentally, is a measure of strength. If it is high the iron is weak, and if it is low the iron is relatively strong. It is evident that a given C.E. may be obtained with bars of widely different chemical compositions. Figure 8 may also be used for sections other than round bars by calculating an equivalent diameter (D_e). Assuming that sections having the same ratio of volume (cubic inches) to surface area (square inches) have about the same cooling rate, D_e may be found by determining the size of a round bar having the same ratio as the given section.

In using Fig. 8 a line is drawn from the "point of rotation" to the carbon equivalent. The intersection of this line with the vertical line, representing the desired or given size, gives the required information on properties,

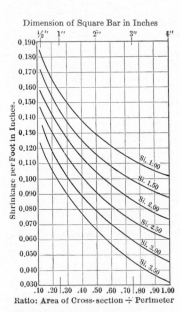

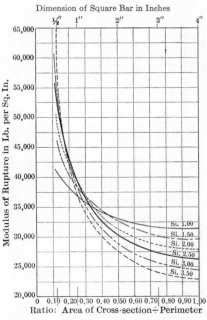

Fig. 9. Influence of silicon on shrinkage of cast-iron specimens of various areas of cross section. (Keep.)

Fig. 10. The variation in cross-breaking modulus of rupture of cast iron for different sizes of bars and for varying percentages of silicon. (Keep.)

read at the left edge. If, for example, a gray cast-iron bar has a carbon equivalent of 3.9 and a diameter of 0.875 in. it may be expected to have a tensile strength of about 40,000 psi, a Brinell hardness of 220, a modulus of rupture of 72,000 psi, and a compressive strength of 130,000 psi. These properties are reduced if a 2.0-in. bar of the same composition is considered. This method may also be extended to alloy gray cast iron by use of suitable factors which take into account the action of the alloying elements.

The very important influence of silicon in reducing shrinkage is well brought out in Fig. 9.

Figure 10 shows the variation in transverse strength for different sizes of bars and different silicon contents. The data emphasize the necessity of testing bars of the same thickness as the finished casting, if a knowledge of the strength of the metal in the casting is wanted.

16. Sulfur in Cast Iron. Sulfur is an undesirable element in cast iron and is generally limited to less than 0.1 per cent. Since it is believed to promote the formation of combined carbon the above limit is often doubled on irons cast in chills. It combines with manganese to form the sulfide (MnS) or, if the manganese is very low and not sufficient to satisfy the sulfur, iron sulfide (FeS) may be formed. Since these sulfides solidify at considerably lower temperatures than cast iron they tend to make castings brittle and weak at high temperatures. Sulfur in high percentages (0.5 per cent or over) also increases shrinkage and causes hard, brittle iron. These evil effects may be neutralized by proper additions of silicon.

17. Phosphorus in Cast Iron. According to Stead, phosphorus occurs in gray iron in a eutectic of iron phosphide plus iron, and in white iron in a eutectic of iron carbide, iron phosphide, and iron. These hard brittle components called *steadite* bulk approximately ten times as much as the weight percentage of phosphorus. When phosphorus does not exceed the usual amount used (0.10 to 0.90 per cent) it has no marked effect on the strength of cast iron. If more than 2 per cent of phosphorus is present the iron is embrittled and the strength diminished. High-phosphorus irons are much more fluid and shrink somewhat less than irons low in phosphorus. High-phosphorus irons, therefore, take a good impression of the mold and are much used in making thin stove castings and ornamental castings where great strength and toughness are not essential.

18. Manganese in Cast Iron. The proportion of manganese ordinarily found in cast iron ranges from 0.4 per cent to 1.2 per cent. When present in such proportions manganese combines with sulfur, forming manganese sulfide (MnS), and—having satisfied sulfur—with carbon to form manganese carbide (Mn_3C). The latter is found in cementite united with iron carbide. Ferromanganese is often added to the molten iron to reduce the sulfur and oxygen contents. This is accomplished by combination and partial withdrawal of the oxides and sulfides of manganese into the slag. Manganese increases the solubility of carbon in iron and opposes the liberation of graphite. Increased shrinkage and hardness are promoted by increasing the manganese content beyond that required to satisfy sulfur. Therefore manganese must be kept low in gray iron which is to be machined; in parts which must withstand abrasion a high manganese content is desirable.

19. Alloying Elements in Cast Iron. In addition to the elements usually present in cast iron, alloying elements such as chromium, copper, molybdenum, nickel, titanium, and vanadium are frequently added in sufficient quantity to produce significant changes in the physical or mechanical properties. The important effects of each of the commonly used alloying elements are given in the following paragraphs.

Additions of *chromium*, a strong carbide-forming element, usually vary between 0.30 and 1.0 per cent. Chromium stabilizes the carbides at high temperatures, increases the depth of chill, and refines the structure. Small amounts of chromium increase the strength, hardness, resistance to corrosion, resistance to wear, but decrease machinability. Chromium contents as high as 35 per cent are used for cast irons that must resist corrosion or heat.

Copper acts as a graphite-forming element, but it is only about one-tenth as effective as silicon. The usual additions of copper for engineering applications vary between 0.50 and 2.0 per cent. In gray cast iron, copper increases the strength, hardness, resistance to wear, and resistance to corrosion.

Molybdenum is a mild carbide-forming element in cast iron. It improves the graphite distribution and refines the grain structure. In the usual amounts, 0.30 to 1.25 per cent, it increases the hardness, tensile strength, and transverse strength. Molybdenum increases the ability of cast iron to maintain good strength at high temperatures and is also believed to improve the fatigue properties of cast iron.

Nickel acts as a graphitizing agent, refines the grain structure, and reduces chill in cast iron. Additions of nickel less than 1.0 per cent are effective in refining the grain and graphite flake size. Engineering gray cast irons may contain as much as 6.0 per cent nickel. Martensitic white cast irons have good strength, toughness, and abrasion resistance, and usually contain about 4.5 per cent nickel and 2.0 per cent chromium. Austenitic cast irons usually contain from 14 to 36 per cent nickel and from 2 to 6 per cent chromium. These cast irons resist heat, corrosion, and usually have low expansivity.

Titanium has a strong affinity for oxygen and nitrogen, decreases the graphite flake size, and exerts a strong graphitizing effect. It is present in small amounts, usually less than 0.10 per cent. It increases the tensile and transverse strength and may also increase the machinability, wear resistance, and corrosion resistance.

Vanadium, usually added in amounts less than 0.50 per cent, is a powerful carbide-forming element that stabilizes cementite and restrains graphitization. It increases tensile and transverse strengths, wear resistance, hardness, and depth of chill.

20. Ductile Cast Iron. The International Nickel Co. has developed * and patented a process for making ductile cast iron in which the graphite

---

* Also developed simultaneously in England.

is present in the form of small nodules or spheroids. The change in the form of the carbon is accomplished by ladle additions of small amounts of magnesium or a magnesium alloy, frequently a nickel-magnesium alloy. Ductile cast iron usually contains 3.1 to 3.6 per cent total carbon, 1.6 to 2.9 per cent silicon, 0.2 to 0.8 per cent manganese, 0.03 to 0.13 per cent phosphorus, less than 0.05 per cent sulfur, 0.6 to 2.0 per cent nickel, and 0.05 to 0.10 per cent magnesium.

Ductile cast iron has good machinability, good pressure tightness, excellent casting qualities, and may be used where moderate shock resistance is required. It is more resistant to growth at high temperatures than ordinary gray cast iron. The mechanical properties of ductile cast iron are superior to those of gray cast iron. The tensile strength of 1-in. sections of ductile cast iron in the as-cast condition usually varies between 85,000 and 110,000 psi, the yield strength measured at an offset of 0.2 per cent varies between 60,000 and 75,000 psi, the elongation measured over a 2-in. gage length does not usually exceed 5 per cent, and the Brinell hardness varies between 225 and 300. Ductile cast iron maintains a proportionality of stress to strain up to high stresses and has a modulus of elasticity of about 25,000,000 psi.

If the pearlitic matrix is changed to a ferritic matrix by annealing, the tensile strength of a 1-in. section is usually decreased to 65,000 to 75,000 psi, the Brinell hardness is decreased to 170 to 200, and the 2-in. elongation is increased to 10 to 20 per cent.

An increase in the size of section from 1 to 6 in. causes moderate decreases in the tensile strength in both the as-cast and annealed conditions, and a marked decrease in the elongation of annealed ductile cast iron.

21. Defects in Cast Iron. Checks, segregation, blow-holes, and coarse grain, the principal defects in cast iron, originate during the cooling of the castings. Checks are small parallel cracks in the surface of a casting. They generally run transverse to the long axis of the piece. Checks may arise from errors in designing the shape of the casting or mold which prevent contraction during cooling. Irons of high sulfur content are likely to have this defect owing to their great shrinkage and lack of strength while at a red heat.

Segregation is very pronounced in high-phosphorus irons, where the eutectics of iron phosphide and iron separate from the main part of the metal and form brittle masses which are more or less well connected, depending on the amount of phosphorus present. Even with smaller percentages of phosphorus there appears to be a well-marked tendency to the formation, here and there, of little knots of metal which are found attached within gas cavities. Analyses of the knots show that the phosphorus and sulfur contents are very much above the mean compositions.

The sulfides are also found in greatest proportion in the top of the casting and in the parts cooled most slowly. Carbon and silicon sometimes segregate in such a manner that interior portions of the metal are white and exterior parts are gray. When such segregations occur at different parts of the surface of a casting, they render it very difficult to machine. Sometimes relief of the non-uniformity can be had by annealing the piece.

Blow-holes are generally due to improper venting of the mold or to a high proportion of sulfur. If pronounced, they seriously affect both strength and toughness of the casting.

A coarse or open grain in the iron is caused by too slow cooling, or it may be due to a very high phosphorus content. In thick parts a coarse open grain is generally found near the center of the section and is quite difficult to prevent. A more compact structure is often secured by lowering the silicon content, by charging turnings or chips of cast iron along with the pig iron, or by adding nickel and chromium.

Besides the above-mentioned defects, spongy spots and "cold shuts" sometimes result from lack of fluidity in the iron or from improper gating. Cold shuts are fault planes in the metal produced by the solidification of part of the casting before the remaining molten metal was run into place. Spongy spots are exaggerated forms of open grain; they are often due to a solidification of metal in the risers before the interior of the casting has solidified. The interior is thus cut off from the supply of metal which is needed to fill voids caused by shrinkage in cooling, and a porous structure results.

22. Compositions Suitable to Different Kinds of Castings. Usually the properties, such as strength and hardness, desired in castings are specified by the purchaser and the composition is left to the discretion of the foundryman. Table 1 shows compositions of irons for some uses. Whereas the major portion of gray-iron castings are made without the alloying elements, nickel, chromium, molybdenum, etc., castings for severe service are frequently made with such additions. Thus nickel cast irons are used in automotive and locomotive cylinders, gears, pump bodies, and crusher frames. Cast irons containing chromium find use in chills, crusher jaws, annealing boxes, and molds for glass. Nickel-chromium cast irons have been used in automotive cylinders, forging dies, brake drums, and clutch plates. Molybdenum, promoting strength and uniformity, has been added to cast irons for brake drums, automotive cylinders, ingot molds, and other high-strength castings. Vanadium cast irons have been used in grate bars, locomotive cylinders, rolls for steel mills, and molds for bottles.

TABLE 1. COMPOSITIONS OF CAST IRONS FOR VARIOUS PURPOSES

(Should not be a basis for specifications.)

Kind of Castings.	Composition in Per Cent.								
	Total Carbon.	Combined Carbon.	Silicon.	Manganese.	Phosphorus.	Sulfur.	Nickel.	Chromium.	Molybdenum.
Agricultural machinery	3.2-3.5	0.4-0.5	2.1-2.3	0.6-0.8	<0.30	<0.10			
Ammonia cylinders....	3.0-3.3	.....	1.0-1.7	0.7-0.9	<0.30	<0.10			
Automobile cylinders...	3.1-3.3	0.4-0.6	2.1-2.3	0.6-0.8	<0.20	<0.13			
Automobile cylinders...	3.1-3.3	.....	1.7-1.9	0.6-0.7	<0.20	<0.13	1.2-1.3		
Automobile cylinders...	3.2-3.4	.....	1.7-1.9	0.6-0.7	<0.20	<0.13	1.4-1.6	0.4-0.5	
Automobile pistons....	3.3-3.5	0.4	2.2-2.4	0.6	<0.20	<0.12	.....	.....	0.4
Automobile piston rings	3.3-3.6	.....	2.8-3.0	0.5-0.7	0.5-0.7	<0.10			
Brake drums..........	3.2-3.3	.....	1.9-2.1	0.6-0.7	<0.20	<0.12	1.2-1.4	0.5-0.6	
Car wheels, chilled.....	3.5-3.7	0.6-0.8	0.6-0.8	0.5-0.7	0.3-0.4	<0.10			
Crusher jaws and rolls..	2.0	.....	1.0	.....	.....	.....	.....	25.0	
Drums, steam.........	3.3-3.4	0.5-0.6	1.4-1.5	0.8-1.0	0.3-0.5	<0.10			
Furnaces and stoves...	3.6-3.7	0.5-0.6	2.1-2.2	0.5-0.6	0.6-0.9	<0.10			
Gears, heavy..........	3.1-3.3	0.6-0.7	1.1-1.2	0.6-0.8	0.2-0.3	<0.10			
Generator frames, steam turbines, pumps.............	3.2-3.3	0.5-0.6	1.9-2.0	0.5-0.6	0.4-0.6	<0.10			
Grinding balls and liners	3.0-3.5	.....	<2.0	.....	.....	.....	.....	3.0	
Heat resisting castings.	3.0-3.5	.....	2.0-2.3	.....	.....	.....	.....	1.2-1.3	
Heavy forming dies....	3.0	.....	1.2-1.3	0.6-0.7	<0.2	<0.10	2.6-2.8	0.7-0.9	
Pipe, centrifugally cast.	3.5-3.6	0.7-0.8	1.6-1.8	0.5-0.6	0.7-0.9	<0.10			
Pipe fittings..........	3.0	.....	1.6-1.8	0.6-0.8	0.5-0.8	<0.10			
Rolls, chilled..........	3.0-3.2	.....	0.6-0.8	1.0-1.2	0.2-0.4	<0.10			
Rope drums, high-strength castings....	2.4-3.0	0.6-0.7	2.0-2.2	0.6-0.7	<0.10	<0.10	1.2-1.3		

PROPERTIES OF CAST IRON

23. Shrinkage. At the moment of complete solidification gray cast iron expands, due to the precipitation of more or less graphite from the eutectic of austenite and cementite. Since graphite occupies more space than if chemically combined in the molten metal the total volume upon solidification is greater than that of the molten metal just before solidification. If phosphorus is high in the iron, the initial expansion is soon augmented by the solidification of the phosphide eutectic which occurs at approximately 1000°C. As the temperature falls these expansions are gradually offset by contraction due to cooling. At 700°C, if the composition is suitable and the rate of cooling slow, another precipitation of graphite with consequent expansion takes place. With high silicon and high total carbon the latter expansion is very pronounced. The casting then shrinks continuously until it reaches room temperature. With proper regulation of the phosphorus, silicon, and total carbon content, it is possible to avoid a coarse open-grained metal and still control shrinkage quite closely. Figure 9 indicates the variations in shrinkage due to changes in silicon and size of casting.

A simple shop test to determine sponginess or shrink cavities consists in molding a K-shaped casting, breaking the branches of the K, and noting the fracture.

24. Hardness of Cast Iron. From the machinist's point of view no property of cast iron is of more importance than its hardness, since the hardness determines the ease with which the iron can be filed or machined. We have seen that hardness increases with the proportion of combined carbon (Fig. 5) and is much influenced by the proportions of manganese and sulfur; that silicon up to about 3 per cent acts as a softener because it promotes the formation of graphite. Therefore, to secure an easily worked iron, the proportion of combined carbon must be reduced to the lowest value consistent with requisite strength. In irons where high strength, closeness of grain, and ease of machining are properties much desired, the total carbon is kept low and silicon high.

Additions of chromium, vanadium, or molybdenum promote combined carbon and hardness. Nickel up to 5 per cent graphitizes the iron and promotes machinability, strength, and uniformity.

For determinations of the hardness and depth of chill which will take place in cast-iron castings of different thicknesses, use sometimes is made of a step-bar casting varying from $\frac{1}{8}$ to 1 in. in thickness. After casting the bar against a chill block, it is broken at different steps, the fracture noted, and hardness tests made.

The Brinell hardness test is probably the most satisfactory for most measurements of hardness of gray iron castings. For indications of hardness of small areas, the Rockwell (B scale) or the Scleroscope are superior. For the harder varieties of white cast irons, the Rockwell (C scale) or Scleroscope provide satisfactory measures of resistance to indentation.

The Brinell hardness number for gray iron runs from 90 for very soft to 200 for dense strong irons, and from 380 to 500 for ordinary chilled white irons. For the special chilled and heat-treated irons it may reach 700.

25. The Tensile Strength of Cast Iron is both an important property and a valuable index of the uniformity of cast iron. The tenacity of gray cast iron varies from 20,000 psi, or less, for soft weak irons to over 60,000 psi for the high-strength irons for special purposes, and as noted in Art. 20 values up to 110,000 psi are obtained for 1-in. sections of ductile cast iron in the as-cast condition. The ASTM standard specifications list seven classes of cast irons based on tensile properties, as shown in Table 2. Suitable composition is chosen by the producing foundry

TABLE 2. ASTM MINIMUM STRENGTH REQUIREMENTS FOR GRAY-IRON CASTINGS

Class.	Required Tensile Strength,* lb./in.^{2}	Minimum Center Breaking Load,† lb. (Optional)			Correlation of Test Bar and Casting.	
		A-Bar, Diam. 0.875 in. Span 12-in.	B-Bar, Diam. 1.2 in. Span 18-in.	C-Bar, Diam. 2.0 in. Span 24-in.	Thickness of Controlling Section of Casting.	Diameter of Test Bar as Cast.
20	20,000	900	1800	6,000	<0.50 in.	0.875
25	25,000	1025	2000	6,800	0.51 to 1.00 in.	1.200
30	30,000	1150	2200	7,600	1.01 to 2.00 in.	2.00
35	35,000	1275	2400	8,300	Over 2.00 in.	2.00, or as
40	40,000	1400	2600	9,100		agreed upon
50	50,000	1675	3000	10,300		
60	60,000	1925	3400	12,500		

* Tests are to be made on threaded end specimens with gaged diameters of 0.505, 0.800, and 1.25 in. for A-, B-, and C-Bar specimens, respectively.
† In transverse tests corrections for deviation in bar diameter, d, may be made by dividing the test load by $(d^3/d_n{}^3)$, where d_n = nominal diameter.

unless otherwise stipulated. Roughly, the cost of the cast iron will increase with the strength specified, the high-test irons being much more expensive than the low-strength irons.

Since the tenacity of the iron is much affected by the size of grain and structure, it will decrease as the size of the bar, or thickness of casting, is increased. The effect is more pronounced for the softer, weaker irons, No. 20 and 25, than for the high-strength irons, No. 40 to 60, as the tests in Table 3 show. Such considerations have led to the adoption of three

TABLE 3. PERCENTAGE VARIATION IN STRENGTH OF CAST IRON WITH SIZE OF BAR. (From Symposium on Cast Iron, *Proc. ASTM,* Vol. 33, Pt. 2, p. 115)

	Tests reported by Gray Iron Institute					Tests of Rother and Mazurie			
	Relative Tensile Strength for Bar Diameters of				Modulus of Rupture of 1-in. Bar as Cast, Span 12-in., lb./in.^{2}	Percentage of Strength of 1-in. Bar for Bar Diameters of			
Class No.	¾-in.	1.1 in.	1.6 in.	2.0 in.		1½ in.	2 in.	2½ in.	3 in.
20	100	79	60	53			Soft Iron		
25	100	81	73	72	49,000	96	88	80	76
30	100	78	71	67	53,000	93	84	83	78
35	100	83	68	66	56,800	95	88	86	84
40	100	85	80	67	——	—	—	—	—
50	100	90	79	72	52,900	95	87	83	79
							Machinery Iron		
					69,400	95	96	92	87
					71,000	94	94	84	81
					——	—	—	—	—
					70,200	95	95	88	84

sizes of test bar, each adapted to furnish information for certain thicknesses of castings, as indicated in Table 2.

In making tensile tests it is well to avoid eccentric loading by using threaded-end specimens like Fig. 3c, Chapter III, held in sockets provided with spherical seats. Nominal speed of head of testing machine should not exceed ⅛ in. per min after a unit stress of 15,000 psi has been imposed on the specimen.

A very comprehensive series of tests on 25 cast irons of different grades was reported by Committee A3 in *Proc. ASTM*, Vol. 33, Pt. 1, p. 87. Information about these irons is given in Tables 4 and 5.

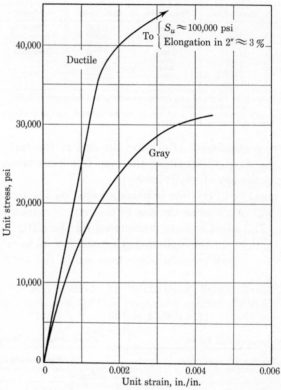

Fig. 11. Tensile stress-strain curves for gray and ductile cast irons.

For these tests twenty 1.4-in. round bars 21 in. long were cast from each of the irons represented in green-sand molds in flasks containing 4 bars each. Irons *J* and *V* were cast in vertical dry-sand molds. All temperatures were carefully measured by the same observers. Bars were machined to a diameter of 1.2 in. prior to testing in impact or bending. Tension and endurance specimens were cut from virgin bars. The tensile strengths reported were obtained from specimens 0.8 in. in diameter, but the tensile moduli of elasticity values were obtained from specimens 0.505 in. in diameter. Compression tests were made on cylindrical specimens 1.2 in. in diameter and 4 in. long, loaded through a spherical bearing. Fatigue tests were made on R. R. Moore machines of the rotating-beam type. Shear tests were made with a double-shear device on cylinders 0.505 in. in diameter. The hardness tests reported were made halfway out on cross sections of 1.2-in. diameter bars. From two to six

Brinell, and three to ten Rockwell, readings were taken on each position. The endurance-test values represent only one test; other test results usually represent the average of three tests. Irons T and X exhibited some shrinkage cavities at the center of the bars which spoiled small specimens cut from these irons. Iron T also showed considerable variations in structure and composition.

The tensile data for these cast irons have been grouped in Table 5 in accordance with the ASTM classification. The first three irons listed in the table are very weak, whereas the last eight irons belong in the high-strength class.

White cast iron, such as is used for making malleable cast iron, has a tensile strength commonly varying between 40,000 and 50,000 psi. In small sections the tenacity may reach 60,000 to 70,000 psi.

Characteristic stress-strain curves for gray and ductile cast irons of 1-in. bars of comparable compositions are shown in Fig. 11. The curves show that ductile cast iron has a sharply defined proportional limit and that gray cast iron does not. The modulus of elasticity of the ductile cast iron is 25,000,000 psi and that of the gray cast iron at a stress of 10,000 psi is about 17,000,000 psi. The marked differences in strength and ductility are readily apparent. The stress-strain curve for white cast iron is a straight line.

The endurance limit for the cast irons listed in Table 5 varied from 43 to 58 per cent of the tensile strength and averaged 49 per cent of the tensile strength.

26. The Compressive Strength of Cast Iron. Since the compressive strength of cast iron is very high it is considerably utilized in construction. Results in Table 5 indicate that the compressive strength of gray cast iron is three to four times the tensile strength, the ratio being greatest for low-strength and least for high-strength irons. When tests are made on small prisms with height at least one and one-half times the least lateral dimension, the crushing strength will range from 60,000 psi for the soft open-grained gray irons to 200,000 psi for the hard close-grained irons. Gray iron of good quality will have a crushing strength of 100,000 to 140,000 psi. White cast iron is one of the strongest metals when subjected to compression, and often has a strength of 250,000 to 275,000 psi. As in tensile tests, the position of the test piece in the casting influences the compressive strength. Pieces cut near the surface of a casting are stronger than those from the interior. Specimens from small castings are stronger than those from large castings of the same metal. Sometimes variations in strength due to these causes amount to 100 per cent of the smallest values.

27. The Transverse Strength of Cast Iron. Transverse tests of cast iron have found much favor because the specimens are quickly prepared

TABLE 4. CASTING AND COMPOSITION OF CAST IRONS TESTED

(Tests of Com. A3, *Proc. ASTM*, Vol. 33, Pt. 1)

Iron.	Furnace.	Pouring.	Freezing.	Steel.	Cast Iron.	Pig Iron.	Total Carbon.	Graphite.	Combined Carbon.	Silicon.	Phosphorus.	Manganese.	Sulfur.	Nickel.	Chromium.	Titanium.	Copper.
		Temperature °C.		Mix Per Cent						Average Chemical Analysis Per Cent							
C	Cupola	1352	1158	10	0	90	3.95	3.09	0.86	1.90	0.07	0.65	0.06	0.01	0.00	0.04	0.32
U	Arc Furnace	1360	1164	12	0	88	3.52	3.68	0.84	2.94	0.04	0.66	0.04	0.01	0.01	0.03	0.34
W	Cupola	1358	1163	37	0	63	3.79	2.99	0.80	1.47	0.12	0.73	0.08	0.01	0.01	0.11	0.21
D	Cupola	1331	1105	13	20	67	3.25	2.66	0.59	2.08	1.99	0.53	0.05	0.03	0.00	0.16	0.02
F	"	1279	1133	10	15	75	3.61	2.93	0.68	2.06	0.75	0.52	0.06	0.00	0.00	0.08	0.02
L	"	1264	1139	0	47	53	3.41	2.85	0.56	2.44	0.63	0.57	0.07	0.01	0.00	0.10	0.03
M	"	1347	1164	25	47	28	3.46	2.82	0.64	2.35	0.15	0.69	0.09	0.65	0.02	0.04	0.03
X	Arc Furnace	1412	1145	0	0	100	3.08	2.32	0.76	2.07	0.04	1.21	0.05	16.3	1.89	0.04	6.12
B	Cupola	1420	1137	12	21	67	3.53	2.69	0.84	1.67	0.68	0.56	0.08	0.00	0.00	0.06	0.06
O	"	1360	1172	13	46	41	3.43	2.75	0.68	2.35	0.20	0.73	0.09	0.01	0.01	0.04	0.03
A	Cupola	1285	1140	10	20	70	3.49	2.72	0.77	1.68	0.74	0.54	0.07	0.00	0.01	0.07	0.10
E	"	1322	1174	4	40	56	3.12	2.44	0.68	2.18	0.63	0.44	0.10	0.00	0.00	0.06	0.02
G	"	1312	1152	20	45	35	3.49	2.78	0.71	2.08	0.19	0.55	0.08	1.17	0.65	0.05	0.02
H	"	1302	1175	10	55	35	3.39	2.75	0.64	2.50	0.43	0.74	0.06	0.01	0.00	0.16	0.04
K	Arc Furnace	1367	1173	20	80	0	3.14	2.30	0.84	2.69	0.18	0.82	0.09	0.25	0.09	0.04	0.06
N	"	1335	1223	0	0	100	2.53	2.03	0.50	3.26	0.02	1.01	0.04	10.6	1.55	0.05	4.07
S	Cupola	1272	1172	40	0	60	3.38	2.59	0.79	1.18	0.14	0.82	0.08	0.95	0.01	0.05	0.05
R	Air Furnace	1356	1177	0	50	50	3.24	2.41	0.83	1.63	0.42	0.56	0.08	0.06	0.01	0.09	0.04
T	Cupola	1306	1180	0	98	2	3.49	2.16	1.33	0.53	0.33	0.42	0.13	0.00	0.01	0.01	0.05
Y	Rotary Coal	1296	1142	12	38	50	3.07	2.22	0.85	1.97	0.40	0.63	0.07	0.01	0.00	0.04	0.12
L*	Arc Furnace	1364	1181	20	80	0	3.05	2.20	0.85	2.70	0.16	0.79	0.09	0.60	0.24	0.03	0.02
Q	Rocking Elec.	1351	1172	23	77	0	2.88	2.25	0.63	1.99	0.43	0.51	0.10	0.01	0.01	0.05	0.04
V	Cupola	1334	1218	85	0	15	2.50	1.50	1.00	2.20	0.04	0.74	0.09	0.00	0.08	0.01	0.12
J	Cupola	1322	1214	85	15	0	2.61	1.73	0.88	2.38	0.06	0.77	0.10	1.08	0.09	0.02	0.05
Z	Arc Furnace	1448	1170	68	0	32	2.79	1.94	0.85	2.44	0.03	0.50	0.06	0.50	0.09	0.02	0.36

* Also contained 0.45 per cent Mo.

TABLE 5. AVERAGE MECHANICAL PROPERTIES OF CAST IRONS

(From Report of Com. A3, *Proc. ASTM*, Vol. 33, Pt. 1)

Iron.	A.S.T.M. Class.	Tension. Strength lb./in.² ×10⁻³	Tension. Mod. of Elasticity at ¼ Ult. ×10⁻⁶ lb./in.²	Compressive Strength, lb./in.² ×10⁻³	Transverse Tests — Mod. of Elasticity at ¼ Ult. ×10⁻⁶ lb./in.²	Max. Center Load, lb.	Max. Defl., in.	Modulus of Rupture lb./in.² ×10⁻³	Energy of Rupture in.lb./in.³	Russell Pendulum Impact — Span 18-in.	Span 8-in.	Shear Strength, 0.505-in. Bar, lb./in.²	Endurance Limit, Bar Diam. 0.303-in., lb./in.²	Brinell	Rockwell B-Scale.
C	<20	18.1	9.1	65.2	10.4	1420	0.352	37.7	15.9	23.2	33.0	28.9	8.8	133	71.5
U	<20	17.7	8.8	72.8	11.1	1651	0.370	43.8	19.1	24.6	37.5	29.6	10.0	146	78.0
W	<20	18.4	9.8	77.9	11.9	1771	0.336	47.0	18.6	25.0	41.6	30.4	8.2	139	74.0
D	20	20.2	12.5	90.9	13.3	1254	0.141	33.3	4.9	7.4	16.7	27.5	12.3	179	89.0
F	20	22.3	12.0	91.0	14.2	1857	0.251	49.2	13.7	21.1	30.7	33.0	11.4	163	84.0
I	20	20.0	11.1	87.2	12.8	1840	0.274	48.8	15.1	20.9	32.0	27.7	9.0	158	78.5
M	20	24.8	13.3	90.8	14.6	2200	0.335	58.3	23.0	33.4	46.5	34.2	12.0	161	84.0
X	20	22.4	12.0	86.0	14.5	1970	0.745	52.2	55.6	54.9	116.5	33.9	10.6	120	68.0
B	25	29.0	12.5	107.2	14.3	2342	0.293	62.2	20.4	24.4	38.2	38.0	14.1	183	88.5
O	25	25.9	13.0	95.0	14.6	2218	0.341	58.7	24.2	30.2	47.9	35.5	11.8	163	82.0
A	30	31.6	13.6	111.0	15.9	2457	0.284	65.1	20.8	27.1	39.0	40.2	14.8	183	89.0
E	30	33.2	16.8	120.8	17.4	2758	0.301	73.2	24.7	31.5	46.0	44.6	16.5	192	90.5
G	30	31.7	12.5	108.8	14.4	2651	0.331	70.3	26.1	28.8	42.4	42.3	13.5	181	86.0
H	30	32.3	14.5	116.1	16.7	2407	0.245	63.9	17.3	22.6	37.5	42.2	18.6	196	90.5
K	30	34.4	15.9	115.9	16.2	2590	0.293	69.7	22.6	31.5	44.5	44.3	16.5	194	93.0
N	30	31.3	9.9	134.2	13.2	2414	0.471	64.4	36.0	93.5	102.2	43.8	12.8	226	92.0
S	30	32.1	15.0	112.0	17.9	2455	0.267	65.0	19.5	29.5	48.7	41.0	16.0	187	91.5
R	35	37.5	15.7	120.8	17.8	2905	0.326	77.0	28.6	34.7	57.1	47.6	17.4	196	93.0
T	35	35.5	17.8	123.5	19.9	2835	0.294	75.2	26.6	28.8	52.9	47.8		207	95.0
Y	35	36.0	15.0	124.5	16.5	2776	0.308	73.5	25.4	27.6	39.6	44.3	16.2	215	94.0
L	40	41.8	16.7	131.2	17.9	3083	0.301	81.8	26.8	39.6	53.9	44.2	18.2	228	96.0
Q	40	41.7	16.7	119.1	19.1	3177	0.439	84.2	46.5	47.2	64.4	47.3	19.6	190	88.5
V	40	48.1	20.9	159.0	22.6	3472	0.230	92.0	21.9	28.4	43.2	60.8	25.2	266	101.5
J	50	51.0	18.6	156.6	19.1	3489	0.272	92.5	26.8	47.5	56.5	61.0	24.0	269	102.5
Z	50	55.5	18.7	135.7	19.9	4200	0.490	111.7	67.2	80.0	103.3	57.1	25.0	236	97.0

at low cost; the required testing machine is simple and readily operated by inexperienced men, and the results measure strength, flexibility, and toughness. Hence this test is much more informative than the tensile test, though the latter is the specification requirement. Tests are now made on the three sizes of round bars shown in Table 2. Bar lengths are 3 in. longer than the indicated test span. Strength is indicated by the center load which the specified bar will carry. A rough measure of toughness may be found by estimating the energy of rupture from half of the product of the maximum load times the corresponding deflection.

The modulus of rupture of cast iron is not usually computed in the foundry, but it forms the best means of comparing bars of the same shape which differ slightly in size. Comparisons cannot well be made between bars differing considerably in size or in shape, since the rate of cooling causes radical changes in the grain structure of the interior. Variations in the moduli of rupture of square bars due to differences in area and in silicon content are shown in Fig. 10. Square bars, in general, exhibit a modulus of rupture 10 to 18 per cent lower than round bars of equal diameter. Variations in the modulus of rupture due to differences in shape of cross sections are illustrated in Table 1, Chapter III. Machined bars are generally weaker than unmachined specimens. Tumbling in a rattler materially improves the strength and increases the hardness of the skin. Bars cast horizontally are strongest when the load is applied against the cope face.

The ratio of the modulus of rupture (S_m) to the tensile strength (S_t) varies from $1\frac{1}{2}$ to $2\frac{1}{2}$. The ratio S_m/S_t decreases as the tensile strength increases. This relation is discernible in values given in Table 5.

The modulus of rupture varies with the span as shown in Fig. III-14. MacKenzie and Donoho reported additional data for strips of pipe iron which they tested (see *Proc. ASTM*, Vol. 37, Pt. 2, p. 71).

Average values for the modulus of rupture of good grades of cast iron may be expected to be not less than the following: No. 20, 48,000 psi; No. 25, 53,000 psi; No. 30, 58,000 psi; No. 35, 64,000 psi; No. 40, 69,000 psi; No. 50, 80,000 psi; and No. 60, 90,000 psi.

Good grades of gray cast iron usually deflect between 0.1 to 0.2 in. when tested in A-bars (Table 2), 0.2 to 0.4 when tested in B-bars, and 0.2 to 0.3 when tested in C-bars.

The energy of rupture in bending, accurately found by evaluating the area under the load-deflection curve and dividing by the volume of the specimen, serves to measure the toughness or resistance to shock of the iron. Where the complete load-deflection data are not obtained, the total energy consumed may be roughly approximated by taking half the product of the maximum load times the corresponding deflection.

Owing to the limited portion of the specimen suffering maximum stress, the energy of rupture decreases markedly with the length of the span, as the data in Fig. 12 show. Also, thick specimens usually show lower energies per unit volume than thin ones. Hence comparisons should be based on standard conditions.

Load-deflection curves obtained at the University of Wisconsin for typical white, gray, and malleable cast iron are given in Fig. 13. The tests were made on bars 0.75 in. in diameter over a 12-in. span. Calculated moduli of rupture for the white, gray, and malleable cast irons were respectively 102,-000, 82,000, and 102,000 psi. The moduli of elasticity were 29,000,000, 19,000,000, and 25,000,000 psi for the white, gray, and malleable cast

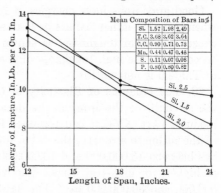

Fig. 12. Influence of length of span on the energy of rupture of 1¼-in. round bars of cast iron. (Mathews.)

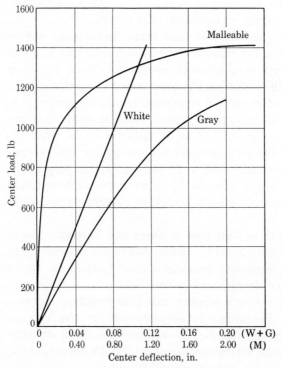

Fig. 13. Cross-bending tests of cast iron.

irons, and the energies of rupture, in the same order, were 15, 26.5, and 550 in-lb per cu in.

Good gray irons have energies of rupture of 18 to 30 in-lb per cu in. when tested in either A-bars or B-bars. Phosphorus in high percentages causes a lack of toughness, as shown by data for the D-iron, Table 5. In contrast, the high toughness of the low-carbon and high-nickel irons of Table 5 is noteworthy.

28. The Modulus of Elasticity of Cast Iron varies considerably with the strength of the iron, as the data in Table 5 show. If the secant modulus (Art. XV-22) is determined for maximum stresses of one-fourth of the ultimate strength, the value for good grades of gray iron usually lies between 13,000,000 and 16,000,000 psi with values of 20,000,000 psi, or higher, for high-test irons. For white cast iron, E lies between 25,-000,000 and 30,000,000 psi. The data from the ASTM Impact Investigation indicated that the moduli in tension and compression were approximately equal but averaged about 11 per cent less than the values calculated from transverse bending tests. The latter discrepancy is undoubtedly due to the presence of stronger and stiffer metal in the outside portions of the specimens tested. Hence for the same quality of cast iron the modulus of elasticity is the same in tension, compression, and bending. The shear modulus of elasticity (E_s) is $0.4E$.

29. Shock Resistance of Cast Iron. In cast-iron car wheels, in rolls and jaw plates for crushers, in grinding balls, and in forming dies, considerable shock must often be sustained. Hence the energy of rupture in cross bending or impact is sometimes a decidedly important property. The energy of rupture in transverse impact is usually 20 to 35 per cent higher than the energy of rupture found in static bending. Good gray irons will usually show 25 to 35 in-lb per cu in. when tested in B-bar specimens. On an 8-in. span the energy per unit volume for 1.2-in.-diameter specimens is 50 to 70 per cent higher than for an 18-in. span (Table 5). When tested in $\frac{3}{4}$-in. bars over an 8-in. span, good iron of No. 30 grade will exhibit energy of rupture values of 28 to 35 in-lb per in.[3]

30. Strength of Cast Iron in Shear and Torsion. The shear strength of cast iron, determined by double-shear tests on small cylindrical or thin rectangular specimens, provides a good method for exploring the uniformity of the strength of a casting.

The shear strength of gray cast iron usually is between 25,000 and 60,000 psi. The property increases with the tensile strength but in a decreasing ratio. For No. 20 cast iron the shear strength is about 1.6 times the tensile strength, whereas for No. 35 the ratio approximates 1.3, and for No. 60 the ratio is about 1.0.

In torsion, cast iron fails on planes at 45° with the torsional shear stresses. Since these failure planes carry tensile stresses of intensities equal to the shears, it is evident that such failures are caused by weakness in tension. Round bars of No. 30 cast iron should exhibit computed twisting strengths (S_s') between 40,000 and 50,000 psi.

31. Shrinkage Stresses. The shrinkage of cast iron in cooling often induces excessive stresses, sometimes sufficiently great to cause failure. Such stresses increase with the thickness of the casting. In a large hollow cylindrical casting the outer and inner surfaces cool first and the subsequent shrinkage of the interior puts these sections in compression. However, with no external force acting, the total internal stress across any diametral section must equal zero and consequently the interior sections of the casting will be in tension. Further the total tensile stress must equal the total compressive stress across the section. The magnitude of the shrinkage stresses in a hollow cylindrical casting may be determined by cutting off a zone included between two transverse sections, laying off a series of concentric rings on the cross section, carefully measuring the diameter of each ring, cutting out the rings, and noting the new diameter. An increase in diameter indicates that the ring had been in compression, and vice versa. The initial stresses may be found from the equation $S' = \epsilon E$, Art. I-4.

32. Strength of Cast Iron Increased by Shocks. Tumbling of castings or imposition of a large number of light blows is likely to produce an increase of 10 to 15 per cent in strength and 20 per cent increase in impact toughness, according to A. E. Outerbridge, *Trans. Am. Inst. Mining Eng.*, Vol. 26, p. 176. This action appears to be due to relief of internal strain and a densification and hardening of the surface where the castings are tumbled in the rattler.

33. Heat Treatment of Cast Iron. Cast iron responds to heat treatment in a manner similar to steel. Internal strains may be relieved by annealing at 430 to 490°C for ½ to 4 hours, in accordance with the mass and thickness of the casting, and cooling slowly. Such treatment slightly decreases hardness and strength properties but materially improves toughness and constancy of shape after machining. The softer, low-strength irons of high graphite content will be weakened more than the high-strength irons of low graphite content by such treatment. Raising the temperature or increasing the annealing period will cause further reductions in hardness and tenacity. Softening of hard castings for purposes of machining can be done by annealing at temperatures of 760 to 820°C.

Wear and abrasive resistance of cast irons carrying fine-grained, uniformly dispersed graphite in a pearlitic matrix can be improved by skillful quenching from above the critical range, 790–850°C. If desired, the drastic hardening effects of quenching may be relieved and the tenacity improved by tempering at temperatures of 300–400°C.

Surface hardness of 800 to 950 Brinell can be produced on finished castings by subjecting irons of low carbon content, containing aluminum and chromium, to the nitriding process.

34. Effect of Repeated Heating on Cast Iron. Repeated heating of high-carbon, gray cast irons at temperatures above 500°C gradually causes a break down of the pearlite into ferrite plus graphite, with accompanying increase in volume or growth. At 725°C, allotropic transformations intensify these growth changes. Furthermore, in connection with such heating, there is likely to be corrosive action which by its nature accentuates growth. Indeed, the action of superheated steam, if corrosive, may effect undesirable growth in gray iron fittings at temperatures below 500°C.

Cast irons of low total carbon, with finely divided, uniformly dispersed graphite flakes and well-stabilized carbide, are the most resistant of the ordinary cast irons. The inclusion of chromium and other ingredients tending to promote stability of iron carbide at high temperatures make the cast iron more resistant to growth from repeated heating. In ordinary amounts silicon promotes graphitization and growth but irons with 6.1 per cent of silicon have shown little growth (see Symposium on Cast Iron, *Proc. ASTM*, Vol. 33, Pt. 2, p. 115).

MALLEABLE CAST IRON

NATURE AND IMPORTANCE

35. Nature. White cast iron of suitable composition can be rendered somewhat malleable and ductile, and very greatly toughened, by surrounding it with a suitable packing material and annealing at a bright red heat for several days. The iron before annealing should have all its carbon in combined form, but the silicon, sulfur, and manganese contents must be so adjusted that the annealing may be accomplished at temperatures just above the critical range (1300° to 1500°F). By the heat treatment the combined carbon is transformed into a special type of graphitic carbon, called *temper* carbon. The temper carbon is made up of finer, more rounded, and more uniformly disseminated grains than the graphite of gray cast iron.

If the packing material is loose and the furnace gases strongly oxidizing, practically all the carbon will be removed from the outer layer of iron, the percentage removed decreasing toward the center of the casting. In American practice the entire annealing period is only 6 or 7 days and the carbon removal is small. Examination of a fractured cross section of malleable cast iron reveals a thin white shell of impure carbonless iron about $\frac{1}{64}$ to $\frac{1}{32}$ in. thick surrounding a black core in which the grains of temper carbon are imprisoned among crystals of iron (ferrite). The color of the core in the fractured casting gives rise to the name *black heart*. In Europe the annealing process is carried on at a higher temperature and for a considerably longer time. This results in the production of a much thicker shell of decarburized iron, and a greater reduction in total carbon than in American practice. The castings so produced have a *white heart*, and are coarser grained and somewhat less strong than black-heart castings. By providing chills in molding the white iron it is possible to make castings up to 4 in. in thickness by the black-heart process. The white-heart process is best adapted to production of parts under $\frac{1}{2}$ in. in thickness.

In strength, malleable cast iron is considerably superior to gray cast iron but inferior to steel castings. It is very much tougher than gray iron and, when well made, compares favorably with cast steel. Owing to lower melting temperature white cast iron shrinks slightly less than steel and in the annealing process an expansion takes place, due to the separation of the temper carbon, which makes the net shrinkage of malleable cast iron about the same as gray cast iron. Malleable castings are in general somewhat smoother and freer from blow-holes than steel castings, and also more resistant to corrosion.

36. Importance of Malleable Cast Iron. On account of good strength, high toughness, and moderate cost, malleable cast iron is much used for a large variety of small castings. About one-half of the 1,000,000 tons of malleable cast iron annually produced in the United States is used by the automotive industry for such parts as steering-gear housings, differential-gear cases, steering knuckles, etc. A large tonnage is also used for pipe fittings. Other important uses include various parts for railroad rolling stock, and for parts of agricultural machinery and implements. The remainder is used for stove plate, hardware, ornamental castings, and cheap tools. About 110 foundries in the United States produce more malleable cast iron than is made in all the rest of the world.

THE MANUFACTURE OF MALLEABLE CAST IRON

37. Melting the Charge. The cupola, the air furnace, and the open-hearth furnace are the types of furnaces most used for melting the charge. Baby Bessemer converters and crucibles are used to some extent in Europe, and the electric furnace is also forcing its way into this field.

The principal use of the cupola in malleable iron works is for making small castings. The process is run in much the same way as in smelting gray cast iron except that a larger proportion of fuel is required in order that the white iron, which is less fluid than gray, may be very hot when poured. The percentage composition of pig iron for such castings according to Moldenke should be about as follows: silicon 1.00 to 1.50, manganese <0.60, phosphorus <0.225 and sulfur <0.05. Small amounts of pig iron and sprues are charged between thin layers of coke or anthracite coal. Malleable or steel scrap cannot be advantageously used in this type of furnace. Iron is run continuously from the tap hole into ladles and poured as rapidly as possible. The cupola is the cheapest in installation, in upkeep and in operation, and the quickest smelting process in general use. However, owing to contact between the fuel and the iron and lack of means of control, burnt metal is sometimes produced. Furthermore, the annealing temperature required for cupola iron is higher than for the air-furnace or open-hearth product.

The air furnace is used most in this country for making malleable castings. It is less expensive to install and operate than the open hearth, although requiring a slightly longer time for smelting. It may be built in a wide variety of sizes, and can be operated discontinuously without impairing the quality of the iron. One of the main difficulties in air-furnace operation is the possibility of burning the thin portions of the bath and consequent production of weak metal. By proper use of the air furnace it is possible to produce a very good grade of malleable iron with less skill than required to run an open-hearth furnace. The charge of metal for the air furnace consists of pig iron, white-iron scrap, and malleable scrap. When necessary to reduce carbon to proper limits (2.25 to 3.00 per cent) a small proportion of steel or wrought-iron scrap is added after the pig iron has melted. For heavy castings the silicon content in the pig iron is run lower than indicated for cupola iron in order to avoid mottling of the hard-iron castings. Figure 6 indicates ranges in carbon and silicon contents in hard iron for making different grades of malleable cast iron.

The open-hearth furnace for malleable iron is built upon the same principle as that used in steel making, but in smaller sizes. With the open-hearth furnace the charge of metal is similar to that used in the air furnace. The fuel, however, is usually producer gas and air, both of which are separately heated by passage through hot checker works before they enter the furnace. Natural gas and vaporized fuel oil are sometimes used instead of producer gas.

Although both the open-hearth and the electric-furnace processes are costly to operate they provide well-controlled melting conditions and furnish excellent malleable cast iron.

38. Molding and Casting. Because of the lack of fluidity in white cast iron and the rapidity with which it chills, patterns must be provided with large runners and sprues. This should be done in order that the metal may be rapidly poured, also in order that a good head of metal may be provided to keep the mold full during solidification. Owing to the high shrinkage of white cast iron especial care should be taken in shaping patterns at the junctions of thick and thin parts. Suitable chills are often required to cool heavy sections with sufficient rapidity to make the iron white and to avoid excessive shrinkage strains at junctions with thin parts.

The molds used for malleable cast iron are similar to those made for gray castings but, owing to the number of castings made from the same pattern, there is a better opportunity for the effective use of molding machines and core-making machines. Metal molds, on account of the chilling action which they exert, are also successfully used for malleable castings.

In casting, it is quite necessary that the white iron be poured at a temperature sufficiently high to render it fluid; yet, on account of danger of burning, the metal cannot be held too long in the furnace. The narrow range of pouring temperature makes it necessary, therefore, to have the metal handled and cast very promptly when it has arrived at a white heat.

After the white castings have cooled they are shaken out of the sand and cleaned by the methods used for gray castings. They are then trimmed of sprues, ground smooth, where necessary, and sorted.

39. The Annealing of the White Castings is an exceedingly important operation in the production of good malleable castings. The hard castings are carefully packed in rectangular boxes, called saggers, which are 16 by 24 in. in plan and 1 ft high. Mill scale from wrought-iron squeezers and siliceous slag are often mixed to form the packing material. Hematite and pulverized magnetic ore are also used for this purpose. Leasman and Storey's * experiments show that the oxidizing character of the packing material exercises no influence upon the decarburization of the iron, but that such change is due to the penetration of carbon dioxide generated in the furnace. The permeability of the packing to this gas is therefore the important factor in determining the carbon content in the skin of the castings.

The saggers are stacked four deep in an annealing furnace, which, in form and in principle of operation, resembles a rectangular down-draft brick kiln. Gas, coal, or oil is used to slowly heat the annealing furnace until the temperature of the castings is above the critical range. Storey states the latter is between 700° and 775°C. The temperature is held just above this range from 60 to 72 hours, and then the castings should be cooled very slowly until well below the critical temperature. For black-heart castings about 6 days are required for annealing.

* See account of experiments at University of Wisconsin in *Foundry,* Vol. 42, p. 474.

After removal from the saggers, the malleable castings are placed in a rattler, which is partly filled with bits of discarded malleable castings, and cleaned. They are then given whatever finishing is necessary. If crooked they are straightened but without heating.

CONSTITUTION AND PROPERTIES OF MALLEABLE CAST IRON

40. Composition and Constitution. Good black-heart malleable castings will generally contain about 2.0 to 2.8 per cent of temper carbon,

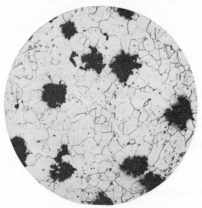 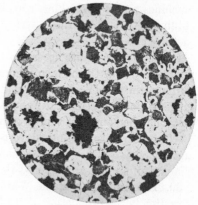

(a) Good malleable iron. Note temper carbon and ferrite grains.

(b) Incompletely annealed malleable iron. Note temper carbon in ferrite masses and pearlite.

Fig. 14. Photomicrographs of malleable iron, ×75. (Malleable Founders' Society.)

0.50 to 1.25 per cent of silicon, manganese under 0.30 per cent, sulfur below 0.05 per cent, and phosphorus under 0.25 per cent. The higher percentages of silicon are in most cases to be found only in small castings. For intricate patterns where fluidity of the molten metal is of great importance phosphorus may run to 0.3 per cent.

If the annealing is properly done no combined carbon will be found and the entire structure will consist of two main elements, ferrite and temper carbon, as shown in Fig. 14a. Such castings should possess maximum ductility. If the annealing period is too short or the temperature too low, cementite will be present in addition to ferrite and temper carbon and the castings will be more brittle, although they may be stronger than the fully annealed iron. When the castings are cooled too rapidly after correct annealing, the structure shows the temper carbon embedded in ferrite which is in turn surrounded by pearlite, Fig. 14b. With too low annealing temperature followed by rapid cooling the structure consists of cementite particles embedded in pearlite masses with more or less temper carbon imprisoned in ferrite. Such iron is likely to be very brittle and non-uniform.

In order to determine whether the iron is of proper constitution a small rectangular lug is cast on the work. After annealing the lug is broken off with a hammer, the toughness of the iron judged by the energy required to remove the lug, and the fracture examined. Good black-heart iron will show a very thin white skin from $\frac{1}{64}$ to $\frac{1}{32}$ in. in thickness surrounding a bluish black or black core. The core should present a velvety appearance and be free from shrink cavities or white crystals.

High-strength *pearlitic malleable cast irons* are made by incompletely graphitizing the combined carbon of the original white cast iron, or by reheating the graphitized metal. Elements like manganese, chromium, or molybdenum are sometimes added to effect retardation graphitization. Although termed pearlitic, different classes of these metals are made with matrices containing any one of the metallographic constituents common in hardened or tempered steel. Successful production of pearlitic malleable cast iron requires very careful control of composition and heat treatment. Tensile strengths range from 60,000 to 100,000 psi, the ductilities are lower than for the black-heart malleables, but the toughnesses may be either higher or lower. The pearlitic malleables are harder, less easy to machine, and shrink less than ordinary malleable cast iron. (See also *ASTM Symposium*, 1936.)

41. Mechanical Properties of Malleable Cast Iron. The ASTM Symposium on Malleable Iron Castings of 1931 furnishes data on the mechanical properties of irons of the following chemical composition: carbon, 1.00 to 2.00; silicon, 0.60 to 1.10; manganese, under 0.30; phosphorus, under 0.20; and sulfur, 0.06 to 0.15 per cent. For such iron the specific gravity was found to vary from 7.15 to 7.45, depending upon the carbon content. The coefficient of thermal expansion up to 400°C (750°F) was 0.000012 per °C, or 0.0000066 per °F. From 20,000 tensile tests, nearly all of which were made on air-furnace iron, the average ultimate strength was 54,040, with a range from 45,000 to 62,860 psi. The yield point, based on an elongation of 1 per cent, varied from 30,000 to 43,000 and averaged 36,350 psi. The elongation varied from 8 to 33 and averaged 18.4 per cent. From a statistical analysis of 5000 tests, representing random heats of many manufacturers, it appears probable that 96 per cent of the tensile strengths were within 4000 psi of the average and 60 per cent of the ductility values were within the range 18.4 ± 3 per cent. The average tensile properties reported from 1210 tests on open-hearth furnace iron were ultimately strength 57,920 psi, yield point, 38,230 psi; and elongation, 25.7 per cent. Cupola iron, use of which is limited principally to making pipe fittings, is more variable in properties. Tensile strengths reported by three manufacturers ranged from 35,000 to 58,200 and averaged 45,200 psi; and the elongation in 2 in. varied from 2 to 16 per cent and averaged 7.2 per cent.

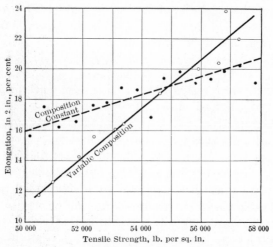

Fig. 15. Relation of tensile strength and elongation of malleable cast irons (*ASTM Symposium*, 1931).

Malleable cast iron is unique in that the elongation increases with the tensile strength. Figure 15 shows relations reported in the symposium and represents several thousand tests. The relations apply only to iron

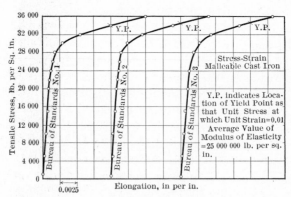

Fig. 16. Stress-strain curves for malleable cast iron in tension (from *ASTM Symposium*, 1931).

without combined carbon. The ASTM *Standards* recognize two grades of malleable cast iron: No. 32510 with a minimum tensile strength of 50,000 psi, yield point of 32,500 psi, and elongation in 2 in. of 10 per cent;

and No. 35018 with a minimum tensile strength of 53,000 psi, yield point of 35,000 psi, and elongation in 2 in. of 18 per cent.

Figure 16 shows stress-strain curves reported in the symposium for these malleable cast irons. Average values of the modulus of elasticity in tension reported by six investigators ranged from 24,000,000 to 27,-900,000 psi and averaged 25,070,000 psi. The modulus of elasticity in compression is approximately the same as in tension; in bending, values usually run from 22,000,000 to 24,000,000 psi.

In compression malleable cast iron takes a permanent set of 1 per cent in the vicinity of 28,000 psi.

In cross bending the extreme fiber stress at maximum load computed from the flexure formula $S = Mc/I$ approximates twice the tensile strength of malleable cast iron when tested in solid square or cylindrical sections. For ¾-in. cylindrical specimens tested on a 12-in. span, the modulus of rupture is usually 85,000 to 100,000 psi, and work to maximum load is generally above 350 in-lb per cu in.

The shear strength approximates 48,000 psi, and the shear modulus of elasticity may be taken at 10,000,000 psi. The modulus of rupture in torsion based on five tests averaged 58,000 psi and the yield point 24,850 psi.

Brinell hardness of malleable cast iron usually lies between 100 and 140, averaging about 115.

In the wedge or curling test for toughness and ductility good malleable cast iron will withstand 25 to 30 blows prior to fracture.

In fatigue the endurance limit has not been thoroughly investigated but available data indicate that it is 0.4 to 0.5 of the tensile strength.

Removal of the skin from black-heart malleable cast iron produces little effect on the tensile strength and yield point as indicated by the data of Table 6. The data in the table do demonstrate that the skin is more ductile than the core metal. Other tests were reported by H. A. Swartz in *Proc. ASTM*, Vol. 20, Pt. 2, p. 70, in which specimens ground before annealing were tested and compared with specimens which had the skin removed to a depth of ¹⁄₁₆

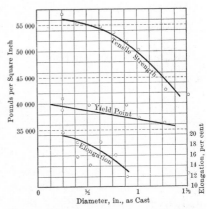

Fig. 17. Tensile properties of malleable cast-iron specimens not machined. (H. A. Swartz.)

in. These showed that the tensile strength was reduced about 7000 psi and the elongation in 2 in. was reduced about 3 per cent for specimens

TABLE 6. TESTS OF MALLEABLE IRON TEST BARS IN "AS-CAST" CONDITION AND MACHINED. (From *ASTM Symposium,* 1931)

Iron made by Frazer and Jones Co. in 1920; tests made by Robert W. Hunt Co.

Set	Diameter of Bar as Cast, in.	How Tested	Tensile Strength, lb. per sq. in.	Yield Point, lb. per sq. in.	Elongation in 2 in., per cent	Reduction of Area, per cent
No. 1	5/8	As cast	55,720	35,410	29.0	30.8
	3/4	Machined to 5/8 in.	55,380	35,350	22.5	22.6
	7/8	Machined to 5/8 in.	54,980	34,950	21.5	21.7
	1	Machined to 5/8 in.	55,140	35,800	19.5	16.9
No. 2	5/8	As cast	55,880	35,040	25.0	26.2
	3/4	Machined to 5/8 in.	54,840	35,310	20.5	19.7
	7/8	Machined to 5/8 in.	53,740	34,980	15.5	14.2
	1	Machined to 5/8 in.	53,600	34,500	14.5	13.0
No. 3	5/8	As cast	56,580	34,600	26.0	30.8
	3/4	Machined to 5/8 in.	55,580	35,760	24.0	24.9
	7/8	Machined to 5/8 in.	55,460	36,320	24.0	20.5
	1	Machined to 5/8 in.	54,820	35,370	24.0	22.1
No. 4	5/8	As cast	55,440	35,220	26.0	29.4
	3/4	Machined to 5/8 in.	55,260	35,960	23.0	24.3
	7/8	Machined to 5/8 in.	54,420	35,310	20.0	21.1
	1	Machined to 5/8 in.	54,540	35,140	23.0	22.6
No. 5	5/8	As cast	55,200	35,310	26.5	20.8
	3/4	Machined to 5/8 in.	55,380	35,340	22.5	23.5
	7/8	Machined to 5/8 in.	55,020	35,340	21.5	19.2
	1	Machined to 5/8 in.	53,840	35,370	24.5	22.9
No. 6	5/8	As cast	55,120	33,720	26.0	29.2
	3/4	Machined to 5/8 in.	54,840	35,120	26.0	25.1
	7/8	Machined to 5/8 in.	55,240	34,310	23.0	23.2
	1	Machined to 5/8 in.	54,920	34,650	24.0	22.6

¼ in. in diameter, whereas the effects on these properties became less as the diameter of the test specimen increased and was negligible for specimens 1¼ in. in diameter or over.

There is an appreciable effect on strength and ductility due to diameter of the specimen as shown in Fig. 17, which is also taken from the tests by Swartz and reported in the *ASTM Symposium,* 1931.

For several years the students in the Materials Testing Laboratory at the University of Wisconsin broke ¾-in. round bars of air-furnace malleable cast iron over an 8-in. span in a Russell impact machine (pendulum type). The majority of these specimens had energies of rupture in impact in excess of 1000 in-lb per cu in., and quite a number have withstood 2000 in-lb per cu in. without rupture.

Constitution of Some of the More Important Non-Ferrous Alloys [*]

By R. A. Ragatz [†]

1. General Principles. In the following pages on the constitution of non-ferrous alloys, it is assumed that the reader is thoroughly familiar with the simple constitution diagrams discussed in Chapter XXI. In addition, the following two rules [‡] will assist greatly in the interpretation of a constitution diagram, and in determining, from the diagram, the transformations that take place when an alloy of known composition is heated or cooled through certain temperature ranges.

Rule 1. To determine the composition of the two phases present at any temperature when in a field where two phases are indicated, draw a temperature horizontal through the field. The compositions corresponding to the two points where this horizontal cuts the boundaries of the field will give the compositions of the two phases present. For example, referring to Fig. 1, which is the constitution diagram for the copper-zinc alloys, consider an alloy composed of 60 per cent copper and 40 per cent zinc. According to the diagram, if this alloy is at a temperature of 700°C, it will consist of two phases, α and β, both of which are solid solutions. At 700°C, the composition of the α solid solution is given by the point k, which is the intersection of the 700°C horizontal with the line aka_1. The composition of the β solid solution at the same temperature is given by point n, which is the intersection of the 700°C horizontal with the line bnb_2. This rule, of course, applies only to fields on the constitution diagram where two phases are indicated.

Rule 2. To determine the relative proportions by weight of the two phases present at any given temperature when in a field where two phases are indicated, draw a temperature horizontal, and note where it intersects the boundaries of the field. The ratio of the weights of the two phases is equal to the inverse ratio of the distances from the vertical corresponding to the average composition of the alloy, to the boundaries of the field.

[*] References: Guillet and Portevin, *Metallography and Macrography*. Gulliver, *Metallic Alloys*. Hoyt, *Metallography*, Vol. II.

[†] Professor of Chemical Engineering, University of Wisconsin.

[‡] Similar to rules given by Hoyt, *Metallography*, Vol. I, pp. 12–13.

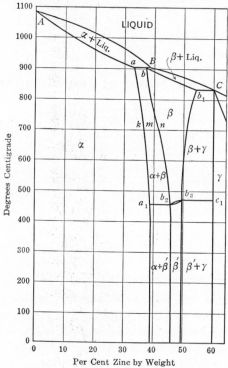

Fig. 1. Part of the constitution diagram for copper-zinc alloys.

For example, referring again to Fig. 1 and considering an alloy containing 60 per cent copper and 40 per cent zinc, at 700°C,

$$\frac{\text{Weight of } \alpha}{\text{Weight of } \beta} = \frac{mn}{km}$$

This rule also applies only to fields on the diagram where two phases are indicated.

Another point that should be understood is that the constitution diagram tells what constituents are present in an alloy at any temperature only if the conditions are such that the alloy is in perfect equilibrium. Usually, if cooling is rapid, equilibrium will not be established, and reactions which would take place if the cooling rate were very slow will not have an opportunity to proceed or go to completion.

2. The Copper-Zinc Constitution Diagram.* The portion of the copper-zinc constitution diagram shown in Fig. 1 covers the composition range of

* Roberts-Austen, *Proc. Inst. Mech. Eng.*, 1897, p. 31; Shepherd, *J. Phys. Chem.*, Vol. 8, p. 421; Carpenter and Edwards, *J. Inst. Metals*, Vol. 5, p. 127. Hudson, *J. Inst. Metals*, Vol. 12, p. 89; *International Critical Tables*, Vol. II, p. 435.

alloys in this series which are of commercial importance. This diagram is of particular interest since it applies to the ordinary brasses, which are the most important non-ferrous alloys.

3. Solidification of Copper-Zinc Alloys. When alloys between A and B in composition cool from temperatures within the liquid field, crystals of α solid solution start to form at temperatures indicated by the line AB. For alloys whose compositions are between A and a, solidification proceeds exactly the same as in any solid solution alloy, as described in detail in Art. XXI-16. Solidification is complete at temperatures indicated by the line Aa, and the entire mass then consists of homogeneous α solid solution. In alloys between a and B in composition, solidification proceeds as in any solid solution alloy until the temperature horizontal abB at 904°C is reached. At this temperature, the following reversible reaction takes place, in the direction indicated by the upper arrow: α (composition a) + liquid (composition B) $\rightleftarrows \beta$ (composition b). If the composition of the alloy is between a and b, all the liquid is used up in the reaction, and solidification will be complete at 904°C. If the composition of the alloy is between b and B, all the α solid solution is used up in the reaction, and solidification will not be complete. The alloy will be composed of β solid solution of composition b and liquid of composition B, after the reaction at 904°C has gone to completion. The temperature will then commence to drop, and solidification will proceed as in any solid solution alloy. Solidification is complete at temperatures indicated by line bb_1, and the entire mass will then consist of homogeneous β solid solution.

The solidification of alloys between B and b_1 in composition is similar to that of any solid solution alloy. Line BC indicates the temperatures at which solidification commences on cooling from temperatures within the liquid field. Solidification is complete at temperatures indicated by line bb_1, and the entire mass consists of homogeneous β solid solution.

4. Transformations in Copper-Zinc Alloys after Solidification. Alloys whose compositions are between A and a consist of homogeneous α solid solution immediately after solidification, and cooling to room temperature causes no transformations.

Alloys between a and b in composition will consist of α of composition a and β of composition b immediately after solidification. On cooling through the $\alpha + \beta$ field, the quantity of α will increase with consequent decrease in β, in accordance with rule 2. At the same time, the compositions of the α and β are constantly changing, and may be determined at any temperature by applying rule 1. If the vertical corresponding to the composition of the alloy intersects the inclined line aka_1, the β phase will disappear entirely at the temperature corresponding to the point of intersection, and the entire alloy will be composed of α solid solution.

Alloys whose compositions are between b and b_1 consist entirely of homogeneous β solid solution immediately after solidification. When alloys between b and b_2 in composition are cooled, α solid solution will start to separate at temperatures indicated by line bnb_2, and will continue to separate till the temperature horizontal a_1b_2 is reached. In a similar manner, alloys between b_1 and b_3 in composition will deposit γ solid solution in cooling between b_1b_3 and b_3c_1.

The transformations indicated by lines a_1b_2, b_2b_3, and b_3c_1 will next be considered. When alloys between a_1 and b_2 in composition are cooled to a temperature indicated by the horizontal line a_1b_2 (453°C), they consist of an aggregate of two solid solutions, the α and the β phases. The α solid solution has the composition a_1, and the β solid solution has the composition b_2. The relative proportion of the α and the β phases depends upon the per cent zinc in the brass, and may be determined for any specific alloy by application of rule 2. At 453°C, the α phase undergoes no change, but the β phase is bodily transformed into an allotropic modification, the β' solid solution. Alloys whose compositions lie between b_2 and b_3 undergo a progressive change from β solid solution into β' solid solution as the temperature drops between the two curved lines connecting b_2 and b_3. When alloys between b_3 and c_1 are cooled to a temperature indicated by the horizontal line b_3c_1 (470°C), they consist of a mixture of two solid solutions, the β and the γ phases. The β solid solution has the composition b_3, and the γ solid solution the composition c_1. The relative proportions of the two phases in any specific alloy may be determined by application of rule 2. At 470°C, the γ phase remains unchanged, but the β phase is completely transformed into β' solid solution.

5. Microstructure of Copper-Zinc Alloys. According to the equilibrium diagram, all alloys whose compositions lie between A and a_1 will be homogeneous solid solutions at room temperature if cooled through the solidification range at a slow enough rate to maintain equilibrium conditions at all times. As a matter of fact, alloys in this range of composition, when cast, cool too rapidly for equilibrium to be established. As a result, these alloys do not appear homogeneous when examined under the microscope, but will exhibit the dendritic structure as shown in Fig. 2. It is possible to produce a homogeneous structure in a cast brass by a prolonged anneal at approximately 700°C.

Brass sheets, rods, and tubing containing more than 63 per cent copper are cold worked to shape from the cast metal. The severe cold working causes distortion of the crystals making up the metal, and causes a great decrease in ductility, and an increase in hardness, tensile strength, and elastic limit. To prevent rupture, it is necessary to anneal the metal several times in the process of reduction to the desired shape. Though the material in the cast condition has the dendritic structure shown in Fig. 2, the cold working and annealing produce perfect homogeneity. Figure 3 is a photomicrograph of sheet brass containing 70 per cent copper. The metal is composed of irregular shaped crystals which are homogeneous in composition. It should be noted that many of the crystal grains are crossed by parallel lines or bands. This effect is known as twinning, and is characteristic of α brass which has been cold worked and then annealed.

  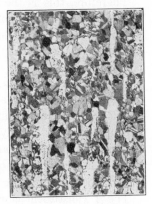

Fig. 2. Cast brass containing 70 per cent copper and 30 per cent zinc. Dark areas of β with light dendrites of α. Etched with chromic acid and hydrogen peroxide. Magnification = $\times$75.

Fig. 3. Sheet brass containing 70 per cent copper and 30 per cent zinc. Homogeneous α solid solution showing pronounced twinning. Etched with ammonia and hydrogen peroxide. Magnification = $\times$75.

Fig. 4. Muntz metal containing 60 per cent copper and 40 per cent zinc. Light elongated areas of β surrounded by small grains of α. Etched with ammonia and hydrogen peroxide. Magnification = $\times$75.

If the copper content is less than a_1, 61 per cent, a new constituent makes its appearance. Figure 4 shows the structure of Muntz metal (60 per cent copper) after etching with ammonia and hydrogen peroxide. The light elongated areas are β' solid solution, and the equi-axed grains that make up the balance of the metal are α solid solution. It should be noted that the relative coloration of the α and β' depends upon the etchant employed, and may be the reverse of that shown in Fig. 4. Acid ferric chloride or chromic acid with hydrogen peroxide blacken the β' and leave the α light, as illustrated by Fig. 2.

If the composition of the alloy is between b_2 and b_3, the entire mass will consist of homogeneous β' solid solution at room temperature. The β' solid solution differs from the α solid solution, in that the β' never exhibits the dendritic structure characteristic of α brass in the cast condition nor the profuse twinning characteristic of α brass which has been cold worked and annealed.

6. Relation between Constitution and Mechanical Properties of Copper-Zinc Alloys. The mechanical properties of the α and β' solid solutions are quite different. Brasses consisting entirely of α solid solution are very ductile when cold, and rather soft, whereas a brass composed entirely of β' solid solution is harder, has practically no ductility, and is so brittle that the tensile strength is low.

The α solid solution has maximum ductility at 70 per cent copper. Therefore, this is the most desirable composition if the brass is to be subjected to severe cold working in the reduction to the desired shape. However, brasses of lower copper content, 63 to 70 per cent, are often used even though they are worked with greater difficulty, since they are cheaper.

If the zinc content is above 39 per cent, the β' constituent will be present. The presence of the β' causes an increase in the tensile strength till the zinc content is approximately 40 per cent, above which the tensile strength drops off quite rapidly. The increase in tensile strength caused by the presence of a small quantity of β' and the decrease in tensile strength when the β' is present beyond a certain limiting value, is somewhat analogous to the effect of cementite upon the tensile strength of steel (Art. XXIV-4). The β' constituent causes a continuous decrease in ductility, and a continuous increase in hardness. Alloys containing less than 55 per cent copper contain so much β' that they are too brittle to be of any use.

The γ solid solution is very brittle, therefore any alloys containing this constituent are of little use.

7. Mechanical Treatment of Brass. Since copper may be worked either hot or cold, it would be expected that the α solid solution low in zinc could be worked either hot or cold. This is the case if the zinc content is not above 10 per cent.

Brasses containing between 63 and 90 per cent copper cannot be worked hot, but must be reduced to shape cold. The most desirable composition, from the standpoint of ease of working, is 70 per cent copper, but economic considerations often make it advisable to use a lower copper content, 63 to 70 per cent. If cold-worked brass is examined under the microscope, it will be seen that the grains are severely distorted and broken up.

The β' constituent is non-malleable at ordinary temperatures. Therefore, if a brass contains a considerable amount of the β' constituent, it must be worked hot. If only a small amount of β' is present, as in brasses containing 60 to 61 per cent copper, it is possible to cold work the metal if care is taken. However, brasses of such composition are usually worked hot.

The γ constituent is so brittle that an alloy containing it in appreciable quantities cannot be worked either hot or cold.

8. Heat Treatment of Brass. It was shown that brass in the cast condition has a non-homogeneous structure. If the composition is above 61 per cent copper, the structure may be rendered homogeneous by a prolonged anneal at approximately 700°C.

The most important heat treatment to which brasses are subjected is the annealing operation in the process of cold working to the desired shape. Cold working produces severe distortion of the grains making up the metal, and a great decrease in ductility, and an increase in hardness, tensile strength, and elastic limit. To prevent failure of the metal, it must be annealed several times in the course of reduction to the desired shape. Annealing causes recrystallization of the strained metal, and restores the ductility. The annealing temperature must be above a certain minimum, or recrystallization of the metal will not take place. The minimum annealing temperature is not fixed, but depends upon the amount of cold work the metal has been subjected to, and upon the composition. In general, the greater the amount of cold work the metal has been subjected to, the lower will be the minimum temperature required. For a given reduction in cross section, the higher the zinc content, the lower will be the minimum temperature required. In annealing cold-worked brass, care must be taken that the annealing temperature is not too high, or the grain size will be large, causing brittleness. Specifications for brass sometimes require that the grain size be within certain limits. The microscope finds an important industrial application in controlling the annealing of cold-worked brass.

Inspection of the equilibrium diagram will tell at once whether the constitution and hence the mechanical properties of an alloy may be altered by quenching. The constitution of alloys containing 68 to 100 per cent copper is unaffected by quenching from temperatures below the line Aa.

If alloys whose compositions are between 61 and 68 per cent copper are heated within the $\alpha + \beta$ field and quenched, the β which was present at the quenching temperature will be retained due to the rapid cooling rate. Retention of the β causes an increase in the tensile strength, and a decrease in ductility.

9. Special Brasses. The effect upon the microstructure and mechanical properties of brass produced by the addition of a third metal has been investigated by Guillet.[*] The addition of a third metal to a brass may affect the microstructure in one of the three following ways:

1. The added metal does not alloy with the brass at ordinary temperatures, but exists in the free state dispersed throughout the mass. If an

---

[*] Guillet, *Comp. rend.*, Vol. 140, p. 307, Vol. 142, p. 1047; *Rév. mét.*, Vol. 2, p. 97, Vol. 3, p. 143.

unetched section of brass to which lead has been added be examined under the microscope, numerous small globules of lead are seen distributed throughout the metal. In general, the presence of the additional constituent will cause a deterioration of the mechanical properties. The addition of lead to brass lowers the tensile strength and decreases the ductility, yet leaded brasses are very widely used because they machine so easily.

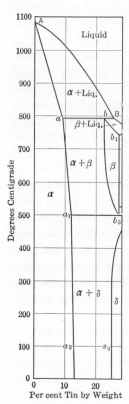

Fig. 5. Part of the constitution diagram for copper-tin alloys.

2. The addition of a third metal causes the appearance of a new constituent. Both phosphorus and tin have this effect. In naval brass (Art. XXX-18) the addition of tin causes the appearance of a constituent similar to the δ constituent in the copper-tin series.

3. The third metal added enters into solid solution, at least up to a certain limiting quantity. Some metals, as for example silicon and aluminum, affect the microstructure in the same manner as the addition of zinc. Certain other metals, as nickel and manganese, for example, have the same effect upon the microstructure as the addition of copper. If the mechanical properties of an ordinary and a ternary brass which both exhibit the same microstructure are compared, it will be found that the mechanical properties of the ternary brass are superior.

10. The Copper-Tin Constitution Diagram.* The copper-rich end of the constitution diagram, Fig. 5, is of interest since it is applicable to the ordinary copper-tin bronzes, which are of considerable industrial importance. The useful alloys in this series usually contain less than 25 per cent tin, therefore, the following discussion on copper-tin alloys will be confined to compositions ranging from 0 to approximately 25 per cent tin.

Figure 5 is similar in many respects to the copper-rich end of the copper-zinc constitution diagram; hence it is unnecessary to give as detailed an account of the process of solidification of the copper-tin alloys, and subsequent transformations in the solid state, as was given for the

* Roberts-Austen and Stansfield, *Proc. Inst. Mech. Eng.*, 1895, p. 269, 1897, p. 67; Heycock and Neville, *Proc. Roy. Soc. (London)*, Vol. 69, p. 320; *Phil. Trans. Roy. Soc. (London) (A)*, Vol. 189, p. 25, Vol. 202-A, p. 1; Shepherd and Blough, *J. Phys. Chem.*, Vol. 10, p. 630.

copper-zinc alloys. Copper-tin alloys between a_1 and b_3 in composition when cooled to 500°C, will consist of α of composition a_1 and β of composition b_3. At 500°C, the β solid solution breaks up into an intimate mixture of α and δ, known as the $\alpha + \delta$ eutectoid. It should be noted that the right-hand boundary of the $\alpha + \delta$ field curves quite sharply to the left between 500 and 300°C. Application of rule 2 to this portion of the $\alpha + \delta$ field shows that the proportion of δ increases considerably as the alloy cools through this temperature range.

11. Microstructure of Copper-Tin Alloys. According to the constitution diagram, alloys between A and a_2 in composition, 0 to 13 per cent tin, will consist of homogeneous α solid solution at room temperature, if the cooling rate was slow enough so equilibrium was maintained throughout the solidification range.   However, bronzes within this range of composition, when in the cast condition, exhibit a dendritic structure similar to that shown in Fig. 6, since cooling is too rapid for equilibrium to be established. If a cast bronze within this range of composition be annealed for an extended period of time, or successively worked and annealed, diffusion will take place within the metal, and a perfectly homogeneous structure will ultimately result.

Fig. 6. Government bronze containing 88 per cent copper, 10 per cent tin, and 2 per cent zinc. Small light areas of $\alpha + \delta$ eutectoid surrounded by skeletons of α. Etched with chromic acid and hydrogen peroxide. Magnification = $\times 75$.

Alloys between a_1 and b_3 in composition, 13 to 25 per cent tin, will be composed of α and the $\alpha + \delta$ eutectoid immediately after the transition at 500°C. In cooling between 500° and 300°C, the amount of δ increases considerably, as indicated by the curved line bounding the right side of the $\alpha + \delta$ field.

12. Relation between Constitution and Mechanical Properties of Copper-Tin Alloys. The α solid solution is more ductile and considerably stronger than pure copper. For rolled bronze, the addition of tin from 0 to 8 per cent causes a continuous increase in the ultimate tensile strength, elastic limit, hardness, and ductility.

The presence of the δ constituent increases the hardness, makes the metal more brittle, and decreases the ductility. At 18 per cent tin, the elongation is nearly zero. The ultimate tensile strength of cast bronze is increased by the presence of δ till the tin content is approximately 19 per cent, above which the tensile strength drops off rapidly.

The usefulness of the ordinary copper-tin bronzes for bearing metals depends upon the fact that the δ constituent imparts desirable antifrictional qualities to the metal. Bronze containing above 11 per cent tin has the structure requisite for a bearing metal, since it is composed of hard particles of δ set in a relatively soft matrix of α. In general, the higher the tin content, and hence the proportion of δ, the greater will be the maximum bearing pressure at which operation will be satisfactory. However, as the quantity of δ increases, the brittleness and difficulty of working increase.

The usefulness of bronze as a material for gears is also due to the presence of the δ constituent. Bronzes containing 10 to 13 per cent tin have sufficient δ to give the gear the necessary strength and resistance to abrasion.

The compound Cu_3Sn is also brittle, and alloys consisting largely of this constituent find few applications in industry. Speculum metal is composed largely of δ with some Cu_3Sn.

13. Mechanical Treatment of Copper-Tin Alloys. The α solid solution may be worked cold, but cannot be worked hot unless the tin content is very low. The δ constituent decreases the ductility and embrittles the metal to such an extent that bronzes containing appreciable quantities cannot be worked cold. Cast bronzes containing 10 to 13 per cent tin are difficult to work, since the metal as cast is not homogeneous, but contains some δ.

The $\alpha + \delta$ bronzes can be worked hot if the temperature of the metal is between 500° and 800°C. In heating above 500°C, the $\alpha + \delta$ eutectoid is converted into β solid solution, which is considerably more malleable and ductile than the δ constituent. The working temperature should not exceed 800°C, since at this temperature the $\alpha + \delta$ bronzes undergo partial liquefaction. Bell metal, 75 to 80 per cent copper, is usually cast to the desired shape in the manufacture of large bells, but in making small bells the metal is sometimes worked to shape at a temperature between 500° and 800°C.

14. Heat Treatment of Copper-Tin Alloys. The heterogeneous structure shown by cast alloys between A and a_2 in composition, 0 to 13 per cent tin, may be effaced by a prolonged anneal. Annealing causes an increase in the ductility, and a decrease in the hardness and tensile strength. Annealing cold-worked bronze causes recrystallization of the distorted metal, with pronounced twinning.

Inspection of the diagram will tell whether the constitution and hence the mechanical properties of an alloy may be altered by quenching. Alloys between A and a in composition will be unaffected by quenching at temperatures below the line Aa, provided that the structure of the metal was initially homogeneous. Alloys between a and a_1 in composition will be composed of α and β if heated to temperatures above the line aa_1 and then quenched. Alloys between a_1 and b_3 in composition will consist of α and β when heated above 500°C, and quenching will result in retention of the β solid solution. The mechanical properties of the β solid solution are superior to those of the δ solid solution, hence the mechanical properties of the $\alpha + \delta$ alloys are considerably improved by quenching at temperatures between 500° and 800°C. The ultimate tensile strength, ductility, and malleability are increased. It has been mentioned that small bells, which usually contain 20 to 25 per cent tin, are often worked to shape at temperatures between 500° and 800°C. An alternative method is to heat above 500°C, quench, and then work to shape cold. Retention of the β solid solution as a result of the quenching operation imparts sufficient malleability to the metal so it may be worked cold.

15. Special Bronzes. Phosphorus, lead, zinc, and silicon are the most important elements that are alloyed with copper-tin bronzes to improve their properties.

(a) *Phosphor Bronzes.* Phosphor bronzes may be divided into two groups, according to their phosphorus contents. (1) The finished bronze contains only a trace of phosphorus, and the improvement in mechanical properties is due simply to the deoxidizing action of the phosphorus. When bronze is melted, oxides of copper and tin are formed, and are a source of weakness in the metal. When phosphorus is added to the molten metal, the oxides of tin and copper are reduced, and the phosphorus pentoxide which is formed enters the slag on the surface of the metal. (2) Phosphorus is present in the finished metal up to approximately 0.4 per cent. In addition to acting as a deoxidizer, the phosphorus added to these bronzes affects the mechanical properties by the formation of the compound Cu_3P. This constituent is hard, brittle, has a low coefficient of friction, and resists abrasion. Phosphor bronzes of this class find their principal application in the manufacture of bearings and gears. The hard particles of δ and Cu_3P are set in a relatively soft matrix of α.

(b) *Lead Bronzes.* If lead is present above 2 per cent, the tensile strength and ductility decrease quite rapidly. The presence of lead makes a bronze easier to machine, and also greatly improves the antifrictional qualities of the metal. Leaded bronze for bearings may contain as high as 30 per cent lead. The lead is practically insoluble in the bronze, and exists in the free state dispersed throughout the metal. A difficulty encountered in the manufacture of high lead bearing bronzes is the tendency of the lead to segregate on cooling. It has been found that this difficulty may be overcome by rapid cooling, and by adding approximately 1 per cent nickel. Plastic bronze has approximately the following composition: 64 per cent copper, 5 per cent tin, 30 per cent lead, and 1 per cent nickel.

In leaded bronze, the soft particles of lead are set in a hard matrix of bronze.

(c) *Zinc Bronzes.* Zinc acts as a deoxidizer, increases the fluidity of the molten metal, and decreases the tendency of the metal to form blowholes. The zinc goes into solution, and has the same effect upon the constitution as the addition of copper. Figure 6 shows the microstructure of a zinc bronze which is used quite extensively. Small light areas of the $\alpha + \delta$ eutectoid are surrounded by skeletons of heterogeneous α solid solution. If the zinc content is below 2 per cent, the mechanical properties are not greatly affected. If the zinc content is greater, the tensile strength and ductility drop off.

(d) *Silicon Bronzes.* Silicon is added as a deoxidizer, and the finished product contains only traces of silicon. Silicon bronze finds its most important application in the manufacture of wire to be used for electrical conductors. It has a greater conductivity than phosphor bronze.

16. The Copper-Aluminum Constitution Diagram.[*] In the copper-aluminum alloy series, both the copper-rich and the aluminum-rich alloys are of industrial importance. The portions of the copper-aluminum constitution diagram shown in Fig. 7 cover the composition range of the useful alloys in this series. Since the alloys of commercial importance contain 0 to 12 per cent copper, and 88 to 100 per cent copper, detailed discussion will be confined to these ranges of composition.

The copper-rich end of Fig. 7 is quite similar to the other two diagrams which have already been discussed in this chapter; therefore a detailed account of the process of solidification and transformations in the solid state will not be necessary for the copper-rich alloys in this series.

17. Copper-Rich Alloys of Aluminum and Copper. (a) *Microstructure.* Alloys between 91 and 100 per cent copper will be composed entirely of homogeneous α solid solution at room temperature, if the rate of cooling during solidification was slow enough so that equilibrium was maintained. Cast alloys within this range of composition exhibit the heterogeneous structure which is characteristic of most solid solution alloys in the cast state.

At room temperature, slowly cooled alloys between a_1 and b_3 in composition will consist of crystals of α mixed with the $\alpha + \delta$ eutectoid. The relative proportions of the free α and of the eutectoid depend upon the composition of the alloy. The quantity of eutectoid varies from 0 to 100 per cent as the composition varies from a_1 to b_3. The eutectoid assumes a coarsely granular form if any free α is present in the alloy, which is the

[*] Curry, *J. Phys. Chem.*, Vol. 11, p. 425; Carpenter and Edwards, *Proc. Inst. Mech. Eng.*, 1907, p. 57; Gwyer, *Ztg. anorg. Chem.*, Vol. 57, p. 113; Andrew, *J. Inst. Metals*, Vol. 13, p. 249; Merica, Waltenberg, and Freeman, National Bur. Standards *Sci. Paper* 337.

case for compositions between a_1 and b_3. If the alloy has an aluminum content greater than b_3, the eutectoid tends to assume a finely laminated structure similar to pearlite in steel. Figure 8 shows the structure of an aluminum bronze, in which the light areas of free α are mixed with the dark $\alpha + \delta$ eutectoid.

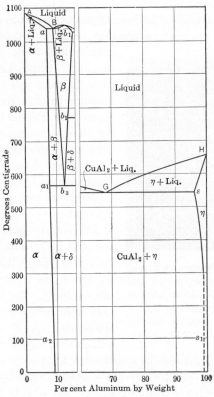

Fig. 7. Part of the constitution diagram for copper-aluminum alloys.

(b) *Relation between Mechanical Properties and Constitution.* The α constituent is strong, ductile, and relatively soft. The tensile strength of the α solid solution shows a continuous increase as the aluminum content increases from 0 to 9 per cent. The ductility shows a maximum value at 7 per cent aluminum, above which the ductility drops off.

The δ constituent is hard and brittle. Its presence causes a continuous decrease in ductility and increases the brittleness. Its presence in small quantities causes an increase in tensile strength. At 10 per cent aluminum, the tensile strength has its maximum value, and drops off quite rapidly when this aluminum content is exceeded.

(c) *Mechanical Treatment.* Alloys composed entirely of α solid solution may be worked either hot or cold. The presence of the δ constituent in appreciable quantities makes the alloys brittle; therefore alloys containing over 9 per cent aluminum cannot be worked cold. However, alloys containing 9 to 12 per cent aluminum may be hot worked between 566° and 1040°C. Heating above 566°C converts the $\alpha + \delta$ eutectoid into β, which may be worked hot.

(d) *Heat Treatment.* The heterogeneous structure of cast alloys containing 91 to 100 per cent copper may be destroyed by annealing, or by mechanical work combined with annealing. Inspection of the constitution diagram will tell at once if it is possible to alter the constitution, and hence the mechanical properties, of an alloy by quenching. The constitution of alloys between A and a in composition, 0 to 7 per cent aluminum, is unaffected by quenching. If alloys between a and a_2, 7 to 9 per cent aluminum, are heated within the $\alpha + \beta$ field and quenched, the β constituent will be retained due to the rapid rate of cooling. When alloys between a_1 and b_3 in composition are heated above 566°C, the $\alpha + \delta$ eutectoid is converted into β. If the alloy is then quenched, the β constituent is retained due to the rapid cooling rate.

Fig. 8. Aluminum bronze containing approximately 91 per cent copper and 9 per cent aluminum. Dark areas of $\alpha + \delta$ eutectoid surrounded by light α. Etched with acid ferric chloride. Magnification = $\times 75$.

The quantity of β present in a quenched alloy depends upon the composition of the alloy and also upon the quenching temperature employed. For example, an alloy containing 12 per cent aluminum when quenched from above 566°C may consist of α and β, or entirely of β, depending upon the quenching temperature employed. The β constituent in quenched alloys often exhibits a striated appearance, similar to martensite in steel. This seems to indicate partial decomposition of the β in spite of the quenching. The retention of the β constituent in a quenched alloy increases the tensile strength and elastic limit, but decreases the ductility and impact resistance.

18. Aluminum-Rich Alloys of Aluminum and Copper. The aluminum-rich alloys of the copper-aluminum alloy series are useful because of their lightness, which is combined with a good degree of strength and ductility. These alloys find their most important application in the automobile industry. The light alloys of copper and aluminum which are of commercial importance usually do not contain over 12 per cent copper.

When alloys between G and H in composition (Fig. 7) are cooled from temperatures within the liquid field, η solid solution will start to deposit at temperatures indicated by line GH. If the composition is between H and s, and the rate of cooling is slow enough so that equilibrium is at all times maintained, the alloys will be completely solid at temperatures indicated by line Hs, and will then consist of homogeneous η solid solution. If the composition is between G and s, η solid solution will separate as the alloy cools between GH and the horizontal Gs at 545°C. At this temperature, the alloy consists of η of composition s, and liquid of composition G. The liquid solidifies at constant temperature to form an intimate mixture of $CuAl_2$ and η. Such an intimate mixture of two phases resulting from the solidification of a liquid is known as a eutectic.

Light aluminum casting alloys usually contain 5 to 12 per cent copper. When examined under the microscope, they are seen to consist of η solid solution mixed with the eutectic. The η constituent may be somewhat heterogeneous due to the fact that the metal was cast, and cooled rather rapidly. However, the heterogeneity is not very pronounced.

The line ss_1 slopes to the right, indicating that the solubility of $CuAl_2$ in aluminum decreases as the temperature drops. At the eutectic temperature, 545°C, the η solid solution can hold approximately 4 per cent copper in solution, and at 300°C the η solid solution can dissolve only 1 per cent copper. It is this decrease in solubility that makes possible the heat treatment of Duralumin, which is discussed below.

The η solid solution has properties similar to aluminum. It is malleable and ductile, and not much heavier than aluminum. The presence of the compound $CuAl_2$ causes an increase in hardness, but a decrease in ductility. The addition of copper to aluminum causes a continuous increase in the tensile strength of sand-cast alloys, to approximately 14 per cent copper. At the same time, the ductility decreases continuously, till at 14 per cent copper the elongation is nearly zero. The mechanical properties of castings are affected to quite a marked degree by the cooling rate. The more rapid the cooling rate, the finer will be the structure as shown by microscopic examination. The finer structure is accompanied by increased tensile strength and ductility. Therefore, chill castings are superior to sand castings, and castings of small cross section have better mechanical properties than those of greater cross section.

Duralumin (Art. XXX-11) is commonly used when the finished object is to be worked to shape rather than cast. It may be worked to shape either hot or cold, but is usually worked while hot. Duralumin is remarkable because of the great improvement in mechanical properties which can be obtained by suitable heat treatment, and the peculiar manner in which this improvement takes place. If Duralumin is heated to 500°C and water quenched, the mechanical properties are about the same as if the alloy had been slowly cooled. However, if it stands at ordinary temperatures, its hardness and tensile strength will start to increase, and after several days will reach maximum values considerably above those of annealed Duralumin of the same composition.

Annealed Duralumin will show particles of $CuAl_2$ imbedded in η solid solution. Some $FeAl_3$ will be present, since iron is always present in the commercial aluminum which is used in making Duralumin. The quenched Duralumin shows less $CuAl_2$ than does the annealed metal, since on heating to the quenching temperature some or all of the $CuAl_2$ dissolves. The $FeAl_3$ does not dissolve on heating to the quenching temperature. No change in the microstructure of Duralumin can be detected on aging after quenching.

19. Copper-Nickel Alloys. Copper and nickel are soluble in one another in all proportions, both in the liquid and solid states. The constitution diagram for this series of alloys is therefore similar to Fig. 8, Art. XXI-16. The curves giving the temperatures of initial and final solidification for these alloys rise continuously from the melting point of copper, 1083°C, to the melting point of nickel, 1452°C. In this alloy series, the only transformation after solidification is a magnetic transformation, which is not accompanied by a change in microstructure.

The copper-nickel alloys as cast have a heterogeneous structure, but may be rendered homogeneous by a prolonged anneal, or by mechanical work combined with annealing. The effect produced by cold working followed by annealing is very similar to the effect produced upon α brass when subjected to a similar treatment. The cold working distorts the crystals, and annealing causes recrystallization of the strained metal, with pronounced twinning.

Quenching has no effect upon the constitution of copper-nickel alloys. The non-magnetic state cannot be retained by quenching from above the magnetic transformation temperature.

Nickel silver (nickeline or German silver) is a copper-nickel alloy carrying considerable zinc. The composition is variable, but is usually within the following limits: * copper, 52 to 80 per cent; nickel, 10 to 35 per cent; zinc, 5 to 30 per cent. Alloys within this range of composition form solid solutions. The cast alloys exhibit the usual dendritic structure, which may be effaced by annealing, or by cold working followed by annealing.

* National Bur. Standards *Circ.* 100.

Monel metal (Art. XXX-29) is used to a considerable extent in making castings, and in this condition has a non-homogeneous structure. Monel metal is also rolled into various shapes, either hot or cold. If rolled cold, the metal must be annealed several times in the process of reduction to the desired shape. The finished material in the annealed state is perfectly homogeneous, as shown in Fig. 9. The small oxide inclusions are characteristic of the microstructure of Monel metal.

Fig. 9.   Rolled Monel metal after annealing. Shows homogeneous solid solution with twinning. Etched with acid ferric chloride. Magnification = ×75.

20. Aluminum-Zinc Alloys.* Aluminum-zinc alloys containing from 0 to 40 per cent zinc form homogeneous solid solutions. Since the alloys of commercial importance fall within this range of composition and hence are solid solution alloys, it is not necessary to give the constitution diagram for this series. These alloys when cast have the usual dendritic structure, which may be effaced by annealing or by mechanical work followed by annealing. Alloys containing up to 25 per cent zinc may be rolled hot; alloys containing up to 15 per cent zinc may be rolled cold. However, the aluminum-zinc alloys are used mostly in the manufacture of light castings. An aluminum-zinc alloy containing 15 per cent zinc, 3 per cent copper, and 82 per cent aluminum is used for a light casting alloy to a great extent in Great Britain, in preference to the ordinary light aluminum-copper alloys which are used so extensively in the United States.

* Rosenhain and Archbutt, *Proc. Inst. Mech. Eng.,* 1912, p. 319; National Bur. Standards *Circ.* 76.

Non-Ferrous Metals and Alloys *

1. Importance and Use of Non-Ferrous Metals. Although the tonnage of iron is in excess of 90 per cent of the total production of all metals and the production of individual non-ferrous metals is small in comparison, the non-ferrous metals play an important part in many engineering structures and industrial processes. Productions of the more important non-ferrous metals, along with the production of pig iron and steel for comparison, in the United States and in the world for 1950, are given in Table 1. The included costs show that the non-ferrous metals are con-

TABLE 1. PRODUCTION AND COST OF IMPORTANT ENGINEERING METALS (1950) [1]

Metal	World Production, 1000 net tons	United States Production, 1000 net tons	Cost, cents per pound
Pig iron	147,000	66,500	2
Steel ingots and castings	205,000	96,500	4
Aluminum	1,630	720	18
Copper	2,760	910	22
Lead	1,875	430	15
Magnesium	44	15	24
Nickel	160	0	48
Tin	183	0	96
Titanium	900 [2]	480 [2]	500
Zinc	2,330	625	15

[1] Based primarily on *Minerals Year Book* (1950).
[2] Titanium concentrates ilmenite and rutile.

siderably more expensive than the ferrous metals. The cost of titanium is exceptionally high because this metal is in the process of development, and its price may be expected to drop sharply.

The non-ferrous metals and their alloys are used despite their high cost because they provide a wide variety of properties. Many non-ferrous

* References: *Metals and Alloys Data Book* by S. L. Hoyt; *ASM Metals Handbook; Modern Metallurgy for Engineers* by F. T. Sisco; *Minerals Year Book,* by the staff of the U. S. Bureau of Mines; *Cast Metals Handbook,* by American Foundrymen's Association.

metals are used because they have good resistance to atmospheric corrosion, some have excellent electrical properties, some have a low melting point and are easily cast, and some have a low density combined with good strength. A more complete discussion of the advantages and disadvantages of the important non-ferrous metals and alloys is given in the following articles.

ALUMINUM AND ITS ALLOYS

2. Production of Aluminum. Aluminum is derived from bauxite whose principal constituents are hydrated oxides of aluminum and iron with some silica. British Guiana, France, Hungary, Indonesia, Russia, Surinam, and the United States lead in the production of bauxite. In the United States, Arkansas, Alabama, and Georgia are the important producing states. The ores usually contain between 30 and 35 per cent of aluminum. Refining of alumina is done principally in Canada, France, Italy, Norway, Russia, and the United States.

The first step in the process of extraction of aluminum is the production of its oxide alumina from bauxite. Alumina is obtained by roasting the coarsely granulated bauxite at a temperature sufficient to drive off the water. The treated bauxite is then finely ground and heated under pressure for several hours with a solution of sodium hydrate. This solution is diluted and filtered and a little sodium hydrate added to the filtrate. It is then agitated for several hours to precipitate the hydrate, which is separated, washed, and calcined at a temperature of approximately 1000°C. The process results in the production of alumina with perhaps 1 per cent of the oxides of sodium, iron, and silicon as impurities.

Aluminum is extracted by electrolytic decomposition of alumina in a molten bath of cryolite (a fluoride of alumina and sodium). The cryolite is placed in a shallow rectangular hearth provided with a coke bottom which serves as the cathode, and several vertical carbon rods are suspended in the bath, which serve as anodes for the electric current. After the cryolite is introduced into the furnace and melted by the passage of the electric current, the alumina is thrown onto the bath. As it melts it is dissociated into aluminum and oxygen, the former settling onto the cathode at the bottom of the bath while the oxygen goes to the anodes and, forming carbon monoxide, escapes from the bath. From time to time a portion of the aluminum is tapped from the furnace and alumina and cryolite are added to replenish the bath. The metallic aluminum thus obtained usually contains from 0.2 to 2 per cent of silicon and iron as impurities. "Pure," or No. 1, aluminum usually carries about ½ per cent of these impurities.

3. Properties and Uses of Aluminum. Aluminum is a white metal of high metallic luster. It is second only to gold in malleability and can be rolled into sheets 0.0005 to 0.0006 in. in thickness. It is one of the lightest metals of construction and, in proportion to its weight, it is very strong. Aluminum of commercial purity has a specific gravity of 2.71.

The mechanical properties of commercially pure aluminum (2S) are given in Table 2.

TABLE 2.   MECHANICAL PROPERTIES OF COMMERCIALLY PURE ALUMINUM

(Courtesy Aluminum Co. of America)

Alloy and Temper [1]	Tension				Hardness	Shear	Fatigue
	Yield Strength at 0.2% Offset, psi	Ultimate Strength, psi	Elongation in 2", per cent		Brinell 500-kg 10 mm Ball	Shearing Strength, psi	Endurance Limit,[2] psi
			Sheet $\frac{1}{16}''$ thick	Round $\frac{1}{2}''$ dia.			
2S–O	5,000	13,000	35	45	23	9,500	5,000
2S–H12	13,000	15,000	12	25	28	10,000	6,000
2S–H14	14,000	17,000	9	20	32	11,000	7,000
2S–H16	17,000	20,000	6	17	38	12,000	8,500
2S–H18	21,000	24,000	5	15	44	13,000	8,500

[1] Temper designation: O, annealed; H18, fully cold worked (hard); H12, H14, H16, intermediate degrees of cold work between O and H18.

[2] Based on 500,000,000 cycles using R. R. Moore type of rotating beam machine.

The modulus of elasticity of aluminum is 10,000,000 psi, and the shearing modulus of elasticity is 3,850,000 psi. Poisson's ratio is 0.33.

Aluminum has a high electric conductivity, 61, based on silver as 100. On account of its light weight, a bar of given length and weight is twice as good a conductor as a similar copper bar. However, copper is generally preferred to aluminum for transmission purposes because copper has better resistance to repeated stress and has a lower coefficient of thermal expansion.

The coefficient of thermal expansion of aluminum is about 0.0000125 per degree Fahrenheit, or roughly about twice that of steel. Its thermal conductivity is 0.52 cal/sq cm/cm/°C/sec.

Commercial aluminum is widely used because of its high resistance to atmospheric corrosion. Aluminum is highly resistant to nitric acid, is slowly dissolved by concentrated sulfuric acid, and is soluble in hydrochloric acid. At ordinary temperatures sulfur gases, carbolic acid, salt water, vinegar, sea water, carbonic acid, and sulfuretted hydrogen do not attack it, but it is rapidly corroded by the caustic alkalies.

Commercial aluminum is used where good formability and good corrosion resistance are required and where high strength is not necessary. Consequently pure aluminum is not used in construction, except for ornamental purposes. It is used chiefly for cooking utensils and for various types of chemical storage equipment.

4. Utility of Aluminum Alloys. Owing to the softness of pure aluminum, it is commonly alloyed with copper, silicon, or magnesium to improve its mechanical properties. Some aluminum alloys also contain one or more of the metals manganese, lead, bismuth, nickel, chromium, zinc, titanium, and beryllium. A large part of the aluminum production is utilized in making light, stiff, corrosion-resistant alloys with these metals. These alloys are widely used in the aircraft industry and the automobile industry, for the manufacture of electric and steam railway rolling stock, and for structural members of bridges and buildings. Aluminum-copper alloys are used for pistons, cylinders, and crankcases for both automobile and airplane engines, also for cooking utensils and strong light parts which are die cast. Aluminum-silicon alloys are used where excellent castability and corrosion resistance are required. Aluminum-magnesium alloys are used where exceptional mechanical properties, resistance to corrosion, and excellent machinability are required. Aluminum alloys containing about 4 per cent copper, 0.5 per cent magnesium, and 0.5 per cent manganese have excellent properties and are used in airplane parts and structural shapes for many types of construction. Other complex aluminum alloys are similarly used. The heavy aluminum bronzes are used in steam valves, pump rods, spindles, springs, propellers, and motor and engine gears where good strength and resistance to corrosion are essential qualities.

5. General Characteristics of Wrought-Aluminum Alloys. In the manufacture of wrought products an ingot of appropriate size and shape is cast and is then hot worked to provide better grain structure. It may then be worked to the finished product without cooling, other than that which takes place during fabrication; or the final fabrication may be cold work. Cold working strain-hardens the metal and increases the strength and hardness in proportion to the amount of work. The effects of cold work may, if desired, be removed by subsequent annealing.

Certain alloys, such as 2S, 3S, and 52S, cannot be heat treated to increase strength and hardness, and the strain-hardening process is the only method of increasing the tensile properties. Increasing amounts of cold work produce alloys varying from soft to hard temper with corresponding increases in strength and hardness. In another group of alloys, such as 17S, 24S, and 61S, the mechanical properties may be improved by heat treatment and strain hardening.

Aluminum alloys can be hot and cold worked by rolling, forging, pressing, extruding, and drawing to produce such products as sheet, plate, wire, bar, tubing, forgings, and rolled or extruded structural sections such as I- and H-beams, channels, angles, and tees. Various fabricating processes, such as welding, shearing, drilling, and punching, may be performed on aluminum alloys with equipment similar to that used for steel. Aluminum alloys may be joined by gas, arc, or resistance welding, and some alloys may also be joined by brazing.

6. General Characteristics of Cast-Aluminum Alloys. Cast-aluminum alloys contain one or more of the elements copper, silicon, magnesium, nickel, iron, zinc, manganese, chromium, and titanium. There are two general classes of cast alloys from the standpoint of methods of improving properties. In one class, improvement of properties results solely from alloying; in the other, control over the alloying elements and various heat treatments are used to effect improvements.

Aluminum alloys are cast in sand molds, in permanent metal molds, and in pressure die-casting machines. Sand casting is used where only a few castings are needed or where large or intricate cored castings are required. When a large number of relatively small castings are wanted the alloy is cast in permanent molds, or die castings are made. Die or permanent-mold castings have a smoother surface, closer dimensional tolerances, and better properties than the same alloy cast in sand.

7. Heat Treatment of Aluminum Alloys. The mechanical properties of some wrought- and cast-aluminum alloys may be varied by three basic heat treatments: solution heat treatment, precipitation heat treatment, and annealing.

Aluminum alloys that are susceptible to aging contain constituents that have a higher solid solubility in aluminum at elevated temperatures than at room temperature. The purpose of the solution heat treatment is to distribute the alloying ingredients throughout the structure so that they will effectively harden the metal. The treatment consists in heating the alloy to a temperature usually between $900°$ and $1000°F$, at which temperature the hardening constituents go into solution, and then quenching the metal to keep these constituents in solution. The as-quenched alloy is then in a state of supersaturation. The hardening constituents will precipitate out with time at room temperatures, and the alloy will increase in strength and hardness and decrease in ductility. Age hardening at room temperatures usually reaches its maximum effect within 4 days, but it may be completely prevented for long periods by keeping the quenched alloys at temperatures around $0°F$.

Aging or precipitation may be accelerated by the precipitation heat treatment, which consists of heating the alloy to a temperature usually between 250° and 400°F. Aging at room temperature is referred to as natural aging; the accelerated precipitation induced by heating is called artificial aging. The strength and hardness are usually increased more by artificial than by natural aging. When aluminum alloys are artificially aged, care must be taken to avoid excessive temperatures or prolonged heating periods, or both, since these conditions produce decreases in strength and hardness. Such excessive treatment is known as overaging. Artificial aging for a short time, however, reduces the resistance to corrosion, and it is therefore necessary to consider the time carefully in view of the conflicting effects. Artificial aging is generally more effective in increasing strength and hardness if the alloy has been cold worked after the solution heat treatment and before aging.

Aluminum alloys may be annealed to remove strain-hardening effects resulting from cold work and also to remove most of the effects of the solution heat treatment and subsequent aging. Annealing is accomplished by heating cast and wrought alloys to 650°F. The cooling rate is not important if the specified temperature is not exceeded, but as a precautionary measure the alloy may be slowly cooled to about 450°F. Where a fully annealed condition is required, such as for severe forming operations, the alloy should be heated to a temperature between 750° and 800°F for 2 hours and slowly cooled in the furnace to a temperature of 500°F. The cooling rate below 500°F is not important.

8. Aluminum-Copper Alloys. Copper was one of the earliest alloying elements used in aluminum, and along with other elements it is still used in many of the commercial alloys. Cast and wrought alloys frequently contain from $3\frac{1}{2}$ to $4\frac{1}{2}$ per cent copper, and some cast alloys contain from 7 to 10 per cent copper. The casting properties of aluminum alloys are improved by the addition of copper, since it decreases hot shortness and shrinkage difficulties. Aluminum-copper alloys are susceptible to age hardening and are nearly always used in the heat-treated condition.

Additions of copper up to about 6 per cent are effective in increasing the yield and tensile strengths, but decrease the ductility. Sand-cast precipitation-hardened alloys containing 6 per cent copper have a tensile strength of almost 50,000 psi and a yield strength close to 40,000 psi; corresponding values for a wrought alloy of the same composition are approximately 60,000 and 40,000 psi, respectively. The per cent elongation in 2 in. for sand-cast alloys decreases from about 40 to 5 per cent as the copper content is increased from 0 to 6 per cent, and under the same conditions the elongation of wrought alloys decreases from 40 to about 20 per cent. Additions of copper to aluminum increase the density, reduce the electrical and thermal conductivities, and, when present in the usual amounts, decrease the coefficient of thermal expansion. Additions of copper in excess of ¼ per cent have an adverse effect on the corrosion-resistant properties of aluminum.

9. Aluminum-Silicon Alloys. Aluminum alloys containing from 5 to 13 per cent silicon are important because their excellent casting qualities, including excellent fluidity and freedom from hot shortness, permit the pouring of thin intricate sections. They also have high resistance to corrosion, are good conductors of electricity and heat, and have low thermal expansion.

The mechanical properties of these alloys are not exceptional. The properties of chill-cast test bars made with variable silicon contents are shown in Fig. 1, and the properties of hard-rolled and annealed aluminum-silicon sheets 0.08 in. thick are shown in Fig. 2. The modulus of elasticity apparently varies between 10,000,000 and 11,000,000 psi as the silicon content increases from 5 to 13 per cent. The yield strength of these alloys is also somewhat dependent on the silicon content, but 10,000 psi may be taken as an average value. The endurance limit for cast aluminum-silicon alloys appears to be in the range of 6000 to 9000 psi.

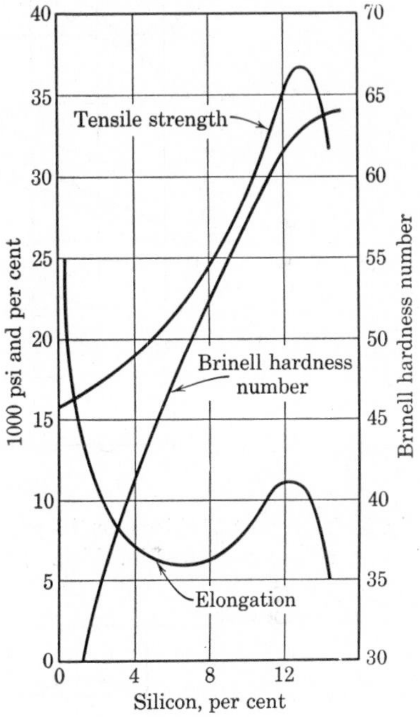

10. Aluminum-Magnesium Alloys. The sand- or die-cast alloys usually contain between 3.8 and 10 per cent magnesium. Those with magnesium contents of 8 to 10 per cent have strengths and ductilities that are among the best obtainable with present cast aluminum alloys. Wrought aluminum-magnesium alloys contain less than 6 per cent magnesium because higher amounts make the reduction of cast ingots difficult. Both the cast and the wrought alloys have good mechanical properties, excellent corrosion resistance, a high strength-weight ratio, and excellent machinability.

The effect of magnesium on the properties of sand-cast aluminum-magnesium alloys is shown in Fig. 3. The curves in Fig. 4 were obtained from tests of solution heat-treated alloys, and a comparison of the curves in the two figures shows the pronounced effect of heat treatment on alloys

Fig. 1.   The effect of silicon on the properties of chill-cast test bars of aluminum-silicon alloys. (From *Metals Handbook,* 1948, p. 805.)

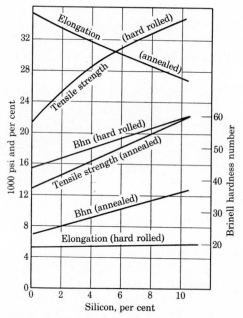

Fig. 2.   The effect of silicon on the properties of hard-rolled and annealed aluminum-
silicon sheet 0.08 in. thick.   (From *Metals Handbook,* 1948, p. 805.)

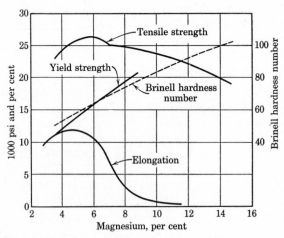

Fig. 3.   The effect of magnesium on the properties of sand-cast aluminum-magnesium
alloys.   (From *Metals Handbook,* 1948, p. 807.)

containing more than 6 per cent magnesium. The effect of magnesium
on the properties of wrought alloys is shown in Fig. 5, and the effect of
elevated temperatures on the properties of alloys containing 4 and 10 per
cent of magnesium is shown in Fig. 6 and 7.

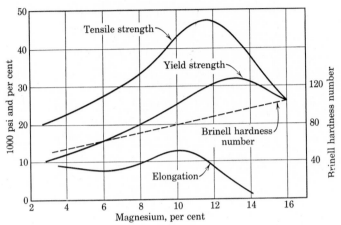

Fig. 4.   The effect of magnesium on the properties of heat-treated sand-cast aluminum-magnesium alloys. (From *Metals Handbook*, 1948, p. 807.)

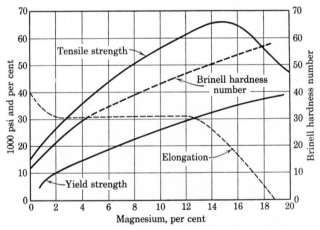

Fig. 5.   The effect of magnesium on the properties of wrought aluminum-magnesium
alloys. (From *Metals Handbook*, 1948, p. 807.)

11. Structural Aluminum Alloys. Although the tensile strength of the
strongest wrought-aluminum alloy is only 90,000 psi, these alloys are
important because of their high strength-weight ratios and their resistance
to atmospheric corrosion. In contrast to the weight of steel, 490 lb per
cu ft, the aluminum alloys weigh only 175 lb per cu ft, or approximately

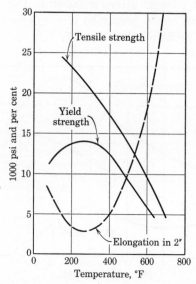

Fig. 6. The effect of high temperatures on the properties of aluminum-magnesium sand-cast specimens (4 per cent magnesium). (From *Metals Handbook,* 1948, p. 808.)

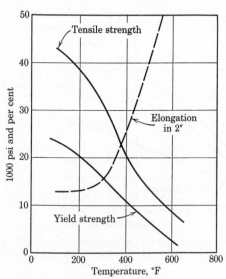

Fig. 7. The effect of high temperatures on the properties of aluminum-magnesium sand-cast specimens (10 per cent magnesium). (From *Metals Handbook,* 1948, p. 808.)

one-tenth of a pound per cu in. The modulus of elasticity is low in comparison and is fairly constant at 10,300,000 psi.

In the system of nomenclature used in the aluminum industry, each cast alloy is assigned a number and the composition of the alloy is specified as in Table 3. Wrought alloys are assigned a number followed by the letter S. The mechanical and/or the heat treatment that the alloy is subjected to is indicated by the letters and numbers that follow the numbers and letters designating composition. In outline form this system is given herewith.

TABLE 3. NOMINAL COMPOSITIONS OF TYPICAL HIGH-STRENGTH ALUMINUM ALLOYS

Alloy Number	Manufacture	Essential Alloying Elements, per cent					
		Cu	Si	Mn	Mg	Cr	Zn
195	Sand cast	4.5					
B195	Permanent-mold cast	4.5	2.5				
218	Die cast				8.0		
220	Sand cast				10.0		
356	Sand and permanent-mold cast		7.0		0.3		
14S	Wrought	4.4	0.8	0.8	0.4		
17S	Wrought	4.0		0.5	0.5		
24S	Wrought	4.5		0.6	1.5		
52S	Wrought				2.5	0.25	
61S	Wrought	0.25	0.6		1.0	0.25	
75S	Wrought	1.5		0.20	2.5	0.30	5.5

F   as fabricated.
O   annealed, recrystallized (wrought products only).
H   strain hardened.
H1   strain hardened only.
H2   strain hardened and then partially annealed.
H3   strain hardened and then stabilized.

(H1, H2, H3 may be followed by additional numbers designating amount of strain hardening.)

W   solution heat treated, unstable temper.
T   treated to produce stable tempers other than F, O, or H.
T2   annealed (cast products only).
T3   solution heat treated and then cold worked.
T4   solution heat treated.
T5   artificially aged only.
T6   solution heat treated, then artificially aged.
T7   solution heat treated, then stabilized.
T8   solution heat treated, cold worked, artificially aged.
T9   solution heat treated, artificially aged, cold worked.
T10   artificially aged and then cold worked.

(Special treatments are designated by adding an additional number after the appropriate T designation)

The nominal compositions of typical high-strength aluminum alloys are given in Table 3. An important group of alloys known as Duralumin contains 3.5 to 4.5 per cent copper, 0.20 to 0.75 per cent magnesium, 0.40 to 1.0 per cent manganese, and over 92 per cent aluminum. Mechanical

TABLE 4. TYPICAL MECHANICAL PROPERTIES OF HIGH-STRENGTH CAST-ALUMINUM ALLOYS

(Based on data compiled by the Aluminum Co. of America)

Alloy and Temper	Tensile Strength, psi	Yield Strength, at 0.2% Off-set, psi	Elongation in 2″ (½″-diam-eter speci-men), per cent	Brinell Hardness Number	Shear Strength, psi	Endur-ance Limit,[1] psi	Compressive Yield Strength, psi
195—T4	32,000	16,000	8.5	60	24,000	6,000	16,000
195—T6	36,000	24,000	5.0	75	30,000	6,500	25,000
195—T62	40,000	30,000	2.0	95	31,000	7,000	38,000
B195—T4	40,000	22,000	10.0	75	30,000	9,500	22,000
B195—T6	45,000	33,000	5.0	90	32,000	10,000	33,000
B195—T7	39,000	20,000	4.5	80	......	......	......
218	42,000	23,000	...	..	......	18,000	......
220—T4	46,000	25,000	14.0	75	33,000	7,000	26,000
356—T6 [2]	35,000	25,000	2.5	80	30,000	......	37,000
356—T7 [2]	38,000	36,000	0.5	85	26,000	8,500	35,000
356—T6 [3]	43,000	27,000	4.0	90	30,000	9,000	26,000
356—T7 [3]	40,000	30,000	2.0	85	30,000	......	......

[1] Based on 500,000,000 cycles using R. R. Moore type of rotating beam machine.
[2] Sand cast.
[3] Permanent mold cast.

properties of high-strength cast alloys are given in Table 4, and values for wrought alloys are given in Table 5.

Although aluminum alloys are generally quite resistant to corrosion, additional protection may be necessary to protect thin sheets exposed to severe corrosion. Additional protection may be obtained by painting the surface or by coating it with a thin layer of pure aluminum (as in the Alclad alloys) produced by an electrochemical method. The tensile and yield strengths, as well as the elongation values, are slightly lower for the Alclad alloys than for the same alloys without any Alclad coating.

Each aluminum alloy has certain individual characteristics that suggest specific uses. Recommended uses for each alloy are provided by the Aluminum Co. of America and other manufacturers. A general listing of the typical uses of the cast alloys given in Table 4 would include machine bases, crane trucks, flywheel housings, bus and aircraft wheels, railroad-car frames, automobile transmission cases, water-cooled cylinder blocks, and fuel-pump bodies. A similar listing for the wrought alloys given in Table 5 would include hardware, structural members for aircraft and railroad cars, structural members for construction purposes, heavy-duty forgings, aircraft fuel lines and tanks, aircraft landing mats, pontoon boats, and canoes.

TABLE 5. TYPICAL MECHANICAL PROPERTIES OF HIGH-STRENGTH
WROUGHT-ALUMINUM ALLOYS

(Based on data compiled by the Aluminum Co. of America)

Alloy and Temper	Tensile Strength, psi	Yield Strength [1] at 0.2% Offset, psi	Elongation in 2" (½"-diameter specimen), per cent	Brinell Hardness Number	Shear Strength, psi	Endurance Limit,[2] psi
14S—O	27,000	14,000	18	45	18,000	11,000
14S—T4	56,000	40,000	25	100	34,000	18,000
14S—T6	70,000	60,000	13	135	42,000	18,000
17S—O	26,000	10,000	22	45	18,000	11,000
17S—T4	62,000	40,000	22	105	38,000	18,000
24S—O	27,000	11,000	22	42	18,000	12,000
24S—T4	68,000	46,000	22	120	41,000	18,000
24S—T36	73,000	57,000	..	130	42,000	......
52S—O	29,000	14,000	30	45	18,000	17,000
52S—H32	34,000	26,000	18	62	20,000	17,500
52S—H34	37,000	29,000	14	67	21,000	18,000
52S—H36	39,000	34,000	10	74	23,000	18,500
52S—H38	41,000	36,000	8	85	24,000	19,000
61S—O	18,000	8,000	30	30	12,500	9,000
61S—T4	35,000	21,000	28	65	24,000	13,500
61S—T6	45,000	40,000	15	95	30,000	13,500
75S—O	33,000	15,000	12	...	......	......
75S—T6	82,000	72,000	10	150	47,000	22,500

[1] The compressive yield strength is approximately the same as the tensile yield strength.

[2] Based on 500,000,000 cycles using R. R. Moore type rotating beam machine.

COPPER AND ITS ALLOYS

12. Production of Copper. Copper ores are among the most widely disseminated. Valuable deposits are found in the United States, in nearly all countries of continental Europe, in Japan, Chile, Mexico, Canada, Spain, Peru, Australia, and Africa. The states which lead in the production of smelted copper are: Arizona, Utah, Montana, Nevada, Michigan, and New Mexico.

In general, copper ores carry a much larger proportion of earthy material than the ores of iron and rarely contain more than 10 or 15 per cent of copper. The three principal groups of copper-bearing ores in order of importance are: the sulfides, native copper, and the oxidized ores. Among the sulfides *chalcopyrite* ($CuFeS_2$, 34.5 per cent copper) and *chalcocite* or *copper glance* (Cu_2S, 79.8 per cent copper) are the chief minerals. Native copper is very extensively mined in northern Michigan; it is also found in New Mexico, Peru, and China. In the Michigan deposits, native copper is found scattered through the lodes in particles of widely varying size. It constitutes up to 4 per cent of the ore mined and is generally very pure, although occasionally contaminated with arsenic; it is often called "Lake" copper. The oxidized ores are derivatives of the sulfides which have been broken down by the action of air and water. The more important are: *cuprite,* the red oxide of copper (Cu_2O, 88.8 per cent copper), and the green carbonate, *malachite* ($CuCO_3 + Cu(OH)_2$, 57.3 per cent copper).

Nearly all copper is extracted by smelting; a small proportion is derived by wet methods in which the copper is withdrawn from the ore in the form of a sulfate or chloride. The oxidized ores are readily smelted in a special type of blast furnace using coke as fuel. Lake copper ores are first concentrated to form a mineral containing 70 per cent or more copper, which is then smelted in a reverberatory furnace. The sulfides, however, require a more complicated treatment, since it is not possible to reduce them directly to metallic copper. Smelting of the sulfide ores is commonly done as follows: The coarse lumpy ore is smelted in a blast furnace with or without previous roasting of a whole or part of the ore charged. The fine portions are usually roasted in reverberatory furnaces. These operations serve to concentrate the copper of the ore into a matte consisting principally of copper and iron sulfides with more or less of the sulfides of nickel, zinc, silver, and lead. Removal of the major portion of the iron and sulfur compounds is effected by placing the molten matte in a converter and oxidizing it with an air blast which enters just above the bath. After the smelting operation the crude copper ("blister copper") is cast into small pigs.

Refining of the crude copper may be accomplished by melting in a reverberatory furnace, or electrolytically. Refining in the reverberatory furnace is brought about by further oxidation of sulfides and by the cleansing action exerted by cuprous oxide on the base metals in the crude copper, the oxide being formed by air blown upon the molten bath. Since a large excess or a deficiency of cuprous oxide in the copper will make it weak and brittle it is necessary to remove any excess which remains after the impurities have been skimmed off. This is accomplished by additions of charcoal and green wood to the bath until the fracture of test ingots presents a flat salmon-red surface of silky texture. The copper is then at "tough pitch" and is ready for casting. Fire refining is used to give crude copper the malleability, ductility, and toughness essential in plates, tubes, and wires. It is also used to refine copper for alloys and to partially refine metal for anodes in the electrolytic process.

Electrolytic refining is used when an especially pure grade is wanted for electrical purposes, also when there is a considerable quantity of gold or silver associated with the crude copper. It is accomplished by passing a current through a copper sulfate solution from an anode consisting of crude copper, or partially refined copper, to a cathode of pure copper. By this method pure copper from the anode is plated upon the cathode and the precious metals settle to the bottom of the bath.

13. Properties and Uses of Copper. Copper possesses high resistance to atmospheric corrosion, has the highest electrical conductivity of all the common metals, is an excellent conductor of heat, is very malleable, and has a high damping capacity. Its specific weight is 560 lb per cu ft, it melts at 1083°C, its coefficient of thermal expansion is 0.0000165 per °C, its thermal conductivity is 0.941 cal/sq cm/cm/°C/sec, and its coefficient of electrical resistivity at 20°C is about 0.15 ohm per meter-gram.

The mechanical properties of copper depend on the mechanical and heat treatments that have been used. Annealed copper has a tensile strength between 30,000 and 35,000 psi and an elongation in 2 in. of 50 to 60 per cent. Hard-drawn high-purity copper may have a tensile strength as high as 70,000 psi and an elongation of about 5 per cent. The modulus of elasticity of hard-drawn copper wire generally varies between 14,-000,000 and 17,000,000 psi.

The combined effects of mechanical and heat treatment on strength and ductility are well illustrated in the process of wire drawing. The strength of hard-drawn copper wire varies from 50,000 psi for wire 0.50 in. in diameter to 70,000 psi for wire 0.05 in. in diameter, and the elongation decreases from approximately 4 per cent for the larger wire to 1 per cent for the smaller. When annealed, wires of the above sizes have a strength of 35,000 to 40,000 psi and elongations of 35 to 25 per cent. They are stronger but less ductile in the smaller sizes. Hard-drawn copper wires may be annealed by heating to some temperature in the range from 700° to 1200°F. Rapid cooling does not interfere with softening of the metal, but repeated alternations of overstrain and annealing at high temperatures cause a marked increase in grain size.

The strength of copper wire may be increased by additions of alloying elements, but such additions greatly reduce the conductivity. Additions of 0.5 to 1.0 per cent of cadmium, however, are effective in increasing strength with only a moderate decrease in conductivity.

About 50 per cent of the copper produced in the United States is used for electrical purposes. A large portion of the remainder is used in making brasses and bronzes, and the rest is used for such purposes as roofing, sheeting, pipes, tubing, and hardware.

14. Compositions of Copper Alloys. The alloying elements most frequently used with copper are zinc, tin, and lead, and considerable use is also made of copper alloys containing aluminum, nickel, manganese, beryllium, and iron. Both cast and wrought alloys are used. Most of the alloys are classed as brasses or bronzes, as shown in Tables 6 and 7.

Brasses are alloys consisting chiefly of copper and 5 to 40 per cent zinc. They may contain in addition significant amounts of other elements. However, as may be noted from Tables 6 and 7, several alloys that are true brasses are commonly called bronzes, as, for example, commercial bronze and manganese bronze. Brasses containing up to 35 per cent zinc exist as a single-phase solid solution known as α brass, as shown by the constitution diagram, Fig. XXIX-1. Alloys containing from 35 to 39 per cent zinc may have a duplex structure at high temperatures and should have a single-phase structure at room temperatures, but the structure is generally complex because rapid cooling rates do not allow establishment of equilibrium conditions.

TABLE 6.   TYPICAL COMPOSITIONS OF CAST-COPPER ALLOYS

Nominal Composition, per cent

Name	Cu	Zn	Sn	Pb	Ni	Al	Fe	Mn
			Brasses					
Composition metal	85	5	5	5				
Leaded red brass	83	7	4	6				
Leaded semi-red brass	80	9	3	7				
Leaded yellow brass	71	25	1	3				
Leaded yellow brass	60	38	1	1				
High-strength yellow brass	62	26				5½	3	3½
Leaded manganese bronze	59	37	¾	¾		¾	1¼	½
Nickel silver	64	8	4	4	20			
			Bronzes					
Leaded tin bronze	88	4½	6	1½				
High-leaded tin bronze	85	1	5	9				
High-leaded tin bronze	70		5	25				
Aluminum bronze	89					10	1	
Aluminum bronze	79				5	11	5	
Zinc bronze [1]	88	2	10					

[1] Also known as government bronze or gun metal.

Many of the bronzes are solid-solution alloys of copper and contain from 1.25 to 10 per cent tin. They are α-phase alloys, as shown in the constitution diagram, Fig. XXIX-5. The Phosphor bronzes have the same basic composition, but in addition have enough phosphorus to remove oxygen during smelting. The tin bronzes may also contain appreciable percentages of zinc and lead. The silicon bronzes contain up to 3 per cent silicon and are single solid solutions of copper and silicon. Two types of aluminum bronzes are used. The first type may have aluminum contents as high as 7½ per cent which are completely soluble in copper. These alloys cannot be strengthened by heat treatment. In the second type the aluminum content is usually between 9.5 and 10 per cent, and a two-phase structure is obtained. The properties of these alloys may be improved by heat treatment.

15. Manufacture of Copper Alloys. The types and sizes of melting equipment used in the production of copper alloy castings are quite variable. The indirect-arc and induction-type electric furnaces and the direct flame gas or oil furnaces are widely used. In the production of cast alloys the liquid metal is usually poured into sand molds because they can be adapted to a wide variety of designs and sizes and because they provide the cheapest method of obtaining the desired product. A shrinkage allowance of about 3/16 in. per ft is required in casting copper alloys. The pouring temperature must be closely controlled if sound

TABLE 7.   TYPICAL COMPOSITIONS OF WROUGHT-COPPER ALLOYS

Nominal Composition, per cent

Name	Cu	Zn	Sn	Pb	Ni	Al	Si	Fe	Mn
				Brasses					
Gilding metal	95	5							
Commercial bronze	90	10							
Red brass	85	15							
Low brass	80	20							
Cartridge brass	70	30							
Yellow brass	65	35							
Muntz metal	60	40							
Low-leaded brass	64½	35		½					
High-leaded brass	62½	35¾		1¾					
Admiralty metal	71	28	1						
Naval brass	60	39¼	¾						
Manganese bronze	58½	39	1					1.4	0.1
Nickel silver	65	17			18				
				Bronzes					
Phosphor bronze	90		10						
Phosphor bronze	98¾		1¼						
Silicon bronze [1]	98						1.5		
Aluminum bronze	95					5			
Aluminum bronze	90					10			
				Miscellaneous Alloys					
Cupro nickel	70				30				
Copper beryllium	97½ (plus 2% Be and 0.25% Co or 0.35% Ni)								

[1] Also contains some manganese, iron, tin.

castings are to be produced. In addition to sand casting, other important methods of casting copper alloys include permanent mold casting, die casting, centrifugal casting, plaster of Paris casting, and casting into a one-piece refractory mold made of refractory cements, known as pre-cision-investment casting. The permanent molds used are usually made of fine-grained gray cast iron. Before use, these molds are heated and coated with a paint that consists of a refractory material, a binder, and a lubricant. After casting, the products are generaly subjected to a variety of surface cleaning, polishing, and protection treatments.

Wrought-copper alloys are first cast into slabs, cakes, bars, billets, and rods. These intermediate products may be hot or cold worked into final form. Hot working at temperatures above the recrystallization tem-perature refines the grain structure and forms the required end product. The hot-working methods used on coper alloys include rolling, extruding, forging, pressing, piercing, and forming.

Cold working copper alloys increases their density and strength and decreases ductility. Roughly a 30 per cent reduction in area will produce a 50 per cent increase in strength, and the elongation will be decreased to about 20 per cent of the value for annealed metal. It is therefore necessary to anneal copper alloys after certain amounts of reduction to avoid failure during fabrication. A wide variety of cold-working methods are available for producing flat products, rods, wires, tubes, cups, and shells. Some of the more important methods used for cold working are rolling, punching, drawing, extruding, flattening, shearing, blanking, stamping, coining, cupping, spinning, and heading.

Copper alloys may be joined by carbon arc welding, metal arc welding, resistance welding, gas welding, and also by soldering and brazing.

16. Heat Treatment of Copper Alloys. Copper and its alloys may be heat treated in different ways to obtain desired properties. A homogenizing treatment may be employed to eliminate segregation by equalizing the chemical composition throughout the metal. With the plain and leaded brasses the temperatures employed in process annealing are usually high enough to produce diffusion and subsequent homogenization. The bronzes and nickel silvers require higher temperatures and prolonged heating periods for homogenization. Temperatures between 1100° and 1450°F are required for high-tin bronzes.

In order that copper and its alloys may be easily hot worked they are heated to some temperature between the recrystallization and the melting temperatures. The temperature range over which these alloys remain plastic varies with the specific alloy, but most alloys are workable in some temperature range between 1150° and 1650°F.

The process of heating a cold-worked metal to the temperature at which it will recrystallize for the purpose of restoring ductility is known as annealing. This treatment, which is necessary for further cold work after a metal has lost most of its ductility, depends on such factors as alloy composition, the amount of the previous cold work, the additional cold working required, and the thickness of the metal. The heating and cooling rates are unimportant except for the alloys that can be precipitation hardened. Temperatures higher than that necessary for complete recrystallization cause an increase in grain growth and ductility and a decrease in strength and hardness. In the usual fabrication process higher annealing temperatures are used initially, since they provide more complete homogenization and because the relatively large grains allow easier and more economical reduction. Lower annealing temperatures, with resultant finer grains, are used at the end of the fabrication process. Annealing temperatures for copper and its alloys are usually within the temperature range of 700° to 1350°F.

Non-uniform plastic deformation below the recrystallization temperature will produce residual stresses. Such metals in service at atmospheric temperatures are susceptible to season cracking (Art. 17). One method of reducing the possibility of season cracking is to heat the metal to a temperature about 100° to 200°F lower than the recrystallization temperature. Thermal stress relief at temperatures as low as possible for periods as long as possible appears to give the best results. The thermal stress relief treatment is usually performed on finished parts.

Certain copper alloys, such as those containing beryllium or chromium, may be solution and precipitation heat treated. The solution heat treatment consists of heating the alloy to a temperature high enough to obtain a single solid solution and then cooling rapidly to obtain a supersaturated condition. In this condition the alloy has high ductility and low hardness and strength. If the solution heat treatment is followed by a second heat treatment at a lower temperature, the unstable constituents will precipitate and the strength and hardness will increase while the ductility will decrease. This precipitation-hardening temperature for beryllium copper is between 625° and 700°F. The exact temperature used depends on the time that the alloy is kept at the temperature. Cold work in addition to the heat treatment may follow the solution heat treatment or may take place after the precipitation-hardening treatment.

17. Season Cracking and Special Tests. Spontaneous cracking of stressed copper alloys in service at room temperatures is known as season cracking. Although all copper alloys are apparently susceptible, the alloys containing between 20 and 40 per cent zinc are most liable to this type of cracking. It is most frequent in drawn rods, tubes, and hollow products.

Two factors causing season cracking are stress and corrosion. The stress results from fabrication procedures, service loading, strain hardening, and non-uniform cooling. The tendency to season crack appears to be related to the magnitude of the stress. Ammonia and its derivatives appear to be the important corrosive reagents that cause stressed copper alloys to crack. Other reagents, such as carbon dioxide, apparently accelerate the rate of cracking caused by ammonia and its derivatives.

Several methods of detecting the tendency of copper alloys to season cracking are available. One test consists of immersing the product in an acidified aqueous solution of mercurous nitrate for a given period of time and then noting whether cracks have formed. This test is not entirely reliable, but, if the product can withstand immersion for 15 min successfully, its susceptibility to season cracking is low. Another method involved the determination of stresses in the metal by evaluating dimensional changes that take place as small successive sections of metal are removed. Investigators have used rod- or tube-, split-ring-, sheet-, and bar-type specimens. Exposure to gaseous atmospheres of ammonia and X-ray diffraction techniques are also used.

The cupping test is used to determine the ductility and drawing qualities of thin sheet metal, especially brass. The test is made on a small sample of metal supported between a die and annular holder. A round-nosed tool is gradually forced against the specimen and forms it into a cup, as shown in Fig. 8. By determining the depth of the cup at fracture, a direct measure of the drawing quality of the metal is obtained.

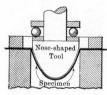

Fig. 8. Arrangement of specimen, tool, and dies on Erichsen Cupping Machine. (*Proc ASTM*, Vol. 17, Pl. 2, p. 200.)

In order to eliminate the possibility of season cracking it is necessary to eliminate the stress in the metal or to eliminate the corrosive factor. In service conditions it is not generally possible to eliminate these factors, but it may be possible to reduce them to the point where they will no longer cause season cracking.

Elimination of residual and assembly stresses may be accomplished as described in Art. 16. Residual stresses may also be reduced by various methods of working, such as stretching, flexing, bending, straightening, and shot blasting.

18. Mechanical Properties of Cast and Wrought Brasses. Because of the wide variation in the compositions of brasses, a wide range in mechanical properties is available. The properties of the cast brasses are not exceptional and usually fall within the following ranges: ultimate tensile strength, 30,000 to 45,000 psi; yield strength at 0.5 per cent offset, 13,000 to 25,000 psi; elongation in 2 in., 15 to 35 per cent; and reduction in area, 15 to 35 per cent. The properties of manganese bronze and the high-strength yellow brasses are better. Sand-cast high-strength yellow brass may have a tensile strength of 115,000 psi, a yield strength of 70,000 psi, and an elongation in 2 in. and reduction in area of about 15 per cent.

The effect of composition on the tensile properties of annealed and cold-worked brass is given in Fig. 9. The tensile strength of the cold-worked alloys increases as the zinc content is increased to around 30 per cent. Annealed alloys show an increase in strength up to 40 per cent zinc. The elongation of the annealed alloys appears to be a maximum for alloys having a zinc content of 30 per cent; the elongation of all cold-worked alloys is usually under 5 per cent and is largely independent of the composition.

Because of the importance of certain classes of brasses, additional information on properties and uses of these alloys is given. *Muntz metal,* an alloy of 60 per cent copper and 40 per cent zinc, is used in the wrought state. It has when annealed a tensile strength of 54,000 psi and a yield strength of 21,000 psi. Cold-rolled sheet of Muntz metal has corresponding values of 80,000 and 57,000 psi. This alloy is used for hot forgings, valve stems, condenser plates, brazing rod, and heat-exchanger tubing.

The tensile strength of cast manganese bronze ranges from 70,000 to 80,000 psi with an elastic limit of about one-third the ultimate strength. The elongation in 2 in. generally lies between 20 and 30 per cent. In

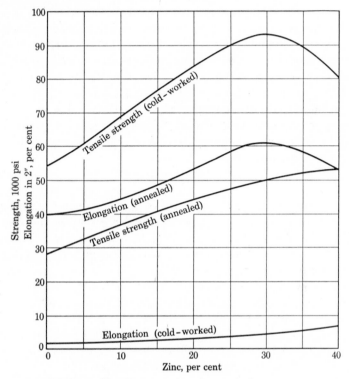

Fig. 9. Tensile properties of wrought brasses.

rolled or forged form the strength is slightly increased, its elastic limit raised to 30,000 or 40,000 psi, and the elongation in 2 in. is raised to 30 or 40 per cent. In compression the strength runs from about 90,000 psi for castings to 150,000 psi for rolled or forged parts. The modulus of elasticity of manganese bronze is about 16,000,000 psi.

On account of its high strength, the facility with which it may be forged or rolled, and its resistance to corrosion and salt water, manganese bronze is used considerably in marine engine parts, for hydraulic rams, cylinders, valve stems, propeller blades and bolts, and condenser tubes. Wrought manganese bronze parts are subject to season cracking and should always be annealed.

Naval brass is used for similar purposes and is much like manganese bronze in composition but lacks manganese and iron. It is slightly weaker and more ductile than manganese bronze. The tenacity in wrought form ranges from 55,000 to 70,000 psi with an elongation in 2 in. of 30 to 45 per cent. Naval brass is also subject to season cracking and should be annealed when used in wrought form.

Wrought leaded brass consists of 60 to 67 per cent copper, 32 to 38 per cent zinc, and 0.5 to 3.0 per cent lead. The metal is sold as low, medium, high, or extra-high leaded brass in accordance with the lead content. The ultimate tensile strength of annealed leaded brass is about 49,000 psi, the yield strength at a deformation of 0.5 per cent varies between 15,000 and 18,000 psi, and the elongation in 2 in. varies between 50 and 60 per cent. In the hard condition the ultimate tensile strength is about 75,000 psi, the yield strength about 60,000 psi, and the elongation in 2 in. varies between 5 and 10 per cent. The modulus of elasticity of these brasses is about 15,000,000 psi. These brasses are used for hardware, clock gears and wheels, nuts, and screws.

Cast leaded brass usually contains between 60 and 85 per cent copper, 1 to 5 per cent tin, 5 to 38 per cent zinc, and 1 to 7 per cent lead. The sand-cast tensile strengths vary between 32,000 and 40,000 psi, the yield strengths at an elongation of 0.5 per cent under load between 12,000 and 15,000 psi, the elongations between 20 and 30 per cent, and the modulus of elasticity between 12,000,000 and 14,000,000 psi. The cast leaded brasses are used for such items as plumbing supplies and fittings, hardware, ornamental castings, and low-pressure valves and fittings.

Nickel silver wrought alloys contain 55 to 65 per cent copper, 18 to 27 per cent zinc, and about 18 per cent nickel. Annealed flat products have ultimate tensile strengths between 55,000 and 60,000 psi, yield strengths between 25,000 and 30,000 psi, and an elongation of about 40 per cent. The modulus of elasticity is equal to 18,000,000 psi. In the hard condition the ultimate strength varies between 85,000 and 100,000 psi, the yield strength varies between 75,000 and 85,000 psi, and the elongation is around 3 per cent. The cast nickel silvers contain from 57 to 66 per cent copper, 2 to 20 per cent zinc, 12 to 25 per cent nickel, 1.5 to 9 per cent lead, and 2 to 4 per cent tin. The properties of the sand-cast alloys are somewhat inferior to those of the annealed wrought alloys given above.

19. Mechanical Properties of Cast and Wrought Bronzes. The Phosphor bronzes are true bronzes, since they are alloys of copper and tin. All the other alloys designated as bronzes contain copper, may or may not contain some tin, and contain other important alloying elements. The tin content of the Phosphor bronzes varies between 1 and 10 per cent, and it may be noted from Fig. 5, Chapter XXIX, that these alloys are all α-phase alloys.

The strength properties of the Phosphor bronzes are increased as the tin content is increased. Annealed sheet Phosphor bronze with 5 per cent tin has an average ultimate strength of 47,000 psi and a yield strength of 20,000 psi; similar values for a Phosphor bronze with 10 per cent tin are 65,000 and 28,000 psi. The elongation in 2 in. varies between 65 and 70 per cent for the annealed grades of Phosphor bronze. The ultimate tensile strength of hard sheet Phosphor bronze alloys increases from 80,000 to 100,000 psi as the tin content is increased from 5 to 10 per cent, and the elongation of these alloys is about 10 per cent. The modulus of elasticity for the Phosphor bronze alloys is about 16,000,000 psi. These alloys are used for such items as bridge bearing plates, Bourdon tubing, chemical hardware, springs, and textile machinery.

The *cast leaded tin bronzes* usually contain from 78 to 88 per cent copper, 5 to 10 per cent tin, 1 to 15 per cent lead, and ¾ to 5 per cent zinc. In a sand-cast condition their ultimate tensile strengths vary between 30,000 and 38,000 psi, their yield strengths at 0.5 per cent elongation under load from 15,000 to 18,000 psi, their elongations from 12 to 35 per cent, and their moduli of elasticity from 13,000,000 to 14,500,000 psi. These alloys are used for bearings, valves, pipe fittings, bushings, and automotive fittings. Alloys with low lead contents (1½ per cent) are used as high-duty bearings where wear resistance and medium to heavy pressures are required, also for steam or valve bodies for use at temperatures up to 550°F. The alloy, consisting of 87 per cent copper, 8 per cent tin, 1 per cent lead, and 4 per cent zinc, is used for high-pressure bearing bushings which are to be used against hardened steel. An alloy used for high-speed heavy-pressure bearings consists of 80 per cent copper, 10 per cent tin, 10 per cent lead, and less than 1 per cent zinc. Bearings for light loads and high-speed operation consist of 70 per cent copper, 5 per cent tin, 25 per cent lead, and less than 1 per cent zinc.

Wrought aluminum bronze alloys contain from 82 to 95 per cent copper, 5 to 10 per cent aluminum, and may also contain some nickel or iron. The cast alloys contain from 79 to 89 per cent copper, 9 to 11 per cent aluminum, 1 to 5 per cent iron, and may also contain some nickel. Aluminum bronze alloys containing up to about 7½ per cent aluminum are solid solutions of aluminum in copper, as may be seen from the constitution diagram, Fig. XXIX-7. These alloys cannot be strengthened by heat-treating processes. Alloys containing more than about 9½ per cent aluminum have a two-phase structure, and these alloys may be quenched and tempered to obtain desired properties.

The ductility of aluminum bronzes remains high, 60 to 70 per cent elongation in 2 in., for alloys having aluminum contents up to about 8 per cent, and then drops sharply. Increasing the aluminum content up to about 10 per cent causes increases in the ultimate and yield tensile strengths. The modulus of elasticity for these alloys is between 15,000,000 and 16,000,000 psi.

Wrought-aluminum bronzes containing 10 per cent aluminum have, in the annealed condition, tensile strengths of 75,000 to 85,000 psi, yield strengths of 35,000 to 45,000 psi, and an elongation in 2 in. of 20 to 25 per cent. The same alloy in a hard-rolled condition may have corresponding values of 120,000 to 135,000 psi, 105,000 to 120,000 psi, and 10 to 15 per cent. Cast-aluminum bronzes have tensile strengths of 65,000 to 90,000 psi, yield strengths of 20,000 to 40,000 psi, and elongations of 15 to 30 per cent. The same alloys when heat treated may have corresponding values of 90,000 to 105,000 psi, 50,000 to 80,000 psi, and 2 to 15 per cent.

The low-alloy α-type aluminum bronzes are used for cold-worked products, as strip, sheet, wire, and tubing. Alloys containing 10 per cent aluminum are used where corrosion resistance, heat resistance, and toughness are required, as in internal-combustion engine parts, marine pumps, bushings, pinions, and bearing plates.

Zinc bronze, or government bronze, is used for valves, fittings, gears, and generally where good strength is desired. This alloy has, when cast in sand molds, a strength of 35,000 to 45,000 psi, with a yield strength of 15,000 to 20,000 psi, and an elongation of 15 to 35 per cent. The ductility of this alloy may be improved by annealing for $\frac{1}{2}$ hour at 700° to 800°C.

The *silicon bronzes* contain between 1.5 and 3.0 per cent silicon and usually some additional alloying elements, such as manganese, iron, zinc, and nickel. The silicon bronzes are single solid solutions. These alloys are used in the wrought form for such purposes as hydraulic pressure lines, marine hardware, chemical equipment, and electrical conduit. Silicon bronzes containing 3 per cent silicon have tensile strengths between 50,000 and 60,000 psi, in the annealed condition, and between 110,000 and 140,000 psi in the hard condition. The corresponding ranges in elongation are 60 to 65 per cent and 3 to 10 per cent. The modulus of elasticity of the silicon bronzes is about 15,000,000 psi.

20. Copper-Beryllium Alloys. These alloys possess exceptional strength, good resistance to corrosion, fair electrical conductivity, and high wear resistance. They are used for springs, gears, electric contacts, bearings, and for non-sparking tools such as chisels and wrenches.

Copper-beryllium alloys contain about 2 per cent beryllium, and in some alloys additions of 0.35 per cent nickel or cobalt may be made to refine the grain structure. These alloys may be hot or cold worked, and respond to precipitation-hardening treatments. Hot-worked alloys are first solutionized by heating to a temperature between 1400° and 1475°F and then quenched in water. The alloys are frequently cold worked after solutionizing and before aging. Aging is carried out at a temperature of about 600°F for a period of 1 to 4 hours. These alloys do not age harden at room temperatures.

Unhardened copper-beryllium alloys have a tensile strength of about 70,000 psi, a yield strength of 30,000 psi, and an elongation in 2 in. of 45 per cent. After a combination of cold work and heat treatment, the tensile strength is about 200,000 psi, the yield strength is around 140,000 psi, and the elongation in 2 in. is about 2 per cent. The modulus of elasticity of the copper-beryllium alloys averages 18,000,000 psi. The Brinell hardness of the hardened alloys is around 350.

LEAD AND ITS ALLOYS

21. Production, Properties, and Uses of Lead. Nearly all lead is derived from ores containing lead sulfide, *galena* (PbS, 86.6 per cent lead). Lead carbonate, *cerussite* ($PbCO_3$), and lead sulfate, *anglesite* ($PbSO_4$), are formed by decomposition of galena and sometimes constitute the out-cropping portions of the galena ore deposits. Lead ores are comparatively lean, averaging in the United States about 5 to 6 per cent of lead. The United States, Mexico, Australia, and Canada normally produce about two-thirds of the world's supply of lead. Within the United States the chief sources of lead are Missouri, Idaho, Utah, Colorado, and Arizona.

The first step in the production of lead is a wet gravity concentration or flotation process by means of which concentrates containing between 40 and 60 per cent of lead are obtained. The lead concentrates are then roasted to convert the sulfides to oxides. The oxides are reduced in a blast furnace to produce a lead-base bullion that contains some gold, silver, and impurities such as antimony, arsenic, copper, and iron. The impurities are removed by an oxidation process, known as softening, carried out in reverberatory furnaces. The precious metals are usually removed by the Parkes desilvering process. In this process the zinc that is added to liquid lead bullion forms an alloy with the gold, silver, and some lead. This alloy rises to the top and is removed, after which the zinc in it is distilled out to leave an alloy rich in precious metals. The zinc left in the refined lead bath is removed by oxidation and skimming. Electrolytic refining processes are also used.

Lead has excellent casting characteristics and is cast into finished form by a wide variety of methods. Many different mold materials, such as sand, rubber, metal, wood, plaster, and papier-mâché, are used. Lead castings shrink about 5/16 in. per ft in cooling. Cast-lead slabs and billets may be rolled into sheet and foil. Extrusion processes are used to manufacture bars, pipe, and cable sheath. Impact extrusion is used in the manufacture of collapsible tubes. Lead parts may be joined by soldering or welding.

Lead has a blue-gray color and a dull metallic luster when freshly fractured. Exposure to moist air causes oxidation and loss of luster. Lead is so soft that it may be scratched with the finger nail and so malleable that it can be readily rolled into thin sheets and foil. It lacks ductility, however, and cannot be drawn into fine wire. It melts at approximately 620°F, weighs about 0.41 lb per cu in., and has a coefficient of thermal expansion of 0.0000293 per °C. The tensile strength of cast lead usually lies between 1500 and 2000 psi; in hard lead wire the strength may reach 3000 psi. The modulus of elasticity is about 2,000,000 psi, and Poisson's ratio varies between 0.40 and 0.45.

About 30 per cent of the lead produced in the United States is used in the manufacture of storage batteries, about 10 per cent is used for cable coverings, about 10 per cent for chemicals such as tetraethyl lead, and somewhat more than 10 per cent for pigments. Lead is also used for ammunition, bearing metal, solder, type metal, terne metal, and other products.

22. Lead-Tin Alloys. These alloys are principally used in making solder, pewter, toys, and for terne plating steel. The tin content for these alloys varies between 5 and 50 per cent. These alloys have rather low melting points, that of the eutectic containing 38.1 per cent lead being only 361°F. Furthermore, the alloys having more than 50 per cent lead remain pasty over a considerable range of temperature before completely solidifying. This property makes these alloys of value for plumber's solder, which ordinarily contains from 2 parts lead and 1 part tin to equal parts of each.

Additions of tin to lead increase the strength and hardness. An alloy consisting of 95 per cent lead and 5 per cent tin has a tensile strength around 3000 psi and a Brinell hardness number of 9; an alloy of 50 per cent lead and 50 per cent tin has corresponding values of 6000 psi and 15.

23. Lead-Antimony Alloys. Antimony, like tin, serves as a hardener when added to lead, but the useful binary alloys of these two metals cover only a limited range. These alloys, known as antimonial lead, hard lead, and grid material, contain from 1 to 15 per cent antimony and are used for such purposes as cable sheathing, rolled sheet, extruded pipe, and battery grids. The tensile strength of an alloy containing 97 per cent lead and 3 per cent antimony is about 5000 psi; the strength of an alloy having 90 per cent lead and 10 per cent antimony is 7500 psi.

24. Lead-Antimony-Tin Alloys. These alloys are widely used for lead-base bearing metals and type metals. The composition ranges for some of the representative alloys are given in Table 8.

TABLE 8.   REPRESENTATIVE COMPOSITIONS OF LEAD, ANTIMONY, AND TIN ALLOYS

| | Composition, per cent | | | |
Name of Metal	Lead	Antimony	Tin	Arsenic
Lead-base bearing metal	75–85	10–15	5–10	
Arsenical lead-base bearing metal	83–85	13–15	1	1–3
Electrotype metal	93–95	2–3	2–4	
Stereotype metal	77–81	13–15	6–8	
Linotype metal	84–86	11–12	3–5	
Monotype metal	64–78	15–24	7–12	

The modulus of elasticity of the lead-base bearing metals is 4,200,000 psi, the ultimate tensile strength is about 10,000 psi, and the percentage elongation is less than 5.

The actual strength properties of the type metals are of little concern, but these alloys must be easily melted and cast, they must take a full sharp impression of the mold, they must have sufficient strength to withstand press action, and they must be hard enough to have good wear resistance.

25. Fusible Alloys.   A wide variety of compositions are used to obtain alloys that melt at specific low temperatures.   They are frequently binary or ternary alloys of lead, tin, bismuth, and cadmium, as shown in Table 9. Considerable use of these alloys is made in automatic sprinkler seystems, fire alarms, and safety devices to prevent overheating.

TABLE 9.   REPRESENTATIVE COMPOSITIONS OF FUSIBLE ALLOYS

Melting Point, °F	Composition, per cent			
	Bismuth	Lead	Tin	Cadmium
520	100			
621		100		
449			100	
610				100
478		82.5		17.5
291	60			40
203	52	32	16	
158	50	26.7	13.3	40
117 [1]	44.7	22.6	8.3	5.3

[1] Also contains 19.1 per cent indium.

MAGNESIUM AND ITS ALLOYS

26. Production, Properties, and Uses of Magnesium.   Production of magnesium has been high during war years and low during the periods of peace. In 1943 the United States produced about 185,000 short tons of magnesium, about 70 per cent of the total world production, but the production in 1949 was only 12,000 short tons. There exists, however, a definite trend toward greater peacetime use of this metal.

Magnesium is produced by electrolysis of molten anhydrous magnesium chloride obtained from natural brines, sea water, dolomite, or magnesite. Thermal reduction of magnesium oxide by means of carbon or ferrosilicon, developed during World War II, is also used in the production of magnesium.

Pure magnesium is used in pyrotechnics, and as a deoxidizer for nickel, silver, and copper-base alloys. The most important use of magnesium is in the production of alloy products where good strength and low weight are required as in aircraft engine parts, landing wheels, and parts of the fuselage. Magnesium alloys are also used in the production of portable equipment such as pneumatic tools, lawn mowers, portable sewing machins, wheelbarrows, and typewriters.

The mechanical properties of pure magnesium metal are low in comparison with those obtained by alloying magnesium with aluminum, manganese, and zinc. Pure cast magnesium has a tensile strength of about 15,000 psi, a yield strength at an offset of 0.2 per cent of about 3000 psi, an elongation in 2 in. of 8 per cent, and a modulus of elasticity of 6,500,000 psi. The alloys of magnesium may have tensile strengths about two to three times as great, and yield strengths about five to ten times as great, but the modulus of elasticity is not appreciably changed, and the changes in per cent elongation are usually not as significant.

27. Structural Magnesium Alloys. Although less strong than the Duralumin alloys, the alloys of magnesium with 12 per cent or less of aluminum have a better strength-weight ratio than the Duralumins, owing to their extreme lightness. The magnesium alloys being relatively soft are the easiest of the commercial metals to machine. These alloys weigh about 112 lb per cu ft, or two-thirds as much as the Duralumins. Unfortunately the modulus of elasticity is low, only 6,500,000 psi, and the alloys are not so ductile or tough as the Duralumins. The coefficient of thermal expansion is 0.000016 per °F, or two and one-half times that of steel. Magnesium-base alloys have good resistance to inland atmospheres, but as a class are less resistant to saline waters or atmospheres than the Duralumins. When properly protected they can be used along the sea coast.

Data on compositions and mechanical properties of some of the more important magnesium-base alloys are given in Table 10. The typical properties are from publications of the Dow Chemical Co., which provide much additional information on these and on other alloys of this type.

The magnesium-base alloys can be cast or wrought into shape in much the same way as the Duralumins. Castings are improved in tenacity

TABLE 10 PROPERTIES OF MAGNESIUM-BASE ALLOYS [1]

ASTM Alloy Number	Dowmetal Alloy Number	Form	Condition [2]	Al	Zn	Mn	Ultimate	Yield [3]	Elongation in 2 in., per cent	Shear Strength, psi	Ultimate Bearing Strength, psi	Brinell Hardness Number	Fatigue Strength,[4] psi
							Tensile Strength, psi						
AZ92	C	Sand and permanent mold castings	AC	9.0	2.0	...	24,000	14,000	2	19,000	60,000	65	11,000
			ACS				24,000	14,000	2	19,000	60,000	...	14,000
			HT				40,000	14,000	10	20,000	75,000	63	13,000
			HTA				40,000	23,000	2	21,000	85,000	84	
AZ31X	FS-1	Sheet	a	3.0	1.0	...	37,000	22,000	21	21,000	75,000	56	12,000
		Sheet	h				42,000	32,000	16	23,000	78,000	73	14,000
		Sheet	r				37,000	22,000	21	21,000	75,000	...	...
		Extruded bars, rods,[5] and solid shapes	Extr.				37,000	26,000	12	19,000	65,000	49	14,000
		Extruded tubing	Extr.				35,000	23,000	12	...	...	46	...
AZ63	H	Sand and permanent mold castings	AC	6.0	3.0	...	29,000	14,000	6	18,000	65,000	50	11,000
			ACS				29,000	14,000	5	19,000	65,000	...	14,000
			HT				40,000	14,000	12	19,000	70,000	55	13,000
			HTA				40,000	19,000	5	21,000	80,000	73	
AZ61X	J-1	Extruded bars, rods [5]	Extr.	6.5	1.0	...	45,000	32,000	14	20,000	76,000	58	18,000
		Extruded solid shapes	Extr.				44,000	28,000	14	...	...	64	...
		Extruded tubing	Extr.				41,000	20,000	13	...	...	50	...
M1	N	Special sand castings	AC	...	...	1.2	14,000	4,500	5	11,000	...	33	9,000
		Sheet	a				33,000	18,000	16	18,000	60,000	48	10,000
		Sheet	h				37,000	28,000	7	...	...	56	...
		Sheet	r				33,000	...	...	...	...	...	...
		Extruded bars, rods,[5] and solid shapes	Extr.				34,000	20,000	9	18,000	56,000	44	9,000
		Extruded tubing	Extr.				32,000	20,000	6	...	...	42	...
AZ80X	O-1	Extruded bars, rods,[5] and solid shapes	Extr.	8.5	0.5	...	48,000	32,000	12	22,000	76,000	60	18,000
		Extruded tubing	HTA				52,000	36,000	5	24,000	90,000	82	19,000
AZ91	R	Die castings	AC	9.0	0.6	...	33,000	22,000	3	20,000	...	60	14,000

[1] Typical values from the publications of the Dow Chemical Co.

[2] Condition: a—annealed, h—hard rolled, r—hot rolled, AC—as cast, ACS—as cast and stabilized, Extr.—as extruded, HT—solution heat treated, HTA—solution heat treated and aged.

[3] Yield strength is defined as the stress at which the stress-strain curve deviates 0.2% from the modulus line.

[4] Based on 500 million cycles of completely reversed stress as determined on the R. R. Moore type of machine and specimen.

[5] The properties for bars, rods, and solid shapes apply to extrusions with a minimum dimension of ¼ to ½ inch.

and ductility by heat treating at temperatures in the vicinity of 700°F and cooling in air. The yield strength is raised by aging castings after treatment at temperatures near 350°F. However, aging reduces the ductility obtained after heat treatment, as indicated for alloy AZ63 in Table 10. Forgings may also be aged to improve the yield strength of the forged metal. Plates and sheets can be obtained in the as-rolled, annealed, or hand-rolled conditions. Structural shapes, bars, and tubing are extruded in forming.

Bars up to 8 in., round tubing up to 12 in. in outer diameter, and H-beams, I-beams, and channels up to 8 in. deep can be obtained. Plates between 0.25 and 0.50 in. thick may be had as large as 60 by 144 in.; plates between 0.020 and 0.024 are available up to a size of 24 by 96 in. Sheets as thin as 0.016 in. are available in widths of 30 in. or less and in lengths up to 6 ft. Extruded shapes range in price from 50 to 80 cents a pound in 1-ton quantities.

Magnesium-base alloys may be joined by arc-, gas-, and electric-resistance welding methods. Brazing and riveting with aluminum rivets may also be used.

The principal field of use for the magnesium-base alloys has been in aircraft construction, for wheels, housings, brackets, crankcases, and engine parts not subject to attrition. Sheets and extruded shapes have found use in the construction of trucks and buses.

NICKEL AND ITS ALLOYS

28. Production, Properties, and Uses of Nickel. Nickel is obtained almost entirely from three sources: the nickeliferous magnetic pyrites found in the Sudbury district of Ontario, Canada, to some extent from the hydrated nickel-magnesium silicate of New Caledonia, an island east of Australia, and also from Russia. The pyrite ore usually contains about 3 per cent nickel, 2 per cent copper, with iron and sulfur constituting the major portion of the residue. The silicate ores generally carry from 6 to 8 per cent of nickel. About 150,000 metric tons is the world's yearly production of metallic nickel.

In order to extract nickel from the sulfide ores, it is first necessary to roast the ore to reduce the sulfur content. The roasted ore is then smelted in a blast furnace, and a crude matte of nickel, iron, and copper is formed. By Bessemerizing this matte the iron is removed, leaving a more pure matte of copper and nickel sulfides. Nickel with 1 to 2 per cent of impurities may be obtained from the Bessemerized matte by smelting in a reverberatory furnace with coke and sodium sulfate. By this process the copper and iron are formed into a matte of lower specific gravity than nickel sulfide. The nickel sulfide is withdrawn from the bottom of the molten bath and resmelted until the desired purity has been obtained. It is then roasted to form nickel oxide which can be reduced to metallic nickel by smelting with charcoal in iron tubes.

The Bessemerized matte may be more completely purified by the Mond process. In the latter process the matte is first crushed, ground, and roasted. The oxides are then treated with dilute sulfuric acid to remove the major portion of the copper. The residue is partially reduced by hot producer gas and volatilized at a lower temperature into nickel carbonyl. By passing the latter through a heated tower the pure nickel is deposited in granular form.

Nickel is a brilliant metal approaching silver in color. It takes a good polish and does not tarnish or corrode in dry air at ordinary temperatures. The melting point of nickel is 1455°C, it weighs 0.32 lb per cu in., and is magnetic up to 665°F. The tensile strength of commercially pure nickel varies from about 50,000 psi for annealed products to 160,000 psi for hard cold-drawn wire. The elongations measured over 2 in. for these products are about 50 and 2 per cent, respectively. The modulus of elasticity of annealed nickel is about 30,000,000 psi.

Nickel and its alloys may be cast, hot worked, and cold worked in much the same maner as steel. They may be soft annealed or given a stress-equalizing anneal. Many of the nickel alloys are solid solutions that do not respond to the usual heat treatments used to secure increases in strength, and the properties of these alloys are controlled by the amount of cold work given them. Additions of alloying elements, such as magnesium, beryllium, aluminum, silicon, and titanium, to nickel and its alloys result in alloys that are susceptible to age hardening.

Nickel is widely used as an alloying element in steel and cast iron and also as an electrodeposited coating over steel to give corrosion protection. Nickel is also used to form alloys with such elements as copper, chromium, and iron. These various alloys are designed to have certain characteristics, such as a high degree of toughness, corrosion resistance, oxidation resistance, low creep rate at high temperatures, and good properties at very low temperatures.

29. Properties of Nickel Alloys. There are a large number of alloy combinations, but most of them may be placed in one of the following four groups: (1) binary alloys with nickel contents in excess of 94 per cent; (2) alloys consisting principally of nickel and copper (Monel metals); (3) alloys consisting principally of nickel, molybdenum, and iron (Hastelloys); (4) alloys consisting principally of nickel, chromium, and iron (Inconel and others). Typical compositions of some of the important nickel-rich alloys are given in Table 11.

The tensile strength of "A" nickel varies from 50,000 psi for annealed specimens up to 160,000 psi for hard-drawn wire. The elongation in 2 in. varies between 65 per cent for hot-rolled rods to 2 per cent for hard wire and strip. This alloy is used for nickel plating, heat-resisting articles,

TABLE 11. TYPICAL COMPOSITIONS OF SOME IMPORTANT
NICKEL ALLOYS

Composition, per cent

Alloy	Ni	Cu	Cr	Fe	Mn	Al	Mo	Si
"A" nickel	99.4							
"D" nickel	95.0				4.5			
"Z" nickel	94.0					4.5		
Cast nickel	97.0							1.5
Monel	67.0	30.0		1.4	1.0			
Cast monel	63.0	32.0		1.5				1.6
"K" monel	66.0	29.0		0.9	0.75	2.75		
"S" monel	63.0	30.0		2.0				4.0
Constantin	45.0	55.0						
Hastelloy A	57.0			20.0			20.0	
Hastelloy B	62.0			5.0			30.0	
Hastelloy C [1]	58.0		15.0	5.0			17.0	
Inconel	80.0		14.0	6.0				
Cast Inconel	78.0		13.5	6.0				2.0
Illium "G"	58.0	6.0	22.0	6.0			6.0	
ASTM B83-46	60.0		16.0	24.0				
Ni-Cr-Fe alloy	35.0		15.0	50.0				

[1] Also contains 5 per cent tungsten

and in the chemical industry. The tensile strength of hot-rolled "D" nickel is about 85,000 psi, its yield strength is about 33,000 psi, its elongation is 40 per cent, and its modulus of elasticity is 30,000,000 psi. This alloy is very resistant to attack by sulfur compounds at elevated temperatures under oxidizing and reducing atmospheres. The tensile strength of "Z" nickel varies from 90,000 psi for annealed products to 250,000 psi for cold-drawn age-hardened wire. The elongation in 2 in. varies from 50 to 2 per cent under the same conditions. The modulus of elasticity is 30,000,000 psi. This alloy is used where a combination of high strength and high resistance to corrosion is required. Sand-cast nickel has a tensile strength between 50,000 and 60,000 psi, an elongation in 2 in. that varies between 20 and 30 per cent, and a modulus of elasticity of 21,-500,000 psi.

The Monel metals are used where high strength, pressure tightness, high resistance to corrosion, and high resistance to wear are required. They are widely used in marine, chemical, power, electrical, and oil-refinery equipment. The tensile strength of cast Monel varies between 70,000 and 90,000 psi, the yield strength is slightly less than half of the tensile strength, the elongation in 2 in. varies between 25 and 40 per cent, and the modulus of elasticity is about 18,500,000 psi. Monel metal in the annealed state has a tensile strength between 70,000 and 80,000 psi and an elongation in 2 in. between 25 and 45 per cent. Cold-drawn wire has a tensile strength between 120,000 and 160,000 psi and an elongation in 2 in. of less than 5 per cent. The modulus of elasticity of Monel is 26,-000,000 psi. The modulus of elasticity and ductility of "K" Monel are similar to those of Monel, but the strength is better. The tensile strength of "K" Monel in the annealed state varies between 90,000 and 120,000 psi and cold-drawn wire and strip may have a strength as high as 200,000 psi. The modulus of elasticity of "S" Monel is about 21,000,000 psi. Its tensile strength varies between 110,000 and 150,000 psi, but the elongation in 2 in. is less than 5 per cent. The Monel alloys in the hot-rolled and especially in the cold-drawn age-hardened condition have very good creep properties.

The Hastelloys A and B are resistant to a wide variety of non-oxidizing acids and salts, and Hastelloy C is resistant to various oxidizing agents. These alloys are also resistant to oxidation at high temperatures and retain good toughness at temperatures of $-200°F$. The tensile strength of the sand-cast Hastelloys varies between 70,000 and 82,000 psi, and that of the annealed alloys between 110,000 and 140,000 psi. The elongation in 2 in. for sand-cast alloys varies between 6 and 15 per cent; the values for the annealed alloys vary between 25 and 50 per cent. The modulus of elasticity of the annealed Hastelloys varies between 27,000,000 and 30,800,000 psi.

The alloys consisting principally of nickel, chromium, and iron have high resistance to corrosion and to oxidation at high temperatures. The tensile strength of Inconel varies from 25,000 to 50,000 psi in the annealed condition to 175,000 psi for cold-drawn wire. The elongation in 2 in. varies between 25 and 50 per cent for the annealed alloys and is less than 5 per cent for the cold-drawn alloys. The modulus of elasticity is 31,-000,000 psi. Cast Inconel has a tensile strength between 70,000 and 100,000 psi, an elongation in 2 in. of 10 to 30 per cent, and a modulus of elasticity of 22,700,000 psi. Illium "G" is a very heat-resistant and corrosion-resistant alloy. The tensile strength of sand-cast Illium "G" varies between 60,000 and 73,000 psi, the elongation in 2 in. varies between 4 and 10 per cent, and the modulus of elasticity is 26,700,000 psi.

TIN AND ITS ALLOYS

30. Production, Properties, and Uses of Tin. Tin is obtained in the Federated Malay States, Bolivia, Indonesia, Thailand, and Africa from the black oxide of tin, cassiterite (SnO_2, 78.6 per cent tin). The total output of tin is about 170,000 tons annually. The principal deposits of the ore are found in alluvial sands, whence the name stream tin, and in veins or lodes, called lode tin. Stream tin deposits commonly contain less than 1 per cent, whereas the lode ore carries about two-thirds tin.

Stream tin ores are concentrated by washing and roasting processes and lode ores are crushed. Ores containing large amounts of sulfur or arsenic are roasted to oxidize these impurities. After these preliminary treatments the dressed or roasted ore is smelted at a high temperature (1000°C) in a reverberatory furnace, or, if the ores are very pure, a blast furnace is sometimes used. The crude tin thus produced carries more or less iron, copper, lead, arsenic, antimony, and tungsten. Since many of the alloys of tin and its impurities have higher melting points than the pure metal, the latter can be separated by raising the temperature of the crude tin just above the melting point of pure tin. Further refining is brought about by aerating the molten tin through violent agitation, thus producing more complete oxidation of the impurities. This is accomplished by submerging logs of green wood in the bath of molten tin (poling) or by repeatedly pouring the molten tin from ladles (tossing).

Considerable quantities of tin are now recovered by electrolytic and chemical methods from scrap tin plate.

Tin is a silvery white, lustrous, and extremely malleable metal as is evidenced by its form in tin foil. It melts at 232°C, and weighs 0.208 lb per cu in. Its tensile strength is within the range 2100 to 3100 psi, and the modulus of elasticity is within the range 6,000,000 to 6,500,000 psi.

Pure tin is seldom used as a casting metal, but it is easily cold worked. It does not harden appreciably with cold work. Tin and tin alloys may be readily joined by soldering with a low-melting solder.

Tin in metal form is rolled into foil, and extruded to make pipes and collapsible tubes. About 50 per cent of the tin produced is used to provide protective coatings. These coatings are applied to wire, plate, and containers by spraying, hot dipping, chemical precipitation, and electro-deposition. Tin is alloyed with other elements, principally lead, copper, zinc, and antimony, to make solder, white-metal bearing alloys, bronze, type metal, and pewter.

31. Properties of Tin Alloys. The use of tin in bronzes and type metals has been discussed under copper alloys and lead alloys, respectively. Besides these uses, tin alloys are used as solders and bearing alloys, and representative compositions for these uses are given in Table 12.

The antimonial tin solder starts to melt at 464°F, and melting is complete at 473°F. The tin-lead solders, whose compositions are given in Table 12, start to melt at 361°F. The eutectic alloy (63 per cent tin and 37 per cent lead) melts completely at that temperature; the other two soft solders melt over a short range of temperature.

TABLE 12. COMPOSITIONS OF TIN SOLDERS AND BEARING METALS

Name of Alloy	Composition, per cent			
	Sn	Sb	Pb	Cu
Antimonial tin solder	95.0	5.0		
Soft solder	70.0		30.0	
Soft solder	63.0		37.0	
Soft solder	50.0		50.0	
Tin babbitt	91.0	4.5		4.5
Tin babbitt	89.0	7.5		3.5
Tin babbitt	83.4	8.3		8.3
Tin babbitt	75.0	12.0	10.0	3.0
Tin babbitt	65.0	15.0	18.0	2.0

The tin-base bearing metals, called babbitts, are used in a large variety of machines that operate under high speeds and light loads. They meet the requirements for good bearing metals, namely, they are easily melted and cast; they adhere well to the backing; they have a structure consisting of a soft, plastic matrix in which are embedded a number of uniformly distributed wear-resisting particles; and they have satisfactory mechanical properties. The tensile strength of the tin-base bearing metals depends on the composition, but the values at room temperature for all the given alloys are within the range 12,800 to 17,600 psi. At a temperature of 212°F these values range between 6700 and 10,000 psi. The modulus of elasticity of the tin-base bearing alloys is 7,400,000 psi.

Fig. 10. Cast babbitt metal containing 83⅓ per cent tin, 8⅓ per cent antimony, and 8⅓ per cent copper, ×100. (R. A. Ragatz.)

The microstructure of a cast babbitt metal, shown in Fig. 10, consists of a dark tin-rich soft matrix in which are set cubes and needles of a hard intermetallic compound, probably SbSn.

TITANIUM AND ITS ALLOYS

32. Production, Properties, and Uses of Titanium and its Alloys.*
This metal in its early stages of development holds promise of becoming a

* Based on data given in the *Handbook on Titanium Metal,* published by the Titanium Metals Corp. of America.

prominent structural metal which will probably compete with aluminum alloys and various alloy steels. It is used as an alloying agent with aluminum, copper, magnesium, steel, and nickel; to refine the grain structure in aluminum alloys; and as a structural metal when alloyed with other elements.

The oxides ilmenite and rutile are chemically reduced to a pure titanium sponge which is then melted into ingots weighing about 1000 lb. The melting process is difficult because titanium absorbs or combines with all chemically active gases which cannot be removed. These gases are undesirable because very small amounts produce harmful embrittlement. The ingots may be forged, rolled, or drawn to produce sheet, strip, plate, wire, and bars. The annual production rate in the United States near the end of 1950 was about 60 tons.

Essentially pure titanium has an ultimate tensile strength of 35,000 psi, a yield strength of 15,000 psi, and an elongation of 55 per cent. It melts at about 3150°F, weighs 280 lb per cu ft, and has a coefficient of expansion of about 0.000005 per °F. It has a higher electrical resistivity and a lower conductivity than aluminum alloys. Titanium has excellent resistance to corrosion, but it is attacked under certain conditions by hydrochloric, hydrofluoric, nitric, phosphoric, and sulfuric acids. It is very resistant to salt water and marine atmospheres.

Commercially pure titanium containing slight amounts of iron, oxygen, and nitrogen and sold under the designation T1-75A has an ultimate tensile strength between 70,000 and 80,000 psi with an elongation between 20 and 30 per cent. An oxygen-nitrogen alloy (T1-100A) used for sheet, plate, strip, and wire has when annealed at 1300°F a tensile strength of 100,000 psi, a yield strength of 75,000 psi, and an elongation of 20 to 25 per cent. Alloy T1-125A used for the same products contains 1.8 per cent chromium, 0.9 per cent iron, and slight amounts of oxygen, carbon, and nitrogen, and has a tensile strength of 125,000 psi, a yield strength of 80,000 psi, and an elongation of 18 to 20 per cent when annealed at 1300°F. Alloys T1-150A and T1-175A are used for bars and forgings. Type T1-150A has a nominal composition of 2.7 per cent chromium, 1.3 per cent iron, 0.25 per cent oxygen, and 0.02 per cent each of nitrogen and carbon. This alloy when annealed at 1300°F has a tensile strength of 150,000 psi, a yield strength of 130,000 psi, and an elongation of 12 to 20 per cent. Alloy T1-175A has a nominal composition of 3.0 per cent chromium, 1.5 per cent iron, 0.5 per cent oxygen, 0.04 per cent nitrogen, and 0.02 per cent carbon. When annealed at 1300°F it has a tensile strength of 175,000 psi, a yield strength of 160,000 psi, and an elongation of 10 per cent. All alloys are work hardenable, but only Types T1-150A and T1-175A are heat treatable. The modulus of elasticity appears dependent on composition and amount of cold working and varies between 14,000,000 and 17,000,000 psi.

Undesirable characteristics of titanium include a rapid drop in the ultimate and the yield strengths at temperatures above 800°F, and embrittlement at temperatures above 1000°F due to the irreversible absorption of oxygen and nitrogen, and a tendency of pure titanium to creep even at room temperatures, which may, however, be modified by cold working and by alloying. The cost of commercially pure and alloy grades of titanium in 1950 was $15.00 per lb for hot- and cold-rolled sheets and $6.00 per lb for hot-rolled and forged bars. Further development of this metal may provide methods for overcoming the disadvantages and for decreasing the cost.

ZINC AND ITS ALLOYS

33. Production, Properties, and Uses of Zinc. Like copper, most of the world's supply of zinc is obtained from sulfide ores, *zinc blende* or *black jack* (ZnS, 67 per cent zinc), which ordinarily carry from one-third to one-half zinc. The ores are very often found associated with the sulfides of lead (galena), iron (pyrites), and copper. The principal sources of supply are Canada, Mexico, Australia, and Russia, and within the United States Oklahoma, New Jersey, Idaho, Arizona, Montana, and Colorado. Zinc carbonate, *calamine* ($ZnCO_3$, 52 per cent zinc); the zinc silicates *hemimorphite* and *willemite*, and *franklinite* (an ore of iron, manganese, and zinc) form less important sources of supply. The carbonate is of chief importance in the Mediterranean countries; the silicates and *franklinite* are the sources of an important supply in New Jersey.

The principal features in the extraction of zinc from its ores are the reduction of the sulfides and carbonates to the oxide form and the subsequent distillation of the oxide. The sulfide ores are finely ground and slowly roasted in reverberatory furnaces until nearly all the sulfur is expelled. Carbonate ores and silicate ores are often calcined in shaft furnaces before being distilled. After roasting or calcination, the ore is mixed with a nearly equal amount of finely ground coal and shoveled into fire clay retorts. By careful control of the temperature of the retorts at a white heat, carbon monoxide is produced and the zinc, thus relieved of its oxygen, is collected and cooled to liquid form in condensers. From time to time molten zinc is tapped from the condensers, skimmed, and poured into molds. The zinc so cast is called spelter. Most of the spelter made in the United States is sufficiently pure for industrial purposes. When contaminated with lead or iron, it is further refined by melting at as low temperature as possible. By so doing a separation of these metals is effected through the differences in their specific gravities. Continuous distillation in vertical retorts and electrolytic refining are also important in the production of zinc.

The most important property of zinc is its resistance to atmospheric corrosion. Zinc weighs 445 lb per cu ft, and it melts at 787°F. Cast zinc is a relatively brittle and weak metal, having a tensile strength of 8000 psi. It becomes sufficiently ductile at 100° to 150°C to be rolled into sheet form. When rolled into plate, its tensile strength may increase up to 25,000 psi, and its elongation in 2 in. varies between 40 and 70 per cent. Across the direction of rolling, the tensile strength is slightly higher, but the ductility is less. Impure types of zinc containing lead, iron, and cadmium have better strength but poorer ductility than pure zinc. Additional alloying elements, as copper, aluminum, and magnesium, are used when better mechanical properties are required.

Zinc, either cast or rolled, shows no well-marked proportional limit or yield point. From a large number of tests, Moore * found that the modulus of elasticity of rolled zinc varied between 10,000,000 and 15,000,000 psi and averaged about 12,000,000 psi. Six tests on cast zinc in tension gave a modulus of 11,025,000 psi, and 4 tests on cast zinc in compression gave an average modulus of only 6,900,000 psi.

Almost 50 per cent of the zinc produced is used in galvanizing, another 30 per cent is used in die castings, and the remainder is used in brass products and for miscellaneous products such as rolled sheets and pigments.

34. Properties of Zinc Alloys. The properties of the brasses made with copper and zinc have been previously described. The most important zinc alloys are those used for die casting. These zinc alloys are ideally adapted to this process of manufacture. In die casting, the molten alloy is forced into a closed steel die by a piston, under pressures up to 2000 psi. Zinc alloys are also used to make rolled sheet zinc. The compositions of some of the important zinc alloys are given in Table 13.

TABLE 13.   COMPOSITIONS OF ZINC ALLOYS

Type of Alloy	Composition, per cent [1]				
	Al	Cu	Mg	Pb	Cd
Die casting	4.0		0.04		
Die casting	4.0	1.0	0.04		
Die casting	4.0	3.0	0.03		
Rolled zinc				0.06	0.06
Rolled zinc				0.30	0.30
Rolled zinc		1.0			
Rolled zinc		1.0	0.01		

[1] Remainder zinc.

The tensile strength of the die-cast alloys depends on the composition and treatment, but varies between 33,000 and 48,000 psi; the elongation in 2 in. varies between 1.5 and 9.0 per cent. The tensile strength of the

* *Bull.* 52, Eng. Expt. Sta., Univ. Ill.

hot-rolled zinc parallel to the direction of rolling varies between 20,000 and 28,000 psi. Cold-rolled zinc has somewhat higher strengths parallel to the direction of rolling. The tensile strengths of hot-rolled and cold-rolled zinc perpendicular to the direction of rolling are higher than the strengths parallel to the direction of rolling. The effects of type of work and location of test specimen with respect to direction of rolling on ductility are opposite to the effects on strength. The elongation in 2 in. for hot-worked zinc parallel to the direction of rolling varies between 20 and 65 per cent.

The Effect of Temperature on the Properties of Metals

EFFECTS OF HIGH TEMPERATURES

1. Importance of High-Temperature Effects. The demands of industry and transportation for metal alloys capable of functioning satisfactorily at high temperatures have become increasingly more urgent and important. Examples of such high-temperature service include turbines, gasoline engines, jet-propelled planes, guided missiles, boilers, furnaces, and various types of stills used by the chemical industry.

In order to evaluate the properties of materials at high temperatures and to determine safe working stresses, short-time tests at elevated temperatures, creep, and creep-rupture tests are used. The short-time high-temperature tests provide information on the properties that measure the ability of a material to withstand high temperatures for a brief period of time, but they provide little information on the ability of the material to withstand continual stress at high temperatures for a long period of time. Since metals under stress at high temperatures continue to deform, creep, it is necessary that the relations between stress, temperature, and rate of deformation be known. With such information available it is possible to design a given member so that the amount of creep will be well within the allowable value during the service life of the member. In addition, the relations between time, temperature, and rupture stress must be known so that failure by fracture will not occur.

2. Stability of Steels at Elevated Temperatures. At high temperatures structural changes within the grains, such as spheroidization and graphitization, may result in undesirable properties. Graphitization, for example, may occur in fine-grained aluminum-killed steel at temperatures as low as 900°F. These undesirable changes may be reduced or eliminated by the addition of chromium, which acts to stabilize the carbides. Another form of instability occurs in the austenitic chrome-nickel steels at temperatures between 800° and 1600°F. At these temperatures chromium carbides form, precipitate at the grain boundaries, and consequently decrease the resistance of the grain boundaries to corrosion. Additions of titanium and columbium are helpful in decreasing this type of carbide precipitation.

Strain aging at high service temperatures is undesirable because it embrittles the steel and greatly decreases impact strength. Considerable difficulty due to strain aging has been encountered in locomotive fireboxes and boilers which operate at 600° to 800°F. As previously noted (Art. XXVI-5), strain aging may be reduced by deoxidizing and normalizing

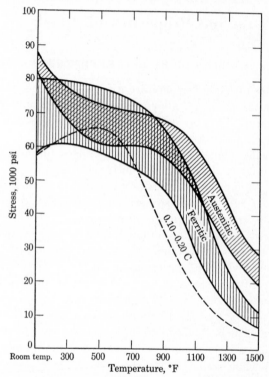

Fig. 1. Tensile strength of various steels as measured at temperatures between room temperature and 1500°F. (From *USS Steels for Elevated Temperature Services,* U. S. Steel Corp.)

the steel. Another form of brittleness is found in steels containing moderate amounts of chromium, manganese, and nickel at temperatures of 800° to 900°F. The embrittlement, believed due to some form of precipitation, may be reduced or prevented by the addition of 0.30 to 0.50 per cent molybdenum. Ferritic chromium steels containing from 12 to 30 per cent chromium may be brittle at temperatures between 700° and 1500°F.

Scaling at high temperatures limits the useful life of steel. Plain carbon steels below 1000°F exhibit negligible amounts of scaling, but the rate of scaling increases rapidly at higher temperatures. The resistance to scaling above 1000°F is greatly increased by additions of chromium, which forms an adherent layer of oxide on the surface that retards the inward diffusion of oxygen. Additions of silicon and aluminum are also effective in increasing scaling resistance. These additions appear to be especially effective when added to steel that contains some chromium.

3. Effect on Tensile Properties of Steels. The details for short-time tensile tests used at elevated temperatures are given in ASTM *Standards* E21. The results of short-time tests performed on a wide variety of steels are summarized in Fig. 1. The curves show that the tensile strength generally decreases as the temperature increases. The strength of the ferritic-alloy steels at 1500°F is only about 15 per cent of the strength at room temperature; the strength of the austenitic steels at 1500°F is about 30 per cent of the strength at room temperature. The plain carbon steels increase in strength from room temperature to about 500°F and then decrease rapidly, and generally the values at room temperatures and at 700°F are approximately equal. Figure 2 shows the same effect of temperature on ultimate strength and in addition shows that reduction in area and elongation decrease from room temperature to about 450°F and increase with temperature thereafter. The increase in strength and decrease in ductility are believed to be due to the precipitation of carbides, oxides, or nitrides during the tensile test. Figure 2 also shows that the yield strength and the proportional limit decrease as the temperature increases.

The short-time high-temperature properties of an important alloy steel (18 per cent chromium and 8 per cent nickel) are shown in Fig. 3. The ultimate and yield strengths decrease with an increase in temperature. The percentage reduction in area curve decreases up to a temperature of about 1500°F before it starts to increase, and the percentage elongation curve decreases as the temperature increases up to about 1300°F before it starts to increase.

4. Effect on Properties of Alloys. Aluminum alloys, as represented by Alloy 24ST in Fig. 4, also show rapid decreases in strength with temperature. The percentage elongation shows only a small drop with temperatures up to 300°F and increases rapidly after that. Aluminum alloys have strengths generally under 5000 psi at temperatures above 600°F; low-carbon steels have similar low strengths at temperatures of 1400°F and above. Most wrought- and cast-aluminum alloys maintain fair strength up to 300°F, but at 600°F the strength is usually between 10 and 35 per cent of the room-temperature strength.

An extensive series of tests upon the effects of elevated temperatures on the mechanical properties of alloys used in valves, shafting, and parts of pumps and engines was reported by Bregowsky and Spring.* The compositions of the various alloys used are given in Table 1; the results of the tension tests are shown in Fig. 5, and the results of torsion tests are

* Sixth Congress of the IATM.

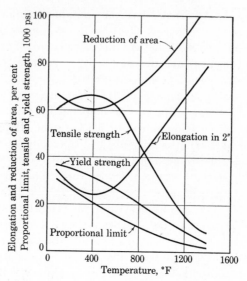

Fig. 2. Effects of high temperatures on the properties of low-carbon steel. (Based on information in *Metals Handbook; Metals and Alloys Data Book* by S. L. Hoyt; *Modern Metallurgy for Engineers* by F. T. Sisco; *Steels for Elevated Temperature Service*, U. S. Steel Corp.)

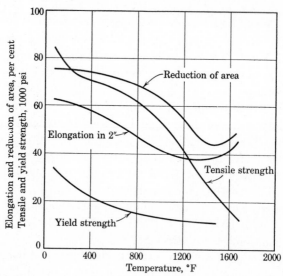

Fig. 3. Effects of high temperatures on the properties of 18 per cent chromium, 8 per cent nickel alloy steel. (Based on information in *Metals Handbook; Metals and Alloys Data Book* by S. L. Hoyt; *Modern Metallurgy for Engineers* by F. T. Sisco; *Steels for Elevated Temperature Service*, U. S. Steel Corp.)

shown in Fig. 6.   Round bars with the gaged portion turned down to a
constant diameter of 0.65 to 0.85 in., depending on the size of the bar as
received, were used.   The gage length of the tension specimens was 2 in.
and that of the torsion specimens was 8 in.   All metal was obtained from
commercial foundries, and all specimens for a given series of tests were
from the same heat.   Each point on the curves represents from two to
ten results.

Figure 5 shows the effects of variations in temperature from room
temperature to 1000°F on 16 alloys.   The non-ferrous alloys show de-

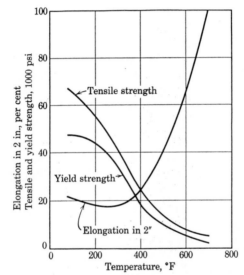

Fig. 4.   Effects of high temperatures on the properties of 24ST aluminum alloy.
(Based on information in *Metals Handbook*; *Metals and Alloys Data Book* by S. L.
Hoyt; *Modern Metallurgy for Engineers* by F. T. Sisco; *Aluminum and Its Alloys*,
Aluminum Co. of America.)

creases in yield and ultimate strengths, although some, like the copper-
tin bronzes and the aluminum bronzes, show little change until the temperature exceeds 400°F.   The curves for the ferrous alloys show general
characteristics similar to those previously described.   It is also apparent
from Fig. 5 that the ductilities of the non-ferrous alloys, with the exception of the manganese bronze and rolled Monel metal, are very low for
temperatures above 600°F.

Data on the torsional strength and angle of twist of 15 alloys are shown
in Fig. 6.   With the exception of the carbon steels, all the alloys show a
progressive decrease in strength as the temperature is increased above
70°F.   The curves for the carbon steels are somewhat similar to the tensile
strength-temperature curves.

TABLE 1. CHEMICAL ANALYSES OF ALLOYS AND METALS USED IN TESTS AT VARIOUS TEMPERATURES (Bregowsky and Spring)

Material		Composition in Per Cent						
Mark	Name	Cu	Sn	Zn	Pb	Fe	Al	P
		Alloys used in Tensile Tests						
1	Copper-tin bronze (3)	87.02	12.46	0.20	0.30	0.06		
2	Copper-tin bronze	89.50	10.22	0.00	tr.	0.38	...	0.035
3	Brass	86.19	5.69	5.03	3.02	0.20		
4	Aluminum bronze	94.94	0.03	...	0.16	0.14	4.90	
5	Aluminum bronze	88.86	0.48	0.15	0.17	0.75	9.67	Mn
6	Cast manganese bronze	58.10	0.51	39.05	tr.	2.21		0.055
7	U. S. navy brass S-C	80.32	3.98	12.80	2.78	0.24	C	
8	U. S. navy bronze M(2)	86.92	7.72	3.62	1.22	0.23		
9	U. S. navy gun bronze G	87.60	10.40	1.31	0.39	0.11		
10	Cast Monel metal	27.11	0.08	64.79	0.13	5.46	0.32	2.33
16	Rolled rod brass	62.30	0.00	34.84	2.53	0.15		
18	Rolled Monel metal	27.22	...	...	(Ni 68.64)	2.38	0.225	1.56
		Alloys used in Torsion Tests					Al	
L	Parsons' manganese bronze	59.58	0.64	38.08	0.00	1.22	0.34	Ni
G	1⅛ in. rolled Monel metal	27.08	(C 0.186)	(Mn 1.52)	0.28	2.50	...	68.40
H	Rod brass	61.08	0.18	35.72	2.34	0.42	...	P
I	Tobin bronze	59.86	0.80	38.94	0.00	0.46	...	0.0015
J	Elephant (Phosphor) bronze	95.52	3.87	0.0	0.00	0.16	...	0.307
K	Delta metal	56.56	0.76	39.36	0.56	2.40	...	0.004

Material		Composition in Per Cent						
Mark	Name	C	Graphitic C	Combined C	Si	Mn	S	P
		Ferrous Metals used in Tensile Tests						
11	Soft cast iron (3)	...	3.31	0.17	2.57	0.60	0.103	0.73
14	Cast steel (2)	0.302		...	0.22	0.61	0.068	0.045
15	Cold-rolled shafting	0.140	Ni	...	0.031	0.80	0.108	0.079
17	30% nickel steel, rolled	0.285	30.92	...	0.14	2.80	0.017	0.011
		Ferrous Metals used in Torsion Tests						
A	Cold-rolled shafting	0.093	...	Va	0.011	0.73	0.117	0.198
B	Cumberland cold-rolled shafting	0.083	...	...	0.024	0.50	0.110	0.101
C	Open hearth machinery steel	0.084	...	...	0.024	0.49	0.029	0.013
D	3½% nickel vanadium steel	0.365	3.25	0.45	0.132	0.45	0.042	0.032
E	25% nickel steel	0.186	25.03					
F	30% nickel steel	0.275	30.92	...	0.140	2.80	0.017	0.011
P	35% C Cumberland cold-rolled	0.375	Cr	...	0.120	0.51	0.50	0.013
N	Vanadium tool steel	0.722	0.49	0.145	0.160	0.32	0.034	0.014

5. Effect on Elastic and Thermal Properties. The effect of elevated temperatures on modulus of elasticity is shown in Fig. 7. With increasing

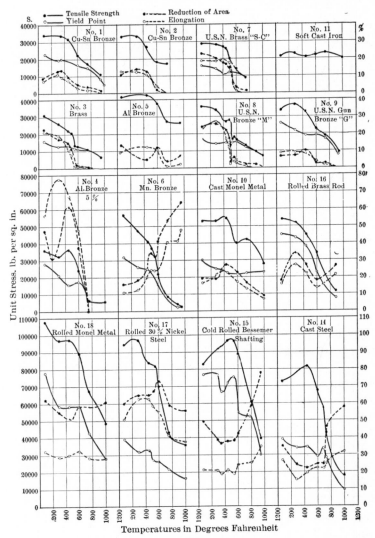

Fig. 5. Effects of temperature on the tensile properties of various alloys. (Bregowsky and Spring.)

temperature the moduli decrease as shown. In a comprehensive series of tests on 21 commercial steels, Garofalo, Malenock, and Smith * have

* The Influence of Temperature on the Elastic Constants of Some Commercial Steels, by F. Garofalo, P. R. Malenock, and G. V. Smith, *ASTM Special Tech. Pub.* 129, 1952.

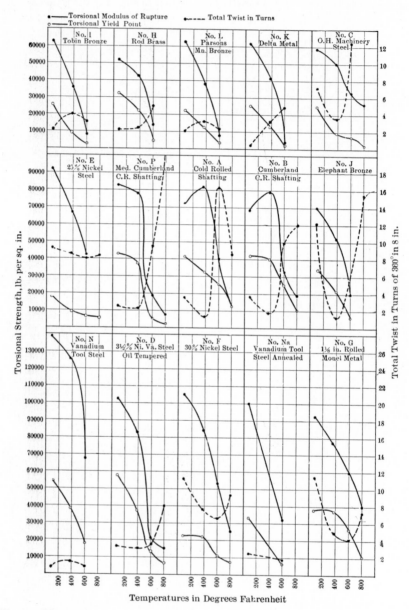

Fig. 6.　Effects of temperature on the torsional properties of various alloys. (Bregowsky and Spring.)

shown also that the shear modulus of elasticity decreases with increasing temperature in a manner similar to that of the tensile modulus. In the same paper the authors found that Poisson's ratio for the 21 commercial steels tested did not change significantly with temperature.

Figure 8 shows the effect of elevated temperatures on the linear thermal expansion for carbon, low-alloy, and stainless steels as they are heated from room temperature to any temperature between 400° and 1200°F.

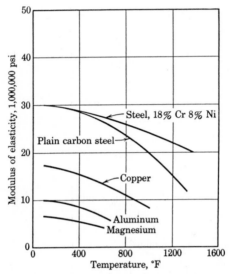

Fig. 7. Effect of high temperatures on the modulus of elasticity. (Based on information in *Metals Handbook; Metals and Alloys Data Book* by S. L. Hoyt; *Modern Metallurgy for Engineers* by F. T. Sisco; *Steels for Elevated Temperature Service,* U. S. Steel Corp.; *Aluminum and Its Alloys,* Aluminum Co. of America.)

The ferritic steels are listed in the order in which their coefficients of expansion increase. The austenitic steels have a higher coefficient of expansion than the ferritic steels at a given temperature.

6. Creep of Metals.* The performance characteristics of metals that are frequently subjected to high temperatures for long periods of time when under ordinary working stresses, as in high-pressure steam lines, oil refineries, and boilers, must be known and properly evaluated in design. For methods of making long-time high-temperature tests see *ASTM Standard* Des. E22. These characteristics, commonly referred to as creep or flow, are obtained by subjecting specimens to a constant dead load while they are in an electric furnace kept at the required temperature and ac-

* For bibliography and much data see *Proc. ASTM,* Vol. 24, Pt. II, p. 9; *Proc. ASTM,* Vol. 38; *Metals Handbook; Steels for Elevated Temperature Service,* United States Steel Corp.

curately determining the elongation for periods exceeding 1000 hours. Information so obtained is then plotted as shown in Fig. 9. The creep curves 1, 2, and 3 are for a given temperature and for specimens subjected to a low stress (curve 1), an intermediate stress (curve 2), and a high

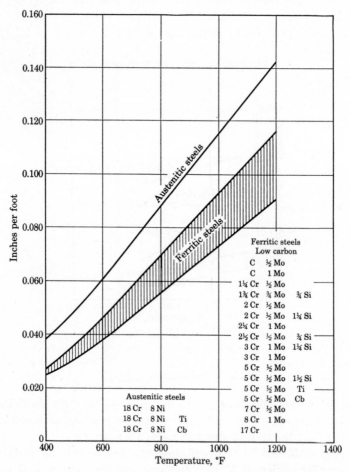

Fig. 8. Influence of temperature on the linear thermal expansion of steel. (From *USS Steels for Elevated Temperature Service,* U. S. Steel Corp.)

stress (curve 3). The curves show that usually there are three stages of creep. In the first stage, creep increases rapidly with time; in the second stage, the creep curve is essentially a straight line; and in the third stage, the straight line may persist if the applied stress is low, or the curve may rise sharply and terminate at rupture if the applied stress is high. *The most useful measure of creep is obtained from the slope of the straight line in the second stage, and is expressed as the stress required to produce a specific rate of creep at a given temperature.* The creep rates most frequently used in design are 0.0001 or 0.00001 per cent per hour often expressed as 1 per cent in 10,000 or 100,000 hours. *Useful creep strength at a given temperature is consequently reported as the stress required to produce a creep rate of 1 per cent in 10,000 or 100,000 hours.*

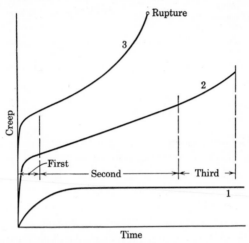

Fig. 9. Characteristic creep-time curves.

7. Creep-Rupture Tests. Creep-rupture or stress-rupture tests are performed in the same manner as the creep tests except that the specimens are dead-loaded so that fracture occurs over periods varying from a few minutes to several thousand hours. Elongations in the creep-rupture test may be as high as 50 per cent in comparison with the elongations in the creep test, which are usually less than 0.5 per cent. The data for each temperature are usually plotted on log-log coordinates with the fracture stress as ordinates and the time for rupture as abscissas. If no structural change at the test temperature takes place, a straight-line relation is obtained, but, if a structural change does occur, an increase in the downward slope of the curve is obtained as shown in the stress-rupture curves for the alloy steel shown in Fig. 10. The rupture strength of a metal is usually reported as the stress required to produce failure in 100, 1000, 10,000, or 100,000 hours at a given temperature.

If steel is structurally stable at a given temperature, the rate of creep during the second stage may be plotted against the stress on a log-log curve and the curve may be extrapolated to a lower creep rate, such as the standard 1 per cent in 10,000 hours, to obtain a prediction of the creep characteristics. This method of predicting long-time creep behavior from short-time tests is useful in quickly evaluating creep behavior of new materials for high-temperature service.

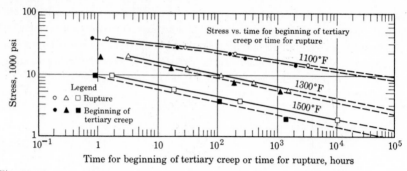

Fig. 10. Stress-rupture curves for type 304L steel (19.5 per cent chromium and 10.2 per cent nickel). (From Creep and Rupture of Chromium-Nickel Austenitic Steels by E. J. Dulis, G. V. Smith, and E. G. Houston, *ASM Preprint* 7, 1952.)

8. Factors Affecting Creep. The creep strength of a metal is greatly affected by differences in chemical composition, microstructure, grain size, and variables in the manufacturing process. In steel, carbon is beneficial in small amounts, and up to 0.20 per cent is normally used. In most instances where desirable creep properties are required, alloying elements, such as molybdenum, chromium, vanadium, tungsten, titanium, and columbium, are added. Aluminum present in the steel for deoxidation purposes decreases creep strength. Non-ferrous alloys, with the exception of the nickel-rich alloys, such as Monel and Inconel and alloys consisting chiefly of cobalt and chromium, generally have lower creep strengths than alloy steels.

The structure and hence the heat treatment used have a great effect on creep strength. It is probable that much of the spread of the creep data obtained by various investigators for a metal with a given composition is due to the heat treatments used and the consequent variation in structures. Steel containing lamellar pearlite, for example, has much better creep properties than steel which has a spheroidized structure. The elevated temperature at which a steel may be used may produce internal changes in the structure (Art. 2) and related changes in properties. Types of structural instability that may be so produced include spheroidization, graphitization, aging, and embrittlement.

Steels with a coarse austenitic grain size generally have better creep properties than fine-grained steels. Care must be exercised, however, in specifying coarse-grained steels where high ductility and impact properties are required. The effect of grain size on the creep strength of non-ferrous alloys appears to be erratic.

Deoxidation practices during melting and refining also have a strong effect on the creep properties of steels. Steels that have been largely deoxidized generally have better creep properties than rimmed steels.

However, the method of deoxidation is also important since aluminum, frequently used for deoxidation, has an adverse effect on creep strength.

9. Creep Values. Kanter and Spring * have determined the creep characteristics for low-carbon cast steel (C = 0.20 to 0.40 per cent), as shown in Fig. 11. Since failure of such steels is accompanied by considerable elongation, they have determined creep curves for elongations of 1 per cent during periods varying between 1 hour and 10 years on the basis that such an elongation in many classes of service, such as high-pressure steam lines, will do little or no harm. It is interesting to note that at

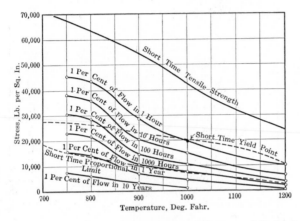

Fig. 11.   Creep in cast carbon steels.   (Kanter and Spring.)

900°F a stress of 29,000 psi will produce a creep of 1 per cent in 1 hour and that a stress of about 3000 psi will produce a creep of 1 per cent in 10 years. At 1200°F a creep of 1 per cent in 1 hour is produced by a stress of only 10,000 psi. Also shown on the figure are the short-time curves for tensile strength, yield point, and proportional limit. The apparent agreement between the short-time proportional limit and the creep curve for 1 per cent of flow in 1000 hours at the higher temperatures is apparently a coincidence.

The creep strengths of a variety of steel alloys for a creep rate of 1 per cent in 10,000 hours are given in Fig. 12. The very rapid decrease in creep strength for temperatures above 800°F is evident. At a temperature of 1100°F the creep strength of plain carbon steel is about 1500 psi, that of the ferritic steel alloys averages about 5000 psi, and that of the austenitic steel alloys averages about 13,000 psi.

The creep properties of various steel alloys are shown in Table 2. The data show that the stress for a creep rate of 1 per cent in 10,000 hours and the stress for rupture at 10,000 hours both decrease rapidly as the

* *Proc. ASTM,* Vol. 28, Pt. 2, p. 80.

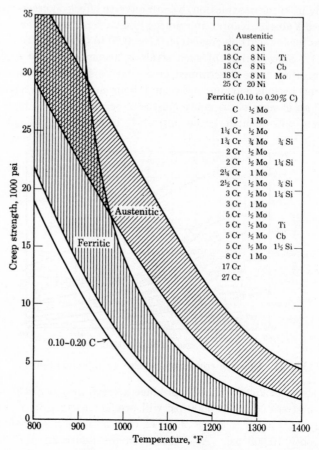

Fig. 12. Creep strength (stress for creep rate of 0.0001 per cent per hour) of various steels at temperatures between 800° and 1400°F. (From *USS Steels for Elevated Temperature Service*, U. S. Steel Corp.)

TABLE 2. CREEP PROPERTIES OF VARIOUS STEELS [1]

Composition of Metal	Stress for a Creep Rate of 1% in 10,000 hours at				Stress for Rupture in 10,000 hours at			
	1100°F	1200°F	1300°F	1500°F	1100°F	1200°F	1300°F	1500°F
Carbon steel (0.08–0.20% C)	1,500	500	—	—	3,000	1,500	500	—
1% Cr ½% Mo <0.15% C	3,000	1,000	—	—	10,000	3,000	—	—
7% Cr ½% Mo <0.15% C	4,000	1,500	500	—	10,000	3,000	1,500	500
18% Cr 8% Ni <0.08% C	12,000	8,000	3,000	1,000	16,000	10,000	5,000	3,000
25% Cr 12% Ni <0.20% C	11,000	9,000	4,000	1,000		15,000	9,000	4,000

[1] Based on information provided in *USS Steels for Elevated Temperature Service*, U. S. Steel Corp.

temperature increases. The beneficial effects of the additions of chromium, molybdenum, and nickel are apparent. Plain carbon steels are seldom used above 900°F; the steels with the higher alloy contents may be used up to 1200°F.

The various high-temperature properties of metals may be plotted on one diagram as shown in Fig. 13 for a plain carbon steel with a carbon content of 0.08 to 0.20 per cent. Curves of this type are valuable for the design of metal products to be used at high temperatures.

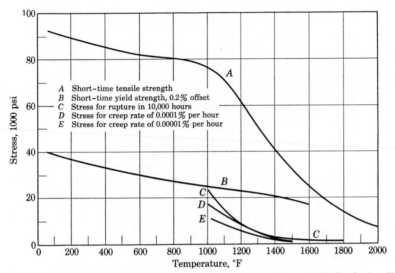

A   Short-time tensile strength
B   Short-time yield strength, 0.2% offset
C   Stress for rupture in 10,000 hours
D   Stress for creep rate of 0.0001% per hour
E   Stress for creep rate of 0.00001% per hour

Fig. 13. High-temperature properties of carbon steel. (From *USS Steels for Elevated Temperature Service*, p. 31, U. S. Steel Corp.)

Stainless steel, hot-rolled Inconel, and cold-drawn and age-hardened "K" Monel have excellent creep resistance. At a temperature of 1000°F the stress required for these three materials to cause a creep rate of 1 per cent in 10,000 hours varies between 20,000 and 25,000 psi. The creep strength of non-ferrous alloys, such as 70–30 brass, Admiralty metal, bronze (88 Cu + 12 Sn), and gun metal, for a creep rate of 1 per cent in 10,000 hours at 400°F, varies from 13,000 to 20,000 psi, and at 600°F from 1000 to 4000 psi. Strong alloys of aluminum and magnesium are not resistant to excessive creep at temperatures greater than 400°F. Non-ferrous alloys consisting largely of cobalt and chromium with appreciable percentages of molybdenum, tungsten, and nickel have unusually good creep properties with rupture stresses at 1000 hours and 1800°F, exceeding 5000 psi. One such alloy consisting of 52 per cent cobalt, 28 per cent chromium, 7½ per cent tungsten, and 12 per cent nickel has a rupture stress at 1000 hours and 1800°F of about 10,000 psi.

TABLE 3.[1]   PROPERTIES OF METALS AT SUBATMOSPHERIC TEMPERATURES

Material	Tensile Strength, psi		Proof or Yield Stress, psi		Elongation in 2″, per cent		Reduction of Area, per cent		Notched-Bar Impact[2] ft-lb	
	Room Temp.	−300°F	Room Temp.	−300°F	Room Temp.	−300°F	Room Temp.	−300°F	Room Temp.	−300°F
Armco iron as rolled	46,000	112,000	—	—	28	None	73	None	57	1
Low C (0.13) steel as rolled	66,000	121,000	52,000	105,000	30	26	72	55	94	3
Medium C (0.40) steel as rolled	92,000	150,000	60,000	135,000	25	3	45	3	35	3
High C (0.80) steel annealed	100,000	155,000	95,000	—	12	None	35	None	—	—
Ni-Cr-Mo steel quenched and drawn	152,000	201,500	137,500	183,500	14	17	65	63	57	22
18% Cr 8% Ni steel	90,000	230,000	35,000	90,000	65	42	70	55	115	100
Annealed Monel	71,000	115,000	21,000	30,000	40	50	75	70	90	95
24ST aluminum alloy	65,000	80,000	45,000	60,000	20	20	30	20	6	6
Copper	32,500	50,500	8,500	11,500	48	58	76	77	43	50
Nickel	65,000	97,500	24,500	28,000	42	53	78	74	89	98
Aluminum	9,750	21,000	4,500	4,500	36	44	91	87	19	27
80% Cu 20% Ni	51,500	74,000	27,000	32,500	25	35	78	72	77	85
54.5% Cu 45.5% Ni	60,000	89,500	19,500	27,000	40	57	77	76	80	86
29% Cu 71% Ni	70,000	112,000	21,000	30,000	40	51	75	72	90	97
Nickel brass	75,000	104,000	28,000	28,500	33	41	50	55	80	87
Aluminum bronze	77,500	96,000	26,500	29,000	26	28	29	30	24	20
Manganese bronze	72,500	94,500	24,000	29,000	28	37	44	41	20	20
70% Cu 30% Zn	51,500	73,500	28,000	30,000	49	74	77	73	65	78

[1] The typical values in this table are based on information given in *Metals Handbook*, ASM (1948); *Impact Resistance and Tensile Properties of Metals at Subatmospheric Temperatures*, ASTM (1941); *Properties of Nickel Alloy Steels at Low Temperatures*, The International Nickel Co.; *Mechanical Properties of Metals at Low Temperatures*, U. S. Dept. Commerce *Circ*. 520.

[2] Since complete details on testing procedure are not available the values given should be used only for comparative purposes between the room- and low-temperature results for any one material.

EFFECTS OF LOW TEMPERATURES

10. Properties of Metals at Subatmospheric Temperatures. Low temperatures, as well as high temperatures, have a marked influence on the properties of metals. Many examples of the use of metals at low temperatures (down to $-60°F$) are found in automobiles, aircraft, and railroad cars; other uses are found in refrigeration equipment and in the chemical industry. Properties of metals at low temperatures are determined after they have been cooled to the desired temperature by means of brines, solid carbon dioxide, liquid air, liquid oxygen, or liquid helium.

Many factors, including some whose full significance is not yet understood, affect the low-temperature properties of metals. Some of these factors are the chemical composition of the metal, the method of production, the amount of deoxidation and the deoxidizing agent used, the magnitude of residual stress, the heat treatment, the grain size, the rate at which the metal is cooled from room conditions down to subatmospheric temperatures and the thermal gradients produced, the presence of notches and other stress raisers, and the rate of testing.

Tests of metals show that usually as the temperature is decreased the coefficient of thermal expansion decreases, the thermal conductivity increases, the modulus of elasticity increases, and the yield and ultimate tensile strengths increase. The data in Table 3 show that the non-ferrous metals when tested at $-300°F$ usually have ductility and toughness values equal to or slightly better than the values determined at room temperature. The plain carbon steels, however, have lower ductility and toughness (as determined from a notched-bar test) values at $-300°F$ than at room temperature. This loss in ductility and toughness which may become pronounced in plain carbon steels at temperatures around $0°F$ seriously restricts their use at low temperatures. A plot of energy absorbed against temperature for ferritic steels will commonly show a temperature range, usually below room temperature, in which the energy values drop steeply with a decrease in temperature, as shown in Fig. 14. In this low transition zone the steel changes from a tough to a brittle material. Within the transition zone energy values are likely to be erratic due to the chance importance of one or more of the many variables involved. The impact resistance of steel increases as the transition-zone temperature is lowered.

Alloying with nickel, chromium, molybdenum, and copper produces improvements in ductility and toughness at low temperatures. Alloying with nickel is especially effective where very low temperatures are involved. Figure 15 provides a comparison of the impact properties of steels containing 0, 3, and 50 per cent nickel. Steels with more than 45 per cent nickel remain austenitic at least down to a temperature of $-300°F$ and also retain their toughness down to that temperature. Stainless steels (18 per cent chromium, 8 per cent nickel) also maintain high

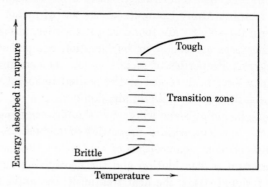

Fig. 14. Typical curve of impact value vs. testing temperature for a ferritic steel, showing transition temperature zone in which erratic values may be expected. (International Nickel Co.)

impact resistance down to temperatures of $-300°F$ if they are properly heat treated. The low-alloy high-strength steels have good resistance to impact at moderately low temperatures (down to $-100°F$) when they have been properly heat treated.

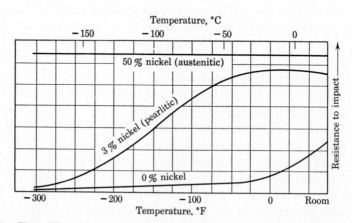

Fig. 15. Chart illustrative of the effects of high and low nickel contents upon the resistance of steels to low-temperature embrittlement. (International Nickel Co.)

Failures of many structures, such as bridges, tanks, pipe lines, and ships, have taken place because of embrittlement at normal low temperatures. In order that this type of failure be avoided, proper materials and correct fabricating procedures must be used. Improper welding procedures, for example, have been responsible for many failures. Where fabrication by welding is required the steel should have a low carbon content and the required amounts of nickel and other desirable alloying elements. The steels to be welded should normally be preheated to some temperature up to 400°F, depending on the composition, to prevent cracking during welding. Where service temperatures below −150°F are anticipated, austenitic chromium-nickel stainless steel electrodes, such as 25 per cent chromium and 20 per cent nickel, should be used. If possible, the heat-affected zone should be given a stress-relief anneal. Where a stress-relief anneal subsequent to welding is not practicable, a steel that will not harden appreciably should be used.

Fatigue of Structural Materials

METALS

1. Definitions. Experience and experiments have shown that a structural material often fails when subjected to many repetitions of a stress less than its ultimate strength or even less than its yield strength. Such failures have been ascribed to *fatigue*. Gough [*] and others have shown that such failures in ductile metals are due to maximum-shear stress components acting upon planes of "easy glide" in the metal crystals. If these stresses are sufficiently high in intensity and applied enough times, they initiate strain lines which upon further stress applications develop into a crack. This causes neighboring crystals to be overstressed, and thus the strain lines and cracks are extended until failure of the part occurs. The conditions by which a fatigue failure proceeds from crystal to crystal prohibit the necking down which takes place in static tension tests of unnotched ductile specimens. Hence an abrupt break without appreciable elongation characterizes fatigue failures.

Fatigue may be caused by several types of stress cycles. A *stress cycle* is the smallest complete stress-time function which is periodically repeated. Thus in a rotating cylindrical beam every longitudinal fiber suffers a complete reversal of stress from tension through compression in every revolution or cycle.

A bridge member may be subjected to a *fluctuating stress* cycle which varies or alternates from a high value S_{max} to a low value S_{min}. S_{max} and S_{min} may be of the same or opposite sign and must be algebraically evaluated. Tension is usually considered positive and compression negative. A crankshaft oscillated back and forth would have its outer elements subjected to alternations of shear stresses, first in one direction and then in the opposite. In such a case $S_{s\ max}$ and $S_{s\ min}$ would have opposite signs.

In a given cycle the *mean*, or steady, *stress*, $S_m = \dfrac{S_{max} + S_{min}}{2}$, algebraically considered. For a *completely reversed* cycle of stress, $S_{max} = -S_{min}$ and $S_m = 0$. The *stress range* $S_r = S_{max} - S_{min}$.

The *alternating component* of the stress cycle $S_a = \dfrac{S_{max} - S_{min}}{2}$.

[*] *Proc. ASTM*, Vol. 33, 1933, p. 3.

The *fatigue life* N is the number of stress cycles sustained under a given test procedure.

An *S-N diagram* is a plot of the stress S against the number of cycles N causing failure. Usually S is plotted as ordinate against log N as abscissa, although log-log paper is also used.

The *fatigue limit* or *endurance limit* S_e is the limiting value of the stress below which the material may be repeatedly stressed an infinite number of times without failure. This value is the stress at which the S-N curve becomes parallel to the N-axis.

Fatigue strength S_n is the greatest unit stress which can be sustained for a given number of cycles. This term becomes useful when the number of cycles to which a member is likely to be subjected is less than N at S_e, also for materials which do not have a well-defined S_e. The number of cycles should always be stated when S_n is mentioned. The ratio of S_e or S_n to the static tensile ultimate strength, S_u, S_e/S_u, or S_n/S_u, is termed the *fatigue ratio*.

2. Early Experiments. The earliest experiments on fatigue appear to have been performed by Captains James and Gaston about 1849. The most exhaustive of the early tests on fatigue were those of Wohler, published in 1858. His experiments included repeated torsion, bending, and axial tension and compression. The following conclusions drawn from Wohler's experiments show the behavior of ductile ferrous metals under the usual fatigue conditions:

1. Wrought iron and steel will rupture at unit stresses below the ultimate and even below the elastic limit, if repeated a sufficient number of cycles.

2. Within certain limits the range of unit stress, not the maximum stress, determines the number of cycles for failure.

3. As the range is decreased, for a given maximum or minimum unit stress, the number of repetitions for rupture increases.

4. For a given maximum or minimum unit stress there appears to be a limiting range within which the repetitions for rupture become infinite.

5. As the maximum unit stress increases, the limiting range decreases.

In the early experiments on fatigue where the number of cycles was not so large, S-N curves were plotted to cartesian coordinates, as shown in Fig. 1c, which represents data from Moore's fatigue tests in completely reversed bending. It later became apparent that the fatigue life of many materials ran far beyond 10 or 20 million cycles and that the fatigue limits could not be readily determined from such plots. Present practice is to plot S-N diagrams either on semi-log paper with the number of cycles plotted to the logarithmic scale, Fig. 1a, or to use log-log paper, as in Fig. 1b. It will be observed that the plots of the four ferrous metals in Fig. 1a and 1b show definite horizontal S-N diagrams at high numbers of cycles, indicating a definite fatigue limit S_e, whereas the aluminum-

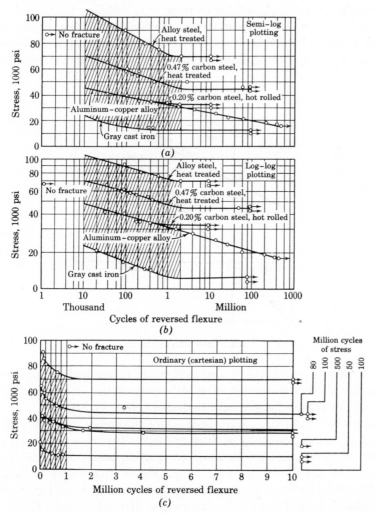

Fig. 1. Typical stress cycle (S-N) diagrams for fatigue tests. (Data by H. F. Moore, courtesy ASM.)

copper alloy 245-T age hardened did not show such a property although it was run some 500,000,000 cycles at a stress of 15,000 psi. The values in psi of S_e for the four ferrous metals shown in Fig. 1 were: chromium-molybdenum alloy steel, 70,000; 0.47 carbon steel, 44,000; 0.20 carbon steel, 32,000; and gray cast iron, 12,000.

From Wohler's data, Goodman devised the diagram of Fig. 2 to show the effect of repetitions of direct stresses, tension or compression, at the right of OE and reversals of stress on the range per cycle at the left of OE. The abscissa axis is dimensionless. In this diagram it was assumed that the number of cycles, 4,000,000 or more, was sufficient to determine the fatigue limits for each range of stress. Obviously the upper right portion of this diagram involving stresses beyond the yield strength of the metal is of little practical value, since the imposition of such high stresses would

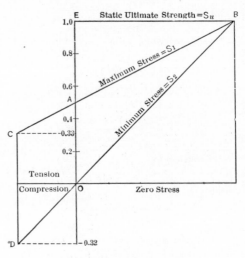

Fig. 2. Goodman's diagram.

be attended by permanent strains that would render useless the parts so stressed. Further discussion of modification of the Goodman diagram and applications of fatigue data to design appear in Art. 4.

Since about 1900 there have been many researches performed on the fatigue of metals. In many of these researches the value of S_e from completely reversed bending tests made on rotating beams was considerably higher than one-third tensile S_u. Furthermore, the scatter in data for repeated axial reversed (push-pull) stresses indicates that eccentric loading probably caused many of the low values. Hence the value of $S_e = \frac{1}{2}S_u$ (tension) has now been quite generally accepted for completely reversed cycles of tension and compression (Art. 4). For references to this field of research, see *Fatigue of Metals*, by Moore and Kommers (1927), and the more recent compilation entitled *Prevention of the Failure of Metals under Repeated Stress*, by the staff of Battelle Memorial Institute (Wiley, 1949). In 1949 the ASTM published its useful *Manual on Fatigue Testing*, which considers the proper nomenclature, types of machines and specimens, and testing procedures, and gives suggestions on the presentation and interpretation of fatigue data.

3. Effect of Range of Stress. The advent of the automobile and the airplane and developments in power field have greatly accentuated the interest in fatigue of metals. Consequently since about 1920 there have been numerous researches made from which has come a better knowledge of the behavior of metals under fatigue than the information obtained by Wohler and other investigators who immediately followed him. Many improvements have also been made in fatigue testing procedures and machines. Some of the latter are shown in Art. II-24 and II-25.

In 1942 J. O. Smith, after an extensive study of the available data on fatigue of metals, presented [*] a satisfactory approach to the general solution of problems involving range of stress on the fatigue strength of metals. On account of the presence of surface irregularities, notches, grooves, and holes in many parts of machines and structures, the stress-raising effects of such factors must be considered, since they materially affect the fatigue limit and fatigue strength, Art. 6. Hence the *stress concentration factor*, K, which is the ratio of the greatest stress at a notch or other stress raiser to the corresponding nominal stress, is included where applicable in the following cases. A summary of Smith's conclusions follows:

1. *Ductile Metals.* (a) Torsion. For notch-free cylindrical specimens the maximum alternating shearing unit stress, S_{sa}, which may be superimposed on a given mean stress in a given cycle, S_{sm}, and repeated indefinitely without causing failure, is constant. Hence, for completely reversed torsional stresses, the maximum

$$S_{sa} = S_{se} \qquad (1)$$

For cylindrical specimens containing a notch or other stress raiser the maximum localized alternating unit stress, KS_{sa}, which may be imposed on a given mean stress, S_{sm}, and repeated indefinitely without failure, is given by

$$KS_{sa} = S_{se}\left(1 - \frac{S_{sm}}{S_{su}}\right) \qquad (2)$$

where S_{su} is the torsional modulus of rupture for solid notch-free specimens. In eq. 2, S_{se}, S_{sm}, and S_{su} are calculated from $S_s = Tr/J$ without taking account of the notch.

(b) Notch-Free and Notched Tension Specimens. In notch-free tension specimens the maximum alternating unit stress S_a which may be imposed upon a mean tensile stress S_m is given by

[*] *Bull.* 334, Univ. Ill., The Effect of Range of Stress on the Fatigue Strength of Metals.

$$S_a = S_e \left(1 - \frac{S_m}{S_u} \right) \tag{3}$$

where S_e is the fatigue limit for completely reversed axial or bending stress cycles and S_u is the ultimate tensile strength.

For notched tension specimens the maximum alternating unit stress which may be imposed is KS_a, where S_a is calculated as in eq. 3 and S_a and S_m are calculated from P/A, $S = Mc/I$ and their combinations without taking account of the notch. Hence

$$KS_a = KS_e \left(1 - \frac{S_m}{S_u} \right) \tag{4}$$

2. *Brittle Metals.* For either notched or notch-free specimens of a brittle metal subjected to repeated axial tension or compression or to torsional shearing stresses the maximum alternating stress appears to be due to the repetition of the maximum tensile stress. Hence the maximum alternating unit stress which may be imposed on a given mean stress and repeated indefinitely is given by

$$S_a = S_e \left(\frac{1 - S_m/S_u}{1 + S_m/S_u} \right) \quad \text{for axial or torsional stresses} \tag{5}$$

For specimens of brittle metals having notches or other stress raisers the value of S_a given in eq. 5 should be multiplied by the proper stress concentration factor, K, for the stress raiser involved to obtain the appropriate maximum alternating stress.

3. *Ductile or Brittle Metals for Ranges in Which the Steady or Mean Stress is Compression.* For either notched or notch-free specimens of ductile or brittle metals under steady compression, S_m, the maximum alternating unit stress S_a which may be superimposed indefinitely upon S_m without failure is

$$S_a \gtreqless S_e \tag{6}$$

where S_e is the fatigue limit for completely reversed tension-compression stresses. Hence, for cast irons under this condition of loading, maximum S_a is much greater than S_e in completely reversed bending.

4. The effect of the stress raiser applies only to the alternating stress component in any range of repeated stress in which the steady stress is tension, and the stress concentration factor K should not be applied in calculating the steady stress.

4. Range of Stress Diagrams. In J. O. Smith's study of fatigue data it became evident that modern experimental evidence showed that the left side of the Goodman diagram would more nearly fit experimental data if the endurance or fatigue limit for completely reversed stress was made $\frac{1}{2}S_u$ instead of $\frac{1}{3}S_u$. Also it was apparent that some appropriate method should be evolved for limiting the stress at which failure would occur through the initial application of a maximum unit stress, $S_{\max}$, that would cause excessive overstrain. For this purpose, Smith plotted the relation of the alternating stress S_a as ordinate to the corresponding steady or

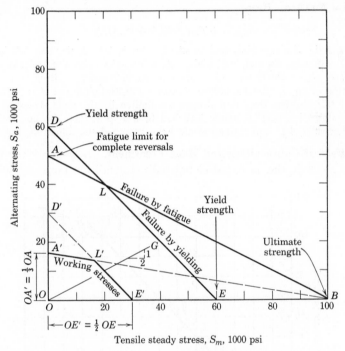

Fig. 3. Working stresses for varying ranges of normal stress for 0.7 per cent carbon steel having a yield ratio of 0.6. (J. O. Smith.)

mean stress S_m as abscissa and drew the appropriate lines limiting fatigue failure and failure by overstrain or yielding. In Fig. 3, representing a steady tensile and alternating stress, these lines are AB and DE, respectively. If L represents the intersection of AB and DE, then failure would be conditioned by fatigue whenever the steady stress is less than the abscissa of L, or 20,000 psi for the scales of Fig. 3. Failure would be conditioned by yielding at first application of the load for values of steady stress greater than the abscissa of L, 20,000 psi.

If a diagram for working stresses is wanted with a factor of safety of 3 against alternating stress and 2 against yield, the line $A'B$ is drawn with $OA' = \frac{1}{3}OA$ and $D'E'$ is drawn with $OD' = \frac{1}{2}OD$ and $OE' = \frac{1}{2}OE$. Then the allowable working stresses are represented by the broken line

$A'L'E'$, and coordinates of points on this line will represent pairs of steady and alternating stresses which have the required safety.

EXAMPLE. Suppose a cylindrical bar with a V-groove is to be made of the steel shown in Fig. 3 and is to carry a load varying from a minimum of 6000 lb tension to a maximum of 18,000 lb tension. For this steel the stress concentration factor K is 1.5. Assuming that the member fails from maximum normal tensile stress, then the steady load $= (18,000 + 6000)/2 = 12,000$ lb, and $S_m = 12,000/A$ and $S_a = KP_{alt}/A = K6000/A$. Hence

$$P_{steady} + P_{alt} = S_m A + (S_a A)/K \qquad (7)$$

Since the ratio of alternating load to steady load is 1 to 2, the line OG is drawn with a 1 to 2 slope through the origin. Its intersection with $L'E'$ provides a safe steady stress $S_m = 20,000$ psi and a safe alternating stress $S_a = 10,000$ psi. Hence, substituting in eq. 7, $12,000 + 6000 = 20,000A + (10,000A)/1.5$ and $A = 0.675$ sq. in. Note for this problem that both stresses are limited by the yield strength. If the ratio of alternating load to steady load had been 2 to 1, then the line OG would have intersected $A'L'$ and fatigue would have governed the allowable stresses.

5. Effect of Composition and Heat Treatment. In general, the fatigue limit of steels in the as-rolled or normalized condition increases with the

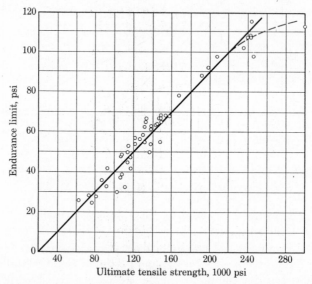

Fig. 4. Relation of fatigue limit of unnotched rotating steel beam specimens to tensile strength. (Data by H. F. Moore, courtesy Republic Steel Corp.)

carbon content up to eutectoid composition. The fatigue limit of unnotched specimens will usually increase with the ultimate strength and hardness of the alloy steels. However, some of the high-strength alloy steels show greater sensitivity to the effect of notches upon their fatigue limits than do other steels of less tensile strength.

Heat treatments which improve the static tensile strength generally increase the fatigue limit,* Fig. 4, but drastic quenching treatments followed by insufficient tempering may cause very strong steels to have smaller fatigue limits than those of lower tensile strength. The very hard steels are more sensitive to notches and stress raisers than those of lesser strength. Hence, for parts which must contain stress raisers, heat treatments to produce tensile strengths in excess of 150,000 psi do not appear to be justified if fatigue resistance is a major consideration, Fig. 5.†

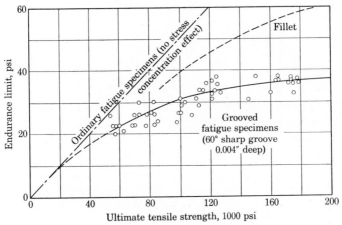

Fig. 5.   Relation of fatigue limit of grooved rotating beam steel specimen to tensile strength.   (Data by Mailaender, courtesy Republic Steel Corp.)

Annealing in general reduces the tensile strength and the fatigue limit. From data available it does not appear that a steel damaged by repetitions of stress can be healed by annealing.

6. Effect of Surface Condition, Notches, and Size.   As previously mentioned, surface flaws, roughness, a notch, a hole, or any abrupt change of cross section cause high localized stress.   Hence the fatigue limit is reduced by any of them.   Consequently, unless these factors are desirable as variables, specimens for fatigue tests are very carefully machined and polished.‡   The injurious effects of surface irregularities and abrupt changes of section cannot be overemphasized wherever fatigue stressing is involved.   Tests by Karpov,§ Fig. 6, show the influence of 60° circumferential notches 0.004 in. deep cut in 0.3-in. diameter rods in decreasing the fatigue limit from 18 to 62 per cent as the tensile strength of the steel rods was increased from 60,000 to 220,000 psi.   The tests show that mill

---

* Moore's tests, Fig. 74, *Republic Alloy Steels.*
† Mailaender data, Fig. **75**, *Republic Alloy Steels.*
‡ See ASTM *Manual on Fatigue Testing,* p. 30.
§ *Trans. ASCE,* Vol. 102, 1937, p. 1184.

scale had a still more potent effect. In general, decarburization of the surface from any heating process has a deleterious effect on the fatigue limit.

Lazan and Blatherwick * have shown that the rolled aluminum alloys 14S-T6, 24S-T4, and 75S-T6 when subjected to a mean tensile stress with alternations are highly sensitive to notches. Their tests show that sharply notching specimens subjected to small ranges of alternating stress caused a marked reduction in the magnitude of the mean stress which the specimens could carry for a given number of cycles. This effect is more pro-

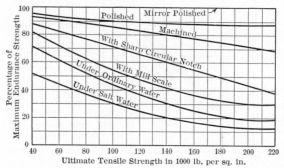

Fig. 6. Reduction in endurance strength of steel alloys due to surface conditions.
(A. V. Karpov.)

nounced when the designated number of cycles is small, in the thousands, than when large, in the millions.

Tests by Kommers and others show that gray cast irons, even those of high strength, show much less sensitivity to notches than do steels when subjected to repeated loadings. Apparently the graphite flakes in cast iron exercise a stress-raising effect which masks the influence of notches.

Carburizing, nitriding, cyaniding, and surface hardening are methods which have been successfully used to increase the fatigue limit of notched steel parts. The data for electroplating with copper and nickel show little effect on the fatigue limit, but some tests show that chromium plating decreases the fatigue limit.

Horger † reports a marked improvement in the fatigue limit of ferrous and non-ferrous metal parts by introducing compressive stresses in the surfaces of such parts through shot peening (blasting with shot). The deleterious effects of holes on fatigue resistance can be reduced by cold working the edges of the holes.

Since most of the fatigue tests on metals have been made on specimens ½ in. or less in diameter or thickness, it is important to note the effects

* *Proc. ASTM*, Vol. 53, 1953, p. 856.
† *Iron Age*, Vol. 155, March 29, 1945, p. 40, and April 5, 1945, p. 66.

of size of specimen on fatigue limit. The data on the effect of size on the fatigue strength of unnotched specimens up to 2 in. in diameter is not conclusive. Tests by R. E. Peterson * on four carbon steels, H. F. Moore on a medium-carbon steel, and R. L. Templin on cast-aluminum alloys all failed to show a size effect; other tests reported † show a material decrease as the size increases. Available data do show conclusively that tests on a small specimen are likely to give much higher fatigue limits than tests on filleted shafts of the same steels. Horger and Neifert ‡ show that in axles tested by them a 6.5-in.-diameter filleted axle had a fatigue limit of only 17,500 psi, whereas rotating-beam specimens from the shaft, 0.3 in. in diameter, had a fatigue limit nearly twice as great. The data presently available indicate that large shafts are more susceptible to notches and fillets than small ones, but the fatigue limit of a fillet may be much improved by rolling the fillet after turning.

7. Effect of Speed of Testing. Moore and Jasper § found that increasing the speed from 200 to 1500 cycles per min caused an increase of 2 per cent in the fatigue limit. A further increase to 5000 cycles per min caused no change. Krouse || and Obert and Johnson ¶ found that the speed could be increased to 10,000 cycles per min with little effect on the ferrous metals. Krouse's data at 30,000 cycles per min showed that there may be an increase of 2 to 10 per cent over that obtained at 1500 cycles per min for the ferrous metals. The tests of brass and aluminum alloys show greater increases in the fatigue limit for higher speeds of testing. Jenkin and Lehmann ** from tests at frequencies of 36,000 to 1,200,000 cycles per min report an increase of 20 per cent in the fatigue limit of flat specimens, but their data showed only a slight decrease when extrapolated for values below 30,000 cycles. As a practical consideration it would seem possible to standardize fatigue tests at a speed of at least 10,000 cycles per min.

8. Effect of Understressing and Overstressing. Considerable improvement in the fatigue limit of steel and cast iron has been obtained by subjecting these metals to several million cycles of stresses just below their fatigue limits, as normally determined, and then proceeding to give the treated specimens a conventional fatigue test.†† Kommers ‡‡ showed that the fatigue limit of a gray cast iron could be raised 25 per cent by understressing. His tests on Armco iron involving understressing followed by

* *Appl. Mech.*, Vol. 1, No. 2, 1933, p. 79.
† *Prevention of Fatigue of Metals*, Battelle, p. 123.
‡ *Proc. ASTM*, Vol. 39, 1939, p. 723.
§ *Bull.* 136, Univ. Ill., 1923, p. 58.
|| *Proc. ASTM*, Vol. 34, 1934, p. 156.
¶ *Proc. ASTM*, Vol. 37, 1937, p. 195.
** *Proc. Roy. Soc. London, A*, Vol. 125, 1929.
†† *Prevention of Fatigue of Metals*, Battelle, p. 88, provides several references.
‡‡ *Proc. ASTM*, 1943, Vol. 43, p. 749.

the gradual application of cycles of stress higher than the normal fatigue limit (coaxing) increased the fatigue limit over 23 per cent and the fatigue life very much more. Sinclair * made coaxing tests on ferrous and non-ferrous metals, some of which were susceptible to strain-aging, Art. XXVI-5, and others not. From his results it appears that the improvement in the fatigue limit due to coaxing depends upon the ability of the metal to strengthen through strain aging which is developed by cyclic stressing with small amplitudes of stress. Repeatedly understressed specimens of low-carbon steel show an increase in tensile strength but a loss in ductility.

Since there is no non-destructive test of short duration which will determine the damage done by overstressing, resort must be made to endurance tests for such information. The damaging or strengthening effect of a number of repetitions of stress above the fatigue limit can be determined by subjecting the overstressed specimen or part to many millions of cycles of stress and comparing the results with the known behavior of specimens given the same cycle but not prestressed.

9. Effect of High Temperatures. The fatigue strength of ferrous alloys usually increases as the temperature is increased up to 550°F, but decreases as the temperature is further increased. At a temperature of 1000°F the fatigue strength of plain carbon steels is only about one-half as great as the fatigue strength at room temperature. The stainless steels are more resistant to high temperatures, and at a temperature of 1200°F they usually have fatigue strengths between 60 and 75 per cent of the fatigue strengths at room temperature.

Comparatively few tests on the fatigue strength of non-ferrous alloys at high temperatures have been made. Information on good-strength aluminum alloys indicates that the fatigue strength decreases rapidly above a temperature of 400°F and that at 500°F the fatigue strength will be only about one-third the fatigue strength at room temperature.

The chromium-nickel-cobalt-molybdenum-iron alloys like N-155 and the cobalt-chromium-molybdenum-nickel alloys like Vitallium when properly heat treated exhibit high resistance to creep † and to fatigue when subjected to tensile loadings at temperatures of 1350° and 1500°F.

10. Influence of Corrosion. The action of corroding agents causes a marked reduction in the fatigue limit of carbon steels and many of the alloy steels. The reduction is more marked when notches or holes are present. McAdam's ‡ tests in which 20 million cycles were used showed that rotating-beam specimens of carbon steels as rolled under completely reversed cycles of tension to compression when subjected to a stream of

---

* *Proc. ASTM,* 1952, Vol. 52, p. 743.

† Lazan and Westberg in *Proc. ASTM,* Vol. 52, 1952, p. 837.

‡ *Prevention of Fatigue of Metals,* Battelle, p. 68.

fresh water would suffer reductions of 40 to 60 per cent below those of similar specimens tested in air. Some of his alloy-steel specimens gave lower values of S_e than the carbon steels. However, the high-chromium 18:8 austenitic and the 27 per cent chromium ferritic-type steels had good endurance limits, approximating 50,000 and 40,000 psi, respectively. These values were somewhat below the corresponding values for tests in air. Only copper of the non-ferrous alloys tested was unaffected. Aluminum, Duralumin, brass, and Monel showed marked reductions in S_e when tested under fresh water. As might be expected, salt water is more damaging to the fatigue resistance of steel than fresh water. McAdam's tests on the resistant 18:8 austenitic high-chromium steel mentioned above gave an S_e of only 25,000 psi when subjected to salt water.

Dolan's [*] tests on chrome-nickel steel SAE 3140 provided fatigue strengths S_n at 10 million cycles, as shown in Table 1.

TABLE 1.   EFFECTS OF NOTCHES AND HOLES ON FATIGUE STRENGTH OF SAE 3140 STEEL (DOLAN)

Condition of Specimen	Rotating-Beam Tests				Completely Reversed Torsion			
	Quenched and Tempered S_u, Tension, 166,300 psi		Hot-Rolled S_u, Tension, 127,000 psi		Hot-Rolled S_u, Tension, 115,000 psi		Quenched and Tempered S_u, Tension, 162,000 psi	
	S_n in Air	S_n in Water	S_n in Air	S_n in Water	S_{sn} in Air	S_{sn} in Water	S_{sn} in Air	S_{sn} in Water
Polished	90,000	13,000	64,000	34,000	44,000	32,500	56,000	32,500
Square notch	36,000	11,000	36,000	19,000	28,000	30,000	37,000	20,000
Drilled hole	31,000	9,000	31,000	16,000	22,000	13,500	30,000	20,000

The diameter of the solid specimens was 0.3 in., of the notched specimens 0.3 in. in torsion tests and 0.25 in. in flexure tests. For the specimens with 0.04-in.-diameter holes the specimen diameter was 0.4 in.

Dolan's data show the drastic effect of notches and holes on the fatigue strength of this steel when it was subjected to the action of fresh water under the various conditions of test.

Karpov's tests, Fig. 6, also support the foregoing statements regarding the effects of fatigue combined with corrosion.

Notches and other stress raisers adversely affect the fatigue strength of aluminum and most of its alloys; of magnesium; and also of copper and its alloys in about the same degree as they affect steels.

When metallic coatings of copper, nickel, or chromium are electroplated upon steel they appear to lower the fatigue strength somewhat if the

[*] *J. Appl. Mech.,* Vol. 5, 1938, p. A143.

specimens are tested in air, but improve the resistance when they are subjected to water spray. Nitriding, according to Mailaender, appears to improve the resistance to corrosion fatigue. Carburizing also appears to be beneficial in improving resistance to corrosion fatigue. Coatings likely to crack or subject to pin holes are of doubtful value in preventing corrosion fatigue. For further information on this subject see *Metals Handbook*.

11. Fatigue Tests on Joints. The recognition of the importance of the action of repeated stresses in machine parts and in structural members, both in bridges and more markedly in airplanes, has increased experimentation on the fatigue properties of full-size members and their connections. The presence of mill scale, rivet holes, abrupt changes of section, and other stress raisers reduce the fatigue limit and the fatigue strength at a given number of cycles below the values given by small polished specimens which have been carefully removed from the given part.

Wilson and Thomas's fatigue tests [*] on riveted joints made with three varieties of structural steel, also on plates and specimens from the joints, are shown in Table 2. The data on fatigue strength are based on the effects of 2 million repetitions of tensile stress varying from zero to the S_n value indicated. The results show that the fatigue strengths of the plates composing the joints were adversely affected by stress raisers, holes, and mill scale, as were the plates similarly drilled. Also as the tensile strength S_u increased, so did the deleterious effects of the stress raisers; see also Fig. 5.

Wilson, Bruckner, McCrackin, and Beede [†] made a comprehensive series of fatigue tests on commercially made butt-welded joints in $7/8$-in. structural steel plates which were 5 in. wide at the weld. The metal had a tensile strength of about 60,000 psi and a yield point of approximately 30,000 psi. Their data for fatigue strength S_n, under favorable operator skill and good supervision, for stresses repeated from zero to S_n gave: for $N = 100,000$, $S_n = 33,100$; for $N = 2,000,000$, $S_n = 22,500$ psi; and for completely reversed cycles of stress for $N = 100,000$, $S_n = 22,300$; for $N = 2,000,000$, $S_n = 14,400$. Each of the foregoing results represented the average of three or more tests. In six series of commercial butt welds, shop-welded in the flat position with a manually operated metallic arc, there was an occasional weld appreciably weaker in fatigue than the basic strengths given above. The ratio of the weakest commercially welded specimen to the average value for the basic series as given above varied from 0.85 to 0.73. The fatigue strength of the commercial butt welds made in the field, having welds either in horizontal or vertical seams

[*] *Bull.* 79, Univ. Ill., 1938.
[†] *Bull.* 344, Univ. Ill., 1943.

TABLE 2. FATIGUE STRENGTH OF VARIOUS TYPES OF STRUCTURAL STEEL SPECIMENS

Type of Specimen	Strength, lb. per sq. in.		Ratio of Fatigue Strength to Static Strength	Ratio of Fatigue Strength to Fatigue Strength of Polished Specimen
	Static	Fatigue		
CARBON STEEL				
Round, machined and polished...............	64,700	47,000	0.73	1.00
Plate, with mill scale on two sides............	61,800	30,300	0.49	0.67
Plate, with mill scale on two sides and 1⅛-in. drilled hole............................	61,800	21,200	0.34	0.47
Plates of riveted joints....................	63,600	25,900	0.41	0.56
SILICON STEEL				
Round, machined and polished...............	81,700	56,000	0.69	1.00
Plate, with mill scale on two sides............	81,800	35,800	0.44	0.64
Plate, with mill scale on two sides and 1⅛-in. drilled hole............................	80,800	23,900	0.30	0.43
Plates of riveted joints....................	80,200	25,600	0.30	0.43
NICKEL STEEL				
Round, machined and polished...............	99,000	74,000	0.75	1.00
Plate, with mill scale on two sides............	99,000	39,500	0.40	0.53
Plate, with mill scale on two sides and 1⅛-in. drilled hole............................	99,000	24,300	0.25	0.33
Plates of riveted joints....................	99,000	26,700	0.27	0.36

in plates held in a vertical plane, indicated that, when these welds were made according to specified directions, values of S_n comparable to the values obtained by commercial operators in the shop were obtainable.

Welded joints and welded connections in ships have produced stress-raising effects which have resulted in failures of a number of merchant ships (Art. XXXI-10). These failures have emphasized the need of the development and use of notch-tough steel for such construction.*

An illuminating article on fatigue characteristics of aircraft materials and fastenings by Piper, Finlay, and Binsacca † gives warning of the grave importance of fatigue failures in aircraft plates and joints. Since the overall factor of safety for aircraft has been progressively reduced, it becomes more and more necessary to ascertain the true permissible

* See symposium on *Fracture and Fatigue of Metals,* The Technology Press, M.I.T., and John Wiley & Sons, p. 52. Reference also gives much additional information on results of recent researches in the field of fatigue.

† *ASTM Bull.,* May 1950, p. 60.

stresses which may be used in design. The problem is complicated further by the lack of a definite fatigue limit for the aluminum-copper alloys used. Hence recourse is made to the use of fatigue strength, S_n, values for 100 or 500 million cycles of stress. These authors show tests of riveted lap joints in Alclad plates 0.065 to 0.066 in. thick and 1 in. wide, fastened by a single 3/16-in. 24S-T aluminum alloy brazier head rivet, in which it was necessary to reduce the tensile unit stresses at net section of the sheet to the following values in order to avoid failures in the sheet at 100 million cycles: for 24S-T, to 3500; 24S-T81, to 1800; 24S-RT, to 2100; 75S-T, to 2100. For 24S-T86, three specimens failed at or below 2300 psi at cycles less than 100 million. They reported results which show that the optimum value of rivet pitch to diameter, p/d, corresponding to the maximum ratio of the fatigue strength of a lap joint to the static ultimate for the plate, is given by the linear relation $p/d = 9.9 - 76t$, for t between 0.032 and 0.091 in.

12. Need for Statistical Approach. It should be apparent from the preceding articles that there are many factors which markedly affect the fatigue strength and fatigue life of engineering materials. Also, it is evident insufficient attention has been given to determining the spread of results either at a given stress S or life N. The need for a better knowledge of the reliability of present data to the designer of aircraft parts and to one who designs parts of engines and machines for high-temperature service is great. Suggestions concerning a proper approach to the solution of this problem are presented in a paper by W. Weibull on *The Statistical Aspects of Fatigue and Its Consequences.** An approximate statistical method for the analysis of fatigue data by R. E. Peterson appeared in *ASTM Bull.*, Jan. 1949, p. 50.

WOOD AND CONCRETE

13. Fatigue of Wood.† Relatively few tests have been carried out to determine the fatigue properties of non-metallic materials. The importance of wood and plywood in aircraft has resulted in a start on the test work required to provide the necessary information.

The Forest Products Laboratory has carried out tests on solid Douglas fir and Sitka spruce specimens, and on five-ply plywoods of yellow birch and yellow poplar in constant deflection flat-plate-type fatigue machines. The cantilever specimens with a 6-in. free length were conditioned to a 12 per cent moisture content prior to test and were tested under controlled temperature and humidity conditions of 75°F and 65 per cent relative

---

* Symposium on the *Fatigue Fracture of Metals*, p. 182, *loc. cit.*

† For additional information see *Repts.* 1327, 1327A, 1539, and 1545, Forest Products Laboratory, Madison, Wis.

humidity, respectively. They were vibrated at 1790 cycles per min until they contacted a microswitch at midlength set for a clearance of 0.003 in., at which time initial failure was presumed to have taken place. Repeated stress cycles and completely reversed stress cycles were used in these tests. The S-N curve out to 50 million cycles did not show any "knee" or endurance limit. The fatigue strength for all materials at 50 million cycles of reversed stress was about 27 per cent of the static modulus of rupture. The fatigue strength of the solid specimens at 50 million cycles of repeated stress was about 36 per cent of the static modulus of rupture. After removal from the fatigue machines, the specimens were tested in static bending, and had about 85 per cent of the strength of control specimens not subjected to fatigue tests.

Rotating beam tests of solid birch and maple specimens carried out at Wright Field gave fatigue strength values at 50 million cycles of 28 and 26 per cent, respectively, of the static modulus of rupture.

Tests have also been carried out at the Forest Products Laboratory to determine the resistance to fatigue stressing of wood-to-metal and wood-to-wood joints. Satisfactory results were obtained with wood-to-metal glues that were believed to be hot-setting mixtures of thermoplastic resins and synthetic rubber, and thermosetting combinations of synthetic rubber and plastics. Satisfactory results for wood-to-wood joints were obtained with resorcinol formaldehyde, alkaline phenol formaldehyde, and melamine.

14. Fatigue of Concrete. In most of its uses, concrete and mortar are not subjected to large numbers of stress cycles, but in some cases, as concrete highways, information on the fatigue properties is very important. The fatigue strength of concrete and cement mortar is influenced by many variables such as mix proportions, type of cement, type of aggregate, curing conditions, age, speed of loading, and previous stress history. From the information available it appears that the behavior characteristics of concrete and metal under repeated stresses are nearly similar.

Fatigue tests on concrete are usually made on concrete that is at least 6 months old in order to avoid marked strength increases during the testing period. When the applied repeated stresses are below the fatigue strength, concrete at first takes on permanent set and suffers a reduction in its modulus of elasticity, but adjustment to the imposed stress cycle produces a straight-line stress-strain curve and a constant but lower modulus of elasticity.

Information secured by many investigators shows that concrete subjected to repeated loads will fail at unit stresses much below the ultimate static strength, that if the applied unit stresses exceed the fatigue strength the number of cycles for rupture increases as the unit stress is decreased, and that the range of stress from minimum to maximum must decrease as the maximum stress is increased if failure is not to occur. As in the case of metals, understressing appears to increase fatigue strength of concrete. The fatigue strength for normal concrete in compression and transverse bending * is equal to about 50 to 55 per cent of the static ultimate strength. Tests † of lightweight concrete made with Haydite aggregate indicate that the approximate fatigue strength under reversed bending is about 50 per cent of the static modulus of rupture, and under repeated bending it is about 40 per cent of the static modulus of rupture. The above-mentioned values are based on 1 to 2 million cycles of stress. Also see Art. XV-18.

* H. F. Clemmer, in *Proc. ASTM,* Vol. 22, 1922, Pt. 2, p. 408.
† H. A. Williams, in *J. Am. Concrete Inst.,* Vol. 14, 1943, p. 441.

Index

1

10   Index